	Cube	Volume = a^3
		Surface area = $6a^2$
	Rectangular Parallel-epiped	Volume = lwh
		Surface area = $2(lw + hw + lh)$
	Any Cylinder or Prism	Volume = (area of base)(altitude)
	Right Cylinder or Prism	Lateral area = (perimeter of base)(altitude) (not incl. bases)
	Sphere	Volume = $\dfrac{4}{3}\pi r^3$
		Surface area = $4\pi r^2$
	Any Cone or Pyramid	Volume = $\dfrac{1}{3}$(area of base)(altitude)
	Right Circular Cone or Regular Pyramid	Lateral area = $\dfrac{1}{2}$(perimeter of base) $\times$ (slant height)
	Any Cone or Pyramid	Volume = $\dfrac{h}{3}(A_1 + A_2 + \sqrt{A_1 A_2})$
	Right Circular Cone or Regular Pyramid	Lateral area = $\dfrac{s}{2}$(sum of base perimeters) = $\dfrac{s}{2}(P_1 + P_2)$
	Corresponding dimensions of plane or solid similar figures are in proportion
	Area of similar plane or solid figures are proportional to the squares of any two corresponding dimensions
	Volumes of similar solid figures are proportional to the cubes of any two corresponding dimensions

SI EDITION

Calter's Technical Mathematics

Paul Calter

Professor of Mathematics
Vermont Technical College

SI Edition prepared by
David Egerton
Professor of Mathematics
St. Lawrence College
Kingston, Ontario

Prentice Hall Canada Career & Technology

Canadian Cataloguing in Publication Data

Calter, Paul
  Technical Mathematics
  SI ed.
  ISBN 0-13-625682-1

  1. Engineering mathematics.
  I. Egerton, David, 1939– . II. Title

  TA330.C343 1998   510 C96-932585-1

 © 1998 Prentice-Hall Canada Inc., Scarborough, Ontario

Allyn and Bacon, Inc., Needham Heights, MA
Prentice-Hall, Inc., Upper Saddle River, New Jersey
Prentice-Hall International (UK) Limited, London
Prentice-Hall of Australia, Pty. Limited, Sydney
Prentice-Hall Hispanoamericana, S.A., Mexico City
Prentice-Hall of India Private Limited, New Delhi
Prentice-Hall of Japan, Inc., Tokyo
Simon & Schuster Southeast Asia Private Limited, Singapore
Editora Prentice-Hall do Brasil, Ltda., Rio de Janeiro

ISBN 0-13-625682-1

Vice President, Editorial Director: Laura Pearson
Acquisitions Editor: David Stover
Signing Representative: Samantha Scully
Developmental Editor: Marta Tomins
Production Editor: Kelly Dickson
Production Coordinator: Julie Preston
Cover Design: Mary Opper
Cover Illustration: Kevin Ghiglione
Art Direction: Mary Opper
Page Layout: Compeer Typographic Services Limited
Technical Artist: Bill Renaud

Original English Language edition published by Prentice-Hall, Inc., Upper Saddle River, New Jersey, 07458. Copyright © 1995.

  2 3 4 5   CC   02 01 00 99 98

Printed and bound in the U.S.A.

Visit the Prentice Hall Canada Web site! Send us your comments, browse our catalogues, and more. **www.phcanada.com** Or reach us through e-mail at **phabinfo_pubcanada@prenhall.com**

To Margaret Jolind
To Jay Egerton

Contents

21

Complex Numbers

22

Analytic Geometry

23

Binary, Hexadecimal, Octal, and BCD Numbers

24

Inequalities and Linear Programming

25

Sequences, Series, and the Binomial Theorem

26

Introduction to Statistics and Probability

Appendices

Indexes

Preface

Technical Mathematics, SI Edition, is intended for students at technical colleges in two- and three-year engineering technology programs. Depending on the pace and amount of material included, it may be used for a two-, three-, or four-semester course.

The introduction of the graphics calculator to our modern set of tools has brought a considerable amount of change. We have modified our presentation to incorporate this new tool for mathematics. The graphics calculator has been integrated into the book, both in text and exercises. We have, however, still retained the former methods, such as manual graphing, for those classes not using graphics calculators.

This edition has been produced to meet the demand for an SI version. The metric system and specifically SI have been adopted by 95 percent of the world's population. Otherwise, we have maintained the same basic structure as the previous edition with the inclusion of a new section dealing with the effects of error in measurement on engineering calculations.

Features of the Book

A mathematics book is never easy reading, so much care has gone into making the material as clear as possible. We follow an intuitive rather than a rigorous approach and give information in small segments. Numerous illustrations and careful page layout are designed to make the material as easy to follow as possible. The book also has the following features. **Chapter Objectives** start each chapter. They state specifically what the student should be able to do upon completion of the chapter. Many fully worked **Examples** form the backbone of the textbook. They are particularly chosen to help the student to do the exercises. We have added dozens of examples to supplement those in previous editions. Examples have markers above and below to separate them clearly from the text discussion.

Practice is essential for learning mathematics, as with other skills, and so we include thousands of **Exercises**. Exercise sets are indicated by title, as well as by number, to further help the student find things in the book. Exercises given after each section are graded by difficulty and grouped by type, to allow practice on a particular area. However those given in the **Chapter Review Problems** are scrambled as to type and difficulty. Answers to all odd-numbered problems are given in Appendix D. Complete solutions to every problem are contained in the **Instructor's Solutions Manual**, and more detailed solutions for every fourth problem are given in the **Student Solutions Manual**.

All important **Formulas**, both mathematical and technical, are boxed and numbered in the text. We also list these formulas in Appendix A, as the **Summary of Facts and Formulas**. We hope it will also help students to see interconnections that might otherwise be overlooked. The formulas are grouped logically in the Summary of Facts and Formulas and are numbered sequentially there. Therefore, the formulas do not necessarily appear in numerical order in the text.

Marginal notes are used for encouragement, to give historical notes, for reminders of things already covered, and for previews of things to come later in their studies.

An instructor quickly learns the pitfalls and traps that "get" students year after year. Many of these are noted in the text as **Common Error Boxes**.

We include discussions in the text of many **technical applications**, such as the use of mathematics for analyzing motion, or for electric circuits. They are included for classes that wish to cover those topics, as well as for motivation, to show that mathematics has real uses. Because space does not permit a full discussion of each application, judgment must be used in assigning applications problems. It is not intended that every student be able to solve every application. We assume that students have sufficient background before attempting the more difficult problems in their own technical area and that they will get technical help not offered in this text. The **Index to Applications** should help in finding specific applications.

The **writing across the curriculum** movement among mathematics educators aims to use writing to help teach mathematics. One difficulty in implementing this idea is the lack of good writing questions, so we have provided one such question per chapter. These will give the instructor something to assign, and also indicate the kinds of questions that can be used so that the instructor can make up others.

Students have never been reluctant to put down a preposterous answer (i.e., the cost of the shirt is $450). In this edition we have tried to show students how to **estimate an answer** in order to check their work. An introductory section on estimating an answer is given as one of the steps in solving a word problem, when word problems are introduced in Chapter 3. Thereafter, almost every applications example begins with an estimation step or ends with a **check for reasonableness** of the answer.

The trend is away from contrived "school" problems with neat solutions and toward **problems with approximate solutions**, that do not yield to many of the methods we teach. These include expressions and equations with approximate constants, and problems that cannot be solved exactly but must be tackled with an approximate method. We include many **numerical methods for the computer**, but these topics are included in such a way so that they can be skipped without impairing the overall study of technical mathematics. Those calculations that are best done by computer are given in the text itself. Elsewhere, computer problems are suggested at the end of exercises, as enrichment activities. Some numerical methods we give are finding roots of equations by the midpoint method, by the false position method, and by simple iteration; solving systems of equations by the Gauss–Seidel method, and by matrix inversion; evaluation of determinants by the method of Chio; numerical evaluation of power series, Fourier series, and limits; numerical differentiation and integration; numerical solution of differential equations, and so forth.

There continues to be interest in collaborative learning, where students work in groups. To provide material for the instructor who wishes to try an occasional group project, we give an introductory Project in Chapter 1 and thereafter have placed **Team Projects** at the end of nearly every chapter. These will also serve as models for Team Projects that the teacher and student can make up themselves.

New Features

A section on the effect of errors, encountered when using instruments to obtain physical quantities, has been added. Comments on percentage error and on accuracy and precision in measurement and number remain unchanged. This new section demonstrates the methods required for dealing with the effect of error in measurement on formula calculations. We believe it to be extremely important for students carrying out experiments in laboratories, and taking measurements in general, to understand the limitations of results obtained from mathematical formulas that are relying on that empirical data.

Additional problems dealing with electrical and electronic technology have been added to the review problems at the end of each chapter. As well, this revision has been prepared to the standards for technical mathematics courses in electronics programs set out by the Committee on National Standards for Applied Science and Engineering Technologists. We have added coverage of such topics as Bessel function theory to meet these standards.

Teaching Resources

There are supplements to assist both the instructor and the student.

An **Instructor's Solution Manual** contains worked out solutions to every problem in the text and a listing of all computer programs. The Instructor's Solution Manual also includes more than 200 problems using Imperial measurements for supplementary use by instructors. The **Student Solutions Manual** gives the solution to every other odd problem.

A **Computerized Test Item File** is a bank of test questions with answers. Questions may be mixed, sorted, changed, or deleted. It consists of a test file disk and a test generator disk, ready to run. **Transparency Masters**, giving additional problems and full explanations, are available.

Acknowledgements

First let us thank the reviewers of the manuscript for the U.S. third edition. These include:

A. David Allen, Ricks College
Donna V. Boccio, Queensboro Community College
James H. Carney, Lorain County Community College

Edgar M. Meyer, St. Cloud State, MN
Nancy J. Sattler, Terra Technical College
Dale H. Thielker, Ranken Technical College
William N. Thomas, Jr., Thomas & Associates Group
Roy A. Wilson, Cerritos College

Reviewers of the earlier editions of the U.S. third edition, the supplements, and the writing questions, and participants in group discussions about the book are:

Byron Angell, Vermont Technical College
David Bashaw, New Hampshire Technical Institute
Elizabeth Bliss, Trident Technical College
Franklin Blou, Essex County College
Jacquelyn Briley, Guilford Technical Community College
Michael Calter, Harvard University
Cheryl Cleaves, State Technical Institute at Memphis
Ray Collings, Tri-County Technical College
Miriam Conlon, Vermont Technical College
Kati Dana, Norwich University
Linda Davis, Vermont Technical College
John Eisley, Mott Community College
Walt Granter, Vermont Technical College
Crystal Gromer, Vermont Technical College
Richard Hanson, Burnsville, MN
Tommy Hinson, Forsythe Community College
Margie Hobbs, State Technical Institute at Memphis
Martin Horowitz, Queensborough Community College
Glenn Jacobs, Greenville Technical College
Wendell Johnson, Akron, OH
Joseph Jordan, John Tyler Community College
Rob Kimball, Wake Technical Community College
John Knox, Vermont Technical College
Ellen Kowalczyk, Madison Area Technical College
Lorraine Lachs, Norwich University
Fran Leach, Delaware Technical College
Jon Luke, Indiana University-Purdue University
Paul Maini, Suffolk County Community College
Harold Oxsen, Walnut Creek, CA
Don Nevin, Vermont Technical College
Donald Reichman, Mercer County Community College
Ursula Rodin, Nashville State Technical Institute
Frank Scalzo, Queensborough Community College
Blin Scatterday, University of Akron Community and Technical College
Edward W. Seabloom, Lane Community College
Robert Seaver, Lorain Community College
Jim Beam, Savannah Area Vo-Tech
Thomas Stark, Cincinnati Technical College
Joel Turner, Blackhawk Technical Institute
Douglas Wolansky, North Alberta Institute of Technology
Henry Zatkis, New Jersey Institute of Technology

The tedious job of solving many of the exercise problems was done by my students, Brett Benner, Keith Crowe, Jim Davis, Nancy Davis, Kelly

Dennehy, Mel Emerson, Ellie Germain, Robert Morel, Jeffery Sloan, and Ray Wells. All problems new to the third edition were solved by Suson Porter of Randolph, who also prepared the Instructor's Solution Manual and checked the proofs for accuracy. George Seki and Terri Bittner of Laurel Technical Services carefully solved and rechecked every example and exercise in the book, both old and new, and proofread the entire text. We also want to express our gratitude to John Morin for his many constructive suggestions on the second edition, to Robert Dickau of Wolfram Research Inc. for his help with the *Mathematica* Instructions, to my wife Margaret for her help with the tedious job of preparing the index, and to Jeffrey Houck of York Production Services for steering the manuscript expertly through the complicated production process.

—*Paul A. Calter, Randolph, Vermont*

Canadian Reviewers

Thank you to the reviewers of *Technical Mathematics*, *SI Edition*. They include: Rob Cassan, Loyalist College; Roger Claus, Humber College; Doug Cole, Confederation College; Erika Crema, British Columbia Institute of Technology; Joe Cygman, DeVry Institute of Technology– Calgary; Frank Donato, Cambrian College; Gary Helmer, Mohawk College; Dave Howard, Canadore College; James Ngok Yeung Lai, Nova Scotia Institute of Technology; Peter Lawrence, Ryerson Polytechnic University; Brian McGregor, Sir Sandford Fleming College; David Sabo, British Columbia Institute of Technology; Donald St. Jean, George Brown College; and Norm Williams, Seneca College.

Thanks also to the technical reviewers of the *SI Edition*. They are Lisa Barrucco, Bernie Brooks, and Jon-Paul Voroney from the University of Guelph.

About the Authors

Paul Calter is Professor Emeritus of Mathematics at Vermont Technical College and Visiting Professor of Mathematics at Dartmouth College. A graduate of The Cooper Union, New York, he received his M.S. from Columbia University.

Professor Calter, a member of the American Society of Mechanical Engineers, has been teaching technical mathematics for nearly 30 years. In 1987, he was the recipient of the Vermont State College Faculty Fellow Award.

A member of the American Mathematical Association of Two Year Colleges, Professor Calter is the Director of the AMATYC Summer Institute in Vermont. He is also a member of the Mathematical Association of America, the National Council of Teachers of Mathematics, the International Society for the Arts, Sciences, and Technology, Volunteers in Technical Assistance, and the Author's Guild.

Professor Calter is the author of several mathematics textbooks including four with Prentice Hall: *Practical Math Handbook for the Building Trades, Mathematics for Computer Technology, Technical Calculus* and *Introductory Algebra and Trigonometry with Applications.*

He resides in rural Vermont and is an accomplished sculptor; he has large pieces installed at several locations, including the Montshire Museum of Science and Vermont Technical College. His work often reflects themes related to mathematics.

David Egerton is a Mathematics Professor at St. Lawrence College in Kingston, Ontario, Canada. He received his B.Sc. (Hons) from Brighton University, UK and a Teachers' Certificate from London University. He came to Canada to teach in 1968 and obtained an M.Sc. (Engineering) in 1973 from Queen's University, Kingston. He is a registered Professional Engineer of Ontario.

Professor Egerton has taught at the college for twenty-seven years, many of those in the Engineering Department. He also taught in Australia, on an exchange programme for one year at Newcastle Technical College, New South Wales.

He was instrumental in the introduction of SI at the college and delivered numerous seminars on the new system to local industries. He has also acted in an advisory capacity for several companies, dealing with their engineering problems. He has been teaching mathematics for seven years and is a strong advocate of new technologies, such as computers and graphics calculators for mathematics.

Professor Egerton is the author of two engineering texts, *A Problem Approach to Statics and Dynamics* and *A Problem Approach to Strength of Materials.*

He lives in Kingston, pursuing numerous hobbies such as painting and cabinet making.

1

Numerical Computation

When you have completed this chapter, you should be able to:

- Perform basic arithmetic operations on signed numbers.
- Perform basic arithmetic operations on approximate numbers.
- Take powers, roots, and reciprocals of signed and approximate numbers.
- Perform combined arithmetic operations to obtain a numerical result.
- Convert numbers between decimal and scientific notation.
- Perform basic arithmetic operations on numbers in scientific notation.
- Convert units of measurement from one denomination to another.
- Substitute given values into equations and formulas.
- Solve common percentage problems.
- Evaluate the effect of measurement errors in calculations.

You are probably already using a *scientific* calculator. Many problems can be solved more easily with the use of a *graphics* calculator. Throughout this text, a calculator symbol is placed beside problems for which the use of a graphics calculator is recommended.

calculator symbol

In this first chapter we cover ordinary arithmetic, but in a different way. The basic operations are explained here in terms of the *calculator*. Although the calculator makes arithmetic easier than before, it also introduces a complication: that of knowing how many of the digits shown in a calculator display should be kept. We will see that it is usually incorrect to keep them all. Then, after performing the algebraic operations on pairs of numbers, we will show how to link these operations to evaluate more complex expressions.

Also in this chapter, we will learn some rules that will help us when we get to algebra.

We also learn *scientific notation*—a convenient way to handle very large or small numbers without having to write down lots of zeros. It is also the way in which calculators and computers display such numbers.

Next we learn how to substitute values into equations and formulas and to evaluate the result, an operation of great practical importance in technical work.

Finally, we cover *percentage*, one of the most often used mathematical ideas in technology as well as in everyday life.

When you finish this chapter you should be able to use most of the keys on your calculator to do some fairly difficult computations. The keys for trigonometry and logarithms are discussed in the chapters on those topics.

1•1

The Real Numbers

Before we start our calculator practice, we must learn a few definitions. In mathematics, as in many fields, you will have trouble understanding the material if you do not clearly understand the meanings of the words that are used.

Integers

The *integers*

$$\ldots, -4, -3, -2, -1, 0, 1, 2, 3, 4, \ldots$$

are the whole numbers, including zero and negative values.

The three dots indicate that the sequence of numbers continues indefinitely.

Rational and Irrational Numbers

The *rational numbers* include the integers and all other numbers that can be expressed as the quotient of two integers, for example,

$$\frac{1}{2}, -\frac{3}{5}, \frac{57}{23}, -\frac{98}{99}, \text{ and } 7$$

Numbers that cannot be expressed as the quotient of two integers are called *irrational*. Some irrational numbers are

$$\sqrt{2}, \sqrt[3]{5}, \sqrt{7}, \pi, \text{ and } e$$

where π is approximately equal to 3.1416 and e is approximately equal to 2.7182.

Real Numbers

The rational and irrational numbers together make up the *real numbers*.

Numbers such as $\sqrt{-4}$ do not belong to the real number system. They are called *imaginary numbers* and are discussed in Chapter 21. Except when otherwise noted, all the numbers we shall work with are real numbers.

Decimal Numbers

Systems having bases other than 10 are used in computer science: *binary* (base 2), *octal* (base 8), and *hexadecimal* (base 16) (see Chapter 23).

Most of our computations are with numbers written in the familiar *decimal* system. The names of the *places* relative to the *decimal point* are shown in Fig. 1•1. We say that the decimal system uses a *base of 10* because it takes 10 units in any place to equal 1 unit in the next-higher place. For example, 10 units in the hundreds position equals 1 unit in the thousands position.

Positional Number Systems

A *positional number system* is one in which the *position* of a digit determines its value. Our decimal system is positional.

FIGURE 1•1 Values of the positions in a decimal number

The numbers 10^2, 10^3, etc., are called *powers of 10*. Don't worry if they are unfamiliar to you. We will explain them in Sec. 1•7.

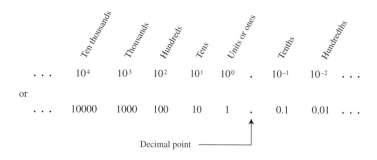

— **Example 1:** In the number 351.3, the digit 3 on the right has the value $\frac{3}{10}$, but the digit 3 on the left has the value 300. Thus

$$351.3 = 300 + 50 + 1 + 0.3$$
$$= 3(10^2) + 5(10^1) + 1(10^0) + 3(10^{-1})$$

The position immediately to the left of the decimal point is called position 0. The position numbers then increase to the left and decrease to the right of the 0 position. —

Place Value

Each position in a number has a *place value* equal to the base of the number system raised to the position number. The place values in the decimal number system, as well as the place names, are shown in Figure 1•1.

Signed Numbers

A *positive* number is a number that is greater than zero, and a *negative* number is *less* than zero. On the *number line* (Fig. 1•2) it is customary to show the positive numbers to the right of zero and the negative numbers to the left of zero. Negative numbers may be integers or fractions, rational numbers or irrational numbers. To distinguish negative numbers from positive numbers we always place a negative sign $(-)$ in front of a negative number.

FIGURE 1•2 The number line

Negative   Positive

$-\sqrt{30}$ $-\frac{7}{2}$ -1.75 $\sqrt{2}$ π $\frac{9}{2}$ 5.6394

-6 -5 -4 -3 -2 -1 0 1 2 3 4 5 6

— **Example 2:** Some negative numbers are

$$-5, \; -6.293, \; -\tfrac{2}{3}, \; -2\tfrac{7}{8}, \; -\sqrt{5}$$ —

We usually omit writing the positive sign $(+)$ in front of a positive number. Thus a number without a sign is always assumed to be positive. In this chapter we will often write a $(+)$ sign for emphasis.

— **Example 3:** Some positive numbers are

$$5, \; +5, \; \tfrac{2}{3}, \; +\tfrac{2}{3}, \; \sqrt{5}$$

The Opposite of a Number

The *opposite* of a number n is the number which, when added to n, gives a sum of zero.

━ **Example 4:** The opposite of 2 is −2, because $2 + (-2) = 0$. The opposite of −6 is +6. ━

Geometrically, the opposite of a number n lies on the opposite side of the zero point of the number line from n, and at an equal distance (see Fig. 1•2).
The opposite of a number is also called the *additive inverse* of that number.

Symbols of Equality and Inequality

Several symbols are used to show the relative positions of two quantities on the number line.

$a = b$ means that *a equals b* and that a and b occupy the same position on the number line.

$a \neq b$ means that a and b are *not equal* and have different locations on the number line.

$a > b$ means that a is *greater than b* and a lies to the right of b on the number line.

$a < b$ means that a is *less than b* and a lies to the left of b on the number line.

$a \cong b$ means that a is *approximately equal to b* and that a and b are *near* each other on the number line.

Absolute Value

The *absolute value* of a number n is its *magnitude*, regardless of its algebraic sign. It is the distance from n to zero on the number line, without regard to direction. When the absolute value of a number is required, the number is written between vertical lines, as in $|n|$ or $|-n|$.

Many calculators have a key for evaluating absolute values. Try to use it to evaluate any of these expressions.

━ **Example 5:**
(a) $|5| = 5$
(b) $|-9| = 9$
(c) $|3 - 7| = |-4| = 4$
(d) $-|-4| = -4$
(e) $-|7 - 21| - |13 - 19| = -|-14| - |-6| = -14 - 6 = -20$ ━

Approximate Numbers

Most of the numbers we deal with in technology are *approximate*.

━ **Example 6:**
(a) All numbers that represent *measured* quantities are approximate. A certain shaft, for example, is approximately 175 mm in diameter.
(b) Many *fractions* can be expressed only approximately in decimal form. Thus $\frac{2}{3}$ is approximately equal to 0.6667.

(c) *Irrational numbers* can be written only approximately in decimal form. The number $\sqrt{3}$ is approximately equal to 1.732.   ▬

Exact Numbers

Exact numbers are those that *have no uncertainty.*

▬ **Example 7:**
(a) There are *exactly* 24 hours in a day, no more, no fewer.
(b) A bicycle has *exactly* two wheels.
(c) Exact numbers are usually integers, but not always. For example, by definition, a vertical column of 10.34 m of water or of 766 mm of mercury is *exactly* one standard atmosphere (101 325 Pa).
(d) On the other hand, not all integers are exact. For example, a certain town has a population of *approximately* 3500 people.   ▬

Significant Digits

In a decimal number, zeros are sometimes used just to locate the decimal point. When used in that way, we say that those zeros are *not significant*. The remaining digits in the number, including zeros, are called *significant digits*.

An overscore is sometimes placed over the last trailing zero that is significant. Thus, the numbers 32.5$\overline{0}$ and 735 $\overline{0}$00 have four significant digits each.

▬ **Example 8:**
(a) The numbers 497.3, 39.05, 8003, and 2.008 each have *four* significant digits.
(b) The numbers 1570, 24 900, 0.0583, and 0.000583 each have *three* significant digits. The zeros in these numbers serve only to locate the decimal point.
(c) The numbers 18.50, 1.490, and 2.000 each have *four* significant digits. The zeros here are not needed to locate the decimal point. They are placed there to show that those digits are in fact zeros, and not something else.   ▬

Accuracy and Precision

The *accuracy* of a decimal number is given by the number of *significant digits* in the number; the *precision* of a decimal number is given by the position of the rightmost significant digit.

▬ **Example 9:**
(a) The number 1.255 is accurate to four significant digits, and precise to three decimal places. We also say that it is precise to the nearest thousandth.
(b) The number 23 800 is accurate to three significant digits, and precise to the nearest hundred.   ▬

Rounding

We will see, in the next few sections, that the numbers we get from a computation often contain *worthless digits* that must be *replaced with zero*. Whenever we do this, we must *round* our answer.

Round down (do not change the last retained digit) when the first digit replaced with zero is 4 or less. *Round up* (increase the last retained digit by one) when the first digit replaced with zero is 6 or more, or a 5 followed by a nonzero digit in any of the decimal places to the right.

■ **Example 10:**

NUMBER	ROUNDED TO THREE DECIMAL PLACES
4.3654	4.365
4.3656	4.366
4.365501	4.366
1.764999	1.765
1.927499	1.927

When the portion of the number replaced by zeros is 5 *exactly*, it does not usually matter whether you round up or down. The exception is when adding or subtracting a long column of figures, as in statistical computations. If, when replacing a 5 with zero, you always rounded up, you could bias the result in that direction. To avoid that you want to round up about as many times as you round down, and a simple way to do that is always to *round to the nearest even number*.

■ **Example 11:**

NUMBER	ROUNDED TO TWO DECIMAL PLACES
4.365	4.36
4.355	4.36
7.76500	7.76
7.75500	7.76

Exercise 1 The Real Numbers

Equality and Inequality Signs

Insert the proper sign of equality or inequality ($=, \cong, >, <$) between each pair of numbers.

1. 7 and 10
2. 9 and -2
3. -3 and 4
4. -3 and -5
5. $\frac{3}{4}$ and 0.75
6. $\frac{2}{3}$ and 0.667

Absolute Value

Evaluate each expression.

7. $-|9 - 23| - |-7 + 3|$
8. $|12 - 5 + 8| - |-6| + |15|$
9. $-|3 - 9| - |5 - 11| + |21 + 4|$

Significant Digits

Determine the number of significant digits in each approximate number:

10. 78.3   **11.** 9274   **12.** 4.008   **13.** 9400
14. 20 000   **15.** 5000.0   **16.** 0.9972   **17.** 1.0000

Round each number to two decimal places:

18. 38.468   **19.** 1.996   **20.** 96.835001   **21.** 55.8650
22. 398.372   **23.** 2.9573   **24.** 2985.339   **25.** 278.382

Round each number to one decimal place:

26. 13.98   **27.** 745.62   **28.** 5.6501   **29.** 0.482
30. 398.36   **31.** 34.927   **32.** 9839.2857   **33.** 0.847

Round each number to the nearest hundred:

34. 28 583   **35.** 7550   **36.** 3 845 240   **37.** 274 837

Round each number to three significant digits:

38. 9.284   **39.** 2857   **40.** 0.04825   **41.** 483 982
42. 0.08375   **43.** 29.555   **44.** 29.45001   **45.** 8372

1•2

Throughout this text, calculator key strokes will be shown in small blue frames, even though the actual key name varies from one calculator to another. You will need to consult your calculator manual to find the right key name.

Addition and Subtraction

Adding and Subtracting Integers

To add two numbers by calculator, simply enter the first number, press $\boxed{+}$, enter the second number, and press the *equals* key $\boxed{=}$, the *execute* key $\boxed{\text{EXE}}$, or the *enter* key $\boxed{\text{ENTER}}$, depending upon your particular calculator. The number we get is called the *sum*.

▬ **Example 12:** Evaluate 2845 + 1172 by calculator.

Solution: There are many types of calculators in use, so the names of the keys and the appearance of the display may be slightly different from those shown here. You should, however, be able to use the keystrokes shown here as a guide in operating your own calculator, but be sure to check your operating manual. The keystrokes are:

> 2845 $\boxed{+}$ 1172 $\boxed{\text{EXE}}$
>
>   4017

If we had wanted to *subtract* 1172 from 2845, we would have simply pressed the $\boxed{-}$ key instead of the $\boxed{+}$ key. ▬

Horizontal and Vertical Addition

Numbers to be added may be arranged vertically or horizontally. Of course, when using the calculator it does not make any difference how the numbers are arranged, as they must be keyed in one at a time anyway.

■ **Example 13:** The addition of 335, 103, and 224 may be represented horizontally

$$335 + 103 + 224 = 662$$

or vertically

$$
\begin{array}{r}
335 \\
103 \\
\underline{224} \\
662
\end{array}
$$

■

Adding Signed Numbers

FIGURE 1·3 The shoe box

Let us say that we have a shoe box (Fig. 1·3) into which we toss all our uncashed cheques and unpaid bills until we have time to deal with them. Let us further assume that the total value of the cheques minus the total value of the bills in the shoebox is $500.

We can think of the amount of a cheque as a positive number because it increases our wealth, and the amount of a bill as a negative number because it decreases our wealth. We thus represent a cheque for $100 as (+$100) and a bill for $200 as (−$200).

Now, let's *add a cheque* for $100 to the box. If we had $500 at first, we must now have $600.

$$\$500 + (+\$100) = \$600$$

or

$$\$500 + \$100 = \$600$$

Here we have added a positive number, and our total has increased by that amount. That is easy to understand. But what does it mean to *add a negative number*.

To find out, let us now *add a bill* for $100 to the box. If we had $500 at first, we must now have $100 less, or $400. Representing the bill by (−$100) we have

$$\$500 + (-\$100) = \$400$$

It seems clear that to add a negative number is no different from subtracting the absolute value of that number.

$$500 + (-100) = 500 - 100$$

This gives us our rule of signs for addition. If b is a positive quantity, then *the operation of adding a negative quantity $(-b)$ to the quantity a is equivalent to the operation of subtracting the positive quantity b from a.*

All boxed and numbered formulas are tabulated in Appendix A. There they are arranged in logical order, by type, and are numbered consecutively. Since the formulas often appear in the text in a different order than in Appendix A, they may not be in numerical order here.

Rule of Signs for Addition	$a + (-b) = a - b$	6

■ **Example 14:**
(a) $7 + (-2) = 7 - 2 = 5$
(b) $-8 + (-3) = -8 - 3 = -11$
(c) $9.92 + (-15.36) = 9.92 - 15.36 = -5.44$

■

Subtracting Signed Numbers

Let us return to our shoebox problem. But now instead of adding cheques or bills to the box, we will *subtract* (remove) cheques or bills from the box.

First we remove (subtract) a cheque for $100 from the box. If we had $500 at first, we must now have $400.

$$\$500 - (+\$100) = \$400$$

or

$$\$500 - \$100 = \$400$$

Here we have subtracted a positive number, and our total has decreased by the amount subtracted, as expected.

Now let us see what it means to *subtract a negative number*. We will remove (subtract) a bill for $100 from the box. If we had $500 at first, we must now have $100 more, or $600, since we have removed a bill. Representing the bill by $(-\$100)$ we have

$$\$500 - (-\$100) = \$600$$

It seems clear that to subtract a negative number is the same as to add the absolute value of that number.

$$500 - (-100) = 500 + 100$$

Thus, if b is a positive quantity, our rule of signs for subtraction is *the operation of subtracting a negative quantity $(-b)$ from a quantity a is equivalent to the operation of adding the positive quantity b to a.*

Rule of Signs for Subtraction	$a - (-b) = a + b$	7

■ **Example 15:**
(a) $15 - (-3) = 15 + 3 = 18$
(b) $-5 - (-9) = -5 + 9 = 4$
(c) $-25.62 - (-5.15) = -25.62 + 5.15 = -20.47$ ■

Subtracting Negative Numbers by Calculator

Note that the negative sign on a calculator is defined in two different ways, and is used for two different purposes:

  1. For the operation of subtraction
  2. To enter a negative quantity

This difference is clear on the calculator, which has separate keys for these two functions. The $\boxed{-}$ key is used only for subtraction; the $\boxed{(-)}$ key is used to enter a negative quantity.

Common Error	These two keys look almost alike, so be careful not to confuse them. Note that the key used to enter a negative quantity has parentheses around the negative sign.

To enter a negative number, simply press the $\boxed{(-)}$ key and then key in the number.

On some calculators a negative number is entered by first keying in the number, then changing its sign by using a *change-sign key*, marked $\boxed{+/-}$ or $\boxed{\text{CHS}}$. Check your manual to see how this key is marked on your calculator.

Try the following examples on your calculator and see if you get the correct answers.

━━ **Example 16:**
(a) $15 - (-3) = 15 + 3 = 18$
(b) $-5 - (-9) = -5 + 9 = 4$
(c) $-25 - (-5) = -25 + 5 = -20$ ━━

Commutative and Associative Laws

These laws are surely familiar to you, even if you do not recognize their names. We will run into them again when studying algebra.

The *commutative law* simply says that you can add numbers in *any order*.

Commutative Law for Addition	$a + b = b + a$	**1**

━━ **Example 17:**

$$2 + 3 = 3 + 2$$
$$= 5$$ ━━

The *associative law* says that you can group numbers to be added in several ways.

Associative Law for Addition	$a + (b + c) = (a + b) + c$ $= (a + c) + b$	**3**

━━ **Example 18:**

$$2 + 3 + 4 = 2 + (3 + 4) = 2 + 7 = 9$$
$$= (2 + 3) + 4 = 5 + 4 = 9$$
$$= (2 + 4) + 3 = 6 + 3 = 9$$ ━━

Addition and Subtraction of Approximate Numbers

Addition and subtraction of integers is simple enough. Now let us tackle the problem mentioned earlier: How many digits do we keep in our answer when adding or subtracting *approximate numbers*?

Rule	When adding or subtracting approximate numbers, keep as many decimal places in your answer as contained in the number having the fewest decimal places.

━━ **Example 19:**

$$32.4 \text{ cm} + 5.825 \text{ cm} = 38.2 \text{ cm} \quad (not\ 38.225 \text{ cm})$$

We do not use the symbol $\cong$ when dealing with approximate numbers. We would not write, for example, $32.4 \text{ cm} + 5.825 \text{ cm} \cong 38.2 \text{ cm}$.

Here we can see the reason for our rule for rounding. In one of the original numbers (32.4 cm) we do not know what digit is to the right of the 4, in the hundredths place. We cannot assume it is zero, for if we *knew* that it was zero it would have been written in (as 32.**40**). This uncertainty in the hundredths place in an original number causes uncertainty in the hundredths place in the answer, so we discard that digit and any to the right of it.　▬

▬ **Example 20:**

$$
\begin{array}{r}
25.8 \\
18.3\,125 \\
\underline{5.4\,07} \\
49.5|195
\end{array}
$$

discard ➝

▬

▬ **Example 21:** A certain stadium contains about 3500 people. It starts to rain and 372 people leave. How many are left in the stadium?

Solution: Subtracting, we obtain

$$3500 - 372 = 3128$$

which we round to 3100, because 3500 here is known to only two significant digits.　▬

It is safer to round the answer *after* adding, rather than to round the original numbers before adding. If you do round before adding, it is prudent to round each original number to *one more* decimal place than you expect in the rounded answer.

Combining Exact and Approximate Numbers

When combining an exact number and an approximate one, the accuracy of the result will be limited by the approximate number. Thus round the result to the number of decimal places found in the approximate number, even though the exact number may *appear* to have fewer decimal places.

▬ **Example 22:** Express 2 hr and 35.8 min in minutes.

Solution: We must add an exact number (120) and an approximate number (35.8):

$$
\begin{array}{r}
120\ \ \ \text{min} \\
+\ \underline{35.8\ \text{min}} \\
155.8\ \text{min}
\end{array}
$$

Since 120 is exact, we do *not* round our answer to the nearest 10 minutes, but retain as many decimal places as in the approximate number. Our answer is thus 155.8 min.　▬

Common Error	Be sure to recognize which numbers in a computation are exact; otherwise, you may perform drastic rounding by mistake.

Students *hate* to throw away those last digits. Remember that by keeping worthless digits you are telling whoever reads that number that it is more precise than it really is.

Exercise 2 Addition and Subtraction

Combine as indicated:

1.	**2.**	**3.**
-955	8275	-748
$+212$	-2163	-212
-347	$-\ 874$	-156

Add each column of figures:

4.	**5.**	**6.**
$99.84	96 256	98 304
24.96	6 016	6 144
6.24	376	384
1.56	141	24 576
12.48	188	3 072
0.98	1 504	144
3.12	752	49 152

Combine as indicated:

7. $926 + 863$

8. $274 + (-412)$

9. $-576 + (-553)$

10. $-207 + (-819)$

11. $-575 - 275$

12. $-771 - (-976)$

13. $1123 - (-704)$

14. $818 - (-207) + 318$

Combine each set of approximate numbers as indicated. Round your answer.

15. $4857 + 73.8$

16. $39.75 + 27.4$

17. $296.44 + 296.997$

18. $385.28 - 692.8$

19. $0.000583 + 0.0008372 - 0.00173$

20. Mont Blanc is 4745 m high, and Mont Tremblant is about 3000 m high. What is the difference in their heights?

21. Ontario covers 1 068 580 km² and Quebec 1 540 680 km². How much larger in land area is Quebec than Ontario?

22. A man willed $125 000 to his wife and two children. To one child he gave $44 675, to the other $26 380, and to his wife the remainder. What was his wife's share?

23. A circular pipe has an inside radius r of 106 mm and a wall thickness of 21.25 mm. It is surrounded by insulation having a thickness of 48 mm (Fig. 1•4). What is the outside diameter d of the insulation?

24. A batch of concrete is made by mixing 267 kg of aggregate, 125 kg of sand, 75.5 kg of cement, and 25.25 kg of water. Find the total mass of the mixture.

25. Three resistors, having values of 27.3 ohms (Ω), 4.0155 Ω, and 9.75 Ω, are wired in series. What is the total resistance? (See Eq. A63, which says that the total series resistance is the sum of the individual resistances.)

Pipe

Insulation

FIGURE 1•4 An insulated pipe

Formula (equation—Eq.) numbers with the prefix "A" are applications. They are listed in Appendix A on pages A•33 to A•38.

1·3

Multiplication

Factors and Product

The numbers we multiply to get a *product* are called *factors*.

$$3 \times 5 = 15$$

factors ⎯⎯⎯⎯⎯   �⎯ product

Multiplication by Calculator

The keystrokes used to multiply the factors 23 and 57 are:

23 ⊠ 57 ⎍EXE⎍

1311

Commutative, Associative, and Distributive Laws

The *commutative law* states that the *order* of multiplication is not important.

Commutative Law for Multiplication	$ab = ba$	**2**

■ **Example 23:** It is no surprise that

$$2 \times 3 = 3 \times 2$$ ■

The *associative law* allows us to group in any way the numbers to be multiplied.

Associative Law for Multiplication	$a(bc) = (ab)c = (ac)b = abc$	**4**

■ **Example 24:**

$$2 \times 3 \times 4 = 2(3 \times 4) = 2(12) = 24$$
$$= (2 \times 3)4 = (6)4 \ = 24$$
$$= (2 \times 4)3 = (8)3 \ = 24$$ ■

The *distributive law* shows how a factor may be *distributed* among several terms.

Distributive Law for Multiplication	$a(b + c) = ab + ac$	**5**

■ **Example 25:**

$$2(3 + 4) = 2(7) = 14$$

But the distributive law enables us to do the same computation in a different way:

$$2(3 + 4) = 2(3) + 2(4) = 6 + 8$$
$$= 14 \quad \text{as before} \quad \blacksquare$$

Multiplying Signed Numbers

To get our rules of signs for multiplication, we use the idea of *multiplication as repeated addition*. For example, to multiply 3 by 4 means to add four 3s (or three 4s).

$$3 \times 4 = 3 + 3 + 3 + 3$$

or

$$3 \times 4 = 4 + 4 + 4$$

Let us return to our shoebox example. Recall that it contains uncashed cheques and unpaid bills. Let's first *add 5 cheques* (+5), each worth $100 (+$100), to the box. The value of the contents of the box then increases by $500. Multiplying,

(number of cheques) $\times$ (value of one cheque) = change in value of contents

$$(+5)(+\$100) = +\$500$$

Thus a positive number times a positive number gave a positive product. This is nothing new.

Now let's *add 5 bills*, each with a value of $100, to the box, thus decreasing its value by $500. To show this multiplication, we use (+5) for the number of bills, (−$100) for the value of each bill, and (−$500) for the change in value of the box contents.

$$(+5)(-\$100) = -\$500$$

Here, a positive number times a negative number gives a negative product.

Next we *remove 5 cheques*, each worth $100, from the box, thus decreasing its value by $500.

$$(-5)(+\$100) = -\$500$$

Here again, the product of a positive number and a negative number is negative. Thus it doesn't matter whether the negative number is the first or the second. This, of course, is what you would expect from the commutative property, which applies to negative numbers as well as to positive numbers.

Finally, we *remove 5 bills*, each with a value of $100, from the box, causing its value to increase by $500.

$$(-5)(-\$100) = +\$500$$

Here, the product of two negative numbers is positive.

We summarize these findings to get our *rules of signs for multiplication*. If a and b are two positive numbers, then *the product of two quantities of like sign is positive*:

Rule of Signs for Multiplication	$(+a)(+b) = (-a)(-b) = +ab$	**8**

and *the product of two quantities of unlike sign is negative*:

Rule of Signs for Multiplication	$(+a)(-b) = (-a)(+b) = -ab$	**9**

■ **Example 26:**
(a) $2(-3) = -6$
(b) $(-2)3 = -6$
(c) $(-2)(-3) = 6$ ■

Multiplying a String of Numbers

When we multiply two negative numbers we get a positive product. Thus, when multiplying a *string* of numbers, if an even number of them are negative, the answer will be positive, and, if an odd number of them are negative, the answer will be negative.

■ **Example 27:**
(a) $2(-3)(-1)(-2) = -12$
(b) $2(-3)(-1)(2) = 12$ ■

Multiplying Negative Numbers by Calculator

As we mentioned earlier, negative numbers are entered into the calculator by using a key marked $\boxed{(-)}$, $\boxed{+/-}$, or $\boxed{\text{CHS}}$. On some calculators you first enter the number and then change its sign using the proper key; on other calculators you enter the minus sign first and then the number, as in the following example.

■ **Example 28:** To multiply -96 and -83, we use the following keystrokes:

$\boxed{(-)}$ 96 $\boxed{\times}$ $\boxed{(-)}$ 83 $\boxed{\text{EXE}}$
7968

■

A simpler way to do the last problem would be to multiply $+96$ and $+83$ and determine the sign by inspection.

Common Error	Do not try to use the $\boxed{-}$ key to enter negative numbers into your calculator. The $\boxed{-}$ key is only for subtraction.

Multiplication of Approximate Numbers

Rule	When multiplying two or more approximate numbers, round the result to as many digits as are in the factor having the fewest significant digits.

▬ **Example 29:**

$$12.1 \quad \times \quad 15.6 \quad = \quad 189$$

three digits	three digits	three digits

▬

When the factors have different numbers of significant digits, keep the same number of digits in your answer as contained in the factor that has the *fewest* significant digits.

▬ **Example 30:**

$$123.56 \quad \times \quad 2.21 \quad = \quad 273$$

five digits	three digits	keep three digits

▬

Common Error	Do not confuse *significant digits* with *decimal places*. The number 274.56 has *five* significant digits and *two* decimal places.
	Decimal places determine how we round after adding or subtracting. Significant figures determine how we round after multiplying, and, as we will soon see, after dividing, raising to a power, or taking roots.

Multiplication with Exact Numbers

When using *exact numbers* in a computation, treat them as if they had *more* significant digits than any of the approximate numbers in that computation.

▬ **Example 31:** If a certain car tire mass is 14.68 kg, how much will four such tires have in total mass?

Solution: Multiplying, we obtain

$$14.68(4) = 58.72 \text{ kg}$$

Since the 4 is an exact number, we retain as many significant figures as contained in 14.68, and round our answer to 58.7 kg. ▬

Exercise 3 Multiplication

Multiply each approximate number and retain the proper number of digits in your answer:

1. 3967×1.84 **2.** 4.900×59.3
3. 93.9×0.0055908 **4.** $4.97 \times 9.27 \times 5.78$
5. $69.0 \times (-258)$ **6.** $-385 \times (-2.2978)$
7. $2.86 \times (4.88 \times 2.97) \times 0.553$ **8.** $(5.93 \times 7.28) \times (8.26 \times 1.38)$

Word Problems

  9. What is the cost of 52.5 tonnes of cement at $63.25 a tonne?
 10. If 100 tonnes of rail are needed for 2 km of track, how many tonnes will be required for 760 km, and what will be the cost at $925 a tonne?
 11. Three barges carry 26 tonnes of gravel each and a fourth carries 35 tonnes. What is the value, to the nearest dollar, of the whole shipment, at $12.75 per tonne?
 12. Two cars start from the same place and travel in opposite directions, one at the rate of 45 km/h, the other at 55 km/h. How far apart will they be at the end of 6.0 h?
 13. What will be the cost of installing a telephone line 274 km long, at $5723 per kilometre?
 14. The current to a projection lamp is measured at 4.7 A when the line voltage is 115.45 V. Using Eq. A65 (power = voltage × current), find the power dissipated in the lamp.
 15. A gear in a certain machine rotates at the speed of 1808 rev/min. How many revolutions will it make in 9.500 min?
 16. Find the mass of 1000 washers if the mass of one washer is 2.375 g.
 17. If there are 360 degrees per revolution, how many degrees are there in 4.863 revolutions?

1•4

Division

Definitions

The *dividend*, when divided by the *divisor*, gives us the *quotient*:

$$\text{dividend} \div \text{divisor} = \text{quotient}$$

or

$$\frac{\text{dividend}}{\text{divisor}} = \text{quotient}$$

A quantity *a/b* is also a *fraction*, and can also be referred to as the *ratio* of *a* to *b*. Fractions and ratios are treated in Chapter 8.

Division by Calculator

■ **Example 32:** To divide 861 by 123, the keystrokes are

> 861 ÷ 123 EXE
>
> 7

When we multiplied two integers, we always got an integer for an answer. This is not always the case when dividing.

■ **Example 33:** When we divide 2 by 3, we get 0.666666666. . . . We must choose how many digits we wish to retain, and round our answer. Rounding to, say, three significant digits, we obtain

$$2 \div 3 \cong 0.667$$

Here it is appropriate to use the $\cong$ symbol.

Division of Approximate Numbers

The rule for rounding is almost the same as with multiplication.

Rule	After dividing one approximate number by another, round the quotient to as many digits as there are in the original number having the fewer significant digits.

■ **Example 34:**

Solution: By calculator,

$$846.2 \div 4.75 = 178.1473684$$

Since 4.75 has three significant digits, we round our quotient to 178. ■

■ **Example 35:** Divide 846.2 into three equal parts.

Solution: We divide by the integer 3, and since we consider integers to be exact, we retain in our answer the same number of significant digits as in 846.2.

$$846.2 \div 3 = 282.1$$ ■

Dividing Signed Numbers

We will use the rules of signs for multiplication to get the rules of signs for division.

We know that the product of a negative number and a positive number is negative. Thus,

$$(-2)(+3) = -6$$

If we divide both sides of this equation by $(+3)$ we get

$$-2 = \frac{-6}{+3}$$

From this we see that *a negative number divided by a positive number gives a negative quotient.*

Again starting with

$$(-2)(+3) = -6$$

we divide both sides by (-2) and get

$$+3 = \frac{-6}{-2}$$

Here we see that *a negative number divided by a negative number gives a positive product.*

We also know that the product of two negative numbers is positive. Thus

$$(-2)(-3) = +6$$

Dividing both sides by (-3) we get

$$-2 = \frac{+6}{-3}$$

Thus *a positive number divided by a negative number gives a negative quotient*. We combine these findings with the fact that the quotient of two positive numbers is positive and get our *rules of signs for division*.

The quotient is positive when dividend and divisor have the same sign.

Rule of Signs for Division	$\dfrac{+a}{+b} = \dfrac{-a}{-b} = \dfrac{a}{b}$	**10**

The quotient is negative when dividend and divisor have opposite signs.

Rule of Signs for Division	$\dfrac{+a}{-b} = \dfrac{-a}{+b} = -\dfrac{a}{b}$	**11**

■ **Example 36:**
(a) $8 \div (-4) = -2$
(b) $-8 \div 4 = -2$
(c) $-8 \div (-4) = 2$ ■

■ **Example 37:** Divide 85.4 by -2.5386 on the calculator.

Solution: The keystrokes are:

$$\boxed{85.4 \; \fbox{÷} \; \fbox{(−)} \; 2.5386 \; \fbox{EXE}}$$
$$-33.6405893$$

which we round to three significant digits, getting -33.6. ■

As with multiplication, the sign could also have been found by inspection.

Zero

Zero divided by any quantity (except zero) is zero. But division *by* zero is not defined. It is an illegal operation in mathematics.

■ **Example 38:** Using your calculator, divide 5 by zero.

Solution: You should get an error message on your calculator. ■

Reciprocals

The *reciprocal* of any number n is $1/n$. Thus the product of a quantity and its reciprocal is equal to 1.

■ **Example 39:**
(a) The reciprocal of 10 is 1/10.
(b) The reciprocal of 1/2 is 2.
(c) The reciprocal of $-\frac{3}{4}$ is $-\frac{4}{3}$. ■

Reciprocals by Calculator

Simply enter the number and press the $\boxed{1/x}$ key or the $\boxed{x^{-1}}$ key. Keep as many digits in your answer as there are significant digits in the original number.

▬ **Example 40:**
(a) The reciprocal of 6.38 is 0.157.
(b) The reciprocal of -2.754 is -0.3631.

Exercise 4 Division

Divide, then round your answer to the proper number of digits.

1. $947 \div 5.82$	**2.** $0.492 \div 0.00478$	**3.** $-99.4 \div 286.5$
4. $-4.8 \div -2.557$	**5.** $5836 \div 8264$	**6.** $5.284 \div 3.827$
7. $94\,840 \div 1.33876$	**8.** $3.449 \div (-6.837)$	
9. $2\,497\,000 \div 150\,000$	**10.** $2.97 \div 4.828$	

Word Problems Involving Division

11. A stretch of roadway 1858.54 m long is to be divided into five equal sections. Find the length of each section.
12. At the rate of 24.5 km in 8.25 h, how many kilometres would a person walk in 12.75 h? (Distance = rate × time)
13. If five masons can build a wall in eight days, how many masons are needed to build it in four days?
14. If 867 shares of railway stock are valued at $84 099, what is the value of each share?

Reciprocals

Find the reciprocal of each number, retaining the proper number of digits in your answer.

15. 693	**16.** 0.00630	**17.** $-396\,000$	**18.** 39.74
19. -0.00573	**20.** 938.4	**21.** 4.992	**22.** -6.93
23. 11.1	**24.** -375	**25.** 1.007	**26.** 3.98

Word Problems Involving Reciprocals

27. Using Eq. A64, find the equivalent resistance of a 473-Ω resistor and a 928-Ω resistor, connected in parallel.
28. When an object is placed 1260 mm in front of a certain thin lens having a focal length f, the image will be formed 2450 mm from the lens. The distances are related as in

$$\frac{1}{f} = \frac{1}{1260} + \frac{1}{2450}$$

Find f from this relationship.
29. The sine of an angle θ (written sin θ) is equal to the reciprocal of the cosecant of θ (csc θ). Find sin θ if csc $\theta = 3.58$.
30. If two straight lines are perpendicular to each other, the slope of one line is the negative reciprocal of the slope of the other. If the slope of a line is -2.55, find the slope of a perpendicular to that line.

1•5

Powers and Roots

Definitions

In the expression 2^4, the number 2 is called the *base* and the number 4 is called the *exponent*. The expression is read "two to the fourth power." Its value is

$$2^4 = 2 \cdot 2 \cdot 2 \cdot 2 = 16$$

Powers by Calculator

To square a number on the calculator, simply enter the number and press the $\boxed{x^2}$ key. To raise a number to other powers, use the $\boxed{y^x}$, $\boxed{x^y}$, or $\boxed{\wedge}$ key, as in the following example. Round your result to the number of significant digits contained *in the base*, not the exponent.

▬ **Example 41:** Find $(3.85)^3$.

    Solution: The keystrokes are:

$$3.85 \ \boxed{\wedge} \ 3 \ \boxed{\text{EXE}}$$
$$57.066625$$

which we round to 57.1. ▬

Negative Base

A negative base raised to an *even* power gives a *positive* number. A negative base raised to an *odd* power gives a *negative* number.

▬ **Example 42:**
(a) $(-2)^2 = (-2)(-2) = 4$
(b) $(-2)^3 = (-2)(-2)(-2) = -8$
(c) $(-1)^{24} = 1$
(d) $(-1)^{25} = -1$ ▬

When using your graphics calculator, do not omit the parentheses, ( ). In Example 42(a), $(-)2^2$ gives -4; $((-)2)^2$ gives 4, the correct result.

Try to do these problems on your calculator, but be aware that you could get an error indication. Some calculators will not work with a negative base, even though this is a valid operation.

    Then how do you do it? Simply enter the base as *positive*, find the power, and determine the sign by inspection.

▬ **Example 43:** Find $(-1.45)^5$.

    Solution: From the calculator,

$$(+1.45)^5 = 6.41$$

Since we know that a negative number raised to an odd power is negative, we write

$$(-1.45)^5 = -6.41$$ ▬

Negative Exponent

A number can be raised to a negative exponent on the calculator with the y^x, x^y, or $\wedge$ key.

■ Example 44: To evaluate $(3.85)^{-3}$, the keystrokes are:

> 3.85 $\boxed{\wedge}$ $\boxed{(-)}$ 3 $\boxed{\text{EXE}}$
>
> 0.01752337

which we round to 0.0175. Notice that raising a positive number to a negative power does not result in a negative number. ■

Fractional Exponents

We'll see later that fractional exponents are another way of writing radicals. For now, we'll just evaluate fractional exponents on the calculator. The keystrokes are the same as before, but we must make sure that the fractional exponent is enclosed in parentheses, as shown in the following example.

■ Example 45: To evaluate $8^{2/3}$, we use the following keystrokes:

> 8 $\boxed{\wedge}$ $\boxed{(}$ 2 $\boxed{\div}$ 3 $\boxed{)}$ $\boxed{\text{EXE}}$
>
> 4
■

Roots

If $a^n = b$, then

$$\sqrt[n]{b} = a \qquad \text{or} \qquad b^{1/n} = a$$

which is read "the nth root of b equals a." The symbol $\sqrt{}$ is a *radical sign*, b is the *radicand*, and n is the *index* of the radical.

■ Example 46:

(a) $\sqrt{4} = 2$ because $2^2 = 4$

(b) $\sqrt[3]{8} = 2$ because $2^3 = 8$

(c) $\sqrt[4]{81} = 3$ because $3^4 = 81$ ■

Principal Root

When we speak about the root of a number we mean, unless otherwise stated, the *principal root*. The principal root of a number has the same sign as the number itself.

The *principal root* of a *positive* number is defined as the *positive* root. Thus $\sqrt{4} = +2$, not ± 2.

The principal root is *negative* when we take an *odd*-numbered root of a *negative* number.

━ **Example 47:**

$$\sqrt[3]{-8} = -2$$

because $(-2)(-2)(-2) = -8$. ━

Roots by Calculator

To find square roots we simply use the $\boxed{\sqrt{}}$ key. To find other roots, use the $\boxed{\wedge}$ key. Retain as many significant digits in the answer as there are significant digits in the original radicand.

Some calculators require that the radicand be entered first, and some require the index to be entered first, as in the following example.

━ **Example 48:** The keystrokes for finding $\sqrt[5]{28.4}$, the fifth root of 28.4, are:

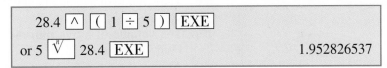

$$28.4 \boxed{\wedge} \boxed{(} 1 \boxed{\div} 5 \boxed{)} \boxed{\text{EXE}}$$

$$\text{or } 5 \boxed{\sqrt[n]{}} 28.4 \boxed{\text{EXE}} \qquad\qquad 1.952826537$$

which we round to 1.95. ━

Odd Roots of Negative Numbers by Calculator

An *even*-numbered root of a negative number is *imaginary* (such as $\sqrt{-4}$). We will study these in Chapter 21. But an *odd*-numbered root of a negative number is *not* imaginary. It is a real, negative, number. As with powers, some calculators will not accept a negative radicand. Fortunately, we can outsmart our calculators and take odd-numbered roots of negative numbers anyway.

━ **Example 49:**

Solution: We know that an odd-numbered root of a negative number is real and negative. So we take the fifth root of $+875$, by calculator,

$$\sqrt[5]{+875} = 3.88 \quad \text{(rounded)}$$

and we only have to place a minus sign before the number.

$$\sqrt[5]{-875} = -3.88$$ ━

Exercise 5 Powers and Roots

Powers

Evaluate each power without using a calculator. Do not round your answers.

1. 2^3	**2.** 5^3	**3.** $(-2)^3$	**4.** 9^2
5. 1^3	**6.** $(-1)^2$	**7.** $(-1)^{40}$	**8.** 3^2
9. 1^8	**10.** $(-1)^3$	**11.** $(-1)^{41}$	**12.** $(-3)^2$

Powers of 10 will be needed for *scientific notation* later. Arrange these powers of 10 in order and try to invent a rule that will enable you to write the value of a power of 10 without doing the computation.

Evaluate each power of 10:

13. 10^2	**14.** 10^1	**15.** 10^0	**16.** 10^{-4}
17. 10^3	**18.** 10^5	**19.** 10^{-2}	**20.** 10^{-1}
21. 10^4	**22.** 10^{-3}	**23.** 10^{-5}	

Evaluate each expression, retaining the correct number of digits in your answer.

24. $(8.55)^3$ **25.** $(1.007)^5$ **26.** $(9.55)^3$ **27.** $(-4.82)^3$
28. $(-77.2)^2$ **29.** $(8.28)^{-2}$ **30.** $(0.0772)^{0.426}$ **31.** $(5.28)^{-2.15}$
32. $(35.2)^{1/2}$ **33.** $(462)^{2/3}$ **34.** $(88.2)^{-2}$ **35.** $(-37.3)^{-3}$

Word Problems Involving Powers

36. The distance travelled by a falling body, starting from rest, is equal to $5t^2$, where t is the elapsed time. In 5.448 s, the distance fallen is $5(5.448)^2$ m. Evaluate this quantity. (Treat 5 here as an approximate number.)

37. The power dissipated in a resistance R through which is flowing a current I is equal to I^2R. Therefore, the power in a 365-Ω resistor carrying a current of 0.5855 A is $(0.5855)^2(365)$ W. Evaluate this power.

38. The volume of a cube of side 358 mm (Fig. 1•5) is $(358)^3$. Evaluate this volume.

39. The volume of a 594-mm-radius sphere (Fig. 1•6) is $\frac{4}{3}\pi (594)^3$ mm³. Find this volume.

40. An investment of $2000 at a compound interest rate of $6\frac{1}{4}\%$, left for $7\frac{1}{2}$ years, will be worth $2000(1.0625)^{7.5}$ dollars. Find this amount, to the nearest cent.

Roots

Find each principal root without using your calculator.

41. $\sqrt{25}$　　　　**42.** $\sqrt[3]{27}$　　　　**43.** $\sqrt{25}$
44. $\sqrt[3]{-27}$　　　**45.** $\sqrt[3]{-8}$　　　**46.** $\sqrt[5]{-32}$

Evaluate each radical by calculator, retaining the proper number of digits in your answer.

47. $\sqrt{49.2}$　　　　**48.** $\sqrt{1.863}$　　　**49.** $\sqrt[3]{88.3}$
50. $\sqrt{772}$　　　　**51.** $\sqrt{3875}$　　　**52.** $\sqrt[3]{7295}$
53. $\sqrt[3]{-386}$　　　**54.** $\sqrt[5]{-18.4}$　　**55.** $\sqrt[3]{-2.774}$

Applications of Roots

56. The period T (time for one swing) of a simple pendulum (Fig. 1•7) 815 mm long is

$$(T =) 2\pi \sqrt{\frac{0.815}{9.8}} \text{ seconds}$$

Evaluate T.

57. The magnitude Z of the impedance in a circuit having a resistance of 3540 Ω and a reactance of 2750 Ω is

$$(Z =) \sqrt{(3540)^2 + (2750)^2} \text{ ohms}$$

Evaluate Z.

58. The geometric mean B between 3.75 and 9.83 is

$$(B =) \sqrt{(3.75)(9.83)}$$

Evaluate B.

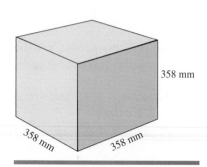
358 mm
358 mm
358 mm

FIGURE 1•5

594 mm

FIGURE 1•6

815 mm

FIGURE 1•7

1•6

Combined Operations

Order of Operations

If the expression to be evaluated does not contain parentheses, perform the operations in the following order.

1. Powers and roots, in any order
2. Multiplications and divisions, from left to right
3. Additions and subtractions, from left to right

Our first group of calculations will be with integers only, and later we will do some problems that require rounding. We first show a problem containing both addition and multiplication.

━ **Example 50:** Evaluate $7 + 3 \times 4$, first without a calculator, and then by calculator.

Solution: The multiplication is done before the addition:

$$7 + 3 \times 4 = 7 + 12 = 19$$

An algebraic or scientific calculator will automatically perform the multiplication before the addition, so we may key in the numbers as written.

$$7 \boxed{+} 3 \boxed{\times} 4 \boxed{\text{EXE}}$$

19 ━

Next we do a calculation having both a power and multiplication.

━ **Example 51:** Evaluate 5×3^2.

Solution: We raise to the power before multiplying:

$$5 \times 3^2 = 5 \times 9 = 45$$

A calculator will do the squaring operation on the 3 only, so there is no need to enter the 3^2 operation first. The keystrokes are:

$$5 \boxed{\times} 3 \boxed{x^2} \boxed{\text{EXE}}$$

45 ━

Parentheses

When an expression contains parentheses, first evaluate the expression within the parentheses and then the entire expression.

━ **Example 52:** Evaluate $(7 + 3) \times 4$.

Solution:

$$(7 + 3) \times 4 = 10 \times 4 = 40$$

The keystrokes are:

40

Note that the use of parentheses was essential here. ▬

If the sum or difference of more than one number is to be raised to a power, those numbers must be enclosed in parentheses.

▬ **Example 53:** Evaluate $(5 + 2)^2$.

Solution: We combine the numbers inside the parentheses before squaring:

$$(5 + 2)^2 = 7^2 = \mathbf{49}$$

There are two ways to do this on a calculator. The first way is to use the $\boxed{=}$, $\boxed{\text{EXE}}$, or $\boxed{\text{ENTER}}$ key to combine the 5 and the 2, before squaring. The keystrokes are:

5 $\boxed{+}$ 2 $\boxed{\text{EXE}}$

7

$\boxed{x^2}$

49

A second way is to use parentheses. The keystrokes are:

$\boxed{(}$ 5 $\boxed{+}$ 2 $\boxed{)}$ $\boxed{x^2}$ $\boxed{\text{EXE}}$

49

On some calculators the result will be displayed immediately after pressing the $\boxed{x^2}$ key. ▬

▬ **Example 54:** Evaluate $(2 + 6)(7 + 9)$.

Solution: The two quantities in parentheses are evaluated before multiplying:

$$(2 + 6)(7 + 9) = 8 + 16 = \mathbf{128}$$

The keystrokes are:

128

On some calculators you do not need the $\boxed{\times}$ key between the two expressions. ▬

■ **Example 55:** Evaluate $\dfrac{8 + 4}{9 - 3}$.

Solution: Here the fraction line acts like parentheses, grouping the 8 and 4, as well as the 9 and 3. Written on a single line, this problem would be

$$(8 + 4) \div (9 - 3)$$

or

$$12 \div 6 = 2$$

The calculator keystrokes are almost the same as for the preceding example. Enter the numerator first and use the $\boxed{\div}$ key instead of the $\boxed{\times}$ key.

$$\boxed{(}\ 8\ \boxed{+}\ 4\ \boxed{)}\ \boxed{\div}\ \boxed{(}\ 9\ \boxed{-}\ 3\ \boxed{)}\ \boxed{\text{EXE}}$$

2

■

Combined Operations with Approximate Numbers

Combined operations with approximate numbers are done the same way. However, we must round our answer properly, using the rules given earlier in this chapter.

■ **Example 56:** Evaluate the expression

$$\left(\frac{118.8 + 4.23}{\sqrt{136}}\right)^3$$

Solution: The keystrokes are:

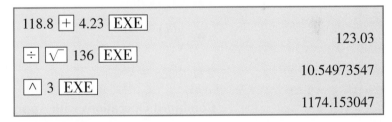

118.8 $\boxed{+}$ 4.23 $\boxed{\text{EXE}}$

123.03

$\boxed{\div}$ $\boxed{\sqrt{\ }}$ 136 $\boxed{\text{EXE}}$

10.54973547

$\boxed{\wedge}$ 3 $\boxed{\text{EXE}}$

1174.153047

Notice that all intermediate results were kept in memory, to the full accuracy of the calculator, and only the answer was rounded. However, if you must write down an intermediate result for later use, keep at least one extra digit and do the final rounding at the end.

How many digits should we keep? In the numerator, we added a number with one decimal place to another with two decimal places, so we are allowed to keep just one. Thus the numerator, after addition, is good to one decimal place, or, in this case, four significant digits. The denominator, however, has just three significant digits, so we round our answer to three significant digits, getting 1170. ■

10 300 mm

6650 mm

x

FIGURE 1•8 A rectangular courtyard

■ **Example 57:** A rectangular courtyard (Fig. 1•8) having sides of 6650 mm and 10 300 mm has a diagonal measurement *x* given by the expression

$$x = \sqrt{(6650)^2 + (10\ 300)^2}$$

Evaluate the expression to find *x*.

Solution: The keystrokes are:

12 260 mm

$x = 12\ 300$ mm   (3 significant digits)

Exercise 6 Combined Operations

Combined Operations with Exact Numbers

Perform each computation by calculator:

1. $(37)(28) + (36)(64)$

2. $(22)(53) - (586)(4) + (47)(59)$

3. $(63 + 36)(37 - 97)$

4. $(89 - 74 + 95)(87 - 49)$

5. $\dfrac{219}{73} + \dfrac{194}{97}$

6. $\dfrac{228}{38} - \dfrac{78}{26} + \dfrac{364}{91}$

7. $\dfrac{647 + 688}{337 + 108}$

8. $\dfrac{809 - 463 + 1858}{958 - 364 + 508}$

9. $(5 + 6)^2$

10. $(422 + 113 - 533)^4$

11. $(423 - 420)^3$

12. $\left(\dfrac{853 - 229}{874 - 562}\right)^2$

13. $\left(\dfrac{141}{47}\right)^3$

14. $\sqrt{434 + 466}$

15. $\sqrt{(8)(72)}$

16. $\sqrt[3]{657 + 553 - 1085}$

17. $\sqrt[4]{(27)(768)}$

18. $\sqrt{\dfrac{2404}{601}}$

19. $\sqrt[4]{\dfrac{1136}{71}}$

20. $\sqrt{961} + \sqrt{121}$

21. $\sqrt[4]{625} + \sqrt{961} - \sqrt[3]{216}$

22. $\sqrt[4]{256} \times \sqrt{49}$

Combined Operations with Approximate Numbers

Perform the computations, keeping the proper number of digits in your answer:

23. $(7.37)(3.28) + (8.36)(2.64)$

24. $(522)(9.53) - (586)(4.70) + (847)(7.59)$

25. $(63.5 + 83.6)(8.37 - 1.72)$

26. $(8.93 - 3.74 + 9.05)(68.70 - 64.90)$

27. $\dfrac{583}{473} + \dfrac{946}{907}$

28. $\dfrac{6.73}{8.38} - \dfrac{5.97}{8.06} + \dfrac{8.63}{1.91}$

29. $\dfrac{6.47 + 8.604}{3.37 + 90.8}$

30. $\dfrac{809 - 463 + 744}{758 - 964 + 508}$

31. $(5.37 + 2.36)^2$

32. $(4.25 + 4.36 - 5.24)^4$

33. $(6.423 + 1.05)^2$

34. $\left(\dfrac{45.3 - 8.34}{8.74 - 5.62}\right)^{2.5}$

35. $\left(\dfrac{8.90}{4.75}\right)^2$

36. $\sqrt{4.34 + 4.66}$

37. $\sqrt[3]{657 + 553 - 842}$

38. $\sqrt{(28.1)(5.94)}$

39. $\sqrt[5]{(9.06)(4.86)(7.93)}$

40. $\sqrt{\dfrac{653}{601}}$

41. $\sqrt[4]{\dfrac{4.50}{7.81}}$

42. $\sqrt{9.74} + \sqrt{12.5}$

43. $\sqrt[4]{528} + \sqrt{94.2} - \sqrt[3]{284}$

44. $\sqrt[4]{653} \times \sqrt{55.3}$

1•7 Scientific Notation

Definitions

Let us multiply two large numbers on the calculator, say, 500 000 and 300 000.

We get a display like [1.5 E + 11] or [1.5 11], depending on the calculator. What has happened?

Our answer (150 000 000 000) is too large to fit the calculator display, so the machine has automatically switched to *scientific notation*. Our calculator display actually contains *two* numbers: a decimal number (1.5) and an integer (11). Our answer is equal to the decimal number, multiplied by 10 raised to the value of the integer.

Calculator display: | 1.5   11 |
Scientific notation: 1.5×10^{11}

decimal part ——————— power of 10

Ten raised to a power (such as 10^{11}) is called a *power of 10*.

A number is said to be in *scientific notation* when it is written as a number whose absolute value is between 1 and 10, multiplied by a power of 10.

▬ **Example 58:**
(a) 2.74×10^3
(b) 8.84×10^9
(c) 5.4×10^{-6}
(d) -1.2×10^{-5}

are numbers written in scientific notation.   ▬

Evaluating Powers of 10

We did some work with powers in Sec. 1•5. We saw, for example, that 2^3 meant

$$2^3 = 2 \cdot 2 \cdot 2 = 8$$

Here, the power 3 tells how many 2s are to be multiplied to give the product. For powers of 10, the power tells how many 10s are to be multiplied to give the product.

■ **Example 59:**

(a) $10^2 = 10 \times 10 = 100$
(b) $10^3 = 10 \times 10 \times 10 = 1000$ ▬

Negative powers, as before, are calculated by means of Eq. 35, $x^{-a} = 1/x^a$.

■ **Example 60:**

(a) $10^{-2} = \dfrac{1}{10^2} = \dfrac{1}{100} = 0.01$

(b) $10^{-5} = \dfrac{1}{10^5} = \dfrac{1}{100\,000} = 0.00001$ ▬

Summarizing some powers of 10 in a table:

POSITIVE POWERS	NEGATIVE POWERS		
$1\,000\,000 = 10^6$	0.1	$= 1/10$	$= 10^{-1}$
$100\,000 = 10^5$	0.01	$= 1/10^2$	$= 10^{-2}$
$10\,000 = 10^4$	0.001	$= 1/10^3$	$= 10^{-3}$
$1\,000 = 10^3$	0.0001	$= 1/10^4$	$= 10^{-4}$
$100 = 10^2$	0.00001	$= 1/10^5$	$= 10^{-5}$
$10 = 10^1$	0.000001	$= 1/10^6$	$= 10^{-6}$
$1 = 10^0$			

Converting Numbers to Scientific Notation

To convert a number to scientific notation, first rewrite the given number with a single digit to the left of the decimal point, discarding any nonsignificant zeros. Then multiply this number by the power of 10 that will make it equal to the original number.

■ **Example 61:**

$$346 = 3.46 \times 100$$
$$= 3.46 \times 10^2$$ ▬

■ **Example 62:**

$$2700 = 2.7 \times 1000$$
$$= 2.7 \times 10^3$$

Note that we have discarded the two nonsignificant zeros. ▬

When converting a number whose absolute value is less than 1, our power of 10 will be negative, as in Example 63.

■ **Example 63:**

$$0.00000950 = 9.50 \times 0.000001$$
$$= 9.50 \times 10^{-6}$$ ▬

The sign of the exponent has nothing to do with the sign of the original number. You can convert a negative number to scientific notation just as you would a positive number, and put the minus sign on afterward.

■ **Example 64:** Convert $-34\ 720$ to scientific notation.

Solution: Converting $+34\ 720$ to scientific notation, we obtain

$$34\ 720 = 3.472 \times 10\ 000$$
$$34\ 720 = 3.472 \times 10^4$$

Then multiplying by -1 gives

$$-34\ 720 = -3.472 \times 10^4$$

To convert from scientific notation, simply reverse the process.

■ **Example 65:**
$$4.82 \times 10^5 = 4.82 \times 100\ 000$$
$$= 482\ 000$$

■ **Example 66:**
$$8.25 \times 10^{-3} = 8.25 \times 0.001$$
$$= 0.00825$$

Addition and Subtraction

If two or more numbers to be added or subtracted have the *same power of 10*, simply combine the numbers and keep the same power of 10.

This is another application of the distributive law, $ab + ac = a(b + c)$. Thus
$$2 \times 10^5 + 3 \times 10^5$$
$$= (2 + 3)10^5$$
$$= 5 \times 10^5$$

■ **Example 67:**
(a) $(2 \times 10^5) + (3 \times 10^5) = 5 \times 10^5$
(b) $(8 \times 10^3) - (5 \times 10^3) + 3 \times 10^3 = 6 \times 10^3$

If the powers of 10 are different, *they must be made equal* before the numbers can be combined. A shift of the decimal point of one place to the *left* will *increase* the exponent by 1. Conversely, a shift of the decimal point one place to the *right* will *decrease* the exponent by 1.

■ **Example 68:**
(a) $(1.5 \times 10^4) + (3 \times 10^3) = (1.5 \times 10^4) + (0.3 \times 10^4)$
$$= 1.8 \times 10^4$$
(b) $(1.25 \times 10^5) - (2 \times 10^4) + (4 \times 10^3)$
$$= (1.25 \times 10^5) - (0.2 \times 10^5) + (0.04 \times 10^5)$$
$$= 1.09 \times 10^5$$

Multiplication

We multiply powers of 10 by *adding their exponents*.

We are really using Eq. 29, $x^a \cdot x^b = x^{a+b}$. This equation is one of the *laws of exponents* that we will study later.

■ **Example 69:**
(a) $10^3 \cdot 10^4 = 10^{3+4} = 10^7$
(b) $10^{-2} \cdot 10^5 = 10^{-2+5} = 10^3$

To multiply two numbers in scientific notation, multiply the decimal parts and the powers of 10 *separately*.

━ **Example 70:**

$$(2 \times 10^5)(3 \times 10^2) = (2 \times 3)(10^3 \times 10^2)$$
$$= 6 \times 10^{5+2} = 6 \times 10^7$$ ━

Division

We divide powers of 10 by subtracting the exponent of the denominator from the exponent of the numerator.

━ **Example 71:**

(a) $\dfrac{10^5}{10^3} = 10^{5-3} = 10^2$ (b) $\dfrac{10^{-4}}{10^{-2}} = 10^{-4-(-2)} = 10^{-2}$ ━

As with multiplication, we divide the decimal parts and the powers of 10 separately.

━ **Example 72:**

(a) $\dfrac{8 \times 10^5}{4 \times 10^2} = \dfrac{8}{4} \times \dfrac{10^5}{10^2} = 2 \times 10^{5-2} = 2 \times 10^3$

(b) $\dfrac{12 \times 10^3}{4 \times 10^5} = 3 \times 10^{3-5} = 3 \times 10^{-2}$ ━

Scientific Notation on Computer or Calculator

A computer or calculator will switch to scientific notation by itself when the printout or display gets too long. For example, a computer might print the number

$$2.75E\text{-}6$$

which we interpret as

$$2.75 \times 10^{-6} \quad \text{or} \quad 0.00000275$$

On a calculator, we can enter numbers in scientific notation with the *enter exponent* key, usually marked $\boxed{\text{EE}}$, $\boxed{\text{EXP}}$, or $\boxed{\text{EEX}}$.

━ **Example 73:** To enter the number 534 000, which is 5.34×10^5 in scientific notation, the keystrokes are

$$5.34 \ \boxed{\text{EE}} \ 5$$ ━

Common Error	Students often enter powers of ten (such as 10^4) incorrectly into their calculators, forgetting that 10^4 is really 1×10^4. Thus to enter 10^4, we press $\qquad\qquad 1 \ \boxed{\text{EE}} \ 4$ *and not* $\qquad\qquad 10 \ \boxed{\text{EE}} \ 4$

Alternatively, we can switch the calculator into scientific notation mode (you may have to select this from a menu; consult your manual). In either case, we then use the same keystrokes as for calculations with decimal numbers, and let the calculator worry about the powers of 10.

━ **Example 74:** To multiply 5.38×10^3 *by* 3.973×10^{-2}, the keystrokes are:

5.38 $\boxed{\text{EE}}$ 3 $\boxed{\times}$ 3.973 $\boxed{\text{EE}}$ $\boxed{(-)}$ 2 $\boxed{\text{EXE}}$
213.7474

which we round to 214.   ━

Exercise 7 Scientific Notation

Powers of 10

Write each number as a power of 10.

1. 100   **2.** 1 000 000   **3.** 0.0001
4. 0.001   **5.** 100 000 000
6. 10^5 **7.** 10^{-2} **8.** 10^{-5}
9. 10^{-1} **10.** 10^4

Scientific Notation

Write each number in scientific notation.

11. 186 000   **12.** 0.0035   **13.** 25 742
14. $80\overline{0}0$ **15.** 98.3×10^3 **16.** 0.0775×10^{-2}

Convert each number from scientific notation to decimal notation.

17. 2.85×10^3 **18.** 1.75×10^{-5} **19.** 9×10^4
20. 9.00×10^4 **21.** 3.667×10^{-3}

Multiplication and Division

Multiply the following powers of 10.

22. $10^5 \cdot 10^2$ **23.** $10^4 \cdot 10^{-3}$ **24.** $10^{-5} \cdot 10^{-4}$
25. $10^{-2} \cdot 10^5$ **26.** $10^{-1} \cdot 10^{-4}$

Divide the following powers of 10.

27. $10^8 \div 10^5$ **28.** $10^4 \div 10^6$ **29.** $10^5 \div 10^{-2}$
30. $10^{-3} \div 10^5$ **31.** $10^{-2} \div 10^{-4}$

Multiply without using a calculator.

32. $(3.0 \times 10^3)(5.0 \times 10^2)$ **33.** $(5 \times 10^4)(8 \times 10^{-3})$
34. $(2 \times 10^{-2})(4 \times 10^{-5})$ **35.** $(7.0 \times 10^4)(3\overline{0}\ 000)$

Divide without using a calculator.

36. $(8 \times 10^4) \div (2 \times 10^2)$

37. $(6 \times 10^4) \div 0.03$

38. $(3 \times 10^3) \div (6 \times 10^5)$

39. $(8 \times 10^{-4}) \div 400\,000$

40. $(9 \times 10^4) \div (3 \times 10^{-2})$

41. $49\,000 \div (7.0 \times 10^{-2})$

Addition and Subtraction

Combine without using a calculator.

42. $(3.0 \times 10^4) + (2.1 \times 10^5)$

43. $(75.0 \times 10^2) + 32\overline{0}0$

44. $(1.557 \times 10^2) + (9.000 \times 10^{-1})$

45. $0.037 - (6.0 \times 10^{-3})$

46. $(7.2 \times 10^4) + (1.1 \times 10^4)$

Scientific Notation on the Calculator

Perform the following computations in scientific notation. Combine the powers of 10 by hand or with your calculator.

47. $(1.58 \times 10^2)(9.82 \times 10^3)$

48. $(9.83 \times 10^5) \div (2.77 \times 10^3)$

49. $(3.87 \times 10^{-2})(5.44 \times 10^5)$

50. $(2.74 \times 10^3) \div (9.13 \times 10^5)$

51. $(5.6 \times 10^2)(3.1 \times 10^{-1})$

52. $(7.72 \times 10^8) \div (3.75 \times 10^{-9})$

$4.98 \times 10^5\,\Omega \quad 2.47 \times 10^4\,\Omega \quad 9.27 \times 10^6\,\Omega$

FIGURE 1•9 Resistors in series

$4.98 \times 10^5\,\Omega$

$2.47 \times 10^4\,\Omega$

$9.27 \times 10^6\,\Omega$

FIGURE 1•10 Resistors in parallel

Applications

53. Three resistors, having resistances of $4.98 \times 10^5\,\Omega$, $2.47 \times 10^4\,\Omega$, and $9.27 \times 10^6\,\Omega$, are wired in series (Fig. 1•9). Find the total resistance, using Eq. A63.

54. Find the equivalent resistance if the three resistors of Problem 53 are wired in parallel (Fig. 1•10). Use Eq. A64.

55. Find the power dissipated in a resistor if a current of 3.75×10^{-3} A produces a voltage drop of 7.24×10^{-4} V across the resistor. Use Eq. A65.

56. The voltage across an 8.35×10^5-Ω resistor is 2.95×10^{-3} V. Find the power dissipated in the resistor, using Eq. A66.

57. Three capacitors, 8.26×10^{-6} farads (F), 1.38×10^{-7} F, and 5.93×10^{-5} F, are wired in parallel. Find the equivalent capacitance by Eq. A73.

58. A wire 4.75×10^4 mm long when loaded is seen to stretch 9.55×10^{-1} mm. Find the strain in the wire, using Eq. A53.

59. How long will it take a rocket traveling at a rate of 5.14×10^6 km/h to travel the 6.08×10^8 km from the earth to the moon? Use Eq. A17.

60. The oil shale reserves of the United States are estimated at 2.0×10^9 tonnes. How long would this last at a rate of consumption of 9.0×10^7 tonnes/year?

1·8

Units of Measurement

A *unit* is a standard of measurement, such as the metre, inch, hour, or pound. The two main systems of units in use are the *British* system (feet, pounds, gallons, etc.) and the SI or *metric* system (metres, kilograms, litres, etc.). SI stands for Le Système International d'Unités, or the *International System of Units*. In addition, some special units, such as a *square* of roofing material, and some obsolete units, such as *rods* and *chains*, must occasionally be dealt with.

Systems of Units

Each physical quantity can be expressed in any one of a bewildering variety of units. Length, for example, can be measured in metres, inches, nautical miles, angstroms, feet, and so on. In this section we will be converting only units that occur in SI.

Abbreviations and Symbols

Most units have an abbreviated form, so that we do not have to write the full word. The abbreviation for millimetres is mm, and the symbol for ohms is Ω. In this section we will usually give the full word *and* the abbreviation. The abbreviations for all the units in this text are given in the table of Conversion Factors, Appendix B.

Metric Units

The *metric system* is a system of weights and measures developed in France in 1793 that has since been adopted by most countries of the world, including Canada. It is widely used in manufacturing and scientific work in the United States.

The basic unit of length in the metric system is the *metre* (m). The unit of area is the *hectare*, or 10 000 square metres (m^2). The unit of volume is the *litre* (L), the volume of a cube one-tenth of a metre along each side. The unit of mass is the *kilogram* (kg), the theoretical mass of a cube of distilled water measuring one-tenth of a metre along each side. For the normal units used in engineering and science, see Table 1·1 on the following page.

The measure for land area is the *hectare* (ha). The term *are* (a) may also be found.

$$1 \text{ ha} = 10\ 000 \text{ m}^2$$

$$1 \text{ a} = 100 \text{ m}^2$$

Metric Prefixes

Converting between metric units is made easy because larger and smaller metric units are related to the basic units by *factors of ten*. These larger or smaller units are indicated by placing a *prefix* before the basic unit. A prefix is a group of letters placed at the beginning of a word to modify the meaning of that word. For example, the prefix *kilo* means 1000, or 10^3. Thus, a *kilogram* is 1000 grams. Other metric prefixes are given in Table 1·2 on the following page.

TABLE 1·1 International System (SI) of Units

NAME	UNIT	SYMBOL	RELATED
Length	metre	m	
Time	second	s	
Mass	kilogram	kg	
Electric Current	ampere	A	
Substance Quantity	mole	mol	
Temperature (absolute)	kelvin	K	
Luminous Intensity	candela	cd	
Force	newton	N	$kg \cdot m/s^2$
Capacity	litre	L	
Volume	cubic metre	m^3	
Area	square metre	m^2	
Pressure	pascal	Pa	N/m^2
Work or Energy	joule	J	$N \cdot m$
Power	watt	W	J/s
Density	mass/unit volume	kg/m^3	
Charge (Electrical)	coulomb	C	
Electrical Potential	volt	V	
Capacitance	farad	F	
Inductance	henry	H	
Resistance	ohm	Ω	
Temperature	°Celsius	°C	
Frequency	hertz	Hz	
Heat Quantity	joule	J	

The first seven units (in the highlighted box) are the *Base Units of SI*.

TABLE 1·2 Metric Prefixes

AMOUNT	MULTIPLES AND SUBMULTIPLES	PREFIX	SYMBOL	PRONUNCIATION	MEANING
1 000 000 000 000	10^{12}	tera	T	ter'à	One trillion times
1 000 000 000	10^9	giga	G	ji'ga	One billion times
1 000 000	10^6	mega	M*	meg'à	One million times
1 000	10^3	kilo	k*	kil'o	One thousand times
100	10^2	hecto	h	hek'to	One hundred times
10	10	deka	da	dek'a	Ten times
0.1	10^{-1}	deci	d	des'i	One tenth of
0.01	10^{-2}	centi	c*	sen'ti	One hundredth of
0.001	10^{-3}	milli	m*	mil'i	One thousandth of
0.000 001	10^{-6}	micro	μ*	mi''kro	One millionth of
0.000 000 001	10^{-9}	nano	n	nan'o	One billionth of
0.000 000 000 001	10^{-12}	pico	p	pē'co	One trillionth of
0.000 000 000 000 001	10^{-15}	femto	f	fem'to	One quadrillionth of
0.000 000 000 000 000 001	10^{-18}	atto	a	at'to	One quintillionth of

* Most commonly used

▬ **Example 75:**

(a) A *kilo*metre (km) is a thousand metres, because *kilo* means one thousand.

$$1 \text{ km} = 1000 \text{ m}$$

(b) A *centi*metre (cm) is one hundredth of a metre, because *centi* means one hundredth.

$$1 \text{ cm} = 1/100 \text{ m}$$

(c) A *milli*metre (mm) is one-thousandth of a metre, because *milli* means one thousandth.

$$1 \text{ mm} = 1/1000 \text{ m}$$ ▬

Converting from One Metric Unit to Another

Converting from one metric unit to another is usually a matter of multiplying or dividing by a power of ten. Most of the time, the names of the units will tell how they are related, so we do not even have to look them up.

▬ **Example 76:** Convert 72 925 metres (m) to kilometres (km)

Solution: A *kilo*metre is a thousand metres,

$$\frac{1 \text{ km}}{1000 \text{ m}} = 1$$

so, as before,

$$72\ 925 \text{ m} = 72\ 925 \text{ m̶} \times \frac{1 \text{ km}}{1000 \text{ m̶}} = 72.925 \text{ km}$$ ▬

For more unusual metric units, simply look up the conversion factor in a table and convert.

▬ **Example 77:** Convert 2.75 newtons (N) to dynes.

Solution: These two metric units of force do not have any basic units in their names, nor any prefixes. Thus we cannot tell just from their names how they are related to each other. However, from Appendix B we find that

$$1 \text{ newton} = 10^5 \text{ dynes}$$

Converting in the usual way,

$$2.75 \text{ newtons} = 2.75 \text{ n̶e̶w̶t̶o̶n̶s̶} \times \frac{10^5 \text{ dynes}}{1 \text{ n̶e̶w̶t̶o̶n̶}} = 2.75 \times 10^5 \text{ dynes}$$

or 275 000 dynes.   ▬

Exercise 8 Units of Measurement

Metric Prefixes

Write each of these quantities with a prefix that reduces the zeros:

1. 15 000 metres (m)
3. 0.000038 farads (F)

2. 0.00012 m
4. 101 000 000 (Pa)

Unit Conversion

Convert each of the quantities in the left-hand column to the units in the right-hand column:

5. 6825 pascals   = **?** kilonewtons/metre^2
6. 32 newtons (N)   = **?** megadynes
7. 8 210 000 watts (W) = **?** kilojoules/second
8. 5150 joules (J)   = **?** kilonewton-metres/second

1-9   Substituting into Equations and Formulas

Substituting into Equations

We get an *equation* when two expressions are set equal to each other.

■ **Example 78:** $x = 5a - 2b + 3c$ is an equation that enables us to find x if we know a, b, and c. ■

We will study equations in detail later, but for now we will simply substitute into equations and use our calculators to compute the results. To *substitute into an equation* means to replace the letter quantities in an equation by their given numerical values, and to perform the computation indicated.

■ **Example 79:** Substitute the values $a = 5$, $b = 3$, and $c = 6$ into the equation

$$x = \frac{3a + b}{c}$$

Solution: Substituting, we obtain

$$x = \frac{3(5) + 3}{6} = \frac{18}{6} = 3$$ ■

When substituting approximate numbers, be sure to round your answer to the proper number of digits. Treat any integers in the equation as exact numbers.

Substituting by Calculator

Problems such as in Example 79 can easily be done by a graphics calculator. In the following example, the key $\boxed{\rightarrow}$ or $\boxed{\text{STO}}$ sends a number to a memory location. Thus

$$5 \boxed{\rightarrow} A$$

means to store the number 5 in memory location A.

■ **Example 80:** Repeating Example 79 by calculator,

25 500 N

1160 mm^2

4750 mm

25 500 N

FIGURE 1·11

It is now possible to go back and replace the given values 5, 3, and 6 with a new set of numbers, if needed, to obtain a new answer. ▬

Substituting into Formulas

A *formula* is an equation expressing some general mathematical or physical fact, such as the formula for the area of a circle of radius r:

Area of a Circle	$A = \pi r^2$	**114**

We substitute into formulas just as we substituted into equations, except that we now carry *units* along with the numerical values.

If the units to be used in a certain formula are specified, convert all quantities to those specified units before substituting into the formula.

▬ **Example 81:** A tensile load of 25 500 N is applied to a bar that is 4750 mm long and has a cross-sectional area of 1160 mm^2 (Fig. 1•11). The elongation is 0.380 mm. Using Eq. A54, find the modulus of elasticity E in newtons per mm^2.

Solution: Substituting the values *with units* into Eq. A54, we obtain

$$E = \frac{PL}{ae} = \frac{25\,500 \text{ N} \times 4750 \text{ mm}}{1160 \text{ mm}^2 \times 0.380 \text{ mm}}$$

$$E = 275\,000 \text{ N/mm}^2 = 275 \times 10^9 \text{ N/m}^2$$

or

$$E = 275 \text{ GPa.}$$ ▬

One pascal (Pa) equals one newton (N) per square metre (m²):

$$1 \text{ Pa} = 1 \text{ N/m}^2$$
$$1 \text{ kPa} = 1 \times 10^3 \text{ N/m}^2$$
$$1 \text{ MPa} = 1 \times 10^6 \text{ N/m}^2$$
$$1 \text{ GPa} = 1 \times 10^9 \text{ N/m}^2$$

Common Error	Students often neglect to include *units* when substituting into a formula, with the result that the units often do not cancel properly.

Exercise 9 Substituting into Equations and Formulas

Substitute the given integers into each equation. Do not round your answer.

1. $y = 5x + 2$ $(x = 3)$
2. $y = 2m^2 - 3m + 5$ $(m = -2)$
3. $y = 2a - 3x^2$ $(x = 3, a = -5)$
4. $y = 3x^3 - 2x^2 + 4x - 7$ $(x = 2)$
5. $y = 2b + 3w^2 - 5z^3$ $(b = 3, w = -4, z = 2)$
6. $y = \dfrac{r^2}{x} - \dfrac{x^3}{r} + \dfrac{w}{x^2}$ $(x = 5, w = 3, r = -4)$

Substitute the given approximate numbers into each equation. Treat the constants in the equations as exact numbers. Round your answer to the proper number of digits.

7. $y = 7x - 5$ $(x = 2.73)$
8. $y = 2w^2 - 3x^2$ $(x = -11.5, w = 9.83)$
9. $y = 8 - x + 3x^2$ $(x = -8.49)$
10. $y = \sqrt[3]{8x} + 7w$ $(x = 1.255, w = 2.304)$
11. $y = \sqrt{x^3 - 3x}$ $(x = 4.25)$
12. $y = (w - 2x)^{1.6}$ $(x = 1.8, w = 7.2))$

13. Use Eq. A19 to find to the nearest dollar the amount to which $3000 will accumulate in five years at a simple interest rate of 6.5%.

14. Using Eq. A18, find the displacement after 1.30 s of a body thrown downward with a speed of 3.87 m/s. Use $a = 9.81$ m/s².

15. Using Eq. A50, convert 128°F to °C.

16. A bar 15 200 mm long, having a cross-sectional area of 1270 mm², is subject to a tensile load of 22 500 N (Fig. 1•12). The elongation is 2.75 mm. Use Eq. A54 to find the modulus of elasticity in newtons per square millimetre.

17. Use Eq. A10 to find to the nearest dollar the amount y obtained when $9570 is allowed to accumulate for five years at a compound interest rate of $6\frac{3}{4}$%.

18. The resistance of a copper coil is 775 Ω at 20°C. The temperature coefficient of resistance is 0.00393 at 20°C. Use Eq. A70 to find the resistance at 80°C.

1•10

$P = 22\ 500$ N

$a = 1270$ mm²

$L = 15\ 200$ mm

FIGURE 1•12 A bar in tension

Percentage

Definition of Percent

The word *percent* means *out of each hundred,* or *per hundred.* It is used with a number, for instance, 12 percent. A percent thus gives the number of parts in every hundred.

■ **Example 82:** If we say that a certain concrete mix is 12% cement by mass, we mean that 12 kg out of every 100 kg of mix will be cement. ■

Rates

The word *rate* is often used to indicate a percent, or percentage rate, as in "rejection rate," "rate of inflation," or "growth rate."

■ **Example 83:** A failure rate of 2% means that, on average, 2 parts out of every 100 would be expected to fail. ■

Percent as a Fraction

Percent is another way of expressing a *fraction* having 100 as the denominator.

■ **Example 84:** If we say that a builder has finished 75% of a house, we mean that he has finished $\frac{75}{100}$ (or $\frac{3}{4}$) of the house. ■

Converting Decimals to Percent

Before working some percentage problems, let us first get some practice in converting decimals and fractions to percents, and vice versa. To convert decimals to percent, simply move the decimal point two places to the right and affix the percent symbol (%).

■ **Example 85:**
(a) $0.75 = 75\%$
(b) $3.65 = 365\%$
(c) $0.003 = 0.3\%$
(d) $1.05 = 105\%$ ■

Converting Fractions or Mixed Numbers to Percent

First write the fraction or mixed number as a decimal, and then proceed as above.

■ **Example 86:**

(a) $\dfrac{1}{4} = 0.25 = 25\%$

(b) $\dfrac{5}{2} = 2.5 = 250\%$

(c) $1\dfrac{1}{4} = 1.25 = 125\%$ ■

Converting Percent to Decimals

Move the decimal point two places to the left and remove the percent sign.

■ **Example 87:**

(a) $13\% = 0.13$ (b) $4.5\% = 0.045$ (c) $155\% = 1.55$
(d) $27\tfrac{3}{4}\% = 0.2775$ (e) $200\% = 2$ ■

Converting Percent to a Fraction

Write a fraction with 100 in the denominator and the percent in the numerator. Remove the percent sign and reduce the fraction to lowest terms.

■ **Example 88:**

(a) $75\% = \dfrac{75}{100} = \dfrac{3}{4}$ (b) $87.5\% = \dfrac{87.5}{100} = \dfrac{875}{1000} = \dfrac{7}{8}$

(c) $125\% = \dfrac{125}{100} = \dfrac{5}{4} = 1\dfrac{1}{4}$ ■

Amount, Base, and Rate

Percentage problems always involve three quantities:

  1. The *percent rate*, P
  2. The *base*, B, the quantity we are taking the percent of
  3. The *amount*, A, we get when we take the percent of the base, also called the *percentage*

In a percentage problem, you will know two of these three quantities (amount, base, or rate) and be required to find the third. This is easily done, for the rate, base, and amount are related by the following equation:

Percentage	Amount = rate × base $A = PB$ where P is expressed as a decimal.	**12**

Finding the Amount When the Base and Rate Are Known

We substitute the given base and rate into Eq. 12 and solve for the amount.

━ **Example 89:** What is 35.0 percent of 80.0?

Solution: In this problem the rate is 35.0%, so

$$P = 0.350$$

But is 80.0 the amount or the base?

Tip	In a particular problem, if you have trouble telling which number is the base and which is the amount, look for the key phrase "*percent of.*" The quantity following this phrase is *always the base*.

We look for the key phrase "percent of."

base
What is 35.0 percent of $\boxed{80.0}$?

Since 80.0 immediately follows *percent of,*

$$B = 80.0$$

From Eq. 12,

$$A = PB = (0.350)80.0 = 28.0 \qquad ━$$

Common Error	Do not forget to convert the percent rate to a *decimal* when using Eq. 12.

━ **Example 90:** Find 0.10% of 5600.

Solution: We substitute into Eq. 12 with

$$P = 0.0010 \quad (not\ 0.10!)$$

and

$$B = 5600$$

So

$$A = PB = (0.0010)5600 = 5.6 \qquad ━$$

Finding the Base When a Percent of It Is Known

We see from Eq. 12 that the base equals the amount divided by the rate (expressed as a decimal), or $B = A/P$.

━ **Example 91:** 12% of what number is 78?

Solution: Finding the key phrase,

12 percent of $\boxed{\text{what number}}$ is 78?
base

it is clear that we are looking for the base. So

$$A = 78 \quad \text{and} \quad P = 0.12$$

By Eq. 12,

$$B = \frac{A}{P} = \frac{78}{0.12} = 650$$

■ **Example 92:** 140 is 25% of what number?

Solution: From Eq. 12,

$$B = \frac{A}{P} = \frac{140}{0.25} = 560$$

Finding the Percent One Number Is of Another Number

From Eq. 12, the rate equals the amount divided by the base, or $P = A/B$.

■ **Example 93:** 42.0 is what percent of 405?

Solution: By Eq. 12, with $A = 42.0$ and $B = 405$,

$$P = \frac{A}{B} = \frac{42.0}{405} = 0.104 = 10.4\%$$

■ **Example 94:** What percent of 1.4 is 0.35?

Solution: From Eq. 12,

$$P = \frac{A}{B} = \frac{0.35}{1.4} = 0.25 = 25\%$$

Percent Change

Percentages are often used to compare two quantities. You often hear statements like the following:

The price of steel rose 3% over last year's price.

The mass of two cars differed by 20% .

Production dropped 5% from last year.

When the two numbers being compared involve a *change* from one to the other, the *original value* is usually taken as the base.

Percent change $= \dfrac{\text{new value} - \text{original value}}{\text{original value}} \times 100$	**13**

■ **Example 95:** A certain price rose from $1.55 to $1.75. Find the percentage change in price.

Be sure to show the *direction* of change with a plus or minus sign, or with words like "increase" or "decrease."

Solution: We use the original value, $1.55, as the base. From Eq. 13,

$$\text{percent change} = \frac{1.75 - 1.55}{1.55} \times 100 = 12.9\% \text{ increase}$$

A common type of problem is to *find the new value* when the original value is changed by a given percent. We see from Eq. 13 that

new value = original value + (original value) × (percent change)

■ **Example 96:** Find the cost of a $156.00 suit after the price increases by $2\frac{1}{2}\%$.

Solution: The original value is 156.00, and the percent change, expressed as a decimal, is 0.025. So

$$\text{new value} = 156.00 + 156.00(0.025) = \$159.90 \quad \blacksquare$$

Percent Efficiency

The power output of any machine or device is always *less* than the power input, because of inevitable power losses within the device. The *efficiency* of the device is a measure of those losses.

Percent efficiency $= \dfrac{\text{output}}{\text{input}} \times 100$	**16**

■ **Example 97:** A certain electric motor consumes 865 W and has an output of 836 W (Fig. 1•13). Find the efficiency of the motor.

By Eq. 16,

$$\text{percent efficiency} = \frac{836}{865} \times 100 = 96.6\%$$

FIGURE 1•13

Percent Error

The accuracy of measurements is often specified by the *percent error*. The percent error is the difference between the measured value and the known or "true" value, expressed as a percent of the known value.

Percent error $= \dfrac{\text{measured value} - \text{known value}}{\text{known value}} \times 100$	**14**

■ **Example 98:** A laboratory mass that is certified to be 500.0 g is placed on a scale (Fig. 1•14). The scale reading is 507.0 g. What is the percent error in the reading?

Solution: From Eq. 14,

$$\text{percent error} = \frac{507.0 - 500.0}{500.0} \times 100 = 1.4\% \text{ high} \quad \blacksquare$$

FIGURE 1•14

As with percent change, be sure to specify the *direction* of the error.

Percent Concentration

In a mixture of two or more ingredients,

Percent concentration of ingredient A $= \dfrac{\text{amount of } A}{\text{amount of mixture}} \times 100$	**15**

■ **Example 99:** A certain fuel mixture contains 18.0 L of alcohol and 84.0 L of gasoline. Find the percentage of gasoline in the mixture.

Solution: The total amount of mixture is

$$18.0 + 84.0 = 102.0 \text{ L}$$

So, by Eq. 15,

$$\text{gasoline percent} = \frac{84.0}{102.0} \times 100 = 82.4\%$$ ■

Common Error	The denominator in Eq. 15 must be the *total amount* of mixture, or the sum of *all* the ingredients. Do not use just one of the ingredients.

Exercise 10 Percentage

Conversions

Convert each decimal to a percent.

1. 3.72   **2.** 0.877   **3.** 0.0055   **4.** 0.563

Convert each fraction to a percent. Round to three significant digits.

5. $\dfrac{2}{5}$ **6.** $\dfrac{3}{4}$ **7.** $\dfrac{7}{10}$ **8.** $\dfrac{3}{7}$

Convert each percent to a decimal.

9. 23%   **10.** 2.97%   **11.** $287\frac{1}{2}\%$ **12.** $6\frac{1}{4}\%$

Convert each percent to a fraction.

13. 37.5%   **14.** $12\frac{1}{2}\%$ **15.** 150%   **16.** 3%

Finding the Amount

Find:

17. 40.0% of 255 tonnes   **18.** 15% of 320 km
19. $33\frac{1}{3}\%$ of 660 kg   **20.** $12\frac{1}{2}\%$ of 72 L
21. 35% of 343 L   **22.** 50.0% of $240
23. A resistance, now 7250 Ω, is to be increased by 15.0%. How much resistance should be added?

24. It is estimated that $\frac{1}{2}$% of the earth's surface receives more energy than the total projected needs for the year 2000. Assuming the earth's surface area to be 5.10×10^8 km², find the required area in hectares.

25. As an incentive to install solar equipment, a tax credit of 40% of the first $1000 and 25% of the next $6400 spent on solar equipment is proposed. How much credit would a homeowner get when installing $5000 worth of solar equipment?

26. How much metal will be obtained from 375 tonnes of ore if the metal is $10\frac{1}{2}$% of the ore?

Finding the Base

Find the number of which:

27. 86.5 is $16\frac{2}{3}$% **28.** 45 is 1.5% **29.** $\frac{3}{8}$% is $1\frac{1}{3}$%
30. $5\overline{0}$ is 25% **31.** $6\overline{0}$ is 60% **32.** $6\overline{0}$ is 75%

33. A Department of Energy report on an experimental electric car gives the range of the car as $16\overline{0}$ km and states that this is "50% better than on earlier electric vehicles." What was the range of earlier electric vehicles?

34. A man withdrew 25% of his bank deposits and spent $33\frac{1}{3}$% of the money withdrawn on the purchase of a radio worth $250. How much money did he have in the bank?

35. Solar panels provide 55% of the heat for a certain building. If $225 per year is now spent for heating oil, what would have been spent if the solar panels were not used?

36. If the United States imports 9.14 billion barrels of oil per day and if this is 48.2% of its needs, how much oil is needed per day?

capacity 50 500 L

5840 L of water

FIGURE 1•15

Finding the Rate

What percent of:

37. 24 is 12? **38.** 36 is 12?
39. 40 is 8? **40.** 840 men are 420 men?
41. 450 h are 150 h? **42.** 450 tonnes are 300 tonnes?

43. A 50 500 L capacity tank contains 5840 L of water (Fig. 1.15). Express the amount of water in the tank as a percentage of the total capacity.

44. In a journey of 1560 km, a person travelled 195 km by car and the rest of the distance by rail. What percent of the distance was travelled by rail?

45. A power supply has a DC output of 50.0 V with a ripple of 0.75 V peak to peak. Express the ripple as a percentage of the DC output voltage.

46. The construction of a factory cost $136 000 for materials and $157 000 for labor. The labor cost was what percentage of the total?

Percent Change

Find the percent change when a quantity changes:

47. from 29.3 to 57.6 **48.** from 107 to 23.75
49. from 227 to 298 **50.** from 0.774 to 0.638

FIGURE 1•16

51. The temperature in a building rose from 19.0°C to 21.0°C during the day. Find the percent change in temperature.
52. A casting initially having a mass of 15 kg has 22.0% of its material machined off. What is its final mass?
53. A certain common stock rose from a value of $35\frac{1}{2}$ per share to $37\frac{5}{8}$ per share. Find the percent change in value.
54. A house that costs $635 per year to heat has insulation installed in the attic, causing the fuel bill to drop to $518 per year. Find the percent change in fuel cost.

Percent Efficiency

55. A certain device (Fig. 1•16) consumes 13 430 W and delivers $895\overline{0}$ W. Find its efficiency.
56. An electric motor consumes 1250 W. Find the power it can deliver if it is 85.0% efficient.
57. A water pump requires an input of 370 W and delivers 4500 kg of water per hour to a house 22 000 mm (22 m) above the pump. Find its efficiency. (*Hint:* Power = 370 W = 370 N·m/s).
58. A certain speed reducer delivers 1270 W with a power input of 1640 W. Find the percent efficiency of the speed reducer.

Percent Error

59. A certain quantity is measured at 125.0 units but is known actually to be 128.0 units. Find the percent error in the measurement.
60. A shaft is known to have a diameter of 35.000 mm. You measure it and get a reading of 34.725 mm. What is the percent error of your reading?
61. A certain capacitor has a working voltage of 125.0 V dc −10%, +150%. Between what two voltages would the actual working voltage lie?
62. A resistor labelled as $550\overline{0}$ Ω with a tolerance of ±5%. Between what two values is the actual resistance expected to lie?

Percent Concentration

63. A solution is made by mixing 75.0 L of alcohol with 125 L of water. Find the percent concentration of alcohol.
64. 8.0 cubic metres of cement is contained in a concrete mixture that is 12% cement by volume. What is the volume of the total mixture?
65. How many litres of alcohol are contained in $50\overline{0}$ L of a gasohol mixture that is 5.0% of alcohol by volume?
66. How many litres of gasoline are there in 1165 L of a methanol-gasoline blend that is 10.0% methanol by volume?

Measurement

1•11

The measurement of physical quantities is a regular part of our daily lives. We count numbers of items, we estimate and calculate the volume and mass of objects, we determine the temperature, pressure, and volume of liquids and gases. The driver of a vehicle uses modern technology to monitor speed, quantity of fuel expended, temperature of the engine, level of charge in the battery, and conditions inside and outside the vehicle. Computer controlled units in the vehicle dispense the fuel and air mixture to the engine, sample running condition, and monitor the pollution controls. All these measurements, with the exception of a *count,* which expresses an *exact* number, are subject to error. We refer to a count as a *digital quantity* and all non-count measurements as *analogue quantities*. There is no *absolute result* for an analogue measurement. For example: we can state that our vehicle has *one* engine (digital) but the 2.3 litre capacity of that engine is an analogue measurement and subject to error. This error is often expressed as a percentage or as a value with a plus or minus quantity. We also have to take into consideration the accuracy and precision of our measurement.

Accuracy

The accuracy of a measurement is controlled by the number of significant digits that are used. When displaying the result of a measurement, great care must be taken to avoid implying an accuracy that is not supported by the method of measurement.

▬ **Example 100:** A measurement of 302, if written 302.0, now has an implied accuracy of one decimal place; this may not be justified. We are indicating by adding the decimal point and the following "0" that the measurement is to a first decimal level of precision. The number 302 has three significant digits, the version 302.0 has four significant digits and is now considered to be a more precise measurement.   ▬

Precision

Precision and accuracy are often treated as though they were interchangeable. In fact, they are very different.

▬ **Example 101:** Consider the numbers 452 and 4.52. Both these numbers have three significant digits, and they are therefore of *equal* accuracy. The number 452 changes by 1 to obtain the next number in the sequence. The number 4.52 changes by .01 to obtain the next number in its sequence. The number 4.52 is therefore designated as a number having greater *precision*.   ▬

Error in Measurement

We have stated previously that analogue values are never exact and they have no absolute *right* value. Values used in scientific and engineering calculations are normally analogue in nature and obtained by taking physical measurements. These values are usually followed by an additional plus or minus quantity to make allowance for possible instrument and operator errors.

▬ **Example 102:** A measurement that yields a value of 15.85 ± .05 mm can be said to be as low as 15.80 mm and as high as 15.90 mm.
    This error allowance is termed *absolute*. The *number* and the *allowance* have the *same* units.   ▬

The error allowance can also be expressed as a percentage of the value.

━ **Example 103:** A value of 24 ± 5% can be as low as 22.8 and as high as 25.2 in *absolute* terms.　　　　　　　　　　　　　　　　━

If a percentage allowance is given, we refer to that quantity as the *relative* error. This is because the larger the number that the percentage error is qualifying, the larger is the quantitative value of that error.

━ **Example 104:** A value of 10.0 ± 2% allows a range from 10.2 to 9.8, whereas a value of 10 000 ± 2% results in a range of 10 200 to 9800. We can clearly see the difference in the *relative effect* of these two errors in measurement. The error range in the first situation is ±0.2 in the value, whereas in the second it is ±200.　　　　　　　　　　　　　　　　━

Error Effect on Calculated Values

Variations in size for engineered components are normally designated as a *tolerance*. The tolerance is a form of error allowance and informs the user of that component that the quantitative value lies between certain limits. The engineering method of expressing error for components is usually in the *absolute* form. We need to consider the effect such errors have on our calculations. Error can affect calculations when the component is to become part of a system where its error, or tolerance, affects quantitative measurement of physical properties.

We shall consider the case of a resistor since it is a component that carries a stated error quantity. When the resistor is incorporated into a circuit, it carries with it the effect of the stated tolerance.

Adding or Subtracting

When adding or subtracting values that have error allowances designated as percentage, we must convert the *relative* or *percentage* error or tolerance into *absolute* values.

━ **Example 105:** A certain resistor has a stated value of $R_1 = 150 \ \Omega \pm 10\%$. If this resistor were combined with another resistor, with, say, a rating of $R_2 = 200 \ \Omega \pm 5\%$, then the resulting *total* resistance and the *new* tolerance or percentage error for the total resistance would have to be calculated.

		Relative Error	Absolute Error
Resistor 1	150	±10%	± 15 Ω
Resistor 2	200	± 5%	± 10 Ω
Adding	350 Ω		± 25 Ω

The total resistance is normally stated in the relative format:

$$\text{Total resistance} = 350 \ \Omega \pm 7.1\%$$ 　━

Multiplying and Dividing

To illustrate how to combine error allowances in circumstances where the values with the allowances must be combined by multiplication or division, we will again use the situation in Example 105.

■ **Example 106:**
We shall again use the resistance value from the previous example and apply a current of ten amperes ($1\overline{0}$A) through the total resistance of the two resistors. The ammeter used to measure the current has a stated accuracy of plus or minus 2.0%. The voltage (V) to be calculated across the resistor is a product of the current (I) and the resistance (R).

Solution:

$$V = I \cdot R = 350(10) = 3500 \text{ V}$$

The total resistance R from the previous example was equal to

$$350 \ \Omega \pm 7.1\%$$

The value from the ammeter is $1\overline{0}$ A $\pm$ 2.0%. It can be shown that the level of error for the combination of current and resistance is the addition of the percentage error for each element of the calculation. The complete proof for this statement is given later. Hence:

$$\text{Voltage across the resistor} = 3500 \text{ V} \pm (7.1 + 2)\%$$

$$V = 3500 \text{ V} \pm 9.1\% \qquad \blacksquare$$

Note that, even if dividing, the percentage errors are still added together.

Exponents

To illustrate how to combine error allowances in circumstances where there is a value with an exponent, this exponent becomes the value of the multiplier of the percentage error. We will again use the situation in Example 105 to demonstrate this.

We shall now determine the electrical power in our circuit, considering the errors in both current and resistor.

■ **Example 107:** For the situation in Example 105, we wish to determine the power in the circuit with the current of 10.0A $\pm$ 2% and the equivalent resistance of $35\overline{0} \ \Omega \pm 7.14\%$.

Solution: Given electrical power $(P) = I^2R$

$$P = 10^2 \times 350 = 35\,000 \text{ W or 35 kW}$$

It can be proved that the error is twice the percentage error for the current, plus the percentage error for the resistor:

$$\text{Total error} = (2)(2.0\%) + (7.14\%) = 11\%$$

The power calculation thus yields

$$\text{Electrical power} = 35 \text{ kW} \pm 11\%$$

The exponent the current is raised to becomes the value of the multiplier of the percentage error. ■

■ **Example 108:** The diameter of a spherical water tank is measured to obtain its volume in cubic metres. The measuring device used to determine the diameter is accurate only to within ± 1.5%. If the measurement of the diameter gives a value of 5.75 m, find (a) volume of the tank (b) percentage error in the volume (c) absolute error in the tank's capacity

Solution:

$$\text{Volume of a sphere} = \frac{4}{3}\,\pi \cdot R^3$$

(a) Volume of the spherical tank $= \dfrac{4}{3} \cdot \pi \cdot 2.875^3$

$$V = 99.5 \text{ m}^3$$

(b) Percentage error $= (3)(1.5\%) = 4.5\%$
The radius is raised to the exponent 3; therefore, the percentage error is multiplied by three.

(c) Absolute error $= 0.045 \times$ volume of tank
$= 0.045 \times 99.5 = \pm 4.48 \text{ m}^3$

The effect of error on calculations is often overlooked when carrying out experiments. The results obtained experimentally are always subject to errors in measurement, equipment variation, and human error. Students should always be aware of the limitations of their results and allow for experimental error. Special care is needed when using any empirically obtained values in calculations.   ■

Proof of Error Effect in Calculations

In this section we shall provide the mathematical proof for the treatment of error in calculations. The level of mathematics required for this proof may be too advanced for some students. The mathematics to be used will be covered later in the text, and therefore it may be advisable simply to accept the theory at this time.

Adding and Subtracting

We have previously shown that adding or subtracting measured elements with an error quantity causes errors in the final calculated results. We also demonstrated that, in the case of addition and subtraction, we had to use the *absolute* error value.

■ **Example 109:** A component with a length of $10\overline{0}$ mm and an expected error of $\pm 2.00\%$ is to be joined with another component of length $20\overline{0}$ mm and an expected error of $\pm 4.00\%$.

Solution: In this case we simply add the two values of length and also the errors in *absolute* form. We use the symbol Δ to indicate a small change in a value.

$$(L_1 + \Delta L_1) + (L_2 + \Delta L_2) = L_T$$

$$(100 \text{ mm} \pm 2 \text{ mm}) + (200 \text{ mm} \pm 8 \text{ mm}) = 300 \text{ mm} \pm 10 \text{ mm}$$

The result is a total value of 300 mm ± 10 mm

$$\text{or } 30\overline{0} \text{ mm} \pm 3.33\%$$

If the two lengths had been subtracted, then the result would have been 100 mm ± 10 mm or 100 mm ± 10%, a much larger error effect. In subtraction, we still add the errors, and the accumulated error is now larger than either individual value of error. ▬

Multiplication and Division

When we multiply or divide quantities with percentage error, we simply add the percentage errors for each component together to obtain the total percentage error in the calculation.

▬ **Example 110:** Consider the calculation of the constant c in the equation, pressure × volume = constant.

$$p \cdot v = c$$

where pressure p has been measured as

$$p = 2\overline{0}0 \pm 5.0\% \text{ kPa}$$

and the volume v has been measured as

$$v = 2.5 \pm 2.0\% \text{ m}^3$$

Solution: Introducing the errors as Δp for the pressure and Δv for the volume, we now rewrite the equation with the error included:

$$(p + \Delta p) \cdot (v + \Delta v) = (c + \Delta c)$$

Expanding the equation gives

$$pv + v\Delta p + p\Delta v + \Delta p\Delta v = (c + \Delta c)$$

We now subtract the original equation, leaving the errors:

$$v\Delta p + p\Delta v + \Delta p\Delta v = \Delta c$$

Multiples and powers of Δ are ignored, because of their very small effect, leaving

$$v\Delta p + p\Delta v = \Delta c$$

We now divide this error set by the original equation:

$$\frac{v\Delta p + p\Delta v}{pv} = \Delta c/c$$

This leaves $\dfrac{\Delta p}{p} \cdot 100\% + \dfrac{\Delta v}{v} \cdot 100\%$ as a percentage error.

We now have the result of addition of individual percentage error to give the final error for the calculated value of the constant c. Therefore

$$p \cdot v = c \pm 7.0\%$$

and the actual value is

$$200 \cdot 10^3 \cdot 2.5 = 5 \cdot 10^5 \pm 7.0\%$$ ▬

Exponents

We now have to consider the effect on a calculation where the measured variable, in this case the radius of the circle, is raised in value by an exponent.

■ **Example 111:** The radius of a circle is measured by an instrument that has an error range of ±10%. The instrument records a value of 1.20 m ± 10%. Find the area of the circle and the expected error range.

Solution: The area of a circle is measured by using an instrument that gives an error of ±$1\bar{0}$%. The radius is measured as 1.2 m.

$$\text{Area of a circle, } A = \pi \cdot r^2$$

Introducing the expected errors, ΔA for the area error from the calculation and ΔR for the error in measurement of the radius of the circle, gives

$$(A + \Delta A) = \pi \cdot (r + \Delta R)^2$$

Expanding the equation gives

$$A + \Delta A = \pi \cdot [r^2 + 2r \cdot \Delta R + (\Delta R)^2]$$

We now subtract the original equation. We also ignore higher powers of ΔR in the belief that they are too small to have any appreciable effect. This assumption does not appear to be unreasonable.

This leaves the error equation

$$\Delta A = \pi \cdot (2r \cdot \Delta R) \qquad \blacksquare$$

We now divide by the original equation and multiply by 100 to convert to percentage error, giving

$$\frac{\Delta A \cdot 100}{A}\% = \frac{2 \cdot \Delta R \cdot 100}{r}\%$$

The percentage error in the area A is the percentage error in the radius, multiplied by the exponent of r, in this case 2. Therefore, the area of the circle and the accompanying error

$$A = \pi \cdot 1.2^2 \pm (2)(10\%) = 4.5 \text{ m}^2 \pm 2\bar{0}\%$$

The value of the area with the expected level of error is

$$\text{Area} = 4.5 \pm 0.9 \text{ m}^2 \qquad \blacksquare$$

We have now shown that exponent errors can be very high. The effect on the final calculated value is not insignificant. If we had been required to calculate the volume of a sphere using the same value for the radius r, the error would have been $3\bar{0}\%$ (r^3).

Exercise 11 Error Effects on Calculations

Adding and Subtracting

1. Two lengths of pipe are to be joined end-to-end. Pipe A is $30\bar{0}$ mm ±5.00% and pipe B is $24\bar{0}$ mm ±3.00%. Find the total length and the accompanying error.
2. Two round rods are to be placed in a circular metal sleeve. The rods are 45.00 mm and 36.00 mm in diameter and both have a stated error of ±12.0%. Find the minimum diameter of the sleeve to ensure the rods fit inside.
3. A $10\bar{0}$-Ω resistor is connected in series to a $50\bar{0}$-Ω resistor in a circuit. The first resistor has an error of ±15.0% and the total resistance is found to be $60\bar{0}$ ± 40.0 Ω. What is the error associated with the $50\bar{0}$-Ω resistor?

Multiplication and Division

4. The sides of a rectangular plate are measured as $18\overline{0}$ mm and $26\overline{0}$ mm. The error in measurement is specified as $\pm 6.0\%$. Find the error in the area calculation, $A = b \cdot d$.

5. The pressure of a gas is measured as 160 kPa $\pm$ 2.5% and the temperature of the gas as $56\overline{0}$ K $\pm$ 5.0%. Find the calculated value of pressure divided by temperature, and the error.

Exponents

6. The area of a circle is found using a value for radius of $68\overline{0}$ mm with an expected error of ± 20.0 mm. Find the area of the circle and the error range.

7. The sides of a cube are measured and found to be 225 mm. The measuring device is known to have an error range of $\pm 4.0\%$. Find the volume of the cube and the error range.

CHAPTER 1   REVIEW PROBLEMS

1. Combine: $1.435 - 7.21 + 93.24 - 4.1116$
2. Give the number of significant digits in:
  (a) 9.886   **(b)** 1.002
  (c) 0.3500   **(d)** $15\,\overline{0}00$
3. Multiply: $21.8(3.775 \times 1.07)$
4. Divide: $88.25 \div 9.15$
5. Find the reciprocal of 2.89.
6. Evaluate: $-|-4 + 2| - |-9 - 7| + 5$
7. Evaluate: $(9.73)^2$
8. Evaluate: $(7.75)^{-2}$
9. Evaluate: $\sqrt{29.8}$
10. Evaluate: $(123)(2.75) - (81.2)(3.24)$
11. Evaluate: $(91.2 - 88.6)^2$
12. Evaluate: $\left(\dfrac{77.2 - 51.4}{21.6 - 11.3}\right)^2$
13. Evaluate: $y = 3x^2 - 2x$ when $x = -2.88$
14. Evaluate: $y = 2ab - 3bc + 4ac$
  when $a = 5$, $b = 2$, and $c = -6$
15. Evaluate: $y = 2x - 3w + 5z$
  when $x = 7.72$, $w = 3.14$, and $z = 2.27$
16. Round to two decimal places:
  (a) 7.977   **(b)** 4.655
  (c) 11.845   **(d)** 1.004
17. Round to three significant digits:
  (a) 179.2   **(b)** 1.076
  (c) 4.8550   **(d)** 45 725
18. A news report states that a new hydroelectric generating station will produce 47 million kWh/yr and that this power, for 20 years of operation, is

equivalent to 2.0 million barrels of oil. Using these figures, how many kilowatt hours is each barrel of oil equivalent to?

19. A certain generator has a power input of 1865 W and delivers $131\overline{0}$ W. Find its percent efficiency.
20. Using Eq. A52, find the stress in newtons per square mm for a force of 1.17×10^3 N distributed over an area of 3.14×10^3 mm^2.
21. Combine:
  $(8.34 \times 10^5) + (2.85 \times 10^6) - (5.29 \times 10^4)$
22. A train running at 42 km/h increases its speed $12\frac{1}{2}\%$. How fast does it then go?
23. The average solar radiation in Canada is about 7.4×10^5 joules per square metre per hour (J/m$^2 \cdot$ h). How many kilowatts would be collected by 15 hectares of solar panels?
24. An item rose in price from \$29.35 to \$31.59. Find the percent increase.
25. Find the percent concentration of alcohol if 2.0 L of alcohol is added to $6\overline{0}$ L of gasoline.
26. A bar, known to be 50.00 mm in diameter, is measured at 50.05 mm. Find the percent error in the measurement.
27. The Department of Energy estimates that there are 700 billion barrels of oil in the oil sands deposits of Alberta. Express this amount in scientific notation.
28. Multiply: $(7.23 \times 10^5) \times (1.84 \times 10^{-3})$
29. Divide: -39.2 by -0.003826
30. Convert 6930 N·m/h to J/s.

31. Divide: 8.24×10^{-3} by 1.98×10^{7}

32. What percent of 40.8 is 11.3?

33. Evaluate: $\sqrt[5]{82.8}$

34. Multiply: $(4.92 \times 10^6) \times (9.13 \times 10^{-3})$

35. Insert the proper sign of equality or inequality between $-\frac{2}{3}$ and -0.660.

36. Convert 0.000426 mA to microamperes.

37. Find 49.2% of 4827.

38. Combine:
$$-385 - (227 - 499) - (-102) + (-284)$$

39. Find the reciprocal of -0.582.

40. Find the percent change in a voltage that increased from $11\overline{0}$ V to 118 V.

41. By insulating, a homeowner's yearly fuel consumption dropped from 6280 L to 4050 L. Her present oil consumption is what percent of the former?

42. Write in decimal notation: 5.28×10^4

43. Convert 49.3 kilograms to newtons.

44. Evaluate: $(45.2)^{-0.45}$

45. Using Eq. A18, find the distance in metres travelled by a falling object in 5.25 s, thrown downward with an initial velocity of 284 m/min.

46. Write in scientific notation: 0.000374

47. 8460 is what percent of 38 400?

48. The Canadian energy consumption of 2.4 million barrels of oil equivalent per day is expected to climb to 3.8 million in six years. Find the percent increase in consumption.

49. The population of a certain town is 8118, which is $12\frac{1}{2}\%$ more than it was three years ago. What was the population then?

50. The temperature of a room rose from 22°C to 26°C. Find the percent increase.

51. Combine: $4.928 + 2.847 - 2.836$

52. Give the number of significant digits in 2003.0.

53. Multiply: 2.84(38.4)

54. Divide: $48.3 \div 2.841$

55. Find the reciprocal of 4.82.

56. Evaluate: $|-2| - |3 - 5|$

57. Evaluate: $(3.84)^2$

58. Evaluate: $(7.62)^{-2}$

59. Evaluate: $\sqrt{38.4}$

60. Evaluate: $(49.3 - 82.4)(2.84)$

61. Evaluate: $x^2 - 3x + 2$ when $x = 3$

62. Round 45.836 to one decimal place.

63. Round 83.43 to three significant digits.

64. Multiply: $(7.23 \times 10^5) \times (1.84 \times 10^{-3})$

65. Convert 30 800 m² to hectares.

66. What percent of 847 is 364?

67. Evaluate: $\sqrt[3]{746}$

68. Find 35.8% of 847.

69. 746 is what percent of 992?

70. Write 0.00274 in scientific notation.

71. Write 73.7×10^{-3} in decimal notation.

72. Evaluate: $(47.3)^{-0.26}$

73. Combine: $6.128 + 8.3470 - 7.23612$

74. Give the number of significant digits in 6013.00.

75. Multiply: 7.184(16.8)

76. Divide: $78.7 \div 8.251$

77. Find the reciprocal of 0.825.

78. Evaluate: $|-5| - |2 - 7| + |-6|$

79. Evaluate: $(0.55)^2$

80. Write 23 800 in scientific notation.

81. Two lengths of steel rod are to be joined end-to-end. Rod A is $80\overline{0}$ mm $\pm 4.00\%$ and rod B is $64\overline{0}$ mm $\pm 2.00\%$. Find the total length of the two rods when joined and the accompanying error.

82. A $20\overline{0}$-Ω resistor is connected in series to a $150\overline{0}$-Ω resistor in a circuit. The first resistor has an error of $\pm 12.0\%$ and the total resistance is found to be $170\overline{0} \pm 5\overline{0}$ Ω. What is the error associated with the 1500-Ω resistor? State the answer as a percentage.

83. A rectangular tank measured as 1180 mm long, 2160 mm wide, and $50\overline{0}$ mm high. The error in measurement is specified as $\pm 6.0\%$ for all the lengths measured. Find the error in the tank volume calculation: $V = b \cdot d \cdot h$.

84. The area of a circle is found using a value for the radius of $88\overline{0}$ mm with an expected error of $\pm 4.00\%$. Find the area of the circle and the expected error range. $A = \pi r^2$

Writing

85. Suppose you have submitted a report that contains calculations in which you have rounded the answers according to the rules given in this chapter. Jones, your company rival, has sharply attacked your work, calling it "inaccurate" because you did not keep enough digits, and your boss seems to agree.

Write a memo to your boss defending your rounding practices. Point out why it is misleading to retain too many digits. Do not write more than one page. You may use numerical examples to prove your point.

Team Projects

You will find a *team project* suggested at the end of most chapters. These projects are generally longer and more complicated than the usual exercise, and are meant to be done by several people working as a team over a few days.

If your class decides to do one or more of these, you should divide into teams of about three to six students. Then each team should:

Study the problem.

Estimate the answer(s).

List possible tools and methods for solution. Choose one combination.

Solve the problem.

Check the answer.

Write a brief report.

Students now have more computational tools at their disposal than anyone has had before. Depending on the problem, you might choose from the following:

Manual computation

Trial and error

Scientific calculator

Graphics calculator

Computer, using BASIC, a spreadsheet like Lotus, mathematical computation software like *MathCad*, or a computer algebra program like *Derive*, *Maple*, or *Mathematica*.

You might choose *more than one* tool, perhaps doing the computation by calculator and checking the results by computer. For some projects you may want to borrow measuring equipment, such as a tape measure or a transit, or consult reference books. Sometimes it may be useful to make a model. Be sure to consider *any* aids that may help you.

2

Introduction to Algebra

OBJECTIVES

When you have completed this chapter, you should be able to:

- Determine the number of terms in an expression, identify the coefficient of each term, and state the degree of the expression.
- Simplify expressions by removing symbols of grouping and by combining like terms.
- Use the laws of exponents to simplify and combine expressions containing powers.
- Add, subtract, multiply, and divide algebraic expressions.

Algebra is a generalization of arithmetic. For example, the statement

$$2 \cdot 2 \cdot 2 \cdot 2 = 2^4$$

can be generalized to

$$a \cdot a \cdot a \cdot a = a^4$$

where *a* can be *any* number, not just 2. We can go further and say that

$$\underbrace{a \cdot a \cdot a \cdot a \cdots a}_{n \text{ factors}} = a^n$$

where *a* can be any number, as before, and *n* can be *any* positive integer, not just 4.

We learn a lot of new words in this chapter. Every field has its special terms, and algebra is no exception. But since algebra is generalized arithmetic, some of what was said in Chapter 1 (such as rules of signs) will be repeated here.

We will redo the basic operations of addition, subtraction, and so on, but now with symbols rather than numbers. Learn this material well, for it is the foundation on which later chapters rest.

In this chapter we review the algebraic operations themselves, with no attempt to show applications. But don't get the idea that algebra has no practical use, for the following chapter will show applications to many branches of technology.

2•1

Algebraic Expressions

Mathematical Expressions

A *mathematical expression* is a grouping of mathematical symbols, such as numbers, letters, and signs of operation.

■ **Example 1:**
(a) $x^2 - 2x + 3$
(b) $4 \sin 3x$
(c) $5 \log x + e^{2x}$

are mathematical expressions. ■

Algebraic Expressions

An *algebraic expression* is one containing only numbers, algebraic symbols and operations (addition, subtraction, multiplication, division, roots, and powers), such as in Example 1(a). All other expressions are called *transcendental*, such as Examples 1(b) and 1(c).

Equations

We mentioned equations briefly in Chapter 1 when we substituted into equations. We treat them in detail in Chapter 3.

None of the expressions above contains an equal sign ($=$). When two expressions are set equal to each other, we get an *equation*.

■ **Example 2:**
(a) $2x^2 + 3x - 5 = 0$
(b) $6x - 4 = x + 1$
(c) $y = 3x - 5$
(d) $3 \sin x = 2 \cos x$

are equations. ■

Constants and Variables

A *constant* is a quantity that does not change in value in a particular problem. It is usually a number, such as 8, 4.67, or π.

A *variable* is a quantity that may change during a particular problem. A variable is usually represented by a letter from the end of the alphabet (x, y, z, etc.).

■ **Example 3:** The constants in the expression

$$3x^2 + 4x + 5$$

are 3, 4, and 5, and the variable is x. ■

A constant can also be represented by a letter. Such a letter is usually chosen from the beginning of the alphabet (a, b, c, etc.). The letter k is often used as a constant. An expression in which the constants are represented by letters is called a *literal* expression.

■ **Example 4:** The constants in the literal expression

$$ax^2 + bx + c$$

are a, b, and c, and the variable is x. ■

Example 5: In the expression

$$ax + by + cz$$

the letters a, b, and c would usually represent constants, and x, y, and z would usually represent variables.

Symbols of Grouping

We will show how to *remove* symbols of grouping in Sec. 2•2. We will also see in Sec. 2•4 that symbols of grouping are used to indicate *multiplication*.

A mathematical expression will often contain parentheses ( ), brackets [ ], and braces { }. These are used to group parts of the expression together, and affect the meaning of the expression.

Example 6:

$$\{[(3 + x^2) - 2] - (2x + 3)\}(x - 3)$$

shows the use of symbols of grouping.

Example 7: The value of the expression

$$2 + 3(4 + 5)$$

is *different* from

$$(2 + 3)4 + 5$$

The first expression has a value of 29 and the second expression has a value of 25. The placement of symbols of grouping *is* important.

Terms

The plus and minus signs divide an expression into *terms*.

Example 8: The expression

$$4x^2 + 3x + 5$$

$$4x^2 \qquad 3x \qquad 4$$

first term second term third term

has *three* terms.

An exception is when the plus or minus sign is *within* a symbol of grouping, and therefore *within* a term.

Example 9: The expression

$$\underbrace{[(x + 2x^2) + 3]}_{\text{first term}} - \underbrace{(2x + 2)}_{\text{second term}}$$

has *two* terms.

Factors

The number 1, and also the entire expression 3*axy*, are also factors. They are not usually stated. See Chapter 8 for a more thorough discussion of factors.

Any divisor of a term is called a *factor* of that term.

Example 10: Some factors of 3*axy* are 3, *a*, *x*, and *y*.

■ **Example 11:** The expression

$$2x + 3yz$$

has two *terms*, $2x$ and $3yz$. The first term has the *factors* 2 and x, and the second term has factors 3, y, and z. ■

Coefficient

The *coefficient* of a term is the constant part of the term.

■ **Example 12:** The coefficient in the term $3axy^2$ is $3a$, where a is a constant. We say that $3a$ is the coefficient of xy^2. ■

When we use the word "coefficient" in this book, it will always refer to the constant part of the term (such as $3a$ in the preceding example), also called the *numerical* coefficient. If there is no numerical coefficient written before a term, it is understood to be 1.

■ **Example 13:** In the expression $\dfrac{w}{2} + x - y - 3z$

the coefficient of w is $\frac{1}{2}$

the coefficient of x is 1

the coefficient of y is -1

the coefficient of z is -3 ■

Do not forget to include the minus sign with the coefficient.

Degree

The *degree* of a term refers to the integer power to which the variable is raised.

The term *degree* is used only when the exponents are *positive integers*. You would not say that $x^{1/2}$ is a "half-degree" term.

■ **Example 14:**
(a) $2x$ is a first-degree term.
(b) $3x^2$ is a second-degree term.
(c) $5y^9$ is a ninth-degree term. ■

If there are more than one variable, their powers are added to obtain the degree of the term.

■ **Example 15:**
(a) $2x^2y^3$ is of fifth degree.
(b) $3xyz^2$ is of fourth degree. ■

The degree of an *expression* is the same as that of the term having the highest degree.

■ **Example 16:** $3x^2 - 2x + 4$ is a second-degree expression. ■

A *multinomial* is an algebraic expression having *more than one term*.

■ **Example 17:** Some multinomials are

(a) $3x + 5$ (b) $2x^3 - 3x^2 + 7$ (c) $\dfrac{1}{x} + \sqrt{2x}$ ■

A *polynomial* is a multinomial in which the powers to which the unknown is raised are all *nonnegative integers*. The first two expressions in Example 17 are polynomials, but the third is not.

A *binomial* is a multinomial with *two* terms, and a *trinomial* is a multinomial having *three* terms. In Example 17, the first expression is a binomial and the second is a trinomial.

Exercise 1 Algebraic Expressions

How many terms are there in each expression below?

1. $x^2 - 3x$

2. $7y - (y^2 + 5)$

3. $(x + 2)(x - 1)$

4. $3(x - 5) + 2(x + 1)$

Write the coefficients of each term, assuming that letters from the beginning of the alphabet ($a, b, c, \ldots$) are constants:

5. $5x^3$

6. $2ay^2$

7. $\dfrac{bx^3}{4}$

8. $\frac{1}{4}(bx)$

9. $\dfrac{3y^2}{2a}$

10. $\dfrac{2c}{a}(4x^2)$

2·2

Addition and Subtraction of Algebraic Expressions

Like Terms

Like terms are those that differ only in their coefficients.

— **Example 18:**

(a) $2wx$ and $-3wx$ are like terms.

(b) $2wx$ and $-3wx^2$ are *not* like terms.   —

This process is also referred to as *collecting terms.*

Algebraic expressions are added and subtracted by *combining like terms*. Like terms are added by adding their coefficients.

— **Example 19:**

(a) $7x + 5x = 12x$

(b) $8w + 2w - 4w - w = 5w$

(c) $9y - 3y = 6y$

(d) $2x - 3y - 5x + 2y = -3x - y$

(e) $4.21x + 1.23x - 3.11x = 2.33x$ —

In Example 19 we combined the terms on a single line. This is sometimes called *horizontal* addition and subtraction. For more complicated problems you may prefer *vertical* addition and subtraction, as shown in the following example.

— **Example 20:** From the sum of $3x^3 + 2x - 5$ and $x^3 - 3x^2 + 7$, subtract $2x^3 + 3x^2 - 4x - 7$.

Solution: Combine the first two expressions:

$$
\begin{array}{r}
3x^3 \qquad\quad + 2x - 5 \\
+ \quad x^3 - 3x^2 \qquad\;\; + 7 \\
\hline
4x^3 - 3x^2 + 2x + 2
\end{array}
$$

and subtract the third expression from their sum:

$$4x^3 - 3x^2 + 2x + 2$$
$$\underline{-(2x^3 + 3x^2 - 4x - 7)}$$
$$2x^3 - 6x^2 + 6x + 9$$

■

Commutative Law of Addition

We mentioned the commutative law (Eq. 1) when adding numbers in Chapter 1. All it means is that the order of addition does not affect the sum $(2 + 3 = 3 + 2)$. The same law applies, of course, when we have letters instead of numbers.

■ **Example 21:**
(a) $a + b = b + a$
(b) $2x + 3x = 3x + 2x$
$$= 5x$$

■

This law enables us to *rearrange the terms* of an expression for our own convenience.

■ **Example 22:** Simplify the expression

$$4y - 2x + 3z - 7z + 4x - 6y$$

Solution: Using the commutative law, we rearrange the expression so as to get like terms together.

$$-2x + 4x + 4y - 6y + 3z - 7z$$

Collecting terms, we obtain
$$2x - 2y - 4z$$

■

With practice, you will soon be able to omit the first step, and collect terms by inspecting the original expression.

Removal of Parentheses

To combine quantities within parentheses with other quantities not within those parentheses, we must first remove the parentheses. If the parentheses (or other symbols of grouping) are preceded only by a + sign (or no sign), the parentheses may be removed.

■ **Example 23:**
(a) $(a + b - c) = a + b - c$
(b) $(x + y) + (w - z) = x + y + w - z$

■

When the parentheses are preceded only by a $(-)$ sign, change the sign of every term within the parentheses upon removing the parentheses.

■ **Example 24:**
(a) $-(a + b - c) = -a - b + c$
(b) $-(x + y) - (x - y) = -x - y - x + y = -2x$
(c) $(2w - 3x - 2y) - (w - 4x + 5y) - (3w - 2x - y)$
$$= 2w - 3x - 2y - w + 4x - 5y - 3w + 2x + y$$
$$= 2w - w - 3w - 3x + 4x + 2x - 2y - 5y + y$$
$$= -2w + 3x - 6y$$

■

When there are groups within groups, start by simplifying the *innermost* groups and then work outward.

■ **Example 25:**

We'll do more complicated problems of this type later.

$$3x - [2y + 5z - (y + 2)] + 3 - 7z = 3x - [2y + 5z - y - 2] + 3 - 7z$$
$$= 3x - [y + 5z - 2] + 3 - 7z$$
$$= 3x - y - 5z + 2 + 3 - 7z$$
$$= 3x - y - 5z + 5 - 7z$$
$$= 3x - y - 12z + 5$$ ■

Good Working Habits

Start now to develop careful working habits. Why make things even harder for yourself by scribbling? Form the symbols with care; work in sequence, from the top of the page to the bottom; do not crowd your work; use a sharp pencil, not a pen; erase mistakes instead of crossing them out. What chance do you have if you cannot read your own work?

Common Error	Do not switch between capitals and lowercase letters without reason. Although b and B are the same alphabetic letter, in a math problem they could stand for entirely different quantities.

Exercise 2 Addition and Subtraction of Algebraic Expressions

Combine as indicated, and simplify:

1. $7x + 5x$

2. $2x + 5x - 4x + x$

3. $6ab - 7ab - 9ab$

4. $9.4x - 3.7x + 1.4x$

5. Add $7a - 3b + m$ and $3b - 7a - c + m$.

6. What is the sum of $6ab + 12bc - 8cd$, $3cd - 7cd - 9bc$, and $12cd - 2ab - 5bc$?

7. What is the sum of $3a + b - 10$, $c - d - a$, and $-4c + 2a - 3b - 7$?

8. Add $7m + 3n - 11p$, $3a - 9n - 11m$, $8n - 4m + 5p$, and $6n - m + 3p$.

9. Add $8ax + 2(x + a) + 3b$, $9ax + 6(x + a) - 9b$, and $11x + 6b - 7ax - 8(x + a)$.

10. Add $a - 9 - 8a^2 + 16a^3$, $5 + 15a^3 - 12a - 2a^2$, and $6a^2 - 10a^3 + 11a - 13$.

11. Subtract $41x^3 - 2x^2 + 13$ from $15x^3 + x - 18$.

12. Subtract $3b - 6d - 10c + 7a$ from $4d + 12a - 13c - 9b$.

13. Add $x - y - z$ and $y - x + z$.

14. What is the sum of $a + 2b - 3c - 10$, $3b - 4a + 5c + 10$, and $5b - c$?

15. Add $72ax^4 - 8ay^3$, $-38ax^4 - 3ay^4 + 7ay^3$, $8 + 12ay^4$, $-6ay^3 + 12$, and $-34ax^4 + 5ay^3 - 9ay^4$.

16. Add $2a(x - y^2) - 3mz^2$, $4a(x - y^2) - 5mz^2$, and $5a(x - y^2) + 7mz^2$.

17. What is the sum of $9b^2 - 3ac + d$, $4b^2 + 7d - 4ac$, $3d - 4b^2 + 6ac$, $5b^2 - 2ac - 12d$, and $4b^2 - d$?

18. From the sum of $2a + 3b - 4c$ and $3b + 4c - 5d$, subtract the sum of $5c - 6d - 7a$ and $-7d + 8a + 9b$.

19. What is the sum of $7ab - m^2 + q$, $-4ab - 5m^3 - 3q$, $12ab + 14m^2 - z$, and $-6m^2 - 2q$?

20. Add $14(x + y) - 17(y + z)$, $4(y + z) - 19(z + x)$, and $-7(z + x) - 3(x + y)$.

21. Add $3.52(a + b)$, $4.15(a + b)$, and $-1.84(a + b)$.

Symbols of Grouping

Remove symbols of grouping and collect terms:

22. $(3x + 5) + (2x - 3)$

23. $3a^2 - (3a - x + b)$

24. $40xy - (30xy - 2b^2 + 3c - 4d)$

25. $(6.4 - 1.8x) - (7.5 + 2.6x)$

26. $7m^2 + 2bc - (3m^2 - bc - x)$

27. $a^2 - a - (4a - y - 3a^2 - 1)$

28. $(2x^4 + 3x^3 - 4) + (3x^4 - 2x^3 - 8)$

29. $a + b - m - (m - a - b)$

30. $(3xy - 2y + 3z) + (-3y + 8z) - (-3xy - z)$

31. $3m - z - y - (2z - y - 3m)$

32. $(2x - 3y) - (5x - 3y - 2z)$

33. $(w + 2z) - (-3w - 5x) + (x + z) - (z - w)$

34. $2a + \{-6b - [3c + (-4b - 6c + a)]\}$

35. $4a - \{a - [-7a - [8a - (5a + 3)] - (-6a - 2a - 9)]\}$

36. $9m - \{3n + [4m - (n - 6m)] - [m + 7n]\}$

Computer

We can use computer mathematics software to solve many of the problems encountered in this text. A computer-screen symbol appears beside (sets of) problems which should be solved using such software, or which require computer programming.

Programs are available that let us do *symbolic* algebra on the computer, in addition to numerical computation. These are called *computer algebra systems* (CAS). Some programs currently available are *Derive*, *Mathematica*, and *Maple*. Each of these systems uses the command *Simplify* to add or subtract algebraic expressions.

37. Using whatever symbolic algebra program is available to you, repeat any of the problems in this exercise. Compare the results with what you calculated by hand.

2·3

Integral Exponents

Definitions

In this section we deal only with expressions that have integers (positive or negative, and zero) as exponents.

■ **Example 26:** We study such expressions as

$$x^3 \qquad a^{-2} \qquad y^0 \qquad x^2 y^3 w^{-1} \qquad (m + n)^5$$

A positive *exponent* shows how many times the *base* is to be multiplied by itself.

■ **Example 27:** In the expression 3^4, 3 is the base and 4 is the exponent.

$$\text{base} \longrightarrow 3^4 \longleftarrow \text{exponent}$$

Its meaning is

$$3^4 = 3(3)(3)(3) = 81$$ ■

In general,

Positive Integral Exponent	a^n means $\underbrace{a \cdot a \cdot a \cdot a \cdot \ldots \cdot a}_{n \text{ factors}}$	**28**

Common Errors	An exponent applies *only* to the symbol directly before it. Thus $$2x^2 \neq 2^2 x^2$$ but $$(2x)^2 = (2x)(2x) = 4x^2$$
	Also, $$-2^2 \neq 4$$ but $$(-2)^2 = (-2)(-2) = 4 \quad \text{and} \quad -2^2 = -(2)(2) = -4$$

Multiplying Powers

Let us multiply the quantity x^2 by x^3. From Eq. 28, we know that

$$x^2 = x \cdot x$$

and that

$$x^3 = x \cdot x \cdot x$$

Multiplying, we obtain

$$x^2 \cdot x^3 = (x \cdot x)(x \cdot x \cdot x)$$
$$= x \cdot x \cdot x \cdot x \cdot x$$
$$= x^5$$

Notice that the exponent in the result is the *sum of the two original exponents*.

$$x^2 \cdot x^3 = x^{2+3} \cdot x^5$$

This will always be so. We summarize this rule as our first *law of exponents*:

Products	$x^a \cdot x^b = x^{a+b}$	**29**

When multiplying powers of the same base, we keep the same base and ***add the exponents***.

■ **Example 28:**
(a) $x^4(x^3) = x^{4+3} = x^7$
(b) $x^5(x^a) = x^{5+a}$
(c) $y^2(y^n)(y^3) = y^{2+n+3} = y^{5+n}$

Every quantity has an exponent of 1, even though it is not usually written.

■ **Example 29:**
(a) $x(x^3) = x^{1+3} = x^4$
(b) $a^2(a^4)(a) = a^{2+4+1} = a^7$
(c) $x^a(x)(x^b) = x^{a+1+b}$

The "invisible 1" appears again. We saw it before as the unwritten coefficient of every term, and now as the unwritten exponent. It is also in the denominator.

$$x = \frac{1x^i}{1}$$

Do not forget about those invisible 1s. *We use them all the time.*

Quotients

Let us divide x^5 by x^3. By Eq. 29,

$$\frac{x^5}{x^3} = \frac{x \cdot x \cdot x \cdot x \cdot x}{x \cdot x \cdot x} = \frac{x \cdot x \cdot x}{x \cdot x \cdot x} \cdot x \cdot x$$

$$= x \cdot x = x^2$$

The same result could have been obtained by *subtracting exponents*:

$$\frac{x^5}{x^3} = x^{5-3} = x^2$$

This always works, and we state it as another law of exponents:

Quotients	$\dfrac{x^a}{x^b} = x^{a-b} \qquad (x \neq 0)$	**30**

When dividing powers of the same base, we keep the same base and ***subtract the exponents***.

■ **Example 30:**

(a) $\dfrac{a^4 b^3}{ab^2} = a^{4-1}b^{3-2} = a^3 b$

(b) $\dfrac{y^{n-m}}{y^{n+m}} = y^{n-m-(n+m)} = y^{-2m}$

Common Error	Remember when using rules 29 and 30 that the quantities to be multiplied or divided **must have the same base.**

Power Raised to a Power

Let us take a quantity raised to a power, say, x^2, and raise the entire expression to *another* power, say, 3.

$$(x^2)^3$$

By Eq. 29,

$$(x^2)^3 = (x^2)(x^2)(x^2)$$

$$= (x \cdot x)(x \cdot x)(x \cdot x)$$

$$= x \cdot x \cdot x \cdot x \cdot x \cdot x = x^6$$

a result that could have been obtained by *multiplying the exponents*:

$$(x^2)^3 = x^{2(3)} = x^6$$

In general,

Powers	$(x^a)^b = x^{ab}$	31

*When raising a power to a power, we keep the same base and **multiply the exponents**.*

━ Example 31:
(a) $(w^5)^2 = w^{5(2)} = w^{10}$
(b) $(a^{-3})^2 = a^{(-3)(2)} = a^{-6}$
(c) $(10^4)^3 = 10^{4(3)} = 10^{12}$
(d) $(b^{x+2})^3 = b^{3x+6}$ ━

Product Raised to a Power

We now raise a product, such as xy, to some power, say 3.

$$(xy)^3$$

By Eq. 28,

$$(xy)^3 = (xy)(xy)(xy)$$

$$= x \cdot y \cdot x \cdot y \cdot x \cdot y$$

$$= x \cdot x \cdot x \cdot y \cdot y \cdot y$$

$$= x^3 y^3$$

In general,

Product Raised to a Power	$(xy)^n = x^n y^n$	32

When a product is raised to a power, each factor may be **separately** raised to the power.

■ **Example 32:**

(a) $(xyz)^5 = x^5y^5z^5$

(b) $(2x)^3 = 2^3x^3 = 8x^3$

(c) $(3.75 \times 10^3)^2 = (3.75)^2 \times (10^3)^2$
$$= 14.1 \times 10^6$$

(d) $(3x^2y^n)^3 = 3^3(x^2)^3(y^n)^3$
$$= 27x^6y^{3n}$$

(e) $(-x^2y)^3 = (-1)^3(x^2)^3y^3 = -x^6y^3$ ■

A good way to test a "rule" that you are not sure of is to *try it with numbers*. In this case, does $(2 + 3)^2$ equal $2^2 + 3^2$? Evaluating each expression, we obtain

$$(5)^2 \overset{?}{=} 4 + 9$$

$$25 \neq 13$$

Common Error	There is *no* similar rule for the *sum* of two quantities raised to a power. $$(x + y)^n \neq x^n + y^n$$

Quotient Raised to a Power

Using the same steps as in the preceding section, see if you can show that

$$\left(\frac{x}{y}\right)^3 = \frac{x^3}{y^3}$$

Or, in general,

Quotient Raised to a Power	$$\left(\frac{x}{y}\right)^n = \frac{x^n}{y^n} \qquad (y \neq 0)$$	**33**

When a quotient is raised to a power, the numerator and denominator may be **separately** raised to the power.

■ **Example 33:**

(a) $\left(\dfrac{x}{5}\right)^2 = \dfrac{x^2}{5^2} = \dfrac{x^2}{25}$

(b) $\left(\dfrac{3a}{2b}\right)^3 = \dfrac{3^3a^3}{2^3b^3} = \dfrac{27a^3}{8b^3}$

(c) $\left(\dfrac{2x^2}{5y^3}\right)^3 = \dfrac{2^3(x^2)^3}{5^3(y^3)^3} = \dfrac{8x^6}{125y^9}$

(d) $\left(-\dfrac{a}{b^2}\right)^3 = (-1)^3\dfrac{a^3}{(b^2)^3} = -\dfrac{a^3}{b^6}$ ■

Zero Exponent

If we divide x^n by itself we get, by Eq. 30,

$$\frac{x^n}{x^n} = x^{n-n} = x^0$$

But any expression divided by itself equals 1, so

Zero Exponent	$x^0 = 1 \qquad (x \neq 0)$	**34**

Any quantity (except 0) raised to the zero power equals 1.

■ **Example 34:**
(a) $(xyz)^0 = 1$
(b) $3862^0 = 1$
(c) $(x^2 - 2x + 3)^0 = 1$
(d) $5x^0 = 5(1) = 5$ ■

Negative Exponent

We now divide x^0 by x^a. By Eq. 30,

$$\frac{x^0}{x^a} = x^{0-a} = x^{-a}$$

Since $x^0 = 1$, we get

Negative Exponent	$x^{-a} = \dfrac{1}{x^a} \qquad (x \neq 0)$	**35**

When taking the reciprocal of a base raised to a power, ***change the sign of the exponent***.

We can, of course, also give Eq. 35 in the form

$$x^a = \frac{1}{x^{-a}} \qquad (x \neq 0)$$

■ **Example 35:**
(a) $5^{-1} = \dfrac{1}{5}$ \qquad\qquad (b) $x^{-4} = \dfrac{1}{x^4}$
(c) $\dfrac{1}{xy^{-2}} = \dfrac{y^2}{x}$ \qquad\qquad (d) $\dfrac{w^{-3}}{z^{-2}} = \dfrac{z^2}{w^3}$
(e) $\left(\dfrac{3x}{2y^2}\right)^{-b} = \left(\dfrac{2y^2}{3x}\right)^{b}$ ■

We can also use negative exponents to rewrite an expression *without fractions*.

■ **Example 36:**
(a) $\dfrac{1}{y} = y^{-1}$ \qquad\qquad (b) $\dfrac{a^2}{b^3} = a^2 b^{-3}$
(c) $\dfrac{x^2 y^{-3}}{w^4 z^{-2}} = x^2 y^{-3} w^{-4} z^2$ ■

Summary of the Laws of Exponents

Definition	$a^n = \underbrace{a \cdot a \cdot a \cdot a \cdot \ldots \cdot a}_{n \text{ factors}}$	28
Products	$x^a \cdot x^b = x^{a+b}$	29
Quotients	$\dfrac{x^a}{x^b} = x^{a-b} \qquad (x \neq 0)$	30
Powers	$(x^a)^b = x^{ab} = (x^b)^a$	31
Product Raised to a Power	$(xy)^n = x^n y^n$	32
Quotient Raised to a Power	$\left(\dfrac{x}{y}\right)^n = \dfrac{x^n}{y^n} \qquad (y \neq 0)$	33
Zero Exponent	$x^0 = 1 \qquad (x \neq 0)$	34
Negative Exponent	$x^{-a} = \dfrac{1}{x^a} \qquad (x \neq 0)$	35

Exercise 3 Integral Exponents

Evaluate each expression.

1. 2^4 **2.** $(-3)^2$ **3.** $(-3)^3$
4. $(|-3|)^3$ **5.** $(0.1)^4$ **6.** $(-2)^5$

Multiply.

7. $a^3 \cdot a^5$ **8.** $x^a(x^2)$ **9.** $y^{a+1} \cdot y^{a-3}$
10. $10^4 \cdot 10^3$ **11.** $10^a \cdot 10^b$ **12.** $10^{n+2} \cdot 10^{2n-1}$

Divide, and write your answers without negative exponents.

13. $\dfrac{y^5}{y^2}$ **14.** $\dfrac{5^5}{5^3}$ **15.** $\dfrac{x^{n+2}}{x^{n+1}}$

16. $\dfrac{10^5}{10}$ **17.** $\dfrac{10^{x+5}}{10^{x+3}}$ **18.** $\dfrac{10^2}{10^{-3}}$

19. $\dfrac{x^{-2}}{x^{-3}}$ **20.** $\dfrac{a^{-5}}{a}$

Simplify.

21. $(x^3)^4$ **22.** $(9^2)^3$ **23.** $(a^x)^y$
24. $(x^{-2})^{-2}$ **25.** $(x^{a+1})^2$

Raise to the power indicated.

26. $(xy)^2$

27. $(2x)^3$

28. $(3x^2y^3)^2$

29. $(3abc)^3$

30. $\left(\dfrac{3}{5}\right)^2$

31. $\left(-\dfrac{1}{3}\right)^3$

32. $\left(\dfrac{x}{y}\right)^5$

33. $\left(\dfrac{2a}{3b^2}\right)^3$

34. $\left(\dfrac{3x^2y}{4wz^3}\right)^2$

Write each expression with positive exponents only.

35. a^{-2}

36. $(-x)^{-3}$

37. $\left(\dfrac{3}{y}\right)^{-3}$

38. $a^{-2}bc^{-3}$

39. $\left(\dfrac{2a}{3b^3}\right)^{-2}$

40. xy^{-4}

41. $2x^{-2} + 3y^{-3}$

42. $\left(\dfrac{x}{y}\right)^{-1}$

Express without fractions, using negative exponents where needed.

43. $\dfrac{1}{x}$

44. $\dfrac{3}{y^2}$

45. $\dfrac{x^2}{y^2}$

46. $\dfrac{x^2y^{-3}}{z^{-2}}$

47. $\dfrac{a^{-3}}{b^2}$

48. $\dfrac{x^{-2}y^{-3}}{w^{-1}z^{-4}}$

Evaluate.

49. $(a + b + c)^0$

50. $8x^0y^2$

51. $\dfrac{a^0}{9}$

52. $\dfrac{y}{x^0}$

53. $\dfrac{x^{2n} \cdot x^3}{x^{3+2n}}$

54. $5\left(\dfrac{x}{y}\right)^0$

Computer

55. Use a computer algebra system to repeat any of the problems in this exercise. Compare your results with what you got by hand.

2•4   Multiplication of Algebraic Expressions

Symbols and Definitions

Multiplication is indicated in several ways: by the usual $\times$ symbol, by a dot, or by parentheses, brackets, or braces. Thus the product of b and d could be written

$$b \cdot d \qquad b \times d \qquad b(d) \qquad (b)d \qquad (b)(d)$$

Most common of all is to use no symbol at all. The product of b and d would usually be written bd. A calculator or computer usually uses the asterisk or star (*) to indicate multiplication.

    We get a *product* when we multiply two or more *factors*:

$$(\text{factor})(\text{factor})(\text{factor}) = \text{product}$$

Avoid using the $\times$ symbol, because it could get confused with the letter x.

Rules of Signs

The product of two factors having the *same* sign is *positive*; the product of two factors having *different* signs is *negative*. If a and b are positive quantities, we have

Rules of Signs	$(+a)(+b) = (-a)(-b) = +ab$	8
	$(+a)(-b) = (-a)(+b) = -(+a)(+b) = -ab$	9

When multiplying more than two factors, the product of every *pair* of negative terms will be positive. Thus, if there is an even number of negative factors, the final result will be positive; if there is an odd number of negative factors, the final result will be negative.

■ **Example 37:**
(a) $x(-y)(-z) = xyz$
(b) $(-a)(-b)(-c) = -abc$
(c) $(-p)(-q)(-r)(-s) = pqrs$ ■

Commutative Law

As we saw when multiplying numbers, the *order* of multiplication does not make any difference. In symbols,

Commutative Law of Multiplication	$ab = ba$	2

■ **Example 38:** Multiply $3y$ by $-2x$.

Solution:
$$(3y)(-2x) = 3(y)(-2)(x)$$
By Eq. 2,
$$= 3(-2)(y)(x)$$
$$= -6yx$$
or
$$= -6xy$$

since it is common practice to write the letters in alphabetical order.   ■

Multiplying Monomials

A *monomial* is an algebraic expression having *one term*.

■ **Example 39:** Some monomials are

(a) $2x^3$ (b) $\dfrac{3wxy}{4}$ (c) $(2b)^3$ ■

To multiply monomials, we make use of the commutative law (Eq. 2), the rules of signs (Eqs. 8 and 9), and the law of exponents for products.

Products	$x^a \cdot x^b = x^{a+b}$	29

Example 40:

$$(4a^3b)(-3ab^2) = (4)(-3)(a^3)(a)(b)(b^2)$$
$$= -12a^{3+1}b^{1+2}$$
$$= -12a^4b^3$$

Example 41: Multiply $5x^2$, $-3xy$, and $-xy^3z$.

> With some practice, you should be able to omit some steps in many of these solutions. But use as many steps as you need to get it right.

Solution: By Eq. 2,

$$5x^2(-3xy)(-xy^3z) = 5(-3)(-1)(x^2)(x)(x)(y)(y^3)(z)$$

By Eq. 29,

$$= 15x^{2+1+1}y^{1+3}z$$
$$= 15x^4y^4z$$

Example 42: Multiply $3x^2$ by $2ax^n$.

Solution: By Eq. 2,

$$3x^2(2ax^n) = 3(2a)(x^2)(x^n)$$

By Eq. 29,

$$= 6ax^{2+n}$$

Multiplying a Multinomial by a Monomial

To multiply a monomial and a multinomial, we use the *distributive law*

> We will later use this law to remove common factors.

Distributive Law for Multiplication	$a(b + c) = ab + ac$	5

The product of a monomial and a polynomial is equal to the sum of the products of the monomial and each term of the polynomial.

Example 43:

$$2x(x - 3x^2) = 2x(x) + 2x(-3x^2)$$
$$= 2x^2 - 6x^3$$

The distributive law, although written for a monomial times a binomial, can be extended for a multinomial having any number of terms. Simply *multiply every term in the multinomial by the monomial.*

Example 44:

(a) $-3x^3(3x^2 - 2x + 4) = -3x^3(3x^2) + (-3x^3)(-2x) + (-3x^3)(4)$
$$= -9x^5 + 6x^4 - 12x^3$$

(b) $4xy(x^2 - 3xy + 2y^2) = 4x^3y - 12x^2y^2 + 8xy^3$

(c) $3.75x(1.83x^2 + 2.27x - 1.49) = 6.86x^3 + 8.51x^2 - 5.59x$

Removing Symbols of Grouping

Symbols of grouping, in addition to indicating that the enclosed expression is to be taken as a whole, also indicate multiplication.

■ **Example 45:**

(a) $x(y)$ is the product of x and y.
(b) $x(y + 2)$ is the product of x and $(y + 2)$.
(c) $(x - 1)(y + 2)$ is the product of $(x - 1)$ and $(y + 2)$.
(d) $-(y + 2)$ is the product of -1 and $(y + 2)$. ■

The parentheses may be removed after the multiplication has been performed.

■ **Example 46:**

(a) $x(y + 2) = xy + 2x$
(b) $5 + 3(x - 2) = 5 + 3x - 6 = 3x - 1$ ■

Common Errors	Do not forget to multiply *every* term within the grouping by the preceding factor. $$-(2x + 5) \neq -2x + 5$$
	Multiply the terms within the parentheses *only* by the factor directly preceding the grouping. $$x + 2(a + b) \neq (x + 2)(a + b)$$

If there are groupings within groupings, start simplifying with the *innermost* groupings.

■ **Example 47:**

(a) $$x - 3[2 - 4(y + 1)] = x - 3[2 - 4y - 4]$$
$$= x - 3[-2 - 4y]$$
$$= x + 6 + 12y$$

(b) $$3\{2[4(w - 4) - (x + 3)] - 2\} - 6x = 3\{2[4w - 16 - x - 3] - 2\} - 6x$$
$$= 3\{2[4w - x - 19] - 2\} - 6x$$
$$= 3\{8w - 2x - 38 - 2\} - 6x$$
$$= 3\{8w - 2x - 40\} - 6x$$
$$= 24w - 6x - 120 - 6x$$
$$= 24w - 12x - 120$$ ■

Multiplying a Multinomial by a Multinomial

Using the distributive law, we multiply one of the multinomials by each term in the other multinomial. We then use the distributive law again to remove the remaining parentheses, and simplify.

■ **Example 48:**

$$(x + 4)(x - 3) = x(x - 3) + 4(x - 3)$$
$$= x^2 - 3x + 4x - 12$$
$$= x^2 + x - 12$$ ■

Some prefer a vertical arrangement for problems like the last one.

■ **Example 49:**

$$
\begin{array}{r}
x + 4 \\
x - 3 \\
\hline
-3x - 12 \\
x^2 + 4x \\
\hline
x^2 + x - 12 \quad \text{as before}
\end{array}
$$

■

■ **Example 50:**

(a) $(x - 3)(x^2 - 2x + 1)$
$$= x(x^2) + x(-2x) + x(1) - 3(x^2) - 3(-2x) - 3(1)$$
$$= x^3 - 2x^2 + x - 3x^2 + 6x - 3$$
$$= x^3 - 5x^2 + 7x - 3$$

(b) $(2x + 3y - 4z)(x - 2y - 3z)$
$$= 2x^2 - 4xy - 6xz + 3xy - 6y^2 - 9yz - 4xz + 8yz + 12z^2$$
$$= 2x^2 - 6y^2 + 12z^2 - xy - 10xz - yz$$

(c) $(1.24x + 2.03)(3.16x^2 - 2.61x + 5.36)$
$$= 3.92x^3 - 3.24x^2 + 6.65x + 6.41x^2 - 5.30x + 10.9$$
$$= 3.92x^3 + 3.17x^2 + 1.35x + 10.9$$

■

When multiplying *more than two* expressions, first multiply any pair, and then multiply that product by the third expression, and so on.

■ **Example 51:** Multiply $(x - 2)(x + 1)(2x - 3)$.

Solution: Multiplying the last two binomials yields

$$(x - 2)(2x^2 - x - 3)$$

Then multiplying that product by (x - 2) gives

$$2x^3 - x^2 - 3x - 4x^2 + 2x + 6$$
$$= 2x^3 - 5x^2 - x + 6$$

■

To raise an expression to a power, simply multiply the expression by itself the proper number of times.

■ **Example 52:**

$$(x - 1)^3 = (x - 1)(x - 1)(x - 1)$$
$$= (x - 1)(x^2 - 2x + 1)$$
$$= x^3 - 2x^2 + x - x^2 + 2x - 1$$
$$= x^3 - 3x^2 + 3x - 1$$

■

Product of the Sum and the Difference of Two Terms

Let us multiply the binomials $(a - b)$ and $(a + b)$. We get

$$(a - b)(a + b) = a^2 + ab - ab - b^2$$

When we multiply two binomials, we get expressions that occur frequently enough in our later work for us to take special note of them here. These are called *special products*. We will need them especially when we study factoring.

The two middle terms cancel, leaving

Difference of Two Squares	$(a - b)(a + b) = a^2 - b^2$	**41**

Thus the product is the *difference of two squares,* the squares of the original numbers.

■ **Example 53:**

$$(x + 2)(x - 2) = x^2 - 2^2 = x^2 - 4$$ ■

Product of Two Binomials Having the Same First Term

When we multiply $(x + a)$ and $(x + b)$, we have

$$(x + a)(x + b) = x^2 + ax + bx + ab$$

Combining like terms, we obtain

Trinomial, Leading Coefficient = 1	$(x + a)(x + b) = x^2 + (a + b)x + ab$	**45**

■ **Example 54:**

$$(w + 3)(w - 4) = w^2 + (3 - 4)w + 3(-4)$$
$$= w^2 - w - 12$$ ■

General Quadratic Trinomial

Some people like the *FOIL* rule. Multiply the *First* terms, then *Outer*, *Inner*, and *Last* terms.

When we multiply two binomials of the form $ax + b$ and $cx + d$, we get

$$(ax + b)(cx + d) = acx^2 + adx + bcx + bd$$

Combining like terms, we obtain

General Quadratic Trinomial	$(ax + b)(cx + d) = acx^2 + (ad + bc)x + bd$	**46**

■ **Example 55:**

$$(3x - 2)(2x + 5) = 3(2)x^2 + [(3)(5) + (-2)(2)]x + (-2)(5)$$
$$= 6x^2 + 11x - 10$$ ■

Powers of Multinomials

As with a monomial raised to a power that is a positive integer, we raise a *multinomial* to a power by multiplying that multinomial by itself the proper number of times.

■ **Example 56:**

$$(x - 3)^2 = (x - 3)(x - 3)$$
$$= x^2 - 3x - 3x + 9$$
$$= x^2 - 6x + 9$$

■ **Example 57:**

$$(x - 3)^3 = (x - 3)(x - 3)(x - 3)$$
$$= (x - 3)(x^2 - 6x + 9) \quad \text{(from Example 56)}$$
$$= x^3 - 6x^2 + 9x - 3x^2 + 18x - 27$$

Combining like terms gives us

$$(x - 3)^3 = x^3 - 9x^2 + 27x - 27$$

Perfect Square Trinomial

When we *square a binomial* such as $(a + b)$, we get

$$(a + b)^2 = (a + b)(a + b) = a^2 + ab + ab + b^2$$

Collecting terms, we obtain

Perfect Square Trinomial	$(a + b)^2 = a^2 + 2ab + b^2$	**47**

This trinomial is called a *perfect square trinomial*, because it is the square of a binomial. Its first and last terms are the squares of the two terms of the binomial; its middle term is twice the product of the terms of the binomial. Similarly, when we square $(a - b)$, we get

Perfect Square Trinomial	$(a - b)^2 = a^2 - 2ab + b^2$	**47**

■ **Example 58:**

$$(3x - 2)^2 = (3x)^2 - 2(3x)(2) + 2^2$$
$$= 9x^2 - 12x + 4$$

Exercise 4 Multiplication of Algebraic Expressions

Multiply the following monomials, and simplify.

1. $x^3(x^2)$
2. $x^2(3axy)$
3. $(-5ab)(-2a^2b^3)$
4. $(3.52xy)(-4.14xyz)$
5. $(6ab)(2a^2b)(3a^3b^3)$
6. $(-2a)(-3abc)(ac^2)$
7. $2p(-4p^2q)(pq^3)$
8. $(-3xy)(-2w^2x)(-xy^3)(-wy)$

Multiply the polynomial by the monomial, and simplify.

9. $2a(a - 5)$
10. $(x^2 + 2x)x^3$
11. $xy(x - y + xy)$
12. $3a^2b^3(ab - 2ab^2 + b)$
13. $-4pq(3p^2 + 2pq - 3q^2)$
14. $2.8x(1.5x^3 - 3.2x^2 + 5.7x - 4.6)$
15. $3ab(2a^2b^2 - 4a^2b + 3ab^2 + ab)$
16. $-3xy(2xy^3 - 3x^2y + xy^2 - 4xy)$

Multiply the following pairs of binomials, and simplify.

17. $(a + b)(a + c)$
18. $(2x + 2)(5x + 3)$
19. $(x + 3y)(x^2 - y)$
20. $(a - 5)(a + 5)$
21. $(m + n)(9m - 9n)$
22. $(m^2 + 2c)(m^2 - 5c)$
23. $(7cd^2 + 4y^3z)(7cd^2 - 4y^3z)$
24. $(3a + 4c)(2a - 5c)$
25. $(x^2 + y^2)(x^2 - y^2)$
26. $(3.50a^2 + 1.20b)(3.80a^2 - 2.40b)$

Multiply the following sets of binomials and trinomials, and simplify.

27. $(a - c - 1)(a + 1)$
28. $(x - y)(2x + 3y - 5)$
29. $(m^2 - 3m - 7)(m - 2)$
30. $(-3x^2 + 3x - 9)(x + 3)$
31. $(x^6 + x^4 + x^2)(x^2 - 1)$
32. $(m - 1)(2m - m^2 + 1)$
33. $(1 - z)(z^2 - z + 2)$
34. $(3a^3 - 2ab - b^2)(2a - 4b)$
35. $(a^2 - ay + y^2)(a + y)$
36. $(y^2 - 7.5y + 2.8)(y + 1.6)$
37. $(a^2 + ay + y^2)(a - y)$
38. $(a^2 + ay - y^2)(a - y)$

Multiply the following sets of binomials and polynomials, and simplify.

39. $[x^2 - (m - n)x - mn](x - p)$
40. $(x^2 + ax - bx - ab)(x + b)$
41. $(m^4 + m^3 + m^2 + m + 1)(m - 1)$

Multiply the following sets of monomials and binomials, and simplify.

42. $(2a + 3x)(2a + 3x)9$
43. $(3a - b)(3a - b)x$
44. $c(m - n)(m + n)$

Multiply the following sets of multinomials, and simplify.

45. $(x + 1)(x + 1)(x - 2)$
46. $(m - 2.5)(m - 1.3)(m + 3.2)$
47. $(x + a)(x + b)(x - c)$
48. $(x - 4)(x - 5)(x + 4)(x + 5)$
49. $(1 + c)(1 + c)(1 - c)(1 + c^2)$

Multiply the following pairs of trinomials, and simplify.

50. $(a + b - c)(a - b + c)$
51. $(2a^3 + 5a)(2a^3 - 5ac^2 + 2a)$
52. $[3(a + b)^2 - (a + b) + 2][4(a + b)^2 - (a + b) - 5]$
53. $(a + b + c)(a - b + c)(a + b - c)$

Multiply the following sets of polynomials, and simplify.

54. $(x^3 - 6x^2 + 12x - 8)(x^2 + 4x + 4)$
55. $(n - 5n^2 + 2 + n^3)(5n + n^2 - 10)$
56. $(mx + my - nx - ny)(mx - my + nx - ny)$

Powers of Algebraic Expressions

Square each binomial.

57. $(a + c)$
58. $(p + q)$
59. $(m - n)$
60. $(x - y)$
61. $(A + B)$
62. $(A - C)$
63. $(3.80a - 2.20x)$
64. $(m + c)$
65. $(2c - 3d)$
66. $(x^2 - x)$
67. $(a - 1)$
68. $(a^2x - ax^3)$
69. $(y^2 - 20)$
70. $(x^n - y^2)$

Square each trinomial.

71. $(a + b + c)$
72. $(a - b - c)$
73. $(1 + x - y)$
74. $(x^2 + 2x - 3)$
75. $(x^2 + xy + y^2)$
76. $(x^3 - 2x - 1)$

Cube each binomial.

77. $(a + b)$
78. $(2x + 1)$
79. $(p - 3q)$
80. $(x^2 - 1)$
81. $(a - b)$
82. $(3m - 2n)$

Symbols of Grouping

Remove symbols of grouping, and simplify.

83. $-3[-(a + b) - c]$
84. $-[x + (y - 2) - 4]$
85. $(p - q) - [p - (p - q) - q]$
86. $-(x - y) - [y - (y - x) - x]$
87. $-5[-2(3y - z) - z] + y$
88. $[(m + 2n) - (2m - n)][(2m + n) - (m - 2n)]$
89. $(x - 1) - \{[x - (x - 3)] - x\}$
90. $(a - b)(a^3 + b^3)[a(a + b) + b^2]$
91. $y - \{4x - [y - (2y - 9) - x] + 2\}$
92. $[2x^2 + (3x - 1)(4x + 5)][5x^2 - (4x + 3)(x - 2)]$

Computer

93. Use a computer algebra system to repeat any of the problems in this exercise. Compare your results with what you got by hand.

2·5   Division of Algebraic Expressions

Symbols for Division

Division may be indicated by any of the symbols ÷, —, and /:

$$x \div y \qquad \frac{x}{y} \qquad x/y$$

The names of the parts are

$$\frac{\text{dividend}}{\text{divisor}} = \frac{\text{numerator}}{\text{denominator}} = \text{quotient}$$

If the divisor does not divide evenly into the dividend, the value left over is called the *remainder*. The quantity x/y is also called a *fraction*, and also the *ratio* of x to y.

Reciprocals

As we saw in Sec. 1·4, the *reciprocal* of a number is 1 divided by that number. The reciprocal of n is $1/n$. We can use the idea of a reciprocal to show how division is related to multiplication. We may write $x \div y$ as

$$\frac{x}{y} = \frac{x}{1} \cdot \frac{1}{y} = x \cdot \frac{1}{y}$$

We see that to *divide by a number* is the same thing as to *multiply by its reciprocal*. This fact will be especially useful for dividing by a fraction.

Division by Zero

Division by zero is not a permissible operation.

If division by zero were allowed, we could, for example, divide 2 by zero and get a quotient x.

$$\frac{2}{0} = x$$

or

$$2 = 0 \cdot x$$

But there is no number x which, when multiplied by zero, gives 2, so we cannot allow this operation.

■ **Example 59:** In the fraction

$$\frac{x + 5}{x - 2}$$

x cannot equal 2, or the illegal operation of division by zero will result.   ■

Rules of Signs

The quotient of two terms of *like* sign is *positive*.

$$\frac{+a}{+b} = \frac{-a}{-b} = \frac{a}{b}$$

The quotient of two terms of *unlike* sign is *negative*.

$$\frac{+a}{-b} = \frac{-a}{+b} = -\frac{a}{b}$$

The fraction itself carries a third sign, which, when negative, reverses the sign of the quotient. These three ideas are summarized in the following rules:

Rules of Signs for Division	$\dfrac{+a}{+b} = \dfrac{-a}{-b} = -\dfrac{-a}{+b} = \dfrac{a}{b}$	**10**
	$\dfrac{+a}{-b} = \dfrac{-a}{+b} = -\dfrac{-a}{-b} = -\dfrac{a}{b}$	**11**

These rules show that a *pair* of negative signs may be removed without changing the value of the fraction.

■ **Example 60:** Simplify $-\dfrac{ax^2}{-y}$.

Solution: Removing the pair of minus signs, we obtain

$$-\frac{ax^2}{-y} = \frac{ax^2}{y}$$ ■

Common Error	Removal of pairs of negative signs pertains only to negative signs that are factors of the numerator, denominator, or the fraction as a whole. Do not try to remove pairs of signs that apply only to single terms. Thus $$\frac{x - 2}{x - 3} \neq \frac{x + 2}{x + 3}$$

Dividing a Monomial by a Monomial

Any quantity (except zero) divided by itself equals *one*. So if the same factor appears in both the divisor and the dividend, it may be eliminated.

■ **Example 61:** Divide $6ax$ by $3a$.

Solution:

$$\frac{6ax}{3a} = \frac{6}{3} \cdot \frac{a}{a} \cdot x = 2x$$

To divide quantities having exponents, we make use of the law of exponents for division:

Quotients	$\dfrac{x^a}{x^b} = x^{a-b}$	30

■ **Example 62:** Divide y^5 by y^3.

Solution: By Eq. 30,

$$\frac{y^5}{y^3} = y^{5-3} = y^2$$

When there are numerical coefficients, divide them separately.

■ **Example 63:**

(a) $\dfrac{15x^6}{3x^4} = \dfrac{15}{3} \cdot \dfrac{x^6}{x^4} = 5x^{6-4} = 5x^2$

(b) $\dfrac{8.35y^5}{3.72y} = \dfrac{8.35}{3.72} \cdot \dfrac{y^5}{y} = 2.24y^{5-1} = 2.24y^4$

If there are more than one unknown, treat each separately.

■ **Example 64:** Divide $18x^5y^2z^4$ by $3x^2yz^3$.

Solution:

$$\frac{18x^5y^2z^4}{3x^2yz^3} = \frac{18}{3} \cdot \frac{x^5}{x^2} \cdot \frac{y^2}{y} \cdot \frac{z^4}{z^3}$$

$$= 6x^3yz$$

Sometimes negative exponents will be obtained.

■ **Example 65:**

$$\frac{6x^2}{x^5} = 6x^{2-5} = 6x^{-3}$$

The answer may be left in this form, or, as is usually done, use Eq. 35 to eliminate the negative exponent. Thus

$$6x^{-3} = \frac{6}{x^3}$$

The process of dividing a monomial by a monomial is also referred to as *simplifying a fraction*, or *reducing a fraction to lowest terms*. We discuss this in Chapter 9.

■ **Example 66:** Simplify the fraction

$$\frac{3x^2yz^5}{9xy^4z^2}$$

Solution: The procedure is no different from that used to *divide* $3x^2yz^5$ by $9xy^4z^2$.

$$\frac{3x^2yz^5}{9xy^4z^2} = \frac{3}{9}x^{2-1}y^{1-4}z^{5-2}$$

$$= \frac{1}{3}xy^{-3}z^3$$

or

$$= \frac{xz^3}{3y^3}$$

Do not be dismayed if the expressions to be divided have negative exponents. Apply Eq. 30, as before.

■ **Example 67:** Divide $21x^2y^{-3}z^{-1}$ by $7x^{-4}y^2z^{-3}$.

Solution: Proceeding as before, we have

$$\frac{21x^2y^{-3}z^{-1}}{7x^{-4}y^2z^{-3}} = \frac{21}{7}x^{2-(-4)}y^{-3-2}z^{-1-(-3)}$$

$$= 3x^6y^{-5}z^2$$

$$= \frac{3x^6z^2}{y^5}$$

Dividing a Multinomial by a Monomial

Divide each term of the multinomial by the monomial.

■ **Example 68:** Divide $9x^2 + 3x - 2$ by $3x$.

Solution:

$$\frac{9x^2 + 3x - 2}{3x} = \frac{9x^2}{3x} + \frac{3x}{3x} - \frac{2}{3x}$$

This is really a consequence of the distributive law (Eq. 5).

$$\frac{9x^2 + 3x - 2}{3x} = \frac{1}{3x}(9x^2 + 3x - 2) = \left(\frac{1}{3x}\right)(9x^2) + \left(\frac{1}{3x}\right)(3x) + \left(\frac{1}{3x}\right)(-2)$$

Each of these terms is now simplified as in the preceding section.

$$\frac{9x^2}{3x} + \frac{3x}{3x} - \frac{2}{3x} = 3x + 1 - \frac{2}{3x}$$

Common Error	Do not forget to divide *every* term of the multinomial by the monomial. $$\frac{x^2 + 2x + 3}{x} \neq x + 2 + 3$$

■ **Example 69:**

(a) $\dfrac{3ab + 2a^2b - 5ab^2 + 3a^2b^2}{15ab} = \dfrac{3ab}{15ab} + \dfrac{2a^2b}{15ab} - \dfrac{5ab^2}{15ab} + \dfrac{3a^2b^2}{15ab}$

$\qquad\qquad\qquad\qquad\quad = \dfrac{1}{5} + \dfrac{2a}{15} - \dfrac{b}{3} + \dfrac{ab}{5}$

(b) $\dfrac{6x^3y - 8xy^2 - 2x^4y^4}{-2xy} = -3x^2 + 4y + x^3y^3$

(c) $\dfrac{8.26x^3 - 6.24x^2 + 7.37x}{2.82x} = 2.93x^2 - 2.21x + 2.61$ ■

Common Error	There is no similar rule for dividing a monomial by a multinomial. $$\dfrac{a}{b+c} \neq \dfrac{a}{b} + \dfrac{a}{c}$$

Dividing a Polynomial by a Polynomial

> This method is used only for *polynomials:* expressions in which the powers are all *positive integers*.

Write the divisor and the dividend in the order of descending powers of the variable. Supply any missing terms, using a coefficient of zero. Set up as a long-division problem, as in the following example.

■ **Example 70:** Divide $x^2 + 4x^4 - 2$ by $1 + x$.

Solution:

> The method works just as well if we write the terms in order of *ascending* powers of the variable.

1. Write the dividend in descending order of the powers.
$$4x^4 + x^2 - 2$$

2. Supply the missing terms with coefficients of zero.
$$4x^4 + 0x^3 + x^2 + 0x - 2$$

3. We write the divisor in descending order of the powers, and set up the problem in long-division format.
$$(x + 1)\overline{)4x^4 + 0x^3 + x^2 + 0x - 2}$$

4. Divide the first term in the dividend ($4x^4$) by the first term in the divisor (x). The result ($4x^3$) is written above the dividend, in line with the term having the same power. It is the first term of the quotient.
$$(x + 1)\overline{)\overset{\displaystyle 4x^3}{4x^4 + 0x^3 + x^2 + 0x - 2}}$$

5. Multiply the divisor by the first term of the quotient. Write the result below the dividend. Subtract it from the dividend.

$$
\begin{array}{r}
4x^3 \\
(x + 1)\overline{)4x^4 + 0x^3 + x^2 + 0x - 2} \\
\underline{4x^4 + 4x^3 } \\
-4x^3 + x^2 + 0x - 2
\end{array}
$$

6. Repeat steps 4 and 5, each time using the new dividend obtained, until the degree of the remainder is less than the degree of the divisor.

$$
\begin{array}{r}
4x^3 - 4x^2 + 5x - 5 \\
(x+1)\overline{)4x^4 + 0x^3 +\ \ x^2 + 0x - 2} \\
\underline{4x^4 + 4x^3} \\
-4x^3 +\ \ x^2 + 0x - 2 \\
\underline{-4x^3 - 4x^2} \\
5x^2 + 0x - 2 \\
\underline{5x^2 + 5x} \\
-5x - 2 \\
\underline{-5x - 5} \\
3
\end{array}
$$

The result is written

$$
\frac{4x^4 + x^2 - 2}{x+1} = 4x^3 - 4x^2 + 5x - 5 + \frac{3}{x+1}
$$

or

$$
4x^3 - 4x^2 + 5x - 5 \quad (\text{R}3)
$$

to indicate a remainder of 3.

Common Error	Errors are often made during the subtraction step (step 5 in the preceding example). $$\begin{array}{r}4x^3 \\ (x+1)\overline{)4x^4 + 0x^3 + x^2 + 0x - 2} \\ \underline{4x^4 + 4x^3} \\ 4x^3 + x^2 + 0x - 2\end{array}$$ No! Should be $-4x^3$.

Example 71: Divide $x^4 - 5x^3 + 9x^2 - 7x + 2$ by $x^2 - 3x + 2$.

Solution: Using long division, we get

$$
\begin{array}{r}
x^2 - 2x + 1 \\
(x^2 - 3x + 2)\overline{)x^4 - 5x^3 + 9x^2 - 7x + 2} \\
\underline{x^4 - 3x^3 + 2x^2} \\
-2x^3 + 7x^2 - 7x \\
\underline{-2x^3 + 6x^2 - 4x} \\
x^2 - 3x + 2 \\
\underline{x^2 - 3x + 2}
\end{array}
$$

Exercise 5 Division of Algebraic Expressions

Divide the following monomials.

1. z^5 by z^3

2. $45y^3$ by $15y^2$

3. $-25x^2y^2z^3 \div 5xyz^2$

4. $20a^5b^5c \div 10abc$

5. $30cd^2f \div 15cd^2$
6. $36ax^2y \div 18ay$
7. $-18x^2yz \div 9xy$
8. $(x - y)^5$ by $(x - y)^3$
9. $15axy^3$ by $-3ay$
10. $-18a^3x$ by $-3ay$
11. $6acdxy^2$ by $2adxy^2$
12. $12a^2x^2$ by $-3a^2x$
13. $15ay^2$ by $-3ay$
14. $45(a - x)^3$ by $15(a - x)^2$
15. $-21vwz^2 \div 7vz^2$
16. $-33r^2s \div 11rs^2$
17. $35m^2nx \div 5m^2x$
18. $20x^3y^3z^3 \div 10x^3yz^3$
19. $16ab$ by $4a$
20. $21acd$ by $7c$
21. ab^2c by ac
22. $(a + b)^4$ by $(a + b)$
23. x^m by x^n
24. $-14a^2x^3y^4 \div 7axy^2$
25. $32r^2s^2q \div 8r^2sq$
26. $-18v^2x^2y \div v^2xy$
27. $24a^{2n}bc^n \div (-a^{2n}bc^n)$
28. $36a^{2n}xy^{3n} \div (-4a^nxy^{2n})$
29. $25xyz^2 \div (-5x^2y^2z)$
30. $-28y^2z^{2m} \div 4y^2z^3x$
31. $-30n^2x^2 \div 6m^2x^3$
32. $28x^2y^2z^2 \div 7xyz$
33. $6abc$ by $2c$
34. ax^3 by ax^2
35. $3mx^6$ by mx
36. $210c^3b$ by $7cd$
37. $42xy$ by xy^2
38. $-21ac$ by $-7a$
39. $-12xy$ by $3y$
40. $72abc$ by $-8c$

Divide the polynomial by the monomial.

41. $2a^3 - a^2$ by a
42. $42a^5 - 6a^2$ by $6a$
43. $21x^4 - 3x^2$ by $3x^2$
44. $35m^4 - 7p^2$ by 7
45. $27x^6 - 45x^4$ by $9x^2$
46. $24x^6 - 8x^3$ by $-8x^3$
47. $34x^3 - 51x^2$ by $17x$
48. $5x^5 - 10x^3$ by $-5x^3$
49. $-3a^2 - 6ac$ by $-3a$
50. $-5x^3 + x^2y$ by $-5x^3$
51. $ax^2y - 2xy^2$ by xy
52. $3xy^2 - 3x^2y$ by xy
53. $4x^3y^2 + 2x^2y^3$ by $2x^2y^2$
54. $3a^2b^2 - 6ab^3$ by $3ab$
55. $abc^2 - a^2b^2c$ by $-abc$
56. $9x^2y^2z + 3xyz^2$ by $3xyz$
57. $x^2y^2 - x^3y - xy^3$ by xy
58. $a^3 - a^2b - ab^2$ by $-a$
59. $a^2b - ab + ab^2$ by $-ab$
60. $xy - x^2y^2 + x^3y^3$ by $-xy$
61. $a^2 - 3ab + ac^2$ by a
62. $x^2y - xy^2 + x^2y^3$ by xy
63. $x^2 - 2xy + y^2$ by x
64. $z^2 - 3xz + 3z^3$ by z
65. $m^2n + 2mn - 3m^2$ by mn
66. $c^2d - 3cd^2 + 4d^3$ by cd
67. $a^2x - abx - acx$ by ax
68. $3x^5y^3 - 3x^4y^3 - 3x^2y^4$ by $3x^3y^3$
69. $a^2b^2 - 2ab - 3ab^3$ by ab
70. $3a^3c^3 + 3a^2c - 3ac^2$ by $3ac$
71. $6a^3x^2 - 15a^4x^2 + 30a^3x^3$ by $-3a^3x^2$
72. $20x^2y^4 - 14xy^3 + 8x^2y^2$ by $2x^2y^2$

Divide the polynomial by the binomial.

73. $x^2 + 15x + 56$ by $x + 7$
74. $x^2 - 15x + 56$ by $x - 7$
75. $x^2 - 4x + 3$ by $x + 2$
76. $2 + 4x - x^2$ by $4 - x$
77. $2a^2 + 11a + 5$ by $2a + 1$

78. $6a^2 - 7a - 3$ by $2a - 3$
79. $27a^3 - 8b^3$ by $3a - 2b$
80. $2x^2 - 5x + 4$ by $x + 1$
81. $4 + 2x - 5x^2$ by $3 - x$
82. $4a^2 + 23a + 15$ by $4a + 3$
83. $3a^2 - 4a - 4$ by $2 - a$
84. $x^4 + x^2 + 1$ by $x^2 + 1$
85. $x^8 + x^4 + 1$ by $x^4 - x$
86. $1 - a^3b^3$ by $1 - ab$
87. $x^3 - 8x - 3$ by $x - 3$
88. $a^2 - 2ab + b^2 - c^2$ by $a - b - c$
89. $a^2 + 2ab + b^2 - c^2$ by $a + b + c$
90. $x^2 - y^2 + 2yz - z^2$ by $x - y + z$
91. $c^4 + 2c^2 - c + 2$ by $c^2 - c + 1$
92. $x^2 - 4y^2 - 4yz - z^2$ by $x + 2y + z$
93. $x^5 + 37x^2 - 70x + 50$ by $x^2 - 2x + 10$
94. $6(x - y)^2 - 7(x - y) - 20$ by $3(x - y) + 4$
95. $23x^2 - 5x^4 - 12 + 12x^5 + 8x - 14x^3$ by $x - 2 + 3x^2$
96. $16(a + b)^4 - 81$ by $2(a + b) - 3$
97. $8x^6 - 4x^5 - 2x^4 + 15x^3 + 3x^2 - 5x - 15$ by $4x^3 - x - 3$
98. $a^2 - 4b^2 - 9c^2 + 12bc$ by $a - 3c + 2b$

Computer

99. Use a computer algebra system to repeat any of the problems in this exercise. Compare your results with what you got by hand.

CHAPTER 2   REVIEW PROBLEMS

1. Multiply: $(b^4 + b^2x^3 + x^4)(b^2 - x^2)$
2. Square: $(x + y - 2)$
3. Evaluate: $(7.28 \times 10^4)^3$
4. Square: $(xy + 5)$
5. Multiply: $(3x - m)(x^2 + m^2)(3x - m)$
6. Divide: $-x^6 - 2x^5 - x^4$ by $-x^4$
7. Cube: $(2x + 1)$
8. Simplify: $7x - \{-6x - [-5x - (-4x - 3x) - 2]\}$
9. Multiply: $3ax^2$ by $2ax^3$
10. Simplify: $\left(\dfrac{3a^2}{2b^3}\right)^3$
11. Square: $(4a - 3b)$
12. Multiply: $(x^3 - xy + y^2)(x + y)$
13. Multiply: $(xy - 2)(xy - 4)$
14. Divide: $x^{m+1} + x^{m+2} + x^{m+3} + x^{m+4}$ by x^4
15. Square: $(2a - 3b)$
16. Multiply: $(a^2 - 3a + 8)(a + 3)$
17. Divide: $a^3b^2 - a^2b^5 - a^4b^2$ by a^2b
18. Multiply: $(2x - 5)(x + 2)$
19. Multiply: $(2m - c)(2m + c)(4m^2 + c^2)$

20. Simplify: $\left(\dfrac{8x^5y^{-2}}{4x^3y^{-3}}\right)^3$
21. Divide: $2a^6$ by a^4
22. Multiply: $(a^2 + a^2y + ay^2 + y^3)(a - y)$
23. Simplify: $y - 3[y - 2(4 - y)]$
24. Divide: $-a^7$ by a^5
25. Multiply: $(2x^2 + xy - 2y^2)(3x + 3y)$
26. Divide: $x^4 - \frac{1}{2}x^3 - \frac{1}{3}x^2 - 2x - 1$ by $2x$
27. Simplify: $-2[w - 3(2w - 1)] + 3w$
28. Multiply: $(a^2 + b)(a + b^2)$
29. Multiply:
$(a^4 - 2a^3c + 4a^2c^2 - 8ac^3 + 16c^4)(a + 2c)$
30. Divide: $16x^3$ by $4x$
31. Divide: $(a - c)^m$ by $(a - c)^2$
32. Divide: $7 - 8c^2 + 5c^3 + 8c$ by $5c - 3$
33. Divide: $-x^2y - xy^2$ by $-xy$
34. Combine:
$(-2x^2 - x + 6) - (7x^2 - 2x + 4) + (x^2 - 3)$
35. Cube: $(b - 3)$

36. Simplify: $(2x^2y^3z^{-1})^3$

37. Divide: $2x^{-2}y^3$ by $4x^{-4}y^6$

38. Simplify: $-\{-[-(a-3)-a]\} + 2a$

39. Multiply: $(x-2)(x+4)$

40. Square: (x^2+2)

41. Evaluate: $(2.83 \times 10^3)^2$

42. Simplify: $(x-3) - [x - (2x+3) + 4]$

43. Multiply: $2xy^3$ by $5x^2y$

44. Divide: $27xy^5z^2$ by $3x^2yz^2$

45. Multiply: $(x-1)(x^2+4x)$

46. Square: (z^2-3)

47. Evaluate: $(1.33 \times 10^4)^2$

48. Simplify: $(y+1) - [y(y+1) + (3y-1) + 5]$

49. Multiply: $2ab^2$ by $3a^2b$

50. Divide: $64ab^4c^3$ by $8a^2bc^3$

Writing

51. In the following chapter we will solve simple equations, something you must have done before. Without looking ahead, write down in your own words whatever you remember about solving equations. You may give a list of steps, or give a description in paragraph form.

Team Project

52. Create a one-hour exam that will test for the most important skills covered in this chapter. Be sure that it is not too long and hard, and not too short and easy. Then work the test and produce an answer key, to be handed in with the test.

3

Simple Equations and Word Problems

O B J E C T I V E S

When you have completed this chapter, you should be able to:

- Solve simple linear equations.
- Check an apparent solution to a linear equation.
- Solve simple fractional equations.
- Write an algebraic expression to describe a given verbal statement.
- Set up and solve word problems that lead to linear equations.
- Solve number problems, financial problems, mixture problems, and statics problems.

When two mathematical expressions are set equal to each other, we get an *equation*. Much of our work in technical mathematics is devoted to *solving equations*. We start in this chapter with the simplest types, and in later chapters cover more difficult ones (quadratic equations, exponential equations, trigonometric equations, and so forth).

Why is it so important to solve equations? The main reason is that equations are used to describe or *model* the way certain things happen in the world. Solving an equation often tells us something important we would not otherwise know. For example, the note produced by a guitar string is not a whim of nature, but can be predicted (solved for) when you know the length, the mass, and the tension in the string, and you know the *equation* relating the pitch, length, mass, and tension.

Thousands of equations exist that link together the various quantities in the physical world, in chemistry, finance, factories, and so on, and their number is still increasing. To be able to solve and to manipulate such equations is essential for anyone who has to deal with these quantities on the job.

3•1

Solving First-Degree Equations

Equations

An equation has two *sides*, or members, and an *equal sign*.

$$3x^2 - 4x = 2x + 5$$

left side ↑ right side

equal sign

Conditional Equations

A *conditional equation* is one whose sides are equal only for certain values of the unknown.

■ **Example 1:** The equation

$$x - 5 = 0$$

is a conditional equation because the sides are equal only when $x = 5$. When we say "equation," we will mean "conditional equation." Other equations that are true for any value of the unknown, such as $x(x + 2) = x^2 + 2x$, are called *identities*. ■

The symbol ≡ is used for identities
We would write $x(x + 2) \equiv x^2 + 2x$.

The Solution

The *solution* to an equation is that value (or values) of the unknown that make the sides equal.

■ **Example 2:** The solution to the equation

$$x - 5 = 0$$

is

$$x = 5$$

The value $x = 5$ is also called the *root* of the equation. We also say that it *satisfies* the equation. ■

First-Degree Equations

A *first-degree* equation (also called a *linear* equation) is one in which the terms containing the unknown are all of first degree.

■ **Example 3:** The equations $2x + 3 = 9 - 4x$, $\dfrac{3x}{2} = 6x + 3$, and $3x + 5y - 6z = 0$ are all of first degree. The first and second equations have one variable, but the third equation has more than one variable. ■

Solving an Equation

To solve an equation, we *perform the same mathematical operation on each side of the equation*. The object is to get the unknown standing alone on one side of the equation.

■ **Example 4:** Solve $3x = 8 + 2x$.

Solution: Subtracting $2x$ from both sides, we obtain

$$3x - 2x = 8 + 2x - 2x$$

Combining like terms yields

$$x = 8$$ ■

Check an apparent solution by substituting it back into the original equation.

■ **Example 5:** Checking the apparent solution to Example 4, we substitute 8 for x in the original equation:

$$3x = 8 + 2x$$

$$3(8) \overset{?}{=} 8 + 2(8)$$

$$24 = 8 + 16 \quad \text{checks}$$ ■

<table>
<tr><td>Common Error</td><td>Check your solution only in the original equation. Later versions may already contain errors.</td></tr>
</table>

Get into the habit of checking your work, for errors creep in everywhere.

■ **Example 6:** Solve the equation $3x - 5 = x + 1$.

Solution: We first subtract x from both sides, and add 5 to both sides.

$$\begin{array}{rcr} 3x - 5 = & x + 1 \\ -x + 5 = & -x + 5 \\ \hline 2x \quad = & 6 \end{array}$$

Dividing both sides by 2, we obtain

$$x = 3$$

Check: Substituting into the original equation yields

$$3(3) - 5 \overset{?}{=} 3 + 1$$

$$9 - 5 = 4 \quad \text{checks}$$ ■

Symbols of Grouping

When the equation contains symbols of grouping, remove them early in the solution.

■ **Example 7:** Solve the equation $3(3x + 1) - 6 = 5(x - 2) + 15$.

Solution: First, remove the parentheses:

$$9x + 3 - 6 = 5x - 10 + 15$$

Combine like terms:
Add $-5x + 3$ to both sides:

$$\begin{array}{rcr} 9x - 3 & = & 5x + 5 \\ -5x + 3 & & -5x + 3 \\ \hline 4x & = & 8 \end{array}$$

Divide by 4:

$$x = 2$$

Check:

$$3(6 + 1) - 6 \overset{?}{=} 5(2 - 2) + 15$$

$$21 - 6 \overset{?}{=} 0 + 15$$

$$15 = 15 \quad \text{checks}$$ ■

> *The mathematical operations you perform must be done* to both sides *of the equation in order to preserve the equality.*

> *The mathematical operations you perform on both sides of an equation must be done to each side as a whole* — not term by term.

Fractional Equations

A *fractional equation* is one that contains one or more fractions. When an equation contains a single fraction, the fraction can be eliminated by *multiplying both sides by the denominator of the fraction*.

■ **Example 8:** Solve:

$$\frac{x}{3} - 2 = 5$$

Solution: Multiplying both sides by 3 gives us

$$3\left(\frac{x}{3} - 2\right) = 3(5)$$

$$3\left(\frac{x}{3}\right) - 3(2) = 3(5)$$

Adding to both sides,

$$
\begin{aligned}
x - 6 &= 15 \\
+ 6 &= +6 \\
\hline
x &= 21
\end{aligned}
$$

Check:

$$\frac{21}{3} - 2 \stackrel{?}{=} 5$$
$$7 - 2 = 5 \quad \text{checks}$$

■

In Chapter 9 we treat fractional equations in detail. There we will see how to find the *least* common denominator.

When there are two or more fractions, multiplying both sides by the product of the denominators (called a *common* denominator) will clear the fractions.

■ **Example 9:** Solve:

$$\frac{x}{2} + 3 = \frac{x}{3}$$

Solution: Multiplying by 2(3), or 6, we have

$$6\left(\frac{x}{2} + 3\right) = 6\left(\frac{x}{3}\right)$$

$$6\left(\frac{x}{2}\right) + 6(3) = 6\left(\frac{x}{3}\right)$$

$$3x + 18 = 2x$$

We now subtract $2x$ from both sides, and also subtract 18 from both sides.

$$3x - 2x = -18$$

$$x = -18$$

Check:

$$\frac{-18}{2} + 3 \stackrel{?}{=} \frac{-18}{3}$$

$$-9 + 3 \stackrel{?}{=} -6$$

$$-6 = -6 \quad \text{checks}$$

Strategy

While solving an equation, you should keep in mind the objective of *getting x by itself on one side of the equal sign, with no x on the other side.* Use any valid operation toward this end.

Equations can be of so many different forms that we cannot give a step-by-step procedure for their solution, but the following tips should help.

1. Eliminate fractions by multiplying both sides by the common denominator of both sides.
2. Remove any parentheses by performing the indicated multiplication.
3. All terms containing x should be moved to one side of the equation, and all other terms moved to the other side.
4. Like terms on the same side of the equation should be combined at any stage of the solution.
5. Any coefficient of x may be removed by dividing both sides by that coefficient.
6. Check the answer in the original equation.

The following example shows the use of these steps.

— Example 10: Solve:

$$\frac{3x - 5}{2} = \frac{2(x - 1)}{3} + 4$$

Solution:

1. We eliminate the fractions by multiplying by 6:

$$6\left(\frac{3x - 5}{2}\right) = 6\left[\frac{2(x - 1)}{3}\right] + 6(4)$$

$$3(3x - 5) = 4(x - 1) + 6(4)$$

2. Then we remove parentheses and combine like terms:

$$9x - 15 = 4x - 4 + 24$$

$$9x - 15 = 4x + 20$$

3. We get all x terms on one side by adding 15 and subtracting $4x$ from both sides:

$$9x - 4x = 20 + 15$$

4. Combining like terms gives us

$$5x = 35$$

5. Dividing by the coefficient of x yields

$$x = 7$$

6. Check:

$$\frac{3(7) - 5}{2} \stackrel{?}{=} \frac{2(7 - 1)}{3} + 4$$

$$\frac{21 - 5}{2} \stackrel{?}{=} \frac{12}{3} + 4$$

$$\frac{16}{2} \stackrel{?}{=} 4 + 4$$

$$8 = 8 \qquad \text{checks}$$

■ **Example 11:** Solve:

$$3(x + 2)(2 - x) = 3(x - 2)(x - 3) + 2x(4 - 3x)$$

Solution: We remove parentheses in two steps. First,

$$3(2x - x^2 + 4 - 2x) = 3(x^2 - 5x + 6) + 8x - 6x^2$$

Then remove the remaining parentheses

$$-3x^2 + 12 = 3x^2 - 15x + 18 + 8x - 6x^2$$

Next we combine like terms:

$$-3x^2 + 12 = -3x^2 - 7x + 18$$

Adding $3x^2$ and subtracting 18 from both sides gives

$$12 - 18 = -7x$$

$$-6 = -7x$$

Dividing both sides by -7 and switching sides, we get

$$x = \frac{6}{7}$$ ■

Other Variables

Up to now we have used only the familiar x as our variable. Of course, any letter can represent the unknown quantity. When we say to "solve" an equation, we mean to isolate the letter quantity, if only one is present. If there are more than one letter, we must be told which to solve for.

■ **Example 12:** Solve the equation

$$4(p - 3) = 3(p + 4) - 5$$

Solution: Removing parentheses and combining like terms,

$$4p - 12 = 3p + 12 - 5$$

$$4p - 12 = 3p + 7$$

Adding 12 and subtracting $3p$ from both sides and combining like terms,

$$4p - 3p = 7 + 12$$
$$p = 19$$

Equations with Approximate Numbers

All of our equations so far have had coefficients and constants that were integers, and we assumed them to be exact numbers. But in technology we must often solve equations containing approximate numbers. The method of solution is no different from that used with exact numbers. Just be sure to round, following the rules given in Chapter 1.

Example 13: Solve for x:

$$5.72(x - 1.15) = 3.22x - 7.73$$

Solution: Removing parentheses gives

$$5.72x - 6.58 = 3.22x - 7.73$$

Collecting terms:

$$5.72x - 3.22x = -7.73 + 6.58$$
$$2.50x = -1.15$$

Dividing both sides by 2.50, we get

$$x = \frac{-1.15}{2.50} = -0.460$$

Literal Equations

A *literal equation* is one in which some or all of the constants are represented by letters.

Example 14: $3x + b = 5$ is a literal equation.

To solve a literal equation for a given quantity means to isolate that quantity on one side of the equal sign. The other side of the equation will, of course, contain the other letter quantities. We do this by following the same procedures as for numerical equations.

Example 15: Solve the equation $3x + b = 5$ for x.

Solution: Subtracting b from both sides gives

$$3x = 5 - b$$

Dividing by 3,

$$x = \frac{5 - b}{3}$$

In this chapter we will solve only the simplest kinds of literal equations. Our main treatment will be in Section 9•7.

Exercise 1 Solving First-Degree Equations

Solve and check each equation.

Treat any integers in these equations as exact numbers. Leave your answers in fractional, rather than decimal, form. When the equation has decimal coefficients, keep as many significant digits in your answer as are contained in those coefficients.

1. $x - 5 = 28$

2. $4x + 2 = 18$

3. $8 - 3x = 7x$

4. $9x + 7 = 25$

5. $9x - 2x = 3x + 2$

6. $x + 8 = 12 - 3x$

7. $x + 4 = 5x + 2$

8. $3y - 2 = 2y$

9. $3x = x + 8$

10. $3x = 2x + 5$

11. $3x + 4 = x + 10$

12. $y - 4 = 7 + 23y$

13. $2.80 - 1.30y = 4.60$

14. $3.75x + 7.24 = 5.82x$

15. $4x + 6 = x + 9$

16. $7x - 19 = 5x + 7$

17. $p - 7 = -3 + 9p$

18. $-3x + 7 = -15 + 2x$

19. $4x - 11 = 2x - 7$

20. $3x - 8 = 12x - 7$

21. $8x + 7 = 4x + 27$

22. $3x + 10 = x + 20$

23. $\dfrac{1}{2}x = 14$

24. $\dfrac{x}{5} = 3x - 25$

25. $5x + 22 - 2x = 31$

26. $4x + 20 - 6 = 34$

27. $\dfrac{n}{3} + 5 = 2n$

28. $5x - \dfrac{2x}{5} = 3$

29. $2x + 5(x - 4) = 6 + 3(2x + 3)$

30. $6x - 5(x - 2) = 12 - 3(x - 4)$

31. $4(3x + 2) - 4x = 5(2 - 3x) - 7$

32. $6 - 3(2x + 4) - 2x = 7x + 4(5 - 2x) - 8$

33. $3(6 - x) + 2(x - 3) = 5 + 2(3x + 1) - x$

34. $3x - 2 + x(3 - x) = (x - 3)(x + 2) - x(2x + 1)$

35. $(2x - 5)(x + 3) - 3x = 8 - x + (3 - x)(5 - 2x)$

36. $x + (1 + x)(3x + 4) = (2x + 3)(2x - 1) - x(x - 2)$

37. $3 - 6(x - 1) = 9 - 2(1 + 3x) + 2x$

38. $7x + 6(2 - x) + 3 = 4 + 3(6 + x)$

39. $3 - (4 + 3x)(2x + 1) = 6x - (3x - 2)(x + 1) - (6 - 3x)(1 - x)$

40. $6.10 - (x + 2.30)(3.20x - 4.30) - 5.20x$
$= 3.30x - x(3.10 + 3.20x) - 4.70$

41. $7r - 2r(2r - 3) - 2 = 2r^2 - (r - 2)(3 + 6r) - 8$

42. $2w - 3(w - 6)(2w - 2) + 6 = 3w - (2w - 1)(3w + 2) + 6$

43. $8.27x - 2.22(2.57 + x)(3.35x - 6.64)$
$= 3.24 - 3.35(2.22x + 5.64)(x - 1.24) - 2.64(2.11x - 3.85)$

44. $1.30x - (x - 2.30)(3.10x - 5.40) - 2.50$
$= 4.60 - (3.10x - 1.20)(x - 5.30) - 4.30x$

Simple Literal Equations

Solve for x.

45. $ax + 4 = 7$

46. $6 + bx = b - 3$

47. $c(x - 1) = 5$

48. $ax + 4 = b - 3$

49. $c - bx = a - 3b$

Computer

50. If you have a computer algebra system, such as *Derive*, *Maple*, or *Mathematica*, it can be used to solve quickly any of the equations in this exercise. Each of these systems uses the *Solve* command to solve an equation. Solve some equations using a computer algebra system, and compare the answers with those you get by hand computation.

3·2

Solving Word Problems

Problems in Verbal Form

We have already done some simple word problems in earlier chapters, and we will have more of them with each new topic, but their main treatment will be here. After looking at these word problems you may ask: "When will I ever have to solve problems like that on the job?"

Maybe never. But you will most likely have to deal with technical material in written form: instruction manuals, specifications, contracts, building codes, handbooks, and so on. This chapter will aid you in coping with precise technical documents, where a mistaken meaning of a word could cost dollars, your job, or even lives.

Some tips on how to approach any word problem are given in the following paragraphs.

Picture the Problem

Try to *visualize* the situation described in the problem. Form a picture in your mind. *Draw a diagram* showing as much of the given information as possible, including the unknown.

Understand the Words

Look up the meanings of unfamiliar words in a dictionary, handbook, or textbook.

■ **Example 16:** A certain problem contains the following statement:

A simply supported beam carries a concentrated load midway between its center and one end.

To understand this statement, you must know what a "simply supported beam" is, and the meaning of "concentrated load." ■

Locate the words and expressions standing for mathematical operations, such as

. . . the difference between . . .
. . . is equal to . . .
. . . the quotient of . . .

■ **Example 17:**
(a) The difference between a and b means $a - b$ (or $b - a$).
(b) Four less than x means $x - 4$.
(c) Three greater than c means $c + 3$.

(d) The sum of x and 4 is equal to three times x, in symbols, is

$$x + 4 = 3x$$

(e) Three consecutive integers, starting with x, are

$$x, x + 1, x + 2$$　　━

Many problems will contain a *rate*, either as the unknown or as one of the given quantities. The word *per* is your tipoff. Look for "km *per* hour," "dollars *per* kilogram," "kilogram *per* litre," "dollars *per* kilometre," and the like. The word *per* also suggests *division*. Kilometres per litre, for example, means kilometres travelled *divided by* litres consumed.

Identify the Unknown

Be sure that you know exactly *what is to be found* in a particular problem. Find the sentence that ends with a question mark, or the sentence that starts with "Find . . ." or "Calculate . . ." or "What is . . ." or "How much . . ." or a similar phrase.

　　Label the unknown with a statement like: "Let x = rate of the train, in km/h." Be sure to include *units of measure* when defining the unknown.

━ **Example 18:** Fifty-five litres of a mixture that is 24% alcohol by volume is mixed with 74 L of a mixture that is 76% alcohol. Find the amount of alcohol in the final mixture.

This step of labelling the unknown annoys many students; they see it as a nitpicking thing that teachers make them do just for show, when they would rather start solving the problem. But realize that this step *is* the start of the problem. It is the crucial first step and *should never be omitted*.

You may be tempted to label the unknown in the following ways:

Let x = alcohol	This is too vague. Are we speaking of volume of alcohol, or weight, or some other property?
Let x = volume of alcohol	The units are missing.
Let x = litres of alcohol	Do we mean litres of alcohol in one of the *initial* mixtures or in the *final* mixture?
Let x = number of litres of alcohol in final mixture	Good

We will do complete solutions of this type of problem in Section 3•4.　━

Define Other Unknowns

If there are more than one unknown, you will often be able to define the additional unknowns *in terms of the original unknown*, rather than introducing another symbol.

━ **Example 19:** A word problem contains the following statement:
　　　"Find two numbers whose sum is 80 and, . . ."
　　Here we have two unknowns. We can label them with separate symbols:

Let x = first number

Let y = second number

but another way is to label the second unknown in terms of the first, thus avoiding the use of a second variable. Since the sum of the two numbers x and y is 80,

$$x + y = 80$$

from which

$$y = 80 - x$$

This enables us to label both unknowns in terms of the single variable x:

Let x = first number

Let $80 - x$ = second number ▬

Sometimes a careful reading of the word problem is needed to *identify* the unknowns before you can define them in terms of one of the variables.

▬ **Example 20:** A word problem contains the following statement: "A person invests part of his \$1000 savings in a bank, at 6%, and the remainder in a certificate of deposit, at 8%." We are then given more information and are asked to find the amount invested at each rate.

Since the investment is in two parts, both of which are unknown, we can say

Let x = amount invested at 6%

and

$1000 - x$ = amount invested at 8%

But isn't it equally correct to say

Let x = amount invested at 8%

and

$1000 - x$ = amount invested at 6%?

We'll finish this problem in Section 3•3.

Yes. You can define the variables either way, as long as you are consistent and *do not change the definition partway through the problem.* ▬

Estimate the Answer

It is a good idea to *estimate* or *guess* the answer before solving the problem, so that you will have some idea whether the answer you finally get is reasonable.

The kinds of problems you may encounter are so diverse that it is not easy to give general rules for estimating. However, we usually make *simplifying assumptions*, or try to *bracket the answer*.

To make a simplifying assumption means to solve a problem simpler than the given one, and use its answer as an estimate for the given problem.

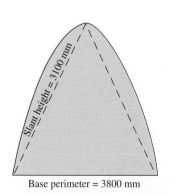

Base perimeter = 3800 mm

FIGURE 3•1 Aircraft nose cone

▬ **Example 21:** To estimate the surface area of the aircraft nose cone shown in Figure 3•1, we could assume that its shape is a right circular cone (shown by dashed lines) rather than the complex shape given. This would enable us to estimate the area using the simple formula (Eq. 131),

$$\text{Area} = \tfrac{1}{2}(\text{perimeter of base}) \times (\text{slant height})$$

For the nose cone,

$$\text{Area} \approx \tfrac{1}{2}(3800)(3100) = 5.9 \times 10^6 \text{ mm}^2$$

We should be suspicious if our "exact" calculation gives an answer much different from this. ▬

To bracket an answer means to find two numbers between which your answer must lie. Don't worry that your two values are far apart. This method will catch more errors than you may suppose.

▬ **Example 22:** It is clear that the length of the bridge cable in Figure 3•2 must be greater that the straight line distances $AB + BC$, but less than the straight line distances $AD + DE + EC$. So the answer must lie between 272 m and 364 m.

FIGURE 3•2 Suspension bridge

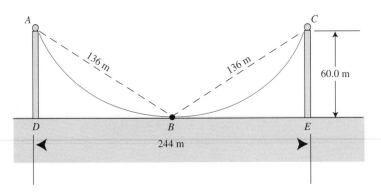

For good problem-solving techniques, read *How to Solve It*, by G. Polya.

Write and Solve the Equation

The unknown quantity must now be related to the given quantities by means of an *equation*. Where does one get an equation? Either the equation is given verbally, right in the problem statement, or else the relationship between the quantities in the problem is one you are expected to know (or to be able to find). These could be mathematical relationships or they could be from any branch of technology. For example:

> *How is the area of a circle related to its radius?*
>
> *How is the current in a circuit related to the circuit resistance?*
>
> *How is the deflection of a steel beam related to its depth?*
>
> *How is the distance traveled by a car related to its speed?*

and so on. The relationships you will need for the problems in this book can be found in the Summary of Facts and Formulas (Appendix A). Of course, each branch of technology has many more formulas than can be shown there. Problems that need some of these formulas are treated later in this chapter. Sometimes, as in the number problems we will solve later in this section, the equation is given verbally in the statement of the problem.

Check Your Answer

There are several things we can do to check an answer.

1. Does the answer look *reasonable*? If the problem is a complicated technical one, you may not yet have the experience to know whether an answer is reasonable, but in many cases you can spot a strange answer.

■ **Example 23:** Does your result show an automobile going 600 km per hour? Did a person's age calculate to be 150 years? Did the depth of the bridge girder come out to be 2 millimetres? ■

Don't just write down the answer and run. Look at it hard to see if it makes sense.

2. Compare your answer with your initial estimate or guess. Do they agree within reason? If you have found two bracketing numbers within which the answer *must* fall, then you must recheck any answers outside that range.

■ **Example 24:** If a calculation showed the length of the bridge cable in Figure 3•2 to be 380 m, you could say with certainty that there is an error, because we saw that the length cannot exceed 364 m. ■

3. Check your answer in the original problem statement. Be sure that the answer(s) meet all the conditions in the problem statement.

■ **Example 25:** A problem asked for three consecutive odd integers whose sum is 39. Four students gave answers of (a) 12, 13, 14, (b) 13, 15, 17, (c) 9, 11, 19, and (d) 11, 13, 15. Determine which, if any, are correct without actually solving the problem.

Solution:
(a) 12, 13, and 14 are consecutive integers whose sum is 39. However, they are not all odd.
(b) 13, 15, 17 are consecutive odd integers, but their sum is not 39.
(c) 9, 11, 19 are odd integers whose sum is 39, but they are not consecutive.
(d) 11, 13, 15 are consecutive odd integers whose sum is 39, and this is the correct answer. ■

Number Problems

Number problems, although of little practical value, will give you practice at picking out the relationship between the quantities in a problem.

■ **Example 26:** If twice a certain number is increased by 9, the result is equal to 2 less than triple the number. Find the number.

Solution: Let x = the number. From the problem statement,

$$2x + 9 = 3x - 2$$

Solving for x, we obtain

$$9 + 2 = 3x - 2x$$

$$x = 11$$

Check: We check our answer in the original problem statement. If the number is 11, then twice the number is 22. Thus twice the number increased by 9 is 31. Further, triple the number is 33. Two less than triple the number is 31. So our answer checks. ▬

Common Error	Checking an answer by substituting in your *equation* is not good enough. The equation itself may be wrong. Check your answer with the problem statement.

Often the solution of a problem involves finding *more than one quantity*.

▬ **Example 27:** Find three consecutive odd integers whose sum is 39.

Solution: We first define our unknowns. Since any odd integer is two greater than the preceding odd integer, we can say

$$\text{Let } x = \text{the first odd integer}$$

Then

$$x + 2 = \text{the second consecutive odd integer}$$

and

$$x + 4 = \text{the third consecutive odd integer}$$

Since the problem states that the sum of the three integers is 39, we write

$$x + (x + 2) + (x + 4) = 39$$

Solving for x gives

$$3x + 6 = 39$$
$$3x = 33$$
$$x = 11$$

But don't stop here; we are not finished. We're looking for *three* numbers. So

$$x + 2 = 13 \quad \text{and} \quad x + 4 = 15$$

Our three consecutive odd integers are then 11, 13, and 15.

Check:

$$11 + 13 + 15 = 39, \text{ as required} \qquad ▬$$

Sometimes, there may seem to be too many unknowns to solve a problem. If so, carefully choose one variable to call x, so that the other unknowns can be expressed in terms of x. Then use the remaining information to write your equation.

▬ **Example 28:** In a group of 102 employees, there are three times as many on the day shift as on the night shift, and two more on the swing shift than on the night shift. How many are on each shift?

Estimate: Let's assume that the night and swing shifts have the *same* number N of employees. Then the day shift would have $3N$ employees, making $5N$ in all. So N would be $102 \div 5$, or 20, rounded. So we might expect about 20 on the night shift, two more than that on the swing shift, and about 60 on the day shift.

Solution: Since the numbers of employees on the day and swing shifts are given in terms of the number on the night shift, we write

Let x = the number of employees on the night shift

Then

$$3x = \text{the number on the day shift}$$

and

$$x + 2 = \text{the number on the swing shift}$$

Since we are told that there are 102 employees in all,

$$x + 3x + (x + 2) = 102$$

from which

$$5x = 100$$

$$x = 20 \text{ on the night shift}$$

$$3x = 60 \text{ on the day shift}$$

$$x + 2 = \underline{22} \text{ on the swing shift}$$
$$ 102 \quad \text{total}$$

These numbers agree well with our estimate.

Exercise 2 Solving Word Problems

Verbal Statements

Rewrite each expression as one or more algebraic expressions.

1. Eight more than 5 times a certain number
2. Four consecutive integers
3. Two numbers whose sum is 83
4. Two numbers whose difference is 17
5. The amounts of antifreeze and of water in 25 L of an antifreeze-water solution
6. A fraction whose denominator is 7 more than 5 times its numerator
7. The angles in a triangle, if one angle is half another
8. The number of litres of antifreeze in a radiator containing x litres of a mixture that is 9% antifreeze
9. The distance travelled in x hours by a car going 82 km/h
10. If x equals the length of a rectangle, write an expression for the width of the rectangle if (*a*) the perimeter is 58; (*b*) the area is 200

Number Problems

11. Nine more than 4 times a certain number is 29. Find the number.
12. Find a number such that the sum of 15 and that number is 4 times that number.

13. Find three consecutive integers whose sum is 174.

14. The sum of 56 and some number equals 9 times that number. Find that number.

15. Twelve less than 3 times a certain number is 30. Find the number.

16. When 9 is added to 7 times a certain number, the result is equal to subtracting 3 from 10 times that number. Find the number.

17. The denominator of a fraction is 2 greater than 3 times its numerator, and the reduced value of the fraction is $\frac{3}{10}$. Find the numerator.

18. Find three consecutive odd integers whose sum is 63.

19. Seven less than 4 times a certain number is 9. Find the number.

20. Find the number whose double exceeds 70 by as much as the number itself is less than 80.

21. If $2x - 3$ stands for 29, for what number does $4 + x$ stand?

22. Separate 197 into two parts such that the smaller part divides into the greater 5 times, with a remainder of 23.

23. After a certain number is diminished by 8, the amount remaining is multiplied by 8; the result is the same as if the number were diminished by 6 and the amount remaining multiplied by 6. What is the number?

24. Thirty-one times a certain number is as much above 40 as 9 times the number is below 40. Find the number.

25. Three times the amount by which a certain number exceeds 6 is equal to the number plus 144. Find the number.

26. In a group of 90 persons, composed of men, women, and children, there are 3 times as many children as men, and twice as many women as men. How many are there of each?

3•3

Financial Problems

We turn now from number problems to ones that have more application to technology, finance, mixture, and statics. Uniform motion problems, which often require the solution of a fractional equation, are left for the chapter on fractions.

■ **Example 29:** A consultant had to pay income taxes of $4867 plus 28% of the amount by which her taxable income exceeded $32 450. Her tax bill was $7285. What was her taxable income? Work to the nearest dollar.

Solution: Let $x =$ taxable income (dollars). The amount by which her income exceeded $32 450 is then

$$x - \$32\,450$$

Her tax is 28% of that amount, plus $4867, so

$$\text{tax} = \$4867 + 0.28(x - \$32\,450) = \$7285$$

We usually work financial problems to the nearest penny or nearest dollar, regardless of the number of significant digits in the problem.

Solving for x, we get

$$0.28(x - \$32\,450) = \$7285 - \$4867 = \$2418$$

$$x - \$32\,450 = \frac{\$2418}{0.28} = \$8636$$

$$x = \$8636 + \$32\,450 = \$41\,086$$

Check: Her income exceeds $32 450 by ($41 086 − $32 450) or $8636. This amount is taxed at 28%, or 0.28($8636) = $2418. To this we add the $4967 tax, getting

$$\$2418 + \$4867 = \$7285 \text{ as required} \qquad \blacksquare$$

■ **Example 30:** A person invests part of his $1000 savings in a bank, at 6%, and part in a certificate of deposit, at 8%, simple interest in both cases. He gets a total of $75 per year in interest from the two investments. How much is invested at each rate?

Solution: Does this look familiar? It is the problem we started in Example 20. There we defined our variables as

$$\text{Let } x = \text{amount invested at } 6\%$$

and

$$\$1000 - x = \text{amount invested at } 8\%$$

If x dollars are invested at 6%, the interest on that investment is $0.06x$ dollars. Similarly, $0.08(1000 - x)$ dollars are earned on the other investment. Since the total earnings are $75, we write

$$0.06x + 0.08(\$1000 - x) = \$75$$
$$0.06x + \$80 - 0.08x = \$75$$
$$-0.02x = -\$5$$
$$x = \$250 \text{ at } 6\%$$

and

$$1000 - x = \$750 \text{ at } 8\% \qquad \blacksquare$$

Check: Does this look reasonable? Suppose that half of the person's savings ($500) was invested at each rate. Then the 6% deposit would earn $30 and the 8% deposit would earn $40, for a total of $70. But he got more than that ($75) in interest, so we would expect more than $500 to be invested at 8% and less than $500 at 6%, as we have found.

Financial problems make heavy use of percentage, so you may want to review Section 1•10.

Exercise 3 Financial Problems

1. The labor costs for a certain project were $1501 per day for 17 technicians and helpers. If the technicians earned $92/day and the helpers $85/day, how many technicians were employed on the project?

2. A company has $86 500 invested in bonds, and earns $6751 in interest annually. Part of the money is invested at 7.4% and the remainder at 8.1%, simple interest. How much is invested at each rate?

3. How much, to the nearest dollar, must a company earn in order to have $95 000 left after paying 27% in taxes?

4. Three equal batches of fiberglass insulation were bought for $408, the first for $17 per tonne, the second for $16 per tonne, and the third for $18 per tonne. How many tonnes of each were bought?

5. A water company changed its rates from $1.95 per 4000 L to $1.16 per 4000 L plus a service charge of $45.00 per month. How much water (to the nearest 4000 L) can you purchase before your new monthly bill would equal the bill under the former rate structure?

6. What salary should a person receive in order to take home $20 000 after deducting 23% for taxes? Work to the nearest dollar.

7. A person was $450.00 in debt, owing a certain sum to a brother, twice that amount to an uncle, and twice as much to a bank as to the uncle. How much was owed to each?

8. A student sold used skis and boots for $210, getting four times as much for the boots as for the skis. What was the price of each?

9. A person used part of a $100 000 inheritance to build a house and invested the remainder for one year, one-third of it at 6% and two-thirds at 5%, simple interest. The total income from the two investments was $320. Find the cost of the house.

10. A used Jeep and a snowplow attachment are worth $1200, the Jeep being worth seven times as much as the plow. Find the value of each.

11. A person spends one-fourth of her annual income for board, one-twelfth for clothes, one-half for other expenses, and saves $2000. What is her income?

12. An estate is to be divided among four children in the following manner: to the first, $2000 more than one-fourth of the whole; to the second, $3400 more than one-fifth of the whole; to the third, $3000 more than one-sixth of the whole; and to the fourth, $4000 more than one-eighth of the whole. What is the value of the estate?

3•4

Mixture Problems

Basic Relationships

The total amount of mixture is, obviously, equal to the sum of the amounts of the ingredients:

Amount of mixture = amount of A + amount of B + . . .	**A1**

These two ideas are so obvious that it may seem unnecessary to write them down. But, because they are obvious, they are often overlooked. They state that the whole is equal to the sum of its parts.

Final amount of each ingredient = initial amount + amount added − amount removed	**A2**

■ **Example 31:** From 100.0 kg of solder, half lead and half zinc, 20.0 kg is removed. Then 30.0 kg of lead is added. How much lead is contained in the final mixture?

Solution:

$$\text{Initial mass of lead} = 0.5(100.0) = 50.0 \text{ kg}$$

$$\text{Amount of lead removed} = 0.5(20.0) = 10.0 \text{ kg}$$

$$\text{Amount of lead added} = 30.0 \text{ kg}$$

By Eq. A2,

$$\text{Final amount of lead} = 50.0 - 10.0 + 30.0 = 70.0 \text{ kg}$$
■

Percent Concentration

The percent concentration of each ingredient is

Percent concentration of ingredient	$= \dfrac{\text{amount of ingredient in mixture}}{\text{total amount of mixture}} \times 100$	**15**

━ **Example 32:** The total mass of the solder in Example 31 is

$$100.0 \text{ kg} - 20.0 \text{ kg} + 30.0 \text{ kg} = 110.0 \text{ kg}$$

so the percent concentration of lead (of which there is 70.0 kg) is

$$\text{percent lead} = \frac{70.0}{110.0} \times 100 = 63.6\%$$

where 110.0 is the total mass (kg) of the final mixture.   ━

Two Mixtures

When *two mixtures* are combined to make a *third* mixture, the amount of any ingredient *A* in the final mixture is

Final amount of *A* = amount of *A* in first mixture + amount of *A* in second mixture	**A3**

━ **Example 33:** One hundred litres of gasohol containing 12% alcohol is mixed with 200 L of gasohol containing 8% alcohol. The volume of alcohol in the final mixture is

$$0.12(100 \text{ L}) + 0.08(200 \text{ L})$$
$$= 12 \text{ L} + 16 \text{ L} = 28 \text{ L}$$ ━

A Typical Mixture Problem

We now make use of these ideas about mixtures to solve a typical mixture problem.

━ **Example 34:** A batch of steel containing 5% nickel and 95% iron is combined with another batch having 2% nickel and 98% iron, to make 3 tonnes of steel having 4% nickel and 96% iron. How many tonnes of each original batch are needed?

Estimate: If we take equal amounts (1.5 tonnes) of each original batch, we would expect a final percentage of nickel halfway between 2% and 5%, or $3\frac{1}{2}\%$. Since we want 4% we need more than half of the 5% steel, or something between 1.5 tonnes and 3 tonnes. Thus the weight of 2% steel should be between 0 tonnes and 1.5 tonnes.

Solution:

Let x = the number of tonnes of steel needed with 5% nickel

FIGURE 3·3

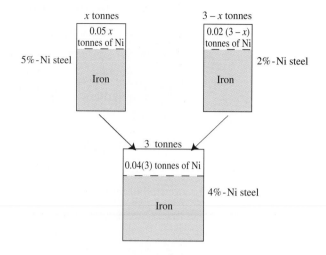

Then

$$3 \text{ tonnes} - x = \text{the number of tonnes of steel needed with 2\% nickel}$$

since 3 tonnes will be made, in all. Figure 3•3 shows the three alloys, with the mass of the steel and the mass of the nickel in each. The amount of nickel in the 5% steel is 5% of its total mass, so

$$0.05x = \text{mass of the nickel in the 5\% steel}$$

Similarly,

$$0.02(3 - x) = \text{mass of the nickel in the 2\% steel}$$

The sum of these must give the mass of nickel in the final mixture:

$$0.05x + 0.02(3 \text{ tonnes} - x) = 0.04(3 \text{ tonnes})$$

Multiplying by 100 and clearing parentheses, we obtain

$$5x + 6 \text{ tonnes} - 2x = 12 \text{ tonnes}$$

$$3x = 6 \text{ tonnes}$$

$$x = 2 \text{ tonnes of 5\% steel}$$

$$3 \text{ tonnes} - x = 1 \text{ tonne of 2\% steel}$$

> Notice that we are ignoring the *iron* in the alloy and writing our equations only for the nickel. Of course, we could have written our equations for the amount of iron and not for the nickel. The point is that you need to write Eq. A3 for *only one of the ingredients*.

Check: The answers agree with our estimate. As a further check, let's compute the percent of nickel in the final batch.

$$\text{Final tonnes of nickel} = 0.05(2) + 0.02(1) = 0.1 + 0.02 = 0.12 \text{ tonne}$$

$$\text{Percent nickel} = \frac{0.12}{3} \times 100 = 4\% \quad \text{checks}$$

Common Error	If you wind up with an equation that looks like this: ( ) kg nickel + ( ) kg iron = ( ) kg nickel you know that something is wrong. When using Eq. A3, all the terms must be *for the same ingredient*.

Exercise 4 Mixture Problems

1. Two different mixtures of gasohol are available, one with 5% alcohol and the other containing 12% alcohol. How many litres of the 12% mixture must be added to $100\overline{0}$ L of the 5% mixture to produce a mixture containing 9% alcohol?

2. How many tonnes of chromium must be added to 2.50 tonnes of stainless steel to raise the percentage of chromium from 11% to 18%?

3. How many kilograms of nickel silver containing 18% zinc and how many kilograms of nickel silver containing 31% zinc must be melted together to produce $70\overline{0}$ kg of a new nickel silver containing 22% zinc?

4. A certain bronze alloy containing 4% tin is to be added to $17\overline{0}$ kg of bronze containing 18% tin to produce a new bronze containing 15% tin. How many kilograms of the 4% bronze are required?

5. How many kilograms of brass containing 63% copper must be melted with $110\overline{0}$ kg of brass containing 72% copper to produce a new brass containing 67% copper?

6. A certain chain saw requires a fuel mixture of 5.5% oil and the remainder gasoline. How many litres of 2.5% mixture and how many of 9% mixture must be combined to produce 40.0 L of 5.5% mixture?

7. A certain automobile cooling system contains 11.0 L of coolant that is 15% antifreeze. How many litres of mixture must be removed so that, when replaced with pure antifreeze, a mixture of 25% antifreeze will result?

8. A vat contains $400\overline{0}$ L of wine with an alcohol content of 10%. How much of this wine must be removed so that, when replaced with wine with a 17% alcohol content, the alcohol content in the final mixture will be 12%?

9. A certain paint mixture of mass 130 kg contains 20% solids suspended in water. How many kilograms of water must be allowed to evaporate to raise the concentration of solids to 25%?

10. Fifteen litres of fuel containing 3.2% oil is available for a certain two-cycle engine. This fuel is to be used for another engine requiring a 5.5% oil mixture. How many litres of oil must be added?

11. A concrete mixture is to be made which contains 35% sand by mass, and $30\overline{0}$ kg of mixture containing 29% sand is already on hand. How many kilograms of sand must be added to this mixture to arrive at the required 35%?

12. How many litres of a solution containing 18% sulfuric acid and how many litres of another solution containing 25% sulfuric acid must be mixed together to make $55\overline{0}$ L of solution containing 23% sulfuric acid? (All percentages are by volume.)

13. The leakage from a microwave oven is found to be 105 mW/mm² at a distance of 100 mm. If the leakage is reduced by 35%, it would be 80% of the amount allowed by the National Safety Standards Association. What amount of safe leakage is allowed?

14. Two different generators running at 100% efficiency in combination would produce $5\overline{0}0$ MW of power. They are connected to the Canadian grid and produce 360 MW of power. If one generator is running at an efficiency of 80% and the other at 60% efficiency, find the power from each generator.

Treat the percent given in this exercise as exact numbers, and work to three significant digits.

3•5

Statics Problems

Moments

The *moment of a force* about some point a is the product of the force F and the perpendicular distance d from the force to the point.

Moment of a Force	$M_a = Fd$	**A12**

◾ **Example 35:** The moment of the force in Figure 3•4 about point a is

$$M_a = 12\overline{0}0 \text{ N} (44\overline{0} \text{ mm}) = 530 \text{ N·m}.$$

FIGURE 3•4 Moment of a force

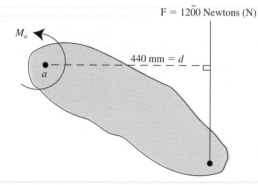

Equations of Equilibrium

If a body is in equilibrium (is not moving, or moves with a constant velocity):

Equations of Equilibrium	The sum of all horizontal forces acting on the body = 0	**A13**
	The sum of all vertical forces acting on the body = 0	**A14**
	The sum of all moments about any point on the body = 0	**A15**

This is Newton's first law of motion.

◾ **Example 36:** A horizontal uniform beam of negligible mass is 6.35 m long and is supported by columns at either end. A concentrated load of 525 N is applied to the beam. At what distance from one end must this load be located so that the vertical reaction at that same end is 315 N, and what will be the reaction at the other end?

Estimate: If the 525-N load were at the midspan, the two reactions would have equal values of $\frac{1}{2}(525)$ or 262.5 N. Since the left reaction (315 N) is greater than that, we deduce that the load is to the left of the midspan and that the reaction at the right will be less than 262.5 N.

Solution: We draw a diagram (Fig. 3•5) and label the required distance as x. By Eq. A14,

$$R + 315 \text{ N} = 525 \text{ N}$$

$$R = 210 \text{ N}$$

FIGURE 3•5

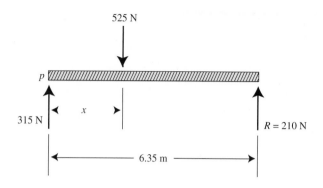

Taking moments about p, we set the moments which tend to turn the bar in a clockwise (CW) direction equal to the moments which tend to turn the bar in the counterclockwise (CCW) direction. By Eq. A15,

$$525x = 210(6.35)$$

$$x = \frac{210(6.35)}{525} = 2.54 \text{ m}$$

━ **Example 37:** Find the reactions R_1 and R_2 in Figure 3•6.

FIGURE 3•6

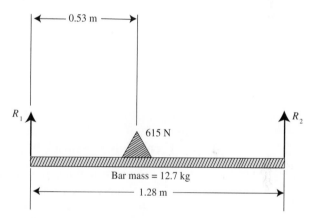

Estimate: Let's assume that the 615 N force is centered on the bar. Then each reaction would equal half the total ($740 \div 2 = 370$ N). But since the weight is to the left of center, we expect R_1 to be a bit larger than 370 N and R_2 to be a bit smaller than 370 N.

Solution: In a statics problem, we may consider all the mass of an object to be concentrated at a single point (called the *center of gravity*) on that object. For a uniform bar, the center of gravity is just where you would expect it to be, at the midpoint. Replacing the masses by forces gives the simplified diagram, Figure 3•7.

The moment of the 615-N force about p is, by Eq. A12,

$$615(0.53)\text{N·m clockwise}$$

Similarly, the other moments about p are

$$12.7 \times 9.81 \text{ N·m clockwise}$$

and

$$1.28 \, R_2 \text{ N·m counterclockwise}$$

FIGURE 3•7

But Eq. A15 says that the sum of the clockwise moments must equal the sum of the counterclockwise moments, so

$$1.28\ R_2 = 615\ \text{N}\ (0.53) + 125\ \text{N}\ (0.64)$$
$$= 406\ \text{N·m}$$
$$R_2 = 317\ \text{N}$$

Also, Eq. A14 says that the sum of the upward forces (R^1 and R^2) must equal the sum of the downward forces (600 N + 120 N), so

$$R_1 + R_2 = 615\ \text{N} + 125\ \text{N}$$
$$R_1 = 615\ \text{N} + 125\ \text{N} - 317\ \text{N}$$
$$R_1 = 423\ \text{N}$$

Exercise 5 Statics Problems

1. A horizontal beam of negligible mass is 5.5 m long and is supported by columns at either end. A vertical load of 65 $\overline{0}$00 N is applied to the beam at a distance x from the left end. Find x so that the reaction at the left column is 47 $\overline{0}$00 N.
2. For the beam of Problem 1, find the reaction at the right column.
3. A certain beam of negligible mass has an additional support 4.00 m from the left end, as shown in Fig. 3•8. The beam is 5.30 m long and has a concentrated load of 10.5 kN at the free end. Find the vertical reactions R_1 and R_2.

FIGURE 3•8

With technical problems involving approximate numbers, be sure to retain the proper number of significant digits in your answer.

4. A horizontal bar of negligible mass has a 245-N load hanging from the left end and a 322-N load hanging from the right end. The bar is balanced at a position 2480 mm from the left end. Find the length of the bar.

5. A horizontal bar of negligible mass is suspended by two cables, one at each end. A vertical force is applied to the bar at a point 1580 mm from the left end. The tension in the cable at the left end is 283 N, and in the cable at the right end, 341 N. Find the length of the bar.

6. A uniform horizontal beam is 2.95-m long and has a mass of 185 kg. It is supported by a column at either end. A vertical load of 17.2 kN is applied to the beam at a distance of x from the left end. Find the value of x at which the reaction at the right end of the beam is 8.91 kN.

7. A uniform horizontal beam is 6.00 m long and has a mass of 1740 kg. It is supported at both ends. A vertical load of 60.5 kN is applied to the beam 2.57 m from the left end. Find the reaction at each end of the beam.

8. A bar of uniform cross-section is 2.14 m long and has a mass of 45.0 kg. A load of 124 kg is suspended from one end. The bar is then to remain horizontal by being supported at the balance point. How far is this point from the end load?

CHAPTER 3 REVIEW PROBLEMS

Solve each equation.

1. $2x - (3 + 4x - 3x + 5) = 4$
2. $5(2 - x) + 7x - 21 = x + 3$
3. $3(x - 2) + 2(x - 3) + (x - 4) = 3x - 1$
4. $x + 1 + x + 2 + x + 4 = 2x + 12$
5. $(2x - 5) - (x - 4) + (x - 3) = x - 4$
6. $4 - 5w - (1 - 8w) = 63 - w$
7. $3z - (z + 10) - (z - 3) = 14 - z$
8. $(2x - 9) - (x - 3) = 0$
9. $3x + 4(3x - 5) = 12 - x$
10. $6(x - 5) = 15 + 5(7 - 2x)$
11. $x^2 - 2x - 3 = x^2 - 3x + 1$
12. $(x^2 - 9) - (x^2 - 16) + x = 10$
13. $x^2 + 8x - (x^2 - x - 2) = 5(x + 3) + 3$
14. $x^2 + x - 2 + x^2 + 2x - 3 = 2x^2 - 7x - 1$
15. $10x - (x - 5) = 2x + 47$
16. $7x - 5 - (6 - 8x) + 2 = 3x - 7 + 106$
17. $3p + 2 = \dfrac{p}{5}$
18. $\dfrac{4}{n} = 3$
19. $\dfrac{2x}{3} - 5 = \dfrac{3x}{2}$
20. $5.90x - 2.80 = 2.40\,x + 3.40$
21. $4.50(x - 1.20) = 2.80(x + 3.70)$
22. $\dfrac{x - 4.80}{1.50} = 6.20x$

23. $6x + 3 - (3x + 2) = (2x - 1) + 9$
24. $3(x + 10) + 4(x + 20) + 5x - 170 = 15$
25. $20 - x + 4(x - 1) - (x - 2) = 30$
26. $5x + 3 - (2x - 2) + (1 - x) = 6(9 - x)$
27. Subdivide a metre of tape into two parts so that one part will be 60 mm longer than the other part.
28. A certain mine yields low-grade oil shale containing 68 L of oil per tonne of rock, and another mine has shale yielding 1200 L/tonne. How many tonnes of each must be sent each day to a processing plant that processes 25 $\overline{0}$00 tonnes of rock per day, so that the overall yield will be 90 L/tonne.
29. A certain automatic soldering machine requires a solder containing half tin and half lead. How much pure tin must be added to 55 kg of a solder containing 61% lead and 39% tin to raise the tin content to 50%?
30. A person owed to A a certain sum, to B four times as much, to C eight times as much, and to D six times as much. A total of $570 would pay all the debts. What was the debt to A?
31. A technician spends $\frac{2}{3}$ of his salary for board and $\frac{2}{3}$ of the remainder for clothing, and saves the rest, $1500 per year. What is his salary?
32. Find four consecutive odd numbers such that the product of the first and third will be 64 less than the product of the second and fourth.

33. The front and rear wheels of a tractor are 3.00 m and 3.66 m, respectively, in circumference. How many metres will the tractor have travelled when the front wheel has made 250 revolutions more than the rear wheel?

Solve each equation.

34. $3x - (x - 4) + (x + 1) = x - 7$
35. $4(x - 3) = 21 + 7(2x - 1)$
36. $8.20(x - 2.20) = 1.30(x + 3.30)$
37. $5(x - 1) - 3(x + 3) = 12$
38. $(x - 2)(x + 3) = x(x + 7) - 8$
39. $5x + (2x - 3) + (x + 9) = x + 1$
40. $1.20(x - 5.10) = 7.30(x - 1.30)$
41. $2(x - 7) = 11 + 2(4x - 5)$
42. $4.40(x - 1.90) = 8.30(x + 1.10)$
43. $8x - (x - 5) + (3x + 2) = x - 14$
44. $7(x + 1) = 13 + 4(3x - 2)$

Solve for x:

45. $bx + 8 = 2$
46. $c + ax = b - 7$
47. $2(x - 3) = 4 + a$
48. $3x + a = b - 5$
49. $8 - ax = c - 5a$
50. Find the reactions R_1 and R_2 in Figure 3•9.

FIGURE 3•9

4

Functions

O B J E C T I V E S

When you have completed this chapter, you should be able to:
- Distinguish between relations and functions.
- Identify types of relations and functions.
- Find the domain and range of a function.
- Use functional notation to manipulate, combine, and evaluate functions.

The equations we have been solving in the last few chapters have contained only *one variable*. For example,

$$x(x - 3) = x^2 + 7$$

contains the single variable x.

But many situations involve *two* (or more) variables that are somehow related to each other. Look, for example, at Figure 4•1, and suppose that you leave your campsite and walk a path up the hill. As you walk, both the horizontal distance x from your camp and the vertical distance y above your camp will change. You cannot change x without changing y, and vice versa (unless you jump into the air or dig a hole). The variables x and y are *related*. In this chapter we study the relation between two variables and introduce the concept of a *function*. The idea of a function provides us with a different way of speaking about mathematical relationships. We could say, for example, that the formula for the area of a circle *as a function of* its radius is $A = \pi r^2$.

It may become apparent as you study this chapter that these same problems could be solved without ever introducing the idea of a function. Does the function concept, then, merely give us new jargon for the same old ideas? Not really.

A new way of *speaking* about something can lead to a new way of *thinking* about that thing, and so it is with functions. It also will lead to the powerful and convenient *functional notation*, which will be especially useful when you study calculus and computer programming. In addition, this introduction to functions will prepare us for the study of *functional variation* later.

FIGURE 4•1

4•1   Functions and Relations

If we have an equation that enables us to find exactly one y for any given x, then y *is said to be a function of* x.

■ **Example 1:** The equation

$$y = 3x - 5$$

is a function. For any x, say $x = 2$, there corresponds exactly one y (in this case, $y = 1$). ■

Thus a function may be in the form of an equation. But *not every equation is a function.*

■ **Example 2:** The equation $y = \pm\sqrt{x}$ is not a function. Each value of x yields *two* values of y. This equation is called a *relation.* ■

We see from Example 2 that a relation need not have only *one* value of y for each value of x, as is required for a function. Thus only some equations that are relations can be called functions.

■ **Example 3:** The equation

$$y^2 = 2x + 4$$

is a relation but is not a function, because for some values of x there are two values of y. When $x = 0$, for example, y has the values 2 and -2. ■

Some older textbooks do not distinguish between relations and functions, but between *single-valued* functions and *two-valued* or *multiple-valued* functions (what we now call relations).

The fact that a relation is not a function does not imply second-class status. Relations are no less useful when they are not functions. In fact for practical work we often do not care whether our relation is a function or not.

The word *function* is commonly used to describe certain types of equations.

■ **Example 4:**

$y = 5x + 3$	is a linear function
$y = 3x^3$	is a power function
$y = 7x^2 + 2x - 5$	is a quadratic function
$y = 3 \sin 2x$	is a trigonometric function
$y = 5^{2x}$	is an exponential function
$y = \log (x + 2)$	is a logarithmic function ■

A More General Definition

When we think about a function or use one, it will most often be in the form of an equation. However, we do not want to limit our definition of a function to equations only, but would like to include other kinds of associations between numbers, such as tables of data, graphs, and verbal statements.

A more general definition of a function that includes all of these is usually given in terms of sets. A *set* is a collection of particular things, such as the set of all automobiles. The objects or members of a set are called *elements.* The only sets we will consider here are those that contain as elements all or some of the real numbers.

We do not intend to study sets here, or to introduce set notation, but will use the idea of a set to define a function, as follows:

> *Let x be an element in set A, and y an element in set B. We say that y is a function of x if there is a rule that associates exactly one y in set B with each x in set A.*

Here, set *A* is called the *domain* and set *B* is called the *range*.

FIGURE 4·2

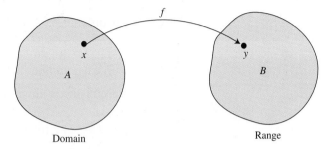

Domain

Range

We can picture a function as in Figure 4·2. Each set is represented by a shaded area, and each element by a point within the shaded area. The function *f* associates exactly one *y* in the range *B* with each *x* in the domain *A*.

Some find it helpful to think of a function as a machine (Figure 4·3). If the machine receives an input of *x* (within the domain of *x*), it uses its built-in rules to produce an output of a single corresponding value of *y*.

FIGURE 4·3 A "function machine."

■ **Example 5:** The equation from Example 1,

$$y = 3x - 5$$

can be thought of as a rule that associates exactly one *y* with any given *x*. The domain of *x* is the set of all real numbers, and the range of *y* is the set of all real numbers. ■

Other Forms of a Function

We have seen that certain equations are functions. But a function may also be (a) a set of ordered pairs, (b) a verbal statement, or (c) a graph. In technical work we must often deal with *pairs* of numbers rather than with single values, and these pairs often make up a function.

■ **Example 6:** In the experiment shown in Figure 4·4, we change the mass on the spring, and for each mass we measure and record the distance that the spring has stretched from its unloaded position. If a mass of 6 kg causes a stretch of 30 mm, then 6 kg and 30 mm are called *corresponding values*. The value 30 mm has no meaning *by itself*, but is meaningful only when it is *paired* with the mass that produced it (6 kg). If we always write the pair of numbers in the *same order* (the mass first and the distance second, in this example), it is then called an *ordered pair* of numbers. It is written (6, 30). ■

FIGURE 4·4

A set or table of ordered pairs is a function if for each x value there is only one y value given. The domain of x is the set of all x values in the table, and the range is the set of all y values.

■ **Example 7:** Suppose that the spring experiment of Example 6 gave the following results:

Mass (kg)	0	1	2	3	4	5	6	7	8
Stretch (mm)	0	5	9	14	21	24	30	36	40

This table of ordered pairs is a function. The domain is the set of numbers (0, 1, 2, 3, 4, 5, 6, 7, 8) and the range is the set of numbers (0, 5, 9, 14, 21, 24, 30, 36, 40). The table associates exactly one number in the range with each number in the domain. ■

A set of ordered pairs is not always given in the table form.

■ **Example 8:** The function of Example 7 can also be written

(0, 0), (1, 5), (2, 9), (3, 14), (4, 21), (5, 24), (6, 30), (7, 36), (8, 40) ■

Functions may also be given in verbal form.

■ **Example 9:** "The shipping charges are 55 cents/kg for the first 50 kg and 45 cents/kg thereafter." This verbal statement is a function relating the shipping costs to the weight of the item. ■

We sometimes want to switch from verbal form to an equation, or vice versa.

■ **Example 10:** Write y as a function of x if y equals twice the cube of x diminished by half of x.

Solution: We replace the verbal statement by the equation

$$y = 2x^3 - \frac{x}{2}$$ ■

There are, of course, many different ways to express this same relationship.

■ **Example 11:** The equation $y = 5x^2 + 9$ can be stated verbally as: "y equals the sum of 9 and 5 times the square of x." ■

■ **Example 12:** Express the volume V of a cone having a base area of 75 units *as a function of* its altitude H.

Solution: This is another way of saying: "Write an equation for *the volume of a cone in terms of its base area and altitude*."

The formula for the volume of a cone is given in the Summary of Facts and Formulas (Appendix A, Eq. 130):

$$V = \tfrac{1}{3}(\text{base area})(\text{altitude}) = \tfrac{1}{3}(75)H$$

So

$$V = 25H$$

is the required expression. ■

FIGURE 4·5

Different Forms of a Relation or Function	
Equation: $$y = x^2 - 3$$	Table of values: $\begin{array}{c\|cccc} x & 0 & 1 & 2 & 3 \\ \hline y & -3 & -2 & 1 & 6 \end{array}$
Verbal statement: "y is equal to the square of x diminished by 3."	
Set of ordered pairs: $(1, -2), \quad (3, 6),$ $(0, -3), \quad (2, 1)$	Graph:

We see, then, that a function or relation can be expressed in several different ways (Figure 4·5): as an equation, as a table, as a set of ordered pairs, or as a verbal statement. A function or relation can also be expressed as a *graph*, as we'll see in Section 5·2.

Finding Domain and Range

To be strictly correct, the domain should be stated whenever an equation is written. However, this is often not done, so we follow the convention:

The domain of the function is assumed to be the largest set of real x values that yield real values of y.

■ **Example 13:** The function

$$y = x^2$$

gives a real y value for every real x value. Thus the domain is all the real numbers, which we can write

Domain: $\qquad\qquad -\infty < x < \infty$

But notice that there is no x that will make y negative. Thus the range of y includes all the positive numbers and zero. This can be written

Range: $\qquad\qquad y \geq 0$ ■

Our next example is one in which certain values of x result in a *negative number under a radical sign*.

■ **Example 14:** Find the domain and range of the function

$$y = \sqrt{x - 2}$$

Solution: Our method is to see what values of x and y "do not work" (give a nonreal result or an illegal operation); then the domain and range will be those values that "do work."

Any value of x less than 2 will make the quantity under the radical sign negative, resulting in an imaginary y. Thus the domain of x is all the positive numbers equal to or greater than 2.

Domain: $\qquad\qquad x \geq 2$

An x equal to 2 gives a y of zero. Any x larger than 2 gives a real y greater than zero. Thus the range of y is

Range: $\qquad\qquad y \geq 0$ ▬

Our next example shows some values of x that result in *division by zero*.

▬ **Example 15:** Find the domain and range of the function

$$y = \frac{1}{x}$$

Solution: Here any value of x but zero will give a real y. Thus the domain is

Domain: $\qquad\qquad x \neq 0$

Notice here that it is more convenient to state which values of x *do not* work, rather than those that do.

Now what happens to y as x varies over its domain? We see that large x values give small y values, and, conversely, that small x values give large y values. Also, negative xs give negative ys. However, there is no x that will make y zero, so,

Range: $\qquad\qquad y \neq 0$ ▬

Our final example shows both division by zero and negative numbers under a radical sign, for certain x values.

▬ **Example 16:** Find the domain and range of the function

$$y = \frac{9}{\sqrt{4 - x}}$$

Solution: Since the denominator cannot be zero, x cannot be 4. Also, any x greater than 4 will result in a negative quantity under the radical sign. The domain of x is then

$$x < 4$$

Restricted to these values, the quantity $4 - x$ is positive, and ranges from very small (when x is nearly 4) to very large (when x is large and negative). Thus the denominator is positive, since we allow only the principal (positive) root, and can vary from near zero to infinity. The range of y, then, includes all the values greater than zero.

Range: $\qquad\qquad y > 0$ ▬

Exercise 1 Functions and Relations

Indicate which of the following relations are also functions:

1. $y = 3x^2 - 5$ $\qquad\qquad$ **2.** $y = \sqrt{2x}$
3. $y = \pm \sqrt{2x}$ $\qquad\qquad$ **4.** $y^2 = 3x - 5$
5. $2x^2 = 3y^2 - 4$ $\qquad\qquad$ **6.** $x^2 - 2y^2 - 3 = 0$

7. Is the set of ordered pairs (1, 3), (2, 5), (3, 8), (4, 12) a function? Explain.

8. Is the set of ordered pairs (0, 0), (1, 2), (1, −2), (2, 3), (2, −3), a function? Explain.

Functions in Verbal Form

For each expression, write y as a function of x, where the value of y is equal to:

9. The cube of x

10. The square root of x, diminished by 5

11. x increased by twice the square of x

12. The reciprocal of the cube of x

13. Two-thirds of the amount by which x exceeds 4

Replace each function by a verbal statement of the type given in Problems 9 to 13:

14. $y = 3x^2$

15. $y = 5 - x$

16. $y = \dfrac{1}{x} + x$

17. $y = 2\sqrt[3]{x}$

18. $y = 5(4 - x)$

Write the equation called for in each of the following statements. Refer to the Summary of Facts and Formulas (Appendix A) if necessary:

19. Express the area A of a triangle as a function of its base b and altitude h.

20. Express the hypotenuse c of a right triangle as a function of its legs, a and b.

21. Express the volume V of a sphere as a function of the radius r.

22. Express the power P dissipated in a resistor as a function of its resistance R and the current I through the resistor.

Write the equations called for in each statement:

23. A car is travelling at a speed of 80 km/h. Write the distance d travelled by the car as a function of time t.

24. To ship their merchandise, a mail-order company charges 65 cents/kg plus \$2.25 for handling and insurance. Express the total shipping charge s as a function of the item mass m.

25. A projectile is shot upward with an initial velocity of 125 m/s. Express the height H of the projectile as a function of time t. (See Eq. A18.)

Domain and Range

State the domain and range of each function:

26. (0, 2), (1, 4), (2, 8), (3, 16), (4, 32)

27. (−10, 20), (5, 7), (−7, 10), (10, 20), (0, 3)

28.

x	2	4	6	8	10
y	0	−2	−5	−9	−15

Find the domain and range for each function:

29. $y = \sqrt{x - 7}$

30. $y = \dfrac{3}{\sqrt{x - 2}}$

31. $y = x - \dfrac{1}{x}$

32. $y = \sqrt{x^2 - 25}$

33. $y = \dfrac{8 - x}{9 - x}$

34. $y = \dfrac{11}{(x + 4)(x + 2)}$

35. $y = \dfrac{4}{\sqrt{1 - x}}$

36. $y = \dfrac{x + 1}{x - 1}$

37. $y = \sqrt{x - 1}$

38. $y = \dfrac{5}{(x + 2)(x - 4)}$

39. Find the range of the function $y = 3x^2 - 5$ whose domain is $0 \le x \le 5$.

Calculator and Computer

40. Many graphics calculators enable you to recall an equation that was entered in the preceding calculation. This enables you to use the equation again with new values of the variables. Some calculators have an ENTRY key for bringing back the last entry, and some use an arrow key for the purpose. Check your manual.

Your calculator or computer can be your own "function machine."

Use your calculator to compute a set of ordered pairs for the function

$$y = 2x^2 - 3x + 5$$

for integer values of x from 0 to 5.

41. If you have a programmable calculator, program it to execute the computation of Problem 40 *automatically*.

42. A program in *Basic* to compute and print a table of ordered pairs for the function in Problem 40 is

```
10    FOR X = 0 to 5
20    LET Y = 2*X↑2 - 3*X + 5
30    PRINT X, Y
40    NEXT X
```

We don't intend to teach computer programming in this text, but we include an occasional problem for those who know simple programming.

Try this program on your computer, if you have *Basic*, or modify it for the language you have available. Then change it for different values of x, different step sizes (say, FOR X = -10 TO 10 STEP .5), and for a different function.

4·2

Functional Notation

Implicit and Explicit Form

When one variable in an equation is isolated on one side of the equal sign, the equation is said to be in *explicit form*.

■ **Example 17:** These equations are all in explicit form:

$$y = 2x^3 + 5 \qquad z = ay + b \qquad x = 3z^2 + 2z - z$$

■

When a variable is *not* isolated, the equation is in *implicit form*.

■ **Example 18:** These equations are all in implicit form:

$$y = x^2 + 4y \qquad x^2 + y^2 = 25 \qquad w + x = y + z$$ ■

Dependent and Independent Variables

In the equation

$$y = x + 5$$

y is called the *dependent variable* because its value depends on the value of x, and x is called the *independent* variable. Of course, the same equation can be written $x = y - 5$, so that x becomes the dependent variable and y the independent variable.

The terms "dependent" and "independent" are used only for an equation in explicit form.

■ **Example 19:** In the implicit equation $y - x = 5$, neither x nor y is called dependent or independent. ■

Functional Notation

Just as we use the symbol x to represent a *number*, without saying which number we are specifying, we use the notation

$$f(x)$$

to represent a *function* without having to specify which particular function we are talking about.

We can also use functional notation to designate a *particular* function, such as

$$f(x) = x^3 - 2x^2 - 3x + 4$$

A functional relation between two variables x and y, in explicit form, such as

$$y = 5x^2 - 6$$

could be written

$$y = f(x)$$

or

$$f(x) = 5x^2 - 6$$

The expression

$$y = f(x)$$

is read "y is a function of x."

Common Error	The expression $y = f(x)$ **does not** mean "y equals f times x"

The independent variable x is sometimes referred to as the *argument* of the function.

■ **Example 20:** We may know that the power P of an engine depends (somehow) on the engine displacement d. We can express this fact by

$$P = f(d)$$

We are saying that P is a function of d, even though we do not know (or perhaps even care, for now) what the relationship is. ■

The letter f is usually used to represent a function, but *other letters* can, of course, be used (g and h being common). Subscripts are also used to distinguish one function from another.

■ **Example 21:** You may see functions written as

$$y = f_1(x) \quad y = g(x)$$
$$y = f_2(x) \quad y = h(x)$$
$$y = f_3(x)$$

■

The letter y itself is often used to represent a function.

■ **Example 22:** The function

$$y = x^2 - 3x$$

will often be written

$$y(x) = x^2 - 3x$$

to emphasize the fact that y is a function of x. ■

Implicit functions can also be represented in functional notation.

■ **Example 23:** The equation $x - 3xy + 2y = 0$ can be represented in functional notation by $f(x, y) = 0$. ■

Functions relating *more than two variables* can be represented in functional notation, as in the following example.

■ **Example 24:**

$$y = 2x + 3z \qquad \text{can be written} \quad y = f(x, z)$$
$$z = x^2 - 2y + w^2 \quad \text{can be written} \quad z = f(x, y, w)$$
$$x^2 + y^2 + z^2 = 0 \quad \text{can be written} \quad f(x, y, z) = 0$$

■

Manipulating Functions

Functional notation provides us with a convenient way of indicating what is to be done with a function or functions. This includes solving an equation for a different variable, changing from implicit to explicit form, or vice versa, combining two or more functions to make another function, or substituting numerical or literal values into an equation.

■ **Example 25:** Write the equation $y = 2x - 3$ in the form $x = f(y)$.

Solution: We are being asked to write the given equation with x, instead of y, as the dependent variable. Solving for x, we obtain

$$2x = y + 3$$

$$x = \frac{y + 3}{2}$$ ■

■ **Example 26:** Write the equation $x = \dfrac{3}{2y - 7}$ in the form $y = f(x)$.

Solution: Here we are asked to rewrite the equation with y as the dependent variable, so we solve for y. Multiplying both sides by $2y - 7$ and dividing by x gives

$$2y - 7 = \frac{3}{x}$$

or

$$2y = \frac{3}{x} + 7$$

Dividing by 2 gives

$$y = \frac{3}{2x} + \frac{7}{2}$$ ■

■ **Example 27:** Write the equation $y = 3x^2 - 2x$ in the form $f(x, y) = 0$.

Solution: We are asked here to go from explicit to implicit form. Rearranging gives us

$$3x^2 - 2x - y = 0$$ ■

Substituting into Functions

If we have a function, say $f(x)$, then the notation $f(a)$ means to replace x by a in the same function.

■ **Example 28:** Given $f(x) = x^3 - 5x$, find $f(2)$.

Solution: The notation $f(2)$ means that 2 is to be *substituted for x* in the given function. Wherever an x appears, we replace it with 2.

$$f(x) = x^3 - 5x$$

$$f(2) = (2)^3 - 5(2)$$

$$= 8 - 10 = -2$$ ■

■ **Example 29:** Given $y(x) = 3x^2 - 2x$, find $y(5)$.

Solution: The given notation means to substitute 5 for x, so

$$y(5) = 3(5)^2 - 2(5)$$

$$= 75 - 10 = 65$$ ■

Often, we must substitute *several values* into a function and combine them as indicated.

━ **Example 30:** If $f(x) = x^2 - 3x + 4$, find
$$\frac{f(5) - 3f(2)}{2f(3)}$$

Solution:

$$f(2) = 2^2 - 3(2) + 4 = 2$$
$$f(3) = 3^2 - 3(3) + 4 = 4$$
$$f(5) = 5^2 - 3(5) + 4 = 14$$

so

$$\frac{f(5) - 3f(2)}{2f(3)} = \frac{14 - 3(2)}{2(4)}$$
$$= \frac{8}{8} = 1$$ ━

The substitution might involve *literal* quantities instead of numerical values.

━ **Example 31:** Given $f(x) = 3x^2 - 2x + 3$, find $f(5a)$.

Solution: We substitute $5a$ for x:
$$f(5a) = 3(5a)^2 - 2(5a) + 3$$
$$= 3(25a^2) - 10a + 3$$
$$= 75a^2 - 10a + 3$$ ━

━ **Example 32:** If $f(x) = 5x - 2$, find $f(2w)$.

Solution:
$$f(2w) = 5(2w) - 2 = 10w - 2$$ ━

━ **Example 33:** If $f(x) = x^2 - 2x$, find $f(w^2)$.

Solution:
$$f(w^2) = (w^2)^2 - 2(w^2) = w^4 - 2w^2$$ ━

It can be confusing when the expression to be substituted contains the same variable as in the original function.

━ **Example 34:** If $f(x) = 5x - 2$, then
$$f(x) = \quad 5x \quad - 2$$
$$f(x + a) = 5(x + a) - 2$$
$$= 5x + 5a - 2$$ ━

■ **Example 35:** If $f(x) = x^2 - 2x$, then

$$f(x - 1) = (x - 1)^2 - 2(x - 1)$$
$$= x^2 - 2x + 1 - 2x + 2$$
$$= x^2 - 4x + 3$$

There may be *more than one function* in a single problem.

■ **Example 36:** Given three different functions,

$$f(x) = 3x \quad g(x) = x^2 \quad h(x) = \sqrt{x}$$

evaluate

$$\frac{2g(3) + 4h(9)}{f(5)}$$

Solution: First substitute into each function:

$$f(5) = 3(5) = 15 \quad g(3) = 3^2 = 9 \quad h(9) = \sqrt{9} = 3$$

Then combine these as indicated:

$$\frac{2g(3) + 4h(9)}{f(5)} = \frac{2(9) + 4(3)}{15} = \frac{18 + 12}{15} = \frac{30}{15} = 2$$

Sometimes we must substitute into a function containing *more than one variable*.

■ **Example 37:** Given $f(x, y, z) = 2y - 3z + x$, find $f(3, 1, 2)$.

Solution: We substitute the given numerical values for the variables. Be sure that the numerical values are taken in the *same order* as the variable names in the functional notation.

$$f(x, y, z)$$
$$\updownarrow \; \updownarrow \; \updownarrow$$
$$f(3, 1, 2)$$

Substituting, we obtain

$$f(3, 1, 2) = 2(1) - 3(2) + 3 = 2 - 6 + 3$$
$$= -1$$

Exercise 2 Functional Notation

Implicit and Explicit Form

Which equations are in explicit form and which are in implicit form?

1. $y = 5x - 8$ **2.** $x = 2xy + y^2$
3. $3x^2 + 2y^2 = 0$ **4.** $y = wx + wz + xz$

Dependent and Independent Variables

Label the variables in each equation as dependent or independent:

5. $y = 3x^2 + 2x$ **6.** $x = 3y - 8$
7. $w = 3x + 2y$ **8.** $xy = x + y$
9. $x^2 + y^2 = z$

Manipulating Functions

10. If $y = 5x + 3$, write $x = f(y)$.

11. If $x = \dfrac{2}{y - 3}$, write $y = f(x)$.

12. If $y = \dfrac{1}{x} - \dfrac{1}{5}$, write $x = f(y)$.

13. If $x^2 + y = x - 2y + 3x^2$, write $y = f(x)$.

14. The power P dissipated in a resistor is given by $P = I^2R$. Write $R = f(P, I)$.

15. Young's modulus E is given by

$$E = \frac{PL}{ae}$$

Write $e = f(P, L, a, E)$.

Substituting into Functions

Substitute the given numerical value(s) into each function:

16. If $f(x) = 2x^2 + 4$, find $f(3)$.   **17.** If $f(x) = 5x + 1$, find $f(1)$.

18. If $f(x) = 15x + 9$, find $f(3)$.   **19.** If $f(x) = 5 - 13x$, find $f(2)$.

20. If $g(x) = 9 - 3x^2$, find $g(-2)$.

21. If $h(x) = x^3 - 2x + 1$, find $h(2.55)$.

22. If $f(x) = 7 + 2x$, find $f(3)$.

23. If $f(x) = x^2 - 9$, find $f(-2)$.

24. If $f(x) = 2x + 7$, find $f(-1)$.

Substitute and combine as indicated:

25. Given $f(x) = 2x - x^2$, find $f(5) + 3f(2)$.

26. Given $f(x) = x^2 - 5x + 2$, find $f(2) + f(3) - f(1)$.

27. Given $f(x) = x^2 - 4$, find $\dfrac{f(2) + f(3)}{4}$.

28. Given **(a)** $f(x) = 2x$ and **(b)** $f(x) = x^2$

evaluate $\dfrac{f(x + d) - f(x)}{d}$ for each given function.

We deal with expressions of this form in calculus, when studying the derivative.

Substitute the literal values into each function:

29. If $f(x) = 2x^2 + 4$, find $f(a)$.

30. If $f(x) = 2x - \dfrac{1}{x} + 4$, find $f(2a)$.

31. If $f(x) = 5x + 1$, find $f(a + b)$.

32. If $f(x) = 5 - 13x$, find $f(-2c)$.

Substitute in each function and combine:

33. If $f(x) = x^2$ and $g(x) = \dfrac{1}{x}$, find $f(3) + g(2)$.

34. If $f(x) = \dfrac{2}{x}$ and $g(x) = 3x$, find $f(4) - g\left(\dfrac{1}{3}\right)$.

35. If $f(x) = 8x^2 - 2x + 1$ and $g(x) = x - 5$, find $2f(3) - 4g(3)$.

36. If $h(z) = 2z$ and $g(w) = w^2$, find

(a) $\dfrac{h(4) + g(1)}{5}$ (b) $h[g(3)]$ (c) $g[h(2)]$

Functions of More Than One Variable

Substitute the values into each function:

37. If $f(x, y) = 3x + 2y^2 - 4$, find $f(2, 3)$.
38. If $f(x, y, z) = 3z - 2x + y^2$, find $f(3, 1, 5)$.
39. If $g(a, b) = 2b - 3a^2$, find $g(4, -2)$.
40. If $f(x, y) = y - 3x$, find $3f(2, 1) + 2f(3, 2)$.
41. If $g(a, b, c) = 2b - a^2 + c$, find $\dfrac{3g(1, 1, 1) + 2g(1, 2, 3)}{g(2, 1, 3)}$.

Applications

42. The distance travelled by a freely falling body is a function of the elapsed time t:

$$f(t) = V_0 t + \tfrac{1}{2}at^2$$

where V_0 is the initial velocity and a is the acceleration due to gravity

$$(a = 9.8 \text{ m/s}^2)$$

If V_0 is 17 m/s, find $f(10.0)$, $f(15.0)$, and $f(20.0)$.
43. The resistance R of a conductor is a function of temperature:

$$f(t) = R_0(1 + \alpha t)$$

where R_0 is the resistance at 0°C and α is the temperature coefficient of resistance (0.00427 for copper). If the resistance of a copper coil is $98\overline{0}0\ \Omega$ at 0°C, find $f(20.0)$, $f(25.0)$, $f(30.0)$.
44. The maximum deflection in mm of a certain cantilever beam (Figure 4•6), with a concentrated load applied r millimetres from the fixed end, is a function of r:

$$f(r) = .00030r^2(8\overline{0} - r)$$

Find the deflections $f(1\overline{0})$ and $f(15)$.

W

$\longleftarrow r \longrightarrow$

FIGURE 4.6 Cantilever beam

4•3

Composite Functions and Inverse Functions

Composite Functions

Just as we can substitute a constant or a variable into a given function, so we can substitute a *function* into a function.

■ **Example 38:** If $g(x) = x + 1$, find

(a) $g(2)$ (b) $g(z^2)$ (c) $g[f(x)]$

Solution:

(a) $g(2) = 2 + 1 = 3$ (b) $g(z^2) = z^2 + 1$ (c) $g[f(x)] = f(x) + 1$ ■

The function $g[f(x)]$ (which we read "g of f of x"), being made up of the two functions $g(x)$ and $f(x)$, is called a *composite function*. If we think of a function as a machine, it is as if we are using the output $f(x)$ of the function machine f as the input of a second function machine g.

In calculus, we will take derivatives of composite functions by means of the *chain rule*.

$$x \longrightarrow \boxed{f} \longrightarrow f(x) \longrightarrow \boxed{g} \longrightarrow g[f(x)]$$

We thus obtain $g[f(x)]$ by replacing x in $g(x)$ by the function $f(x)$.

■ **Example 39:** Given the functions $g(x) = x + 1$, and $f(x) = x^3$, write the composite function $g[f(x)]$

Solution: In the function $g(x)$, we replace x by $f(x)$, since $f(x) = x^3$:

$$g(x) \;\; = \;\; x \;\; + 1$$
$$\downarrow \qquad\quad \downarrow \qquad \downarrow$$
$$g[f(x)] = f(x) + 1$$
$$\qquad\qquad\quad \downarrow$$
$$\qquad = \;\; x^3 \;\; + 1 \qquad\qquad ■$$

As we have said, the notation $g[f(x)]$ means to substitute $f(x)$ into the function $g(x)$. On the other hand, the notation $f[g(x)]$ means to substitute $g(x)$ into $f(x)$.

$$x \longrightarrow \boxed{g} \longrightarrow g(x) \longrightarrow \boxed{f} \longrightarrow f[g(x)]$$

In general, $f[g(x)]$ *will not be the same as* $g[f(x)]$. ■

■ **Example 40:** Given $g(x) = x^2$ and $f(x) = x + 1$, find

(a) $f[g(x)]$ (b) $g[f(x)]$ (c) $f[g(2)]$ (d) $g[f(2)]$

Solution:

(a) $f[g(x)] = g(x) + 1 = x^2 + 1$
(b) $g[f(x)] = f[g(x)]^2 = (x + 1)^2$
(c) $f[g(2)] = 2^2 + 1 = 5$
(d) $g[f(2)] = (2 + 1)^2 = 9$

Notice that here $f[g(x)]$ is not equal to $g[f(x)]$. ■

Inverse of a Function

Consider a function f that, given a value of x, returns some value of y.

$$x \longrightarrow \boxed{f} \longrightarrow y$$

If that y is now put into a function g that *reverses the operations* in f so that its output is the original x, then g is called the *inverse* of f.

$$x \longrightarrow \boxed{f} \longrightarrow y \longrightarrow \boxed{g} \longrightarrow x$$

The inverse of a function $f(x)$ is often designated by $f^{-1}(x)$.

$$x \longrightarrow \boxed{f} \longrightarrow y \longrightarrow \boxed{f^{-1}} \longrightarrow x$$

Common Error	Do not confuse f^{-1} with $1/f$

■ **Example 41:** Two such inverse operations are "cube" and "cube root."

$$x \longrightarrow \boxed{\text{cube } x} \longrightarrow x^3 \longrightarrow \boxed{\text{take cube root}} \longrightarrow x$$ ■

Thus, if a function $f(x)$ has an inverse $f^{-1}(x)$ that reverses the operations in $f(x)$, then the *composite* of $f(x)$ and $f^{-1}(x)$ should have no overall effect. If the input is x, then the output must also be x. In symbols, if $f(x)$ and $f^{-1}(x)$ are inverse functions, then

$$f^{-1}[f(x)] = x$$

and

$$f[f^{-1}(x)] = x$$

Conversely, if $g[f(x)] = x$ and $f[g(x)] = x$, then $f(x)$ and $g(x)$ are inverse functions.

■ **Example 42:** Using the example of the cube and cube root, if

$$f(x) = x^3 \qquad \text{and} \qquad g(x) = \sqrt[3]{x}$$

then

$$g[f(x)] = \sqrt[3]{f(x)} = \sqrt[3]{x^3} = x$$

and

$$f[g(x)] = [g(x)]^3 = (\sqrt[3]{x})^3 = x$$

This shows that here $f(x)$ and $g(x)$ are indeed inverse functions. ▬

To find the inverse of a function $y = f(x)$:

1. Solve the given equation for x.
2. Interchange x and y.

■ **Example 43:** We use the cube, cube root example one more time. Find the inverse $g(x)$ of the function

$$y = f(x) = x^3$$

Solution: We solve for x and get

$$x = \sqrt[3]{y}$$

It is then customary to interchange variables so that the dependent variable is (as usual) y. This gives

$$y = f^{-1}(x) = \sqrt[3]{x}$$

Thus $f^{-1}(x) = \sqrt[3]{x}$ is the inverse of $f(x) = x^3$, as verified earlier. ▬

■ **Example 44:** Find the inverse $f^{-1}(x)$ of the function

$$y = f(x) = 2x + 5$$

Solution: Solving for x gives

$$x = \frac{y - 5}{2}$$

Interchanging x and y, we obtain

$$y = f^{-1}(x) = \frac{x - 5}{2}$$

━

Sometimes the inverse of a function will *not* be a function itself, but may be a relation.

━ **Example 45:** Find the inverse of the function $y = x^2$.

Solution: Taking the square root of both sides.

$$x = \pm\sqrt{y}$$

Interchanging x and y, we get

$$y = \pm\sqrt{x}$$

Thus a single value of x (say 4) gives *two* values of y ($+2$ and -2), so our inverse does not meet the definition of a function. It is, however, a relation. ━

Sometimes the inverse of a function gets a special name. The inverse of the sine function, for example, is called the *arcsin*, and the inverse of an exponential function is a *logarithmic* function.

Exercise 3   Composite Functions and Inverse Functions

Composite Functions

1. Given the functions $g(x) = 2x + 3$ and $f(x) = x^2$, write the composite function $g[f(x)]$.
2. Given the functions $g(x) = x^2 - 1$ and $f(x) = 3 + x$, write the composite function $f[g(x)]$.

Given $g(x) = x^3$ and $f(x) = 4 - 3x$, find:

3. $f[g(x)]$ **4.** $g[f(x)]$
5. $f[g(3)]$ **6.** $g[f(3)]$

Inverse Functions

Find the inverse of:

7. $y = 8 - 3x$
8. $y = 5(2x - 3) + 4x$
9. $y = 4x + 2(5 - x)$
10. $y = 3(x - 2) - 4(x + 3)$

Computer

Programming languages usually have a command for defining a function. BASIC, for example, uses the DEF FN statement, as in

```
50   DEF FND(X) = 3*X + 5
```

Here the *name* of the function is D, and the *independent variable or argument* is x. Functions of more than one variable can also be defined, as in

```
100   DEF FNB(X,Y,Z) = 3*X + Y/2 - Z
```

11. Using the *define* instructions on your machine, compute and print

$$y = \frac{4f_1(x)}{f_2(x) + 3}$$

for integer values of x from 1 to 10, where

$$f_1(x) = 2x - 5 \qquad \text{and} \qquad f_2(x) = 3x^2 + 2x - 3$$

CHAPTER 4 REVIEW PROBLEMS

1. Which of the following relations are also functions?
  (a) $y = 5x^3 - 2x^2$
  (b) $x^2 + y^2 = 25$
  (c) $y = \pm\sqrt{2x}$

2. Write y as a function of x if y is equal to half the cube of x, diminished by twice x.

3. Write an equation to express the surface area S of a sphere as a function of its radius r.

4. Find the largest possible domain and range for each function.

  (a) $y = \dfrac{5}{\sqrt{3 - x}}$

  (b) $y = \dfrac{1 + x}{1 - x}$

5. Label each of the following functions as implicit or explicit. If explicit, name the dependent and independent variables.
  (a) $w = 3y - 7$
  (b) $x - 2y = 8$

6. Given $y = 3x - 5$, write $x = f(y)$.

7. Given $x^2 + y^2 + 2w = 3$, write $w = f(x, y)$.

8. Write the inverse of the function $y = 9x - 5$.

9. If $y = 3x^2 + 2z$ and $z = 2x^2$, write $y = f(x)$.

10. If $f(x) = 5x^2 - 7x + 2$, find $f(3)$.

11. If $f(x) = 9 - 3x$, find $2f(3) + 3f(1) - 4f(2)$.

12. If $f(x) = 7x + 5$ and $g(x) = x^2$, find $3f(2) - 5g(3)$.

13. If $f(x, y, z) = x^2 + 3xy + z^2$, find $f(3, 2, 1)$.

14. If $f(x) = 8x + 3$ and $g(u) = u^2 - 4$, write $f[g(u)]$.

15. If $f(x) = 5x$, $g(x) = 1/x$, and $h(x) = x^3$, find

$$\frac{5h(1) - 2g(3)}{3f(2)}$$

16. Is the relation $x^2 + 3xy + y^2 = 1$ a function? Why?

17. Replace the function $y = 5x^3 - 7$ by a verbal statement.

18. What are the domain and range of the function $(10, -8)$, $(20, -5)$, $(30, 0)$, $(40, 3)$, and $(50, 7)$?

19. If $y = 6 - 3x^2$, write $x = f(y)$.

20. If $x = 6w - 5y$ and $y = 3z + 2w$, write $x = f(w, z)$.

Writing

21. State, in your own words, what is meant by "function" and "relation," and how a function differs from a relation. You may use examples to help describe these terms.

5

Graphs

O B J E C T I V E S

When you have completed this chapter, you should be able to:

- Graph points and empirical data in rectangular coordinates.
- Make a complete graph of a relation or a function.
- Graph parametric functions in rectangular coordinates.
- Solve equations graphically.

In this chapter we study graphing, a topic that has seen renewed interest with the availability of the graphics calculator. We start by explaining the rectangular coordinate system and the plotting of single points, and continue with the graphing of functions and relations. The idea of a complete graph is stressed.

The equation of a straight line is also introduced in this chapter. We conclude by showing how to solve any equation approximately using a graphical method. This is extremely important because it enables us to obtain solutions that would not be attainable by any other method.

5•1

Rectangular coordinates are also called *Cartesian* coordinates, after the French mathematician René Descartes (1596–1650). Another type of coordinate system we will use is called the *polar* coordinate system.

Rectangular Coordinates
The Rectangular Coordinate System

In Chapter 1 we plotted numbers on the number line. Suppose, now, that we take a second number line and place it at right angles to the first one, so that each intersects the other at the zero mark, as in Figure 5•1. We call this a *rectangular coordinate system*.

The horizontal number line is called the *x axis* and the vertical line is called the *y axis*. They intersect at the *origin*. These two axes divide the plane into four *quadrants*, numbered counterclockwise, as in the figure.

Graphing Ordered Pairs

Figure 5•2 shows a point *P* in the first quadrant. Its horizontal distance from the origin, called the *x coordinate* or *abscissa* of the point, is 3 units. Its vertical distance from the origin, called the *y coordinate* or *ordinate* of the point, is 2 units. The numbers in the *ordered pair* (3, 2) are called the *rectangular coordinates* (or simply *coordinates*) of the point. They are always written in the same order, with the *x* coordinate first. The letter identifying the point is sometimes written before the coordinates, as *P*(3, 2).

FIGURE 5·1 The rectangular coordinate system

FIGURE 5·2 Is it clear from this figure why we call these rectangular coordinates?

FIGURE 5·3

To plot any ordered pair (h, k), simply place a point at a distance h units from the y axis and k units from the x axis. Remember that negative values of x are located to the left of the origin and negative ys are below the origin.

■ **Example 1:** The points

$$P(4, 1) \quad Q(-2, 3) \quad R(-1, -2) \quad S(2, -3) \quad T(1.3, 2.7)$$

are shown plotted in Figure 5·3.

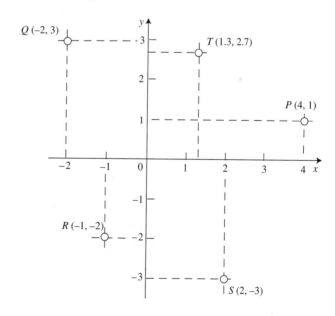

Notice that the abscissa is negative in the second and third quadrants, and that the ordinate is negative in the third and fourth quadrants. Thus the signs of the coordinates of a point tell us the quadrant in which the point lies. ■

■ **Example 2:** The point $(-3, -5)$ lies in the third quadrant, for that is the only quadrant in which the abscissa and the ordinate are both negative.

■

Exercise 1 Rectangular Coordinates

Rectangular Coordinates

If h and k are positive quantities, in which quadrants would the following points lie?

1. $(h, -k)$ **2.** (h, k)
3. $(-h, k)$ **4.** $(-h, -k)$
5. Which quadrant contains points having a positive abscissa and a negative ordinate?
6. In which quadrants is the ordinate negative?
7. In which quadrants is the abscissa positive?
8. The ordinate of any point on a certain straight line is -5. Give the coordinates of the point of intersection of that line and the y axis.
9. Find the abscissa of any point on a vertical straight line that passes through the point $(7, 5)$.

Graphing Ordered Pairs

10. Write the coordinates of points A, B, C, and D in Figure 5•4.

FIGURE 5•4

11. Write the coordinates of points E, F, G, and H in Figure 5•4.
12. Graph each point.
    (a) $(3, 5)$ (b) $(4, -2)$ (c) $(-2.4, -3.8)$
    (d) $(-3.75, 1.42)$ (e) $(-4, 3)$ (f) $(-1, -3)$

Graph each set of points, connect them, and identify the geometric figure formed.

13. $(0.7, 2.1)$, $(2.3, 2.1)$, $(2.3, 0.5)$, and $(0.7, 0.5)$
14. $(2, -\frac{1}{2})$, $(3, -1\frac{1}{2})$, $(1\frac{1}{2}, -3)$, and $(\frac{1}{2}, -2)$
15. $(-1\frac{1}{2}, 3)$, $(-2\frac{1}{2}, \frac{1}{2})$, and $(-\frac{1}{2}, \frac{1}{2})$

16. $(-3, -1), (-1, -\frac{1}{2}), (-2, -3),$ and $(-4, -3\frac{1}{2})$

17. Three corners of a rectangle have the coordinates $(-4, 9), (8, 3),$ and $(-8, 1)$. Graphically find the coordinate of the fourth corner.

5•2

The Graph of a Function

If the function is given as a set of ordered pairs, simply plot each ordered pair. We usually connect the points with a smooth curve unless we have reason to believe that there are sharp corners, breaks, or gaps in the graph.

If the function is in the form of an *equation*, we obtain a table of ordered pairs by selecting values of x over the required domain, and then computing corresponding values of y. Since we are usually free to select any x values we like, we pick "easy" integer values. We then plot the set of ordered pairs.

Our first graph will be of the straight line.

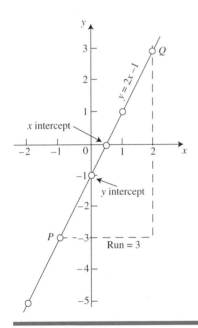

FIGURE 5•5 A first-degree equation will always plot as a straight line—hence the name *linear* equation.

■ Example 3: Graph the function $y = f(x) = 2x - 1$ for values of x from -2 to 2.

Solution: Substituting into the equation, we obtain

$$f(-2) = 2(-2) - 1 = -5$$
$$f(-1) = 2(-1) - 1 = -3$$
$$f(0) \ = 2(0) \ - 1 = -1$$
$$f(1) \ = 2(1) \ - 1 = 1$$
$$f(2) \ = 2(2) \ - 1 = 3$$

Thus our points are $(-2, -5), (-1, -3), (0, -1), (1, 1),$ and $(2, 3)$. Note that each of these pairs of numbers satisfies the given equation.

These points plot as a straight line (Fig. 5•5). Had we known in advance that the graph would be a straight line, we could have saved time by plotting just two points, with perhaps a third as a check. **■**

In Section 5•3 we will discuss the straight line in more detail and show another way to graph it.

Our next graph will be of a curve called the *parabola*. We graph it, and any function, in the same way that we graphed the straight line. Make a table of point pairs, plot the points, and connect them.

If we had plotted an infinite number of points, they would be crowded so close together that they would seem to form a continuous line. The curve can be thought of as a *collection* of all points that satisfy the equation. Such a curve (or the set of points) is called a *locus* of the equation.

■ Example 4: Graph the function $y = f(x) = x^2 - 4x - 3$ for values of x from -1 to 5.

Solution: Substituting into the equation, we obtain

$$f(-1) = (-1)^2 - 4(-1) - 3 = 1 + 4 - 3 = 2$$
$$f(0) \ = 0^2 - 0 - 3 = -3$$
$$f(1) \ = 1^2 - 4(1) - 3 = 1 - 4 - 3 = -6$$
$$f(2) \ = 2^2 - 4(2) - 3 = 4 - 8 - 3 = -7$$
$$f(3) \ = 3^2 - 4(3) - 3 = 9 - 12 - 3 = -6$$

FIGURE 5·6 This curve is called a *parabola*, which we will meet again later. Note the *vertex* and the *axis of symmetry*.

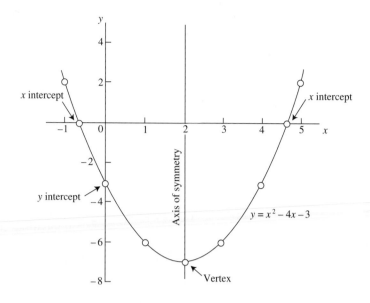

The straight line and the parabola are covered in much greater detail in Analytic Geometry, Chapter 22.

$$f(4) = 4^2 - 4(4) - 3 = 16 - 16 - 3 = -3$$
$$f(5) = 5^2 - 4(5) - 3 = 25 - 20 - 3 = 2$$

The points obtained are plotted in Figure 5·6.

Common Error	Be especially careful when substituting negative values into an equation. It is easy to make an error.

Exercise 2 The Graph of a Function

Graphing Sets of Ordered Pairs

Graph each set of ordered pairs. Connect them with a curve that seems to you to fit the data best.

1. $(-3, -2), (9, 6), (3, 2), (-6, -4)$
2. $(-7, 3), (0, 3), (4, 10), (-6, 1), (2, 6), (-4, 0)$
3. $(-10, 9), (-8, 7), (-6, 5), (-4, 3), (-2, 4), (0, 5), (2, 6), (4, 7)$
4. $(0, 4), (3, 3.2), (5, 2), (6, 0), (5, -2), (3, -3.2), (0, -4)$

Graph of a Straight Line

Graph each straight line by plotting two points on the line plus a third as a check.

5. $y = 3x + 1$
6. $y = 2x - 2$
7. $y = 3 - 2x$
8. $y = -x + 2$

Graph of Any Function

For each function, make a table of ordered pairs, taking integer values of x from -3 to 3. Plot the point pairs and connect them with a smooth curve.

9. $y = x^2$

10. $y = 4 - 2x^2$

11. $y = \dfrac{x^2}{x + 3}$

12. $y = x^2 - 7x + 10$

13. $y = x^2 - 1$

14. $y = 5x - x^2$

15. $y = x^3$

16. $y = x^3 - 2$

Computer

17. Write a program to generate a table of x, y point pairs for any function you enter. You should also be able to enter the domain of x, and the interval between your points. Use your program to obtain plotting points for any of the equations in this exercise, and plot the points by hand.

18. There are many graphing programs available for the computer. Most mathematical software, such as *MathCAD* and *Derive*, have built-in graphing capabilities. Some spreadsheet programs, such as LOTUS 123, are able to create graphs of data in a spreadsheet. If you have any such program available, learn how to use it. Practice with any of the graphs in this exercise.

5·3

Graphing the Straight Line

We graphed a straight line in Sec. 5·2 by finding the coordinates of two points on the line, plotting those points, and connecting them. Here, we will show how to plot a straight line by using the steepness of the line, called the *slope*, and the point where it crosses the y axis, called the *y intercept*.

This is still introductory material; our main study of the straight line will come in Chapter 22.

Slope

The horizontal distance between any two points on a straight line is called the *run* and the vertical distance between the same points is called the *rise*. For points P and Q in Fig. 5·5 the rise is 6 in a run of 3. The rise divided by the run is called the *slope* of the line, and is given the symbol m:

$$\text{Slope} = m = \frac{\text{rise}}{\text{run}}$$

■ **Example 5:** The straight line in Fig. 5·5 has a rise of 6 in a run of 3, so

$$\text{the slope } m = \frac{\text{rise}}{\text{run}} = \frac{6}{3} = 2 \qquad ■$$

■ **Example 6:** Find the slope of a straight line that drops half a unit as we move one unit in the positive x direction.

Solution: The rise is $-1/2$ in a run of 1, so the slope is

$$(\text{slope } m) = \frac{-1/2}{1} = -\frac{1}{2} \qquad ■$$

Example 7: Find the slope of the line in Fig. 5•7.

FIGURE 5•7

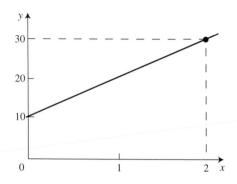

Solution: The rise is $30 - 10 = 20$ and the run is $2 - 0 = 2$, so

$$m = \frac{20}{2} = 10$$

Further, if (x_1, y_1) and (x_2, y_2) are two points on the line, the slope

Slope	$m = \dfrac{\text{rise}}{\text{run}} = \dfrac{y_2 - y_1}{x_2 - x_1}$	**284**

The slope is equal to the rise divided by the run.

Example 8: Find the slope of the line connecting the points $(-3, 5)$ and $(4, -6)$ (Fig. 5•8).

Solution: We will see that it does not matter which is called point 1 and which is point 2. Let us choose

$$x_1 = -3 \qquad y_1 = 5 \qquad x_2 = 4 \qquad y_2 = -6$$

Then, by Eq. 284,

$$\text{slope } m = \frac{-6 - 5}{4 - (-3)} = \frac{-11}{7} = -\frac{11}{7}$$

would have given the same result.

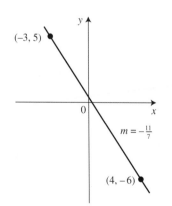

FIGURE 5•8

Common Error	Be careful not to mix up the subscripts. $m \neq \dfrac{y_2 - y_1}{x_1 - x_2}$

Horizontal and Vertical Lines

For any two points on a horizontal line, the values of y_1 and y_2 in Eq. 284 are equal, making the slope equal to zero. For a vertical line, the values of x_1 and x_2 are equal, giving division by zero. Hence the slope is undefined for a vertical line. The slopes of various lines are shown in Fig. 5•9.

FIGURE 5•9

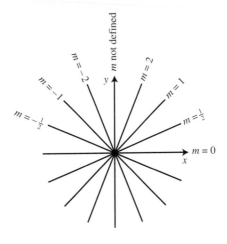

Intercepts

Some graphics calculators can automatically find the *y* intercept of a plotted function. Check your calculator manual.

The *intercepts* of a curve are the places where the curve crosses the *x* and *y* axes. The term *intercept* is used for any curve, not just the straight line.

■ **Example 9:** The *x* intercept for the straight line in Fig. 5•5 is $(1/2, 0)$ and the *y* intercept is $(0, -1)$. ■

Equation of a Straight Line

Suppose that $P(x, y)$ is any point on a straight line. We seek an equation that links *x* and *y* in a functional relationship, so that, for any *x*, a value of *y* can be found. We can get such an equation by applying the definition of slope to our point *P*, and some *known* point on the line. Let us use the *y* intercept $(0, b)$ as the coordinates for the known point. For *P*, a general point on the line, we use coordinates (x, y). For a line that intersects the *y* axis *b* units from the origin (Fig. 5•10) the rise is $y - b$ and the run is $x - 0$, so by Eq. 284,

FIGURE 5•10

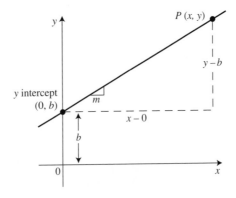

$$m = \frac{y - b}{x - 0}$$

Simplifying, $mx = y - b$, or

Straight Line: Slope-Intercept Form	$y = mx + b$	**289**

This is called the slope-intercept form of the equation of a straight line because the slope m and y intercept b are easily identified once the equation is in this form. For example, in the equation $y = 2x + 1$,

$$y = 2x + 1$$

slope ⤒ ⤒ y intercept

Here m, the slope, is 2 and b, the y intercept, is 1.

■ **Example 10:** Write the equation of the straight line, in slope-intercept form, that has a slope of 2 and a y intercept of 3. Make a graph.

Solution: Substituting $m = 2$ and $b = 3$ into Eq. 289 gives

$$y = 2x + 3$$

To graph the line, we first locate the y intercept, 3 units up from the origin. The slope of the line is 2, so to get another point on the line we move 1 unit to the right and 2 units up, from the y intercept, Fig. 5•11.

FIGURE 5•11

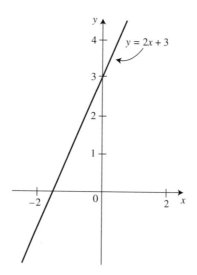

■ **Example 11:** Find the slope and y intercept of the line $y = 3x - 4$. Make a graph.

Solution: By inspection, we see that the slope is the coefficient of x, and that the y intercept is the constant term. So,

$$m = 3 \qquad \text{and} \qquad b = -4$$

We plot the y intercept 4 units below the origin, and through it draw a line with a rise of 3 units in a run of 1 unit, Fig. 5•12.   ▬

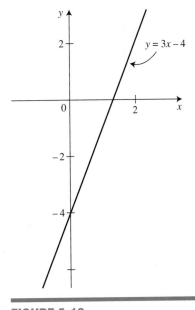

$y = 3x - 4$

FIGURE 5•12

Exercise 3   Graphing the Straight Line

Find the slope of each straight line.

1. Rise = 4; run = 2
2. Rise = 6; run = 4
3. Rise = -4; run = 4
4. Rise = -9; run = -3
5. Connecting (2, 4) and (5, 7)
6. Connecting (5, 2) and (3, 6)
7. Connecting $(-2, 5)$ and $(5, -6)$
8. Connecting $(3, -3)$ and $(-6, 2)$

Write the equation of each straight line in slope-intercept form, and make a graph.

9. Slope = 4; y intercept = -3
10. Slope = -1; y intercept = 2
11. Slope = 3; y intercept = -1
12. Slope = -2; y intercept = 3
13. Slope = 2.3; y intercept = -1.5
14. Slope = -1.5; y intercept = 3.7

Find the slope and y intercept for each equation, and make a graph.

15. $y = 3x - 5$
16. $y = 7x + 2$
17. $y = -\frac{1}{2}x - \frac{1}{4}$
18. $y = -3x + 2$

5•4   The Graphics Calculator

The *graphics calculator* will help us to make graphs quickly. To do this we must:

1. Set the domain and range.
2. Enter the function.

You should now look at your calculator manual to find out which keys are used. To set the domain and range, look for a key marked $\boxed{\text{Range}}$. To enter the function you will need a key probably marked $\boxed{Y=}$ or $\boxed{\text{Graph}}$.

▬ **Example 12:** Graph the parabola of Example 4 (page 137) using a graphics calculator. Use the same domain and range as in that example.

Solution: We first set the domain and range. Pressing the $\boxed{\text{Range}}$ key will give you a screen that will look something like this:

```
Range
Xmin = −10
Xmax = 10
Xscl = 1
Ymin = −10
Ymax = 10
Yscl = 1
```

Here, Xmin and Xmax define the domain, and Ymin and Ymax give the range. This screen shows both domain and range set to *default values* of −10 to 10 (your calculator may show different values). The Xscl value shows the spacing of the tick marks on the x axis. With an Xscl setting 1, there will be a tick mark at each unit. The Yscl value does the same thing for the y axis.

We will now change these values. We know from Example 4 that y will vary from −7 to 2, when x has the given domain, so we set Ymin to −8 and Ymax to 3. If we were graphing this curve for the first time, we would not know these values and would have to find them by trial and error. We'll do this in a later example.

The calculator *cursor* should be at the Xmin value (−10). Key in −1 and press ENTER or EXE. The cursor should now be at the Xmax value. Key in 5 and press ENTER. Continue through the list. If the value shown is not the one you want, simply replace it. If it is already correct, press ENTER to proceed to the next line.

Set Xscl and Yscl each to a value of 1. When you finish, your screen should look something like this:

```
Range
Xmin = −1
Xmax = 5
Xscl = 1
Ymin = −8
Ymax = 3
Yscl = 1
```

Next we enter the function. Press the Y= key or the Graph key and the screen will display something like

```
Y =
```

Enter the function $x^2 - 4x - 3$ to the right of the equal sign. Your screen should look something like this:

```
Y = X² − 4X − 3
```

To see the graph, press the Graph G <> T key. You should get the same graph as in Example 4.

FIGURE 5•15

FIGURE 5•13

FIGURE 5•14

Complete Graph

In the preceding examples we were told which x values to use for the graph. If we want to graph a function to see how it behaves, we would not bother with those regions where the curve is simply rising or falling without change, but would include those x values that show *all the features of interest*. Those features of interest include

> *Intercepts* on the x and/or y axes
> Peaks on the curve, called *maximum points*, such as A in Figure 5•13
> Valleys on the curve, called *minimum points*, such as B in Figure 5•13
> The *domain* of the function, and those regions where the curve does not exist, such as the shaded regions in Figure 5•14

A graph showing all the features of interest is sometimes called a *complete graph*. With some experience you will often be able to tell just by looking at a function if its graph will have certain features, such as how many maximum and minimum points it will have. But until you have such experience you can find the features of interest simply by trial and error. The graphics calculator is ideal for such exploration, as shown in the following example.

■ **Example 13:** Make a complete graph of the function

$$y = 0.054x^3 - 23x - 80$$

Solution: Let us set our ranges for both x and y from -10 to 10. We key in the given function and get the graph in Figure 5•15(a). We notice an x intercept at about $x = -3$.

Suspecting there is more to the graph than what shows in this viewing window, we reset both ranges from -100 to $+100$. We get the graph of Figure 5•15(b), and see two more x intercepts. However, the curve seems to be "clipped" at the top and bottom, so let us increase the y range to -200 to $+200$, keeping the x range unchanged. We get Figure 5•15(c), and observe a maximum point in the second quadrant and a y intercept below the origin. The curve still seems clipped at the bottom, so let us change Ymin to -300. This reveals a minimum point, Figure 5•15(d). We are fairly sure now (but not positive) that all the features of interest are within the viewing window. Let us finally adjust the ranges so that the curve nicely fills the viewing window. We set the x range from -30 to 30 and the y range from -300 to 300.

Most graphing calculators have a zoom feature which allows you to quickly make both ranges larger or smaller. Check your manual to see how it is used.

We have been ignoring the Xscl and Yscl settings until we found suitable ranges. Let us now set the x scale to 10 and the y scale to 50, getting the graph of Figure 5•15(e).

We see three x intercepts, one y intercept, a maximum point, and a minimum point. We shall show how to get the approximate coordinates of those points in the following section. ▬

Using the TRACE Key

When the TRACE key is pressed a small cursor will appear on the curve in the viewing window. Further, the x and y coordinates of the cursor will be displayed on the screen. (Some calculators show only the x coordinate. Use the X <> Y key to show the y coordinate.) Pressing the left and right arrow keys will cause the cursor to move along the curve, with the new coordinate(s) displayed as you move. This provides an easy way of finding the approximate coordinates of any point of interest on the graph.

▬ **Example 14:** Using the TRACE key, find the approximate coordinates of the intercepts and the maximum and minimum points on the curve of Example 13.

Solution: Going from left to right along the curve we read:

$$x \text{ intercept at } x = -18.6$$
$$\text{Maximum at } (-11.7, 102.6)$$
$$x \text{ intercept at } x = -3.5$$
$$y \text{ intercept at } y = -72.7$$
$$\text{Minimum at } (11.7, -262.6)$$
$$x \text{ intercept at } x = 22.4$$

Note that these coordinates are not very accurate, because the scale for this graph is very large. But we need not be satisfied with this accuracy. All we have to do is *zoom in* to any particular point of interest to get more accuracy. In fact, *we can zoom in repeatedly* to get whatever degree of accuracy we want.

Exercise 4 The Graphics Calculator

Graph these functions from Exercise 2, using a graphics utility. Compare your graphs with those you obtained manually.

1. $y = x^2$ **2.** $y = 4 - 2x^2$

3. $y = \dfrac{x^2}{x+3}$ **4.** $y = x^2 - 7x + 10$

5. $y = x^2 - 1$ **6.** $y = 5x - x^2$

7. $y = x^3$ **8.** $y = x^3 - 2$

Make a complete graph of each function, choosing a viewing window that includes all features of interest. Use your graphics calculator's graphing features to find the approximate coordinates of any x intercepts, maximum points, and minimum points:

9. $y = 2x^2 - 14x + 22$ **10.** $y = 7x^2 + 9x - 14$
11. $y = 4x^3 - 4x^2 + 11x - 24$ **12.** $y = 5x^4 + 13x^2 - 31$

5·5

Graphing Empirical Data, Formulas, and Parametric Equations

Graphing Empirical Data

Data obtained from an experiment or by observation is called *empirical* data. Empirical data is graphed just like any other set of point pairs. Be sure to label the graph completely, including units on the axes.

■ **Example 15:** Graph the following data for the temperature rise in a certain furnace.

Time (h)	0	1	2	3	4	5	6	7	8	9	10
Temperature (°C)	102	463	748	1010	1210	1370	1510	1590	1710	1770	1830

Solution: We plot each point, connect them, and label the graph, as in Figure 5•16. ■

FIGURE 5·16 Note the use of different scales on the two axes.

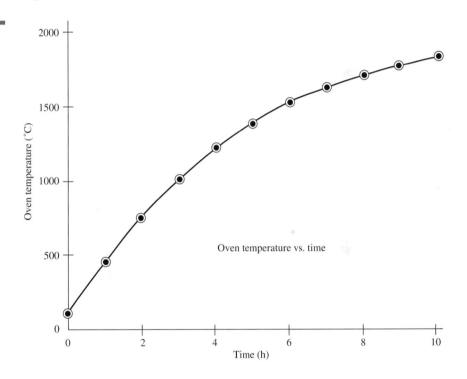

Graphing Formulas

A formula is graphed in the same way that we graph a function; we substitute suitable values of the independent variable into the formula and compute the corresponding values of the dependent variable. We then plot the ordered pairs and connect the points obtained with a smooth curve. But with formulas we must be careful to handle the units properly and to label the graph more fully.

Example 16: The formula for the power P dissipated in a resistor carrying a current of I amperes (A) is

$$P = I^2R \qquad \text{watts (W)}$$

where R is the resistance in ohms. Graph P versus I, for a resistance of 10 000 Ω. Take I from 0 to 10 A.

Let us choose values of I of 0, 1, 2, 3, . . . , 10, and make a table of ordered pairs by substituting these into the formula.

I(A)	0	1	2	3	...
P(W)	0	10 000	40 000	90 000	...

At this point we notice that the figures for wattage are so high that it will be more convenient to work in kilowatts (kW), where 1 kW = 1000 W.

I(A)	0	1	2	3	4	5	6	7	8	9	10
P(kW)	0	10	40	90	160	250	360	490	640	810	1000

These points are plotted in Figure 5•17. Note the labelling of the graph and of the axes.

FIGURE 5•17 Power dissipated in a 10 000 Ω resistor calculated using $P = i^2R$ with $R = 10\,000$ Ω

Graphing Parametric Equations

For the equations we have graphed so far, y has been expressed as a function of x.

$$y = f(x)$$

But x and y can also be related to each other by means of a third variable, say t, if both x and y are given as functions of t.

$$x = g(t)$$

and

$$y = h(t)$$

In a later chapter we'll plot parametric equations in *polar* coordinates. We'll also use polar coordinates to describe the *trajectory* of a projectile.

Such equations are called *parametric equations*. The third variable t is called the *parameter*.

To graph parametric equations we assign values to the parameter t and compute x and y for each t. The table of (x, y) pairs is then plotted.

Example 17: Graph the parametric equations

$$x = 2t \qquad \text{and} \qquad y = t^2 - 2$$

for $t = -3$ to 3.

Solution: We make a table with rows for t, x, and y. We take values of t from -3 to 3, and for each compute x and y.

t	-3	-2	-1	0	1	2	3
x	-6	-4	-2	0	2	4	6
y	7	2	-1	-2	-1	2	7

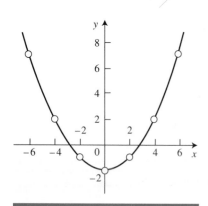

FIGURE 5•18

We now plot the (x, y) pairs, $(-6, 7)$, $(-4, 2)$, . . . , $(6, 7)$ and connect them with a smooth curve (Fig. 5•18). The curve obtained is a parabola, as in Example 4, but here it is obtained with parametric equations.

We can quickly plot parametric equations with a graphics calculator.

■ **Example 18:** Plot the parametric equations from the preceding example with a graphics calculator.

Solution: We first put the calculator into parametric equation mode. This option may have to be selected from a menu; check your calculator manual.

Next we enter the equations:

$$
\begin{aligned}
XIT &= 2T \\
YIT &= T^2 - 2
\end{aligned}
$$

Finally, we set the range:

$$
\begin{aligned}
Tmin &= -3 \\
Tmax &= 3 \\
Tstep &= .1 \\
Xmin &= -6 \\
Xmax &= 6 \\
Xscl &= 1 \\
Ymin &= -2 \\
Ymax &= 7 \\
Yscl &= 1
\end{aligned}
$$

The graph obtained will be the same as in Fig. 5•18.   ■

Exercise 5 Graphing Empirical Data, Formulas, and Parametric Equations

Graphing Empirical Data

Graph the following three sets of experimental data. Label each graph completely. Take the first quantity in each table as the abscissa, and the second quantity as the ordinate. Connect the points with a smooth curve.

1. The current I (mA) through a tungsten lamp and the voltage V (V) that is applied to the lamp, related as shown in the following table:

V	10	20	30	40	50	60	70	80	90	100	110	120
I	158	243	306	367	420	470	517	559	598	639	676	710

2. The melting point $T(°C)$ of a certain alloy and the percent of lead P in the alloy, related as shown in the following table:

P	40	50	60	70	80	90
T	186	205	226	250	276	304

3. A steel wire in tension, with the stress σ (N/m^2) and the strain ϵ (mm/mm) related as follows:

σ	5000	10 000	20 000	30 000	40 000	50 000	60 000	70 000
ϵ	0	0.00019	0.00057	0.00094	0.00134	0.00173	0.00216	0.00256

Graphing Formulas

4. A milling machine having a purchase price P of $15 600 has an annual depreciation A of $1600. Graph the book value y at the end of each year, for $t = 10$ years, using the equation $y = P - At$.

5. The force F required to pull a block along a rough surface is given by $F = \mu R$, where R is the normal force and μ is the coefficient of friction. Plot F for values of R from zero to 1000 N, taking μ as 0.45.

6. A 2580-Ω resistor is wired in parallel with a resistor R_1. Graph the equivalent resistance R for values of R_1 from 0 to 5000 Ω, in steps of 500 Ω. Use Eq. A64.

7. Use Eq. A67 to graph the power P, in watts (w), dissipated in a 2500-Ω resistor for values of the current I from 0 to 10 A.

8. A resistance of 5280 Ω is placed in series with a device that has a reactance of X ohms (Fig. 5•19). Using Eq. A99, plot the absolute value of the impedance Z for values of X from 0 to 10 000 Ω.

FIGURE 5•19

Graphing Parametric Equations

Plot the following parametric equations for values of t from -3 to 3:

9. $x = t, y = t$

10. $x = 3t, y = t^2$

11. $x = -t, y = 2t^2$

12. $x = -2t, y = t^2 + 1$

5•6

Graphical Solution of Equations

Solving Equations Graphically

We can use our knowledge of graphing functions to solve equations of the form $f(x) = 0$.

We mentioned earlier that a point at which a graph of a function $y = f(x)$ crosses or touches the x axis is called an x intercept. Such an x intercept is also called a zero of that function.

In Figure 5•20 there are two zeros, since there are two x values for which $y = 0$, and hence $f(x) = 0$. Those x values for which $f(x) = 0$ are called *roots* or *solutions* to the equation $f(x) = 0$.

Thus if we were to graph the function $y = f(x)$, any value of x at which y is equal to zero would be a solution to $f(x) = 0$. To solve an equation graphically, we simply put it into the form $f(x) = 0$ and then graph the function $y = f(x)$. Each x intercept is then an approximate solution to the equation.

We can get two different expressions when we put the given equation into the form $f(x) = 0$. Thus, if $x^2 = 2x + 2$ we could write

$$f(x) = x^2 - 2x - 2$$

or

$$f(x) = -x^2 + 2x + 2$$

It doesn't matter which we use because both cross the x axis at the same points.

■ **Example 19:** Graphically find the approximate root(s) of the equation

$$4.1x^3 - 5.9x^2 - 3.8x + 7.5 = 0 \qquad (1)$$

FIGURE 5•20

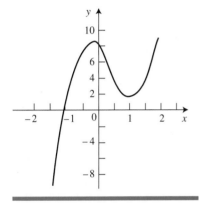

FIGURE 5•21 The shape of this curve is typical of a third-degree (cubic) function.

Some graphics calculators can automatically find a root, when the cursor is moved to a point on the curve near that root. Again, read your calculator manual for the proper instructions to use.

Solution: Let us represent the left side of the given equation by *f(x)* and reverse sides, giving

$$f(x) = 4.1x^3 - 5.9x^2 - 3.8x + 7.5$$

Any value of x for which $f(x) = 0$ will clearly be a solution to (1), so we simply plot $f(x)$ and look for the x intercepts. Not knowing the shape of the curve, we compute $f(x)$ at various values of x until we are satisfied that we have located each region in which an x intercept is located. We then make a table of point pairs for this region.

x	−2	−1	0	1	2	3
$f(x)$	−41.3	1.3	7.5	1.9	9.1	53.7

We graph the function (Fig. 5•21) and read the approximate value of the x intercept,

$$x \cong -1.1$$

This, then, is an approximate solution to the given equation. Have we found *every* root? If we compute y for values of x outside the region we have graphed, we would see that the curve moves even farther from the x axis, so we are reasonably sure that we have found the only root. With other functions it may not be so easy to tell if the curve will reverse direction somewhere and cross the x axis again. ▬

Solving Equations with the Graphics Calculator

In Section 5•2 we showed how to use the TRACE features of a graphics calculator to find intercepts. Since the graphical solution of an equation requires finding an x intercept, the same method will work here.

▬ **Example 20:** Repeat Example 19 using TRACE on a graphics calculator.

Solution: We key in the function and display the graph in the standard viewing window, with the x range set at −10 to 10. We see that the curve crosses the x axis at about $x = -1$. Let us reduce the x range in steps, each time using TRACE to locate the x intercept as closely as we can. Also, as we reduce the x range we also reduce the y range (values not shown) so that the curve is steep enough to see clearly where it appears to cross the x axis. The cursor jumps in steps and may not land right on the intercept, so we get as close as we can. The following table shows the coordinates of the point closest to the intercept, for the various x ranges tried.

x range	x	y
−2 to 0	−1.052632	0.18056568
−1.1 to −1	−1.061053	−0.00814060
−1.07 to −1.05	−1.060526	0.00373216
−1.061 to −1.060	−1.060695	−0.00006597

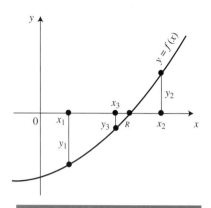

FIGURE 5·22 The midpoint method for finding roots

This method is also called the *half-interval method* or the *bisection method*.

Now, if we were exactly *at* the intercept, the value of y would be *zero*. Thus the smaller the value of y, the closer we are to the intercept. We can make the value of y as small as we please, within the limits of the calculator, by zooming in even further.

To get a measure of the accuracy of the root, subtract the x value at any point from the x value one step to the right. This will give you the *step size* in the x direction.

Thus for the final x range in our example, suppose the step size is found to be 0.000011. This shows that the fifth decimal place in our intercept has some uncertainty, but that any digits to the right of that are unreliable. Thus we give our root as

$$x = -1.0607$$

Computer Solution of Equations by the Midpoint Method

There are several methods for finding the roots of equations by computer. In Chapter 14 we show the method of *simple iteration*, and when you study calculus you will learn the popular *Newton's method*. Here we cover the simple *midpoint* method.

Figure 5·22 shows a graph of some function $y = f(x)$. It is a smooth, continuous curve which crosses the x axis at R, which is a root of the equation $f(x) = 0$. We determine two values x_1 and x_2 that lie to the left and right of R, a fact that we verify by testing whether y_1 and y_2 have opposite signs. We then locate x_3 midway between x_1 and x_2, and determine whether it is to the left or right of R by comparing the sign of y_3 with that of y_1. Thus x_3 becomes a new endpoint (either the left or the right, as determined by the test), and we repeat the computation, halving the interval again and again until we get as close to R as we wish.

Following is an algorithm for the midpoint method.

1. Make two initial guesses, x_1 and x_2, which must lie on either side of the root R.
2. Go to Step 3 if y_1 and y_2 have opposite signs. Otherwise, go back to Step 1.
3. Compute the abscissa x_3 of the point midway between the two original points, with

$$x_3 = \frac{x_1 + x_2}{2}$$

4. Compute y_1 and y_3 by substituting x_1 and x_3 into the equation of the curve.
5. If the absolute value of y_3 is "small," then print the value of x_3 and end the computation.
6. Determine whether x_3 is to the right or left of the root by comparing the signs of y_1 and y_3.
7. If y_1 and y_3 have the same signs, replace x_1 with x_3. Otherwise, replace x_2 with x_3.
8. Go to Step 3 and repeat the computation.

A technique such as this one, in which we repeat a computation many times, each time getting an approximate result that is (with luck) closer to the true value, is called *iteration*. Iteration methods are used often on the computer, and we give several in this text.

Using this algorithm as a guide, try to program the midpoint method on your computer. Save your program carefully because you can use it to check your manual solutions to the various equations in this text.

Exercise 6 Graphical Solution of Equations

The following equations all have at least one root between $x = -10$ and $x = 10$. Put each equation into the form $y = f(x)$ and plot just enough of each to find the approximate value(s) of the root(s).

1. $2.4x^3 - 7.2x^2 - 3.3 = 0$

2. $9.4x = 4.8x^3 - 7.2$

3. $25x^2 - 19 = 48x + x^3$

4. $1.2x + 3.4x^3 = 2.8$

5. $6.4x^4 - 3.8x = 5.5$

6. $621x^4 - 284x^3 - 25 = 0$

Can you guess the significance of the point of intersection? Look ahead at Section 10•1.

In each of Problems 7 to 10, two equations are given. Graph each equation as if the other were not there, but on the same coordinate axes. Each equation will graph as a straight line. Give the approximate coordinates of the point of intersection of the two lines.

7. $y = 2x + 1$
$y = -x + 2$

8. $x - y = 2$
$x + y = 6$

9. $y = -3x + 5$
$y = x - 4$

10. $2x + 3y = 9$
$3x - y = -4$

Computer

11. Write a program for solving equations by the midpoint method. Use it to solve any of the equations in Problems 1 to 6.

CHAPTER 5   REVIEW PROBLEMS

1. Graph the following points and connect them with a smooth curve:

x	0	1	2	3	4	5	6
y	2	$2\frac{1}{4}$	3	4	6	9	13

2. Plot the function $y = x^3 - 2x$ for $x = -3$ to $+3$. Label any roots or intercepts.

3. Graph the function $y = 3x - 2x^2$ from $x = -3$ to $x = 3$. Label any roots or intercepts.

4. Graphically find the approximate value of the roots of the equation

$$(x + 3)^2 = x - 2x^2 + 4$$

5. Graphically find the point of intersection:

$$2.5x - 3.7y = 5.2$$
$$6.3x + 4.2y = 2.6$$

6. Using the following data, make a graph of the pressure p (kPa) in an engine cylinder, where v is the volume (cm³) above the piston.

p	39.6	44.7	53.8	73.5	85.8	113.2	135.8	178.2
v	10.61	9.73	8.55	7.00	6.23	5.18	4.59	3.87

In Problems 7 and 8, plot the parametric equations, for $t = -2$ to 2.

7. $x = 3t$
$y = t^3$

8. $x = 2t^2$
$y = 4t$

In Problems 9 to 12, make a complete graph of each function, choosing a domain and range that include all the features of interest.

9. $y = 5x^2 + 24x - 12$ **10.** $y = 9x^2 + 22x - 17$
11. $y = 6x^3 + 3x^2 - 14x - 21$
12. $y = 3x^4 + 21x^2 + 21$

In Problems 13 and 14, write the equation of the straight line and draw a graph of the line.

13. Slope $= -2$, y intercept $= 4$

14. Slope $= 4$, y intercept $= -6$

In Problems 15 and 16, find the slope and y intercept of the straight line and draw a graph of the line.

15. $y = 12x - 4$ **16.** $y = -2x + 11$

Writing

17. The sales of skis by a ski manufacturer are shown for a two year period in Fig. 5•23. Study the graph and write a verbal summary of the sales pattern for the period shown.

Team Project

18. Graph the function

$$y = 1.24x^3 + 0.482x^2 + 2.85x + 0.394$$

Find to the nearest hundredth any roots or maximum and minimum points.

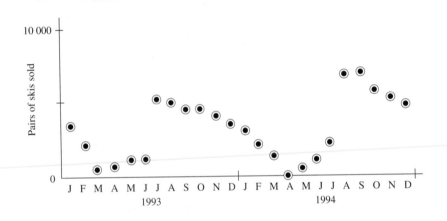

FIGURE 5•23 Ski Sales for 1993–1994

6

Geometry

O B J E C T I V E S

When you have completed this chapter, you should be able to:

- Find the angles formed by intersecting straight lines.
- Solve practical problems that require finding the sides and angles of right triangles.
- Solve practical problems in which the area of a triangle or quadrilateral must be found.
- Solve problems involving the circumference, diameter, or area of a circle, or a tangent to a circle.
- Compute surface areas and volumes of spheres, cylinders, cones, and other solid figures.

We present in this chapter some of the more useful facts from geometry, together with examples of their use in solving practical problems. Geometrical theorems—provable statements—are treated as facts and are presented almost "cookbook" style, with no proofs given and with the emphasis on the applications of these facts. Our main concern will be the computation of lengths, areas, and volumes of various geometric figures.

Much of the material on angles, triangles, and radian measure will be good preparation for the later chapters on trigonometry.

6•1

FIGURE 6•1

Straight Lines and Angles
Straight Line

A *line segment* is that portion of a straight line lying between two endpoints [Fig. 6•1(a)]. A *ray*, or *half-line*, is the portion of a line lying to one side of a point (endpoint) on the line [Fig. 6•1(b)].

Angles

An *angle* is formed when two rays intersect at their endpoints (Fig. 6•2). The point of intersection is called the *vertex* of the angle, and the two rays are called the *sides* of the angle.

The angle shown in Fig. 6•2 can be *designated* in any of the following ways:

angle ABC angle CBA angle B angle θ

FIGURE 6·2 An angle

FIGURE 6·3 An angle formed by rotation

The symbol ∠ means *angle*, so ∠*B* means angle *B*.

An angle can also be thought of as having been *generated* by a ray turning from some *initial position* to a *terminal position* (Fig. 6·3).

One *revolution* is the amount a ray would turn to return to its original position.

The *units of angular measure* in common use are the *degree* and the *radian* (Sec. 6·4). The *measure* of an angle is the number of units of measure it contains. Two angles are *equal* if they have the same measure.

The *degree* is a unit of angular measure equal to 1/360 of a revolution. Thus, there are 360 degrees in one complete revolution.

Figure 6·4 shows (a) a *right* angle ($\frac{1}{4}$ revolution, or 90°), usually marked with a small square at the vertex; (b) an *acute* angle (less than $\frac{1}{4}$ revolution); (c) an *obtuse* angle (greater than $\frac{1}{4}$ revolution but less than $\frac{1}{2}$ revolution); and (d) a *straight* angle ($\frac{1}{2}$ revolution, or 180°).

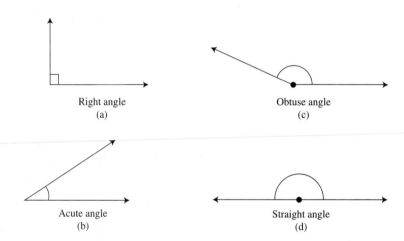

FIGURE 6·4 Types of angles

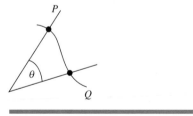

FIGURE 6·5

Two lines at right angles to each other are said to be *perpendicular*. Two angles are called *complementary* if their sum is a right angle, and *supplementary* if their sum is a straight angle.

Two more words we use in reference to angles are *intercept* and *subtend*. In Figure 6·5, we say that the angle θ *intercepts* the section *PQ* of the curve. Conversely, we say that angle θ is *subtended by PQ*.

Angles between Intersecting Lines

Angles *A* and *B* of Figure 6·6 are called *opposite* or *vertical* angles. It should be apparent that *A* and *B* are equal.

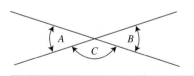

FIGURE 6·6

Opposite angles of two intersecting straight lines are equal.	104

Two angles are called *adjacent* when they have a common side and a common vertex, such as angles *A* and *C* of Figure 6·6. When two lines intersect, the adjacent angles are *supplementary*.

For brevity, we say "angle *A*" instead of the cumbersome but more correct "the measure of angle *A*." We will learn how to convert angles from one system of measurement to another (such as degrees to radians) in Chapter 7.

■ **Example 1:** Find the measure (in degrees) of angles *A* and *B* in the structure shown in Figure 6·7.

FIGURE 6·7

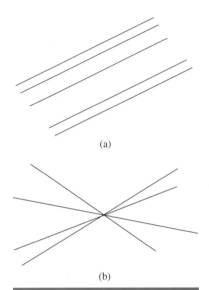

(a)

(b)

FIGURE 6·8 Families of lines

Solution: We see from the diagram that RQ and PS are straight intersecting lines (we will often assume relationships from the diagram rather than prove them). Since angle A is opposite the 34° angle, angle $A = 34°$. Angle B and the 34° angle are supplementary, so

$$B = 180° - 34° = 146°$$

Families of Lines

A *family* of lines is a group of lines that are related to each other in some way. Figure 6·8(a) shows a family of lines, none of which intersect. They are called *parallel*. Figure 6·8(b) shows a family of lines that all pass through the same point, but have different slopes.

In a later chapter, we will talk about *families of curves*.

Transversals

(a)

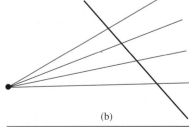

(b)

FIGURE 6·9 Transversals

A *transversal* is a line that intersects a family or system of lines. In Fig. 6·9, the lines labelled T are transversals. In Fig. 6·9(a), two parallel lines, L_1 and L_2, are cut by transversal T. Angles A, B, G, and H are called *exterior* angles, and C, D, E, and F are called *interior* angles. Angles A and E are called *corresponding* angles. Other corresponding angles in Fig. 6·9(a) are C and G, B and F, and D and H. Angles C and F are called *alternate interior angles*, as are D and E. We have a theorem:

If two parallel straight lines are cut by a transversal, corresponding angles are equal, and alternate interior angles are equal.	**105**

Thus, in Figure 6·9(a), $\angle A = \angle E$, $\angle C = \angle G$, $\angle B = \angle F$, and $\angle D = \angle H$. Also, $\angle D = \angle E$ and $\angle C = \angle F$.

━ **Example 2:** The top girder PQ in the structure of Fig. 6•7 is parallel to the ground and angle C is $73°$. Find angle D.

Solution: We have two parallel lines, PQ and RS, cut by transversal PS. By Statement 105

$$\angle D = \angle C = 73°$$

Another useful theorem applies when a number of parallel lines are cut by *two* transversals, such as in Figure 6•10. The portions of the transversals lying between the same parallels are called *corresponding segments*. (In Fig. 6•10, a and b are corresponding segments, c and d are corresponding segments, and e and f are corresponding segments.)

When a number of parallel lines are cut by two transversals, the ratios of corresponding segments on the transversals are equal.	**106**

In Figure 6•10,

$$\frac{a}{b} = \frac{c}{d} = \frac{e}{f}$$

FIGURE 6•10

━ **Example 3:** A portion of a street map is shown in Figure 6•11. Find the distances PQ and QR.

FIGURE 6•11

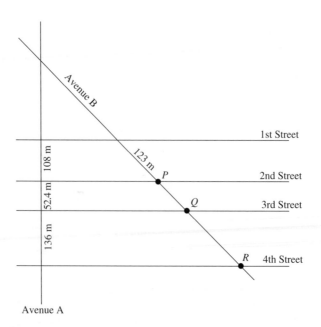

Solution: From Statement 106,

$$\frac{PQ}{52.4} = \frac{123}{108}$$

$$PQ = \frac{123}{108}(52.4) = 59.7 \text{ m}$$

Similarly,

$$\frac{QR}{136} = \frac{123}{108}$$

$$QR = \frac{123}{108}(136) = 155 \text{ m}$$

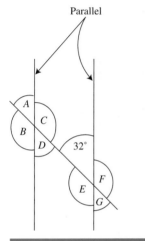

FIGURE 6•13

FIGURE 6•14

FIGURE 6•15

Exercise 1 Straight Lines and Angles

1. Find angle θ in Figure 6•12 (a), (b), and (c).

FIGURE 6•12

2. Find angles A, B, C, D, E, F, and G in Figure 6•13.

3. Find distance x in Figure 6•14.

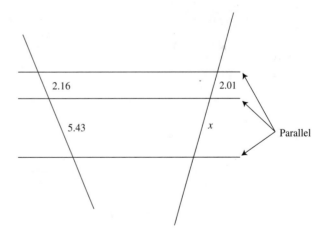

4. Find angles A and B in Figure 6•15.

FIGURE 6·16

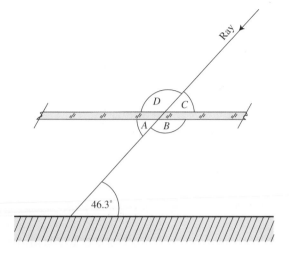

The *angle of elevation* of some object above the observer is the angle between the line of sight to that object and the horizontal, as in Chaper 7, Figure 7·13.

5. On a certain day, the angle of elevation of the sun is 46.3° (Figure 6·16). Find the angles *A*, *B*, *C*, and *D* that a ray of sunlight makes with a horizontal sheet of glass.

6. Three parallel steel cables hang from a girder to the deck of a bridge (Fig. 6·17). Find distance *x*.

FIGURE 6·17

6·2

Triangles

Polygons

A *polygon* is a plane figure formed by three or more line segments, called the *sides* of the polygon, joined at their endpoints, as in Figure 6·18. The points where the sides meet are called *vertices*. We say that the sides of a polygon are equal if their measures (lengths) are equal. If all the sides and angles of a polygon are equal, it is called a *regular* polygon, as in Figure 6·19. The *perimeter* of a polygon is simply the sum of its sides.

FIGURE 6•18 A polygon

FIGURE 6•18 A polygon

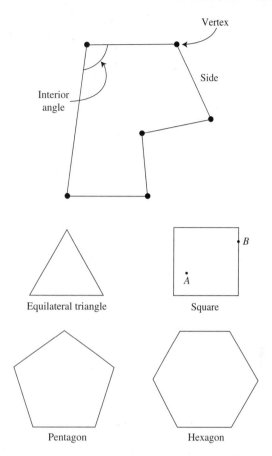

FIGURE 6•19 Some regular polygons

Equilateral triangle

Square

Pentagon

Hexagon

Modern definitions of plane figures exclude the *interior* as part of the figure. Thus, in Figure 6•19, point *A* is *not* on the square, while point *B is* on the square. The interior is referred to as a *region*.

Sum of Interior Angles

A polygon of *n* sides has *n* interior angles, such as those shown in Figure 6•20. The sum of these angles is given by Rule 112.

Interior Angles of a Polygon	Sum of Angles $= (n - 2)180°$	**112**

■ **Example 4:** Find angle θ in Figure 6•20.

FIGURE 6•20

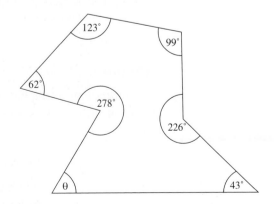

Solution: The polygon shown has seven sides, so $n = 7$. By Eq. 112,

$$\text{sum of angles} = (7 - 2)(180°) = 900°$$

Adding the six given angles gives us

$$278° + 62° + 123° + 99° + 226° + 43° = 831°$$

So

$$\theta = 900° - 831° = 69°$$

Triangles

A *triangle* is a polygon having three *sides*. The angles between the sides are the *interior angles* of the triangle, usually referred to as simply the angles of the triangle.

A *scalene* triangle (Figure 6•21) has no equal sides, an *isosceles* triangle has two equal sides, and an *equilateral* triangle has three equal sides.

An *acute* triangle has three acute angles, an *obtuse* triangle has one obtuse angle, and a *right* triangle has one right angle.

FIGURE 6•21 Types of triangles

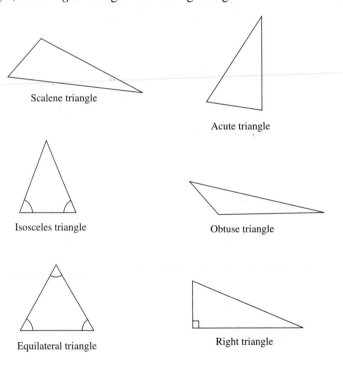

Scalene triangle

Acute triangle

Isosceles triangle

Obtuse triangle

Equilateral triangle

Right triangle

Altitude and Base

The *altitude* of a triangle is the perpendicular distance from a vertex to the opposite side called the *base*, or an extension of that side (Fig. 6•22).

FIGURE 6•22

Altitude

Base

Altitude

Base

Area of a Triangle

We make use of a familiar formula:

The measuring of areas, volumes, and lengths is sometimes referred to as *mensuration*.

Area of a Triangle	Area equals one-half the product of the base and the altitude to that base: $$A = \frac{bh}{2}$$	137

▬ **Example 5:** Find the area of the triangle in Figure 6•22 if the base is 52.0 and the altitude is 48.0.

Solution: By Eq. 137,

$$\text{area} = \frac{52.0(48.0)}{2} = 1250 \text{ (rounded)}$$ ▬

Named for Hero (or Heron) of Alexandria, a Greek mathematician and physicist of the 1st century A.D.

If the altitude is not known but we have instead the lengths of the three sides, we may use *Hero's formula*. If a, b, and c are the lengths of the sides,

Hero's Formula	Area of triangle $= \sqrt{s(s-a)(s-b)(s-c)}$ where s is half the perimeter $$s = \frac{a+b+c}{2}$$	138

▬ **Example 6:** Find the area of a triangle having sides of lengths 3.25, 2.16, and 5.09.

Solution: We first find s, which is half the perimeter,

$$s = \frac{3.25 + 2.16 + 5.09}{2} = 5.25$$

$$Area = \sqrt{5.25(5.25 - 3.25)(5.25 - 2.16)(5.25 - 5.09)} = 2.28$$ ▬

Sum of the Angles

An extremely useful relationship exists between the interior angles of any triangle.

Sum of the Angles	The sum of the three interior angles A, B, and C of any triangle is 180 degrees. $$A + B + C = 180°$$	139

▬ **Example 7:** Find angle A in a triangle if the other two interior angles are 38° and 121°.

Solution: By Eq. 139,

$$A = 180° - 121° - 38° = 21°$$ ▬

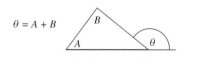

$\theta = A + B$

FIGURE 6·23 An exterior angle

FIGURE 6·24 Congruent triangles

$$\frac{a}{d} = \frac{b}{e} = \frac{c}{f}$$

FIGURE 6·25 Similar triangles

We will see in a later chapter that these relationships also hold for similar figures *other than* triangles, and for similar *solids* as well.

Exterior Angles

An exterior angle is the angle between the side of a triangle and an extension of the adjacent side, such as angle θ in Figure 6·23. The following theorem applies to exterior angles:

Exterior Angle of a Triangle	An exterior angle equals the sum of the two opposite interior angles $\theta = A + B$	**142**

Congruent Triangles

Two triangles (or any other polygons, for that matter) are said to be *congruent* if the angles and sides of one are equal to the angles and sides of the other, as in Figure 6·24.

Similar Triangles

Two triangles are said to be *similar* if they have the *same shape*, even if one triangle is larger than the other. This means that the angles of one of the triangles must equal the angles of the other triangle, as in Figure 6·25. Sides that lie between the same pair of equal angles are called *corresponding sides*, such as sides a and d. Sides b and e, as well as sides c and f, are also corresponding side. We have two theorems:

Similar Triangles	If two angles of a triangle are equal to two angles of another triangle, their third angles must be equal, and the triangles are similar.	**143**
	If two triangles are similar, their corresponding sides are in proportion.	**144**

■ **Example 8:** Two beams, *AB* and *CD*, in the framework of Figure 6·26 are parallel. Find distance *AE*.

FIGURE 6·26

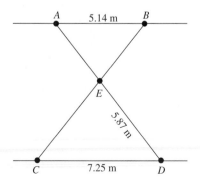

Solution: By Statement 104, we know that angle *AEB* equals angle *DEC*. Also, by statement 105, angle *ABE* equals angle *ECD*. Thus, triangle *ABE* is similar to triangle *CDE*. Since *AE* and *ED* are corresponding sides,

$$\frac{AE}{5.87} = \frac{5.14}{7.25}$$

$$AE = 5.87\left(\frac{5.14}{7.25}\right) = 4.16 \text{ m}$$

Right Triangles

In a right triangle (Fig. 6•27) the side opposite the right angle is called the *hypotenuse*, and the other two sides are called *legs*. The legs and the hypotenuse are related by the well-known *Pythagorean theorem*:

$a^2 + b^2 = c^2$

FIGURE 6•27 The Pythogorean theorem, named for the Greek mathematician Pythagoras (ca. 580–500 B.C.)

Pythagorean Theorem	The square of the hypotenuse of a right triangle is equal to the sum of the squares of the two legs: $a^2 + b^2 = c^2$	145

Example 9: A right triangle has legs of length 6 units and 11 units. Find the length of the hypotenuse.

Solution: Letting c = the length of the hypotenuse,

$$c^2 = 6^2 + 11^2 = 36 + 121 = 157$$

$$c = \sqrt{157} = 12.5 \quad \text{(rounded)}$$

Example 10: A right triangle has a hypotenuse 5 units in length and a leg of 3 units. Find the length of the other leg.

Solution:

$$a^2 = c^2 - b^2$$
$$= 5^2 - 3^2 = 16$$
$$a = \sqrt{16} = 4$$

The 3–4–5 right triangle is a good one to remember.

Common Error	Remember that the Pythagorean theorem applies *only to right triangles*. Later we will use trigonometry to find the sides and angles of *oblique* triangles (triangles with no right angles).

Some Special Triangles

In a *30–60–90* right triangle [Fig. 6•28(a)], the side opposite the 30° angle is half the length of the hypotenuse.

A *45° right triangle* [Fig. 6•28(b)] is also *isosceles*, and the hypotenuse is $\sqrt{2}$ times the length of either side.

FIGURE 6•28 Some special right triangles

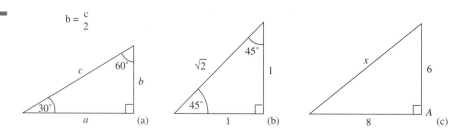

A *3–4–5 triangle* is a right triangle in which the sides are in the ratio of 3 to 4 to 5.

■ **Example 11:** In Figure 6•28(c), side *x* is 10 units. ■

Exercise 2 Triangles

For practice, do these problems using only geometry, even if you know some trigonometry.

1. What is the cost, to the nearest dollar, of a triangular piece of land whose base is 828 m and altitude 412 m, at $1125 a hectare?

2. A house (Fig. 6•29) is 7.30 m wide, the ridge is 2.74 m higher than the side walls, and the rafters project 0.460 m beyond the sides of the house. How long are the rafters?

FIGURE 6•29

To help you solve each problem, draw a diagram and label it completely. Look for rectangles, special triangles, or right triangles contained in the diagram. Be sure to look up any word that may be unfamiliar, such as "diagonal," "radius," or "diameter."

3. What is the length of a handrail to a flight of stairs (Fig. 6•30) if each step is 305 mm wide and 223 mm high?

4. At $3.50 a square metre, find to the nearest dollar the cost of paving a triangular court, its base being 32.0 m and its altitude 19.2 m.

5. A vertical pole 15.0 m high is supported by three guy wires attached to the top and reaching the ground at distances of 20.0 m, 30.0 m, and 60.0 m from the foot of the pole. What are the lengths of the wires?

6. A ladder 12.0 m long reaches to the top of a building when its foot stands 5.00 m from the building. How high is the building?

7. Two streets, one 16.2 m wide and the other 31.5 m wide, cross at right angles. What is the diagonal distance between the opposite corners?

8. A room is 6.0 m long, 5.0 m wide, and 4.0 m high. What is the diagonal distance from one of the lower corners to the opposite upper corner?

FIGURE 6•30

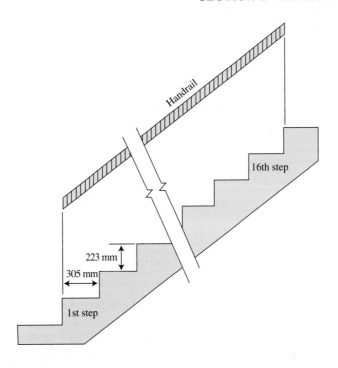

9. What is the side of a square whose diagonal is 50.0 m?
10. A rectangular park 125 m long and 233 m wide has a straight walk running through it joining diagonally opposite corners. What is the length of the walk?
11. A ladder 10.0 m long stands flat against the side of a building. How many metres must it be drawn out at the bottom so that the top may be lowered 1.30 m?
12. The slant height of a cone (Fig. 6•31) is 552 mm and the diameter of the base is 465 mm. How high is the cone?
13. A house (Fig. 6•32) that is 15.2 m long and 12.2 m wide has a pyramidal roof whose height is 4.60 m. Find the length PQ of a hip rafter that reaches from a corner of the building to the vertex of the roof.

FIGURE 6•31

FIGURE 6·32

FIGURE 6·33

We have not studied the hexagon as such, but you can solve Problems 15 and 16 by dividing the hexagon into equal right triangles. This also works for other regular polygons.

FIGURE 6·34

14. An antenna, 125 m high, is supported by cables of length L that reach the ground at a distance D from the base of the antenna. If D is three-quarters of the length of a cable, find L and D.

15. A hex head bolt (Fig. 6·33) measures 12.7 mm across the flats. Find the distance x across the corners.

16. A 1.00-m-long piece of hexagonal steel stock measuring 30.0 mm across the flats has a 10.0-mm-diameter hole running lengthwise from end to end. Find the mass of the bar. (Density $= 7850$ kg/m³.)

17. Find the distance AB between the centers of the two rollers in Figure 6·34.

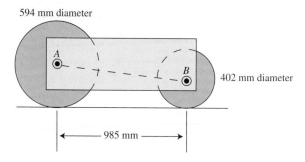

18. A 60° screw thread is measured by placing three wires in the thread and measuring the distance T, as in Figure 6·35. Find the distance D if the wire diameters are 2.500 mm and the distance T is 38.00 mm, assuming that the root of the thread is a sharp V shape.

19. A highway, Figure 6·36, cuts a corner from a parcel of land. Find the number of hectares in the triangular lot ABC (1 hectare $= 10\ 000$ m²). (Use Eq. 138.)

20. A surveyor starts at A in Figure 6·37 and lays out lines AB, BC, and CA. Find the three interior angles of the triangle.

21. A beam AB is supported by two crossed beams (Fig. 6·38). Find distance x.

22. Find dimension x in Figure 6·39.

23. Find dimension x on the bevelled end of the shaft in Figure 6·40.

FIGURE 6·35 Measuring a screw thread "over wires"

FIGURE 6·36

FIGURE 6·37

FIGURE 6·38

FIGURE 6•39

FIGURE 6•40

Computer

24. Write a program that will accept as input any two sides of a right triangle and will then display or print the length of the third side.

25. Write a program that will accept as input the three sides of any triangle and compute and display the area by Hero's formula.

6•3

Quadrilaterals

A *quadrilateral* is a polygon having four sides. The familiar figures shown in Figure 6•41 are quadrilaterals. The formula for the area of each region is given right on the figure. Lengths of line segments are measured in units of length (such as metres and millimetres), and areas of regions are measured in *square* units (such as square metres and square millimetres).

For the *parallelogram*, opposite sides are parallel and equal. Opposite angles are equal, and each diagonal cuts the other diagonal into two equal parts (they *bisect* each other).

The *rhombus* is also a parallelogram, so the previous facts apply to it as well. In addition, its diagonals bisect each other at *right angles* and bisect the angles of the rhombus.

FIGURE 6•41 Quadrilaterals

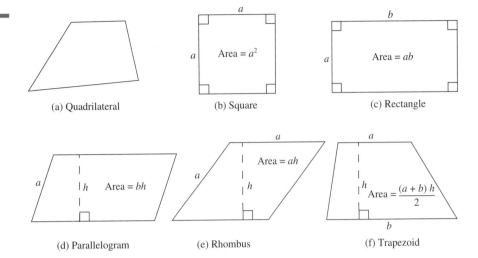

(a) Quadrilateral   (b) Square   (c) Rectangle

(d) Parallelogram   (e) Rhombus   (f) Trapezoid

FIGURE 6•42

FIGURE 6•43

FIGURE 6•44

Work to the nearest dollar throughout this exercise, where costs are involved.

The *trapezoid* has two parallel sides, which are called the bases, and the altitude is the distance between the bases.

■ **Example 12:** A solar collector array consists of six rectangular panels, each 1150 mm × 2350 mm, each with a blocked rectangular area (needed for connections) measuring 120 mm × 223 mm. Find the total collecting area in square mm.

Estimate: If the panels were 1200 mm × 2400 mm, or 3×10^6 mm^2 each, six of them would be $6 \times 3 \times 10^6$) or 18×10^6 mm^2. Since we have estimated each dimension larger than it really is, and have also ignored the blocked areas, we would expect this answer to be larger than the actual area.

Solution:

The area of each panel is $1150 \times 2350 = 2.7 \times 10^6$ mm^2

The blocked area is 0.0267×10^6 mm^2

Subtracting yields

Collecting area per panel = $(2.7 - 0.0267) \times 10^6$ mm^2

There are six panels, so

Total collecting area = $6 \times (2.673 \times 10^6)$ mm^2

$= 16.0$ m^2 ■

Exercise 3   Quadrilaterals

1. Find the area of the parallelogram in Figure 6•42.
2. Find the area of the rhombus in Figure 6•43.
3. Find the area of the trapezoid in Figure 6•44.
4. Find the cost of shingling a flat roof, 19.8 m long and 13.7 m wide, at $9.50 per square metre.
5. What will be the cost of flagging a sidewalk 95 metres long and 2.0 metres wide at $15.75 per square metre?
6. How many 230-mm-square tiles are needed to cover a floor 14.6 metres by 3.65 metres?

7. What will it cost to carpet a floor, 6.25 m by 7.18 m, at $7.75 per square metre?

8. How many rolls of paper, each 7.30 m long and 460 mm wide, are needed to paper the walls of a room 4.82 m by 4.25 m and 3.00 m high, deducting 11.5 square metres for doors and windows?

9. What is the cost of plastering the walls and ceiling of a room 12 m long, 11 m wide, and 6.7 m high, at $8.50 per square metre, allowing 13.0 m² for doors, windows, and baseboard?

10. What will it cost to cement a cellar 7.70 m long and 5.65 m wide, at $3.20 per square metre?

11. Find the cost of lining a topless rectangular tank 1.73 m long, 1.37 m wide, and 1.22 m deep, with zinc, mass 50.0 kg per square metre and costing $3.55 per kg installed.

6·4 The Circle

Circumference and Area

For a circle of diameter d and radius r (Fig. 6·45),

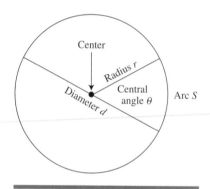

FIGURE 6·45 A circle

Circle of Radius r and Diameter d $\pi \cong 3.1416$	Circumference $= 2\pi r = \pi d$	113
	Area $= \pi r^2 = \dfrac{\pi d^2}{4}$	114

■ **Example 13:** The circumference and area of a 257-mm-radius circle are

$$C = 2\pi(257) = 1615 \text{ mm}$$

and

$$A = \pi(257)^2 = 207\,500 \text{ mm}^2$$

■

Radian Measure

We cover radian measure, and compute areas of sectors and segments in Chapter 16.

A *central angle* (Fig. 6·45) is one whose vertex is at the center of the circle. An *arc* is a portion of the circumference of a circle. If an arc is marked off along a circle with a length equal to the radius of the circle, the central angle subtended by this arc is defined as one *radian*.

Other Parts of a Circle

A *sector* (Fig. 6·46) is the region bounded by two radii and one of the arcs that they intercept. A *chord* is a line segment connecting two points on the circle. A *segment* is the region bounded by a chord and one of the arcs that it intercepts. When a circle has two intersecting chords, the following theorem applies:

FIGURE 6·46

Intersecting Chords	If two chords in a circle intersect, the product of the parts of one chord is equal to the product of the parts of the other chord.	121

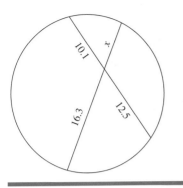

FIGURE 6·47

■ **Example 14:** Find the length x in Figure 6·47.

Solution: By Statement 121,

$$16.3x = 10.1(12.5)$$

$$x = \frac{10.1(12.5)}{16.3} = 7.75$$
■

Tangents and Secants

A *tangent* (Fig. 6·48) is a straight line that touches a circle at just one point. A *secant* cuts the circle at *two* points. A chord is that portion of a secant lying within the circle.

We have two very useful theorems about tangents. First:

Tangents to a Circle	A tangent is perpendicular to the radius drawn through the point of contact.	**119**

Thus, in Figure 6·48, angle *OPB* is a right angle.

FIGURE 6·48 Tangent and secant

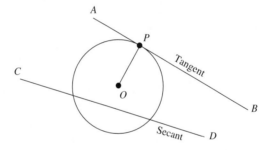

■ **Example 15:** Find the distance *OP* in Figure 6·49.

Solution: By Theorem 119 we know that angle *PQO* is a right angle. Also,

$$PQ = 342 - 115 = 2270 \text{ mm}$$

So, by the Pythagorean theorem,

$$OP = \sqrt{(115)^2 + (227)^2} = 2540 \text{ mm}$$
■

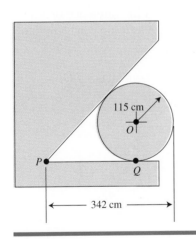

FIGURE 6·49

The second theorem is:

Tangents to a Circle	Two tangents drawn to a circle from a point outside the circle are equal, and they make equal angles with a line from the point to the center of the circle.	**120**

Thus, in Figure 6·50,

$$AB = AD \qquad \text{and} \qquad \angle BAC = \angle CAD$$

FIGURE 6·50

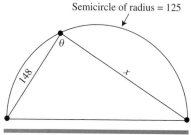

Semicircle of radius = 125

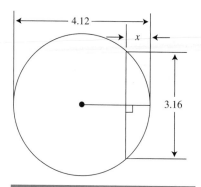

FIGURE 6•51

FIGURE 6•52

By cutting from both sides, it is possible to fell a tree whose diameter is twice the length of the chain-saw bar.

FIGURE 6•53

FIGURE 6•54

Semicircle

The angle between two lines drawn from the two ends of the diameter of a semicircle to any single point on the circumference will be a right angle.	**118**

■ **Example 16:** Find the distance x in Figure 6•51.

Solution: By Statement 118 we know that $\theta = 90°$. Then, by Eq. 145,

$$x = \sqrt{(250)^2 - (148)^2} = 201$$
■

Exercise 4 The Circle

1. In a park is a circular fountain whose basin is 22.5 m in circumference. What is the diameter of the basin?
2. How much larger is the side of a square circumscribing a circle 1550 mm in diameter than a square inscribed in the same circle?
3. The area of the bottom of a circular pan is 126 000 mm². What is its diameter?
4. Find the diameter of a circular solar pond enclosing 125 m².
5. What is the circumference of a circular lake 33.0 m in diameter?
6. The radius of a circle is 5.00 m. Find the diameter of another circle containing four times the area of the first.
7. The distance around a circular park is $40\overline{0}0$ m. How many hectares does it contain?
8. A woodcutter uses a tape measure and finds the circumference of a tree to be 2.40 m. Assuming the tree to be circular, determine what length of chain-saw bar is needed to fell the tree.
9. Find the distance x in Figure 6•52.
10. In Figure 6•53, distance OP is 8.65 units. Find the distance PQ.

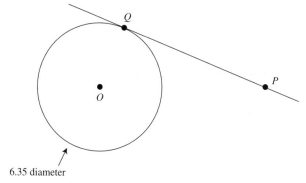

6.35 diameter

11. Figure 6•54 shows a semicircle with a diameter of 105. Find distance PQ.

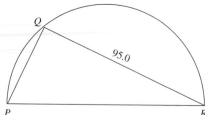

1 pascal = 1 N/m²

$$\text{pressure} = \frac{\text{force}}{\text{area}}$$

FIGURE 6•55

FIGURE 6•56

FIGURE 6•57

12. What must be the diameter d of a cylindrical piston so that a pressure of 750 000 N/m² (750 kPa) on its circular end will result in a total force of 15 000 N?

13. Find the length of belt needed to connect the three 150-mm-diameter pulleys in Figure 6•55. *Hint: The total* curved *portion of the belt is equal to the circumference of one pulley.*

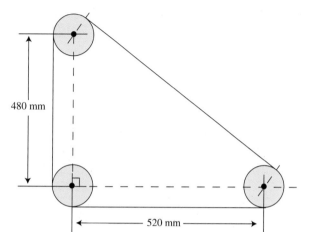

14. Seven cables of equal diameter are contained within a circular conduit, as in Figure 6•56. If the inside diameter of the conduit is 256 mm, find the cross-sectional area *not* occupied by the cables.

15. A circular tile walk is 1.00 m wide and surrounds a circular garden 21.0 m in diameter. Find the area of the tiled walk.

16. Figure 6•57 shows two of the supports for a hemispherical dome. Find the length of girder AB.

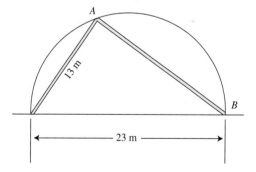

17. A certain car tire is 785 mm in diameter. How far will the car move forward with one revolution of the wheel?

18. Archimedes claimed that the area of a circle is equal to the area of a triangle that has an altitude equal to the radius of the circle and a base equal to the circumference of the circle. Use the formulas of this chapter to show that this is true.

Computer

19. A lens in a certain optical instrument has a diameter of 75.0 mm. This diameter is reduced by a series of circular "stops" (Fig. 6•58), with each stop reducing the area of the opening by 15% of its previous area. Write a program or use a spreadsheet that will compute the required diameter of each stop, and will display both the stop diameter and the area in mm². Continue until the stop diameter falls below 20 mm.

FIGURE 6·58

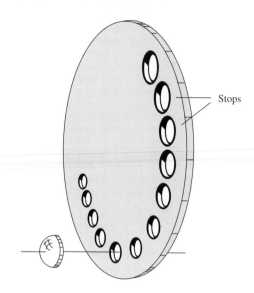

Stops

Volumes and Areas of Solids

Volume

The volume of a solid is a measure of the space it occupies or encloses. It is measured in cubic units (mm³ or m³) or, usually for liquids, in litres (L). Our main task in this chapter is to compute the volumes of various solids.

Area

We speak about three different kinds of areas. *Surface area* will be the *total* area of the surface of a solid, including the ends, or bases. The *lateral area*, which will be defined later for each solid, does *not* include the areas of the bases. The *cross-sectional area* is the area of the plane figure obtained when we slice the solid in a specified way.

The formulas for the areas and volumes of some common solids are given in Figure 6·59.

Note that the formulas for the cone and the frustum of a cone are the same as for the pyramid and the frustum of a pyramid.

■ **Example 17:** Find the volume of a cone having a base area of 12 500 mm² and an altitude of 112 mm.

Solution: By Eq. 130,

$$\text{Volume} = \frac{12\ 500(112)}{3} = 467\ 000 \text{ mm}^3$$

■

FIGURE 6•59 Some solids, with formulas and formula numbers

	Cube	Volume $= a^3$	122
		Surface area $= 6a^2$	123
	Rectangular parallel-epiped	Volume $= lwh$	124
		Surface area $= 2(lw + hw + lh)$	125
	Any cylinder or prism	Volume $=$ (area of base)(altitude)	126
	Right cylinder or prism	Lateral area $=$ (perimeter of base)(altitude) (not including bases)	127
	Sphere	Volume $= \frac{4}{3}\pi r^3$	128
		Surface area $= 4\pi r^2$	129
	Any cone or pyramid	Volume $= \frac{h}{3}$ (area of base)	130
	Right circular cone or regular pyramid	Lateral area $= \frac{s}{2}$ (perimeter of base)	133
	Any cone or pyramid	Volume $= \frac{h}{3}(A_1 + A_2 + \sqrt{A_1 A_2})$	132
	Right circular cone or regular pyramid	Lateral area $= \frac{s}{2}$(sum of base perimeters) $= \frac{s}{2}(P_1 + P_2)$	133

Dimension

A geometric figure that has length but no area or volume (such as a line or a curve) is said to be of *one dimension*. A geometric figure having area but not volume (such as a circle) is said to have *two* dimensions, or to be *two dimensional*. A figure having volume (such as a sphere) is said to have *three* dimensions.

Fractals

Named for the Swedish mathematician Helge von Koch who constructed this curve in 1904

Can you imagine a curve so complex that it is misleading to call it one dimensional? The coastline of England is often given as an example. Another example is the *Koch Snowflake*, Figure 6•60(d).

We start with an equilateral triangle, as in Figure 6•60(a). On each of the three sides we place another equilateral triangle whose side is $\frac{1}{3}$ that of the sides of the original triangle [Fig. 6•60(b)]. Our figure now has 12 sides, and a perimeter $\frac{4}{3}$ times the original perimeter. Next, on each of the 12 new sides we place an equilateral triangle whose side is $\frac{1}{3}$ the length of the sides of the

FIGURE 6·60

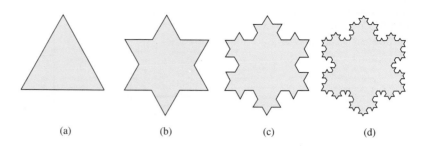

(a) (b) (c) (d)

The term *fractal* was coined by Benoit B. Mandelbrot to describe objects that have dimensions other than one, two, or three.

preceding triangle [Fig.6·60(c)]. We continue indefinitely, and get a boundary that has a dimension not of one, but of approximately 1.2619.

The snowflake curve is called a *fractal*.

Exercise 5 Volumes and Areas of Solids

Prism and Rectangular Parallelepiped

For some of these problems we need Eq. A43: the weight (or mass) equals the volume of the solid times the density of the material.

1. Find the volume of the triangular prism in Figure 6·61.
2. A 25.0 mm cube of steel is placed in a surface grinding machine, and the vertical feed set so that 0.130 mm of metal is removed from the top of the cube at each cut. How many cuts are needed to reduce the mass of the cube by 0.017 kg?

The density of steel ≅ 7650 kg/m³.

3. A rectangular tank is being filled with liquid, with each cubic metre of liquid increasing the depth by 20.0 mm. The length of the tank is 12.0 m.
   (a) What is the width of the tank?
   (b) How many cubic metres will be required to fill the tank to a depth of 3.00 m?

FIGURE 6·61

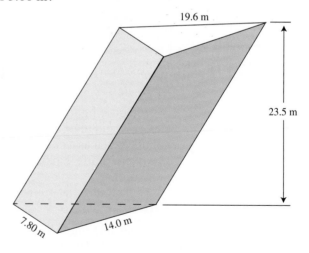

19.6 m

23.5 m

7.80 m   14.0 m

4. How many loads of gravel will be needed to cover 3.50 km of roadbed, 100$\overline{0}$ m wide, to a depth of 76.2 mm, if one truckload contains 8.00 m³ of gravel?

Cylinder

5. Find the volume of the cylinder in Figure 6·62.
6. Find the volume and lateral area of a right circular cylinder having a base radius of 128 and a height of 285.

FIGURE 6·62

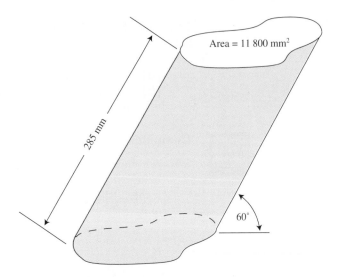

7. A 2.13 m long piece of steel tubing has an outside diameter of 90.0 mm and mass 57.0 kg. Find the wall thickness.
8. A certain bushing is in the shape of a hollow cylinder 18.0 mm in diameter and 25.0 mm long, with an axial hole 12.0 mm in diameter. If the density of the material from which they are made is 7150 kg/m^3, find the mass of 1000 bushings.
9. A steel gear is to be lightened by drilling holes through the gear. The gear is 90.0 mm thick. Find the diameter d of the holes if each hole is to remove 0.34 kg.

The engine *displacement* is the total volume swept out by all the pistons.

10. A certain gasoline engine has four cylinders, each with a bore of 82.0 mm and a piston stroke of 95.0 mm. Find the engine displacement in litres.

Cone and Pyramid

11. The circumference of the base of a right circular cone is 1020 mm and the slant height is 965 mm. What is the area of the lateral surface?
12. Find the volume of a circular cone whose altitude is 240 mm and whose base diameter is 310 mm.
13. Find the mass of the mast of a ship, its height being 15.24 m, the circumference at one end 1.524 m and at the other 0.914 m, if the density of the wood is 642.0 kg/m^3.
14. The slant height of a right pyramid is $28\overline{0}$ mm, and the base is a 102 mm square. Find the area of the entire surface.
15. How many cubic metres are in a piece of timber 10.0 m long, one end being a 382 mm square, and the other a 302 mm square?
16. Find the total surface area and volume of a tapered steel roller 4.0 m long and having end diameters of 310 mm and 380 mm.

Sphere

17. Find the volume and surface area of a sphere having a radius of 744.
18. Find the volume and radius of a sphere having a surface area of 462.
19. Find the surface area and radius of a sphere that has a volume of 5.88.

A *great circle* of a sphere is one that has the same diameter as the sphere.

20. How many great circles of a sphere would have the same area as that of the surface of the sphere?

21. Find the mass in kilograms of 100 steel balls each 63 mm in diameter.

22. A spherical radome encloses a volume of $90\overline{0}0$ m³. Assume that the sphere is complete.

(a) Find the radome radius, r.

(b) If constructed of a material of mass 2.00 kg/m², find the mass of the radome.

Computer

23. A conical tank (Fig. 6•63) that has a base diameter equal to its height is being filled with water at the rate of 2.25 m³/h. Write a program or use a spreadsheet that will compute and display the volume of water in the tank (m³) and the depth D (m), for every 5 m., up to 1 h.

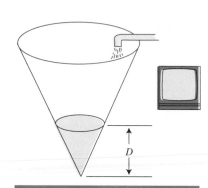

FIGURE 6•63

CHAPTER 6   REVIEW PROBLEMS

1. A rocket ascends at an angle of 60.0° with the horizontal. After 1 min, it is directly over a point that is a horizontal distance of 20.0 km from the launch point. Find the speed of the rocket.

2. A rectangular beam 410 mm thick is cut from a log 510 mm in diameter. Find the greatest depth beam that can be obtained.

3. A cylindrical tank 4.00 m in diameter is placed with its axis vertical and is partially filled with water. A spherical diving bell is completely immersed in the tank, causing the water level to rise 1.00 m. Find the diameter of the diving bell.

4. Two vertical piers are 80 m apart and support a circular bridge arch. The highest point of the arch is 10 m higher than the piers. Find the radius of the arch.

5. Two antenna masts are $1\overline{0}$ m and 15 m high and are 12 m apart. How long a wire is needed to connect the tops of the two masts?

6. Find the area and side of a rhombus whose diagonals are $1\overline{0}0$ and 140.

7. Find the area of a triangle that has sides of length 573, 638, and 972.

8. Two concentric circles have radii of 5.00 and 12.0. Find the length of a chord of the larger circle, which is tangent to the smaller circle.

9. A belt that does not cross goes around two pulleys, each with a radius of 120 mm and whose centers are 230 mm apart. Find the length of the belt.

10. A regular triangular pyramid has an altitude of 12.0 m, and the base is 4.00 m on a side. Find the area of a section made by a plane parallel to the base and 4.00 m from the vertex.

11. A fence parallel to one side of a triangular field cuts a second side into segments of 15.0 m and 21.0 m long. The length of the third side is 42.0 m. Find the length of the shorter segment of the third side.

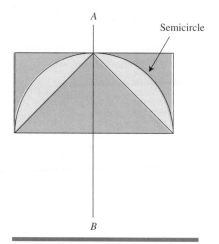

FIGURE 6•64

12. When Figure 6•64 is rotated about axis AB, we generate a cone inscribed in a hemisphere which is itself inscribed in a cylinder. Show that the volumes of these three solids are in the ratio 1:2:3. (Archimedes was so pleased with this discovery, it is said, that he ordered this figure to be engraved on his tomb.)

13. Four interior angles of a certain irregular pentagon are 38°, 96°, 112°, and 133°. Find the fifth interior angle.

14. Find the area of a trapezoid whose parallel sides have lengths of 837 m and 583 m and are separated by a perpendicular distance of 746 m.

15. A plastic drinking cup has a base diameter of 49.00 mm, is 63.00 mm wide at the top, and is 86.00 mm tall. Find the volume of the cup.

16. A spherical balloon is 5.30 m in diameter and is made of a material mass 0.127 kg/m² of surface area. Find the volume of the balloon and the mass of the balloon material.

17. Find the area of a triangle whose base is 982 mm and whose altitude is 1370 mm.

18. Find the volume of a sphere of radius 338 mm.

19. Find the area of a parallelogram of base 39.2 m and height 29.3 m.

20. In "The Musgrave Ritual," Sherlock Holmes calculates the length of the shadow of an elm tree that is no longer standing. He does know that the elm was 19.5 m high and that the shadow was cast at the instant that the sun was grazing the top of a certain oak tree. Holmes held a 1.80 m-long fishing rod vertical and measured the length of its shadow at the proper instant. It was 2.44 m long. How long was the shadow of the elm?

21. Find the volume of a cylinder with base radius 223 mm and height 562 mm.

22. Find the surface area of a sphere having a diameter of $99\overline{0}$ mm.

23. Find the volume of a right circular cone with base diameter 865 mm and height 1590 mm.

24. Find the volume of a box measuring 890 mm × 970 mm × 1840 mm.

25. Find the volume of a triangular prism having a length of 46.5 mm if the area of one end is $250\overline{0}$ mm².

26. To find the diameter of a circle when the center is inaccessible, a scale can be placed as in Figure 6•65, and the chord c and the perpendicular distance h measured. Find the radius of the curve if the chord length is 82.5 mm and h is 11.6 mm.

Writing

27. Write a section in an instruction manual for machinists on how to find the root diameter of a screw thread (Fig. 6•35, page 168) by measuring "over wires." Your entry should have two parts. First, a "how to" section giving step-by-step instructions, and then a "theory" section explaining why this method works. Keep the entry to one page or less.

Team Projects

28. Actually use the method that Sherlock Holmes used in "The Musgrave Ritual," Problem 20, to find the height of a flagpole or building on your campus. Find some way of checking your result.

29. Estimate which weighs more, a million dollars in dollar bills, or a million dollars in gold.

30. Writing about trees, Leonardo da Vinci said that "every division of the branches, when joined together, adds up to the thickness of the branch at their meeting point." (From the Codex Urbino.) In other words, the sum of the diameters at B, in Fig. 6•66, should be approximately equal to the diameter at A, and also be equal to the sum of the diameters at C. Try to verify this by actual measurement on some tree branches, assuming that the branch cross-sections are circular. Also compare the sum of the *areas* at A, B, and C.

FIGURE 6•65

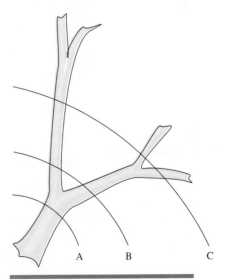

FIGURE 6•66

7

Right Triangles and Vectors

When you have completed this chapter, you should be able to:

- Convert angles between decimal degrees, radians, and degrees, minutes, and seconds.
- Find the trigonometric functions of an angle.
- Find the acute angle that has a given trigonometric function.
- Find the missing sides and angles of a right triangle.
- Solve practical problems involving the right triangle.
- Resolve a vector into components, and, conversely, combine components into a resultant vector.
- Solve practical problems using vectors.

With this chapter we begin our study of trigonometry, the branch of mathematics that enables us to solve triangles. The trigonometric functions are introduced here and are used to solve right triangles. Other kinds of triangles (oblique triangles) are discussed in Chapter 15, and other applications of trigonometry are given in Chapters 16, 17, and 18.

We build on what we learned about triangles in Chapter 5, mainly the Pythagorean theorem and the fact that the sum of the angles of a triangle is 180°. Here we make use of coordinate axes, described in Section 5•1.

Also introduced in this chapter are vectors, the study of which will be continued in Chapter 15.

7•1   Angles and Their Measures

Angles Formed by Rotation

We can think of an angle as the figure generated by a ray rotating from some initial position (Fig. 7•1) to some terminal position. We usually consider angles formed by rotation in the *counterclockwise* direction as *positive*, and angles formed by *clockwise* rotation as *negative*. A rotation of one *revolution* brings the ray back to its initial position.

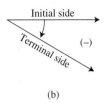

(a)   (b)

Degrees, Minutes, and Seconds

The degree (°) is a unit of angular measure equal to 1/360 of a revolution; thus, 360° = one revolution. A fractional part of a degree may be expressed as a common fraction (like $36\frac{1}{2}°$), as a decimal (28.74°), or as *minutes* and *seconds*.

A *minute* (′) is equal to 1/60 of a degree; a *second* (″) is equal to 1/60 of a minute, or 1/3600 of a degree.

Note that minutes or seconds less than 10 are written with an initial zero. Thus 6′ is written 06′.

■ **Example 1:** Some angles written in degrees, minutes, and seconds are

$$85°18'42''\qquad 62°12'\qquad 69°55'25.4''\qquad 75°06'03''$$ ■

We will sometimes abbreviate "degrees, minutes, and seconds" as DMS.

Radian Measure

A *central angle* in a circle is one whose vertex is at the center of the circle. An *arc* is a portion of the circle. If an arc is marked off along a circle with a length equal to the radius of the circle, the central angle subtended by this arc is defined as one *radian* (Fig. 7•2). A radian (rad) is a unit of angular measure commonly used in trigonometry. We will study radian measure in detail in Chapter 16.

An arc having a length of twice the radius will subtend a central angle of two radians. Similarly, an arc with a length of 2π times the radius (the circumference) will subtend a central angle of 2π radians. Thus our conversion factor is

$$2\pi \text{ radians} = 1 \text{ revolution} = 360°$$

One radian

Conversion of Angles

We convert angles in the same way as we convert any other units. A summary of the conversions needed is:

You may prefer to use π rad = 180°. Some calculators have special keys for angle conversions. Check your manual.

Angle Conversions	1 rev = 360° = 2π rad 1° = 60′ 1′ = 60″	**117**

■ **Example 2:** Convert 47.6° to radians and revolutions.

Solution: By Eq. 117,

$$47.6°\left(\frac{2\pi \text{ rad}}{360°}\right) = 0.831 \text{ rad}$$

Note that we keep the *same number of significant digits* as we had in the original angle. To convert to revolutions,

$$47.6° \left(\frac{1 \text{ rev}}{360°} \right) = 0.132 \text{ rev}$$ ▬

▬ **Example 3:** Convert 1.8473 rad to degrees and revolutions.

Solution: By Eq. 117,

$$1.8473 \text{ rad} \left(\frac{360°}{2\pi \text{ rad}} \right) = 105.84°$$

and

$$1.8473 \text{ rad} \left(\frac{1 \text{ rev}}{2\pi \text{ rad}} \right) = 0.29401 \text{ rev}$$ ▬

▬ **Example 4:** Convert 1.0000 radians to degrees.

Solution:

$$1.0000 \text{ rad} \left(\frac{360°}{2\pi \text{ rad}} \right) = 57.296 \text{ degrees}$$

This is a good conversion factor to memorize.   ▬

Conversions involving degrees, minutes, and seconds require several steps. Further, to know how many digits to retain, we note the following:

$$1 \text{ min} = 1/60 \text{ degree} \approx 0.02°$$

and

$$1 \text{ sec} = 1/3600 \text{ degree} \approx 0.0003°$$

Note that a second of an arc is an extremely small angle. Angle measurements accurate to the nearest second are rare, and require special equipment and techniques.

Thus an angle known to the nearest minute is about as accurate as a decimal angle known to two decimal places. Also, an angle known to the nearest second is about as accurate as a decimal angle known to the fourth decimal place. Thus we would treat an angle like 28°17′37″ as if it had four decimal places and six significant digits.

▬ **Example 5:** Convert 28°17′37″ to decimal degrees and radians.

Solution: We separately convert the minutes and the seconds to degrees, and add them. Since the given angle is known to the nearest second, we will work to four decimal places.

$$37 \text{ sec} \left(\frac{1 \text{ deg}}{3600 \text{ sec}} \right) = 0.0103°$$

$$17 \text{ min} \left(\frac{1 \text{ deg}}{60 \text{ min}} \right) = 0.2833°$$

$$28° = \underline{28.0000°}$$

Adding gives   28.2936°

Now, by Equ. 117,

$$28.2936° \left(\frac{2\pi \text{ rad}}{360 \text{ deg}} \right) = 0.493817 \text{ rad}$$ ▬

■ **Example 6:** Convert 1.837520 rad to degrees, minutes, and seconds.

Solution: We first convert to decimal degrees:

$$1.837520 \text{ rad} \left(\frac{360°}{2\pi \text{ rad}} \right) = 105.2821°$$

Then we convert the decimal part (0.2821°) to minutes:

$$0.2821° \left(\frac{60'}{1 \text{ deg}} \right) = 16.93'$$

and convert the decimal part of 16.93 to seconds:

$$0.93' \left(\frac{60''}{1 \text{ min}} \right) = 56''$$

So

$$1.837520 \text{ rad} = 105°16'56''$$ ■

Common Error	When reading an angle quickly, it is easy to mistake decimal degrees with degrees and minutes. Don't mistake 28°50' for 28.50°

Angle Conversions by Calculator

Another unit of angular measure is the *grad*. There are 400 grads in one revolution.

Scientific calculators have a key or switch to put the calculator into the desired angular mode, degrees or radians (and sometimes grads). Further, most advanced calculators, such as the graphics calculator, enable you to enter angles in degrees, in radians, or in degrees, minutes, and seconds (DMS). The calculator will automatically convert the entered angle into the angular units previously set using the MODE key.

For example, if your calculator is set in *degree* mode and you then enter an angle in *radians*, the calculator can be made to convert the angle and display it in *degrees*.

■ **Example 7:** Convert 0.845 radians to degrees using an advanced calculator.

Solution: We first set the mode to *degrees*.

> Key in 0.845.
> Press the radian key. *This is not the same key as for entering radian mode.* (Your calculator may not have this function.)
> Pressing ENTER or EXE will display the given angle in degrees.

Thus,

$$0.845 \text{ radians} = 48.4 \text{ degrees}$$ ■

Some calculators allow you to enter angles in DMS, using a key that is marked ° ' '', or something similar. The entered angle is then displayed in whatever angular units were set with the MODE key.

■ **Example 8:** Convert 23°15′21″ to radians by calculator.

Solution: Put the calculator into radian mode. Then:

Enter 23 and press $\boxed{\circ\ '\ ''}$

Enter 15 and press $\boxed{\circ\ '\ ''}$

Enter 21 and press $\boxed{\circ\ '\ ''}$

Pressing $\boxed{\text{ENTER}}$ or $\boxed{\text{EXE}}$ should now display the angle in radians, as 0.405891, to six significant digits. ■

Exercise 1 Angles and Their Measures

Angle Conversions

Convert to radians.

1. 27.8°	**2.** 38.7°	**3.** 35°15′
4. 270°27′25″	**5.** 0.55 rev	**6.** 0.276 rev

Convert to revolutions.

7. 4.772 rad	**8.** 2.38 rad	**9.** 68.8°
10. 3.72°	**11.** 77°18′	**12.** 135°27′42″

Convert to degrees (decimal).

13. 2.83 rad	**14.** 4.275 rad	**15.** 0.475 rev
16. 0.236 rev	**17.** 29°27′	**18.** 275°18′35″

Convert to degrees, minutes, and seconds.

19. 4.2754 rad	**20.** 1.773 rad	**21.** 0.44975 rev
22. 0.78426 rev	**23.** 185.972°	**24.** 128.259°

Computer

25. Write a program that will accept an angle in decimal degrees and compute and print the angle in degrees, minutes, and seconds.

7·2 The Trigonometric Functions

Definitions

We start with coordinate axes (Fig. 7·3) upon which we draw an angle. We always draw such angles the same way, with the vertex at the origin, in this case called O, and with one side along the x axis. Such an angle is said to be in *standard position*. We can think of the angle as being generated by a line rotating counterclockwise, whose initial position is on the x axis. We now select any point P on the terminal side of the angle θ, and we let the coordinates of P be x and y. We form a *right triangle OPQ* by dropping a perpendicular from P to the x axis. The side OP is the *hypotenuse* of the right

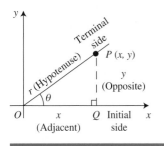

FIGURE 7·3 An angle in standard position

We do only *acute* angles here and discuss larger angles in Chapter 15.

The cotangent is sometimes abbreviated *ctn*.

triangle; we label its length *r*. Note that by the Pythagorean theorem, $r^2 = x^2 + y^2$. Also, side *OQ* is *adjacent* to angle *θ* and has a length *x*, and side *PQ* is *opposite* angle *θ* and has a length *y*.

If we had chosen to place point *P* farther out on the terminal side of the angle, the lengths *x*, *y*, and *r* would all be greater than they are now. But the *ratio* of any two sides will be the same regardless of where we place *P*, because all the triangles thus formed are similar to each other. Such a ratio will change only if we change the angle *θ*. A ratio between any two sides of a right triangle is called a *trigonometric ratio* or *trigonometric function*.

The six trigonometric functions are defined as follows:

Trigono-metric Functions	Sine $\theta = \sin \theta = \dfrac{y}{r} = \dfrac{\text{opposite side}}{\text{hypotenuse}}$	**146**
	Cosine $\theta = \cos \theta = \dfrac{x}{r} = \dfrac{\text{adjacent side}}{\text{hypotenuse}}$	**147**
	Tangent $\theta = \tan \theta = \dfrac{y}{x} = \dfrac{\text{opposite side}}{\text{adjacent side}}$	**148**
	Cotangent $\theta = \cot \theta = \dfrac{x}{y} = \dfrac{\text{adjacent side}}{\text{opposite side}}$	**149**
	Secant $\theta = \sec \theta = \dfrac{r}{x} = \dfrac{\text{hypotenuse}}{\text{adjacent side}}$	**150**
	Cosecant $\theta = \csc \theta = \dfrac{r}{y} = \dfrac{\text{hypotenuse}}{\text{opposite side}}$	**151**

Note that each of the trigonometric ratios is *related to* the angle *θ*. Take the ratio *y/r*, for example. The values of *y/r* depend only on the measure of *θ*, not on the lengths of *y* or *r*. To convince yourself of this, draw an angle of, say, 30°, as in Figure 7·4(a). Then form a right triangle by drawing a perpendicular from any point on side *L* or from any point on side *M* [Fig. 7·4(b) and (c)]. No matter how you draw the triangle, the side opposite the 30° angle *will always be half the hypotenuse* (sin 30° = $\frac{1}{2}$). You would get a similar result for any other angle and for any other trigonometric ratio. *The value of the trigonometric ratio depends only on the measure of the angle.* We have a *relation*, such as the relations we studied in Chapter 4.

Furthermore, for any angle *θ*, there exists *only one* value for each trigonometric ratio. Thus, *each ratio is a function of θ*, which is why we call them the *trigonometric functions of θ*. In functional notation, we could write

$$\sin \theta = f(\theta)$$

$$\cos \theta = g(\theta)$$

$$\tan \theta = h(\theta)$$

and so forth. The angle *θ* is called the *argument* of the function.

(a)

(b)

(c)

FIGURE 7·4

Note that, while there is one and only one value of each trigonometric function for a given angle θ, we will see that for any given value of a trigonometric function (say, $\sin \theta = \frac{1}{2}$) there are *indefinitely many* values of θ. We treat this idea more fully in Section 15•1.

The trigonometric functions are sometimes called *circular* functions.

Reciprocal Relationships

From the trigonometric functions we see that

$$\sin \theta = \frac{y}{r}$$

and that

$$\csc \theta = \frac{r}{y}$$

Obviously, $\sin \theta$ and $\csc \theta$ are reciprocals.

$$\sin \theta = \frac{1}{\csc \theta}$$

Inspection of the trigonometric functions below shows two more sets of reciprocals (see also Fig. 7•5).

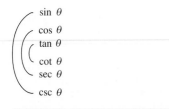

Reciprocal Relationships	$\sin \theta = \dfrac{1}{\csc \theta}$	**152(a)**
	$\cos \theta = \dfrac{1}{\sec \theta}$	**152(b)**
	$\tan \theta = \dfrac{1}{\cot \theta}$	**152(c)**

FIGURE 7•5 This diagram shows which functions are reciprocals of each other.

This is a good place to use the $\boxed{1/x}$ key on your calculator.

■ **Example 9:** Find $\tan \theta$ if $\cot \theta = 0.638$.

Solution: From the reciprocal relationships,

$$\tan \theta = \frac{1}{\cot \theta} = \frac{1}{0.638} = 1.57$$

Finding the Trigonometric Functions of an Angle

The six trigonometric functions of an angle can be written if we know the angle or if we know two of the sides of a right triangle containing the angle.

■ **Example 10:** A right triangle (Fig. 7•6) has sides of 4.37 and 2.83. Write the six trigonometric functions of angle θ.

Solution: We first find the hypotenuse by the Pythagorean theorem:

$$c = \sqrt{(2.83)^2 + (4.37)^2} = \sqrt{27.1}$$
$$= 5.21$$

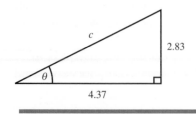

FIGURE 7•6

We also note that the opposite side is 2.83 and the adjacent side is 4.37. Then by Eqs. 146 to 151,

$$\sin \theta = \frac{\text{opposite side}}{\text{hypotenuse}} = \frac{2.83}{5.21} = 0.543$$

$$\cos \theta = \frac{\text{adjacent side}}{\text{hypotenuse}} = \frac{4.37}{5.21} = 0.839$$

$$\tan \theta = \frac{\text{opposite side}}{\text{adjacent side}} = \frac{2.83}{4.37} = 0.648$$

$$\cot \theta = \frac{\text{adjacent side}}{\text{opposite side}} = \frac{4.37}{2.83} = 1.54$$

$$\sec \theta = \frac{\text{hypotenuse}}{\text{adjacent side}} = \frac{5.21}{4.37} = 1.19$$

$$\csc \theta = \frac{\text{hypotenuse}}{\text{opposite side}} = \frac{5.21}{2.83} = 1.84$$

Common Error	Do not omit the angle when writing a trigonometric function. To write "sin = 0.543," for example, has no meaning.

■ Example 11: A point P on the terminal side of an angle B (in standard position) has the coordinates (8.84, 3.15). Write the sine, cosine, and tangent of angle B.

Solution: We are given $x = 8.84$ and $y = 3.15$. We find r from the Pythagorean theorem:

$$r = \sqrt{(8.84)^2 + (3.15)^2} = 9.38$$

Then, by Eqs. 146 to 151,

$$\sin B = \frac{y}{r} = \frac{3.15}{9.38} = 0.336$$

$$\cos B = \frac{x}{r} = \frac{8.84}{9.38} = 0.942$$

$$\tan B = \frac{y}{x} = \frac{3.15}{8.84} = 0.356$$

■

Trigonometric Functions by Calculator

A trigonometric function is found by calculator by using a trig function key: sin , cos , or tan . On some calculators you enter the angle first and then press the trig function key; on other calculators you must press the trig function key first. You must find out which way your calculator works. We will show examples in which the trigonometric function is entered before the angle. Make sure that your calculator is in the degree mode if the entered angle is in degrees, or in the radian mode if the angle is in radians.

■ **Example 12:** Find the sine of 38.6° by calculator to four significant digits.

Solution: We set the mode to degrees. Then

> | sin | 38.6 | ENTER |
>
> 0.6238795967

which we round to 0.6239.   ■

■ **Example 13:** Find tan 1.174 rad by calculator to five significant digits.

Solution: Put the calculator into radian mode. Then

> | tan | 1.174 | ENTER |
>
> 2.386509704

which we round to 2.3865.   ■

To find the cotangent, secant, or cosecant, first find the reciprocal function (tangent, cosine, or sine), and then press the $\boxed{1/x}$ or $\boxed{x^{-1}}$ key to get the reciprocal.

■ **Example 14:** Find sec 72.8° to four significant digits.

Solution: With our calculator in degree mode, the keystrokes are

> | cos | 72.8 | 1/x | ENTER |
>
> 3.381713822

which we round to 3.382.   ■

■ **Example 15:** Find the cosecant of 0.748 rad to four significant digits.

Solution: With our calculator in radian mode, the keystrokes are

> | sin | .748 | 1/x | ENTER |
>
> 1.470211991

which we round to 1.470.   ■

Common Error	It is easy to forget to set your calculator in the proper degree/radian mode. Be sure to check it each time.

Evaluating Trigonometric Expressions

Trigonometric functions may be combined with numbers or variables to get more complex expressions, such as

$$2 \sin 35° - 5 \cos 12°$$

In this section we will evaluate some very simple expressions of this kind, and cover more complex ones later.

Simply perform the indicated operations. Just remember that angles are assumed to be in *radians* unless marked otherwise.

◾ **Example 16:** Evaluate, to three significant digits,

$$7.82 - 3.15 \cos 67.8°$$

Solution: By calculator, we find that $\cos 67.8° = 0.3778$, so our expression becomes

$$7.82 - 3.15(0.3778) = 6.63$$

As is usual when doing such calculations, we keep all the figures in the calculator whenever possible. If you must write down an intermediate result, as we did here just to show the steps, retain one or two digits more than required in the final answer. ◾

◾ **Example 17:** Evaluate, to four significant digits,

$$1.836 \sin 2 + 2.624 \tan 3$$

Solution: Here no angular units are indicated, so we assume them to be radians. Switching to radian mode, we get

$$1.836 \sin 2 + 2.624 \tan 3 = 1.836(0.90930) + 2.624(-0.14255)$$
$$= 1.295$$ ◾

Exercise 2   The Trigonometric Functions

For Problems 1 to 4 below, use a protractor to mark off the given angle on coordinate axes. Drop a perpendicular from any point on the terminal side and measure the distances x, y, and r, as in Figure 7•3 (page 187). Use these measured distances to write the six trigonometric ratios of the angle to two decimal places. Check your answer by calculator.

1. 30°
2. 55°
3. 14°
4. 37°

For Problems 5 to 8, plot the given coordinate and connect it to the origin. With a protractor, measure the angle formed with the x axis. Check by taking the tangent of your measured angle. It should equal the ratio y/x.

5. (3, 4)   **6.** (5, 3)   **7.** (1, 2)   **8.** (5, 4)

9. Write the six trigonometric ratios for angle θ in Figure 7•7.

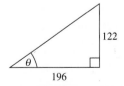

FIGURE 7•7

Each of the points given in Problems 10 to 15 is on the terminal side of an angle. Compute the distance r from the origin to the point and write the sin, cos, and tan of the angle. Work to three significant digits.

10. (3, 5)   **11.** (4, 2)
12. (5, 3)   **13.** (2, 3)
14. (4, 5)   **15.** (4.75, 2.68)

Evaluate. Work to four decimal places.

16. sin 47.3°   **17.** tan 44.4°   **18.** sec 29.5°
19. cot 18.2°   **20.** csc 37.5°   **21.** cos 21.27°
22. cos 86.75°   **23.** sec 12.3°   **24.** csc 12.67°

Write the sin, cos, and tan for each angle. Keep three decimal places.

25. 72.8°   **26.** 19.2°
27. 33.1°   **28.** 41.4°
29. 0.744 rad   **30.** 0.385 rad

Evaluate each trigonometric expression to three significant digits.

31. 5.27 sin 45.8° − 1.73
32. 2.84 cos 73.4° − 3.83 tan 36.2°
33. 3.72(sin 28.3° + cos 72.3°)
34. 11.2 tan 5 + 15.3 cos 3
35. 2.84(5.28 cos 2 − 2.82) + 3.35
36. 2.63 sin 2.4 + 1.36 cos 3.5 + 3.13 tan 2.5

7·3   Finding the Angle When the Trigonometric Function Is Given

The operation of finding the angle when the trigonometric function is given is the *inverse* of finding the function when the angle is given. There is special notation to indicate the inverse trigonometric function. If

$$A = \sin \theta$$

we write

$$\theta = \arcsin A$$

or

$$\theta = \sin^{-1} A$$

which is read "θ is the angle whose sine is A." Similarly, we use the symbols arccos A, $\cos^{-1} A$, arctan A, and so on.

Common Error	Do not confuse the **inverse** with the **reciprocal**. $$\frac{1}{\sin \theta} = (\sin \theta)^{-1} \neq \sin^{-1} \theta$$

Here we use the inverse trigonometric function keys, $\boxed{\sin^{-1}}$, $\boxed{\cos^{-1}}$, or $\boxed{\tan^{-1}}$ on the calculator. If you do not have such keys, look for an $\boxed{\text{arc}}$ or $\boxed{\text{inv}}$ key and consult your manual on its use.

Some calculators require that the inverse function key be pressed before entering the number, and some after entering the number. To save space, we show only examples where the inverse function key is pressed first. Be sure to reverse the order if you have to.

━ **Example 18:** If $\sin \theta = 0.7337$, find θ in degrees to three significant digits.

Solution: Switch the calculator into the degree mode. Then

$\boxed{\sin^{-1}}$ .7335 $\boxed{\text{ENTER}}$
47.19748165

which we round to 47.2°. Note that a calculator gives us acute angles only.   ━

━ **Example 19:** If $\tan x = 2.846$, find x in radians to four significant digits.

Solution: With the calculator in the radian mode,

$\boxed{\tan^{-1}}$ 2.846 $\boxed{\text{ENTER}}$
1.232901233

which we round to 1.233.   ━

In this chapter we limit our work with inverse functions to *first-quadrant* angles only, and consider any angle in Chapter 15.

If the cotangent, secant, or cosecant is given, we first take the reciprocal of that value and then use the appropriate reciprocal relationship,

$$\sin \theta = \frac{1}{\csc \theta} \qquad \cos \theta = \frac{1}{\sec \theta} \qquad \tan \theta = \frac{1}{\cot \theta}$$

━━━━━ **Example 20:** If $\sec \theta = 1.573$, find θ in degrees to four significant digits.

Solution: Put the calculator into the degree mode. Then, since

$$\cos \theta = \frac{1}{\sec \theta} = \frac{1}{1.573}$$

we first find the reciprocal of 1.573 and then take the inverse cosine.

1.573 $\boxed{x^{-1}}$
0.6357279085
$\boxed{\cos^{-1}}$ $\boxed{\text{ANS}}$ $\boxed{\text{ENTER}}$
50.53 (rounded)

or, in one line,

$\boxed{\cos^{-1}}$ 1.573 $\boxed{x^{-1}}$ $\boxed{\text{ENTER}}$
50.53 (rounded)

━

Exercise 3 Finding the Angle When the Trigonometric Function Is Given

Find the acute angle (in decimal degrees) whose trigonometric function is given. Keep three significant digits.

1. $\sin A = 0.500$ **2.** $\tan D = 1.53$ **3.** $\sin G = 0.528$
4. $\cot K = 1.77$ **5.** $\sin B = 0.483$ **6.** $\cot E = 0.847$

Without using tables or a calculator, write the sin, cos, and tan of angle A. Leave your answer in fractional form.

7. $\sin A = \dfrac{3}{5}$

8. $\cot A = \dfrac{12}{5}$

9. $\cos A = \dfrac{12}{13}$

Evaluate the following, giving your answer in decimal degrees to three significant digits:

10. $\arcsin 0.635$ **11.** $\text{arcsec } 3.86$ **12.** $\tan^{-1} 2.85$
13. $\cot^{-1} 1.17$ **14.** $\cos^{-1} 0.229$ **15.** $\text{arccsc } 4.26$

7·4

Solution of Right Triangles

Right Triangles

The right triangle (Fig. 7·8) was introduced in Section 6·2, where we also had the Pythagorean theorem.

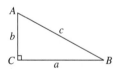

FIGURE 7·8 A right triangle. We will usually *label* a right triangle as shown here. We label the angles with capital letters A, B, and C, with C always the right angle. We label the sides with lowercase letters a, b, and c, with side a opposite angle A, side b opposite angle B, and side c (the hypotenuse) opposite angle C (the right angle).

Pythagorean Theorem	$c^2 = a^2 + b^2$	145
Sum of the Angles	$A + B + C = 180°$	139
Trigonometric Functions	$\sin \theta = \dfrac{\text{side opposite } \theta}{\text{hypotenuse}}$	146
	$\cos \theta = \dfrac{\text{side adjacent to } \theta}{\text{hypotenuse}}$	147
	$\tan \theta = \dfrac{\text{side opposite } \theta}{\text{side adjacent to } \theta}$	148

These five equations will be our tools for solving any right triangle.

Solving Right Triangles When One Side and One Angle Are Known

To *solve* a triangle means to find all missing sides and angles (although in most practical problems we need find only one missing side or angle). We can solve any right triangle if we know one side and either another side or one angle.

To solve a right triangle when one side and one angle are known:

1. Make a sketch.
2. Find the missing angle by using Eq. 139.
3. Relate the known side to one of the missing sides by one of the trigonometric ratios. Solve for the missing side.
4. Repeat Step 3 to find the second missing side.
5. Check your work with the Pythagorean theorem.

■ **Example 21:** Solve right triangle ABC if $A = 18.6°$ and $c = 135$.

Solution:

1. We make a sketch (Fig. 7•9).
2. Then, by Eq. 139,

$$B = 90° - A = 90° - 18.6° = 71.4°$$

3. Let us now find side a. We must use one of the trigonometric ratios. But *how do we know which one to use?* And further, *which of the two angles, A or B, should we write the trig ratio for?*

It is simple. First, always work with the *given angle*, because, if you made a mistake in finding angle B and then used it to find the sides, they would be wrong also. Then, to decide which trigonometric ratio to use, we note that side a is *opposite* angle A and that the given side is the *hypotenuse*. Thus, our trig function must be one that relates the *opposite side* to the *hypotenuse*. Our obvious choice is Eq. 146.

$$\sin A = \frac{\text{opposite side}}{\text{hypotenuse}}$$

Substituting the given values, we obtain

$$\sin 18.6° = \frac{a}{135}$$

Solving for a,

$$a = 135 \sin 18.6°$$

$$= 135(0.3190) = 43.1$$

4. We now find side b. Note that side b is *adjacent to* angle A. We therefore use Eq. 147,

$$\cos 18.6° = \frac{b}{135}$$

So

$$b = 135 \cos 18.6°$$

$$= 135(0.9478) = 128$$

We have thus found all the missing parts of the triangle.

FIGURE 7•9

Realize that either of the two legs can be called *opposite* or *adjacent*, depending on which angle we are referring them to. Here b is adjacent to angle A but opposite angle B.

As a rough check of any triangle, see if the longest side is opposite the largest angle and if the shortest side is opposite the smallest angle. Also check that the hypotenuse is greater than either leg but less than their sum.

5. For a check, we see if the three sides will satisfy the Pythagorean theorem.

Check: $(43.1)^2 + (128)^2 \overset{?}{=} (135)^2$
$$18\ 242 \overset{?}{=} 18\ 225$$

Since we are working to three significant digits, this is close enough for a check. ▬

▬ **Example 22:** In right triangle, *ABC*, angle $B = 55.2°$ and $a = 207$. Solve the triangle.

Solution:

1. We make a sketch (Fig. 7•10).
2. By Eq. 139,
$$A = 90° - 55.2° = 34.8°$$

3. By Eq. 147,
$$\cos 55.2° = \frac{207}{c}$$
$$c = \frac{207}{\cos 55.2°} = \frac{207}{0.5707} = 363$$

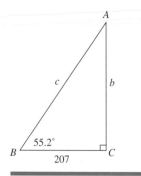

FIGURE 7•10

4. Then by Eq. 148,
$$\tan 55.2° = \frac{b}{207}$$
$$b = 207 \tan 55.2° = 207(1.439) = 298$$

5. Checking with the Pythagorean theorem,
$$(363)^2 \overset{?}{=} (207)^2 + (298)^2$$
$$131\ 769 \overset{?}{=} 131\ 653 \quad \text{checks to within three significant digits} \quad ▬$$

This, of course, is good advice for *any* computation, not just for solving right triangles.

Tip	Whenever possible, use the *given information* for each computation, rather than some quantity previously calculated. This way, any errors in the early computation will not be carried along.

Solving Right Triangles When Two Sides Are Known

1. Draw a diagram of the triangle.
2. Write the trigonometric ratio that relates one of the angles to the two given sides. Solve for the angle.
3. Subtract the angle just found from 90° to get the second angle.
4. Find the missing side by the Pythagorean theorem.
5. Check the computed side and angles with trigonometric ratios, as shown in Example 23.

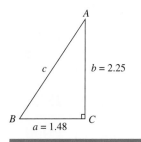

FIGURE 7•11

━ **Example 23:** Solve right triangle *ABC* if $a = 1.48$ and $b = 2.25$.

Solution:

1. We sketch the triangle (Fig. 7•11).

2. To find angle *A*, we note that the 1.48 side is *opposite* angle *A* and that the 2.25 side is *adjacent to* angle *A*. The trig ratio relating *opposite* and *adjacent* is the *tangent* (Eq. 148).

$$\tan A = \frac{1.48}{2.25} = 0.6578$$

from which

$$\tan^{-1} 0.6578 = A$$

$$A = 33.3°$$

3. Solving for angle *B*,

$$B = 90° - A = 90 - 33.3 = 56.7°$$

4. We find side *c* by the Pythagorean theorem,

$$c^2 = (1.48)^2 + (2.25)^2 = 7.253$$

$$c = 2.69$$

5. Check:

$$\sin 33.3° \stackrel{?}{=} \frac{1.48}{2.69}$$

$$0.549 \cong 0.550 \qquad \text{checks}$$

and

$$\sin 56.7° \stackrel{?}{=} \frac{2.25}{2.69}$$

$$0.836 = 8.836 \qquad \text{checks}$$

(Note that we could just as well have used another trigonometric function, such as the cosine, for our check.)   ━

Cofunctions

The sine of angle *A* in Figure 7•8 is

$$\sin A = \frac{a}{c}$$

But *a/c* is *also* the cosine of the complementary angle *B*. Thus we can write

$$\sin A = \cos B$$

Here sin *A* and cos *B* are called *cofunctions*. Similarly, cos *A* = sin *B*. These cofunctions and others in the same right triangle are given in the following table.

Cofunctions where $A + B = 90°$ or $A + B = \dfrac{\pi}{2}$ rad	$\sin A = \cos B$	**154(a)**
	$\cos A = \sin B$	**154(b)**
	$\tan A = \cot B$	**154(c)**
	$\cot A = \tan B$	**154(d)**
	$\sec A = \csc B$	**154(e)**
	$\csc A = \sec B$	**154(f)**

In general, *a trigonometric function of an acute angle is equal to the corresponding cofunction of the complementary angle.*

━ **Example 24:** If the cosine of the acute angle A in a right triangle ABC is equal to 0.725, find the sine of the other acute angle, B.

Solution: By Eq. 154(b),

$$\sin B = \cos A = 0.725$$ ━

Exercise 4　Solution of Right Triangles

Right Triangles with One Side and One Angle Given

Sketch each right triangle below and find all the missing parts. Assume the triangles to be labelled as in Figure 7•8 (page 194). Work to three significant digits.

1. $a = 155$　$A = 42.9°$ 　　**2.** $b = 82.6$　$B = 61.4°$
3. $a = 1.74$　$B = 31.9°$ 　　**4.** $b = 7.74$　$A = 22.5°$
5. $a = 284$　$A = 1.13$ rad 　　**6.** $b = 73.2$　$B = 0.655$ rad
7. $b = 9.26$　$B = 55.2°$ 　　**8.** $a = 1.73$　$A = 39.3°$
9. $b = 82.4$　$A = 31.4°$ 　　**10.** $a = 18.3$　$B = 44.1°$

Right Triangles with Two Sides Given

Sketch each right triangle and find all missing parts. Work to three significant digits and express the angles in decimal degrees.

11. $a = 382$　$b = 274$ 　　**12.** $a = 3.88$　$c = 5.37$
13. $b = 3.97$　$c = 4.86$ 　　**14.** $a = 63.9$　$b = 84.3$
15. $a = 27.4$　$c = 37.5$ 　　**16.** $b = 746$　$c = 957$
17. $a = 41.3$　$c = 63.7$ 　　**18.** $a = 4.82$　$b = 3.28$
19. $b = 228$　$c = 473$ 　　**20.** $a = 274$　$c = 429$

Cofunctions

Express as a function of the complementary angle.

21. $\sin 38°$ 　　**22.** $\cos 73°$ 　　**23.** $\tan 19°$
24. $\sec 85.6°$ 　　**25.** $\cot 63.2°$ 　　**26.** $\csc 82.7°$
27. $\tan 35°14'$ 　　**28.** $\cos 0.153$ rad 　　**29.** $\sin 0.475$ rad

Computer

30. Write a program or use a spreadsheet to compute the perimeter of a regular polygon of *n* sides inscribed in a circle having a diameter of one unit. Let *n* vary from 3 to 20, and for each *n* print **(a)** the number of sides, *n*; **(b)** the perimeter of the polygon; and **(c)** the difference between the circumference of the circle and the perimeter of the polygon.

31. Write a program to solve any right triangle. Have the program accept as input a known side and angle, or two known sides, and compute and print all the sides and angles.

7•5

Applications of the Right Triangle

There are, of course, a huge number of applications for the right triangle, a few of which are given in the following exercises. A typical application is that of finding a distance that cannot be measured directly.

■ **Example 25:** To find the height of a flagpole, Figure 7•12, a person measures 10 m from the base of the pole, and then measures an angle of 40.8° from a point 1.82 m above the ground to the top of the pole. Find the height of the flagpole.

FIGURE 7•12

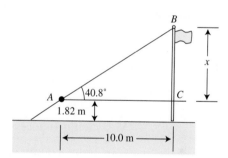

Estimate: If angle *A* was 45°, then *BC* would be the same length as *AC*, or 10 m. But our angle is a bit less than 45°, so we expect *BC* to be less than 10 m, say 9 m. Thus our guess for the entire height is about 10.82 m.

Solution: In right triangle *ABC*, *BC* is opposite the known angle and *AC* is adjacent. Using the tangent we get

$$\tan 40.8° = \frac{x}{10}$$

where *x* is the height of the pole above the observer. Then

$$x = 10 \tan 40.8° = 8.63 \text{ m}$$

Adding 1.82 m, the total pole height is 10.50 m, measured from the ground.

■

■ **Example 26:** From a plane at an altitude of 842 m, the pilot observes the angle of depression of a lake to be 18.6°. How far is the lake from a point on the ground directly beneath the plane?

(a) Angle of elevation

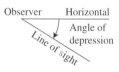

(b) Angle of depression

FIGURE 7·13 Angles of elevation and depression

FIGURE 7·14

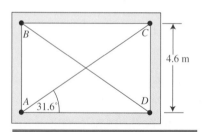

FIGURE 7·15

Solution: We first note that an *angle of depression*, and also an *angle of elevation*, are defined as the angle between a line of sight and the *horizontal*, as shown in Figure 7·13. We then make a sketch for our problem (Fig. 7·14). Since the ground and the horizontal line drawn through the plane are parallel, angle *A* the angle of depression (18.6°) are alternate interior angles. Therefore, $A = 18.6°$. Then

$$\tan 18.6° = \frac{842}{x}$$

$$x = \frac{842}{\tan 18.6°} = 2500 \text{ m} \quad \blacksquare$$

■ Example 27: The frame, Figure 7·15, is braced by wires *AC* and *BD*. Find the length of each wire.

Estimate: We can make a quick estimate if we remember that the sine of 30° is 0.5. Thus we expect wire *AC* to be a little shorter than twice side *CD*, or around 9.00 m.

Solution: Noting that, in right triangle *ACD*, *CD* is opposite the given angle and *AC* is the hypotenuse, we choose the sine.

$$\sin 31.6° = \frac{4.6}{AC}$$

$$AC = \frac{4.6}{\sin 31.6°} = 8.8 \text{ m} \quad \blacksquare$$

Exercise 5 Applications of the Right Triangle

Measuring Inaccessible Distances

1. From a point on the ground 255 m from the base of a tower, the angle of elevation to the top of the tower is 57.6°. Find the height of the tower.

2. A pilot 4220 m directly above the front of a straight train observes that the angle of depression of the end of the train is 68.2°. Find the length of the train.

3. From the top of a lighthouse 48 m above the surface of the water, the angle of depression of a boat is observed to be 28.7°. Find the horizontal distance from the boat to the lighthouse.

4. An observer in an airplane 463 m above the surface of the ocean observes that the angle of depression of a ship is 28.8°. Find the straight-line distance from the plane to the ship.

5. The distance *PQ* across a swamp is desired. A line *PR* of length 59.3 m is laid off at right angles to *PQ*. Angle *PRQ* is measured at 47.6°. Find the distance *PQ*.

6. The angle of elevation of the top of a building from a point on the ground 83.8 m from its base is 51.3°. Find the height of the building.

7. The angle of elevation of the top of a building from a point on the ground 68.58 m from its base is 28.0°. How high is the building?

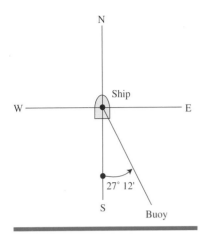

FIGURE 7•16 A compass direction of S27°12′E means an angle of 27•12′ measured from due south to the east. Also, remember that 1 minute (1′) of arc is equal to 1/60 degree, or,

$$60' = 1°$$

FIGURE 7•17

8. From the top of a hill 38 m above a stream, the angles of depression of a point on the near shore and of a point on the opposite shore are 42.3° and 40.6°. Find the width of the stream between these two points.

9. From the top of a tree 15.0 m high on the shore of a pond, the angle of depression of a point on the other shore is 6.70°. What is the width of the pond?

Navigation

10. A passenger on a ship sailing due north at 8.20 km/h noticed that at 1:00 P.M. a buoy was due east of the ship. At 1:45 P.M., the bearing of the buoy from the ship was S27°12′E (Fig. 7•16). How far was the ship from the buoy at 1:00 P.M.?

11. An observer at a point P on a coast sights a ship in a direction N43°15′E. The ship is at the same time directly east of a point Q, 15.6 km due north of P. Find the distance of the ship from point P and from point Q.

12. A ship sailing parallel to a straight coast is directly opposite one of two lights on the shore. The angle between the lines of sight from the ship to these lights is 27°50′, and it is known that the lights are 355 m apart. Find the perpendicular distance of the ship from the shore. *Hint:* Use parallel lines and alternate interior angles.

13. An airplane left an airport and flew 504 km in the direction N15°18′E, then turned and flew 474 km in the direction S74°42′E. How far, and in what direction, should it fly to return to the airport?

14. A ship is sailing due south at a speed of 7.50 km/h when a light is sighted with a bearing S35°28′E. One hour later the ship is due west of the light. Find the distance from the ship to the light at that instant.

15. After leaving port a ship holds a course N46°12′E for 360 km. Find how far north and how far east of the port the ship is now located.

Structures

16. A guy wire from the top of an antenna is anchored 16.3 m from the base of the antenna and makes an angle of 85.2° with the ground. Find (a) the height h of the antenna; (b) the length L of the wire.

17. Find the angle θ and length AB in the truss shown in Figure 7•17.

18. A house (Fig. 7•18, page 202) is 8.75 m wide and its roof has an angle of inclination of 34.0°. Find the length L of the rafters.

19. A guy wire 25.0 m long is stretched from the ground to the top of a telephone pole 19.8 m high. Find the angle between the wire and the pole.

Geometry

20. What is the angle between a diagonal AB of a cube and a diagonal AC of a face of that cube (Fig. 7•19, page 202)?

21. Two of the sides of an isosceles triangle have a length of 152 mm, and each of the base angles is 68.0°. Find the altitude and the base of the triangle.

22. The diagonal of a rectangle is three times the length of the shorter side. Find the angle between the diagonal and the longer side.

FIGURE 7·18

FIGURE 7·19

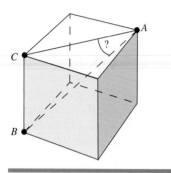

Trigonometry has many uses in the machine shop. Given here are some standard shop calculations.

FIGURE 7·20

23. Find the angles between the diagonals of a rectangle whose dimensions are 580 units × 940 units.

24. Find the area of a parallelogram if the lengths of the sides are 2550 mm and 4820 mm and if one angle is 83.2°.

25. Find the length of a side of a regular hexagon inscribed in a 1250 mm radius circle. *Hint:* Draw lines from the center of the hexagon to each vertex and to the midpoint of each side, to form right triangles.

26. Find the length of the side of a regular pentagon circumscribed about a circle of radius 6200 mm.

Shop Trigonometry

27. Find the dimension x in Figure 7·20.

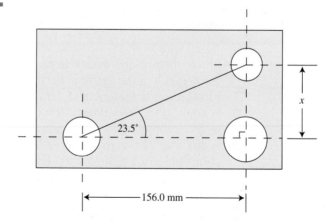

28. A bolt circle (Fig. 7·21, page 203) is to be made on a jig borer. Find the dimensions x_1, y_1, x_2, and y_2.

29. A bolt circle with a radius of 360.00 mm contains 24 equally spaced holes. Find the straight-line distance between the holes so that they may be stepped off with dividers.

30. A 228.60-mm-long shaft (Fig. 7·22, page 203) is to taper 3.500° and be 25.40 mm in diameter at the narrow end. Find the diameter d of the larger end. *Hint:* Draw a line (shown dashed in the figure) from the small end to the large, to form a right triangle. Solve that triangle.

FIGURE 7·22 Tapered shaft

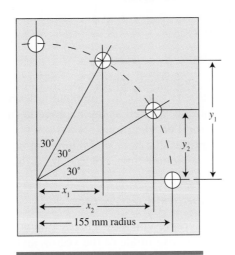

FIGURE 7·21 A bolt circle

31. A measuring square having an included angle of 60.0° is placed over the pulley fragment of Figure 7·23. The distance d from the corner of the square to the pulley rim is measured at 140.46 mm. Find the pulley radius r.

32. A common way of measuring dovetails is with the aid of round plugs, as in Figure 7·24. Find the distance x over the 12.0-mm-diameter plugs. *Hint:* Find the length of side AB in the 30–60–90 triangle ABC, and then use AB to find x.

33. A bolt head (Fig. 7·25) measures 7.50 mm across the flats. Find the distance p across the corners and the width r of each flat.

FIGURE 7·24 Measuring a dovetail

FIGURE 7·23 Measuring the radius of a broken pulley

FIGURE 7·25

7·6

Vectors

Definition

A *vector quantity* is one that has *direction* as well as magnitude. For example, a velocity cannot be completely described without giving the direction of the motion, as well as the magnitude (the speed). Other vector quantities are force and acceleration.

Quantities that have magnitude but no direction are called *scalar* quantities. These include time, volume, mass, and so on.

Representation of Vectors

A vector is represented by a line segment (Fig. 7·26) whose length is proportional to the magnitude of the vector, and whose direction is the same as the direction of the vector quantity.

Vectors are represented by boldface type. Thus **B** is a vector quantity, whereas *B* is a scalar quantity. A vector can be designated by a single letter, or by two letters representing the endpoints, with the starting point given first. Thus, the vector in Figure 7·26 can be labelled

V   or   **AB**

FIGURE 7·26 Representation of a vector

or, when handwritten,

$$\vec{V} \quad \text{or} \quad \vec{AB}$$

Boldface letters are not practical in handwritten work. Instead, it is customary to place an *arrow* over vector quantities.

The *magnitude* of a vector can be designated with absolute value symbols, or by ordinary (nonboldface) type. Thus the magnitude of vector **V** in Figure 7·26 is

$|\mathbf{V}|$ or V or $|\mathbf{AB}|$ or AB

Polar and rectangular Form

A vector is usually specified by giving its magnitude and direction. It is then said to be in *polar* form.

■ **Example 28:** A certain vector has a magnitude of 5 units and makes an angle of 38° with the positive *x* axis. We often write such a vector in the form

$5\underline{/38°}$

which is read *5 at an angle of 38°*.   ■

A vector drawn from the origin can also be designated by the *coordinates of its endpoint*.

■ **Example 29:**
(a) The ordered pair (3, 5) is a vector. It designates a line segment drawn from the origin to the point (3, 5).
(b) The *ordered triple* of numbers (4, 6, 3) is a vector in three dimensions. It designates a point drawn from the origin to the point (4, 6, 3).

We cover vectors such as these in Chapter 15.

A vector written this way is said to be in *rectangular* form.   ■

FIGURE 7·27

FIGURE 7·28

FIGURE 7·29 Rectangular components of a vector

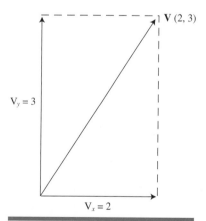

FIGURE 7·30

The component of a vector along an axis is also referred to as the *projection* of the vector onto that axis.

Drawing a Vector on Coordinate Axes

When a vector is specified by its magnitude and direction, simply draw an arrow whose length is equal to its magnitude (using a suitable scale for the axes) in the given direction. The tail of the vector is placed at the origin and the angle is measured, as usual, counterclockwise from the positive *x* direction.

■ **Example 30:** Draw the vector whose magnitude is 5 and whose direction is 38°.

Solution: We measure 38° counterclockwise from the positive *x* axis (Fig. 7·27), and draw the vector from the origin, with length 5 units. ■

When a vector is given by the coordinates of its endpoint, simply plot the point and connect it to the origin.

■ **Example 31:** Draw the vector (3.2, 4.8).

Solution: We plot the point (3.2, 4.8) (Fig. 7·28), and connect it to the origin. We draw the arrow at the given point, not at the origin. ■

Rectangular Components of a Vector

Any vector can be replaced by two (or more) vectors which, acting together, exactly duplicate the effect of the original vector. They are called the *components* of the vector. The components are usually chosen perpendicular to each other and are then called *rectangular components*. To *resolve* a vector means to replace it by its components.

■ **Example 32:** A ball thrown from one person to another moves simultaneously in both the horizontal direction and the vertical direction. The ball thus has a horizontal and a vertical component of velocity. ■

■ **Example 33:** Figure 7·29(a) shows a vector **V** resolved into its *x* component $\mathbf{V}_x$ and its *y* component $\mathbf{V}_y$. ■

■ **Example 34:** Figure 7·29(b) shows a block on an inclined plane with its force *W* resolved into a component *N* normal (perpendicular) to the plane and a component *T* tangential (parallel) to the plane. ■

■ **Example 35:** Figure 7·30, shows the vector **V** (2, 3) resolved into its *x* and *y* components. It is clear that the *x* component is 2 units, and the *y* component is 3 units. Note that the coordinates of the endpoint are also the magnitudes of the components. ■

Resolution of Vectors

We see in Figure 7·29 that a vector and its rectangular components form a rectangle that has two *right triangles*. Thus we can resolve a vector into its rectangular components with the right-triangle trigonometry of this chapter. Since, in Figure 7·29(a),

$$\sin \theta = \frac{V_y}{V}$$

we get

$$V_y = V \sin \theta$$

Similarly,

$$V_x = V \cos \theta$$

■ **Example 36:** The vector **V** in Figure 7•29(a) has a magnitude of 248 units and makes an angle θ of 38.2° with the x axis. Find the x and y components.

Finding the rectangular components of a vector on coordinate axes is no different from converting the vector from polar to rectangular form. Some calculators have a key for converting between rectangular and polar coordinates, which can also be used to find resultants and components of vectors. Check your manual.

Solution:

$$\sin 38.2° = \frac{V_y}{248}$$

$$V_y = 248 \sin 38.2° = 153$$

Similarly,

$$V_x = 248 \cos 38.2° = 195$$

Thus we can write

$$\mathbf{V} = 248\underline{/38.3°} = (195, 153)$$

in rectangular form.   ■

■ **Example 37:** A cable exerts a force of 558 N at an angle of 47.2° with the horizontal [Fig. 7.31(a)]. Resolve this force into vertical and horizontal components.

Solution: We draw a vector diagram [Fig. 7•31(b)]. Then

$$\sin 47.2° = \frac{V_y}{558}$$

$$V_y = 558 \sin 47.2° = 409 \, N$$

Similarly,

$$V_x = 558 \cos 47.2° = 379 \, N$$ ■

558 N

558 N

V_y

47.2°

47.2°

V_x

(a)   (b)

FIGURE 7•31

Resultant of Perpendicular Vectors

Just as any vector can be *resolved* into components, so can several vectors be *combined* into a single vector called the *resultant*, or *vector sum*. The process of combining vectors into a resultant is called *vector addition*.

When combining or adding two mutually perpendicular vectors, we can use right-triangle trigonometry, just as we did for resolving a vector into rectangular components.

■ **Example 38:** Find the resultant of two mutually perpendicular vectors whose magnitudes are 485 and 627, and the angle it makes with the 627 magnitude vector.

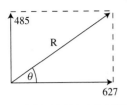

FIGURE 7•32 Resultant of two vectors

Solution: We draw a vector diagram (Fig. 7•32). Then, by the Pythagorean theorem,

$$R = \sqrt{(485)^2 + (627)^2} = 793$$

and by Eq. 148,

$$\tan \theta = \frac{485}{627} = 0.774$$

$$\theta = 37.7°$$

━ **Example 39:** If the components of vector **A** are

$$A_x = 735 \quad \text{and} \quad A_y = 593$$

find the magnitude of **A** and the angle θ it makes with the x axis.

Solution: By the Pythagorean theorem,

$$A^2 = A_x^2 + A_y^2$$
$$= (735)^2 + (593)^2 = 891\ 900$$
$$A = 944$$

and

$$\tan \theta = \frac{A_y}{A_x}$$
$$= \frac{593}{735}$$
$$\theta = 38.9°$$

In other words

$$\mathbf{A} = (735, 593) = 944\underline{/38.9°}$$

Resultant of Nonperpendicular Vectors

We can use right triangle trigonometry to find the resultant of any number of nonperpendicular vectors, such as those shown in Figure 7•33(a).

1. Resolve each vector into its x and y components.
2. Combine the x components into a single vector R_x in the x direction, and combine the y components into a single vector R_y in the y direction.
3. Find the resultant **R** of R_x and R_y.

━ **Example 40:** Find the resultant of the three vectors in Figure 7•33(a):

$$6.34\underline{/29.5°}, \quad 4.82\underline{/47.2°}, \quad \text{and} \quad 5.52\underline{/73.0°}$$

Solution: We first resolve each given vector into x and y components. We will arrange the computation in table form for convenience.

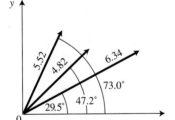

(a)

(b)

FIGURE 7•33

x components	y components
$6.34 \cos 29.5° = 5.52$	$6.34 \sin 29.5° = 3.12$
$4.82 \cos 47.2° = 3.27$	$4.82 \sin 47.2° = 3.54$
$5.52 \cos 73.0° = 1.61$	$5.52 \sin 73.0° = 5.28$
Sums: $R_x = 10.4$	$R_y = 11.9$

We now find the resultant of R_x and R_y [Figure 7•33(b)]. The magnitude of the resultant is

$$R = \sqrt{R_x^2 + R_y^2} = \sqrt{(10.4)^2 + (11.9)^2} = 15.8$$

Now finding the angle,

$$\tan \theta = \frac{R_y}{R_x} = \frac{11.9}{10.4} = 1.14$$

$$\text{Angle } \theta = 48.8°$$

$$\text{Resultant vector} = 15.8\underline{/48.8°}.$$

Exercise 6   Vectors

Drawing Vectors

Draw each vector on coordinate axes.

1. Magnitude = 3.84   Angle = 72.4°
2. Magnitude = 9.46   Angle = 28.4°
3. 36.2$\underline{/44.8°}$ **4.** 1.63$\underline{/29.4°}$
5. (2.84, 5.37)   **6.** (72.4, 58.3)

Resolution of Vectors

Given the magnitude of each vector and the angle θ that it makes with the x axis, find the x and y components.

7. Magnitude = 4.93 $\theta = 48.3°$ **8.** Magnitude = 835 $\theta = 25.8°$
9. Magnitude = 1.884 $\theta = 58.24°$ **10.** Magnitude = 362 $\theta = 13.8°$

Resultant of Perpendicular Vectors

In the following problems, the magnitudes of perpendicular vectors **A** and **B** are given. Find the resultant and the angle it makes with vector **B**.

11. $A = 483$ $B = 382$ **12.** $A = 2.85$ $B = 4.82$
13. $A = 7364$ $B = 4837$ **14.** $A = 46.8$ $B = 38.6$
15. $A = 1.25$ $B = 2.07$ **16.** $A = 274$ $B = 529$

In the following problems, vector **A** has x and y components A_x and A_y. Find the magnitude of **A** and the angle it makes with the x axis.

17. $A_x = 483$ $A_y = 382$ **18.** $A_x = 6.82$ $A_y = 4.83$
19. $A_x = 58.3$ $A_y = 37.2$ **20.** $A_x = 2.27$ $A_y = 3.97$

Resultant of Nonperpendicular Vectors

Find the resultant of each set of vectors.

21. 4.83$\underline{/18.3°}$ and 5.99$\underline{/83.5°}$
22. 13.5$\underline{/29.3°}$ and 27.8$\underline{/77.2°}$
23. 635$\underline{/22.7°}$ and 485$\underline{/48.8°}$
24. 83.2$\underline{/49.7°}$ and 52.5$\underline{/66.3°}$
25. 1.38$\underline{/22.4°}$, 2.74$\underline{/49.5°}$, and 3.32$\underline{/77.3°}$
26. 736$\underline{/15.8°}$, 586$\underline{/69.2°}$, and 826$\underline{/81.5°}$

Applications of Vectors

Any vector quantity such as force, velocity, or impedance can be combined or resolved by the methods in the preceding section.

Force Vectors

■ **Example 41:** A cable running from the top of a telephone pole (Fig. 7•34) creates a horizontal pull of 875 N. A support cable running to the ground is inclined 71.5° from the horizontal. Find the tension in the support cable.

Solution: We draw the forces acting at the top of the pole (Fig. 7•35). We see that the horizontal component of the tension T in the support cable must equal the horizontal pull of 875 N. So

$$\cos 71.5° = \frac{875}{T}$$

$$T = \frac{875}{\cos 71.5°} = 2760 \text{ N}$$ ■

Velocity Vectors

■ **Example 42:** A river flows at the rate of 4.70 km/h. A rower, who can travel 7.51 km/h in still water, heads directly across the current. Find the rate and direction of travel of the boat.

Solution: The boat (Fig. 7•36) is crossing the current and at the same time is being carried downstream. Thus the velocity **V** has one component of 7.51 km/h across the current and another component of 4.70 km/h downstream. We find the resultant of these two components by the Pythagorean theorem,

$$V^2 = (7.51)^2 + (4.70)^2$$

from which

$$V = 8.86 \text{ km/h}$$

Now finding the angle θ yields

$$\tan \theta = \frac{4.70}{7.51}$$

from which

$$\theta = 32.0°$$ ■

Impedance Vectors

Vectors find extensive application in electrical technology, and one of the most common applications is in the calculation of impedances. Figure 7•37 shows a resistor, an inductor, and a capacitor, connected in series with an AC source. The *reactance X* is a measure of how much the capacitance and inductance retard the flow of current in such a circuit. It is the difference between the *capacitive reactance X_C* and the *inductive reactance X_L*.

7•7

875 N

71.5°

FIGURE 7•34

875 N   875 N

T

FIGURE 7•35

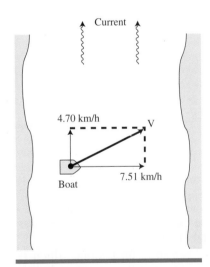

Current

4.70 km/h   V

7.51 km/h

Boat

FIGURE 7•36

R

ac source L

C

FIGURE 7•37

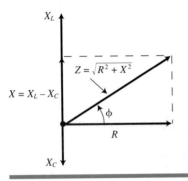

FIGURE 7•38 Vector impedance diagram

FIGURE 7•39

| Reactance | $X = X_L - X_c$ | **A98** |

The *impedance Z* is a measure of how much the flow of current in an AC circuit is retarded by all circuit elements, including the resistance. The magnitude of the impedance is related to the total resistance R and reactance X by

| Magnitude of Impedance | $|Z| = \sqrt{R^2 + X^2}$ | **A99** |

The impedance, resistance, and reactance form the three sides of a right triangle, the *vector impedance diagram* (Fig. 7•38). The angle ϕ between Z and R is called the *phase angle*.

| Phase Angle | $\phi = \arctan \dfrac{X}{R}$ | **A100** |

━ **Example 43:** The capacitive reactance of a certain circuit is 2720 Ω, the inductive reactance is 3260 Ω, and the resistance is 1150 Ω. Find the reactance and magnitude of the impedance of the circuit, and the phase angle.

Solution: By Eq. A98,

$$X = 3260 - 2720 = 540 \ \Omega$$

By Eq. A99,

$$|Z| = \sqrt{(1150)^2 + (540)^2} = 1270 \ \Omega$$

and by Eq. A100,

$$\phi = \arctan \frac{540}{1150} = 25.2° \qquad ━$$

Exercise 7 Applications of Vectors

Force Vectors

You will need the equations of equilibrium, Eqs. A13 and A14, for some of these problems.

1. What force, neglecting friction, must be exerted to drag a 56.5-N mass up a slope inclined 12.6° from the horizontal?
2. What is the largest load that a tractor can drag up a slope which is inclined 21.2° from the horizontal if it is able to pull up the slope with a force of 12 200 N? Neglect the force due to friction.
3. Two ropes (Fig. 7•39) hold a crate. One rope is pulling with a force of 994 N in a direction 15.5° with the vertical and the other with a force of 624 N in a direction 25.2° with the vertical. How much does the crate weigh?
4. A truck having a mass of 3306 kg moves up a bridge inclined 4.80° from the horizontal. Find the force of the truck normal (perpendicular) to the bridge.

Wind, 23.6 km/h

212 km/h

Track

N

FIGURE 7•40

FIGURE 7•41 Flight terminology: The *heading* of an aircraft is the direction in which the craft is *pointed*. Because of air current, it will not usually travel in that direction, but in an actual path called the *track*. The angle between the heading and the track is the *drift angle*. The *air speed* is the speed relative to the surrounding air, and the *ground speed* is the craft's speed relative to the earth.

5. A person has just enough strength to pull a 129-kg mass up a certain slope. Neglecting friction, find the angle at which the slope is inclined to the horizontal if the person is able to exert a pull of 551 N.

6. A person wishes to pull a 102-kg mass up an incline to the top of a wall 5.0 m high. Neglecting friction, what is the length of the shortest incline (measured along the incline) that can be used if the person's pulling strength is 650 N?

7. A truck of mass 18.6 tonnes stands on a hill inclined 15.4° from the horizontal. How large a force must be counteracted by brakes to prevent the truck from rolling downhill?

Velocity Vectors

8. A plane is headed due west with an air speed of 212 km/h (Fig. 7•40). It is driven from its course by wind from due north blowing at 23.6 km/h. Find the ground speed of the plane and the actual direction of travel. Refer to Figure 7•41 for definitions of flight terminology.

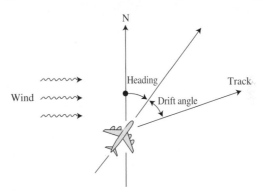

9. At what air speed should an airplane head due west in order to follow a course S80°15′W if a 20.5 km/h wind is blowing from due north?

10. A pilot heading his plane due north finds the actual direction of travel to be N5°12′E. The plane's air speed is 525 km/h and the wind is from due west. Find the plane's ground speed and the velocity of the wind.

11. A certain escalator travels at a rate of 10.6 m/min and its angle of inclination is 32.5°. What is the vertical component of the velocity? How long will it take a passenger to travel 10.0 m vertically?

12. A projectile is launched at an angle of 55.6° to the horizontal with a speed of 7550 m/min. Find the vertical and horizontal components of this velocity.

13. At what speed with respect to the water should a ship head due north in order to follow a course N5°15′E if a current is flowing due east at the rate of 1.65 km/h?

Impedance Vectors

14. A circuit has a reactance of 2650 Ω and a phase angle of 44.6°. Find the resistance and the magnitude of the impedance.

15. A circuit has a resistance of 115 Ω and a phase angle of 72.0°. Find the reactance and the magnitude of the impedance.

See Figure 7•16 (page 201) if you've forgotten how compass directions are written.

16. A circuit has an impedance of 975 Ω and a phase angle of 28.0°. Find the resistance and the reactance.

17. A circuit has a reactance of 5.75 Ω and a resistance of 4.22 Ω. Find the magnitude of the impedance and the phase angle.

18. A circuit has a capacitive reactance of 1776 Ω, an inductive reactance of 5140 Ω, and a total impedance of 5560 Ω. Find the resistance and the phase angle.

CHAPTER 7   REVIEW PROBLEMS

Perform the angle conversions, and fill in the missing quantities

DECIMAL DEGREES	DEGREES– MINUTES– SECONDS	RADIANS	REVOLUTIONS
1. 38.2			
2.	25°28′45″		
3.		2.745	
4.			0.275

The following points are on the terminal side of an angle θ. Write the six trigonometric functions of the angle and find the angle in decimal degrees, to three significant digits.

5. (3, 7)
6. (2, 5)
7. (4, 3)
8. (2.3, 3.1)

Write the six trigonometric functions of each angle. Keep four decimal places.

9. 72.9°
10. 35°13′33″
11. 1.05 rad

Find acute angle θ in decimal degrees.

12. $\sin \theta = 0.574$
13. $\cos \theta = 0.824$
14. $\tan \theta = 1.345$

Evaluate each expression. Give your answer as an acute angle in degrees.

15. arctan 2.86
16. $\cos^{-1} 0.385$
17. arcsec 2.447

Solve right triangle ABC.

18. $a = 746$ $A = 37.2°$
19. $b = 3.72$ $A = 28.5°$
20. $c = 45.9$ $A = 61.4°$
21. Find the *x* and *y* components of a vector that has a magnitude of 885 and makes an angle of 66.3° with the *x* axis.
22. Find the magnitude of the resultant of two mutually perpendicular vectors that have magnitudes of 54.8 and 39.4 and find the angle the resultant makes with the 54.8 vector.
23. A vector has *x* and *y* components of 385 and 275. Find the magnitude and direction of that vector.
24. A telephone pole casts a shadow 13.5 m long when the angle of elevation of the sun is 15.4°. Find the height of the pole.
25. From a point 38.10 m in front of a church, the angles of elevation of the top and base of its steeple are 22.5° and 19.6°, respectively. Find the height of the steeple.
26. A circuit has a resistance of 125 Ω, an impedance of 256 Ω, an inductive reactance of 312 Ω, and a positive phase angle. Find the capacitive reactance and the phase angle.

Evaluate to four decimal places.

27. cos 59.2°
28. csc 19.3°
29. tan 52.8°
30. sec 37.2°
31. cot 24.7°
32. sin 42.9°

Find the acute angle whose trigonometric function is given, to the nearest tenth of a degree.

33. $\tan \theta = 1.7362$
34. $\sec \theta = 2.9914$
35. $\sin \theta = 0.7253$

36. csc θ = 3.2746
37. cot θ = 0.9475
38. cos θ = 0.3645

Evaluate each trigonometric expression to three significant digits.

39. 8.23 cos 15.8° + 8.73
40. 5.82 − 5.89 sin 16.2°
41. 9.26(cos 88.3 + sin 22.3°)
42. 52.2 sin 3 + 45.3 cos 2

Draw each vector on coordinate axes.

43. Magnitude = 726, angle = 32.4°
44. 12.6$\underline{/74.8°}$ **45.** (7.84, 8.37)

Find the resultant of each set of vectors.

46. 633$\underline{/68.3°}$ and 483$\underline{/23.5°}$
47. 13.2$\underline{/22.7°}$ and 22.6$\underline{/76.8°}$
48. 8.28$\underline{/82.3°}$, 9.14$\underline{/15.5°}$, and 7.72$\underline{/47.9°}$
49. The equation for electric power is $P = I \cdot V \cdot \cos\theta$ watts in an alternating current circuit. Find the phase angle θ, if the power is given as 250 W when the voltage is 110 V with a current of 2.8A.

50. Two voltages are acting on an electrical circuit. Voltage $V_1 = 200\angle30°$ and $V_2 = 320\angle25°$. Find a single voltage that will replace these two voltages in both magnitude and direction.

Writing

51. Write a short paragraph, with examples, on how you might possibly use an idea from this chapter in a real-life situation: on the job, in a hobby, or around the house.

Team Project

52. Make a device for measuring angles in the horizontal plane, using a sighting tube of some sort and a protractor. Use this "transit" and a rope of known length to find some distance on your campus, such as the distance across a ball field, using the method of Problem 5 in Exercise 4. Compare your results with the actual taped distance. Give a prize to the team that gets closest to the taped value.

8

Factors and Factoring

When you have completed this chapter, you should be able to:

- Factor expressions by removing common factors.
- Factor binomials that are the difference of two squares.
- Factor the sum or difference of two cubes.
- Factor trinomials.
- Factor the perfect square trinomial.
- Factor expressions by grouping.
- Use factoring techniques in applications.

The idea of a factor is not entirely new to us. You might glance back at Sections 1•3 and 2•1 before starting this chapter.

In Chapter 2 we learned how to multiply expressions together—here we do the reverse. We find those quantities (factors) which, when multiplied together, give the original product.

Why bother factoring? What is the point of changing an expression from one form to another? Because factoring, which may seem complicated at first, is actually essential to simplifying expressions and solving equations, especially the quadratic equations in Chapter 14. The value of factoring will become clear as we use it toward the end of this chapter to solve literal equations and to manipulate the formulas that are so important in technology. We also use factoring in Chapter 9 to simplify fractions.

8•1

Common Factors

Factors of an Expression

The *factors of an expression* are those quantities whose product is the original expression.

— **Example 1:** The factors of $x^2 - 9$ are $x + 3$ and $x - 3$, because

$$(x + 3)(x - 3) = x^2 + 3x - 3x - 9$$

$$= x^2 - 9$$
—

Prime Factors

Many expressions have no factors other than 1 and themselves. Such expressions are called *prime*.

■ **Example 2:** Two factors of 30 are 5 and 6. The 5 is prime because it cannot be factored. However, the 6 is not prime because it can be factored into 2 and 3. Thus the prime factors of 30 are 2, 3, and 5. ■

■ **Example 3:** The expressions x, $x - 3$, and $x^2 - 3x + 7$ are all prime. They cannot be factored further. ■

■ **Example 4:** The expressions $x^2 - 9$ and $x^2 + 5x + 6$ are not prime, because they can be factored. They are said to be *factorable*. ■

Factoring

Factoring is the process of finding the factors of an expression. It is *the reverse of finding the product* of two or more quantities.

Multiplication (Finding the Product)
$x(x + 4) = x^2 + 4x$
Factoring (Finding the Factors)
$x^2 + 4x = x(x + 4)$

We factor an expression by *recognizing the form* of that expression and then applying standard rules for factoring. In the first type of factoring we will cover, we look for *common factors*.

Common Factors

If each term of an expression contains the same quantity (called the *common factor*), that quantity may be *factored out*.

This is nothing but the *distributive law* that we studied earlier.

Common Factor	$ab + ac = a(b + c)$	5

■ **Example 5:** In the expression

$$2x + x^2$$

each term contains an x as a common factor, so we write

$$2x + x^2 = x(2 + x)$$

Most of the factoring we will do will be of this type. ■

■ **Example 6:**
(a) $3x^3 - 2x + 5x^4 = x(3x^2 - 2 + 5x^3)$
(b) $3xy^2 - 9x^3y + 6x^2y^2 = 3xy(y - 3x^2 + 2xy)$

(c) $3x^3 - 6x^2y + 9x^4y^2 = 3x^2(x - 2y + 3x^2y^2)$
(d) $2x^2 + x = x(2x + 1)$

When factoring, don't confuse superscripts (powers) with subscripts.

■ **Example 7:** The expression $x^3 + x^2$ is factorable:

$$x^3 + x^2 = x^2(x + 1)$$

but the expression

$$x_3 + x_2$$

is not factorable.

Common Error	Students are sometimes puzzled over the 1 in Example 7. Why should it be there? After all, when you remove a chair from a room, it is *gone*; there is nothing (zero) remaining where the chair used to be. If you remove an x by factoring, you might assume that nothing (zero) remains where the x used to be. $$2x^2 + x = x(2x + 0)?$$ Prove to yourself that this is not correct by multiplying the factors to see if you get back the original expression.

Factors in the Denominator

Common factors may appear in the denominators of the terms as well as in the numerators.

■ **Example 8:**

(a) $\dfrac{1}{x} + \dfrac{2}{x^2} = \dfrac{1}{x}\left(1 + \dfrac{2}{x}\right)$

(b) $\dfrac{x}{y^2} + \dfrac{x^2}{y} + \dfrac{2x}{3y} = \dfrac{x}{y}\left(\dfrac{1}{y} + x + \dfrac{2}{3}\right)$

Checking

This check will tell us whether we have factored correctly, but, of course, not whether we have factored *completely*, that is, found the prime factors.

To check whether factoring has been done correctly, simply multiply your factors together and see if you get back the original expression.

■ **Example 9:** Are $2xy$ and $x + 3 - y^2$ the factors of

$$2x^2y + 6xy - 2xy^3?$$

Solution: Multiplying the factors, we obtain

$$2xy(x + 3 - y^2) = 2x^2y + 6xy - 2xy^3 \qquad \text{checks}$$

Exercise 1 Common Factors

Factor each expression and check your result.

1. $3y^2 + y^3$
2. $6x - 3y$
3. $x^5 - 2x^4 + 3x^3$
4. $9y - 27xy$
5. $3a + a^2 - 3a^3$
6. $8xy^3 - 6x^2y^2 + 2x^3y$
7. $5(x + y) + 15(x + y)^2$
8. $\dfrac{a}{3} - \dfrac{a^2}{4} + \dfrac{a^3}{5}$
9. $\dfrac{3}{x} + \dfrac{2}{x^2} - \dfrac{5}{x^3}$
10. $\dfrac{3ab^2}{y^3} - \dfrac{6a^2b}{y^2} + \dfrac{12ab}{y}$
11. $5a^2b + 6a^2c$
12. $a^2c + b^2c + c^2d$
13. $4x^2y + cxy^2 + 3xy^3$
14. $4abx + 6a^2x^2 + 8ax$
15. $3a^3y - 6a^2y^2 + 9ay^3$
16. $2a^2c - 2a^2c^2 + 3ac$
17. $5acd - 2c^2d^2 + bcd$
18. $4b^2c^2 - 12abc - 9c^2$
19. $8x^2y^2 + 12x^2z^2$
20. $6xyz + 12x^2y^2z$
21. $3a^2b + abc - abd$
22. $5a^3x^2 - 5a^2x^3 + 10a^2x^2z$

Applications

23. When a bar of length L_0 is changed in temperature by an amount t, its new length L will be $L = L_0 + L_0\alpha t$, where α is the coefficient of thermal expansion. Factor the right side of this equation.
24. A sum of money a when invested for t years at an interest rate n will accumulate to an amount y, where $y = a + ant$. Factor the right side of this equation.

Compare your result with Eq. A70.

25. When a resistance R_1 is heated from a temperature t_1 to a new temperature t, it will increase in resistance by an amount $\alpha(t - t_1)R_1$, where α is the temperature coefficient of resistance. The final resistance will then be $R = R_1 + \alpha(t - t_1)R_1$. Factor the right side of this equation.
26. An item costing P dollars is reduced in price by 15%. The resulting price C is then $C = P - 0.15P$. Factor the right side of this equation.
27. The displacement of a uniformly accelerated body is given by

$$s = v_0t + \frac{a}{2}t^2$$

Factor the right side of this equation.

FIGURE 8•1

28. The sum of the voltage drops across the resistors in Fig. 8•1 must equal the battery voltage E.

$$E = IR_1 + IR_2 + IR_3$$

Factor the right side of this equation.

29. The mass of a spherical shell having an outside radius of r_2 and an inside radius r_1 is

$$(\text{Mass} =) \tfrac{4}{3}\pi r_2^3 D - \tfrac{4}{3}\pi r_1^3 D$$

where D is the mass density of the material. Factor the right side of this equation.

8•2 Difference of Two Squares

Form

An expression of the form

where one perfect square is subtracted from another, is called a *difference of two squares*. It arises when $(a - b)$ and $(a + b)$ are multiplied together.

Remember this from Chapter 2?

Difference of Two Squares	$a^2 - b^2 = (a + b)(a - b)$	**41**

Factoring the Difference of Two Squares

Once we recognize its form, the difference of two squares is easily factored.

■ **Example 10:**

$$4x^2 - 9 = (2x)^2 - (3)^2$$

$$(2x)^2 - (3)^2 = (2x \quad)(2x \quad)$$

square root of the first term

$$(2x)^2 - (3)^2 = (2x \quad 3)(2x \quad 3)$$

square root of the last term

$$4x^2 - 9 = (2x + 3)(2x - 3)$$

opposite signs

■ **Example 11:**

(a) $y^2 - 1 = (y + 1)(y - 1)$

(b) $9a^2 - 16b^2 = (3a + 4b)(3a - 4b)$

(c) $49x^2 - 9a^2y^2 = (7x - 3ay)(7x + 3ay)$
(d) $1 - a^2b^2c^2 = (1 - abc)(1 + abc)$ ▬

Common Error	There is no similar rule for factoring the *sum* of two squares. $$a^2 + b^2$$

The difference of any two quantities that have *even powers* can be factored as the difference of two squares. *Express each quantity as a square* by means of the law of powers:

Powers	$x^{ab} = (x^a)^b$	**31**

▬ **Example 12:**
(a) $\begin{aligned} a^4 - b^6 &= (a^2)^2 - (b^3)^2 \\ &= (a^2 + b^3)(a^2 - b^3) \end{aligned}$
(b) $\begin{aligned} x^{2a} - y^{6b} &= (x^a)^2 - (y^{3b})^2 \\ &= (x^a + y^{3b})(x^a - y^{3b}) \end{aligned}$ ▬

Sometimes one or both terms in the given expression may be fractions.

▬ **Example 13:**

$$\frac{1}{x^2} - \frac{1}{y^2} = \left(\frac{1}{x}\right)^2 - \left(\frac{1}{y}\right)^2$$

$$= \left(\frac{1}{x} + \frac{1}{y}\right)\left(\frac{1}{x} - \frac{1}{y}\right)$$ ▬

Sometimes one (or both) of the terms in an expression is itself a binomial.

▬ **Example 14:**

$$(a + b)^2 - x^2 = [(a + b) + x][(a + b) - x]$$ ▬

Factoring Completely

After factoring an expression, see if any of the factors themselves can be factored *again*.

▬ **Example 15:** Factor $a - ab^2$.

Solution: Always remove any common factors first. Factoring, we obtain

$$a - ab^2 = a(1 - b^2)$$

Now, factoring the difference of two squares, we get

$$a - ab^2 = a(1 + b)(1 - b)$$ ▬

■ **Example 16:**

$$x^4 - y^4 = (x^2 + y^2)(x^2 - y^2)$$

Now factoring the difference of two squares again, we obtain

$$x^4 - y^4 = (x^2 + y^2)(x + y)(x - y)$$ ■

Exercise 2 Difference of Two Squares

Factor completely.

1. $4 - x^2$ **2.** $x^2 - 9$
3. $9a^2 - x^2$ **4.** $25 - x^2$
5. $4x^2 - 4y^2$ **6.** $9x^2 - y^2$
7. $x^2 - 9y^2$ **8.** $16x^2 - 16y^2$
9. $9c^2 - 16d^2$ **10.** $25a^2 - 9b^2$
11. $9y^2 - 1$ **12.** $4x^2 - 9y^2$

Expressions with Higher Powers or Literal Powers

Factor completely.

13. $m^4 - n^4$ **14.** $a^8 - b^8$
15. $m^{2n} - n^{2m}$ **16.** $9^{2n} - 4b^{4n}$
17. $a^{16} - b^8$ **18.** $9a^2b^2 - 4c^4$
19. $25x^4 - 16y^6$ **20.** $36y^2 - 49z^6$
21. $16a^4 - 121$ **22.** $121a^4 - 16$
23. $25a^4b^4 - 9$ **24.** $121a^2 - 36b^4$

FIGURE 8·2 Circular washer

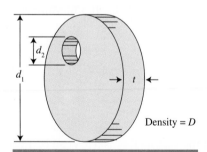

FIGURE 8·3 Flywheel

Applications

25. The thrust washer in Figure 8·2 has a surface area of

$$\pi r_2^2 - \pi r_1^2$$

Factor this expression.

26. A flywheel of diameter d_1 (Fig. 8·3) has a balancing hole of diameter d_2 drilled through it. The mass m of the flywheel is then

$$\frac{\pi d_1^2}{4} Dt - \frac{\pi d_2^2}{4} Dt$$

Factor this expression.

27. A spherical balloon shrinks from radius r_1 to radius r_2. The change in surface area is, from Eq. 129, $4\pi r_1^2 - 4\pi r_2^2$. Factor this expression.

28. When an object is released from rest, the distance fallen between time t_1 and time t_2 is $\frac{1}{2}at_2^2 - \frac{1}{2}at_1^2$, where a is the acceleration due to gravity. Factor this expression.

29. When a body of mass m slows down from velocity v_1 to velocity v_2, the decrease in kinetic energy is $\frac{1}{2}mv_1^2 - \frac{1}{2}mv_2^2$. Factor this expression.

30. The work required to stretch a spring from a length x_1 (measured from the unstretched position) to a new length x_2 is $\frac{1}{2}kx_2^2 - \frac{1}{2}kx_1^2$. Factor this expression.

31. The formula for the volume of a cylinder of radius r and height h is $v = \pi r^2 h$. Write an expression for the volume of a hollow cylinder that has an inside radius r, an outside radius R, and a height h. Then factor the expression completely.

32. A body at temperature T will radiate an amount of heat kT^4 to its surroundings and will absorb from the surroundings an amount of heat kT_s^4, where T_s is the temperature of the surroundings. Write an expression for the net heat transfer by radiation (amount radiated minus amount absorbed) and factor this expression completely.

8·3

Factoring Trinomials

Trinomials

A *trinomial*, you will recall, is a polynomial having *three terms*.

━ **Example 17:** $2x^3 - 3x + 4$ is a trinomial.   ━

A *quadratic trinomial* has an x^2 term, an x term, and a constant term.

━ **Example 18:** $4x^2 + 3x - 5$ is a quadratic trinomial.   ━

In this section we factor only quadratic trinomials.

Test for Factorability

Not all quadratic trinomials can be factored. We test for factorability as follows:

$b^2 - 4ac$ is called the *discriminant*, Eq. 101. We will use it later to predict the nature of the roots of a quadratic equation.

Test for Factorability	The trinomial $ax^2 + bx + c$ (where a, b, and c are constants) is factorable if $b^2 - 4ac$ is a perfect square.	**44**

━ **Example 19:** Can the trinomial $6x^2 + x - 12$ be factored?

Solution: Using the test for factorability, Eq. 44 with $a = 6$, $b = 1$, and $c = -12$,

$$b^2 - 4ac = 1^2 - 4(6)(-12) = 289$$

By taking the square root of 289 on the calculator, we see that it is a perfect square ($289 = 17^2$), so the given trinomial is factorable. We will see later that its factors are $(2x + 3)$ and $(3x - 4)$.   ━

The coefficient of the x^2 term in a quadratic trinomial is called the *leading coefficient*. (It is the constant a in Eq. 44). We will first factor the easier type of trinomial, in which the leading coefficient is 1.

Trinomials with a Leading Coefficient of 1

We get such a trinomial when we multiply two binomials if the coefficients of the x terms in the binomials are also 1.

$$(x + a)(x + b) = x^2 + (a + b)x + ab$$

Note that the coefficient of the middle term of the trinomial equals the *sum* of a and b, and that the last term equals the *product* of a and b. Knowing this, we can reverse the process and find the factors when the trinomial is given.

Trinomials: Leading Coefficient $= 1$	$$x^2 + (a + b)x + ab = (x + a)(x + b)$$ sum ⌐ product ⌐	**45**

━ **Example 20:** Factor the trinomial $x^2 + 8x + 15$.

Solution: From Eq. 45 this trinomial, if factorable, will factor as $(x + a)(x + b)$, where a and b have a sum of 8 and a product of 15. The integers 5 and 3 have a sum of 8 and a product of 15, so,

$$x^2 + 8x + 15 = (x + 5)(x + 3)$$

━

Using the Signs to Aid Factoring

The signs of the terms of the trinomial can tell you the signs of the factors.

1. If the sign of the last term is *positive*, the signs in the factors will be the same (both positive or both negative). The sign of the middle term of the trinomial will tell whether the signs in the factors are both positive or both negative.

━ **Example 21:**

positive, so signs in the factors are the same

(a) $x^2 + 6x + 8 = (x + 4)(x + 2)$

positive, so signs in both the factors are positive

positive, so signs in the factors are the same

(b) $x^2 - 6x + 8 = (x - 4)(x - 2)$

negative, so signs in both the factors are negative

━

2. If the sign of the last term of the trinomial is *negative*, the signs of a and b in the factors will differ (one positive, one negative). The sign of the middle term of the trinomial will tell which quantity, a or b, is larger (in absolute value), the positive one or the negative one.

━ **Example 22:**

negative, so the signs in the factors differ, one positive and one negative

$x^2 - 2x - 8 = (x - 4)(x + 2)$

negative, so the larger number (4) has a negative sign

━

■ **Example 23:** Factor $x^2 + 2x - 15$.

Solution: We first look at the sign of the last term (-15). The negative sign tell us that the signs of the factors will differ.

$$x^2 + 2x - 15 = (x - \quad)(x + \quad)$$

We then find two numbers whose product is -15 and whose sum is 2. These two numbers must have opposite signs in order to have a negative product. Also, since the middle coefficient is $+2$, the positive number must be 2 greater than the negative number. Two numbers that meet these conditions are $+5$ and -3. So

$$x^2 + 2x - 15 = (x + 5)(x - 3)$$ ■

Remember to remove any *common factors* before factoring a trinomial.

■ **Example 24:**

$$2x^3 + 4x^2 - 30x = 2x(x^2 + 2x - 15)$$
$$= 2x(x - 3)(x + 5)$$ ■

Trinomials Having More Than One Variable

■ **Example 25:** Factor $x^2 + 5xy + 6y^2$.

As with the difference of two squares, many trinomials can be factored that at first glance do not seem to be in the proper form. Here are some common types.

Solution: One way to factor such a trinomial is, first, to drop the second variable (y in this example) temporarily:

$$x^2 + 5x + 6$$

Then factor the resulting trinomial:

$$(x + 2)(x + 3)$$

Finally, note that if we tack y onto the second term of each factor, this will cause y to appear in the middle term of the trinomial and y^2 to appear in the last term of the trinomial. The required factors are then

$$(x + 2y)(x + 3y)$$ ■

■ **Example 26:** Factor $w^2x^2 + 3wxy - 4y^2$.

Solution: Temporarily dropping w and y yields

$$x^2 + 3x - 4$$

which factors into

$$(x - 1)(x + 4)$$

We then note that, if a w were appended to each x term and a y to the second term in each binomial,

$$(wx - y)(wx + 4y)$$

the product of these factors will give the original expression. ■

Trinomials with Higher Powers

Trinomials with powers *greater than two* may be factored if one exponent can be expressed as a *multiple of two*, and if that exponent is *twice the other*.

■ **Example 27:**

$$x^6 - x^3 - 6 = (x^3)^2 - (x^3) - 6$$
$$= (x^3 - 3)(x^3 + 2)$$ ■

Trinomials with Variables in the Exponents

If one exponent is *twice the other*, you may be able to factor such a trinomial.

■ **Example 28:**

$$x^{2n} + 5x^n + 6 = (x^n)^2 + 5(x^n) + 6$$
$$= (x^n + 3)(x^n + 2)$$ ■

Substitution

This technique will be valuable when we solve *equations of quadratic type* in Chapter 14.

You may prefer to handle some expressions by making a *substitution*, as in the following examples.

■ **Example 29:** Factor $x^{6n} + 2x^{3n} - 3$.

Solution: We see that one exponent is twice the other. Let us substitute a new letter for x^{3n}. Let

$$w = x^{3n}$$

Then

$$x^{6n} = (x^{3n})^2 = w^2$$

and our expression becomes

$$w^2 + 2w - 3$$

which factors into

$$(w + 3)(w - 1)$$

or, substituting back, we have

$$(x^{3n} + 3)(x^{3n} - 1)$$ ■

■ **Example 30:** Factor $(x + y)^2 + 7(x + y) - 30$.

Solution: We might be tempted to expand this expression, but notice that if we make the substitution

$$w = x + y$$

we get

$$w^2 + 7w - 30$$

which factors into $(w + 10)(w - 3)$. Substituting back, we get the factors

$$(x + y + 10)(x + y - 3)$$ ■

Exercise 3 Factoring Trinomials

Test for Factorability

Test each trinomial for factorability.

1. $3x^2 - 5x - 9$

2. $3a^2 + 7a + 2$

3. $2x^2 - (-12x) + 18$

4. $5z^2 - 2z - 1$

5. $x^2 - 30x - 64$

6. $y^2 + 2y - 7$

Trinomials with Leading Coefficient of 1

Factor completely.

7. $x^2 - 10x + 21$

8. $x^2 - 15x + 56$

9. $x^2 - 10x + 9$

10. $x^2 + 13x + 30$

11. $x^2 + 7x - 30$

12. $x^2 + 3x + 2$

13. $x^2 + 7x + 12$

14. $c^2 + 9c + 18$

15. $x^2 - 4x - 21$

16. $x^2 - x - 56$

17. $x^2 + 6x + 8$

18. $x^2 + 12x + 32$

19. $b^2 - 8b + 15$

20. $b^2 + b - 12$

21. $b^2 - b - 12$

22. $3b^2 - 30b + 63$

23. $2y^2 - 26y + 60$

24. $4z^2 - 16z - 84$

25. $3w^2 + 36w + 96$

Trinomials Having More than One Variable

Factor completely.

26. $x^2 - 13xy + 36y^2$

27. $x^2 + 19xy + 84y^2$

28. $a^2 - 9ab + 20b^2$

29. $a^2 + ab - 6b^2$

30. $a^2 + 3ab - 4b^2$

31. $a^2 + 2ax - 63x^2$

32. $x^2y^2 - 19xyz + 48z^2$

33. $a^2 - 20abc - 96b^2c^2$

34. $x^2 - 10xyz - 96y^2z^2$

35. $a^2 + 49abc + 48b^2c^2$

Trinomials with Higher Powers or with Variables in the Exponents

Factor completely.

36. $a^{6p} + 13a^{3p} + 12$

37. $(a + b)^2 - 7(a + b) - 8$

38. $w(x + y)^2 + 5w(x + y) + 6w$

39. $x^4 - 9x^2y^2 + 20y^4$

40. $a^6b^6 - 23a^3b^3c^2 + 132c^4$

Applications

41. To find the thickness t of the angle iron in Figure 8•4, it is necessary to solve the quadratic equation

$$t^2 - 140t + 2400 = 0$$

Factor the left side of this equation. Show how the equation was obtained.

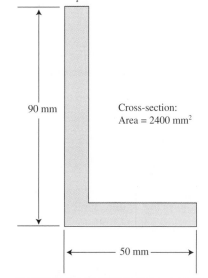

90 mm

Cross-section:
Area = 2400 mm²

t

50 mm

FIGURE 8•4

FIGURE 8·5

8·4

We'll use this same grouping idea later to factor certain trinomials.

42. To find the dimensions of a rectangular field having a perimeter of 70 m and an area of 300 m², we must solve the equation

$$x^2 - 35x + 300 = 0$$

Factor the left side of this equation.

43. To find the width of the frame in Fig. 8·5, we must solve the equation

$$x^2 - 110x + 1000 = 0$$

Factor the left side of this equation.

44. To find two resistors that will give an equivalent resistance of 400 Ω when wired in series and 75 Ω when wired in parallel, we must solve the equation.

$$R^2 - 400R + 30\,000 = 0$$

Factor the left side of this equation.

Factoring by Grouping

When the expression to be factored has four or more terms, these terms can sometimes be arranged in smaller groups that can be factored separately.

▬ **Example 31:** Factor $ab + 4a + 3b + 12$.

Solution: Group the two terms containing the factor a, and the two containing the factor 3. Remove the common factor from each pair of terms.

$$(ab + 4a) + (3b + 12) = a(b + 4) + 3(b + 4)$$

Both terms now have the common factor $(b + 4)$, which we factor out.

$$(b + 4)(a + 3)$$ ▬

▬ **Example 32:** Factor $x^2 - y^2 + 2x + 1$.

Solution: Taking our cue from Example 31, we try grouping the x terms together,

$$(x^2 + 2x) + (-y^2 + 1)$$

and are no better off than before. We then might notice that if the $+1$ term were grouped with the x terms, we would get a trinomial that could be factored. Thus we have

$$(x^2 + 2x + 1) - y^2$$

$$= (x + 1)(x + 1) - y^2$$

or

$$(x + 1)^2 - y^2$$

We now have the difference of two squares. Factoring again gives

$$(x + 1 + y)(x + 1 - y)$$ ▬

Exercise 4 Factoring by Grouping

Factor completely.

1. $a^3 + 3a^2 + 4a + 12$
2. $x^3 + x^2 + x + 1$
3. $x^3 - x^2 + x - 1$
4. $2x^3 - x^2 + 4x - 2$
5. $x^2 - bx + 3x - 3b$
6. $ab + a - b - 1$
7. $3x - 2y - 6 + xy$
8. $x^2y^2 - 3x^2 - 4y^2 + 12$
9. $x^2 + y^2 + 2xy - 4$
10. $x^2 - 6xy + 9y^2 - a^2$
11. $m^2 - n^2 - 4 + 4n$
12. $p^2 - r^2 - 6pq + 9q^2$

Expressions with Three or More Letters

Factor completely.

13. $ax + bx + 3a + 3b$
14. $x^2 + xy + xz + yz$
15. $a^2 - ac + ab - bc$
16. $ay - by + ab - y^2$
17. $2a + bx^2 + 2b + ax^2$
18. $2xy + wy - wz - 2xz$
19. $6a^2 + 2ab - 3ac - bc$
20. $x^2 + bx + cx + bc$
21. $b^2 - bc + ab - ac$
22. $bx - cx + bc - x^2$
23. $x^2 - a^2 - 2ab - b^2$
24. $p^2 - y^2 - x^2 - 2xy$

8·5

General Quadratic Trinomial

When we multiply the two binomials $(ax + b)$ and $(cx + d)$, we get a trinomial with a leading coefficient of ac, a middle coefficient of $(ad + bc)$, and a constant term of bd.

General Quadratic Trinomial	$(ax + b)(cx + d) = acx^2 + (ad + bc)x + bd$	**46**

The general quadratic trinomial may be factored by trial and error or by the grouping method.

Trial and Error

To factor the general quadratic trinomial by trial and error, we look for four numbers, a, b, c, and d, such that

$$ac = \text{the leading coefficient}$$

$$ad + bc = \text{the middle coefficient}$$

$$bd = \text{the constant term}$$

Also, the *signs* in the factors are found in the same way as for trinomials with a leading coefficient of 1.

━ **Example 33:** Factor $2x^2 + 5x + 3$.

Solution: The leading coefficient $ac = 2$ and the constant term $bd = 3$. Try

$$a = 1, c = 2 \text{ and } b = 3, d = 1$$

Then $ad + bc = 1(1) + 3(2) = 7$. No good. It is supposed to be 5. We next try

$$a = 1, c = 2, \text{ and } b = 1, d = 3$$

Then $ad + bc = 1(3) + 1(2) = 5$. This works. So

$$2x^2 + 5x + 3 = (x + 1)(2x + 3)$$ ━

Grouping Method

The grouping method eliminates the need for trial and error.

Some people have a knack for factoring and can quickly factor a trinomial by trial and error. Others rely on the longer but surer grouping method.

━ **Example 34:** Factor $3x^2 - 16x - 12$.

Solution:

1. Multiply the leading coefficient and the constant term.
$$3(-12) = -36$$

2. Find two numbers whose product equals -36 and whose sum equals the middle coefficient, -16. Two such numbers are 2 and -18.

3. Rewrite the trinomial, splitting the middle term according to the selected factors $(-16x = 2x - 18x)$,
$$3x^2 + 2x - 18x - 12$$
and group the first two terms together and the last two terms together.
$$(3x^2 + 2x) + (-18x - 12)$$

4. Remove common factors from each grouping.
$$x(3x + 2) - 6(3x + 2)$$

5. Remove the common factor $(3x + 2)$ from the entire expression.
$$(3x + 2)(x - 6)$$

These are the required factors.

| Common Error | It is easy to make a mistake when factoring out a negative quantity. Thus, when we factored out a -6 in going from Step 3 to Step 4 above, we got

$$(-18x - 12) = -6(3x + 2)$$

but not

$$-6(3x - 2)$$
$\quad\quad\quad\quad$↑— Incorrect! |

Notice that, if we had grouped the terms differently in Step 3, we would have arrived at the same factors:

$$3x^2 - 18x + 2x - 12$$
$$3x(x - 6) + 2(x - 6)$$
$$(3x + 2)(x - 6)$$

as before.

Sometimes an expression may be simplified before factoring, as we did in Section 8•3.

■ **Example 35:** Factor $12(x + y)^{6n} - (x + y)^{3n}z - 6z^2$.

Solution: If we substitute $a = (x + y)^{3n}$ our expression becomes

$$12a^2 - az - 6z^2$$

Temporarily dropping the z's gives

$$12a^2 - a - 6$$

which factors into

$$(4a - 3)(3a + 2)$$

Replacing the z's, we get

$$12a^2 - az - 6z^2 = (4a - 3z)(3a + 2z)$$

Finally, substituting back $(x + y)^{3n}$ for a, we have

$$12(x + y)^{6n} - (x + y)^{3n}z - 6z^2 = [4(x + y)^{3n} - 3z][3(x + y)^{3n} + 2z]$$ ■

Exercise 5 General Quadratic Trinomial

Factor completely.

1. $4x^2 - 13x + 3$ **2.** $5a^2 - 8a + 3$
3. $5x^2 + 11x + 2$ **4.** $7x^2 + 23x + 6$
5. $12b^2 - b - 6$ **6.** $6x^2 - 7x + 2$
7. $2a^2 + a - 6$ **8.** $2x^2 + 3x - 2$
9. $5x^2 - 38x + 21$ **10.** $4x^2 + 7x - 15$
11. $3x^2 + 6x + 3$ **12.** $2x^2 + 11x + 12$
13. $3x^2 - x - 2$ **14.** $7x^2 + 123x - 54$

15. $4x^2 - 10x + 6$
16. $3x^2 + 11x - 20$
17. $4a^2 + 4a - 3$
18. $9x^2 - 27x + 18$
19. $9a^2 - 15a - 14$
20. $16c^2 - 48c + 35$

Expressions Reducible to Quadratic Trinomials

Factor completely.

21. $49x^6 + 14x^3y - 15y^2$
22. $-18y^2 + 42x^2 - 24xy$
23. $4x^6 + 13x^3 + 3$
24. $5a^{2n} - 8a^n + 3$
25. $5x^{4n} + 11x^{2n} + 2$
26. $12(a + b)^2 - (a + b) - 6$
27. $3(a + x)^{2n} - 3(a + x)^n - 6$

Applications

28. An object is thrown upward with an initial velocity of 10 m/s from a building 40 m above the ground. The height, s, of the object above the ground at any time t is given by

$$s = 40 + 10t - 5t^2$$

Factor the right side of this equation when $s = 0$.

29. An object is thrown into the air with an initial velocity of 20 m/s. To find the time it takes for the object to reach a height of 15 m, we must solve the quadratic equation

$$5t^2 - 20t + 15 = 0$$

Factor the left side of this equation.

30. To find the depth of cut h needed to produce a flat of a certain width on a 25-mm-radius bar (Fig. 8•6) we must solve the equation

$$4h^2 - 200\,h + 1600 = 0$$

Factor the left side of this equation.

FIGURE 8•6

8•6

The Perfect Square Trinomial

The Square of a Binomial

In Chapter 2 we saw that the expression obtained when a binomial is squared is called a *perfect square trinomial*.

━ **Example 36:** Squaring the binomial $(2x + 3)$, we obtain

$$(2x + 3)^2 = 4x^2 + 6x + 6x + 9$$

$$= 4x^2 + 12x + 9$$ ━

Note that, in the perfect square trinomial obtained in Example 36, the first and last terms are the squares of the first and last terms of the binomial

Any quadratic trinomial can be manipulated into the form of a perfect square trinomial by a procedure called *completing the square*. We will use that method in Section 14•2 to derive the quadratic formula.

and that the middle term is twice the product of the terms of the binomial.

$$(2x + 3)^2$$

product

$6x$

twice the product

$$4x^2 + 12x + 9$$

and that the constant term is always positive. In general,

Perfect Square Trinomials	$(a + b)^2 = a^2 + 2ab + b^2$	**47**
	$(a - b)^2 = a^2 - 2ab + b^2$	**48**

Factoring a Perfect Square Trinomial

We can factor a perfect square trinomial in the same way we factored the general quadratic trinomial in Section 8•5. However, the work is faster if we recognize that a trinomial is a perfect square. If it is, its factors will be the square of a binomial. The terms of that binomial are the square roots of the first and last terms of the trinomial. The sign in the binomial will be the same as the sign of the middle term of the trinomial.

■ **Example 37:** Factor $a^2 - 4a + 4$.

Solution: The first and last terms are both perfect squares, and the middle term is twice the product of the square roots of the first and last terms. Thus the trinomial is a perfect square. Factoring, we obtain

$$a^2 - 4a + 4$$

square root   same   square root

$$(a - 2)^2$$

■ **Example 38:**

$$9x^2y^2 - 6xy + 1 = (3xy - 1)^2$$

Common Error	$(a + b)^2 \neq a^2 + b^2$

Exercise 6 The Perfect Square Trinomial

Factor completely.

1. $x^2 + 4x + 4$ **2.** $x^2 - 30x + 225$
3. $y^2 - 2y + 1$ **4.** $x^2 + 2x + 1$
5. $2y^2 - 12y + 18$ **6.** $9 - 12a + 4a^2$

7. $9 + 6x + x^2$
8. $4y^2 - 4y + 1$
9. $9x^2 + 6x + 1$
10. $16x^2 + 16x + 4$
11. $9y^2 - 18y + 9$
12. $16n^2 - 8n + 1$
13. $16 + 16a + 4a^2$
14. $1 + 20a + 100a^2$
15. $49a^2 - 28a + 4$

Perfect Square Trinomials with Two Variables

Factor completely.

16. $a^2 - 2ab + b^2$
17. $x^2 + 2xy + y^2$
18. $a^2 - 14ab + 49b^2$
19. $a^2w^2 + 2abw + b^2$
20. $a^2 - 10ab + 25b^2$
21. $x^2 + 10ax + 25a^2$
22. $c^2 - 6cd + 9d^2$
23. $x^2 + 8xy + 16y^2$

Expressions That Can Be Reduced to Perfect Square Trinomials

Factor completely.

24. $1 + 2x^2 + x^4$
25. $z^6 + 16z^3 + 64$
26. $36 + 12a^2 + a^4$
27. $49 - 14x^3 + x^6$
28. $a^2b^2 - 8ab^3 + 16b^4$
29. $a^4 - 2a^2b^2 + b^4$
30. $16a^2b^2 - 8ab^2c^2 + b^2c^4$
31. $4a^{2n} + 12a^nb^n + 9b^{2n}$

32. To find the width $2n$ of a road that will give a sight distance of 1000 m on a curve of radius 500 m we must solve the equation

$$n^2 - 1000n + 250\,000 = 0$$

Factor the left side of this equation.

8·7

Sum or Difference of Two Cubes

Definition

An expression such as

$$x^3 + 27$$

is called the sum of two cubes, x^3 and 3^3. In general, when we multiply the binomial $(a + b)$ and the trinomial $(a^2 - ab + b^2)$, we obtain

$$(a + b)(a^2 - ab + b^2) = a^3 - a^2b + ab^2 + a^2b - ab^2 + b^3$$
$$= a^3 + b^3$$

All but the cubed terms drop out, leaving the sum of two cubes. In general,

Sum of Two Cubes	$a^3 + b^3 = (a + b)(a^2 - ab + b^2)$	**42**

and similarly,

Difference of Two Cubes	$a^3 - b^3 = (a - b)(a^2 + ab + b^2)$	**43**

When we recognize that an expression is the sum (or difference) of two cubes, we can write the factors immediately.

▬ **Example 39:** Factor $x^3 + 27$.

Solution: This is the sum of two cubes, $x^3 + 3^3$. Substituting into Eq. 42, with $a = x$ and $b = 3$, yields

$$x^3 + 27 = x^3 + 3^3 = (x + 3)(x^2 - 3x + 9)$$

same sign

opposite sign

always +

▬

▬ **Example 40:** Factor $27x^3 - 8y^3$.

Solution: This is the difference of two cubes, $(3x)^3 - (y)^3$. Factoring gives us

$$27x^3 - 8y^3 = (3x)^3 - (2y)^3 = (3x - 2y)(9x^2 + 6xy + 4y^2)$$

same sign

opposite sign

always +

▬

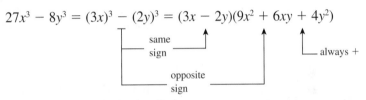

Common Error	The middle term of the trinomials in Eqs. 42 and 43 is often mistaken as $2ab$. $$a^3 + b^3 \neq (a + b)(a^2 - 2ab + b^2)$$ no!

When the powers are multiples of 3, we may be able to factor the expression as the sum or difference of two cubes.

▬ **Example 41:**

$$a^6 - b^9 = (a^2)^3 - (b^3)^3$$

Factoring, we obtain

$$= (a^2 - b^3)(a^4 + a^2b^3 + b^6)$$

▬

Factoring by Computer

Computer algebra systems (CAS) such as *Derive*, *Maple*, or *Mathematica* can, of course, factor very well. In fact, you might feel that they factor *too* well. For example, the expression

$$x^2 - 2$$

might be factored by CAS into

$$(x - \sqrt{2})(x + \sqrt{2})$$

Now this may be just what you want. However, if you want to avoid irrational factors like these you can *adjust the level of factoring*. *Derive*, for example, has five levels of factoring: trivial, square-free, rational, radical, and complex, and *Mathematica* has similar commands.

Trivial factoring removes common factors. Thus, $2x^3 - 4x^2 - 16x$ would be factored into

$$2x(x^2 - 2x - 8)$$

and *not* into $2x(x - 4)(x + 2)$.

Square-free factoring removes common factors, and also factors trinomials, but will not factor the difference of two squares. Thus

$$x^4 + 2x^3 - 3x^2 - 8x - 4$$

would factor into

$$(x + 1)^2 (x^2 - 4)$$

but not into

$$(x + 1)^2(x - 2)(x + 2)$$

Rational factoring does what we normally refer to in this chapter as complete factoring. It will factor

$$2x^2 - 18 = 2(x - 3)(x + 3)$$

It will not factor $x^2 - 2$ into irrational factors.

Radical factoring will introduce radical factors, causing $x^2 - 2$ to be factored into $(x - \sqrt{2})(x + \sqrt{2})$.

Complex factoring may introduce complex factors. Thus, $x^2 + 4$ would be factored into $(x - j2)(x + j2)$, where j is equal to $\sqrt{-1}$, as explained in Chapter 21.

Exercise 7   Sum or Difference of Two Cubes

Factor completely.

1. $64 + x^3$

2. $1 - 64y^3$

3. $2a^3 - 16$

4. $a^3 - 27$

5. $x^3 - 1$

6. $x^3 - 64$

7. $x^3 + 1$

8. $a^3 - 343$

9. $a^3 + 64$

10. $x^3 + 343$

11. $x^3 + 125$

12. $64a^3 + 27$

13. $216 - 8a^3$

14. $343 - 27y^3$

15. $343 + 64x^3$

More Difficult Types

Factor completely.

16. $27x^9 + 512$

17. $y^9 + 64x^3$

18. $64a^{12} + x^{15}$

19. $27x^{15} + 8a^6$

20. $8x^{6p} + 8a^6$

21. $8a^{6x} - 125b^{3x}$

22. $64x^{12a} - 27y^{15a}$

23. $64x^{3n} - y^{9n}$

24. $x^3y^3 - z^3$

Applications

25. The volume of a hollow spherical shell having an inside radius of r_1 and an outside radius of r_2 is $\frac{4}{3}\pi r_2^3 - \frac{4}{3}\pi r_1^3$. Factor this expression completely.

26. A cistern is in the shape of a hollow cube whose inside dimension is s and whose outside dimension is S. If made of concrete of density d, it weighs $dS^3 - ds^3$. Factor completely.

CHAPTER 8   REVIEW PROBLEMS

Factor completely.

1. $x^2 - 2x - 15$
2. $2a^2 + 3a - 2$
3. $x^6 - y^4$
4. $2ax^2 + 8ax + 8a$
5. $2x^2 + 3x - 2$
6. $a^2 + ab - 6b^2$
7. $(a - b)^3 + (c + d)^3$
8. $8x^3 - \dfrac{y^3}{27}$
9. $\dfrac{x^2}{y} - \dfrac{x}{y}$
10. $2ax^2y^2 - 18a$
11. $xy - 2y + 5x - 10$
12. $3a^2 - 2a - 8$
13. $x - bx - y + by$
14. $\dfrac{2a^2}{12} - \dfrac{8b^2}{27}$
15. $(y + 2)^2 - z^2$
16. $2x^2 - 20ax + 50a^2$
17. $x^2 - 7x + 12$
18. $4a^2 - (3a - 1)^2$
19. $16x^{4n} - 81y^{8n}$
20. $xy - y^2 + xz - yz$
21. $9a^2 + 12az^2 + 4z^4$
22. $4a^6 - 4b^6$
23. $x^{2m} + 2x^m + 1$
24. $4x^{6m} + 4x^{3m}y^m + y^{2m}$
25. $(x - y)^2 - z^2$
26. $x^2 - 2x - 3$
27. $1 - 16x^2$
28. $a^2 - 2a - 8$
29. $9x^4 - x^2$
30. $x^2 - 21x + 110$
31. $(p - q)^3 - 27$
32. $5a^2 - 20x^2$
33. $27a^3 - 8w^3$
34. $3x^2 - 6x - 45$

35. $16x^2 - 16xy + 4y^2$
36. $64m^3 - 27n^3$
37. $6ab + 2ay + 3bx + xy$
38. $15a^2 - 11a - 12$
39. $2y^4 - 18$
40. $ax - bx + ay - by$
41. The reduction in power in a resistance R caused by lowering the voltage across the resistor from V_2 to V_1 is

$$\frac{V_2^2}{R} - \frac{V_1^2}{R}$$

Factor this expression.

42. A conical tank of height h is filled to a depth d. The volume of liquid that can still be put into the tank is

$$V = \frac{\pi}{3}r_1^2 h - \frac{\pi}{3}r_2^2 d$$

where r_1 is the base radius of the tank and r_2 is the base radius of the liquid. Factor the right side of this equation.

Computer

43. If you have access to a computer algebra system, use it to factor any of the expressions in this chapter. Be sure to set the level of factoring appropriately (**Rational** in *Derive*, for example).

Writing

44. We have studied the factoring of seven different types of expression in this chapter. List them and give an example of each. State in words how to recognize each and to tell one from the other. Also list at least four other expressions that are *not* one of the given seven, and state why each is different from those we have studied.

Team Project

45. The area of a rectangle is the *product* of its sides, so we can think of the product $5x$ as the area of a rectangle of sides 5 and x.

Similarly, the trinomial $2x^2 + 5x + 2$ can be thought of as the area of a rectangle of sides $(2x + 1)$ and $(x + 2)$, because

$$2x^2 + 5x + 2 = (2x + 1)(x + 2)$$

Thus to factor a trinomial using areas, cut rectangles of paper with areas equal to the terms in the trinomial. Thus the trinomial $2x^2 + 5x + 2$ can be represented by two squares of side x, five rectangles with side 1 and x, and two squares of side 1. Choose any size for x, but avoid making it an integer value.

Arrange the individual squares to form a rectangle. There will be only one way to do this. The sides $(2x + 1)$ and $(x + 2)$ of this rectangle will be the factors of the trinomial.

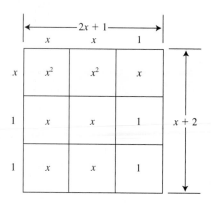

Use this method to factor the following trinomials:

$$x^2 + 3x + 2$$

$$2x^2 + 7x + 6$$

$$x^2 + 13x + 30$$

Expand the method to handle trinomials with *negative* terms. Use it to factor

$$x^2 + 2x - 3$$

$$x^2 + 7x - 30$$

9

Fractions and Fractional Equations

O B J E C T I V E S

When you have completed this chapter, you should be able to:

- Determine values of the variables that result in undefined fractions.
- Convert common fractions to decimals, and vice versa.
- Reduce algebraic fractions.
- Add, subtract, multiply, and divide algebraic fractions.
- Simplify complex fractions.
- Solve fractional equations.
- Solve applied problems requiring fractional equations.
- Solve literal equations and formulas.

Although the calculator, the computer, and the metric system (all of which use decimal notation) have somewhat reduced the importance of common fractions, they are still widely used. Algebraic fractions are, of course, as important as ever. We must be able to handle them in order to solve fractional equations and the word problems from which they arise.

This material is not all new to us. Some was covered in Chapter 2 and simple fractional equations were solved in Chapter 3. We also make heavy use of factoring in order to simplify algebraic fractions.

9•1 Simplification of Fractions

Parts of a Fraction

A fraction has a *numerator,* a *denominator*, and a *fraction line.*

$$\text{fraction line} \longrightarrow \frac{a}{b} \begin{array}{l} \longleftarrow \text{numerator} \\ \longleftarrow \text{denominator} \end{array}$$

Quotient

A fraction is a way of indicating a *quotient* of two quantities. The fraction a/b can be read "*a* divided by *b*."

Ratio

The quotient of two numbers or quantities is also spoken of as the *ratio* of those quantities. Thus the ratio of x to y is x/y.

Division by Zero

Since division by zero is not permitted, it should be understood in our work with fractions that *the denominator cannot be zero.*

■ **Example 1:** What values of x are not permitted in the fraction

$$\frac{3x}{x^2 + x - 6}?$$

Solution: Factoring the denominator, we get

$$\left(\frac{3x}{x^2 + x - 6} = \right)\frac{3x}{(x - 2)(x + 3)}$$

We see that an x equal to 2 or to -3 will make $(x - 2)$ or $(x + 3)$ equal to zero. This will result in division by zero, so these values are not permitted. ■

Common Fractions

A fraction whose numerator and denominator are both integers is called a *common fraction*.

■ **Example 2:**

$$\frac{2}{3}, \quad -\frac{9}{5}, \quad \frac{-124}{125}, \quad \text{and} \quad \frac{18}{-11}$$

are common fractions. ■

Algebraic Fractions

An *algebraic fraction* is one whose numerator and/or denominator contains a *literal* quantity.

■ **Example 3:**

$$\frac{x}{y}, \quad \frac{\sqrt{x + 2}}{x}, \quad \frac{3}{y}, \quad \text{and} \quad \frac{x^2}{x - 3}$$

are algebraic fractions. ■

Rational Algebraic Fractions

Recall that a polynomial is an expression in which the exponents are nonnegative integers.

An algebraic fraction is called *rational* if the numerator and denominator are both *polynomials*.

■ **Example 4:**

$$\frac{x}{y}, \quad \frac{3}{w^3}, \quad \text{and} \quad \frac{x^2}{x-3}$$

are rational fractions but $\dfrac{\sqrt{x+2}}{x}$ is not.   ■

Proper and Improper Fractions

A *proper* common fraction is one whose numerator is smaller than its denominator.

■ **Example 5:** $\frac{3}{5}$, $\frac{1}{3}$, and $\frac{9}{11}$, are proper fractions, whereas $\frac{8}{5}$, $\frac{3}{2}$, and $\frac{7}{4}$ are *improper* fractions.   ■

A proper *algebraic* fraction is a rational fraction whose numerator is of *lower degree* than the denominator.

■ **Example 6:**

$$\frac{x}{x^2+2} \quad \text{and} \quad \frac{x^2+2x-3}{x^3+9}$$

are proper fractions, while

$$\frac{x^3-2}{x^2+x-3} \quad \text{and} \quad \frac{x^2}{y}$$

are improper fractions.   ■

Mixed Form

A *mixed number* is the sum of an integer and a fraction.

■ **Example 7:**

$$2\frac{1}{2}, \quad 5\frac{3}{4}, \quad \text{and} \quad 3\frac{1}{3}$$

are mixed numbers.   ■

A *mixed expression* is the sum of or difference between a polynomial and a rational algebraic fraction.

■ **Example 8:**

$$3x - 2 + \frac{1}{x} \quad \text{and} \quad y - \frac{y}{y^2+1}$$

are mixed expressions.   ■

Decimals and Fractions

To change a fraction to an equivalent decimal, simply divide the numerator by the denominator.

Repeating decimals are often written with a bar over the repeating part: $0.\overline{81}$.

■ **Example 9:** To write $\frac{9}{11}$ as a decimal, we divide 9 by 11:

$$\frac{9}{11} = 0.818181818\overline{1}\ldots$$

We get a *repeating decimal;* the dots following the number indicate that the digits continue indefinitely. ■

To change a decimal number to a fraction, write a fraction with the decimal number in the numerator and 1 in the denominator. Multiply numerator and denominator by a multiple of 10 that will make the numerator a whole number. Finally, reduce to lowest terms.

■ **Example 10:** Express 0.875 as a fraction.

Solution:

$$0.875 = \frac{0.875}{1} = \frac{875}{1000} = \frac{7}{8}$$ ■

To express a *repeating* decimal as a fraction, follow the steps in the next example.

■ **Example 11:** Change the repeating decimal $0.81\overline{81}$ to a fraction.

Solution: Let $x = 0.81\overline{81}$. Multiplying by 100, we have

$$100x = 81.\overline{81}$$

Subtracting the first equation, $x = 0.81\overline{81}$, from the second gives us

$$99x = 81 \quad \text{(exactly)}$$

Dividing by 99 yields

$$x = \frac{81}{99} = \frac{9}{11} \quad \text{(reduced)}$$ ■

Simplifying a Fraction by Reducing to Lowest Terms

We reduce a fraction to lowest terms by dividing both numerator and denominator by any factor that is contained in both.

$$\frac{ab}{bd} = \frac{a}{b}$$	**50**

■ **Example 12:** Reduce to lowest terms. Write the answer without negative exponents.

(a) $\dfrac{9}{12} = \dfrac{3(3)}{4(3)} = \dfrac{3}{4}$

(b) $\dfrac{3x^2yz}{9xy^2z^3} = \dfrac{3}{9} \cdot \dfrac{x^2}{x} \cdot \dfrac{y}{y^2} \cdot \dfrac{z}{z^3} = \dfrac{x}{3yz^2}$ ■

When possible, factor the numerator and denominator. Then divide both numerator and denominator by any factors common to both.

■ **Example 13:**

(a) $\dfrac{2x^2 + x}{3x} = \dfrac{(2x + 1)x}{3(x)} = \dfrac{2x + 1}{3}$

(b) $\dfrac{ab + bc}{bc + bd} = \dfrac{b(a + c)}{b(c + d)} = \dfrac{a + c}{c + d}$

(c) $\dfrac{2x^2 - 5x - 3}{4x^2 - 1} = \dfrac{(2x + 1)(x - 3)}{(2x + 1)(2x - 1)} = \dfrac{x - 3}{2x - 1}$

(d) $\dfrac{x^2 - ax + 2bx - 2ab}{2x^2 + ax - 3a^2} = \dfrac{x(x - a) + 2b(x - a)}{(x - a)(2x + 3a)}$

$\qquad\qquad = \dfrac{(x - a)(x + 2b)}{(x - a)(2x + 3a)} = \dfrac{x + 2b}{2x + 3a}$ ■

The process of striking out the same factors from numerator and denominator is called *canceling*.

	If a factor is missing from *even one term* in the numerator or denominator, that factor *cannot* be canceled. $$\dfrac{xy - z}{wx} \neq \dfrac{y - z}{w}$$
Common Errors	We may divide (or multiply) the numerator and denominator by the same quantity (Eq. 50), but we *may not add or subtract* the same quantity in the numerator and denominator, as this will change the value of the fraction. For example, $$\dfrac{3}{5} \neq \dfrac{3 + 1}{5 + 1} = \dfrac{4}{6} = \dfrac{2}{3}$$

Most students love canceling because they think they can cross out any term that stands in their way. If you use canceling, use it carefully!

Simplifying Fractions by Changing Signs

Recall from Chapter 2 that any two of the three signs of a fraction may be changed without changing the value of a fraction.

Rules of Signs	$\dfrac{+a}{+b} = \dfrac{-a}{-b} = -\dfrac{-a}{+b} = -\dfrac{+a}{-b} = \dfrac{a}{b}$	**10**
	$\dfrac{+a}{-b} = \dfrac{-a}{+b} = -\dfrac{-a}{-b} = -\dfrac{a}{b}$	**11**

We can sometimes use this idea to simplify a fraction, that is, to reduce it to lowest terms.

■ **Example 14:** Simplify the fraction

$$-\frac{3x - 2}{2 - 3x}$$

Solution: We change the sign of the denominator *and* the sign of the entire fraction:

$$-\frac{3x-2}{2-3x} = +\frac{3x-2}{-(2-3x)} = \frac{3x-2}{-2+3x} = \frac{3x-2}{3x-2} = 1$$

changed

Exercise 1 Simplification of Fractions

In each fraction below, what values of x, if any, are not permitted?

Hint: Factor the denominators in Problems 4, 5, and 6.

1. $\dfrac{12}{x}$

2. $\dfrac{x}{12}$

3. $\dfrac{18}{x-5}$

4. $\dfrac{5x}{x^2-49}$

5. $\dfrac{7}{x^2-3x+2}$

6. $\dfrac{3x}{8x^2-14x+3}$

Change each fraction to a decimal. Work to four decimal places.

7. $\dfrac{7}{12}$

8. $\dfrac{5}{9}$

9. $\dfrac{15}{16}$

10. $\dfrac{125}{155}$

11. $\dfrac{11}{3}$

12. $\dfrac{25}{9}$

Change each decimal to a fraction.

13. 0.4375

14. 0.390625

15. 0.6875

16. 0.28125

17. 0.7777 . . .

18. 0.636363 . . .

Simplify each fraction by manipulating the algebraic signs.

19. $\dfrac{a-b}{b-a}$

20. $-\dfrac{2x-y}{y-2x}$

21. $\dfrac{(a-b)(c-d)}{b-a}$

22. $\dfrac{w(x-y-z)}{y-x+z}$

Reduce to lowest terms. Write your answers without negative exponents.

23. $\dfrac{14}{21}$

24. $\dfrac{81}{18}$

25. $\dfrac{75}{35}$

26. $\dfrac{36}{44}$

27. $\dfrac{2ab}{6b}$

28. $\dfrac{12m^2n}{15mn^2}$

29. $\dfrac{21m^2p^2}{28mp^4}$

30. $\dfrac{abx-bx^2}{acx-cx^2}$

31. $\dfrac{4a^2-9b^2}{4a^2+6ab}$

32. $\dfrac{3a^2+6a}{a^2+4a+4}$

33. $\dfrac{x^2 + 5x}{x^2 + 4x - 5}$

34. $\dfrac{xy - 3y^2}{x^3 - 27y^3}$

35. $\dfrac{x^2 - 4}{x^3 - 8}$

36. $\dfrac{2a^3 + 6a^2 - 8a}{2a^3 + 2a^2 - 4a}$

37. $\dfrac{2m^3n - 2m^2n - 24mn}{6m^3 + 6m^2 - 36m}$

38. $\dfrac{9x^3 - 30x^2 + 25x}{3x^4 - 11x^3 + 10x^2}$

39. $\dfrac{2a^2 - 2}{a^2 - 2a + 1}$

40. $\dfrac{3a^2 - 4ab + b^2}{a^2 - ab}$

41. $\dfrac{x^2 - z^2}{x^3 - z^3}$

42. $\dfrac{2x^2}{6x - 4x^2}$

43. $\dfrac{2a^2 - 8}{2a^2 - 2a - 12}$

44. $\dfrac{2a^2 + ab - 3b^2}{a^2 - ab}$

45. $\dfrac{x^2 - 1}{2xy + 2y}$

46. $\dfrac{x^3 - a^2x}{x^2 - 2ax + a^2}$

47. $\dfrac{2x^4y^4 + 2}{3x^8y^8 - 3}$

48. $\dfrac{18a^2c - 6bc}{42a^2d - 14bd}$

49. $\dfrac{(x + y)^2}{x^2 - y^2}$

50. $\dfrac{mw + 3w - mz - 3z}{m^2 - m - 12}$

51. $\dfrac{b^2 - a^2 - 6b + 9}{5b - 15 - 5a}$

52. $\dfrac{3w - 3y - 3}{w^2 + y^2 - 2wy - 1}$

Computer

53. A computer algebra system (CAS) will simplify fractions, given the proper command. In *Derive*, *Mathematica*, and *Maple*, for example, the command SIMPLIFY will reduce a fraction to lowest terms. This same command will simplify nonfractional algebraic expressions as well. If you have access to a computer algebra system, use it to simplify any of the fractions in this exercise.

9·2

Multiplication and Division of Fractions

Multiplication

We multiply a fraction *a/b* by another fraction *c/d* as follows:

Multiplying Fractions	$\dfrac{a}{b} \cdot \dfrac{c}{d} = \dfrac{ac}{bd}$	**51**

The product of two or more fractions is a fraction whose numerator is the product of the numerators of the original fractions, and whose denominator is the product of the denominators of the original fractions.

▬ **Example 15:**

(a) $\dfrac{2}{3} \cdot \dfrac{5}{7} = \dfrac{2(5)}{3(7)} = \dfrac{10}{21}$

(b) $\dfrac{1}{2} \cdot \dfrac{2}{3} \cdot \dfrac{3}{5} = \dfrac{1(2)(3)}{2(3)(5)} = \dfrac{1}{5}$

(c) $5\dfrac{2}{3} \cdot 3\dfrac{1}{2} = \dfrac{17}{3} \cdot \dfrac{7}{2} = \dfrac{119}{6}$ ▬

Common Error	When multiplying mixed numbers, students sometimes try to multiply the whole parts and the fractional parts separately. $$2\frac{2}{3} \times 4\frac{3}{5} \neq 8\frac{6}{15}$$ The correct way is to write each mixed number as an improper fraction and to multiply as shown. $$2\frac{2}{3} \times 4\frac{3}{5} = \frac{8}{3} \times \frac{23}{5} = \frac{184}{15} = 12\frac{4}{15}$$

Leave your product in factored form until after you simplify.

■ **Example 16:**

(a) $\dfrac{2a}{3b} \cdot \dfrac{5c}{4a} = \dfrac{10ac}{12ab} = \dfrac{5c}{6b}$

(b) $\dfrac{x}{x+2} \cdot \dfrac{x^2-4}{x^3} = \dfrac{x(x^2-4)}{(x+2)x^3}$

$$= \dfrac{x(x+2)(x-2)}{(x+2)x^3} = \dfrac{x-2}{x^2}$$

(c) $\dfrac{x^2+x-2}{x^2-4x+3} \cdot \dfrac{2x^2-3x-9}{2x^2+7x+6} = \dfrac{(x-1)(x+2)(x-3)(2x+3)}{(x-1)(x-3)(x+2)(2x+3)} = 1$ ■

Division

To divide one fraction, *a/b*, by another fraction, *c/d*,

$$\dfrac{\dfrac{a}{b}}{\dfrac{c}{d}}$$

Can you say why it is permissible to multiply numerator and denominator by d/c?

we multiply numerator and denominator by *d/c*:

$$\dfrac{\dfrac{a}{b}\cdot\dfrac{d}{c}}{\dfrac{c}{d}\cdot\dfrac{d}{c}} = \dfrac{\dfrac{a}{b}\cdot\dfrac{d}{c}}{\dfrac{cd}{cd}} = \dfrac{\dfrac{a}{b}\cdot\dfrac{d}{c}}{1} = \dfrac{a}{b}\cdot\dfrac{d}{c} = \dfrac{ad}{bc}$$

We see that dividing by a fraction is the same as *multiplying by the reciprocal* of that fraction.

Division of Fractions	$\dfrac{a}{b} \div \dfrac{c}{d} = \dfrac{a}{b}\cdot\dfrac{d}{c} = \dfrac{ad}{bc}$	**52**

When dividing fractions, invert the divisor and multiply.

■ **Example 17:**

(a) $\dfrac{2}{3} \div \dfrac{5}{7} = \dfrac{2}{3} \cdot \dfrac{7}{5} = \dfrac{14}{15}$

(b) $3\dfrac{2}{5} \div 2\dfrac{4}{15} = \dfrac{17}{5} \div \dfrac{34}{15}$

$\qquad\qquad = \dfrac{17}{5} \times \dfrac{15}{34} = \dfrac{3}{2}$

(c) $\dfrac{x}{y} \div \dfrac{x+2}{y-1} = \dfrac{x}{y} \cdot \dfrac{y-1}{x+2}$

$\qquad\qquad = \dfrac{x(y-1)}{y(x+2)}$

(d) $\dfrac{x^2 + x - 2}{x} \div \dfrac{x+2}{x^2} = \dfrac{x^2 + x - 2}{x} \cdot \dfrac{x^2}{x+2}$

$\qquad\qquad = \dfrac{(x+2)(x-1)x^2}{x(x+2)} = x(x-1)$

(e) $x \div \dfrac{\pi r^2 x}{4} = \dfrac{x}{1} \div \dfrac{\pi r^2 x}{4} = \dfrac{x}{1} \cdot \dfrac{4}{\pi r^2 x} = \dfrac{4}{\pi r^2}$ ▬

> Remember that all literal fractions have nonzero denominators, since division by zero is not permitted.

Common Error	We invert the *divisor* and multiply. Be sure not to invert the dividend.

Changing Improper Fractions to Mixed Form

To write an improper fraction in mixed form, divide the numerator by the denominator and express the remainder as the numerator of a fraction whose denominator is the original denominator.

■ **Example 18:** Write $\frac{45}{7}$ as a mixed number.

Solution: Dividing 45 by 7, we get 6 with a remainder of 3, so

$$\frac{45}{7} = 6\frac{3}{7}$$ ▬

The procedure is the same for changing an *algebraic* fraction to mixed form. Divide the numerator by the denominator.

■ **Example 19:**

$$\frac{x^2 + 3}{x} = \frac{x^2}{x} + \frac{3}{x}$$

$$= x + \frac{3}{x}$$ ▬

Exercise 2 Multiplication and Division of Fractions

Multiply and reduce.

1. $\dfrac{1}{3} \times \dfrac{2}{5}$ 　　　　**2.** $\dfrac{3}{7} \times \dfrac{21}{24}$ 　　　　**3.** $\dfrac{2}{3} \times \dfrac{9}{7}$

4. $\dfrac{11}{3} \times 7$

5. $\dfrac{2}{3} \times 3\dfrac{1}{5}$

6. $3 \times 7\dfrac{2}{5}$

7. $3\dfrac{3}{4} \times 2\dfrac{1}{2}$

8. $\dfrac{3}{5} \times \dfrac{2}{7} \times \dfrac{5}{9}$

9. $3 \times \dfrac{5}{8} \times \dfrac{4}{5}$

10. $\dfrac{15a^2}{7b^2} \cdot \dfrac{28ab}{9a^3c}$

11. $\dfrac{a^4b^4}{2a^2y^n} \cdot \dfrac{a^2x}{xy^n}$

12. $\dfrac{3x^2y^2z^3}{4a^2b^2c^2} \cdot \dfrac{8a^3b^2c^2}{9x^2yz^3}$

13. $\dfrac{5m^2n^2p^4}{3x^2yz^3} \cdot \dfrac{21xyz^2}{20m^2n^2p^2}$

14. $\dfrac{x+y}{x-y} \cdot \dfrac{x^2-y^2}{(x+y)^2}$

15. $\dfrac{x^2-a^2}{xy} \cdot \dfrac{xy}{x+a}$

16. $\dfrac{x^4-y^4}{a^2x^2} \cdot \dfrac{ax^3}{x^2+y^2}$

17. $\dfrac{a}{x-y} \cdot \dfrac{b}{x+y}$

18. $\dfrac{x+y}{10} \cdot \dfrac{ax}{3(x+y)}$

19. $\dfrac{c}{x^2-y^2} \cdot \dfrac{d}{x^2-y^2}$

20. $\dfrac{x-2}{2x+3} \cdot \dfrac{2x^2+x-3}{x^2-4}$

21. $\dfrac{x^2-1}{x^2+x-6} \cdot \dfrac{x^2+2x-8}{x^2-4x-5}$

22. $\dfrac{5x-1}{x^2-x-2} \cdot \dfrac{x-2}{10x^2+13x-3}$

23. $\dfrac{2x^2+x-1}{3x^2-11x-4} \cdot \dfrac{3x^2+7x+2}{2x^2-7x+3}$

24. $\dfrac{x^3+1}{x+1} \cdot \dfrac{x+3}{x^2-x+1}$

25. $\dfrac{2x^2+x-6}{4x^2-3x-1} \cdot \dfrac{4x^2+5x+1}{x^2-4x-12}$

Divide and reduce.

26. $\dfrac{7}{9} \div \dfrac{5}{3}$

27. $3\dfrac{7}{8} \div 2$

28. $\dfrac{7}{8} \div 4$

29. $\dfrac{9}{16} \div 8$

30. $24 \div \dfrac{5}{8}$

31. $\dfrac{5}{8} \div 2\dfrac{1}{4}$

32. $2\dfrac{7}{8} \div 1\dfrac{1}{2}$

33. $2\dfrac{5}{8} \div \dfrac{1}{2}$

34. $50 \div 2\dfrac{3}{5}$

35. $\dfrac{5abc^3}{3x^2} \div \dfrac{10ac^3}{6bx^2}$

36. $\dfrac{7x^2y}{3ad} \div \dfrac{2xy^2}{3a^2d}$

37. $\dfrac{4a^3x}{6dy^2} \div \dfrac{2a^2x^2}{8a^2y}$

38. $\dfrac{5x^2y^3z}{6a^2b^2c} \div \dfrac{10xy^3z^2}{8ab^2c^2}$

39. $\dfrac{3an+cm}{x^2-y^2} \div (x^2+y^2)$

40. $\dfrac{a^2+4a+4}{d+c} \div (a+2)$

41. $\dfrac{ac+ad+bc+bd}{c^2-d^2} \div (a+b)$

42. $\dfrac{5(x+y)^2}{x-y} \div (x+y)$

43. $\dfrac{1}{x^2 + 17x + 30} \div \dfrac{1}{x + 15}$

44. $\dfrac{5xy}{a - x} \div \dfrac{10xy}{a^2 - x^2}$

45. $\dfrac{3x - 6}{2x + 3} \div \dfrac{x^2 - 4}{4x^2 + 2x - 6}$

46. $\dfrac{a^2 - a - 2}{5a - 1} \div \dfrac{a - 2}{10a^2 + 13a - 3}$

47. $\dfrac{2p^2 + p - 6}{4p^2 - 3p - 1} \div \dfrac{2p^2 - 5p + 3}{4p^2 + 9p + 2}$

48. $\dfrac{x^3 + 1}{x + 1} \div \dfrac{x^2 - x + 1}{3x + 9}$

49. $\dfrac{z^2 - 1}{z^2 + z - 6} \div \dfrac{z^2 - 4z - 5}{z^2 + 2z - 8}$

50. $\dfrac{x^2 + 5x + 6}{2x^2 - 3x + 1} \div \dfrac{x^2 - 9}{2x^2 - 7x + 3}$

Improper Fractions and Mixed Form

Change each improper fraction to a mixed number.

51. $\dfrac{5}{3}$ **52.** $\dfrac{11}{5}$ **53.** $\dfrac{29}{12}$

54. $\dfrac{17}{3}$ **55.** $\dfrac{47}{5}$ **56.** $\dfrac{125}{12}$

Change each improper algebraic fraction to a mixed expression.

57. $\dfrac{x^2 + 1}{x}$ **58.** $\dfrac{1 - 4x}{2x}$ **59.** $\dfrac{4x - x^2}{2x^2}$

Applications

60. For a thin lens, the relationship between the focal length f, the object distance p, and the image distance q is

$$f = \frac{pq}{p + q}$$

A second lens of focal length f_1 has the same object distance p but a different image distance q_1:

$$f_1 = \frac{pq_1}{p + q_1}$$

Find the ratio f/f_1 and simplify.

61. The density of an object is its mass divided by its volume. Write and simplify an expression for the density of a sphere having a mass m and a volume equal to $4\pi r^3/3$.

62. The pressure on a surface is equal to the total force divided by the area. Write and simplify an expression for the pressure on a circular surface of area $\pi d^2/4$ subjected to a distributed load F.

FIGURE 9•1

FIGURE 9•2

63. The stress on a bar in tension is equal to the load divided by the cross-sectional area. Write and simplify an expression for the stress in a bar having a trapezoidal cross-section of area $(a + b)h/2$, subject to a load P.

64. The acceleration on a body is equal to the force on the body divided by its mass, and the mass equals the volume of the object times the density. Write and simplify an expression for the acceleration of a sphere having a volume $4\pi r^3/3$ and a density D, subjected to a force F.

65. To find the moment of the area A in Figure 9•1, we must multiply the area $A = \dfrac{\pi d^2}{4}$ by the distance to the pivot, $16d/3$. Multiply and simplify.

66. The circle in Figure 9•2 has an area $\pi d^2/4$, and the sector has an area equal to $ds/4$. Find the ratio of the area of the circle to the area of the sector.

Computer

67. If you have a computer algebra system, use it to do any of the multiplications or divisions in this exercise. You need not tell the computer to multiply or divide; the instruction SIMPLIFY is all you need.

9•3   Addition and Subtraction of Fractions

Similar Fractions

Similar fractions (also called *like* fractions) are those having the same (common) denominator. To add or subtract similar fractions, *combine the numerators and place them over the common denominator*.

Addition and Subtraction of Fractions	$\dfrac{a}{b} + \dfrac{c}{b} = \dfrac{a \pm c}{b}$	**53**

■ **Example 20:**

(a) $\dfrac{2}{3} + \dfrac{5}{3} = \dfrac{2 + 5}{3} = \dfrac{7}{3}$

(b) $\dfrac{1}{x} + \dfrac{3}{x} = \dfrac{1 + 3}{x} = \dfrac{4}{x}$

(c) $\dfrac{3x}{x + 1} - \dfrac{5}{x + 1} + \dfrac{x^2}{x + 1} = \dfrac{3x - 5 + x^2}{x + 1}$ ■

Least Common Denominator

The least common denominator is also called the *least common multiple* (LCM) of the denominators.

The *least common denominator*, LCD (also called the *lowest* common denominator), is the smallest expression that is exactly divisible by each of the denominators. Thus the LCD must contain all the prime factors of each of the denominators. The common denominator of two or more fractions is simply the product of the denominators of those fractions. To find the *least* common denominator, drop any prime factor from one denominator that also appears in another denominator before multiplying.

■ **Example 21:** Find the LCD for the two fractions $\frac{3}{8}$ and $\frac{1}{18}$.

Solution: Factoring each denominator, we obtain

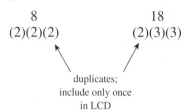

$$
\begin{array}{cc}
8 & 18 \\
(2)(2)(2) & (2)(3)(3)
\end{array}
$$

duplicates;
include only once
in LCD

Our LCD is then the product of these factors, dropping one of the 2s that appears in both sets of factors.

$$\text{LCD} = (2)(2)(2)(3)(3) = 8(9) = 72$$ ■

For this simple problem you probably found the LCD by inspection in less time than it took to read this example, and are probably wondering what all the fuss is about. What we are really doing is developing a *method* that we can use on algebraic fractions, where the LCD will *not* be obvious.

■ **Example 22:** Find the LCD for the fractions

$$\frac{5}{x^2 + x}, \quad \frac{x}{x^2 - 1}, \quad \text{and} \quad \frac{9}{x^3 - x^2}$$

Solution: The denominator $x^2 + x$ has the prime factors x and $x + 1$; the denominator $x^2 - 1$ has the prime factors $x + 1$ and $x - 1$; and the denominator $x^3 - x^2$ has the prime factors x, x, and $x - 1$. Our LCD is thus

$$(x)(x)(x + 1)(x - 1) \quad \text{or} \quad x^2(x^2 - 1)$$ ■

Combining Fractions with Different Denominators

First find the LCD. Then multiply numerator and denominator of each fraction by that quantity that will make the denominator equal to the LCD. Finally, combine as shown above, and simplify.

■ **Example 23:** Add $\frac{1}{2}$ and $\frac{2}{3}$.

Solution: The LCD is 6, so

$$\frac{1}{2} + \frac{2}{3} = \frac{1}{2}\left(\frac{3}{3}\right) + \frac{2}{3}\left(\frac{2}{2}\right)$$

$$= \frac{3}{6} + \frac{4}{6}$$

$$= \frac{7}{6}$$ ■

■ **Example 24:** Add $\frac{3}{8}$ and $\frac{1}{18}$.

Solution: The LCD, from Example 21, is 72. So

$$\frac{3}{8} + \frac{1}{18} = \frac{3}{8} \cdot \frac{9}{9} + \frac{1}{18} \cdot \frac{4}{4}$$

$$= \frac{27}{72} + \frac{4}{72}$$

$$= \frac{31}{72}$$

It is not necessary to write the fractions with the *least* common denominator; any common denominator will work as well. But your final result will then have to be reduced to lowest terms.

The method for adding and subtracting unlike fractions can be summarized by the formula that follows.

Combining Unlike Fractions	$\dfrac{a}{b} \pm \dfrac{c}{d} = \dfrac{ad}{bd} \pm \dfrac{bc}{bd} = \dfrac{ad \pm bc}{bd}$	**54**

■ **Example 25:** Combine: $x/2y - 5/x$.

Solution: The LCD will be the product of the two denominators, or $2xy$. So

$$\frac{x}{2y} - \frac{5}{x} = \frac{x}{2y}\left(\frac{x}{x}\right) - \frac{5}{x}\left(\frac{2y}{2y}\right)$$

$$= \frac{x^2}{2xy} - \frac{10y}{2xy}$$

$$= \frac{x^2 - 10y}{2xy}$$

The procedure is the same, of course, even when the denominators are more complicated.

■ **Example 26:** Combine the fractions

$$\frac{x + 2}{x - 3} + \frac{2x + 1}{3x - 2}$$

Solution: Our LCD is $(x - 3)(3x - 2)$, so

$$\frac{x + 2}{x - 3} + \frac{2x + 1}{3x - 2} = \frac{(x + 2)(3x - 2)}{(x - 3)(3x - 2)} + \frac{(2x + 1)(x - 3)}{(3x - 2)(x - 3)}$$

$$= \frac{(3x^2 + 4x - 4) + (2x^2 - 5x - 3)}{(x - 3)(3x - 2)}$$

$$= \frac{5x^2 - x - 7}{3x^2 - 11x + 6}$$

Always factor the denominators completely. This will show whether the same factor appears in more than one denominator.

■ **Example 27:** Combine and simplify:

$$\frac{1}{x-3} + \frac{x-1}{x^2+3x+9} + \frac{x^2+x-3}{x^3-27}$$

Solution: Factoring gives

$$\frac{1}{x-3} + \frac{x-1}{x^2+3x+9} + \frac{x^2+x-3}{(x-3)(x^2+3x+9)}$$

Our LCD is then $x^3 - 27$ or $(x-3)(x^2+3x+9)$. Multiplying and adding, we have

$$\frac{(x^2+3x+9) + (x-1)(x-3) + (x^2+x-3)}{(x-3)(x^2+3x+9)}$$

$$= \frac{x^2+3x+9+x^2-4x+3+x^2+x-3}{(x-3)(x^2+3x+9)}$$

$$= \frac{3x^2+9}{x^3-27}$$ ■

Combining Integers and Fractions

Treat the integer as a fraction having 1 as a denominator, and combine as shown above.

■ **Example 28:**

$$3 + \frac{2}{9} = \frac{3}{1} + \frac{2}{9} = \frac{3}{1} \cdot \frac{9}{9} + \frac{2}{9}$$

$$= \frac{27}{9} + \frac{2}{9} = \frac{29}{9}$$ ■

The same procedure may be used to change a *mixed number* to an *improper fraction*.

■ **Example 29:**

$$2\frac{1}{3} = 2 + \frac{1}{3} = \frac{6}{3} + \frac{1}{3}$$

$$= \frac{7}{3}$$ ■

Changing a Mixed Algebraic Expression to an Improper Fraction

The procedure is no different from that in the preceding section. Write the nonfractional expression as a fraction with 1 as the denominator, find the LCD, and combine, as shown in the following example.

■ **Example 30:**

$$x^2 + \frac{5}{2x} = \frac{x^2}{1}\left(\frac{2x}{2x}\right) + \frac{5}{2x}$$

Adding,

$$= \frac{2x^3 + 5}{2x}$$

━

Partial Fractions

Those fractions whose sum is equal to a given fraction are called *partial fractions*.

━ **Example 31:** If we add the two fractions $2/x$ and $3/x^2$, we get

$$\frac{2}{x} + \frac{3}{x^2} = \frac{2x}{x^2} + \frac{3}{x^2} = \frac{2x + 3}{x^2}$$

Turned around, we say that the fraction $(2x + 3)/x^2$ has the partial fractions $2/x$ and $3/x^2$. To be able to separate a fraction into its partial fraction is important in calculus. We mention partial fractions here, but will not calculate any until later. ━

Exercise 3 Addition and Subtraction of Fractions

Common Fractions and Mixed Numbers

Don't use your calculator for these numerical problems. The practice you get working with common fractions will help you when doing algebraic fractions.

Combine and simplify.

1. $\dfrac{3}{5} + \dfrac{2}{5}$

2. $\dfrac{1}{8} - \dfrac{3}{8}$

3. $\dfrac{2}{7} + \dfrac{5}{7} - \dfrac{6}{7}$

4. $\dfrac{5}{9} + \dfrac{7}{9} - \dfrac{1}{9}$

5. $\dfrac{1}{3} - \dfrac{7}{3} + \dfrac{11}{3}$

6. $\dfrac{1}{5} - \dfrac{9}{5} + \dfrac{12}{5} - \dfrac{2}{5}$

7. $\dfrac{1}{2} + \dfrac{2}{3}$

8. $\dfrac{3}{5} - \dfrac{1}{3}$

9. $\dfrac{3}{4} + \dfrac{7}{16}$

10. $\dfrac{2}{3} + \dfrac{3}{7}$

11. $\dfrac{5}{9} - \dfrac{1}{3} + \dfrac{3}{18}$

12. $\dfrac{1}{2} + \dfrac{1}{3} + \dfrac{1}{5}$

13. $2 + \dfrac{3}{5}$

14. $3 - \dfrac{2}{3} + \dfrac{1}{6}$

15. $\dfrac{1}{5} - 7 + \dfrac{2}{3}$

16. $\dfrac{1}{5} + 2 - \dfrac{1}{3} + 5$

17. $\dfrac{1}{7} + 2 - \dfrac{3}{7} + \dfrac{1}{5}$

18. $5 - \dfrac{3}{5} + \dfrac{2}{15} - 2$

Rewrite each mixed number as an improper fraction.

19. $2\dfrac{2}{3}$

20. $1\dfrac{5}{8}$

21. $3\dfrac{1}{4}$

22. $2\dfrac{7}{8}$

23. $5\dfrac{11}{16}$

24. $9\dfrac{3}{4}$

Expressions of this form arise in calculus, when taking the derivative of a fraction by the delta method.

Algebraic Fractions

Combine and simplify.

25. $\dfrac{1}{a} + \dfrac{5}{a}$

26. $\dfrac{3}{x} + \dfrac{2}{x} - \dfrac{1}{x}$

27. $\dfrac{2a}{y} + \dfrac{3}{y} - \dfrac{a}{y}$

28. $\dfrac{x}{3a} - \dfrac{y}{3a} + \dfrac{z}{3a}$

29. $\dfrac{5x}{2} - \dfrac{3x}{2}$

30. $\dfrac{7}{x+2} - \dfrac{5}{x+2}$

31. $\dfrac{3x}{a-b} + \dfrac{2x}{b-a}$

32. $\dfrac{a}{x^2} - \dfrac{b}{x^2} + \dfrac{c}{x^2}$

33. $\dfrac{7}{a+1} + \dfrac{9}{1+a} - \dfrac{3}{-a-1}$

34. $\dfrac{2a}{x(x-1)} - \dfrac{3\,a}{x^2-x} + \dfrac{a}{x-x^2}$

35. $\dfrac{3a}{2x} + \dfrac{2a}{5x}$

36. $\dfrac{1}{x} + \dfrac{1}{y} + \dfrac{1}{z}$

37. $\dfrac{a}{3} + \dfrac{2}{x} - \dfrac{1}{2}$

38. $\dfrac{1}{x+3} + \dfrac{1}{x-2}$

39. $\dfrac{a+b}{3} - \dfrac{a-b}{2}$

40. $\dfrac{3}{a+b} + \dfrac{2}{a-b}$

41. $\dfrac{4}{x-1} - \dfrac{5}{x+1}$

42. $\dfrac{x+1}{x-1} - \dfrac{x-1}{x+1}$

43. $\dfrac{b}{a+b} - \dfrac{a}{b-a} - \dfrac{a-b}{a+b}$

44. $\dfrac{y^2-2xy+x^2}{x^2-xy} + \dfrac{x}{x-y}$

45. $\dfrac{1}{2(x-1)} - \dfrac{1}{2(x+1)} + \dfrac{1}{x^2}$

46. $\dfrac{1+x}{1+x+x^2} + \dfrac{1-x}{1-x+x^2}$

47. $\dfrac{1}{x+1} + \dfrac{2}{x+2} + \dfrac{3}{x-3}$

48. $\dfrac{a-b}{ab} + \dfrac{b-c}{bc} + \dfrac{c-a}{ac}$

49. $\dfrac{x}{x^2-9} + \dfrac{x}{x+3}$

50. $\dfrac{x+3}{x^2-2x-8} - \dfrac{2x}{x-4}$

51. $\dfrac{5}{x-2} - \dfrac{3x+4}{x^3-8}$

52. $\dfrac{3x}{x-1} + \dfrac{5}{x^3+x^2-2x} + \dfrac{2}{x} + \dfrac{x-1}{x+2}$

53. $\dfrac{1}{x+d+1} - \dfrac{1}{x+1}$

54. $\dfrac{1}{(x+d)^2} - \dfrac{1}{x^2}$

55. $x + d + \dfrac{1}{x+d} - \left(x + \dfrac{1}{x}\right)$

56. $\dfrac{x+d}{(x+d-1)^2} - \dfrac{x}{(x-1)^2}$

Mixed Form

Rewrite each mixed expression as an improper fraction.

57. $x + \dfrac{1}{x}$

58. $\dfrac{1}{2} - x$

59. $\dfrac{x}{x-1} - 1 - \dfrac{1}{x+1}$

60. $a + \dfrac{1}{a^2 - b^2}$

61. $3 - a - \dfrac{2}{a}$

62. $\dfrac{5}{x} - 2x + \dfrac{3}{x^2}$

63. $\left(3b + \dfrac{1}{x}\right) - \left(2b - \dfrac{b}{ax}\right)$

64. $\left(5x + \dfrac{x+2}{3}\right) - \left(2x - \dfrac{2x-3}{4}\right)$

Do this group of problems without using your calculator, and leave your answers in fractional form.

Hint: In Problem 65, first find the amount that each crew can do in one day (e.g., the first crew can grade 13/3 km per day). Then add the separate amounts to get the daily total. You can use a similar approach to the other work problems in this group.

Applications

65. A certain work crew can grade 13 km of roadbed in three days, and another crew can do 19 km in four days. How much can both crews together grade in one day?

66. Liquid is running into a tank from a pipe that can fill four tanks in three days. Meanwhile, liquid is running out from a drain that can empty two tanks in four days. What will be the net change in volume in one day?

67. A planer makes a 1-m cutting stroke at a rate of 15 m/min and returns at 75 m/min. How long does it take for the cutting stroke and return? (See Eq. A17.)

68. Two resistors, 5 Ω and 15 Ω, are wired in parallel. What is the resistance of the parallel combination? (See Eq. A64.)

69. One crew can put together five machines in eight days. Another crew can assemble three of these machines in four days. How much can both crews together assemble in one day?

70. One crew can assemble M machines in p days. Another crew can assemble N of these machines in q days. Write an expression for the number of machines that both crews together can assemble in one day, combine into a single term, and simplify.

71. A steel plate in the shape of a trapezoid (Fig. 9•3) has a hole of diameter d. The area of the plate, less the hole, is

$$\dfrac{(a+b)h}{2} - \dfrac{\pi d^2}{4}$$

FIGURE 9•3

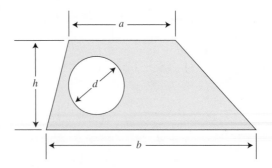

Combine these two terms and simplify.

FIGURE 9•4

72. The resistance R (Fig. 9•4) is

$$\frac{R_1 R_2}{R_1 + R_2} + R_3$$

Combine into a single term and simplify.

73. If a car travels a distance d at a rate V, the time required will be d/V. The car then continues for a distance d_1 at a rate V_1, and a third distance d_2 at rate V_2. Write an expression for the total travel time; then combine the three terms into a single term and simplify.

Computer

74. If you have a computer algebra system, use it to do any of the additions or subtractions in this exercise.

9•4   Complex Fractions

Fractions that have only *one* fraction line are called *simple* fractions. Fractions with *more than* one fraction line are called *complex* fractions.

 Example 32:

$$\frac{\dfrac{a}{b}}{c} \quad \text{and} \quad \frac{x - \dfrac{1}{x}}{\dfrac{x}{y} - x}$$

are complex fractions.

We show how to simplify complex fractions in the following examples.

 Example 33: Simplify the complex fraction,

$$\frac{\dfrac{1}{2} + \dfrac{2}{3}}{3 + \dfrac{1}{4}}$$

Solution: We can simplify this fraction by multiplying numerator and denominator by the least common denominator for all the individual fractions. The denominators are 2, 3, and 4, so the LCD is 12. Multiplying, we obtain

$$\frac{\left(\dfrac{1}{2} + \dfrac{2}{3}\right)12}{\left(3 + \dfrac{1}{4}\right)12} = \frac{6 + 8}{36 + 3} = \frac{14}{39}$$

 Example 34: Simplify the complex fraction

$$\frac{1 + \dfrac{a}{b}}{1 - \dfrac{b}{a}}$$

Solution: The LCD for the two small fractions a/b and b/a is ab. Multiplying, we obtain

$$\frac{1 + \dfrac{a}{b}}{1 - \dfrac{b}{a}} \cdot \frac{ab}{ab} = \frac{ab + a^2}{ab - b^2}$$

or, in factored form,

$$\frac{a(b + a)}{b(a - b)}$$ ▬

In the following example, we simplify a small section at a time and work outward. Try to follow the steps.

▬ **Example 35:**

$$\frac{a + \dfrac{1}{b}}{a + \dfrac{1}{b + \dfrac{1}{a}}} \cdot \frac{ab}{ab + 1} = \frac{\dfrac{ab + 1}{b}}{a + \dfrac{1}{\dfrac{ab + 1}{a}}} \cdot \frac{ab}{ab + 1}$$

$$= \frac{\dfrac{ab + 1}{b}}{a + \dfrac{a}{ab + 1}} \cdot \frac{ab}{ab + 1}$$

$$= \frac{\dfrac{ab + 1}{b}}{\dfrac{a(ab + 1) + a}{ab + 1}} \cdot \frac{ab}{ab + 1}$$

$$= \frac{ab + 1}{b} \cdot \frac{ab + 1}{a(ab + 1) + a} \cdot \frac{ab}{ab + 1}$$

$$= \frac{a(ab + 1)}{a(ab + 1) + a} = \frac{ab + 1}{ab + 2}$$ ▬

Exercise 4 Complex Fractions

Simplify.

1. $\dfrac{\dfrac{2}{3} + \dfrac{3}{4}}{\dfrac{1}{5}}$

2. $\dfrac{\dfrac{3}{4} - \dfrac{1}{3}}{\dfrac{1}{2} + \dfrac{1}{6}}$

3. $\dfrac{\dfrac{1}{2} + \dfrac{1}{3} + \dfrac{1}{4}}{3 - \dfrac{4}{5}}$

4. $\dfrac{\dfrac{4}{5}}{\dfrac{1}{5} + \dfrac{2}{3}}$

5. $\dfrac{5 - \dfrac{2}{5}}{6 + \dfrac{1}{3}}$

6. $\dfrac{1}{2} + \dfrac{3}{\dfrac{2}{5} + \dfrac{1}{3}}$

7. $\dfrac{x + \dfrac{y}{4}}{x - \dfrac{y}{3}}$

8. $\dfrac{\dfrac{a}{b} + \dfrac{x}{y}}{\dfrac{a}{z} - \dfrac{x}{c}}$

9. $\dfrac{1 + \dfrac{x}{y}}{1 - \dfrac{x^2}{y^2}}$

10. $\dfrac{x + \dfrac{a}{c}}{x + \dfrac{b}{d}}$

11. $\dfrac{a^2 + \dfrac{x}{3}}{4 + \dfrac{x}{5}}$

12. $\dfrac{3a^2 - 3y^2}{\dfrac{a + y}{3}}$

13. $\dfrac{x + \dfrac{2d}{3ac}}{x + \dfrac{3d}{2ac}}$

14. $\dfrac{4a^2 - 4x^2}{\dfrac{a + x}{a - x}}$

15. $\dfrac{x^2 - \dfrac{y^2}{2}}{\dfrac{x - 3y}{2}}$

16. $\dfrac{\dfrac{ab}{7} - 3d}{3c - \dfrac{ab}{d}}$

17. $\dfrac{1 + \dfrac{1}{x + 1}}{1 - \dfrac{1}{x - 1}}$

18. $\dfrac{xy - \dfrac{3x}{ac}}{\dfrac{ac}{x} + 2c}$

19. $\dfrac{\dfrac{2m + n}{m + n} - 1}{1 - \dfrac{n}{m + n}}$

20. $\dfrac{\dfrac{x^3 + y^3}{x^2 - y^2}}{\dfrac{x^2 - xy + y^2}{x - y}}$

21. $\dfrac{1}{a + \dfrac{1}{1 + \dfrac{a + 1}{3 - a}}}$

22. $\dfrac{x + y}{x + y + \dfrac{1}{x - y + \dfrac{1}{x + y}}}$

23. $\dfrac{3abc}{bc + ac + ab} - \dfrac{\dfrac{a - 1}{a} + \dfrac{b - 1}{b} + \dfrac{c - 1}{c}}{\dfrac{1}{a} + \dfrac{1}{b} + \dfrac{1}{c}}$

24. $\dfrac{\dfrac{1}{a} + \dfrac{1}{b+c}}{\dfrac{1}{a} - \dfrac{1}{b+c}} \left(1 + \dfrac{b^2 + c^2 - a^2}{2bc} \right)$

25. $\dfrac{\dfrac{x^2 - y^2 - z^2 - 2yz}{x^2 - y^2 - z^2 + 2yz}}{\dfrac{x - y - z}{x + y - z}}$

Applications

26. A car travels a distance d_1 at a rate V_1, then another distance d_2 at a rate V_2. The average speed for the entire trip is

$$\dfrac{d_1 + d_2}{\dfrac{d_1}{V_1} + \dfrac{d_2}{V_2}}$$

Simplify this complex fraction.

27. The equivalent resistance of two resistors in parallel is

$$\dfrac{R_1 R_2}{R_1 + R_2}$$

If each resistor is made of wire of resistivity ρ, with R_1 using a wire of length L_1 and cross-sectional area A_1, and R_2 having a length L_2 and area A_2, our expression becomes

See Eq. A71, $R = \rho L/A$.

$$\dfrac{\dfrac{\rho L_1}{A_1} \cdot \dfrac{\rho L_2}{A_2}}{\dfrac{\rho L_1}{A_1} + \dfrac{\rho L_2}{A_2}}$$

Simplify this complex fraction.

Computer

28. If you have a computer algebra system, use it to simplify any of the expressions in this exercise.

9·5

Fractional Equations

Solving Fractional Equations

An equation in which one or more terms is a fraction is called a *fractional equation*. To solve a fractional equation, first eliminate the fractions by multiplying both sides of the equation by the least common denominator (LCD) of every term. We can do this because multiplying both sides of an equation by the same quantity (the LCD in this case) does not unbalance the equation. With the fractions thus eliminated, the equation is then solved like any non-fractional equation.

━━ **Example 36:** Solve for x:

$$\frac{3x}{5} - \frac{x}{3} = \frac{2}{15}$$

Solution: Multiplying both sides of the equation by the LCD (15), we obtain

$$15\left(\frac{3x}{5} - \frac{x}{3}\right) = 15\left(\frac{2}{15}\right)$$

$$9x - 5x = 2$$

$$x = \frac{1}{2}$$

Equations with the Unknown in the Denominator

The procedure is the same when the unknown appears in the denominator of one or more terms. However, the LCD will now contain the unknown. Here it is understood that x cannot have a value that will make any of the denominators in the problem equal to zero. It should also be noted that x cannot be equal to zero.

■ **Example 37:** Solve for x:

$$\frac{2}{3x} = \frac{5}{x} + \frac{1}{2} \qquad (x \neq 0)$$

Solution: The LCD is $6x$. Multiplying both sides of the equation yields

$$6x\left(\frac{2}{3x}\right) = 6x\left(\frac{5}{x} + \frac{1}{2}\right)$$

$$6x\left(\frac{2}{3x}\right) = 6x\left(\frac{5}{x}\right) + 6x\left(\frac{1}{2}\right)$$

$$4 = 30 + 3x$$

$$3x = -26$$

$$x = -\frac{26}{3}$$

We assume the integers in these equations to be exact numbers. Thus we leave our answers in fractional form rather than converting to (approximate) decimals.

Check:

$$\frac{2}{3\left(-\dfrac{26}{3}\right)} \overset{?}{=} \frac{5}{-\dfrac{26}{3}} + \frac{1}{2}$$

$$-\frac{2}{26} \overset{?}{=} -\frac{15}{26} + \frac{13}{26}$$

$$-\frac{2}{26} = -\frac{2}{26} \qquad \text{checks}$$

■ **Example 38:** Solve for x:

$$\frac{8x + 7}{5x + 4} = 2 - \frac{2x}{5x + 1}$$

Solution: Multiplying by the LCD $(5x + 4)(5x + 1)$ yields

$$(8x + 7)(5x + 1) = 2(5x + 4)(5x + 1) - 2x(5x + 4)$$

$$40x^2 + 35x + 8x + 7 = 2(25x^2 + 5x + 20x + 4) - 10x^2 - 8x$$

$$40x^2 + 43x + 7 = 50x^2 + 50x + 8 - 10x^2 - 8x$$

$$43x + 7 = 42x + 8$$

$$x = 1$$

Check:

$$\frac{8(1) + 7}{5(1) + 4} \stackrel{?}{=} 2 - \frac{2(1)}{5(1) + 1}$$

$$\frac{15}{9} \stackrel{?}{=} 2 - \frac{2}{6}$$

$$\frac{5}{3} = \frac{6}{3} - \frac{1}{3} \quad \text{checks}$$

Common Error	The technique of multiplying by the LCD in order to eliminate the denominators is valid *only when we have an equation*. Do not multiply through by the LCD when there is no equation!

■ Example 39: Solve for x:

$$\frac{3}{x - 3} = \frac{2}{x^2 - 2x - 3} + \frac{4}{x + 1}$$

Solution: The denominator of the second fraction factors into

$$x^2 - 2x - 3 = (x - 3)(x + 1)$$

The LCD is therefore $(x - 3)(x + 1)$. Multiplying both sides of the given equation by the LCD gives

$$3(x + 1) = 2 + 4(x - 3)$$

$$3x + 3 = 4x - 10$$

$$x = 13 \qquad ■$$

Exercise 5 Fractional Equations

Solve for x.

1. $2x + \dfrac{x}{3} = 28$

2. $4x + \dfrac{x}{5} = 42$

3. $x + \dfrac{x}{5} = 24$

4. $\dfrac{x}{6} + x = 21$

5. $3x - \dfrac{x}{7} = 40$

6. $x - \dfrac{x}{6} = 25$

7. $\dfrac{2x}{3} - x = -24$

8. $\dfrac{3x}{5} + 7x = 38$

9. $\dfrac{x}{2} + \dfrac{x}{3} + \dfrac{x}{4} = 26$

10. $\dfrac{x - 1}{2} = \dfrac{x + 1}{3}$

11. $\dfrac{3x - 1}{4} = \dfrac{2x + 1}{3}$

12. $x + \dfrac{2x}{3} + \dfrac{3x}{4} = 29$

13. $2x + \dfrac{x}{3} - \dfrac{x}{4} = 50$

14. $3x - \dfrac{2x}{3} - \dfrac{5x}{6} = 18$

15. $3x - \dfrac{x}{6} + \dfrac{x}{12} = 70$

16. $\dfrac{x}{4} + \dfrac{x}{6} + \dfrac{x}{8} = 26$

17. $\dfrac{6x - 19}{2} = \dfrac{2x - 11}{3}$

18. $\dfrac{7x - 40}{8} = \dfrac{9x - 80}{10}$

19. $\dfrac{3x - 116}{4} + \dfrac{180 - 5x}{6} = 0$

20. $\dfrac{3x - 4}{2} - \dfrac{3x - 1}{16} = \dfrac{6x - 5}{8}$

21. $\dfrac{x - 1}{8} - \dfrac{x + 1}{18} = 1$

22. $\dfrac{3x}{4} + \dfrac{180 - 5x}{6} = 29$

23. $\dfrac{15x}{4} = \dfrac{9}{4} - \dfrac{3 - x}{2}$

24. $\dfrac{x}{4} + \dfrac{x}{10} + \dfrac{x}{8} = 19$

Equations with Unknown in Denominator

Solve for x:

25. $\dfrac{2}{3x} + 6 = 5$

26. $9 - \dfrac{4}{5x} = 7$

27. $4 + \dfrac{1}{x + 3} = 8$

28. $\dfrac{x + 5}{x - 2} = 5$

29. $\dfrac{x - 3}{x + 2} = \dfrac{x + 4}{x - 5}$

30. $\dfrac{3}{x + 2} = \dfrac{5}{x} + \dfrac{4}{x^2 + 2x}$

31. $\dfrac{9}{x^2 + x - 2} = \dfrac{7}{x - 1} - \dfrac{3}{x + 2}$

32. $\dfrac{3x + 5}{2x - 3} = \dfrac{3x - 3}{2x - 1}$

33. $\dfrac{4}{x^2 - 1} + \dfrac{1}{x - 1} + \dfrac{1}{x + 1} = 0$

34. $\dfrac{x}{3} - \dfrac{x^2 - 5x}{3x - 7} = \dfrac{2}{3}$

35. $\dfrac{3}{x + 1} - \dfrac{x + 1}{x - 1} = \dfrac{x^2}{1 - x^2}$

36. $\dfrac{x + 1}{2(x - 1)} - \dfrac{x - 1}{x + 1} = \dfrac{17 - x^2}{2(x^2 - 1)}$

37. $\dfrac{9x + 20}{36} - \dfrac{x}{4} = \dfrac{4x - 12}{5x - 4}$

38. $\dfrac{10x + 13}{18} - \dfrac{x + 2}{x - 3} = \dfrac{5x - 4}{9}$

39. $\dfrac{6x + 7}{10} - \dfrac{3x + 1}{5} = \dfrac{x - 1}{3x - 4}$

40. $\dfrac{5x}{1 - x} - \dfrac{7x}{3 + x} = \dfrac{12(1 - x^2)}{x^2 + 2x - 3}$

Computer

41. If you have a computer algebra system, use it to solve any of the equations in this exercise.

Word Problems Leading to Fractional Equations

9·6

Solving Word Problems

The method for solving the word problems in this chapter (and in any other chapter) is no different from that given in Chapter 3. The resulting equations, however, will now contain fractions.

■ **Example 40:** One-fifth of a certain number is 3 greater than one-sixth of that same number. Find the number.

Solution: Let x = the number. Then, from the problem statement,

$$\frac{1}{5}x = \frac{1}{6}x + 3$$

Multiplying by the LCD (30), we obtain

$$6x = 5x + 90$$

$$x = 90$$

Check: Is one-fifth of 90 (which is 18) 3 greater than one-sixth of 90 (which is 15)? Yes.   ▬

Rate Problems

Fractional equations often arise when we solve problems involving *rates*. Problems of this type include:

Uniform motion: *Amount traveled = Rate of travel × time traveled*
Work: *Amount of work done = Rate of work × time worked*
Fluid flow: *Amount of flow = Flow rate × duration of flow*
Energy flow: *Amount of energy = Rate of energy flow × time*

Notice that these equations are mathematically identical. Word problems involving motion, flow of fluids or solids, flow of heat, electricity, solar energy, mechanical energy, and so on can be handled in the same way.

To convince yourself of the similarity of all these types of problems, consider the following word problem: *If worker M can do a certain job in 5 h, and N can do the same job in 8 h, how long will it take M and N together to do that same job?* Are the following problems really any different?

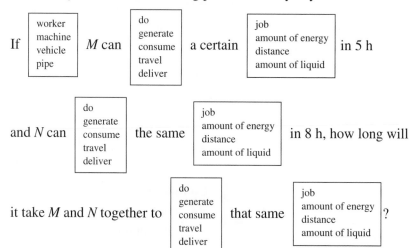

We will first do a uniform motion problem and then proceed to work and flow problems.

Uniform Motion

Motion is called *uniform* when the speed does not change. The distance traveled at constant speed is related to the rate of travel and the elapsed time by the following equation.

Be careful not to use this formula for anything but *uniform* motion.

Uniform Motion	Distance = rate × time	A17

■ **Example 41:** A train departs at noon, traveling at a speed of 64 km/h. A car leaves the same station $\frac{1}{2}$ h later to overtake the train, traveling on a road parallel to the track. If the car's speed is 96 km/h, at what time and at what distance from the station will it overtake the train?

Estimate: The train gets a head start of (1/2)(64), or 32 km, but the car goes 32 km/h faster than the train. Thus every hour the distance between car and train is reduced by 32 km. So it should take one hour for the car to overtake the train. The distance will be one hour's travel distance for the car, or 96 km.

Solution: Let x = time traveled by car (hours). Then $x + \frac{1}{2}$ = time traveled by train (hours). The distance traveled by the car is

$$(\text{distance} =) \text{ rate} \times \text{time} = 96x$$

and for the train

$$\text{distance} = 64\left(x + \frac{1}{2}\right)$$

But the distance is the same for car and train, so we can write the equation

$$96x = 64\left(x + \frac{1}{2}\right)$$

Removing parentheses yields

$$96x = 64x + 32$$
$$96x - 64x = 32$$
$$32x = 32$$
$$x = 1 \text{ h} = \text{time for car}$$
$$x + \frac{1}{2} = 1\tfrac{1}{2} \text{ h} = \text{time for train}$$

So the car overtakes the train at 1:30 P.M. at a distance of 96 km from the station. ■

Work Problems

To tackle work problems, we need one simple idea:

Work	Amount done = (rate of work) × (time)	A5

We often use this equation to find the rate of work for a person or a machine.

In a typical work problem, there are two or more persons or machines doing work, each at a different rate. For each worker the work rate is the amount done by that worker divided by the time taken to do the work. That is, if a person can stamp 9 parts in 13 min, that person's work rate is $\frac{9}{13}$ part per minute.

■ **Example 42:** Crew A can assemble two cars in five days, and crew B can assemble three cars in seven days. If both crews together assemble 100 cars, with crew B working 10 days longer than crew A, how many days (rounded to the nearest day) must each crew work?

Estimate: Working alone, crew A does two cars in five days, or 100 cars in 250 days. Similarly, crew B does 100 cars in about 231 days. Together they do 200 cars in $250 + 231$ or 481 days, or about 100 cars in 240 days. Thus we would expect each crew to work about half that, or about 120 days each. But crew B works 10 days longer than A, so we guess that they work about five days longer than 120 days while crew A works about five days less than 120 days.

Solution:

$$\text{Let } x = \text{days worked by crew } A$$

and

$$x + 10 = \text{days worked by crew } B$$

The work rate of each crew is

$$\text{crew } A: \quad \text{rate} = \frac{2}{5} \text{ car per day}$$

$$\text{crew } B: \quad \text{rate} = \frac{3}{7} \text{ car per day}$$

The amount done by each crew equals their work rate times the number of days worked. The sum of the amounts done by the two crews must equal 100 cars.

$$\frac{2}{5}x + \frac{3}{7}(x + 10) = 100$$

We clear fractions by multiplying by the LCD, 35:

$$14x + 15(x + 10) = 3500$$

$$14x + 15x + 150 = 3500$$

$$29x = 3350$$

$$x = 116 \text{ days for crew } A$$

$$x + 10 = 126 \text{ days for crew } B \quad\blacksquare$$

Fluid Flow and Energy Flow

For flow problems, we make use of the simple equation

$$\text{amount of flow} = \text{flow rate} \times \text{time}$$

Here we assume, of course, that the flow rate is constant.

■ **Example 43:** A certain small hydroelectric generating station can produce 17 megawatthours (MWh) of energy per year. After 4.0 months of operation, another generator is added which, by itself, can produce 11 MWh in 5.0 months. How many additional months are needed for a total of 25 MWh to be produced?

Solution: Let x = additional months. The original generating station can produce 17/12 MWh per month for $4 + x$ months. The new generator can produce 11/5 MWh per month for x months. The problem states that the total amount produced (in MWh) is 25, so

$$\frac{17}{12}(4.0 + x) + \frac{11}{5.0}x = 25$$

Multiplying by the LCD, 60, we obtain

$$5.0(17)(4.0 + x) + 12(11)x = 25(60)$$
$$340 + 85x + 132z = 1500$$
$$217x = 1160$$
$$x = \frac{1160}{217} = 5.3 \text{ months.} \quad \blacksquare$$

Exercise 6 Word Problems

Number Problems

1. There is a number such that if $\frac{1}{5}$ of it is subtracted from 50 and this difference is multiplied by 4, the result will be 70 less than the number. What is the number?

2. The number 100 is separated into two parts such that if $\frac{1}{3}$ of one part is subtracted from $\frac{1}{4}$ of the other, the difference is 11. Find the two parts.

3. The second of two numbers is 1 greater than the first, and $\frac{1}{2}$ of the first plus $\frac{1}{5}$ of the first is equal to the sum of $\frac{1}{3}$ of the second and $\frac{1}{4}$ of the second. What are the numbers?

4. Find two consecutive numbers such that one-half the larger exceeds one-third of the smaller by 9.

5. The difference between two positive numbers is 20, and $\frac{1}{7}$ of one is equal to $\frac{1}{3}$ of the other. What are the numbers?

Uniform Motion Problems

Depending on how you set them up, some of these problems may not result in fractional equations.

6. A person sets out from Ottawa and walks toward Montréal at the rate of 5.0 km/h. Three hours afterward, a second person sets out from the same place and walks in the same direction at the rate of 8.0 km. How far from Ottawa will the second person overtake the first?

7. A courier who goes at the rate of 10 km/h is followed, after 4.0 h, by another who goes at the rate of 12 km/h. In how many hours will the second courier overtake the first?

8. A person walks to the top of a mountain at the rate of 3.20 km/h and down the same way at the rate of 6.40 km/h. If he walks for 6.00 h, how far is it to the top of the mountain?

9. In going a certain distance, a train traveling at the rate of 64.0 km/h takes 2.00 h less than a train traveling 50.0 km/h. Find the distance.

10. Spacecraft A is over Toronto at noon on a certain day and traveling at a rate of $3\overline{0}0$ km/h. Spacecraft B, attempting to overtake and dock with A, is over Toronto at 1:15 P.M. and is traveling in the same direction as A, at 410 km/h. At what time will B overtake A? At what distance from Toronto?

Work Problems

11. A laborer can do a certain job in five days, a second can do the job in six days, and a third in eight days. In what time can the three together do the job?

12. Three masons build 318 m of wall. Mason *A* builds 7.0 m/day, *B* builds 6.0 m/day, and *C* builds 5.0 m/day. Mason *B* works twice as many days as *A*, and *C* works half as many days as *A* and *B* combined. How many days did each work?

13. If a carpenter can roof a house in 10 days and another can do the same in 14 days, how many days will it take if they work together?

14. A technician can assemble an instrument in 9.5 h. After working for 2.0 h she is joined by another technician who, alone, could do the job in 7.5 h. How many additional hours are needed to finish the job?

15. A certain screw machine can produce a box of parts in 3.3 h. A new machine is to be ordered; this machine will have a speed which will allow both machines working together to produce a box of parts in 1.4 h. How long would it take the new machine alone to produce a box of parts?

Fluid Flow Problems

16. A tank can be filled by a pipe in 3.0 h and emptied by another pipe in 4.0 h. How much time will be required to fill an empty tank if both are running?

17. Two pipes empty into a tank. One pipe can fill the tank in 8.0 h and the other in 9.0 h. How long will it take both pipes together to fill the tank?

18. A tank has three pipes connected. The first, by itself, could fill the tank in $2\frac{1}{2}$ h, the second in 2 h, and the third in 1 h 40 min. In how many minutes will the tank be filled?

19. A tank can be filled by a certain pipe in 18.0 h. Five hours after this pipe is opened, it is supplemented by a smaller pipe which, by itself, could fill the tank in 24.0 h. Find the total time, measured from the opening of the larger pipe, required to fill the tank.

20. At what rate must liquid be drained from a tank in order to empty it in 1.50 h if the tank takes 4.70 h to fill at the rate of 3.50 m³/min?

Energy Flow Problems

21. A certain power plant consumes 1500 tonnes of coal in 4.0 weeks. There is a stockpile of $1\overline{0}\,000$ tonnes of coal available when the plant starts operating. After 3.0 weeks in operation, an additional boiler, capable of using 2300 tonnes in 3.0 weeks, is put on line with the first boiler. In how many more weeks will the stockpile of coal be consumed?

22. A certain array of solar cells can generate 2.0 megawatthours (MWh) in 5.0 months (under standard conditions). After operating for 3.0 months, another array of cells is added which alone can generate 5.0 MWh in 7.0 months. How many additional months, after the new array has been added, are needed for the total energy generated from both arrays to be $1\overline{0}$ MWh?

23. A landlord owns a house that consumes 9240 L of heating oil in three winters. He buys another house, better insulated than the first, and the two houses together use 8140 L of oil in two winters. How many winters would it take the insulated house alone to use 5500 L of oil?

The humorist Stephen Leacock, in his *A, B, and C—The Human Element in Mathematics*, tells of those word problem heroes: *A*, full-blooded and having great strength and endurance; *B*, quiet and easy going; and *C*, the weakling. Here's a sample.

"The first time I ever saw these men was one evening after a regatta. They had all been rowing in it, and it had transpired that *A* could row as much in one hour as *B* in two or *C* in four. *B* and *C* had come in dead fagged and *C* was coughing badly. . . . Just then *A* came blustering in and shouted, "I say, you fellows, Smith has shown me three cisterns in his garden and he says we can pump them until tomorrow night. I bet I can beat you both . . . . I heard *B* growl . . . but they went, and presently I could tell from the sound of the water that *A* was pumping four times as fast as *C*."

In this group of problems, as in the previous ones, we assume that the rates are constant.

24. A wind generator can charge 20 storage batteries in 24 h. After this wind generator has been charging for 6.0 h, another generator, which can charge the batteries in 36 h, is also connected to the batteries. How many additional hours are needed to charge the batteries?

25. A certain solar collector can absorb 9405 kJ in 7.0 h. Another panel is added and together they collect 36 575 kJ in 5.0 h. How long would it take the new panel alone to collect 36 575 Btus?

Financial Problems

26. After spending $\frac{1}{4}$ of my money, then $\frac{1}{5}$ of the remainder, I had $66 left. How many dollars did I start with?

27. A person who had inherited some money spent $\frac{3}{8}$ of it the first year, $\frac{4}{5}$ of the remainder the next year, and had $1420 left. What was the inheritance?

28. Three children were left an inheritance of which the eldest received $\frac{2}{3}$, the second $\frac{1}{5}$, and the third the rest, which was $20 000. How much did each receive?

29. A's capital was $\frac{3}{4}$ of B's. If A's had been $500 less, it would have been only $\frac{1}{2}$ of B's. What was the capital of each?

9·7 Literal Equations and Formulas

Literal Equations

A *literal equation* is one in which some or all of the constants are represented by letters.

■ **Example 44:**

$$a(x + b) = b(x + c)$$

is a literal equation, whereas

$$2(x + 5) = 3(x + 1)$$

is a numerical equation.

Formulas

A *formula* is a literal equation that relates two or more mathematical or physical quantities. These are the equations, mentioned in the introduction of this chapter, that describe the workings of the physical world. A listing of some of the common formulas used in technology is given in the Applications section of the Summary of Facts and Formulas (Appendix A, pages A·32 to A·38).

■ **Example 45:**

Newton's second law	$F = ma$	**A20**

is a formula relating the force acting on a body with its mass and acceleration.

Solving Literal Equations and Formulas

When we solve a literal equation or formula, we cannot, of course, get a *numerical* answer, as we could with equations that had only one unknown. Our object here is to *isolate* one of the letters on one side of the equal sign. We "solve for" one of the literal quantities.

■ **Example 46:** Solve for x:

$$a(x + b) = b(x + c)$$

Solution: Our goal is to isolate x on one side of the equation. Removing parentheses, we obtain

$$ax + ab = bx + bc$$

Subtracting bx and then ab will place all the x terms on one side of the equation.

$$ax - bx = bc - ab$$

Factoring to isolate x yields

$$x(a - b) = b(c - a)$$

Dividing by $(a - b)$, where $a \neq b$, gives us

$$x = \frac{b(c - a)}{a - b}$$

■

■ **Example 47:** Solve for x:

$$b\left(b + \frac{x}{a}\right) = d$$

Solution: Dividing both sides by b, we have

$$b + \frac{x}{a} = \frac{d}{b}$$

Subtracting b yields

$$\frac{x}{a} = \frac{d}{b} - b$$

Multiplying both sides by a gives us

$$x = a\left(\frac{d}{b} - b\right)$$

■

■ **Example 48:** The formula for the amount of heat q flowing by conduction through a wall of thickness L, conductivity k, and cross-sectional area A is

$$q = \frac{kA(t_1 - t_2)}{L}$$

where t_1 and t_2 are the temperatures of the warmer and cooler sides, respectively. Solve this equation for t_1.

Solution: Multiplying both sides by L/kA gives

$$\frac{qL}{kA} = t_1 - t_2$$

Then adding t_2 to both sides, we get

$$t_1 = \frac{qL}{kA} + t_2$$

■

Checking Literal Equations

As with numerical equations, we can substitute our expression for x back into the original equation and see if it checks.

■ **Example 49:** We check the solution of Example 47 by substituting $a(d/b - b)$ for x in the original equation.

$$b\left(b + \frac{x}{a}\right) \overset{?}{=} d$$

$$b\left[b + \frac{a(d/b - b)}{a}\right] \overset{?}{=} d$$

$$b\left(b + \frac{d}{b} - b\right) \overset{?}{=} d$$

$$b\left(\frac{d}{b}\right) = d \qquad \text{checks}$$

■

Another simple "check" is to substitute numerical values. Avoid simple values 0 and 1 that may make an incorrect solution appear to check, and we avoid any values that will make a denominator zero.

■ **Example 50:** Check the results from Example 47.

Solution: Let us *choose* values for a, b, and d, say,

$$a = 2, \quad b = 3, \quad \text{and} \quad d = 6$$

With these values,

$$x = a\left(\frac{d}{b} - b\right) = 2\left(\frac{6}{3} - 3\right) = -2$$

We now see if these values check in the original equation.

$$b\left(b + \frac{x}{a}\right) = d$$

$$3\left(3 + \frac{-2}{2}\right) \overset{?}{=} 6$$

$$3(3 - 1) \overset{?}{=} 6$$

$$3(2) = 6 \qquad \text{checks}$$

Realize that this is not a rigorous check, because we are testing the solution only for the specific values chosen. However, if it checks for those values, we can be *reasonably* sure that our solution is correct.

■

Literal Fractional Equations

To solve literal fractional equations, the procedure is the same as for other fractional equations; multiply by the LCD to eliminate the fractions.

■ **Example 51:** Solve for x in terms of a, b, and c:

$$\frac{x}{b} - \frac{a}{c} = \frac{x}{a}$$

Solution: Multiplying by the LCD (abc) yields

$$acx - a^2b = bcx$$

Rearranging so that all x terms are together on one side of the equation, we obtain

$$acx - bcx = a^2b$$

Factoring gives us

$$x(ac - bc) = a^2b$$

$$x = \frac{a^2b}{ac - bc}$$ ■

■ **Example 52:** Solve for x:

$$\frac{x}{x - a} - \frac{x + 2b}{x + a} = \frac{a^2 + b^2}{x^2 - a^2}$$

Solution: The LCD is $x^2 - a^2$, that is, $(x - a)(x + a)$. Multiplying each term by the LCD gives

$$x(x + a) - (x + 2b)(x - a) = a^2 + b^2$$

Removing parentheses and rearranging so that all the x terms are together, we obtain

$$x^2 + ax - (x^2 + 2bx - ax - 2ab) = a^2 + b^2$$
$$x^2 + ax - x^2 - 2bx + ax + 2ab = a^2 + b^2$$
$$2ax - 2bx = a^2 - 2ab + b^2$$

Then we factor:

$$2x(a - b) = (a - b)^2$$

and divide by $2(a - b)$:

$$x = \frac{(a - b)^2}{2(a - b)} = \frac{a - b}{2}$$ ■

Sometimes a fractional equation will have some terms that themselves are not fractions, but the method of solution is the same.

■ **Example 53:** Solve for x:

$$\frac{x}{b} + c = \frac{2x}{a + b} + b$$

Solution: We multiply both sides by the LCD, $b(a + b)$:

$$x(a + b) + c(b)(a + b) = 2x(b) + b(b)(a + b)$$

Removing parentheses and moving all the x terms to one side gives

$$ax + bx + abc + b^2c = 2bx + ab^2 + b^3$$

$$ax + bx - 2bx = ab^2 + b^3 - abc - b^2c$$

Factoring yields

$$x(a - b) = b(ab + b^2 - ac - bc)$$

$$x = \frac{b(ab + b^2 - ac - bc)}{a - b}$$

Exercise 7 Literal Equations and Formulas

Solve for x.

1. $2ax = bc$
2. $ax + dx = a - c$
3. $a(x + y) = b(x + z)$
4. $4x = 2x + ab$
5. $4acx - 3d^2 = a^2d - d^2x$
6. $a(2x - c) = a + c$
7. $a^2x - cd = b - ax + dx$
8. $3(x - r) = 2(x + p)$
9. $\dfrac{a}{2}(x - 3w) = z$
10. $cx - x = bc - b$
11. $3x + m = b$
12. $ax + m = cx + n$
13. $ax - bx = c + dx - m$
14. $3m + 2x - c = x + d$
15. $ax - ab = cx - bc$
16. $p(x - b) = qx + d$
17. $3(x - b) = 2(bx + c) - c(x - b)$
18. $a(bx + d) - cdx = c(dx + d)$

Literal Fractional Equations

19. $\dfrac{w + x}{x} = w(w + y)$

20. $\dfrac{ax + b}{c} = bx - a$

21. $\dfrac{p - q}{x} = 3p$

22. $\dfrac{bx - c}{ax - c} = 5$

23. $\dfrac{a - x}{5} = \dfrac{b - x}{2}$

24. $\dfrac{x}{a} - b = \dfrac{c}{d} - x$

25. $\dfrac{x}{a} - a = \dfrac{a}{c} - \dfrac{x}{c - a}$

26. $\dfrac{x}{a - 1} - \dfrac{x}{a + 1} = b$

27. $\dfrac{x - a}{x - b} = \left(\dfrac{2x - a}{2x - b}\right)^2$

28. $\dfrac{a - b}{bx + c} + \dfrac{a + b}{ax - c} = 0$

29. $\dfrac{x + a}{x - a} - \dfrac{x - b}{x + b} = \dfrac{2(a + b)}{x}$

30. $\dfrac{ax}{b} - \dfrac{b - x}{2c} + \dfrac{a(b - x)}{3d} = a$

Word Problems with Literal Solutions

31. Two persons are d km apart. They set out at the same time and travel toward each other; one travels at the rate of m km/h and the other at the rate of n km/h. How far will each have traveled when they meet?

32. If A can do a piece of work in p hours, B in q hours, C in r hours, and D in s hours, how many hours will it take to do the work if all work together?

33. After spending $1/n$ and $1/m$ of my money, I had a dollars left. How many dollars had I at first?

Formulas

Be careful to distinguish between capitals and lowercase letters—they are not the same. A given equation might have, for example, both T and t, each with a different meaning.

34. The correction C for the sag in a surveyor's tape weighing w kg/m and pulled with a force of P newtons is

$$C = \frac{w^2 L^3}{24 P^2} \quad \text{metres}$$

Solve this equation for the distance measured, L.

35. When a bar of length L_0 having a coefficient of linear thermal expansion α is increased in temperature by an amount Δt, it will expand to a new length L, where

$$L = L_0(1 + \alpha \Delta t)$$

Solve this equation for Δt.

36. Solve the equation given in the preceding problem for the initial length L_0.

37. A rod of cross-sectional area a and length L will stretch by an amount e when subject to a tensile load of P. The modulus of elasticity is given by

$$E = \frac{PL}{ae}$$

Solve this equation for a.

38. The formula for the displacement s of a freely falling body having an initial velocity v_0 and acceleration a is

$$s = v_0 t + \tfrac{1}{2} a t^2$$

Solve this equation for a.

39. The formula for the amount of heat flowing through a wall by conduction is

$$q = \frac{kA(t_1 - t_2)}{L}$$

Solve this equation for t_2.

40. An amount a invested at a simple interest rate n for t years will accumulate to an amount y, where $y = a + ant$. Solve for a.

FIGURE 9•5

FIGURE 9•6

FIGURE 9•7

FIGURE 9•8

41. The formula for the equivalent resistance R for the parallel combination of two resistors, R_1 and R_2, is

$$\frac{1}{R} = \frac{1}{R_1} + \frac{1}{R_2}$$

Solve this formula for R_2.

42. Applying Kirchhoff's law (Eq. A68) to loop 1 in Figure 9•5, we get $E = I_1R_1 + I_1R_2 - I_2R_2$. Solve for I_1.

43. If the resistance of a conductor is R_1 at temperature t_1, the resistance will change to a value R when the temperature changes to t, where

$$R = R_1[1 + \alpha(t - t_1)]$$

and α is the temperature coefficient of resistance at temperature t_1. Solve this equation for t_1.

44. Solve the equation given in the preceding problem for the initial resistance R_1.

45. Taking the moment M about point p in Figure 9•6, we get $M = R_1L - F(L - x)$. Solve for L.

46. Three masses, m_1, m_2, and m_3, are attached together and accelerated by means of a force F, where,

$$F = m_1a + m_2a + m_3a$$

Solve for the acceleration a.

47. A bar of mass m_1 is attached to a sphere of mass m_2 (Fig. 9•7). The distance x to the center of gravity is

$$x = \frac{10m_1 + 25m_2}{m_1 + m_2}$$

Solve for m_1.

48. A ball of mass m is swung in a vertical circle (Fig. 9•8). At the top of its swing, the tension T in the cord plus the ball's mass effect m is just balanced by the centrifugal force mv^2/R:

$$T + ma = \frac{mv^2}{R}$$

Solve for m.

49. The total energy of a body of mass m, moving with velocity v and located at a height y above some datum, is the sum of the potential energy may and the kinetic energy $\frac{1}{2}mv^2$:

$$E = may + \tfrac{1}{2}mv^2$$

Solve for m.

Computer

50. A computer algebra system is great for solving literal equations. If you have a CAS, use it to solve any of the equations in this exercise. In DERIVE, you would highlight the equation to be solved, and give the command SOLVE. You then have to tell the computer *which variable* to solve for.

CHAPTER 9   REVIEW PROBLEMS

Perform the indicated operations and simplify.

1. $\dfrac{a^2 + b^2}{a - b} - a + b$

2. $\dfrac{3}{5x^2} - \dfrac{2}{15xy} + \dfrac{1}{6y^2}$

3. $\dfrac{3m + 1}{3m - 1} + \dfrac{m - 4}{5 - 2m} - \dfrac{3m^2 - 2m - 4}{6m^2 - 17m + 5}$

4. $\dfrac{\dfrac{1}{1 - x} - \dfrac{1}{1 + x}}{\dfrac{1}{1 - x^2} - \dfrac{1}{1 + x^2}}$

5. $(a^2 + 1 + a)\left(1 - \dfrac{1}{a} + \dfrac{1}{a^2}\right)$

6. $\dfrac{\dfrac{a - 1}{6} - \dfrac{2a - 7}{2}}{\dfrac{3a}{4} - 3}$

7. $\dfrac{1 + \dfrac{a - c}{a + c}}{1 - \dfrac{a - c}{a + c}}$

8. $\left(1 + \dfrac{x + y}{x - y}\right)\left(1 - \dfrac{x - y}{x + y}\right)$

9. $\dfrac{x^2 + 8x + 15}{x^2 + 7x + 10} - \dfrac{x - 1}{x - 2}$

10. $\dfrac{x^2 - 5ax + 6a^2}{x^2 - 8ax + 15a^2} - \dfrac{x - 7a}{x - 5a}$

11. $\dfrac{1}{a^2 - 7a + 12} + \dfrac{2}{a^2 - 4a + 3} - \dfrac{3}{a^2 - 5a + 4}$

12. $\dfrac{x^4 - y^4}{(x - y)^2} \times \dfrac{x - y}{x^2 + xy}$

13. $\dfrac{a^3 - b^3}{a^3 + b^3} \times \dfrac{a^2 - ab + b^2}{a - b}$

14. $\dfrac{3wx^2y^3}{7axyz} \times \dfrac{4a^3xz}{6aw^2y}$

15. $\dfrac{4a^2 - 9c^2}{4a^2 + 6ac}$

16. $\dfrac{b^2 - 5b}{b^2 - 4b - 5}$

17. $\dfrac{3a^2 + 6a}{a^2 + 4a + 4}$

18. $\dfrac{20(a^3 - c^3)}{4(a^2 + ac + c^2)}$

19. $\dfrac{x^2 - y^2 - 2yz - z^2}{x^2 + 2xy + y^2 - z^2}$

20. $\dfrac{2a^2 + 17a + 21}{3a^2 + 26a + 35}$

21. $\dfrac{(a + b)^2 - (c + d)^2}{(a + c)^2 - (b + d)^2}$

22. $\dfrac{1}{x - 2a} + \dfrac{a^2}{x^3 - 8a^3} - \dfrac{x + a}{x^2 + 2ax + 4a^2}$

Solve for x.

23. $cx - 5 = ax + b$

24. $a(x - 3) - b(x + 2) = c$

25. $\dfrac{5 - 3x}{4} + \dfrac{3 - 5x}{3} = \dfrac{3}{2} - \dfrac{5x}{3}$

26. $\dfrac{3x - 1}{11} - \dfrac{2 - x}{10} = \dfrac{6}{5}$

27. $\dfrac{x + 3}{2} + \dfrac{x + 4}{3} + \dfrac{x + 5}{4} = 16$

28. $\dfrac{2x + 1}{4} - \dfrac{4x - 1}{10} + \dfrac{5}{4} = 0$

29. $x^2 - (x - p)(x + q) = r$

30. $mx - n = \dfrac{nx - m}{p}$

31. $p = \dfrac{q - rx}{px - q}$

32. $m(x - a) + n(x - b) + p(x - c) = 0$

33. $\dfrac{x - 3}{4} - \dfrac{x - 1}{9} = \dfrac{x - 5}{6}$

34. $\dfrac{1}{x - 5} - \dfrac{1}{4} = \dfrac{1}{3}$

35. $\dfrac{3}{y - 4} + \dfrac{5}{2(y - 4)} + \dfrac{9}{2(y - 4)} = \dfrac{1}{2}$

36. $\dfrac{2}{x - 2} = \dfrac{5}{2(x - 1)}$

37. $\dfrac{10-7x}{6-7x}=\dfrac{5x-4}{5x}$

38. $\dfrac{9x+5}{6(x-1)}+\dfrac{3x^2-51x-71}{18(x^2-1)}=\dfrac{15x-7}{9(x+1)}$

39. It is estimated that a bulldozer can prepare a certain site in 15.0 days and that a larger bulldozer can prepare the same site in 11.0 days. If we assume that they do not get in each other's way, how long will it take the two machines, working together, to prepare the site?

40. The acceleration a_1 of a body of mass m_1 subjected to a force F_1 is, by Eq. A20, $a_1=F_1/m_1$. Write an expression for the difference in acceleration between that body and another having a mass m_2 and force F_2. Combine the terms of that expression and simplify.

41. Multiply $2\dfrac{3}{5}\times 7\dfrac{5}{9}$

42. Divide $\dfrac{8x^3y^2z}{5a^4b^3c}$ by $\dfrac{4xy^5z^3}{15abc^3}$

43. Multiply $\dfrac{3wx^2y^3}{7axyz}$ by $\dfrac{4a^3xz}{6aw^3y}$

44. Divide $9\dfrac{5}{7}\div 3\dfrac{4}{9}$

45. The charge in a capacitor is given by $Q=CV$ (A74).

Find the value of C in a circuit where the capacitors are in series.

Rewrite the equation $\dfrac{1}{C}=\dfrac{1}{C_1}+\dfrac{1}{C_2}$

46. If the voltage in the above equation is given as 32.8 V, find **(a)** the total capacitance C with a charge of $Q=68.0$ coulombs; and **(b)** C_2, given $C_1=85.6$ F.

Writing

47. Suppose that a vocal member of your local school board says that the study of fractions is no longer important now that we have computers and insists that it be cut from the curriculum to save money.

Write a short letter to the editor of your local paper in which you agree or disagree. Give your reasons for retaining or eliminating the study of fractions.

Team Project

48. The ancient Egyptians wrote each fraction (except for $\frac{2}{3}$) as the sum of unit fractions (a fraction with a numerator of 1). Thus,

$\frac{3}{5}$ would be written as $\frac{1}{2}+\frac{1}{10}$

and

$\frac{5}{7}$ would be written as $\frac{1}{2}+\frac{1}{7}+\frac{1}{14}$

This is called the *decomposition* of a fraction. Repetitions were not allowed. Thus $\frac{3}{5}$ would not be written as

$\frac{1}{5}+\frac{1}{5}+\frac{1}{5}$.

Decompose each following proper fraction into unit fractions.

$\dfrac{3}{4}\quad\dfrac{2}{5}\quad\dfrac{4}{5}\quad\dfrac{5}{6}\quad\dfrac{2}{7}\quad\dfrac{3}{7}\quad\dfrac{4}{7}\quad\dfrac{6}{7}$

$\dfrac{3}{8}\quad\dfrac{5}{8}\quad\dfrac{7}{8}\quad\dfrac{2}{9}\quad\dfrac{4}{9}\quad\dfrac{5}{9}\quad\dfrac{7}{9}\quad\dfrac{8}{9}$

10

Systems of Linear Equations

O B J E C T I V E S

When you have completed this chapter, you should be able to:

- Find an approximate graphical solution to a system of two equations.
- Solve a system of two equations in two unknowns by the addition–subtraction method.
- Solve a system of two equations by substitution, or by a computer technique.
- Solve a system of two equations having fractional coefficients or having the unknowns in the denominators.
- Solve a system of three or more equations by addition–subtraction or by substitution.
- Write a system of equations to describe a given word problem and to solve those equations.

Usually, a physical situation can be described by a single equation. For example, the displacement of a freely falling body is described by Eq. A18, $s = v_0 t + \frac{1}{2}at^2$. Often, however, a situation can be described only by *more than one* equation. For example, to find the two currents I_1 and I_2 in the circuit of Figure 10•1, we must solve the two equations

$$98I_1 - 43I_2 = 5$$

$$43I_1 - 115I_2 = 10$$

We must find values for I_1 and I_2 that satisfy *both* equations at the same time. In this chapter we learn how to solve such sets of two or three linear equations, and we also get practice in writing systems of equations to describe a variety of technical problems. In Chapter 11 we will learn how to solve systems of equations by means of determinants, and in Chapter 12 we will solve sets of equations using matrices.

FIGURE 10•1

10•1

Systems of Two Linear Equations

Linear Equations

We have previously defined a *linear equation* as one of *first degree*.

FIGURE 10·2

Systems of equations are also called *simultaneous* equations.

Note that some variables may have zero coefficients and may not appear in every equation.

■ **Example 1:** The equation

$$3x + 5 = 20$$

is a linear equation in *one unknown*. We learned how to solve these in Chapter 3. ■

■ **Example 2:** The equation

$$2x - y = 3$$

is a linear equation in *two* unknowns. A linear equation with the terms written in this order is said to be in *general form*. If we graph this equation we get a *straight line*, Figure 10·2. Glance back at Section 5·4 if you've forgotten how to make such a graph. ■

If a linear equation in two unknowns is solved for y, we get an equation in *slope-intercept* form, as explained in Section 5·4.

■ **Example 3:** If we solve the equation from Example 2 for y, we get the same equation in slope–intercept form:

$$y = 2x - 3$$

Recall from Section 5·4 that the coefficient of the x term is the *slope* and the constant term is the y *intercept*. Thus, in our example,

$$\text{slope} = 2 \qquad y \text{ intercept} = -3$$

The graph is, of course, the same as in Example 2. ■

A linear equation can have *any number* of unknowns.

■ **Example 4:**
(a) $x - 3y + 2z = 5$ is a linear equation with three unknowns.
(b) $3x + 2y - 5z - w = 6$ is a linear equation with four unknowns. ■

Systems of Equations

A set of two or more equations that simultaneously impose conditions on all the variables is called a *system of equations*.

■ **Example 5:**
(a) $3x - 2y = 5$
$\quad x + 4y = 1$
is a system of two linear equations with two unknowns.
(b) $x - 2y + 3z = 4$
$\quad 3x + y - 2z = 1$
$\quad 2x + 3y - z = 3$
is a system of three linear equations with three unknowns.
(c) $2x - y = 5$
$\quad x + 2z = 3$
$\quad 3y - z = 1$
is also a system of three linear equations with three unknowns.

(d) $y = 2x^2 - 3$
$y^2 = x + 5$

is a system of two quadratic equations with two unknowns. ▬

Solution to a System of Equations

The solution to a *system* of equations is a set of values of the unknowns that will *satisfy every equation* in the system.

▬ **Example 6:** The system of equations

$$x + y = 5$$
$$x - y = 3$$

is satisfied *only* by the values $x = 4$ and $y = 1$, and by *no other* set of values. Thus, the pair (4, 1) is the solution to the system, and the equations are said to be *independent*. ▬

To get a numerical solution for all the unknowns in a system of linear equations, if one exists, *there must be as many independent equations as there are unknowns*. We first solve two equations with two unknowns, then later, three equations with three unknowns, and then larger systems, but, for a solution to be possible, the number of equations must always equal the number of unknowns.

Approximate Graphical Solution to a Pair of Equations

Since any point on a curve satisfies the equation of that curve, the coordinates of the *points of intersection* of two curves will satisfy the equations of *both* curves. Thus we merely have to plot the two curves and find their point or points of intersection; these will be the solution to the pair of equations.

▬ **Example 7:** Graphically find the approximate solution to the pair of linear equations

$$3x - y = 1$$
$$x + y = 3$$

Solution: We plot the lines as in Chapter 5, as shown in Figure 10·3. The lines are seen to intersect at the point (1, 2). Our solution is then $x = 1$, $y = 2$. ▬

A *linear* equation with two unknowns plots as a *straight line*. Thus two linear equations plot as two straight lines. If the lines intersect at a single point, the coordinates of that point will satisfy both equations, and hence are a solution to the set of equations. If the lines are *parallel*, there is no point whose coordinates satisfy both equations, and the set of equations is said to be *inconsistent*. If the two lines *coincide* at every point, the coordinates of any point on one line will satisfy both equations. Such a set of equations is called *dependent*.

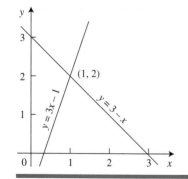

FIGURE 10·3 Graphical solution to a pair of equations. This is also a good way to get an approximate solution to a pair of *nonlinear* equations. See Exercise 2, Problem 19 (page 290).

Solution by Graphics Utility

The ability of the graphics calculator or graphing software on the computer to show the graphs of two equations on the screen at the same time makes it ideal for getting an approximate solution to a pair of equations. Further, the ability to magnify any portion of the display by *zooming in* or by changing the range, combined with the TRACE feature, enable us to find points of intersection to any desired accuracy.

■ **Example 8:** Solve the pair of equations

$$1.53x + 3.35y = 7.62$$
$$2.84x - 1.94y = 4.82$$

to the nearest hundredth, using the graphics calculator.

Solution: The equations must be entered into the calculator in slope–intercept form, so we first solve each for y. Solving the first equation gives

$$3.35y = -1.53x + 7.62$$
$$y = -0.457x + 2.27 \qquad (1)$$

From the second equation,

$$1.94y = 2.84x - 4.82$$
$$y = -1.46x - 2.48 \qquad (2)$$

Next we enter equations (1) and (2) into the graphics calculator and draw the graph. With both the x and y ranges set from -10 to $+10$, we get the graph shown in Figure 10•4.

Turning on TRACE, we move the cursor as close to the point of intersection as we can, and read the x and y coordinates.

$$x \approx 2.421 \qquad y \approx 1.156$$

However, if we move the cursor one step, we see that the x and y values change more than 0.01 at this range setting. Thus we cannot get the required accuracy here. We must zoom in (see your calculator manual for how to do this) until the cursor step size is smaller than 0.01. This occurs when the x range is from 2 to 3, and the y range is from 0.5 to 2, approximately, depending on the calculator used. We read then

$$x = 2.47 \qquad y = 1.13$$

good to the nearest hundredth.   ■

Solving a Pair of Linear Equations by the Addition–Subtraction Method

The method of *addition–subtraction*, and the method of *substitution* that follows, have the objective of *eliminating* one of the unknowns.

In the addition–subtraction method, this is accomplished by first (if necessary) multiplying each equation by numbers that will make the coefficients of one unknown in both equations equal in absolute value. The two equations are then added or subtracted so as to eliminate that variable.

Let us first use this method for the same system that we solved graphically in Example 7.

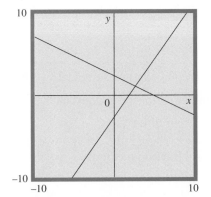

FIGURE 10•4

Some graphics calculators will automatically find the point of intersection of two plotted curves. Consult your user's manual to see if your calculator has this feature.

In Chapter 12 we will use the matrix features of the graphics calculator to solve sets of equations.

■ **Example 9:** Solve by the addition–subtraction method:

$$3x - y = 1$$
$$x + y = 3$$

Solution: Simply adding the two equations causes y to drop out.

$$3x - y = 1$$
$$\underline{x + y = 3}$$

Add:
$$4x \quad = 4$$
$$x = 1$$

Substituting into the second given equation yields

$$1 + y = 3$$
$$y = 2$$

Our solution is then $x = 1$, $y = 2$, as found graphically in Example 7. ■

In the next example, we must multiply one equation by a constant before adding.

■ **Example 10:** Solve by the addition–subtraction method:

$$2x - 3y = -4$$
$$x + \quad y = \quad 3$$

Solution: Multiply the second equation by 3:

$$2x - 3y = -4$$
$$\underline{3x + 3y = \quad 9}$$

Add:
$$5x \quad = \quad 5$$

We have thus reduced our two original equations to a single equation in one unknown. Solving for x gives

$$x = 1$$

Substituting into the second original equation, we have

$$1 + y = 3$$
$$y = 2$$

So the solution is $x = 1$, $y = 2$.

Check: Substitute into the first original equation:

$$2(1) - 3(2) \overset{?}{=} -4$$
$$2 - 6 \quad = -4 \qquad \text{checks}$$

and into the second original equation:

$$1 + 2 = 3 \qquad \text{checks} \qquad \blacksquare$$

Often it is necessary to multiply *both* given equations by suitable factors, as shown in the following example.

■ **Example 11:** Solve by addition or subtraction:

$$5x - 3y = 19$$
$$7x + 4y = 2$$

Solution: Multiply the first equation by 4 and the second by 3:

$$20x - 12y = 76$$
$$21x + 12y = 6$$

Add:
$$41x \quad\quad = 82$$
$$x = 2$$

Substituting $x = 2$ into the first equation gives

$$5(2) - 3y = 19$$
$$3y = -9$$
$$y = -3$$

So the solution is $x = 2$, $y = -3$.

These values check when substituted into each of the original equations (work not shown). Notice that we could have eliminated the x terms by multiplying the first equation by 7 and the second by -5, and adding. The results, of course, would have been the same: $x = 2$, $y = -3$. ■

The coefficients in the preceding examples were integers, but in applications they will usually be approximate numbers. If so, we must retain the proper number of significant digits, as in the following example.

■ **Example 12:** Solve for x and y.

$$2.64x + 8.47y = 3.72$$
$$1.93x + 2.61y = 8.25$$

> We are less likely to make a mistake adding rather than subtracting, so it is safer to multiply by a negative number and add the resulting equations, as we do here.

Solution: Let us eliminate y. We multiply the first equation by 2.61 and the second equation by -8.47. Let us carry at least three digits and/or two decimal places in our calculation, and round our answer to three digits at the end.

$$6.89x + 22.11y = 9.71$$
$$-16.35x - 22.11y = -69.88$$

$$-9.46x \quad\quad = -60.17$$
$$x = 6.36$$

> Another approach is to divide each equation by the coefficient of its x term, thus making each x coefficient equal to 1. Then subtract one equation from the other.

Substituting into the first equation yields

$$2.64(6.36) + 8.47y = 3.72$$
$$8.47y = 3.72 - 16.79 = -13.07$$
$$y = -1.54$$ ■

Substitution Method

To use the *substitution method* to solve a pair of linear equations, first solve either original equation for one unknown in terms of the other unknown.

Then substitute this expression into the other equation, thereby eliminating one unknown.

■ **Example 13:** Solve by substitution:

$$7x - 9y = 1$$
$$y = 5x - 17 \qquad (1)$$

Solution: We substitute $(5x - 17)$ for y in the first equation and get

$$7x - 9(5x - 17) = 1$$
$$7x - 45x + 153 = 1$$
$$-38x = -152$$
$$x = 4$$

Substituting $x = 4$ into the second original equation gives

$$y = 5(4) - 17$$
$$y = 3$$

So our solution is $x = 4$, $y = 3$. ■

> If, as in this example, one or both of the given equations are already in explicit form, then the substitution method is probably the easiest. Otherwise, many students find the addition–subtraction method easier.

Systems Having No Solution

Certain systems of equations have no unique solution. If you try to solve either of these types, *both variables will vanish.*

■ **Example 14:** Solve the system

$$2x + 3y = 5$$
$$6x + 9y = 2$$

Solution: Multiply the first equation by 3:

$$\begin{array}{r} 6x + 9y = 15 \\ \underline{6x + 9y = 2} \end{array}$$

Subtract: $0 = 13$ no solution ■

> It does not matter much whether a system is inconsistent or dependent; in either case we get no useful solution. But the practical problems we solve here will always have numerical solutions, so if your variables vanish go back and check your work.

If both variables vanish and an *inequality* results, as in Example 14, the system is called *inconsistent.* The equations would plot as two *parallel lines.* There is no point of intersection and hence no solution.

If both variables vanish and an *equality* results (such as $4 = 4$), the system is called *dependent.* The two equations would plot as a *single line,* indicating that there are infinitely many solutions.

A Computer Technique: The Gauss-Seidel Method

The *Gauss-Seidel method* is a simple computer technique for solving systems of equations. Suppose that we wish to solve the set of equations

$$x - 2y + 2 = 0 \qquad (1)$$
$$3x - 2y - 6 = 0 \qquad (2)$$

We first solve the first equation for x in terms of y and the second equation for y in terms of x.

$$x = 2y - 2 \tag{3}$$

$$y = \frac{3x - 6}{2} \tag{4}$$

We then *guess* at the value of y, substitute this value into (3), and obtain a value for x. This x is substituted into (4) and a value of y is obtained. These values for x and y will not be the correct values; they are only our *first approximation* to the true values.

The latest value for y is then put into (3), producing a new x; which is then put into (4), producing a new y; which is then put into (3); and so on. We repeat the computation until the values no longer change (we say that they *converge* on the true values). If the values of x and y get very large (*diverge* instead of converge), we solve the first equation for y and the second equation for x, and the computation will converge.

This type of repetitive process is called *iteration*, or the *method of successive approximations*.

■ **Example 15:** Calculate x and y for the equations above using the Gauss-Seidel method. Take $y = 0$ for the first guess.

Solution: From equation (3) we get

$$x = 2(0) - 2 = -2$$

Substituting $x = -2$ into (4),

$$y = \frac{3(-2) - 6}{2} = -6$$

With y equal to -6, we then use (3) to find a new x, and so on. We get the values

x	y
-2	-6
-14	-24
-50	-78
-158	-240
-482	-726
$-1\,454$	$-2\,184$
$-4\,370$	$-6\,558$
$-13\,118$	$-19\,680$
$-39\,362$	$-59\,046$
.	.
.	.
.	.

Note that the values are *diverging*. We try again, this time solving equation (1) for y,

$$y = \frac{x + 2}{2}$$

and solving (2) for x,

$$x = \frac{2y + 6}{3}$$

Repeating the computation, starting with $x = 0$, gives the values

x	y
2.666667	1
3.555556	2.333334
3.851852	2.777778
3.950617	2.925926
3.983539	2.975309
3.994513	2.991769
3.998171	2.997256
3.99939	2.999086
3.999797	2.999695
3.999932	2.999899
3.999977	2.999966
3.999992	2.999989
3.999998	2.999996
3.999999	2.999999
4	3
4	3
.	.
.	.
.	.

which converge on $x = 4$ and $y = 3$. ▬

How do we know what value to take for our first guess? Choose whatever values seem "reasonable." If you have no idea, then choose any values, such as the zeros in this example. Actually, it does not matter much what values we start with. If the computation is going to converge, it will converge regardless of the initial values chosen. However, the closer your guess, the *faster* the convergence.

Exercise 1 Systems of Two Linear Equations

Graphical Solution

Graphically find the approximate solution to each system of equations below. If you have a graphics calculator, use the ZOOM and TRACE features to find the solution to two decimal places.

1. $2x - y = 5$
$x - 3y = 5$

2. $x + 2y = -7$
$5x - y = 9$

3. $x - 2y = -3$
$3x + y = 5$

4. $4x + y = 8$
$2x - y = 7$

5. $2x + 5y = 4$
$5x - 2y = -3$

6. $x - 2y + 2 = 0$
$3x - 6y + 2 = 0$

Algebraic Solution

Solve each system of equations by addition–subtraction, by substitution, or by computer.

7. $2x + y = 11$
$3x - y = 4$

8. $5x + 7y = 101$
$y = 7x - 55$

9. $3x - 2y = -15$
$5x + 6y = 3$

10. $7x + 6y = 20$
$2x + 5y = 9$

11. $x + 5y = 11$
$3x + 2y = 7$

12. $4x - 5y = -34$
$2x - 3y = -22$

13. $x = 11 - 4y$
$5x - 2y = 11$

14. $2x - 3y = 3$
$4x + 5y = 39$

15. $7x - 4y = 81$
$5x - 3y = 57$

16. $3x + 4y = 85$
$5x + 4y = 107$

17. $3x - 2y = 1$
$2x + y = 10$

18. $5x - 2y = 3$
$2x + 3y = 5$

19. $y = 9 - 3x$
$x = 8 - 2y$

20. $y = 2x - 3$
$x = 19 - 3y$

21. $29.1x - 47.6y = 42.8$
$11.5x + 72.7y = 25.8$

22. $4.92x - 8.27y = 2.58$
$6.93x + 2.84y = 8.36$

23. $4n = 18 - 3m$
$m = 8 - 2n$

24. $5p + 4q - 14 = 0$
$17p = 31 + 3q$

25. $3w = 13 + 5z$
$4w - 7z - 17 = 0$

26. $3u = 5 + 2v$
$5v + 2u = 16$

27. $3.62x = 11.7 + 4.73y$
$4.95x - 7.15y - 12.8 = 0$

28. $3.03a = 5.16 + 2.11b$
$5.63b + 2.26a = 18.8$

There are no applications given here.
They are located in Exercise 3.

29. $4.17w = 14.7 - 3.72v$
$v = 8.11 - 2.73w$

30. $5.66p + 4.17q - 16.9 = 0$
$13.7p = 32.2 + 3.61q$

31. Use your graphics calculator to solve any of the systems in this exercise. Work to three significant digits.

Computer

32. Write a program or use a spreadsheet for the Gauss-Seidel method described in Section 10•1. Use it to solve any of the sets of equations in this exercise.

33. A computer algebra system (CAS) will easily solve a set of equations. Using *Derive*, for example, the equations from Problem 1 of this exercise would be entered enclosed in brackets and separated by a comma;

$$[2x - y = 5, x - 3y = 5]$$

You would then highlight this expression and enter the SOLVE command to get the solution. In *Maple*, you would give the command

$$\text{Solve}(\{2x - y = 5, x - 3y = 5\})$$

and in *Mathematica* the instruction is

$$\text{Solve}[\{2x - y = = 5, x - 3y = = 5\}, \{x, y\}]$$

Use your CAS to solve any of the sets of equations in this exercise.

10•2

Other Systems of Equations

Systems with Fractional Coefficients

When one or more of the equations in our system have fractional coefficients, simply multiply the entire equation by the LCD, and proceed as before.

The techniques in this section apply not only to two equations in two unknowns, but also to larger systems as well.

■ **Example 16:** Solve for x and y:

$$\frac{x}{2} + \frac{y}{3} = \frac{5}{6} \tag{1}$$

$$\frac{x}{4} - \frac{y}{2} = \frac{7}{4} \tag{2}$$

Solution: Multiply (1) by 6 and (2) by 4:

$$
\begin{array}{rll}
3x + 2y = & 5 & \text{(3)} \\
\underline{x - 2y = } & 7 & \text{(4)} \\
\end{array}
$$

Add (3) and (4):

$$
\begin{array}{rl}
4x = & 12 \\
x = & 3
\end{array}
$$

Having x, we can now substitute back to get y. It is not necessary to substitute back into one of the original equations. We choose instead the easiest place to substitute, such as equation (4). (However, when checking, be sure to substitute your answers into both of the *original equations*.) Substituting $x = 3$ into (4) gives

$$3 - 2y = 7$$

$$2y = 3 - 7 = -4$$

$$y = -2$$

■

To save space we will not show the check in many of these examples.

Fractional Equations with Unknowns in the Denominator

The same method (multiplying by the LCD) can be used to clear fractions when the unknowns appear in the denominators. Note that such equations are not linear (that is, not of first degree) as were the equations we have solved so far, but we are able to solve them by the same methods.

Of course, neither x nor y can equal zero in this system.

■ **Example 17:** Solve the system

$$\frac{10}{x} - \frac{9}{2y} = 6 \tag{1}$$

$$\frac{20}{3x} + \frac{15}{y} = 1 \tag{2}$$

Solution: We multiply (1) by $2xy$ and (2) by $3xy$:

$$20y - 9x = 12xy \tag{3}$$

$$20y + 45x = 3xy \tag{4}$$

Subtracting (4) from (3) gives

$$-54x = 9xy$$

$$y = -6$$

Substituting $y = -6$ back into (1),

$$\frac{10}{x} - \frac{9}{2(-6)} = 6$$

$$\frac{10}{x} = 6 - \frac{3}{4} = \frac{21}{4}$$

$$\frac{x}{10} = \frac{4}{21}$$

$$x = \frac{40}{21}$$

So our solution is $x = 40/21$, $y = -6$. ▬

A convenient way to solve nonlinear systems like these is to *substitute new variables* to make the equations linear. Solve in the usual way and then substitute back.

This technique of substitution is very useful, and we will use it again later to reduce certain equations to quadratic form. Do not confuse this kind of substitution with the method of substitution we studied in Section 10•1.

▬ **Example 18:** Solve the nonlinear system of equations

$$\frac{2}{3x} + \frac{3}{5y} = 17 \tag{1}$$

$$\frac{3}{4x} + \frac{2}{3y} = 19 \tag{2}$$

Solution: We substitute $m = 1/x$ and $n = 1/y$ and get the linear system

$$\frac{2m}{3} + \frac{3n}{5} = 17 \tag{3}$$

$$\frac{3m}{4} + \frac{2n}{3} = 19 \tag{4}$$

Again, we clear fractions by multiplying each equation by its LCD. Multiplying (3) by 15 gives

$$10m + 9n = 255 \tag{5}$$

and multiplying (4) by 12 gives

$$9m + 8n = 228 \tag{6}$$

Using the addition–subtraction method, we multiply (5) by 8 and multiply (6) by -9.

$$80m + 72n = 2040$$
$$-81m - 72n = -2052$$

Add:
$$-m = -12$$
$$m = 12$$

Substituting $m = 12$ into (5) yields

$$120 + 9n = 255$$

$$n = 15$$

Finally, we substitute back to get x and y:

$$x = \frac{1}{m} = \frac{1}{12} \quad \text{and} \quad y = \frac{1}{n} = \frac{1}{15}$$ ▬

Common Error	Students often forget that last step. We are not solving for m and n, but for x and y.

Literal Equations

We use the method of addition–subtraction or the method of substitution for solving systems of equations with literal coefficients, treating the literals as if they were numbers.

■ **Example 19:** Solve for x and y in terms of m and n.

$$2mx + ny = 3$$
$$mx + 3ny = 2$$

Solution: We will use the addition–subtraction method. Multiply the second equation by -2:

$$
\begin{array}{r}
2mx + ny = 3 \\
-2mx - 6ny = -4 \\
\hline
\end{array}
$$

Add:
$$-5ny = -1$$
$$y = \frac{1}{5n}$$

Substituting back into the second original equation, we obtain

$$mx + 3n\left(\frac{1}{5n}\right) = 2$$

$$mx + \frac{3}{5} = 2$$

$$mx = 2 - \frac{3}{5} = \frac{7}{5}$$

$$x = \frac{7}{5m}$$

■

■ **Example 20:** Solve for x and y by the addition–subtraction method:

$$a_1x + b_1y = c_1$$
$$a_2x + b_2y = c_2$$

Solution: Multiplying the first equation by b_2 and the second equation by b_1, we obtain

$$
\begin{array}{r}
a_1b_2x + b_1b_2y = b_2c_1 \\
a_2b_1x + b_1b_2y = b_1c_2 \\
\hline
\end{array}
$$

Subtract:
$$(a_1b_2 - a_2b_1)x = b_2c_1 - b_1c_2$$

Dividing by $a_1b_2 - a_2b_1$ gives

$$x = \frac{b_2c_1 - b_1c_2}{a_1b_2 - a_2b_1}$$

Now solving for y, we multiply the first equation by a_2 and the second equation by a_1. Writing the second equation above the first, we get

$$
\begin{array}{r}
a_1a_2x + a_1b_2y = a_1c_2 \\
a_1a_2x + a_2b_1y = a_2c_1 \\
\hline
\end{array}
$$

Subtract:
$$(a_1b_2 - a_2b_1)y = a_1c_2 - a_2c_1$$

Dividing by $a_1b_2 - a_2b_1$ yields

$$y = \frac{a_1c_2 - a_2c_1}{a_1b_2 - a_2b_1}$$ ▬

This result may be summarized as follows:

	The solution to the set of equations $$a_1x + b_1y = c_1$$ $$a_2x + b_2y = c_2$$ is $$x = \frac{b_2c_1 - b_1c_2}{a_1b_2 - a_2b_1} \qquad y = \frac{a_1c_2 - a_2c_1}{a_1b_2 - a_2b_1}$$ $$(a_1b_2 - a_2b_1 \neq 0)$$	
Two Linear Equations in Two Unknowns (Cramer's Rule)		**63**

Thus Eq. 63 is a formula for solving a pair of linear equations. We simply have to identify the six numbers a_1, b_1, c_1, a_2, b_2, and c_2, and substitute them into the equations. But be sure to put the equations into standard form first.

▬ **Example 21:** Solve, using Eq. 63:

$$9y = 7x - 15$$

$$-17 + 5x = 8y$$

Solution: Rewrite our equations in the form given in Eq. 63:

$$7x - 9y = 15$$

$$5x - 8y = 17$$

Then substitute, with

$$a_1 = 7 \qquad b_1 = -9 \qquad c_1 = 15$$
$$a_2 = 5 \qquad b_2 = -8 \qquad c_2 = 17$$

$$x = \frac{b_2c_1 - b_1c_2}{a_1b_2 - a_2b_1} = \frac{-8(15) - (-9)(17)}{7(-8) - 5(-9)}$$

$$= -3$$

$$y = \frac{a_1c_2 - a_2c_1}{a_1b_2 - a_2b_1} = \frac{7(17) - (5)(15)}{-11}$$

$$= -4$$ ▬

Exercise 2 Other Systems of Equations

Fractional Coefficients

Solve simultaneously.

1. $\dfrac{x}{5} + \dfrac{y}{6} = 18$

$\dfrac{x}{2} - \dfrac{y}{4} = 21$

2. $\dfrac{x}{2} + \dfrac{y}{3} = 7$

$\dfrac{x}{3} + \dfrac{y}{4} = 5$

3. $\dfrac{x}{3} + \dfrac{y}{4} = 8$

$x - y = -3$

4. $\dfrac{x}{2} + \dfrac{y}{3} = 5$

$\dfrac{x}{3} + \dfrac{y}{2} = 5$

5. $\dfrac{3x}{5} + \dfrac{2y}{3} = 17$

$\dfrac{2x}{3} + \dfrac{3y}{4} = 19$

6. $\dfrac{x}{7} + 7y = 251$

$\dfrac{y}{7} + 7x = 299$

7. $\dfrac{m}{2} + \dfrac{n}{3} - 3 = 0$

$\dfrac{n}{2} + \dfrac{m}{5} = \dfrac{23}{10}$

8. $\dfrac{p}{6} - \dfrac{q}{3} + \dfrac{1}{3} = 0$

$\dfrac{2p}{3} - \dfrac{3q}{4} - 1 = 0$

9. $\dfrac{r}{6.20} - \dfrac{s}{4.30} = \dfrac{1}{3.10}$

$\dfrac{r}{4.60} - \dfrac{s}{2.30} = \dfrac{1}{3.50}$

Unknowns in the Denominator

Solve simultaneously.

10. $\dfrac{8}{x} + \dfrac{6}{y} = 3$

$\dfrac{6}{x} + \dfrac{15}{y} = 4$

11. $\dfrac{1}{x} + \dfrac{3}{y} = 11$

$\dfrac{5}{x} + \dfrac{4}{y} = 22$

12. $\dfrac{5}{x} + \dfrac{6}{y} = 7$

$\dfrac{7}{x} + \dfrac{9}{y} = 10$

13. $\dfrac{2}{x} + \dfrac{4}{y} = 14$

$\dfrac{6}{x} - \dfrac{2}{y} = 14$

14. $\dfrac{6}{x} + \dfrac{8}{y} = 1$

$\dfrac{7}{x} - \dfrac{11}{y} = -9$

15. $\dfrac{2}{5x} + \dfrac{5}{6y} = 14$

$\dfrac{2}{5x} - \dfrac{3}{4y} = -5$

16. $\dfrac{5}{3a} + \dfrac{2}{5b} = 7$

$\dfrac{7}{6a} - 3 = \dfrac{1}{10b}$

17. $\dfrac{1}{5z} + \dfrac{1}{6w} = 18$

$\dfrac{1}{4w} - \dfrac{1}{2z} + 21 = 0$

18. $\dfrac{8.10}{5.10t} + \dfrac{1.40}{3.60s} = 1.80$

$\dfrac{2.10}{1.40s} - \dfrac{1.30}{5.20t} + 3.10 = 0$

 ### Graphics Calculator

19. We can use a graphics calculator to solve approximately a pair of non-linear equations just as we solved linear equations in Section 10.1. We graph the two equations and use the ZOOM and TRACE features to find the point of intersection to any desired accuracy. Remember that the equations must be solved for y before entering them into the calculator. Use the graphics calculator to solve any of the preceding pairs of equations in this exercise.

Use the graphics calculator to solve the following sets of nonlinear equations.

20. $y = 4.83x + 7.82$
$y = 3.44x^2 + 2.08x$

21. $y = 7.14 - 8.83x^2$
$y = 1.89x^3 + 2.87x$

22. $y = 3.75x^4 + 4.75$
$y = 5.82 - 3.35x$

23. $y = 4.82x - 3.82x^3$
$y = 2.84x + 6.27$

Literal Equations

Solve for x and y in terms of the other literal quantities.

24. $3x - 2y = a$
$2x + y = b$

25. $ax + by = r$
$ax + cy = s$

26. $ax - dy = c$
$mx - ny = c$

27. $px - qy + pq = 0$
$2px - 3qy = 0$

Computer

28. Program Eq. 63 into your computer so that x and y will be computed and printed whenever the six coefficients

$$a_1, b_1, c_1 \quad \text{and} \quad a_2, b_2, c_2$$

are entered into the program. Test the program on a system of equations that you have already solved algebraically.

29. A computer algebra system will solve a pair of equations with literal coefficients, except now you will not get numerical answers but will get expressions containing the literal quantities.

Enter the two literal equations just as you do for equations with numerical coefficients. Now, however, the program will prompt you to enter the solution variables (usually x and y).

Use your CAS to solve any of the literal equations in this exercise.

10·3   Word Problems with Two Unknowns

In many problems there are two or more unknowns that must be found. To solve such problems, we must write *as many independent equations as there are unknowns*. Otherwise, it is not possible to obtain numerical answers, although one unknown could be expressed in terms of another.

Set up these problems as we did in Chapters 3 and 9 and solve the resulting system of equations by any of the methods in this chapter.

We will start with a financial problem. We did financial problems with one unknown in Section 3·3. You may want to flip through that section before starting here.

■ **Example 22:** A certain investment in bonds had a value of \$248 000 after four years, and of \$260 000 after five years, at simple interest (Fig. 10·5). Find the amount invested and the interest rate. (The formula $y = P(1 + nt)$ gives the amount y obtained by investing an amount P for t years at an interest rate n.)

FIGURE 10•5

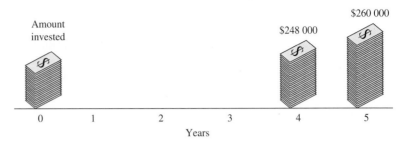

Estimate: We know that the original investment has to be less than $248 000. We might also reason that the investment cannot be too small, if it is to grow to $248 000 in only four years. Also, some familiarity with bonds (or a quick inquiry of someone who is familiar with them) reveals that, historically, any kind of bond has yields somewhere between a few percent and about 15%.

Solution: For the 4-year investment, $t = 4$ years and $y = $248 000$. Substituting into the given formula yields

$$\$248\ 000 = P(1 + 4n)$$

Then substitute again, with $t = 5$ years and $y = $260 000$:

$$\$260\ 000 = P(1 + 5n)$$

Thus we get two equations in two unknowns, P (the amount invested) and n (the interest rate). Next we remove parentheses:

$$\$248\ 000 = P + 4Pn \qquad (1)$$

$$\$260\ 000 = P + 5Pn \qquad (2)$$

At this point we may be tempted to subtract one of these equations from the other to eliminate P. But this will not work because P remains in the term containing Pn. Instead, we multiply (1) by 5 and (2) by -4 to eliminate the Pn term:

$$\begin{aligned} \$\ 1\ 240\ 000 &= \quad 5P + 20Pn \\ -1\ 040\ 000 &= -4P - 20Pn \\ \hline \end{aligned}$$

Add: $\qquad \$\quad 200\ 000 = P$

Substituting back into (1) gives us

$$\$248\ 000 = \$200\ 000 + 4(\$200\ 000)n$$

from which

$$n = 0.06$$

Thus a sum of $200 000 was invested at 6%.

Check: For the 4-year period:

$$y = \$200\ 000[1 + 4(0.06)] = \$248\ 000 \qquad \text{checks}$$

and for the 5-year period:

$$y = \$200\ 000[1 + 5(0.06)] = \$260\ 000 \qquad \text{checks} \qquad \blacksquare$$

We'll now do a **mixture** problem. We did mixture problems with one unknown in Section 3•4.

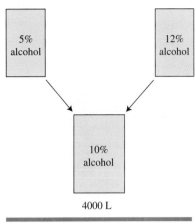

FIGURE 10•6

■ **Example 23:** Two different gasohol mixtures are available; one contains 5.00% alcohol, and the other 12.0% alcohol. How much of each, to the nearest litre, should be mixed to obtain $40\overline{0}0$ L of gasohol containing 10.0% alcohol (Fig. 10•6)?

Estimate: Note that using 2000 L of each original mixture would give the 4000 L needed, but with a percentage of alcohol midway between 5% and 12%, or around 8.5%. This is lower than needed, so we reason that we need more than 2000 L of the 12% and less than 2000 L of the 5% mixture.

Solution: We let

$$x = \text{litres of 5\% gasohol needed}$$
$$y = \text{litres of 12\% gasohol needed}$$

So

$$x + y = 4000$$

and

$$0.05x + 0.12y = 0.10\,(4000)$$

are our two equations in two unknowns. Multiplying the first equation by 5 and the second equation by 100,

$$5x + 5y = 20\,000$$
$$5x + 12y = 40\,000$$

Subtracting the first equation from the second,

$$7y = 20\,000$$
$$y = 2860\,L$$

So

$$x = 4000 - y = 1140\,L \qquad\qquad ■$$

Our next application is a work problem. Glance back at Section 9•6 to see how we set up work problems in one unknown.

■ **Example 24:** During a certain day, two computer printers are observed to process 1705 form letters, with the slower printer in use for 5.5 h and the faster for 4.0 h (Fig. 10•7). On another day the slower printer works for 6.0 h and the faster for 6.5 h, and together they print 2330 form letters. How many letters can each print in an hour, working alone?

Estimate: Assume for now that both printers worked at the same rate. On the first day they worked a total of 9.5 h and printed 1705 letters, or 1705 ÷ 9.5 ≈ 180 letters per hour, and on the second day, 2330 ÷ 121.5 ≈ 186 letters per hour. But we expect more from the fast printer, say, around 200 letters/h, and less from the slow printer, say, around 150 letters/h.

Solution: We let

$$x = \text{rate of slow printer, letters/h}$$
$$y = \text{rate of fast printer, letters/h}$$

FIGURE 10•7

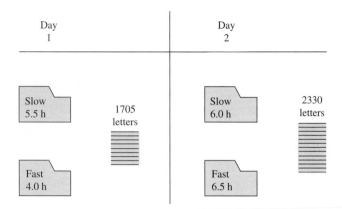

We write two equations to express, for each day, the total amount of work produced, remembering from Chapter 9 that

$$\text{amount of work} = \text{work rate} \times \text{time}$$

On the first day, the slow printer produces $5.5x$ letters while the fast printer produces $4.0y$ letters. Together they produce

$$5.5x + 4.0y = 1705$$

Similarly, for the second day,

$$6.0x + 6.5y = 2330$$

Using the addition–subtraction method, we multiply the first equation by 6.5 and the second by -4.0.

$$35.75x + 26y = 11\ 083$$
$$-24x - 26y = -9\ 320$$

Add:
$$11.75x \qquad = 1\ 763$$
$$x = 150 \text{ letters/h}$$

Substituting back yields

$$5.5(150) + 4y = 1705$$

$$y = 220 \text{ letters/h}$$

Our next example will be from statics. Refer back to Section 3•5 for the basic formulas, and to Section 7•6 for the resolution of vectors.

■ **Example 25:** Find the forces F_1 and F_2 (Fig. 10•8).

Solution: We resolve each vector into its x and y components. We will take components to the right and upwards as positive. As in Section 7•6, we will arrange the values in a table, for convenience.

FIGURE 10•8

Force	x component	y component
F_1	$-F_1 \cos 41.5° = -0.749F_1$	$F_1 \sin 41.5° = 0.663F_1$
F_2	$F_2 \cos 27.6° = 0.886F_2$	$-F_2 \sin 27.6° = -0.463F_2$
6800 N	$6800 \cos 51.3° = 4252$ N	$6800 \sin 51.3° = 5307$ N
9500 N	$-9500 \cos 25.8° = -8553$ N	$-9500 \sin 25.8° = -4135$ N

We then set the sum of the x components to zero,

$$\Sigma F_x = -0.749F_1 + 0.886F_2 + 4252 - 8553 = 0$$

or

$$-0.749F_1 + 0.886F_2 = 4301 \text{ N} \tag{1}$$

and set the sum of the y components to zero,

$$\Sigma F_y = 0.663F_1 - 0.463F_2 + 5307 - 4135 = 0$$

or

$$0.663F_1 - 0.463F_2 = -1172 \tag{2}$$

Now we divide (1) by 0.749, and divide (2) by 0.663 and get:

$$\begin{array}{r} -F_1 + 1.183F_2 = 5742 \\ F_1 - 0.698F_2 = -1768 \end{array} \tag{3}$$

Adding:
$$\begin{array}{r} 0.485F_2 = 3974 \\ F_2 = 8194 \text{ N} \end{array}$$

Substituting back into (3) gives

$$\begin{aligned} F_1 &= 1.183F_2 - 5742 \text{ N} \\ &= 1.183(7736.66 \text{ N}) - 5520.3 \text{ N} \\ F_1 &= 3951 \text{ N} \end{aligned}$$

Some of these problems can be set up using just one unknown, but for now use two unknowns for the practice.

Exercise 3 Word Problems with Two Unknowns

Number Problems

1. The sum of two numbers is 24 and their difference is 8. What are the numbers?
2. The sum of two numbers is 29 and their difference is 5. What are the numbers?
3. There is a fraction such that if 3 is added to the numerator its value will be $\frac{1}{3}$, and if 1 is subtracted from the denominator its value will be $\frac{1}{5}$. What is the fraction?
4. The sum of the two digits of a certain number is 9. If 9 is added to the original number, the new number will have the original digits reversed. Find the number. (*Hint:* Let $x =$ the tens digit and $y =$ the ones digit, so that the value of the number is $10x + y$.)
5. A number consists of two digits. The number is 2 more than 8 times the sum of the digits, and, if 54 is subtracted from the number, the digits will be reversed. Find the number.
6. If the larger of two numbers is divided by the smaller, the quotient is 7 and the remainder is 4. But if three times the greater is divided by twice the smaller, the quotient is 11 and the remainder is 4. What are the numbers?
7. The sum of two numbers divided by 2 gives a quotient of 24, and their difference divided by 2 gives a quotient of 17. What are the numbers?

Geometry Problems

8. If the width of a certain rectangle is increased by 3 and the length decreased by 3, the area is seen to increase by 6 [Fig. 10•9(a)]. But if

FIGURE 10•9

FIGURE 10•10

FIGURE 10•11

FIGURE 10•12

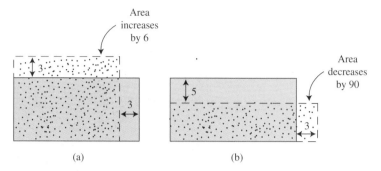

the width is reduced by 5 and the length increased by 3, the area decreases by 90 [Fig. 10•9(b)]. Find the original dimensions.

9. If the width of a certain rectangle is increased by 3 and the length reduced by 4, we get a square with the same area as the original rectangle (Fig. 10•10). Find the length and width of the original rectangle.

Trigonometry Problems

10. A surveyor measures the angle of elevation of a hill at $15.8°$ (Fig. 10•11). She then moves 105 m closer, on level ground, and measures the angle of elevation at $21.4°$. Find the height h of the hill and the distance d. (*Hint:* Write the expression for the tangent of the angle of elevation, at each location, and solve the two resulting equations simultaneously.)

11. A ship travelling a straight course, Figure 10•12, sights a lighthouse at an angle of $32.8°$. After sailing another 4.5 km, the lighthouse is at an angle of $77.2°$. Find the distances x and y.

Uniform Motion Problems

12. In a first race, A gives B a headstart of 30.0 m and overtakes him in 4.0 min. In a second race he gains 255 m on B when B runs 2740 m. Find the rate at which each runs.

13. A and B run two races of 85 m. In the first race, A gives B a start of 21 m and they tie the race. In the second race, A gives B a start of $1\overline{0}$ m and beats him by $6\frac{2}{3}$ s. How many metres can each run in a second?

14. A certain river has a speed of 4.0 km/h. A rower travels downstream for 1.50 h and returns in 4.50 h. Find his rate in still water, and the one-way distance travelled.

15. A canoeist can paddle 32.0 km down a certain river and back in 8.0 h (64.0 km round trip). She can also paddle 8.0 km downriver in the same time as she paddles 4.8 km upriver. Find her rate in still water, and the rate of the current.

16. A space shuttle and a damaged satellite are 615 km apart (Fig. 10•13). The shuttle travels at 1340 km/h and the satellite at 1090 km/h, in the same direction. How long will it take the shuttle to overtake the satellite, and in what distance?

Nonuniform Motion Problems

17. The arm of an industrial robot starts at a speed v_0 and drops 348 mm in 4.28 s, at constant acceleration a. Its motion is described by

$$s = v_0 t + at^2/2$$

1340 km/h   1090 km/h

615 km

FIGURE 10•13

v_0

FIGURE 10•14

Railway Bond 6.2%

Provincial Bond 9.7%

FIGURE 10•15

$370/hectare

$450/hectare

FIGURE 10•16

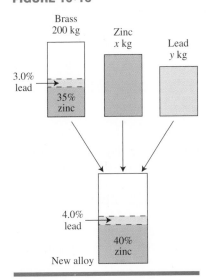

Brass 200 kg   Zinc x kg   Lead y kg

3.0% lead

35% zinc

4.0% lead

40% zinc

New alloy

FIGURE 10•17

or

$$348 = 4.28\,v_0 + a(4.28)^2/2$$

In another trial, the arm is found to drop 583 mm in 5.57 s, with the same initial speed and acceleration. Find v_0 and a.

18. Crates start at the top of an inclined roller ramp (Fig. 10•14) with a speed of v_0. They roll down with constant acceleration, reaching a speed of 4.97 m/s after 5.58 s. The motion is described by Eq. A19,

$$v = v_0 + at$$

or

$$4.97 = v_0 + 5.58a$$

The crates are also seen to reach a speed of 5.64 m/s after 7.03 s. Find v_0 and a.

Financial Problems

19. A certain investment, at simple interest, amounted in five years to $3000 and in six years to $3100. Find the amount invested, to the nearest dollar, and the rate of interest (see Eq. A9).

20. A shipment of 21 computer keyboards and 33 monitors cost $35 564.25. Another shipment of 41 keyboards and 36 monitors cost $49 172.50. Find the cost of each keyboard and each monitor.

21. A person invested $4400, part of it in railway bonds bearing 6.2% interest and the remainder in provincial bonds bearing 9.7% interest (Fig. 10•15), and received the same income from each. How much, to the nearest dollar, was invested in each?

22. A farmer bought $10\overline{0}$ hectares of land, part at $370 and part at $450 a hectare (Fig. 10•16), paying for the whole $42 200. How much land was there in each part?

23. If I lend my money at 6% simple interest for a given time, I shall receive $720 interest; but if I lend it for three years longer, I shall receive $1800. Find the amount of money and the time.

Mixture Problems

24. A certain brass alloy contains 35% zinc and 3.0% lead (Fig. 10•17). Then x kg of zinc and y kg of lead are added to $20\overline{0}$ kg of the original alloy to make a new alloy that is $4\overline{0}$% zinc and 4.0% lead. **(a)** Show that the amount of zinc in the new alloy is given by

$$0.35(200) + x = 0.40(200 + x + y)$$

and that the amount of lead is given by

$$0.03(200) + y = 0.04(200 + x + y)$$

(b) Solve for x and y.

25. A certain concrete mixture contains 5.00% cement and 8.00% sand (Fig. 10•18). How many kilograms of this mixture and how many kilograms of sand should be combined with 255 kg of cement to make a batch that is 12.0% cement and 15.0% sand?

FIGURE 10•18

26. A distributor has two gasohol blends: one that contains 5.00% alcohol and another with 11.0% alcohol. How many litres of each must be mixed to make $50\overline{0}$ L of gasohol containing 9.50% alcohol?

27. A potting mixture contains 12.0% peat moss and 6.00% vermiculite. How much peat and how much vermiculite must be added to $10\overline{0}$ kg of this mixture to produce a new mixture having 15.0% peat and 15.0% vermiculite?

Statics

28. Find the forces F_1 and F_2 in Figure 10•19.

FIGURE 10•19

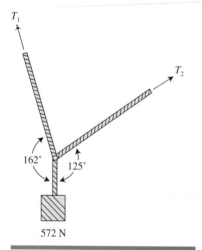

FIGURE 10•20

29. Find the tensions in the ropes in Figure 10•20.

30. When the 45.3-kg mass in Figure 10•21 is increased to $10\overline{0}$ kg, the balance point shifts 154 mm. Find the length of the bar and the original distance from the balance point to the 45.3-kg mass.

FIGURE 10•21

Work Problems

31. A carpenter and a helper can do a certain job in 15 days. If the carpenter works 1.5 times as fast as the helper, how long would it take each to do the job, working alone?

32. During one week two machines produce a total of 27 210 parts, with the faster machine working for 37.5 h and the slower for 28.2 h. During another week, they produce 59 830 parts, with the faster machine working 66.5 h and the slower machine working 88.6 h. How many parts can each produce in an hour working alone?

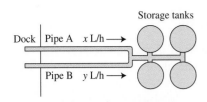

FIGURE 10·22

Flow Problems

33. Two different-sized pipes lead from a dockside to a group of oil storage tanks (Fig. 10·22). On one day the two pipes are seen to deliver 117 000 L with pipe A in use for 3.5 h and pipe B for 4.5 h. On another day the two pipes deliver 151 200 L with pipe A operating for 5.2 h and pipe B for 4.8 h. If pipe A can deliver x L/h and pipe B can deliver y L/h, **(a)** show that the total litres of oil delivered for the two days are given by the equations

$$3.5x + 4.5y = 117\ 000$$

$$5.2x + 4.8y = 151\ 200$$

(b) Solve for x and y.

34. Two conveyors can fill a certain bin in 6.00 h, working together. If one conveyor works 1.8 times as fast as the other, how long would it take each to fill the bin working alone?

Energy Flow

35. A hydroelectric generating plant and a coal-fired generating plant together supply a city of 255 000 people, with the hydro plant producing 1.75 times the power of the coal plant. How many people could each plant service alone?

36. During a certain week a small wind generator and a small hydro unit together produce 5880 kWh, with the wind generator operating only 85% of the time. During another week the two units produce 6240 kWh, with the wind generator working 95% of the time and the hydro unit down 7.50 h for repairs. Assuming that each unit has a constant output when operating, find the number of kilowatts produced by each in 1 h.

FIGURE 10·23

Electrical

37. To find the currents I_1 and I_2 in Figure 10·23 we use Eq. A68 in each loop and get the pair of equations

$$6.00 - R_1I_1 - R_2I_1 + R_2I_2 = 0$$

$$12.0 - R_3I_2 - R_2I_2 + R_2I_1 = 0$$

Solve for I_1 and I_2 if $R_1 = 736\ \Omega$, $R_2 = 386\ \Omega$, and $R_3 = 375\ \Omega$.

38. Use Eq. A68 to write a pair of equations for the circuit of Figure 10·24 as in Problem 37. Solve these equations for I_1 and I_2.

39. The resistance R of a conductor at temperature t is given by Eq. A70

$$R = R_1 (1 + \alpha t)$$

where R_1 is the temperature at 0°C and α is the temperature coefficient of resistance. A coil of this conductor is found to have a resistance of 31.2 Ω at 25.4°C and a resistance of 35.7 Ω at 57.3°C. Find R_1 and α.

40. The resistance R of two resistors in parallel, Figure 10·25, is given by Eq. A64,

$$1/R = 1/R_1 + 1/R_2$$

R is found to be 283.0 Ω, but, if R_1 is doubled and R_2 halved, then R is found to be 291.0 Ω. Find R_1 and R_2.

FIGURE 10·24

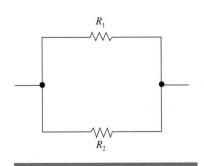

FIGURE 10·25

Systems of Three Linear Equations

Our strategy here is to reduce a given system of three equations with three unknowns to a system of two equations in two unknowns, which we already know how to solve.

In the following chapter we will use *determinants* to solve sets of three or more equations.

Addition–Subtraction Method

We take any two of the given equations and, by addition–subtraction or substitution, eliminate one variable, obtaining a single equation in two unknowns. We then take another pair of equations (which must include the one not yet used, as well as one of those already used), and similarly obtain a second equation in the *same two* unknowns. This pair of equations can then be solved simultaneously, and the values obtained are substituted back to obtain the third variable.

■ **Example 26:** Solve

$$6x - 4y - 7z = 17 \tag{1}$$
$$9x - 7y - 16z = 29 \tag{2}$$
$$10x - 5y - 3z = 23 \tag{3}$$

Solution: Let us start by eliminating x from equations (1) and (2).

It is a good idea to number your equations, as in this example, to help keep track of your work.

Multiply (1) by 3:	$18x - 12y - 21z = 51$	(4)
and multiply (2) by -2:	$-18x + 14y + 32z = -58$	(5)
Add:	$2y + 11z = -7$	(6)

We now eliminate the same variable, x, from equations (1) and (3).

Multiply (1) by -5:	$-30x + 20y + 35z = -85$	(7)
and multiply (3) by -3:	$30x - 15y - 9z = 69$	(8)
Add:	$5y + 26z = -16$	(9)

Now we solve (6) and (9) simultaneously.

Multiply (6) by 5:	$10y + 55z = -35$
and (9) by -2:	$-10y - 52z = 32$
Add:	$3z = -3$
	$z = -1$

Substituting $z = -1$ into (6) gives us

$$2y + 11(-1) = -7$$
$$y = 2$$

Substituting $y = 2$ and $z = -1$ into (1) yields

$$6x - 4(2) - 7(-1) = 17$$
$$x = 3$$

Our solution is then $x = 3$, $y = 2$, and $z = -1$.

Check: We check a system of three (or more) equations in the same way that we checked a system of two equations, by substituting back into the original equations.

Substituting into (1) gives

$$6(3) - 4(2) - 7(-1) = 17$$
$$18 - 8 + 7 = 17 \qquad \text{checks}$$

Substituting into (2) we get

$$9(3) - 7(2) - 16(-1) = 29$$
$$27 - 14 + 16 = 29 \qquad \text{checks}$$

Finally we substitute into (3):

$$10(3) - 5(2) - 3(-1) = 23$$
$$30 - 10 + 3 = 23 \qquad \text{checks} \qquad ▬$$

Substitution Method

A *sparse* system (one in which many terms are missing) is often best solved by substitution, as in the following example.

▬ **Example 27:** Solve by substituting:

$$x - y = 4$$
$$x + z = 8$$
$$x - y + z = 10$$

Solution: From the first two equations we can write both y and z in terms of x:

$$y = x - 4$$

and

$$z = 8 - x$$

Substituting these back into the third equation yields

$$x - (x - 4) + (8 - x) = 10$$

from which

$$x = 2$$

Substituting back gives

$$y = x - 4 = 2 - 4 = -2$$

and

$$z = 8 - x = 8 - 2 = 6$$

Our solution is then $x = 2$, $y = -2$, and $z = 6$. ▬

Fractional Equations

We use the same techniques for solving a set of three fractional equations that we did for two equations: (1) multiply each equation by its LCD to eliminate fractions; and (2) if the unknowns are in the denominators, substitute new variables which are the reciprocals of the originals.

■ **Example 28:** Solve for x, y, and z.

$$\frac{4}{x} + \frac{9}{y} - \frac{8}{z} = 3 \tag{1}$$

$$\frac{8}{x} - \frac{6}{y} + \frac{4}{z} = 3 \tag{2}$$

$$\frac{5}{3x} + \frac{7}{2y} - \frac{2}{z} = \frac{3}{2} \tag{3}$$

Solution: We make the substitution

$$p = \frac{1}{x}, \quad q = \frac{1}{y}, \quad \text{and} \quad r = \frac{1}{z}$$

and also multiply (3) by its LCD, 6, to clear fractions.

$$4p + 9q - 8r = 3 \tag{4}$$

$$8p - 6q + 4r = 3 \tag{5}$$

$$10p + 21q - 12r = 9 \tag{6}$$

We multiply (5) by 2 and add it to (4), eliminating the r terms,

$$20p - 3q = 9 \tag{7}$$

Then we multiply (5) by 3 and add it to (6):

$$34p + 3q = 18 \tag{8}$$

Adding (7) and (8) gives

$$54p = 27$$

$$p = \frac{1}{2}$$

Then from (8),

$$3q = 18 - 17 = 1$$

$$q = \frac{1}{3}$$

and from (5),

$$4r = 3 - 4 + 2 = 1$$

$$r = \frac{1}{4}$$

Returning to our original variables, $x = 2$, $y = 3$, and $z = 4$. ■

■ **Example 29:** Find the forces F_1, F_2, and F_3 in Figure 10•26.

FIGURE 10•26

Solution: We resolve each force into its x and y components (see Section 7•6 to refresh your memory). Then by Equations A13 to A15, the sum of the vertical forces, the sum of the horizontal forces, and the sum of the moments about any point, must each equal zero.

$$\Sigma F_y = F_{1y} + F_{2y} - F_{3y} - 4430 = 0 \tag{1}$$

$$\Sigma F_x = F_{1x} - F_{2x} - F_{3x} = 0 \tag{2}$$

$$\Sigma M_p = 300(4430) + 655F_{3y} - 1155F_{2y} = 0 \tag{3}$$

Using the trigonometric functions, these equations become
Eq. (1) becomes:

$$F_1 \sin 47.0° + F_2 \sin 51.3° - F_3 \sin 77.4° - 4430 = 0 \tag{4}$$

Eq. (2) becomes:

$$F_1 \cos 47.0° - F_2 \cos 51.3° - F_3 \cos 77.4° = 0 \tag{5}$$

Eq. (3) becomes:

$$300(4430) + 655F_3 \sin 77.4° - 1155 F_2 \sin 51.3° = 0 \tag{6}$$

After evaluating the trigonometric functions and simplifying, our three equations become

$$0.731F_1 + 0.780F_2 - 0.976F_3 = 4430 \text{ N} \tag{7}$$

$$0.682F_1 - 0.625F_2 - 0.218F_3 = 0 \tag{8}$$

$$-901F_2 + 639F_3 = -1\,330\,000 \text{ N} \tag{9}$$

Solving (9) for F_3 gives

$$F_3 = 1.41F_2 - 2080 \tag{10}$$

Substituting this into (7) and (8) and simplifying, we get

$$F_1 - 0.815F_2 = 3283 \tag{11}$$

$$F_1 - 1.367F_2 = -665$$

Subtracting, we get $0.552F_2 = 3948$, from which

$$F_2 = 7150 \text{ N}$$

Substituting back into (11) gives

$$F_1 = 3283 + 0.815(7150) = 9110 \text{ N}$$

and substituting into (10) we get

$$F_3 = 1.41\,(7150) - 2080 = 8000 \text{ N}$$

■

Exercise 4 Systems of Three Linear Equations

Solve each system of equations.

1. $x + y = 35$
$x + z = 40$
$y + z = 45$

2. $x + y + z = 12$
$x - y \quad = 2$
$x \quad - z = 4$

3. $3x + y = 5$
$2y - 3z = -5$
$x + 2z = 7$

4. $x - y = 5$
$y - z = -6$
$2x - z = 2$

5. $x + y + z = 18$
$x - y + z = 6$
$x + y - z = 4$

6. $x + y + z = 90$
$2x - 3y \quad = -20$
$2x \quad + 3z = 145$

7. $x + 2y + 3z = 14$
$2x + y + 2z = 10$
$3x + 4y - 3z = 2$

8. $x + y + z = 35$
$x - 2y + 3z = 15$
$y - x + z = -5$

9. $x - 2y + 2z = 5$
$5x + 3y + 6z = 57$
$x + 2y + 2z = 21$

10. $1.21x + 1.48y + 1.63z = 6.83$
$4.94x + 4.27y + 3.63z = 21.7$
$2.88x + 4.15y - 2.79z = 2.76$

11. $2.51x - 4.48y + 3.13z = 10.8$
$2.84x + 1.37y - 1.66z = 6.27$
$1.58x + 2.85y - 1.19z = 27.3$

12. $5a + b - 4c = -5$
$3a - 5b - 6c = -20$
$a - 3b + 8c = -27$

13. $p + 3q - r = 10$
$5p - 2q + 2r = 6$
$3p + 2q + r = 13$

Fractional Equations

Solve each system of equations.

14. $x + \dfrac{y}{3} = 5$

$x + \dfrac{z}{3} = 6$

$y + \dfrac{z}{3} = 9$

15. $\dfrac{1}{x} + \dfrac{1}{y} = 5$

$\dfrac{1}{y} + \dfrac{1}{z} = 7$

$\dfrac{1}{x} + \dfrac{1}{z} = 6$

16. $\dfrac{x}{10} + \dfrac{y}{5} + \dfrac{z}{20} = \dfrac{1}{4}$

$x + y + z = 6$

$\dfrac{x}{3} + \dfrac{y}{2} + \dfrac{z}{6} = 1$

17. $\dfrac{1}{x} + \dfrac{2}{y} - \dfrac{1}{z} = -3$

$\dfrac{3}{x} + \dfrac{1}{y} + \dfrac{1}{z} = 4$

$\dfrac{1}{x} - \dfrac{1}{y} + \dfrac{2}{z} = 6$

Literal Equations

Solve for x, y, and z.

18. $x - y = a$
$y + z = 3a$
$5z - x = 2a$

19. $x + a = y + z$
$y + a = 2x + 2z$
$z + a = 3x + 3y$

20. $ax + by = (a + b)c$
$by + cz = (c + a)b$
$ax + cz = (b + c)a$

21. $x + y + 2z = 2(b + c)$
$x + 2y + z = 2(a + c)$
$2x + y + z = 2(a + b)$

Solving Problem 22 gives us formulas
for solving a set of three equations. We'll
find them useful in the next chapter.

22. $a_1x + b_1y + c_1z = k_1$
$a_2x + b_2y + c_2z = k_2$
$a_3x + b_3y + c_3z = k_3$

Number Problems

23. The sum of the digits in a certain 3-digit number is 21. The sum of the first and third digits is twice the middle digit. If the hundreds and tens digits are interchanged, the number is reduced by 90. Find the number.

24. There are two fractions which have the same denominator. If 1 is subtracted from the numerator of the smaller fraction, its value will be $\frac{1}{3}$ of the larger fraction; but if 1 is subtracted from the numerator of the larger, its value will be twice that of the smaller fraction. The difference between the fractions is $\frac{1}{3}$. What are the fractions?

25. A certain number is expressed by three digits whose sum is 10. The sum of the first and last digits is $\frac{2}{3}$ of the second digit; and if 198 is subtracted from the number, the digits will be reversed. What is the number?

Electrical Problems

26. When writing Kirchhoff's law (Eq. A68) for a certain three-loop network, we get the set of equations

$$3I_1 + 2I_2 - 4I_3 = 4$$
$$I_1 - 3I_2 + 2I_3 = -5$$
$$2I_1 + I_2 - I_3 = 3$$

where I_1, I_2, and I_3 are the loop currents in amperes. Solve for these currents.

27. For the three-loop network of Fig. 10•27 **(a)** use Kirchhoff's law to show that the currents may be found from

$$159I_1 - 50.9I_2 = 1$$
$$407I_1 - 2400I_2 + 370I_3 = 1$$
$$142I_2 - 380I_3 = 1$$

(b) Solve this set of equations for the three currents.

FIGURE 10•27

Statics Problems

28. Find the forces F_1, F_2, and F_3 in Figure 10•28.

FIGURE 10•28

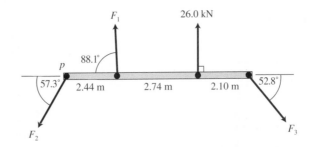

29. Find the forces F_1, F_2, and F_3 in Figure 10•29.

FIGURE 10·29

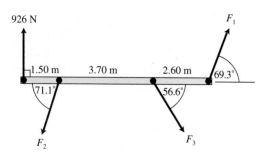

Computer

30. The Gauss-Seidel method described in Section 10•1 works for any number of equations. For three equations in three unknowns, for example, write the equations in the form

$$x = f(y, z)$$

$$y = g(x, z)$$

$$z = h(x, y)$$

and proceed as before. Try it on one of the systems given in this exercise. If the computation diverges, then solve each equation for a different variable than before and try again. It may take two or three tries to find a combination that works.

31. We used a computer algebra system to solve a set of two equations in Exercise 1. Such programs can, of course, solve larger systems. The equations are entered in the same way.

Use a CAS to solve any of the equations in this exercise.

CHAPTER 10 REVIEW PROBLEMS

Solve each system of equations by any method.

1. $4x + 3y = 27$
$2x - 5y = -19$

2. $\dfrac{x}{3} + \dfrac{y}{2} = \dfrac{4}{3}$

$\dfrac{x}{2} + \dfrac{y}{3} = \dfrac{7}{6}$

3. $\dfrac{15}{x} + \dfrac{4}{y} = 1$

$\dfrac{5}{x} - \dfrac{12}{y} = 7$

4. $2x + 4y - 3z = 22$
$4x - 2y + 5z = 18$
$6x + 7y - z = 63$

5. $5x + 3y - 2z = 5$
$3x - 4y + 3z = 13$
$x + 6y - 4z = -8$

6. $3x - 5y - 2z = 14$
$5x - 8y - z = 12$
$x - 3y - 3z = 1$

7. $\dfrac{3}{x + y} + \dfrac{4}{x - z} = 2$

$\dfrac{6}{x + y} + \dfrac{5}{y - z} = 1$

$\dfrac{4}{x - z} + \dfrac{5}{y - z} = 2$

8. $4x + 2y - 26 = 0$
$3x + 4y = 39$

9. $2x - 3y + 14 = 0$
$3x + 2y = 44$

10. $\dfrac{2}{x} + \dfrac{1}{y} = \dfrac{4}{3}$

$\dfrac{3}{x} + \dfrac{5}{y} = \dfrac{19}{6}$

11. $\dfrac{9}{x} + \dfrac{8}{y} = \dfrac{43}{6}$

$\dfrac{3}{x} + \dfrac{10}{y} = \dfrac{29}{6}$

12. $\dfrac{x}{a} + \dfrac{y}{b} = p$

$\dfrac{x}{b} + \dfrac{y}{a} = q$

13. $x + y = a$

$x + z = b$

$y + z = c$

14. $\dfrac{5x}{6} + \dfrac{2y}{5} = 14$

$\dfrac{3x}{4} - \dfrac{2y}{5} = 5$

15. $\dfrac{2x}{7} + \dfrac{2y}{3} = \dfrac{16}{3}$

$x + y = 12$

16. $x + y + z = 35$

$5x + 4y + 3z = 22$

$3x + 4y - 3z = 2$

17. $2x - 4y + 3z = 10$

$3x + y - 2z = 6$

$x + 3y - z = 20$

18. $5x + y - 4z = -5$

$3x - 5y - 6z = -20$

$x - 3y + 8z = -27$

19. $x + 3y - z = 10$

$5x - 2y + 2z = 6$

$3x + 2y + z = 13$

20. $x + 21y = 2$

$2x + 27y = 19$

21. $2x - y = 9$

$5x - 3y = 14$

22. $6x - 2y + 5z = 53$

$5x + 3y + 7z = 33$

$x + y + z = 5$

23. $9x + 4y = 54$

$4x + 9y = 89$

24. A sum of money was divided between A and B so that A's share was to B's share as 5 is to 3. Also, A's share exceeded $\frac{5}{9}$ of the whole sum by $50. What was each share?

25. A and B can do a job in 12 days, and B and C can do the same job in 16 days. How long would it take them all working together to do the job if A does $1\frac{1}{2}$ as much as C?

26. If the numerator of a certain fraction is increased by 2 and its denominator diminished by 2, its value will be 1. If the numerator is increased by the denominator and the denominator is diminished by 5, its value will be 5. Find the fraction.

27. Develop the equations for the three-loop network shown in Figure 10•30, and solve for I_1, I_2, and I_3.

FIGURE 10•30 Three-branch network

Writing

28. Suppose that you have a number of pairs of equations to solve in order to find the loop currents in a circuit you are designing. Each pair of equations has different values of the variables. You must leave for a week but want your assistant to solve the equations in your absence. Write step-by-step instructions to be followed, using the addition–subtraction method, including instructions as to the number of digits to be retained.

Team Project

29. A certain nickel-silver alloy contains:

Copper	55.9%	Lead	0.10%
Zinc	31.25%	Nickel	12.00%
Tin	0.50%	Manganese	0.25%

How many kilograms of zinc, tin, lead, nickel, and manganese must be added to 400 kg of this alloy to make a new "leaded nickel-silver" with the following composition.

Copper	44.50%	Lead	1.00%
Zinc	42.00%	Nickel	10.00%
Tin	0.50%	Manganese	2.00%

11

Determinants

OBJECTIVES

When you have completed this chapter, you should be able to:

- Evaluate second-order determinants.
- Evaluate third-order determinants by minors.
- Use the properties of determinants to reduce the order of a determinant.
- Evaluate determinants by a systematic method suitable for the computer.
- Solve a system of any number of linear equations by determinants.

In Chapter 10, we learned how to solve sets of two or three equations by graphing, addition–subtraction, substitution, and by computer using the Gauss-Seidel method. These methods, however, become unwieldy when the number of equations to be solved is greater than three.

In this chapter we introduce the idea of a determinant. We learn how to evaluate determinants and then how to use them to solve a set of equations. We start with sets of two equations and then expand our use of determinants so that we can solve systems with any number of equations.

11•1   Second-Order Determinants

Definitions

In Chapter 10 we studied the set of equations

$$a_1x + b_1y = c_1$$

$$a_2x + b_2y = c_2$$

Now let us refer to the values

$$\begin{vmatrix} a_1 \\ a_2 \end{vmatrix} \text{ as the column of } x \text{ coefficients,}$$

$$\begin{vmatrix} b_1 \\ b_2 \end{vmatrix} \text{ as the column of } y \text{ coefficients, and}$$

$$\begin{vmatrix} c_1 \\ c_2 \end{vmatrix} \text{ as the column of constants.}$$

When we solved this set of equations we got the solution

$$x = \frac{b_2 c_1 - b_1 c_2}{a_1 b_2 - a_2 b_1} \qquad \text{and} \qquad y = \frac{a_1 c_2 - a_2 c_1}{a_1 b_2 - a_2 b_1}$$

The denominator $(a_1 b_2 - a_2 b_1)$ of each of these fractions is called the *determinant* of the coefficients a_1, b_1, a_2, and b_2. It is commonly expressed by the symbol

$$\begin{vmatrix} a_1 & b_1 \\ a_2 & b_2 \end{vmatrix}$$

It is common practice to use the same word *determinant* to refer to the *symbol*

$$\begin{vmatrix} a_1 & b_1 \\ a_2 & b_2 \end{vmatrix}$$

as well as to the value $(a_1 b_2 - a_2 b_1)$. We'll follow this practice.

with its being understood that this signifies the product of the upper left and lower right numbers, minus the product of the upper right and lower left numbers. Thus

$$\begin{vmatrix} a_1 & b_1 \\ a_2 & b_2 \end{vmatrix} = a_1 b_2 - a_2 b_1$$

■ **Example 1:** In the determinant

$$\begin{vmatrix} 2 & 5 \\ 6 & 1 \end{vmatrix}$$

each of the numbers 2, 5, 6, and 1 is called an *element*. There are two *rows*, the first row containing the elements 2 and 5, and the second row having the elements 6 and 1. There are also two *columns*, the first with elements 2 and 6, and the second with elements 5 and 1. The *value* of this determinant is

$$2(1) - 5(6) = 2 - 30 = -28$$ ■

Thus a determinant is written as a *square array*, enclosed between vertical bars. The number of rows equals the number of columns. The *order* of a determinant is equal to the number of rows or columns it contains. Thus the determinants above are of second order.

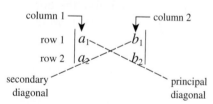

The diagonal running from upper left to lower right is called the *principal diagonal*. The other is called the *secondary diagonal*. Thus

Second-Order Determinant	$\begin{vmatrix} a_1 & b_1 \\ a_2 & b_2 \end{vmatrix} = a_1 b_2 - a_2 b_1$	**65**

The value of a second-order determinant is equal to the product of the elements on the principal diagonal minus the product of the elements on the secondary diagonal.

■ **Example 2:**

$$\begin{vmatrix} 2 & -1 \\ 3 & 5 \end{vmatrix} = 2(5) - 3(-1) = 13$$ ■

Common Errors	Students sometimes add the numbers on a diagonal instead of *multiplying*. Be careful not to do that.
	Don't just ignore a zero element. It causes the product along its diagonal to be zero.

■ **Example 3:**

$$\begin{vmatrix} 4 & a \\ x & 3b \end{vmatrix} = 4(3b) - x(a) = 12b - ax \qquad ■$$

■ **Example 4:**

$$\begin{vmatrix} 0 & 3 \\ 5 & 2 \end{vmatrix} = 0(2) - 3(5) = -15 \qquad ■$$

Evaluating Determinants on a Computer Algebra System

A computer algebra system can evaluate determinants, even when the elements contain symbols.

■ **Example 5:** Use a CAS to evaluate the determinant

$$\begin{vmatrix} x & 3 \\ 2y & w \end{vmatrix}$$

Solution: We enter the elements row by row, enclosed by parentheses, brackets, or braces. In *Derive*, we enter

$$[[x, 3], [2y, w]]$$

and give the command SIMPLIFY to return the value of the determinant, $wx - 6y$. In *Maple*, we enter

$$A: = \text{matrix } (2,2, [[x,3], [2y,w]]);$$

Then the command

$$\det(A);$$

returns the value of the determinant. Similarly, in *Mathematica*, we write

$$a = \{\{x, 3\}, \{2y, w\}\}$$

and give the command Det[a] to obtain the value. ■

Solving a System of Equations by Determinants

We now return to the set of equations

$$a_1x + b_1y = c_1 \qquad (1)$$
$$a_2x + b_2y = c_2$$

If, in the solution for x,

$$x = \frac{b_2c_1 - b_1c_2}{a_1b_2 - a_2b_1} \qquad (2)$$

This denominator is called the *determinant of the coefficients*, or sometimes the *determinant of the system*. It is usually given the Greek capital letter delta (Δ). If this determinant equals zero, there is no solution to the set of equations.

we replace the denominator by the square array,

$$\begin{vmatrix} a_1 & b_1 \\ a_2 & b_2 \end{vmatrix} = a_1 b_2 - a_2 b_1$$

we get

$$x = \frac{b_2 c_1 - b_1 c_2}{\begin{vmatrix} a_1 & b_1 \\ a_2 & b_2 \end{vmatrix}} \tag{3}$$

Now look at the numerator of (3), which is $b_2 c_1 - b_1 c_2$. If this expression were the value of some determinant, it is clear that the elements on the principal diagonal would be b_2 and c_1 and that the elements on the secondary diagonal would be b_1 and c_2. One such determinant is

$$\overbrace{\begin{vmatrix} c_1 & b_1 \\ c_2 & b_2 \end{vmatrix}}^{\text{column of constants}} = b_2 c_1 - b_1 c_2$$

Our solution for x can then be expressed

$$x = \frac{\begin{vmatrix} c_1 & b_1 \\ c_2 & b_2 \end{vmatrix}}{\begin{vmatrix} a_1 & b_1 \\ a_2 & b_2 \end{vmatrix}}$$

An expression for y can be developed in a similar way. Thus the solution to the system of equations (1), in terms of determinants, is

This rule is named after the Swiss mathematician Gabriel Cramer, 1704–1752. Cramer's rule, as we will see, is valid for systems with any number of linear equations.

Cramer's Rule	$x = \dfrac{\begin{vmatrix} c_1 & b_1 \\ c_2 & b_2 \end{vmatrix}}{\begin{vmatrix} a_1 & b_1 \\ a_2 & b_2 \end{vmatrix}}$ and	$y = \dfrac{\begin{vmatrix} a_1 & c_1 \\ a_2 & c_2 \end{vmatrix}}{\begin{vmatrix} a_1 & b_1 \\ a_2 & b_2 \end{vmatrix}}$	**70**

The solution for any variable is a fraction whose denominator is the determinant of the coefficients, and whose numerator is that same determinant, except that the column of coefficients for the variable for which we are solving is replaced by the column of constants.

Of course, the denominator Δ cannot be zero or we get division by zero. This would indicate that the set of equations has no unique solution.

■ **Example 6:** Solve by determinants:

$$2x - 3y = 1$$
$$x + 4y = -5$$

Solution: We first evaluate the determinant of the coefficients, because if $\Delta = 0$ there is no unique solution, and we have no need to proceed further.

$$\Delta = \begin{vmatrix} 2 & -3 \\ 1 & 4 \end{vmatrix} = 2(4) - 1(-3) = 8 + 3 = 11$$

Solving for x, we have

$$x = \frac{\begin{vmatrix} 1 & -3 \\ -5 & 4 \end{vmatrix}}{\Delta} = \frac{1(4) - (-5)(-3)}{11} = \frac{4 - 15}{11} = -1$$

Solving for y yields

It's easier to find y by substituting x back into one of the previous equations, but we use determinants instead, to show how it is done.

We would, of course, check our answers by substituting back into the original equations, as we did in Chapter 10.

$$y = \frac{\begin{vmatrix} 2 & 1 \\ 1 & -5 \end{vmatrix}}{\Delta} = \frac{2(-5) - 1(1)}{11} = \frac{-10 - 1}{11} = -1$$

Common Error	Don't forget to arrange the given equations into the form $$a_1x + b_1y = c_1$$ $$a_2x + b_2y = c_2$$ before writing the determinants.

Example 7: Solve for x and y by determinants:

$$2ax - by + 3a = 0$$
$$4y = 5x - a$$

Solution: We first rearrange our equations.

$$2ax - by = -3a$$
$$5x - 4y = \quad a$$

The determinant of the coefficients is

$$\Delta = \begin{vmatrix} 2a & -b \\ 5 & -4 \end{vmatrix} = 2a(-4) - 5(-b) = -8a + 5b$$

So

$$x = \frac{\begin{vmatrix} -3a & -b \\ a & -4 \end{vmatrix}}{\Delta} = \frac{(-3a)(-4) - a(-b)}{5b - 8a}$$

$$= \frac{12a + ab}{5b - 8a}$$

and

$$y = \frac{\begin{vmatrix} 2a & -3a \\ 5 & a \end{vmatrix}}{\Delta} = \frac{2a(a) - 5(-3a)}{5b - 8a} = \frac{2a^2 + 15a}{5b - 8a}$$

Exercise 1 Second-Order Determinants

Find the value of each second-order determinant.

1. $\begin{vmatrix} 3 & 2 \\ 1 & -4 \end{vmatrix}$

2. $\begin{vmatrix} -2 & 5 \\ 3 & -3 \end{vmatrix}$

3. $\begin{vmatrix} 0 & 5 \\ -3 & -4 \end{vmatrix}$

4. $\begin{vmatrix} 8 & 3 \\ -1 & 2 \end{vmatrix}$

5. $\begin{vmatrix} -4 & 5 \\ 7 & -2 \end{vmatrix}$

6. $\begin{vmatrix} 7 & -6 \\ -5 & 4 \end{vmatrix}$

7. $\begin{vmatrix} 4.82 & 2.73 \\ 2.97 & 5.28 \end{vmatrix}$

8. $\begin{vmatrix} 48.7 & -53.6 \\ 4.93 & 9.27 \end{vmatrix}$

9. $\begin{vmatrix} -2/3 & 2/5 \\ -1/3 & 4/5 \end{vmatrix}$

10. $\begin{vmatrix} 1/2 & 1/4 \\ -1/2 & -1/4 \end{vmatrix}$

11. $\begin{vmatrix} a & b \\ c & d \end{vmatrix}$

12. $\begin{vmatrix} 2m & 3n \\ -m & 4n \end{vmatrix}$

13. $\begin{vmatrix} \sin\theta & 3 \\ \tan\theta & \sin\theta \end{vmatrix}$

14. $\begin{vmatrix} 2i_1 & i_2 \\ -3i_1 & 4i_2 \end{vmatrix}$

15. $\begin{vmatrix} 3i_1 & i_2 \\ \sin\theta & \cos\theta \end{vmatrix}$

16. $\begin{vmatrix} 3x & 2 \\ x & 5 \end{vmatrix}$

Solve each pair of equations by determinants.

17. $2x + y = 11$
$3x - y = 4$

18. $5x + 7y = 101$
$7x - y = 55$

19. $3x - 2y = -15$
$5x + 6y = 3$

20. $7x + 6y = 20$
$2x + 5y = 9$

21. $x + 5y = 11$
$3x + 2y = 7$

22. $4x - 5y = -34$
$2x - 3y = -22$

23. $x + 4y = 11$
$5x - 2y = 11$

24. $2x - 3y = 3$
$4x + 5y = 39$

25. $7x - 4y = 81$
$5x - 3y = 57$

26. $3x + 4y = 85$
$5x + 4y = 107$

27. $3x - 2y = 1$
$2x + y = 10$

28. $5x - 2y = 3$
$2x + 3y = 5$

29. $y = 9 - 3x$
$x = 8 - 2y$

30. $y = 2x - 3$
$x = 19 - 3y$

31. $29.1x - 47.6y = 42.8$
$11.5x + 72.7y = 25.8$

32. $4.92x - 8.27y = 2.58$
$6.93x + 2.84y = 8.36$

33. $4n = 18 - 3m$
$m = 8 - 2n$

34. $5p + 4q - 14 = 0$
$17p = 31 + 3q$

35. $3w = 13 + 5z$
$4w - 7z - 17 = 0$

36. $3u = 5 + 2v$
$5v + 2u = 16$

Fractional and Literal Equations

Solve for x and y by determinants.

37. $\dfrac{x}{3} + \dfrac{y}{2} = 1$

$\dfrac{x}{2} - \dfrac{y}{3} = -1$

38. $px - qy + pq = 0$
$2px - 3qy = 0$

39. $ax + by = p$
$cx + dy = q$

40. $\dfrac{x}{2} - \dfrac{3y}{4} = 0$

$\dfrac{x}{3} + \dfrac{y}{4} = 0$

41. $\dfrac{3}{x} + \dfrac{8}{y} = 3$

$\dfrac{15}{x} - \dfrac{4}{y} = 4$

42. $4mx - 3ny = 6$

$3mx + 2ny = -7$

Graphics Calculator

Some graphics calculators can evaluate determinants, if all the elements are numbers. To evaluate the determinant in Example 1 on the TI-81 or TI-85 graphics calculator:

Your own calculator will probably have a different way to enter and evaluate a determinant than that shown here. Be sure to check your manual.

(a) Call up the MATRX menu and select EDIT.
(b) Name the matrix to edit. We choose A.
(c) Enter the number of rows and columns. Since we have a square array, the number of rows will equal the number of columns. We enter 2×2.
(d) Enter the elements, row by row, starting with the upper left.
(e) Return to the MATRX menu and choose DET.
(f) Enter the matrix of which you wish to find the determinant. We enter A.

Pressing $\boxed{\text{ENTER}}$ will display the value (-28) of the determinant.

43. Use your graphics calculator to evaluate any of the determinants in Problems 1 through 10.

44. Use your graphics calculator to solve any of the sets of equations in Problems 17 through 32. Remember, the value of each variable is the quotient of *two* determinants.

Computer

45. Use a computer algebra system to evaluate any of the determinants in this exercise, having numerical *or* literal elements.

46. Use a computer algebra system to solve any of the sets of equations in this exercise. Remember, the value of each variable is the quotient of *two* determinants.

11·2

Third-Order Determinants

The technique we used for finding the value of a second-order determinant cannot be used for higher-order determinants. We will now show two other methods. First, what we'll call the *diagonal* method, which works *only for third-order determinants*, and then *development by minors*, which works for *any* determinant.

The Diagonal Method

We will not emphasize this method, because it works only for third-order determinants, and also is not suitable for computer solution.

The value of a third-order determinant can be found as follows. To the right of the determinant, rewrite the first two columns:

$$\begin{vmatrix} a_1 & b_1 & c_1 \\ a_2 & b_2 & c_2 \\ a_3 & b_3 & c_3 \end{vmatrix} \begin{matrix} a_1 & b_1 \\ a_2 & b_2 \\ a_3 & b_3 \end{matrix}$$

We then multiply the elements along each of the six diagonals. The value of the determinant is the sum of the products along those diagonals running downward to the right, *minus* the products along those diagonals running downward to the left.

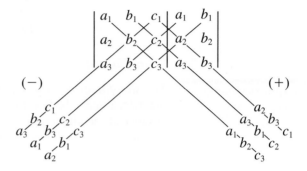

The value of the determinant is then

Third-Order Determinant	$\begin{vmatrix} a_1 & b_1 & c_1 \\ a_2 & b_2 & c_2 \\ a_3 & b_3 & c_3 \end{vmatrix} = \begin{aligned} & a_1b_2c_3 + a_3b_1c_2 + a_2b_3c_1 \\ & - a_3b_2c_1 + a_1b_3c_2 + a_2b_1c_3 \end{aligned}$	**66**

■ **Example 8:** Evaluate the third-order determinant

$$\begin{vmatrix} 2 & 1 & 0 \\ 3 & -2 & 1 \\ 5 & 1 & 0 \end{vmatrix}$$

Solution: Rewriting the first two columns to the right of the determinant, we have

$$\begin{vmatrix} 2 & 1 & 0 \\ 3 & -2 & 1 \\ 5 & 1 & 0 \end{vmatrix}\begin{matrix} 2 & 1 \\ 3 & -2 \\ 5 & 1 \end{matrix}$$

Multiplying along the diagonals, we obtain

$$2(-2)(0) + 1(1)(5) + 0(3)(1) - [0(-2)(5) + 2(1)(1) + 1(3)(0)]$$
$$= \quad 0 \quad + \quad 5 \quad + \quad 0 \quad - [\quad 0 \quad + \quad 2 \quad + \quad 0]$$
$$= 5 - 2 = 3$$

■

Minors

The *minor of an element in a determinant* is a determinant of next lower order, obtained by deleting the row and the column in which that element lies.

■ **Example 9:** The minor of element c in the determinant

$$\begin{vmatrix} a & b & c \\ d & e & f \\ g & h & i \end{vmatrix}$$

is found by striking out the first row and third column

$$\begin{vmatrix} a & b & \cancel{c} \\ d & e & \cancel{f} \\ g & h & \cancel{i} \end{vmatrix} \qquad \text{or} \qquad \begin{vmatrix} d & e \\ g & h \end{vmatrix}$$

Sign Factor

A minor, with the sign factor attached, is called a *signed minor*. It is also called a *cofactor* of the given element.

The *sign factor* for an element depends upon the position of the element in the determinant. To find the sign factor, add the row number and the column number of the element. If the sum is even, the sign factor is $(+1)$; if the sum is odd, the sign factor is (-1).

Example 10:
(a) For the determinant in Example 9, element c is in the first row and third column. The sum of the row and column numbers

$$1 + 3 = 4$$

is even, so the sign factor for the element c is $(+1)$.
(b) The sign factor for the element b in Example 9 is (-1).

The sign factor for the element in the upper left-hand corner of the determinant is $(+1)$ and the signs alternate according to the pattern

$$\begin{vmatrix} + & - & + & - & + & - & \cdot \\ - & + & - & + & - & \cdot & \cdot \\ + & - & + & - & \cdot & \cdot & \cdot \\ - & + & - & \cdot & \cdot & \cdot & \cdot \\ + & - & \cdot & \cdot & \cdot & \cdot & \cdot \\ - & \cdot & \cdot & \cdot & \cdot & \cdot & \cdot \\ \cdot & \cdot & \cdot & \cdot & \cdot & \cdot & \cdot \end{vmatrix}$$

so that the sign factor may be found simply by *counting off* from the upper left corner.

Thus for any element in a determinant we can write three quantities:

1. The element itself.
2. The sign factor of the element.
3. The minor of the element.

Example 11: For the element in the second row and first column in the determinant

$$\begin{vmatrix} -2 & 5 & 1 \\ 3 & -2 & 4 \\ 1 & -4 & 2 \end{vmatrix}$$

1. The element itself is 3.
2. The sign factor of that element is (-1).
3. The minor of that element is

$$\begin{vmatrix} 5 & 1 \\ -4 & 2 \end{vmatrix}$$

Evaluating a Determinant by Minors

We now define the value of a determinant as follows:

Value of a Determinant	To find the value of a determinant of order n: 1. Multiply each of the n elements in any row (or column) by the sign factor of that element and the minor of that element. 2. Take the algebraic sum of those n products.	**68**

━━ **Example 12:** Evaluate by minors:

$$\begin{vmatrix} 3 & 2 & 4 \\ 1 & 6 & -2 \\ -1 & 5 & -3 \end{vmatrix}$$

Solution: We first choose a row or a column for development. The work of expansion is greatly reduced if that row or column contains zeros. Our given determinant has no zeros, so let us choose column 1, which at least contains some 1s.

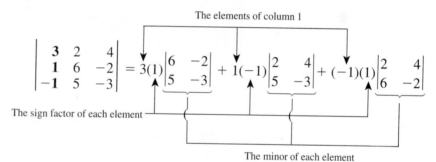

$$= 3[(6)(-3) - (-2)(5)] - 1[(2)(-3) - (4)(5)] - 1[(2)(-2) - 4(6)]$$

$$= -24 + 26 + 28$$

$$= 30$$ ━━

━━ **Example 13:** Evaluate by minors:

$$\begin{vmatrix} a_1 & b_1 & c_1 \\ a_2 & b_2 & c_2 \\ a_3 & b_3 & c_3 \end{vmatrix}$$

We would get the same result if we had chosen another row or column for development.

Solution: Choosing, say, the first row for development, we get

$$a_1 \begin{vmatrix} b_2 & c_2 \\ b_3 & c_3 \end{vmatrix} - b_1 \begin{vmatrix} a_2 & c_2 \\ a_3 & c_3 \end{vmatrix} + c_1 \begin{vmatrix} a_2 & b_2 \\ a_3 & b_3 \end{vmatrix}$$

$$= a_1(b_2c_3 - b_3c_2) - b_1(a_2c_3 - a_3c_2) + c_1(a_2b_3 - a_3b_2)$$

$$= a_1b_2c_3 - a_1b_3c_2 - a_2b_1c_3 + a_3b_1c_2 + a_2b_3c_1 - a_3b_2c_1$$

$$= a_1b_2c_3 + a_3b_1c_2 + a_2b_3c_1 - a_3b_2c_1 - a_1b_3c_2 - a_2b_1c_3$$ ━━

The value of the determinant is thus given by the following formula:

| Third-Order Determinant | $\begin{vmatrix} a_1 & b_1 & c_1 \\ a_2 & b_2 & c_2 \\ a_3 & b_3 & c_3 \end{vmatrix} = a_1b_2c_3 + a_3b_1c_2 + a_2b_3c_1 \\ \quad - a_3b_2c_1 - a_1b_3c_2 - a_2b_1c_3$ | **66** |

Solving a System of Three Equations by Determinants

The solution of this system was given as an exercise in Chapter 10, Exercise 4.

If we were to *algebraically* solve the system of equations

$$a_1x + b_1y + c_1z = k_1$$
$$a_2x + b_2y + c_2z = k_2$$
$$a_3x + b_3y + c_3z = k_3$$

we would get the solution

| Three Equations with Three Unknowns | $x = \dfrac{b_2c_3k_1 + b_1c_2k_3 + b_3c_1k_2 - b_2c_1k_3 - b_3c_2k_1 - b_1c_3k_2}{a_1b_2c_3 + a_3b_1c_2 + a_2b_3c_1 - a_3b_2c_1 - a_1b_3c_2 - a_2b_1c_3}$

 $y = \dfrac{a_1c_3k_2 + a_3c_2k_1 + a_2c_1k_3 - a_3c_1k_2 - a_1c_2k_3 - a_2c_3k_1}{a_1b_2c_3 + a_3b_1c_2 + a_2b_3c_1 - a_3b_2c_1 - a_1b_3c_2 - a_2b_1c_3}$

 $z = \dfrac{a_1b_2k_3 + a_3b_1k_2 + a_2b_3k_1 - a_3b_2k_1 - a_1b_3k_2 - a_2b_1k_3}{a_1b_2c_3 + a_3b_1c_2 + a_2b_3c_1 - a_3b_2c_1 - a_1b_3c_2 - a_2b_1c_3}$ | **64** |

Notice that the three denominators are identical and are equal to the value of the determinant formed from the coefficients of the unknowns (Eq. 66). As before, we call it the *determinant of the coefficients*, Δ.

Furthermore, the numerator of each can be obtained from the determinant of the coefficients by replacing the coefficients of the variable in question with the constants k_1, k_2, and k_3. The solution to our set of equations

$$a_1x + b_1y + c_1z = k_1$$
$$a_2x + b_2y + c_2z = k_2$$
$$a_3x + b_3y + c_3z = k_3$$

is then

| Cramer's Rule | $x = \dfrac{\begin{vmatrix} k_1 & b_1 & c_1 \\ k_2 & b_2 & c_2 \\ k_3 & b_3 & c_3 \end{vmatrix}}{\Delta} \qquad y = \dfrac{\begin{vmatrix} a_1 & k_1 & c_1 \\ a_2 & k_2 & c_2 \\ a_3 & k_3 & c_3 \end{vmatrix}}{\Delta} \qquad z = \dfrac{\begin{vmatrix} a_1 & b_1 & k_1 \\ a_2 & b_2 & k_2 \\ a_3 & b_3 & k_3 \end{vmatrix}}{\Delta}$

 where

 $\Delta = \begin{vmatrix} a_1 & b_1 & c_1 \\ a_2 & b_2 & c_2 \\ a_3 & b_3 & c_3 \end{vmatrix} \neq 0$ | **71** |

Cramer's rule, although we do not prove it, works for higher-order systems as well. We restate it now in words.

Cramer's Rule	The solution for any variable is a fraction whose denominator is the determinant of the coefficients, and whose numerator is the same determinant, except that the column of coefficients for the variable for which we are solving is replaced by the column of constants.	**69**

━ **Example 14:** Solve by determinants:

$$x + 2y + 3z = 14$$

$$2x + y + 2z = 10$$

$$3x + 4y - 3z = 2$$

Solution: We first write the determinant of the coefficients:

$$\Delta = \begin{vmatrix} 1 & 2 & 3 \\ 2 & 1 & 2 \\ 3 & 4 & -3 \end{vmatrix}$$

and expand it by minors. Choosing the first row for expansion gives

$$\Delta = \begin{vmatrix} 1 & 2 & 3 \\ 2 & 1 & 2 \\ 3 & 4 & -3 \end{vmatrix} = 1 \begin{vmatrix} 1 & 2 \\ 4 & -3 \end{vmatrix} - 2 \begin{vmatrix} 2 & 2 \\ 3 & -3 \end{vmatrix} + 3 \begin{vmatrix} 2 & 1 \\ 3 & 4 \end{vmatrix}$$

$$= 1(-3 - 8) - 2(-6 - 6) + 3(8 - 3)$$

$$= -11 + 24 + 15 = 28$$

As when solving a set of two equations, a Δ of zero would mean that the system had no unique solution, and we would stop here.

We now make a new determinant by replacing the coefficients of x, $\begin{vmatrix} 1 \\ 2 \\ 3 \end{vmatrix}$, by the column of constants, $\begin{vmatrix} 14 \\ 10 \\ 2 \end{vmatrix}$, and expand it by, say, the second column.

$$\begin{vmatrix} 14 & 2 & 3 \\ 10 & 1 & 2 \\ 2 & 4 & -3 \end{vmatrix} = -2 \begin{vmatrix} 10 & 2 \\ 2 & -3 \end{vmatrix} + 1 \begin{vmatrix} 14 & 3 \\ 2 & -3 \end{vmatrix} - 4 \begin{vmatrix} 14 & 3 \\ 10 & 2 \end{vmatrix}$$

$$= -2(-30 - 4) + 1(-42 - 6) - 4(28 - 30)$$

$$= 68 - 48 + 8 = 28$$

Dividing this value by Δ gives x:

$$x = \frac{28}{\Delta} = \frac{28}{28} = 1$$

Next we replace the coefficients of y with the column of constants and expand the first column by minors.

$$\begin{vmatrix} 1 & 14 & 3 \\ 2 & 10 & 2 \\ 3 & 2 & -3 \end{vmatrix} = 1 \begin{vmatrix} 10 & 2 \\ 2 & -3 \end{vmatrix} - 2 \begin{vmatrix} 14 & 3 \\ 2 & -3 \end{vmatrix} + 3 \begin{vmatrix} 14 & 3 \\ 10 & 2 \end{vmatrix}$$

$$= 1(-30 - 4) - 2(-42 - 6) + 3(28 - 30)$$

$$= -34 + 96 - 6 = 56$$

Dividing by Δ gives the value of y:

$$y = \frac{56}{\Delta} = \frac{56}{28} = 2$$

We can get z also by determinants or, more easily, by substituting back. Substituting $x = 1$ and $y = 2$ into the first equation, we obtain

$$1 + 2(2) + 3z = 14$$
$$3z = 9$$
$$z = 3$$

The solution is thus $(1, 2, 3)$. ▬

Often, some terms will have zero coefficients or decimal coefficients. Further, the terms may be out of order, as in the following example.

▬ **Example 15:** Solve for x, y, and z.

$$23.7y + 72.4x = 82.4 - 11.3x$$
$$25.5x - 28.4z + 19.3 = 48.2y$$
$$13.4 + 66.3z = 39.2x - 10.5$$

Solution: We rewrite each equation in the form $ax + by + cz = k$, combining like terms as we go, and putting in the missing terms with zero coefficients. We do this *before* writing the determinant.

$$83.7x + 23.7y + 0z = 82.4 \qquad (1)$$
$$25.5x - 48.2y - 28.4z = -19.3$$
$$-39.2x + 0y + 66.3z = -23.9 \qquad (2)$$

The determinant of the system is then

$$\Delta = \begin{vmatrix} 83.7 & 23.7 & 0 \\ 25.5 & -48.2 & -28.4 \\ -39.2 & 0 & 66.3 \end{vmatrix}$$

Let us develop the first row by minors.

$$\Delta = 83.7 \begin{vmatrix} -48.2 & -28.4 \\ 0 & 66.3 \end{vmatrix} - 23.7 \begin{vmatrix} 25.5 & -28.4 \\ -39.2 & 66.3 \end{vmatrix} + 0$$

$$= 83.7 \,(-48.2)(66.3) - 23.7[25.5(66.3) - (-28.4)(-39.2)]$$

$$= -281\,000 \qquad \text{(to three significant digits)}$$

Now solving for x gives us

$$x = \frac{\begin{vmatrix} 82.4 & 23.7 & 0 \\ -19.3 & -48.2 & -28.4 \\ -23.9 & 0 & 66.3 \end{vmatrix}}{\Delta}$$

Let us develop the first row of the determinant by minors. We get

$$82.4\begin{vmatrix} -48.2 & -28.4 \\ 0 & 66.3 \end{vmatrix} - 23.7\begin{vmatrix} -19.3 & -28.4 \\ -23.9 & 66.3 \end{vmatrix} + 0$$

$$= 82.4(-48.2)(66.3) - 23.7[(-19.3)(66.3) - (-28.4)(-23.9)]$$

$$= -217\,000$$

Dividing by Δ yields

$$x = \frac{-217\,000}{-281\,000} = 0.772$$

We solve for y and z by substituting back. From (1) we get

$$23.7y = 82.4 - 83.7(0.772) = 17.8$$

$$y = 0.751$$

and from (2)

$$66.3z = -23.9 + 39.2(0.772) = 6.36$$

$$z = 0.096$$

The solution is then $x = 0.772$, $y = 0.751$, and $z = 0.096$.

Exercise 2 Third-Order Determinants

Evaluate each determinant.

1. $\begin{vmatrix} 1 & 0 & 2 \\ 3 & 1 & 0 \\ 1 & 2 & 1 \end{vmatrix}$
　　　　　　　
2. $\begin{vmatrix} 2 & -1 & 3 \\ 0 & 2 & 1 \\ 3 & -2 & 4 \end{vmatrix}$

3. $\begin{vmatrix} -3 & 1 & 2 \\ 0 & -1 & 5 \\ 6 & 0 & 1 \end{vmatrix}$
　　　　　　　
4. $\begin{vmatrix} -1 & 0 & 3 \\ 2 & 0 & -2 \\ 1 & -3 & 4 \end{vmatrix}$

5. $\begin{vmatrix} 5 & 1 & 2 \\ -3 & 2 & -1 \\ 4 & -3 & 5 \end{vmatrix}$
　　　　　　　
6. $\begin{vmatrix} 1.0 & 2.4 & -1.5 \\ -2.6 & 0 & 3.2 \\ -2.9 & 1.0 & 4.1 \end{vmatrix}$

7. $\begin{vmatrix} 2 & 1 & 3 \\ 0 & -2 & 4 \\ 0 & 1 & 5 \end{vmatrix}$
　　　　　　　
8. $\begin{vmatrix} 1 & 5 & 4 \\ -3 & 6 & -2 \\ -1 & 5 & 3 \end{vmatrix}$

Some of these are identical to those given in Chapter 10, Exercise 4.

Solve by determinants.

9. $\begin{aligned} x + y + z &= 18 \\ x - y + z &= 6 \\ x + y - z &= 4 \end{aligned}$
　　　　
10. $\begin{aligned} x + y + z &= 12 \\ x - y &= 2 \\ x - z &= 4 \end{aligned}$

11. $\begin{aligned} x + y &= 35 \\ x + z &= 40 \\ y + z &= 45 \end{aligned}$
　　　　
12. $\begin{aligned} x + y + z &= 35 \\ x - 2y + 3z &= 15 \\ y - x + z &= -5 \end{aligned}$

13. $\begin{aligned} x + 2y + 3z &= 14 \\ 2x + y + 2z &= 10 \\ 3x + 4y - 3z &= 2 \end{aligned}$
　　　　
14. $\begin{aligned} x + y + z &= 90 \\ 2x - 3y &= -20 \\ 2x + 3z &= 145 \end{aligned}$

15. $\begin{aligned} x - 2y + 2z &= 5 \\ 5x + 3y + 6z &= 57 \\ x + 2y + 2z &= 21 \end{aligned}$

16. $\begin{aligned} 3x + y &= 5 \\ 2y - 3z &= -5 \\ x + 2z &= 7 \end{aligned}$

17. $\begin{aligned} 2x - 4y + 3z &= 10 \\ 3x + y - 2z &= 6 \\ x + 3y - z &= 20 \end{aligned}$

18. $\begin{aligned} x - y &= 5 \\ y - z &= -6 \\ 2x - z &= 2 \end{aligned}$

19. $\begin{aligned} 1.15x + 1.95y + 2.78z &= 15.3 \\ 2.41x + 1.16y + 3.12z &= 9.66 \\ 3.11x + 3.83y - 2.93z &= 2.15 \end{aligned}$

20. $\begin{aligned} 1.52x - 2.26y + 1.83z &= 4.75 \\ 4.72x + 3.52y + 5.83z &= 45.2 \\ 1.33x + 2.61y + 3.02z &= 18.5 \end{aligned}$

Fractional Equations

Solve by determinants.

21. $x + \dfrac{y}{3} = 5$

$x + \dfrac{z}{3} = 6$

$y + \dfrac{z}{3} = 9$

22. $\dfrac{1}{x} + \dfrac{1}{y} = 5$

$\dfrac{1}{y} + \dfrac{1}{z} = 7$

$\dfrac{1}{x} + \dfrac{1}{z} = 6$

23. $\dfrac{x}{10} + \dfrac{y}{5} + \dfrac{z}{20} = \dfrac{1}{4}$

$x + y + z = 6$

$\dfrac{x}{3} + \dfrac{y}{2} + \dfrac{z}{6} = 1$

24. $\dfrac{1}{x} + \dfrac{2}{y} - \dfrac{1}{z} = -3$

$\dfrac{3}{x} + \dfrac{1}{y} + \dfrac{1}{z} = 4$

$\dfrac{1}{x} - \dfrac{1}{y} + \dfrac{2}{z} = 6$

Graphics Calculator

25. We use a graphics calculator to evaluate third-order determinants in the same way as for second-order determinants, which we showed in Section 11•1. Be sure to change the dimensions from 2 × 2 to 3 × 3. Use the graphics calculator to evaluate any of the determinants in this exercise.

26. Use a graphics calculator to solve any of the systems of equations in this exercise. Evaluate the determinant of the system and the determinant for x, and divide to get x. Repeat for the other unknowns.

Computer

27. To evaluate a determinant on a CAS, enter the elements in the same form as we showed in Section 11•1, and give the command SIMPLIFY. Use a CAS to evaluate any determinant in this exercise.

28. Use a CAS to solve any system of equations in this exercise, by evaluating and then dividing the appropriate determinants.

11•3

Higher-Order Determinants

We can evaluate a determinant of any order by repeated use of the method of minors. Any row or column of a fifth-order determinant can be developed, thus reducing the determinant to five fourth-order determinants. Each of these can then be developed into four third-order determinants, and so on, until only second-order determinants remain.

Obviously, this is lots of work. To avoid this, we first *simplify* the determinant, using the properties of determinants in the following section, and then apply a systematic method for reducing the determinants by minors shown after that.

Properties of Determinants

A determinant larger than third order can usually be evaluated faster if we first reduce its order before expanding by minors. We do this by applying the various properties of determinants as shown in the following examples.

Zero Row or Column	If all elements in a row (or column) are zero, then the value of the determinant is zero.	72

■ **Example 16:**

$$\begin{vmatrix} 4 & 8 & 0 \\ 5 & 2 & 0 \\ 3 & 9 & 0 \end{vmatrix} = 0$$

■

Identical Rows or Columns	If two rows (or columns) are identical, then the value of a determinant is zero.	73

■ **Example 17:** The value of the determinant

$$\begin{vmatrix} 2 & 1 & 3 \\ 4 & 2 & 5 \\ 4 & 2 & 5 \end{vmatrix}$$

is found by expanding by minors using, say, the first row,

$$2\begin{vmatrix} 2 & 5 \\ 2 & 5 \end{vmatrix} - 1\begin{vmatrix} 4 & 5 \\ 4 & 5 \end{vmatrix} + 3\begin{vmatrix} 4 & 2 \\ 4 & 2 \end{vmatrix}$$

$$= 2(10 - 10) - 1(20 - 20) + 3(8 - 8)$$

$$= 0$$

■

Zeros below the Principal Diagonal	If all elements below the principal diagonal are zeros, then the value of the determinant is the product of the elements along the principal diagonal.	74

■ **Example 18:** The determinant

$$\begin{vmatrix} 2 & 9 & 7 & 8 \\ 0 & 1 & 5 & 9 \\ 0 & 0 & 3 & 4 \\ 0 & 0 & 0 & 1 \end{vmatrix}$$

Expand this determinant by minors and see for yourself that its value is indeed 6.

has the value

$$(2)(1)(3)(1) = 6$$

■

| Interchanging Rows with Columns | If we change the rows to columns and the columns to rows, the value of a determinant will be unchanged. | **75** |

■ Example 19: The value of the determinant

$$\begin{vmatrix} 5 & 2 \\ 4 & 3 \end{vmatrix}$$

is

$$(5)(3) - (2)(4) = 7$$

If the first column now becomes the first row, and the second column becomes the second row, we get the determinant

$$\begin{vmatrix} 5 & 4 \\ 2 & 3 \end{vmatrix}$$

which has the value

$$(5)(3) - (4)(2) = 7$$

as before. ■

| Interchange of Two Rows (or Columns) | A determinant will change sign when we interchange two rows (or columns). | **76** |

■ Example 20: The value of the determinant

$$\begin{vmatrix} 3 & 0 & 2 \\ 1 & 4 & 3 \\ 2 & 1 & 2 \end{vmatrix}$$

is found by expanding by minors using the first row.

$$3\begin{vmatrix} 4 & 3 \\ 1 & 2 \end{vmatrix} - 0 + 2\begin{vmatrix} 1 & 4 \\ 2 & 1 \end{vmatrix} = 3(8 - 3) + 2(1 - 8) = 1$$

Let us now interchange, say, the first and second columns.

$$\begin{vmatrix} 0 & 3 & 2 \\ 4 & 1 & 3 \\ 1 & 2 & 2 \end{vmatrix}$$

Its value is again found by expanding using the first row,

$$0 - 3\begin{vmatrix} 4 & 3 \\ 1 & 2 \end{vmatrix} + 2\begin{vmatrix} 4 & 1 \\ 1 & 2 \end{vmatrix} = -3(8 - 3) + 2(8 - 1) = -1$$

So interchanging two columns has reversed the sign of the determinant. ■

| Multiplying by a Constant | If each element in a row (or column) is multiplied by some constant, then the value of the determinant is multiplied by that constant. | **77** |

■ **Example 21:** We saw that the value of the determinant in Example 20 was equal to 1.

$$\begin{vmatrix} 3 & 0 & 2 \\ 1 & 4 & 3 \\ 2 & 1 & 2 \end{vmatrix} = 1$$

Let us now multiply the elements in the third row by some constant, say, 3.

$$\begin{vmatrix} 3 & 0 & 2 \\ 1 & 4 & 3 \\ 6 & 3 & 6 \end{vmatrix}$$

This new determinant has the value

$$3(24 - 9) + 2(3 - 24) = 45 - 42 = 3$$

or three times its previous value. ■

We can also use this rule *in reverse*, to *remove a factor* from a row or column.

■ **Example 22:** The determinant

$$\begin{vmatrix} 3 & 1 & 0 \\ 30 & 10 & 15 \\ 3 & 2 & 1 \end{vmatrix}$$

could be evaluated as it is, but let us first factor a 3 from the first column,

$$\begin{vmatrix} 3 & 1 & 0 \\ 30 & 10 & 15 \\ 3 & 2 & 1 \end{vmatrix} = 3 \begin{vmatrix} 1 & 1 & 0 \\ 10 & 10 & 15 \\ 1 & 2 & 1 \end{vmatrix}$$

and then factor a 5 from the second row,

$$3 \begin{vmatrix} 1 & 1 & 0 \\ 10 & 10 & 15 \\ 1 & 2 & 1 \end{vmatrix} = 3(5) \begin{vmatrix} 1 & 1 & 0 \\ 2 & 2 & 3 \\ 1 & 2 & 1 \end{vmatrix}$$

$$= 15[(2 - 6) - (2 - 3)] = -45$$ ■

Multiples of One Row (or Column) Added to Another	If the elements of a row (or column) are multiplied by some factor, and then added to the corresponding elements of another row or column, the value of a determinant is unchanged.	**78**

■ **Example 23:** Again using the determinant from Example 20,

$$\begin{vmatrix} 3 & 0 & 2 \\ 1 & 4 & 3 \\ 2 & 1 & 2 \end{vmatrix} = 1$$

let us get a new second row by multiplying the third row by -4 and adding those elements to the second row. The new elements in the second row are then

$$1 + 2(-4) = -7, \qquad 4 + 1(-4) = 0, \qquad \text{and} \qquad 3 + 2(-4) = -5$$

giving a new determinant

$$\begin{vmatrix} 3 & 0 & 2 \\ -7 & 0 & -5 \\ 2 & 1 & 2 \end{vmatrix}$$

whose value we find by developing the second column by minors,

$$-1\begin{vmatrix} 3 & 2 \\ -7 & -5 \end{vmatrix} = -1[3(-5) - 2(-7)] = -[-15 + 14] = 1$$

as before. Notice, however, that we have *introduced another zero* into the determinant, making it easier to evaluate. This, of course, is the point of the whole operation. ■

A Systematic Method for Evaluating a Determinant

In one method for evaluating a determinant, you first select the row or column having the most zeros, then use the properties of determinants to introduce zeros into all but one element of that row or column, and then develop that row or column by minors. That method is fine for manual computation, but not as good for a computer. Although we could program a computer to select the best row for development, the logic gets complicated.

The following algorithm, based on the properties of determinants in Eqs. 77 and 78, gives a systematic method for manual or computer evaluation of a determinant of any size. It is sometimes called the *method of Chió*.

1. Factor out the element in row 1, column 1, from each element in row 1.
2. Multiply each element in row 1 by the first element in row 2. Subtract these products from the corresponding elements in row 2.
3. Repeat Step 2 for each row until all but the first element in the first column are zeros.
4. Delete the first row and first column, thus reducing the order of the determinant by 1.
5. Repeat Steps 1 through 4 until the determinant is reduced to a single element. The value of the determinant is then the product of that element and all the factors removed in Step 1.

■ **Example 24:** Evaluate the following determinant by the method of Chió. Work to three significant digits.

$$\begin{vmatrix} 5 & 3 & 8 \\ 2 & 6 & 1 \\ 4 & 7 & 9 \end{vmatrix}$$

Solution:

-------------------- **First Pass** --------------------

If the element in row 1, column 1, happens to be zero, the method will not work. If this happens, interchange two rows or two columns and try again. Remember to change the sign of the determinant when interchanging rows or columns.

Step 1: We factor out the 5.

$$5\begin{vmatrix} 1 & 0.6 & 1.6 \\ 2 & 6 & 1 \\ 4 & 7 & 9 \end{vmatrix}$$

Step 2: Multiply row 1 by 2 and subtract the result from row 2 (leaving row 1 as it was after Step 1).

$$5\begin{vmatrix} 1 & 0.6 & 1.6 \\ 0 & 4.8 & -2.2 \\ 4 & 7 & 9 \end{vmatrix}$$

Step 3: Multiply row 1 by 4 and subtract the result from row 3 (leaving row 1 as after Step 1).

$$5\begin{vmatrix} 1 & 0.6 & 1.6 \\ 0 & 4.8 & -2.2 \\ 0 & 4.6 & 2.6 \end{vmatrix}$$

Step 4: We develop the first column by minors. Since the first element is a 1 and the others are zeros, we simply delete the first row and first column.

$$5(1)\begin{vmatrix} 4.8 & -2.2 \\ 4.6 & 2.6 \end{vmatrix}$$

Thus we have reduced the order of the determinant from three to two. We then repeat the whole process.

-------------------- **Second Pass** --------------------

Step 1: Factor out 4.8.

$$5(4.8)\begin{vmatrix} 1 & -0.458 \\ 4.6 & 2.6 \end{vmatrix}$$

Step 2: Multiply row 1 by 4.6 and subtract from row 2.

$$5(4.8)\begin{vmatrix} 1 & -0.458 \\ 0 & 4.707 \end{vmatrix}$$

Step 3: Not needed.

Step 4: Delete the first row and first column. The value of the determinant is then

$$5(4.8)(4.707) = 113$$

━

━ **Example 25:** Evaluate the following fourth-order determinant by the method of Chió. Work to three significant digits.

$$\begin{vmatrix} 5 & 2 & 6 & 1 \\ 4 & 2 & 9 & 4 \\ 3 & 6 & 1 & 0 \\ 7 & 1 & 3 & 4 \end{vmatrix}$$

Solution:

-------------------- **First Pass** --------------------

Step 1: We factor out the 5.

$$5\begin{vmatrix} 1 & 0.4 & 1.2 & 0.2 \\ 4 & 2 & 9 & 4 \\ 3 & 6 & 1 & 0 \\ 7 & 1 & 3 & 4 \end{vmatrix}$$

Step 2: Multiply row 1 by 4 and subtract the result from row 2.

$$5\begin{vmatrix} 1 & 0.4 & 1.2 & 0.2 \\ 0 & 0.4 & 4.2 & 3.2 \\ 3 & 6 & 1 & 0 \\ 7 & 1 & 3 & 4 \end{vmatrix}$$

Step 3: Multiply row 1 by 3 and subtract the result from row 3. Multiply row 1 by 7 and subtract the result from row 4.

$$5\begin{vmatrix} 1 & 0.4 & 1.2 & 0.2 \\ 0 & 0.4 & 4.2 & 3.2 \\ 0 & 4.8 & -2.6 & -0.6 \\ 0 & -1.8 & -5.4 & 2.6 \end{vmatrix}$$

Step 4: Delete the first row and first column.

$$5\begin{vmatrix} 0.4 & 4.2 & 3.2 \\ 4.8 & -2.6 & -0.6 \\ -1.8 & -5.4 & 2.6 \end{vmatrix}$$

-------------------- **Second Pass** --------------------

Step 1: Factor out 0.4.

$$5(0.4)\begin{vmatrix} 1 & 10.5 & 8 \\ 4.8 & -2.6 & -0.6 \\ -1.8 & -5.4 & 2.6 \end{vmatrix}$$

Steps 2 and 3:

$$5(0.4)\begin{vmatrix} 1 & 10.5 & 8 \\ 0 & -53 & -39 \\ 0 & 13.5 & 17 \end{vmatrix}$$

Step 4: Delete the first row and first column.

$$5(0.4)\begin{vmatrix} -53 & -39 \\ 13.5 & 17 \end{vmatrix}$$

-------------------- **Third Pass** --------------------

Step 1: Factor out -53.

$$5(0.4)(-53)\begin{vmatrix} 1 & 0.736 \\ 13.5 & 17 \end{vmatrix}$$

Step 2: Multiply row 1 by 13.5 and subtract the result from row 2.

$$5(0.4)(-53)\begin{vmatrix} 1 & 0.736 \\ 0 & 7.06 \end{vmatrix}$$

Step 3: Not needed.

Step 4: Delete the first row and first column. The value of the determinant is then

$$5(0.4)(-53)(7.06) = -748 \qquad \blacksquare$$

Exercise 3 Higher-Order Determinants

Evaluate each determinant.

1. $\begin{vmatrix} 4 & 3 & 1 & 0 \\ -1 & 2 & -3 & 5 \\ 0 & 1 & -1 & 2 \\ 0 & 2 & -3 & 5 \end{vmatrix}$

2. $\begin{vmatrix} -1 & 3 & 0 & 2 \\ 2 & -1 & 1 & 0 \\ 5 & 2 & -2 & 0 \\ 1 & -1 & 3 & 1 \end{vmatrix}$

3.
$$\begin{vmatrix} 2 & 0 & -1 & 0 \\ 0 & 0 & 2 & -1 \\ 1 & 3 & 2 & 1 \\ 3 & 1 & 1 & -2 \end{vmatrix}$$

4.
$$\begin{vmatrix} 1 & 2 & -1 & 1 \\ -1 & 1 & 2 & 3 \\ 3 & -1 & 1 & 2 \\ 1 & 2 & -1 & 1 \end{vmatrix}$$

5.
$$\begin{vmatrix} 3 & 1 & 0 & 2 & 4 \\ 1 & 2 & 4 & 0 & 1 \\ 2 & 3 & 1 & 4 & 2 \\ 1 & 2 & 0 & 2 & 1 \\ 3 & 4 & 1 & 3 & 1 \end{vmatrix}$$

6.
$$\begin{vmatrix} 2 & 1 & 5 & 3 & 6 \\ 1 & 4 & 2 & 4 & 3 \\ 3 & 1 & 2 & 4 & 1 \\ 5 & 2 & 3 & 1 & 4 \\ 4 & 5 & 2 & 3 & 1 \end{vmatrix}$$

Four Equations with Four Unknowns

Solve by determinants.

7.
$$\begin{aligned} x + y + 2z + w &= 18 \\ x + 2y + z + w &= 17 \\ x + y + z + 2w &= 19 \\ 2x + y + z + w &= 16 \end{aligned}$$

8.
$$\begin{aligned} 2x - y - z - w &= 0 \\ x - 3y + z + w &= 0 \\ x + y - 4z + w &= 0 \\ x + y + w &= 36 \end{aligned}$$

9.
$$\begin{aligned} 3x - 2y - z + w &= -3 \\ -x - y + 3z + 2w &= 23 \\ x + 3y - 2z + w &= -12 \\ 2x - y - z - 3w &= -22 \end{aligned}$$

10.
$$\begin{aligned} x + 2y &= 5 \\ y + 2z &= 8 \\ z + 2u &= 11 \\ u + 2x &= 6 \end{aligned}$$

11.
$$\begin{aligned} x + y &= a + b \\ y + z &= b + c \\ z + w &= a - b \\ w - x &= c - b \end{aligned}$$

12.
$$\begin{aligned} 2x - 3y + z - w &= -6 \\ x + 2y - z &= 8 \\ 3y + z + 3w &= 0 \\ 3x - y + w &= 0 \end{aligned}$$

Five Equations with Five Unknowns

Solve by determinants.

13.
$$\begin{aligned} x + y &= 9 \\ y + z &= 11 \\ z + w &= 13 \\ w + u &= 15 \\ u + x &= 12 \end{aligned}$$

14.
$$\begin{aligned} 3x + 4y + z &= 35 \\ 3z + 2y - 3w &= 4 \\ 2x - y + 2w &= 17 \\ 3z - 2w + v &= 9 \\ w + y &= 13 \end{aligned}$$

15.
$$\begin{aligned} w + v + x + y &= 14 \\ w + v + x + z &= 15 \\ w + v + y + z &= 16 \\ w + x + y + z &= 17 \\ v + x + y + z &= 18 \end{aligned}$$

16. Separate 125 into four parts such that if the first is increased by 4, the second diminished by 4, the third multiplied by 4, and the fourth divided by 4, these four quantities will all be equal.

17. A person divided a sum of money among four children so that the share of the eldest was $\frac{1}{2}$ of the sum of the shares of the other three, the share of the second was $\frac{1}{3}$ of the sum of the shares of the other three, and the share of the third was $\frac{1}{4}$ of the sum of the shares of the other three. The eldest has $14 000 more than the youngest. What was the share of each?

18. Applying Kirchhoff's law to a certain four-loop network gives the equations

$$57.2I_1 + 92.5I_2 - 23.0I_3 - 11.4I_4 = \;\;\; 38.2$$
$$95.3I_1 - 14.9I_2 + 39.0I_3 + 59.9I_4 = \;\;\; 29.3$$
$$66.3I_1 + 81.4I_2 - 91.5I_3 + 33.4I_4 = -73.6$$
$$38.2I_1 - 46.6I_2 + 30.1I_3 + 93.2I_4 = \;\;\; 55.7$$

Solve for the four loop currents, by any method.

19. We have available four bronze alloys containing the following percentages of copper, zinc, and lead.

	ALLOY 1	ALLOY 2	ALLOY 3	ALLOY 4
Copper	52.0	53.0	54.0	55.0
Zinc	30.0	38.0	20.0	38.0
Lead	3.0	2.0	4.0	3.0

How many kilograms of each alloy should be taken to produce $60\overline{0}$ kg of a new alloy that is 53.8% copper, 30.1% zinc, and 3.2% lead?

Graphics Calculator

20. We use a graphics calculator to evaluate any order determinant in the same way as for second-order determinants, as we showed in Section 11.1. Be sure to enter the dimensions of the determinant to be evaluated. Use the graphics calculator to evaluate any of the determinants in this exercise.

21. Use a graphics calculator to solve any of the systems of equations in this exercise. Evaluate the determinant of the system and the determinant for x, and divide to get x. Repeat for the other unknowns.

Computer

22. To evaluate a determinant on a computer algebra system, enter the elements in the same form as we showed in Section 11.1 and give the command SIMPLIFY. Use a CAS to evaluate any determinant in this exercise.

23. Use a CAS to solve any system of equations in this exercise, by evaluating and then dividing the appropriate determinants.

24. Write a program to evaluate a determinant of any order. Use the algorithm given for the method of Chió. Use DATA statements to input the order of the determinant, and then the elements, row by row. Use it to evaluate any of the determinants in this chapter.

CHAPTER 11 REVIEW PROBLEMS

Evaluate.

1.
$$\begin{vmatrix} 6 & 1/2 & -2 \\ 3 & 1/4 & 4 \\ 2 & -1/2 & 3 \end{vmatrix}$$

2.
$$\begin{vmatrix} 2 & 7 & -2 & 8 \\ 4 & 1 & 1 & -3 \\ 0 & 3 & -1 & 4 \\ 6 & 4 & 2 & -8 \end{vmatrix}$$

3.
$$\begin{vmatrix} 0 & n & m \\ -n & 0 & l \\ -m & -l & 0 \end{vmatrix}$$

4.
$$\begin{vmatrix} 8 & 2 & 0 & 1 & 4 \\ 0 & 1 & 4 & 2 & 7 \\ 2 & 6 & 3 & 8 & 0 \\ 1 & 4 & 2 & 6 & 5 \\ 4 & 6 & 8 & 3 & 5 \end{vmatrix}$$

5. $\begin{vmatrix} 25 & 23 & 19 \\ 14 & 11 & 9 \\ 21 & 17 & 14 \end{vmatrix}$

6. $\begin{vmatrix} x+y & x-y \\ x-y & x+y \end{vmatrix}$

7. $\begin{vmatrix} 9 & 13 & 17 \\ 11 & 15 & 19 \\ 17 & 21 & 25 \end{vmatrix}$

8. $\begin{vmatrix} 5 & -3 & -2 & 0 \\ 4 & 1 & -6 & 2 \\ -1 & 4 & 3 & -5 \\ 0 & 6 & -4 & 2 \end{vmatrix}$

9. $\begin{vmatrix} 1 & 2 & 3 \\ 3 & 1 & 2 \\ 2 & 3 & 1 \end{vmatrix}$

10. $\begin{vmatrix} 2 & -3 & 1 \\ -2 & 4 & 5 \\ 3 & -1 & -4 \end{vmatrix}$

11. $\begin{vmatrix} 1 & 2 & 2 & 4 \\ 1 & 4 & 4 & 1 \\ 1 & 1 & 2 & 2 \\ 4 & 8 & 11 & 13 \end{vmatrix}$

12. $\begin{vmatrix} a-b & -2a \\ 2b & a-b \end{vmatrix}$

13. $\begin{vmatrix} 3 & 1 & 5 & 2 \\ 4 & 10 & 14 & 6 \\ 8 & 9 & 1 & 4 \\ 6 & 15 & 21 & 9 \end{vmatrix}$

14. $\begin{vmatrix} 7 & 8 & 9 \\ 28 & 35 & 40 \\ 21 & 26 & 30 \end{vmatrix}$

15. $\begin{vmatrix} 1 & 5 & 2 \\ 4 & 7 & 3 \\ 9 & 8 & 6 \end{vmatrix}$

16. $\begin{vmatrix} 3 & -6 \\ -5 & 4 \end{vmatrix}$

17. $\begin{vmatrix} 6 & 4 & 7 \\ 9 & 0 & 8 \\ 5 & 3 & 2 \end{vmatrix}$

18. $\begin{vmatrix} 3 & 2 & 1 & 3 \\ 4 & 2 & 2 & 4 \\ 2 & 3 & 1 & 6 \\ 10 & 4 & 5 & 8 \end{vmatrix}$

Solve by determinants.

19. $\begin{aligned} x + y + z + w &= -4 \\ x + 2y + 3z + 4w &= 0 \\ x + 3y + 6z + 10w &= 9 \\ x + 4y + 10z + 20w &= 24 \end{aligned}$

20. $\begin{aligned} x + 2y + 3z &= 4 \\ 3x + 5y + z &= 18 \\ 4x + y + 2z &= 12 \end{aligned}$

21. $\begin{aligned} 4x + 3y &= 27 \\ 2x - 5y &= -19 \end{aligned}$

22. $\begin{aligned} 8x - 3y - 7z &= 85 \\ x + 6y - 4z &= -12 \\ 2x - 5y + z &= 33 \end{aligned}$

23. $\begin{aligned} x + 2y &= 10 \\ 2x - 3y &= -1 \end{aligned}$

24. $\begin{aligned} x + y + z + u &= 1 \\ 2x + 3y - 4z + 5u &= -31 \\ 3x - 4y + 5z + 6u &= -22 \\ 4x + 5y - 6z - u &= -13 \end{aligned}$

25. $\begin{aligned} 2x - 3y &= 7 \\ 5x + 2y &= 27 \end{aligned}$

26. $\begin{aligned} 6x + y &= 60 \\ 3x + 2y &= 39 \end{aligned}$

27. $\begin{aligned} 2x + 5y &= 29 \\ 2x - 5y &= -21 \end{aligned}$

28. $\begin{aligned} 4x + 3y &= 7 \\ 2x - 3y &= -1 \end{aligned}$

29. $\begin{aligned} 4x - 5y &= 3 \\ 3x + 5y &= 11 \end{aligned}$

30. $\begin{aligned} x + 5y &= 41 \\ 3x - 2y &= 21 \end{aligned}$

31. $\begin{aligned} x + 2y &= 7 \\ x + y &= 5 \end{aligned}$

32. $\begin{aligned} 8x - 3y &= 22 \\ 4x + 5y &= 18 \end{aligned}$

33. $\begin{aligned} 3x + 4y &= 25 \\ 4x + 3y &= 21 \end{aligned}$

Writing

34. Suppose that you often solve sets of three or more equations on the job. Write a memo to your boss asking for a desktop computer to do the work. It should include a description of the method of Chió which can be understood by an engineer who does not have extensive computer experience.

Team Project

35. Solve by any method.

$\begin{aligned} 28.3x + 29.2y - 33.1z + 72.4u + 29.4v &= 39.5 \\ 73.2x - 28.4y + 59.3z - 27.4u + 49.2v &= 82.3 \\ 33.7x + 10.3y + 72.3z + 29.3u - 21.2v &= 28.4 \\ 92.3x - 39.5y + 29.5z - 10.3u + 82.2v &= 73.4 \\ 88.3x + 29.3y + 10.3z + 84.2u + 29.3v &= 39.4 \end{aligned}$

12

Matrices

O B J E C T I V E S

When you have completed this chapter, you should be able to:

- Identify various types of arrays, matrices, and vectors, and give their dimensions.
- Write the transpose of a matrix.
- Add, subtract, and multiply matrices.
- Solve systems of equations using matrix inversion.

The method of determinants is fine for solving a set of equations by hand, but it is not easy to program for the computer. One popular method of solving sets of equations by computer and graphics calculator is called *matrix inversion*. We will learn that method later in this chapter, but first we must learn about matrices and how to manipulate them.

12•1   Definitions

Arrays

A set of numbers, called *elements*, arranged in a pattern, is called an array. Arrays are named for the shape of the pattern made by the elements.

■ **Example 1:** The array

$$\begin{pmatrix} 7 & 3 & 9 & 1 \\ & 8 & 3 & 2 \\ & & 9 & 1 \\ & & & 5 \end{pmatrix}$$

is called a *triangular array*.   ■

Vectors

A *vector* is an array consisting of a single row or a single column.

■ **Example 2:** The array $(2, 6, -2, 8)$ is called a *row vector*, and the array

$$\begin{pmatrix} 7 \\ 3 \\ 9 \\ 2 \end{pmatrix}$$

is called a *column vector*.   ■

What has this got to do with the vectors we defined in Chapter 7, where we used vectors to represent directed quantities such as force and velocity?

The two apparently different definitions agree, if we think of a vector as the *coordinates of the endpoint* of a line segment drawn from the origin.

■ **Example 3:**
(a) The vector $(4, 7)$ represents a line segment in a plane drawn from the origin to the point $(4, 7)$.
(b) The vector $(2, 3, 4)$ represents a line segment in three dimensions, drawn from the origin to the point $(2, 3, 4)$.
(c) The vector $(5, 8, 1, 3, 6)$ can be thought of as representing a line segment in five dimensions, although we cannot draw it. However, we can work mathematically with this vector using the same rules as for the others. ■

Matrices

A matrix is sometimes referred to as a *vector of vectors*.

A *matrix* is a *rectangular* array.

■ **Example 4:** The rectangular arrays

(a) $\begin{pmatrix} 2 & 5 & 7 \\ 6 & 3 & 1 \end{pmatrix}$ (b) $\begin{pmatrix} 7 & 3 & 5 \\ 1 & 9 & 3 \\ 8 & 3 & 2 \end{pmatrix}$

are matrices. Further, (b) is a *square* matrix. For a square matrix, the diagonal running from the upper left element to the lower right element is called the *main diagonal*. In (b), the elements on the main diagonal are 7, 9, and 2. The diagonal from upper right to lower left is called the secondary diagonal. In our example, the elements 5, 9, and 8 are on the *secondary* diagonal. ■

In everyday language, an array is a *table* and a vector is a *list*.

Subscripts

Each element in an array is located in a horizontal *row* and a vertical *column*. We indicate the row and column by means of *subscripts*.

■ **Example 5:** The element a_{25} is located in row 2 and column 5. ■

Thus, an element in an array needs *double subscripts* to give its location. An element in a list, such as b_7, needs only a *single subscript*.

Dimensions

A matrix will have, in general, m rows and n columns. The numbers m and n are the *dimensions* of the matrix, as, for example, a 4×5 matrix.

■ **Example 6:** The matrix

$$\begin{pmatrix} 2 & 3 & 5 & 9 \\ 1 & 0 & 8 & 3 \end{pmatrix}$$

has the dimensions 2×4, and the matrix

$$\begin{pmatrix} 5 & 3 & 8 \\ 1 & 0 & 3 \\ 2 & 5 & 2 \\ 1 & 0 & 7 \end{pmatrix}$$

has the dimensions 4×3.

Scalars

A single number, as opposed to an array of numbers, is called a *scalar*.

Example 7: Some scalars are 5, 693.6, and -24.3.

A scalar can also be thought of as an array having just one row and one column.

Naming a Matrix

We will often denote or *name* a matrix with a single letter.

Example 8: We can let

$$\mathbf{A} = \begin{pmatrix} 2 & 5 & 1 \\ 0 & 4 & 3 \end{pmatrix}$$

Thus we can represent an entire array by a single symbol.

The Null or Zero Matrix

A matrix in which all elements are zero is called the *null* or *zero* matrix.

Example 9: The matrix

$$\mathbf{O} = \begin{pmatrix} 0 & 0 & 0 \\ 0 & 0 & 0 \end{pmatrix}$$

is a 2×3 zero matrix. We will denote the zero matrix by the boldface letter **O**.

The Unit Matrix

If all the elements *not* on the main diagonal of a square matrix are 0, we have a *diagonal matrix*. If, in addition, the elements on the main diagonal are equal, we have a *scalar matrix*. If the elements on the main diagonal of a scalar matrix are 1s, we have a *unit matrix* or *identity matrix*.

Example 10: The matrices

$$\mathbf{A} = \begin{pmatrix} 3 & 0 & 0 \\ 0 & 5 & 0 \\ 0 & 0 & 7 \end{pmatrix} \quad \mathbf{B} = \begin{pmatrix} 6 & 0 & 0 \\ 0 & 6 & 0 \\ 0 & 0 & 6 \end{pmatrix} \quad \mathbf{I} = \begin{pmatrix} 1 & 0 & 0 \\ 0 & 1 & 0 \\ 0 & 0 & 1 \end{pmatrix}$$

are all diagonal matrices. **B** and **I** are, in addition, scalar matrices, and **I** is a unit matrix. We usually denote the unit matrix by the letter **I**.

Equality of Matrices

When comparing two matrices *of the same dimension*, elements in each matrix having the same row and column subscripts are called *corresponding elements*. Two matrices of the same dimension are equal if their corresponding elements are equal.

■ **Example 11:** The matrices

$$\begin{pmatrix} x & 2 & 5 \\ 3 & 1 & 7 \end{pmatrix} \quad \text{and} \quad \begin{pmatrix} 4 & 2 & 5 \\ 3 & 1 & y \end{pmatrix}$$

are equal only if $x = 4$ and $y = 7$.   ■

Transpose of a Matrix

The *transpose* $\mathbf{A}'$ of a matrix $\mathbf{A}$ is obtained by changing the rows to columns and changing the columns to rows.

■ **Example 12:** The transpose of the matrix

$$\begin{pmatrix} 1 & 2 & 3 & 4 \\ 5 & 6 & 7 & 8 \end{pmatrix}$$

is

$$\begin{pmatrix} 1 & 5 \\ 2 & 6 \\ 3 & 7 \\ 4 & 8 \end{pmatrix}$$

■

Determinant of a Square Matrix

We form the determinant of a square matrix by writing the same elements enclosed between vertical bars.

■ **Example 13:** The determinant of the square matrix

$$\begin{pmatrix} a & b & c & d \\ e & f & g & h \\ i & j & k & l \\ m & n & o & p \end{pmatrix}$$

is

$$\begin{vmatrix} a & b & c & d \\ e & f & g & h \\ i & j & k & l \\ m & n & o & p \end{vmatrix}$$

■

We'll see later when we want to find the *inverse* of a square matrix that the inverse exists only for a nonsingular matrix.

In Chapter 11 we learned how to evaluate determinants, so we'll not repeat that material here. We do, however, need a definition that will be useful later in this chapter.

A square matrix is called *singular* if its determinant is zero, and is called *nonsingular* if its determinant is not zero.

Exercise 1 Definitions

Given

$$A = \begin{pmatrix} 2 & 5 & 1 \\ 6 & 3 & 7 \\ 1 & 6 & 9 \\ 7 & 4 & 2 \end{pmatrix} \qquad B = \begin{pmatrix} 7 \\ 3 \\ 9 \\ 2 \end{pmatrix} \qquad C = \begin{pmatrix} f & i & q & w \\ & g & w & k \\ & & c & z \\ & & & b \end{pmatrix}$$

$$D = \begin{pmatrix} 6 & 2 & 0 & 1 \\ 2 & 8 & 3 & 9 \end{pmatrix} \qquad E = \begin{pmatrix} x & y \\ z & w \end{pmatrix} \qquad F = \begin{pmatrix} 0 & 0 & 0 & 0 \\ 0 & 0 & 0 & 0 \end{pmatrix}$$

$$G = 7 \qquad H = \begin{pmatrix} 3 & 8 \\ & 5 \end{pmatrix} \qquad I = (3 \quad 8 \quad 4 \quad 6)$$

Which of the nine arrays shown above is:

1. A rectangular array?
2. A square array?
3. A triangular array?
4. A column vector?
5. A row vector?
6. A table?
7. A list?
8. A scalar?
9. A null matrix?
10. A matrix?

For the matrix **A** above, find the element:

11. a_{32}
12. a_{41}

Give the dimensions of:

13. Matrix **A**
14. Matrix **B**
15. Matrix **D**
16. Matrix **E**

Write the transpose of:

17. Matrix **F**
18. Matrix **D**
19. Under what conditions will the matrices

$$\begin{pmatrix} 6 & x \\ w & 8 \end{pmatrix} \quad \text{and} \quad \begin{pmatrix} y & 2 \\ 7 & z \end{pmatrix}$$

be equal?

Graphics Calculator

20. Some graphics calculators can do matrix manipulations. On the TI-81, for example, you would enter a matrix in the following way.

1. Press $\boxed{\text{MATRX}}$ to display the matrix menu.
2. Select $\boxed{\text{EDIT}}$.
3. Choose which matrix, **A**, **B**, or **C**, you wish to edit.
4. Enter the matrix dimensions, rows first, then columns.
5. Enter the elements, one row at a time, from left to right.

To find the transpose of a matrix:

1. Enter the name of the matrix. If it is matrix **A** you would enter

$$\boxed{\text{2nd}}, \boxed{\text{A}}$$

2. Display the matrix menu and choose $^\text{T}$. The display will then be

$$\boxed{\text{A}}^\text{T}$$

3. Pressing $\boxed{\text{ENTER}}$ will cause the transposed matrix to be displayed.

   Use a graphics calculator to find the transpose of any matrix in this exercise.

Computer

21. Using subscripted variables, write a *Basic* program to find and print the transpose of any matrix. Use DATA statements to enter the number of rows and columns, and then the elements of the original matrix, row by row, into your program.

22. A computer algebra system is ideal for manipulating matrices. In *Derive*, the matrix

$$\begin{matrix} 1 & 2 & 3 & 4 \\ 5 & 6 & 7 & 8 \end{matrix}$$

is entered

$$[[1, 2, 3, 4], [5, 6, 7, 8]]$$

To transpose a matrix, *Derive* uses the opening quote (').

$$[[1, 2, 3, 4], [5, 6, 7, 8]]`$$

Then SIMPLIFY will display the transposed matrix. In *Maple*, enter the same matrix in the form

$$\text{A} := (2, 4[[1, 2, 3, 4], [5, 6, 7, 8]]);$$

Then evalm(A) will display the matrix and transpose(A); will transpose the matrix. In *Mathematica* the matrix is entered as

$$a = \{\{1, 2, 3, 4\}, \{5, 6, 7, 8\}\}$$

The command MatrixForm [a] will display the matrix, and Transpose[a] will transpose the matrix.

   Use a computer algebra system to find the transpose of any matrix in this exercise.

12·2 Operations with Matrices

In earlier chapters we have learned how to add, subtract, and multiply numbers and algebraic quantities. We now perform these operations on matrices.

Addition and Subtraction of Matrices

Addition and subtraction are *not defined* for two matrices of *different* dimensions.

To add two matrices *of the same dimensions*, simply combine corresponding elements.

■ **Example 14:**

$$\begin{pmatrix} 2 & -3 & 4 & 1 \\ 0 & 5 & 6 & -8 \end{pmatrix} + \begin{pmatrix} 5 & 8 & 1 & 2 \\ 9 & -3 & 0 & 1 \end{pmatrix} = \begin{pmatrix} 7 & 5 & 5 & 3 \\ 9 & 2 & 6 & -7 \end{pmatrix}$$ ■

Subtraction is done in a similar way.

■ **Example 15:**

$$\begin{pmatrix} 2 & -3 & 4 & 1 \\ 0 & 5 & 6 & -8 \end{pmatrix} - \begin{pmatrix} 5 & 8 & 1 & 2 \\ 9 & -3 & 0 & 1 \end{pmatrix} = \begin{pmatrix} -3 & -11 & 3 & -1 \\ -9 & 8 & 6 & -9 \end{pmatrix}$$ ■

As with ordinary addition, the *commutative law* (Eq. 1) and the *associative law* (Eq. 3) apply.

Commutative Law	$\mathbf{A} + \mathbf{B} = \mathbf{B} + \mathbf{A}$	79

Associative Law	$\mathbf{A} + (\mathbf{B} + \mathbf{C}) = (\mathbf{A} + \mathbf{B}) + \mathbf{C}$ $\qquad\qquad\quad = (\mathbf{A} + \mathbf{C}) + \mathbf{B}$	80

Product of a Scalar and a Matrix

Worked in reverse, we can *factor* a scalar from a matrix. Thus, in the example shown, we can think of the number 3 as being *factored out*.

To multiply a matrix by a scalar, multiply each element in the matrix by the scalar.

■ **Example 16:**

$$3\begin{pmatrix} 2 & 4 & 1 \\ 5 & 7 & 3 \end{pmatrix} = \begin{pmatrix} 6 & 12 & 3 \\ 15 & 21 & 9 \end{pmatrix}$$ ■

In symbols

Product of a Scalar and a Matrix	$k\begin{pmatrix} a & b \\ c & d \end{pmatrix} = \begin{pmatrix} ka & kb \\ kc & kd \end{pmatrix}$	87

Multiplication of Vectors and Matrices

Not all matrices can be multiplied. Further, for matrices **A** and **B**, it may be possible to find the product **AB** but *not* the product **BA**.

Two matrices for which multiplication is defined are called *conformable matrices*.

Conformable Matrices	The product **AB** of two matrices **A** and **B** is defined only when the number of columns in **A** equals the number of rows in **B**.	82

■ **Example 17:** If

$$\mathbf{A} = \begin{pmatrix} 3 & 5 \\ 2 & 1 \\ 7 & 4 \\ 9 & 0 \end{pmatrix} \quad \text{and} \quad \mathbf{B} = \begin{pmatrix} 7 & 3 & 8 \\ 4 & 7 & 1 \end{pmatrix}$$

we can find the product **AB**, because the number of columns in **A** (2 columns) equals the number of rows in **B** (2 rows). However, we *cannot* find the product **BA** because the number of columns in **B** (3 columns) does not equal the number of rows in **A** (4 rows).   ▬

For two or more conformable matrices, the *associative* law and the *distributive* law for multiplication applies.

Associative Law	$\mathbf{A(BC) = (AB)C = ABC}$	84

Distributive Law	$\mathbf{A(B + C) = AB + AC}$	85

These are similar to Eqs. 4 and 5 for ordinary multiplication.

The *dimensions* of the matrix obtained by multiplying an $m \times p$ matrix with a $p \times n$ matrix is equal to $m \times n$. In other words, the product matrix **AB** will have the same number of *rows* as **A** and the same number of *columns* as **B**.

Dimensions of the Product	$(m \times p)(p \times n) = (m \times n)$	86

▬ **Example 18:** The product **AB** of a 3×5 matrix **A** and a 5×7 matrix **B** is a 3×7 matrix.   ▬

Scalar Product of Two Vectors

Whatever we say about matrices applies, of course, to vectors as well.

We will show matrix multiplication first with vectors, and then extend it to other matrices.

The *scalar product* (also called the *dot product* or *inner product*) of a row vector **A** and a column vector **B** is defined only when the number of columns in **A** is equal to the number of rows in **B**.

If each vector contains m elements, the dimensions of the product will be, by Eq. 86,

$$(1 \times m)(m \times 1) = 1 \times 1$$

Thus, the product is a scalar, hence the name *scalar product*.

To multiply a row vector by a column vector, multiply the first elements of each, then the second, and so on, and add the products obtained.

▬ **Example 19:**

$$(2 \quad 6 \quad 4 \quad 8)\begin{pmatrix} 3 \\ 5 \\ 1 \\ 7 \end{pmatrix} = [2(3) + 6(5) + 4(1) + 8(7)]$$

$$= (6 + 30 + 4 + 56) = 96 \qquad ▬$$

Stated as a formula, we have

$$
(a \quad b \quad . \ . \ .)\begin{pmatrix} x \\ y \\ . \\ . \\ . \end{pmatrix} = (ax + by + . \ . \ .) \qquad \textbf{88}
$$

■ **Example 20:** A certain store has four types of radios, priced at \$71, \$62, \$83, and \$49. On a particular day, they sell quantities of 8, 3, 7, and 6, respectively. If we represent the prices by a row vector and the quantities by a column vector, and multiply, we get

$$
(71 \quad 62 \quad 83 \quad 49)\begin{pmatrix} 8 \\ 3 \\ 7 \\ 6 \end{pmatrix} = [71(8) + 62(3) + 83(7) + 49(6)]
$$

$$
= 1629
$$

The interpretation of this number is obviously the total dollar income from the sale of the four types of radios on that day. ■

Product of a Row Vector and a Matrix

By Eq. 86, the product of a row vector and a matrix having n columns will be a row vector having n elements.

$$
(1 \times p)(p \times n) = (1 \times n)
$$

We saw earlier that the product of a row vector and a column vector is a single number, or scalar. Thus, the product of the given row vector and the first column of the matrix will give a scalar. This scalar will be *the first element in the product vector.*

The *second* element in the product vector is found by multiplying the second column in the matrix by the row vector, and so on.

■ **Example 21:** Multiply

$$
(1 \quad 3 \quad 0)\begin{pmatrix} 7 & 5 \\ 1 & 0 \\ 4 & 9 \end{pmatrix}
$$

Solution: The dimensions of the product will be

$$
(1 \times 3)(3 \times 2) = (1 \times 2)
$$

Multiplying the vector and the first column of the matrix gives

> Here we use the asterisk (*) as a placeholder to denote the other element still to be computed.

$$
(1 \quad 3 \quad 0)\begin{pmatrix} \mathbf{7} & 5 \\ \mathbf{1} & 0 \\ \mathbf{4} & 9 \end{pmatrix} = [\mathbf{1(7)} + \mathbf{3(1)} + \mathbf{0(4)} \quad * \quad]
$$

$$
= (\mathbf{10} \quad *)
$$

Multiplying the vector and the second column of the matrix yields

$$
(1 \quad 3 \quad 0)\begin{pmatrix} 7 & \mathbf{5} \\ 1 & \mathbf{0} \\ 4 & \mathbf{9} \end{pmatrix} = [10 \quad \mathbf{1(5)} + \mathbf{3(0)} + \mathbf{0(9)}]
$$

$$
= (10 \quad 5)
$$

■

■ **Example 22:** Continuing Example 20, let us suppose that on the second day, the store sells quantities of 5, 9, 1, and 4, respectively, of the four radios. If we again represent the prices by a row vector, but now represent the quantities by a matrix and multiply, we get

$$(71 \quad 62 \quad 83 \quad 49)\begin{pmatrix} 8 & 5 \\ 3 & 9 \\ 7 & 1 \\ 6 & 4 \end{pmatrix} = \begin{bmatrix} 71(8) + 62(3) + 83(7) + 49(6) \\ 71(5) + 62(9) + 83(1) + 49(4) \end{bmatrix}$$

$$= (1629 \quad 1192)$$

We interpret these numbers as the total dollar income from the sale of the four radios on each of the two days.   ■

Product of Two Matrices

We now multiply two matrices **A** and **B**. We already know how to multiply a row vector and a matrix. So let us think of the matrix **A** as several row vectors. Each of these row vectors, multiplied by the matrix **B**, will produce a row vector in the product **AB**.

■ **Example 23:** Find the product **AB** of the matrices

$$\mathbf{A} = \begin{pmatrix} 1 & 0 \\ 3 & 2 \end{pmatrix} \qquad \mathbf{B} = \begin{pmatrix} 5 & 4 & 8 \\ 6 & 7 & 9 \end{pmatrix}$$

Solution: The dimensions of the product will be

$$(2 \times 2)(2 \times 3) = (2 \times 3)$$

We think of the matrix **A** as being two row vectors, each of which, when multiplied by matrix **B**, will produce a row vector in the product matrix.

$$\underset{\mathbf{A}}{\begin{pmatrix} 1 & 0 \\ 3 & 2 \end{pmatrix}} \underset{\mathbf{B}}{\begin{pmatrix} 5 & 4 & 8 \\ 6 & 7 & 9 \end{pmatrix}} = \underset{\mathbf{AB}}{\begin{pmatrix} * & * & * \\ * & * & * \end{pmatrix}}$$

Multiplying by the first row vector in **A**,

$$\underset{\mathbf{A}}{\begin{pmatrix} \mathbf{1} & \mathbf{0} \\ 3 & 2 \end{pmatrix}} \underset{\mathbf{B}}{\begin{pmatrix} 5 & 4 & 8 \\ 6 & 7 & 9 \end{pmatrix}} = \underset{\mathbf{AB}}{\begin{bmatrix} \mathbf{1(5)} + \mathbf{0(6)} & \mathbf{1(4)} + \mathbf{0(7)} & \mathbf{1(8)} + \mathbf{0(9)} \\ * & * & * \end{bmatrix}}$$

$$= \begin{bmatrix} \mathbf{5} & \mathbf{4} & \mathbf{8} \\ * & * & * \end{bmatrix}$$

Then, multiplying by the second row vector in **A**,

$$\underset{\mathbf{A}}{\begin{pmatrix} 1 & 0 \\ \mathbf{3} & \mathbf{2} \end{pmatrix}} \underset{\mathbf{B}}{\begin{pmatrix} 5 & 4 & 8 \\ 6 & 7 & 9 \end{pmatrix}} = \underset{\mathbf{AB}}{\begin{bmatrix} 5 & 4 & 8 \\ \mathbf{3(5)} + \mathbf{2(6)} & \mathbf{3(4)} + \mathbf{2(7)} & \mathbf{3(8)} + \mathbf{2(9)} \end{bmatrix}}$$

giving the final product

$$\underset{\mathbf{A}}{\begin{pmatrix} 1 & 0 \\ 3 & 2 \end{pmatrix}} \underset{\mathbf{B}}{\begin{pmatrix} 5 & 4 & 8 \\ 6 & 7 & 9 \end{pmatrix}} = \underset{\mathbf{AB}}{\begin{pmatrix} 5 & 4 & 8 \\ 27 & 26 & 42 \end{pmatrix}}$$

■

■ **Example 24:** Find the product **AB** of the matrices

$$\begin{pmatrix} 1 & 0 & 2 \\ 0 & 1 & 1 \\ 3 & 0 & 2 \\ 1 & 1 & 0 \\ 2 & 1 & 1 \end{pmatrix} \begin{pmatrix} 3 & 0 & 1 & 1 \\ 1 & 2 & 3 & 0 \\ 0 & 1 & 2 & 1 \end{pmatrix}$$

$$\quad\quad\quad\quad\quad \mathbf{A} \quad\quad\quad\quad\quad \mathbf{B}$$

Solution: We think of the matrix **A** as five row vectors. Each of these five row vectors, multiplied by the matrix **B**, will produce a row vector in the product **AB**.

$$\begin{matrix} (1 & 0 & 2) \\ (0 & 1 & 1) \\ (3 & 0 & 2) \\ (1 & 1 & 0) \\ (2 & 1 & 1) \end{matrix} \begin{pmatrix} 3 & 0 & 1 & 1 \\ 1 & 2 & 3 & 0 \\ 0 & 1 & 2 & 1 \end{pmatrix} = \begin{matrix} (& &) \\ (& &) \\ (& &) \\ (& &) \\ (& &) \end{matrix}$$

$$\quad \mathbf{A} \quad\quad\quad \mathbf{B} \quad\quad\quad \mathbf{AB}$$
$$(5 \times 3) \quad (3 \times 4) \quad\quad (5 \times 4)$$

Multiplying the *first* row vector (1   0   2) in **A** by the matrix **B** gives the first row vector in **AB**.

$$\begin{matrix} (\mathbf{1} & \mathbf{0} & \mathbf{2}) \\ (0 & 1 & 1) \\ (3 & 0 & 2) \\ (1 & 1 & 0) \\ (2 & 1 & 1) \end{matrix} \begin{pmatrix} 3 & 0 & 1 & 1 \\ 1 & 2 & 3 & 0 \\ 0 & 1 & 2 & 1 \end{pmatrix} = \begin{matrix} (\mathbf{3} & \mathbf{2} & \mathbf{5} & \mathbf{3}) \\ (& & &) \\ (& & &) \\ (& & &) \end{matrix}$$

$$\quad \mathbf{A} \quad\quad\quad \mathbf{B} \quad\quad\quad \mathbf{AB}$$

Multiplying the *second* row vector in **A** and the matrix **B** gives a second row vector in **AB**.

$$\begin{matrix} (1 & 0 & 2) \\ (\mathbf{0} & \mathbf{1} & \mathbf{1}) \\ (3 & 0 & 2) \\ (1 & 1 & 0) \\ (2 & 1 & 1) \end{matrix} \begin{pmatrix} 3 & 0 & 1 & 1 \\ 1 & 2 & 3 & 0 \\ 0 & 1 & 2 & 1 \end{pmatrix} = \begin{matrix} (3 & 2 & 5 & 3) \\ (\mathbf{1} & \mathbf{3} & \mathbf{5} & \mathbf{1}) \\ (& & &) \\ (& & &) \end{matrix}$$

$$\quad \mathbf{A} \quad\quad\quad \mathbf{B} \quad\quad\quad \mathbf{AB}$$

The *third* row vector in **A** produces a third row vector in **AB**.

$$\begin{matrix} (1 & 0 & 2) \\ (0 & 1 & 1) \\ (\mathbf{3} & \mathbf{0} & \mathbf{2}) \\ (1 & 1 & 0) \\ (2 & 1 & 1) \end{matrix} \begin{pmatrix} 3 & 0 & 1 & 1 \\ 1 & 2 & 3 & 0 \\ 0 & 1 & 2 & 1 \end{pmatrix} = \begin{matrix} (3 & 2 & 5 & 3) \\ (1 & 3 & 5 & 1) \\ (\mathbf{9} & \mathbf{2} & \mathbf{7} & \mathbf{5}) \\ (& & &) \end{matrix}$$

$$\quad \mathbf{A} \quad\quad\quad \mathbf{B} \quad\quad\quad \mathbf{AB}$$

And so on, until we get the final product

$$\begin{pmatrix} 1 & 0 & 2 \\ 0 & 1 & 1 \\ 3 & 0 & 2 \\ 1 & 1 & 0 \\ 2 & 1 & 1 \end{pmatrix} \begin{pmatrix} 3 & 0 & 1 & 1 \\ 1 & 2 & 3 & 0 \\ 0 & 1 & 2 & 1 \end{pmatrix} = \begin{pmatrix} 3 & 2 & 5 & 3 \\ 1 & 3 & 5 & 1 \\ 9 & 2 & 7 & 5 \\ 4 & 2 & 4 & 1 \\ 7 & 3 & 7 & 3 \end{pmatrix}$$

$$\quad\quad \mathbf{A} \quad\quad\quad\quad \mathbf{B} \quad\quad\quad\quad \mathbf{AB}$$

■

We can state the product of two matrices as a formula as follows:

This formula works, of course, for conformable matrices with any number of elements.

Product of Two Matrices	$\begin{pmatrix} a & b & c \\ d & e & f \end{pmatrix}\begin{pmatrix} u & x \\ v & y \\ w & z \end{pmatrix} = \begin{pmatrix} au + bv + cw & ax + by + cz \\ du + ev + fw & dx + ey + fz \end{pmatrix}$	**92**

Product of Square Matrices

We multiply square matrices **A** and **B** just as we do other matrices. But, unlike for rectangular matrices, both the products **AB** and **BA** will be defined, although they will not usually be equal.

■ **Example 25:** Find the products **AB** and **BA** for the square matrices

$$\mathbf{A} = \begin{pmatrix} 0 & 1 & 2 \\ 1 & 1 & 0 \\ 2 & 3 & 1 \end{pmatrix} \qquad \mathbf{B} = \begin{pmatrix} 2 & 1 & 0 \\ 1 & 0 & 3 \\ 3 & 1 & 1 \end{pmatrix}$$

and show that the products are not equal.

Solution: Multiplying as shown earlier,

$$\mathbf{AB} = \begin{pmatrix} 0 & 1 & 2 \\ 1 & 1 & 0 \\ 2 & 3 & 1 \end{pmatrix}\begin{pmatrix} 2 & 1 & 0 \\ 1 & 0 & 3 \\ 3 & 1 & 1 \end{pmatrix} = \begin{pmatrix} 7 & 2 & 5 \\ 3 & 1 & 3 \\ 10 & 3 & 10 \end{pmatrix}$$

and

$$\mathbf{BA} = \begin{pmatrix} 2 & 1 & 0 \\ 1 & 0 & 3 \\ 3 & 1 & 1 \end{pmatrix}\begin{pmatrix} 0 & 1 & 2 \\ 1 & 1 & 0 \\ 2 & 3 & 1 \end{pmatrix} = \begin{pmatrix} 1 & 3 & 4 \\ 6 & 10 & 5 \\ 3 & 7 & 7 \end{pmatrix}$$

■

We see that multiplying the matrices in the reverse order does *not* give the same result.

Commutative Law	**AB ≠ BA** Matrix multiplication is *not* commutative.	**83**

Product of a Matrix and a Column Vector

We have already multiplied a row vector **A** by a matrix **B**. Now we multiply a matrix **A** by a column vector **B**.

■ **Example 26:** Multiply

$$\begin{pmatrix} 3 & 1 & 2 & 0 \\ 1 & 3 & 5 & 2 \end{pmatrix}\begin{pmatrix} 2 \\ 1 \\ 3 \\ 4 \end{pmatrix}$$

Here, of course, we use the same rules as for finding the product of any two matrices.

Solution: The dimensions of the product will be

$$(2 \times 4)(4 \times 1) = (2 \times 1)$$

Multiply the column vector by the first row in the matrix:

$$\begin{pmatrix} 3 & 1 & 2 & 0 \\ 1 & 3 & 5 & 2 \end{pmatrix}\begin{pmatrix} 2 \\ 1 \\ 3 \\ 4 \end{pmatrix} = \Big(3(2) + 1(1) + 2(3) + 0(4) \Big) = \begin{pmatrix} 13 \end{pmatrix}$$

and then by the second row:

$$\begin{pmatrix} 3 & 1 & 2 & 0 \\ 1 & 3 & 5 & 2 \end{pmatrix}\begin{pmatrix} 2 \\ 1 \\ 3 \\ 4 \end{pmatrix} = \begin{pmatrix} 13 \\ 1(2) + 3(1) + 5(3) + 2(4) \end{pmatrix} = \begin{pmatrix} 13 \\ 28 \end{pmatrix}$$

Most of the matrix multiplication we do later will be of a matrix and a column vector.

Note that the product of a matrix and a column vector is a column vector.

■ **Example 27:** Five students decided to raise money by selling T-shirts for three weeks. The following table shows the number of shirts sold by each student during each week.

	Week 1	2	3
Student 1	8	2	6
2	3	5	2
3	6	5	4
4	7	3	1
5	2	3	4

They charged $7.50 per shirt the first week, and then lowered the price to $6.00 the second week, and then $5.50 for the third week. Find the total amount raised by each student for the three weeks.

Solution: To get the total amounts, we know that we must multiply the matrix **B** representing the number of T-shirts sold,

$$\mathbf{B} = \begin{pmatrix} 8 & 2 & 6 \\ 3 & 5 & 2 \\ 6 & 5 & 4 \\ 7 & 3 & 1 \\ 2 & 3 & 4 \end{pmatrix}$$

by a vector **C** representing the price per shirt. But should **C** be a row vector of a column vector? And should we find the product **BC** or the product **CB**?

If we let **C** be a 1×3 row vector and try to multiply it by the 5×3 matrix **B**, we see that we cannot, because these matrices are not conformable for either product **BC** or product **CB**.

On the other hand, if we let **C** be a 3×1 column vector,

$$\mathbf{C} = \begin{pmatrix} 7.50 \\ 6.00 \\ 5.50 \end{pmatrix}$$

the product **CB** is not defined, but the product **BC** gives a column vector

$$\mathbf{BC} = \begin{pmatrix} 8 & 2 & 6 \\ 3 & 5 & 2 \\ 6 & 5 & 4 \\ 7 & 3 & 1 \\ 2 & 3 & 4 \end{pmatrix} \begin{pmatrix} 7.50 \\ 6.00 \\ 5.50 \end{pmatrix} = \begin{pmatrix} 105.00 \\ 63.50 \\ 97.00 \\ 76.00 \\ 55.00 \end{pmatrix}$$

which represents the total earned by each student. ▬

Exercise 2 Operations with Matrices

Addition and Subtraction of Matrices

Combine the following vectors and matrices.

1. $(3 \quad 8 \quad 2 \quad 1) + (9 \quad 5 \quad 3 \quad 7)$

2. $\begin{pmatrix} 6 & 3 & 9 \\ 2 & 1 & 3 \end{pmatrix} + \begin{pmatrix} 8 & 2 & 7 \\ 1 & 6 & 3 \end{pmatrix}$

3. $\begin{pmatrix} 5 \\ -3 \\ 5 \\ 8 \end{pmatrix} + \begin{pmatrix} 7 \\ 0 \\ -4 \\ 8 \end{pmatrix} - \begin{pmatrix} -2 \\ 7 \\ -5 \\ 2 \end{pmatrix}$

4. $\begin{pmatrix} 6 & 2 & -7 \\ -3 & 5 & 9 \\ 2 & 5 & 3 \end{pmatrix} - \begin{pmatrix} 5 & 2 & 9 \\ 1 & 4 & 8 \\ 7 & -3 & 4 \end{pmatrix} + \begin{pmatrix} 1 & -6 & 7 \\ 2 & 4 & -9 \\ -6 & 2 & 7 \end{pmatrix}$

5. $\begin{pmatrix} 1 & 5 & -2 & 1 \\ 0 & -2 & 3 & 5 \\ -2 & 9 & 3 & -2 \\ 5 & -1 & 2 & 6 \end{pmatrix} - \begin{pmatrix} -6 & 4 & 2 & 8 \\ 9 & 2 & -6 & 3 \\ -5 & 2 & 6 & 7 \\ 6 & 3 & 7 & 0 \end{pmatrix}$

Product of a Scalar and a Matrix

Multiply each scalar and vector.

6. $6 \begin{pmatrix} 9 \\ -2 \\ 6 \\ -3 \end{pmatrix}$

7. $-3(5 \quad 9 \quad -2 \quad 7 \quad 3)$

Multiply each scalar and matrix.

8. $7 \begin{pmatrix} 7 & -3 & 7 \\ -2 & 9 & 5 \\ 9 & 1 & 0 \end{pmatrix}$

9. $-3 \begin{pmatrix} 4 & 2 & -3 & 0 \\ -1 & 6 & 3 & -4 \end{pmatrix}$

Remove any factors from the vector or matrix.

10. $\begin{pmatrix} 25 \\ -15 \\ 30 \\ -5 \end{pmatrix}$

11. $\begin{pmatrix} 21 & 7 & -14 \\ 49 & 63 & 28 \\ 14 & -21 & 56 \\ -42 & 70 & 84 \end{pmatrix}$

If $\quad \mathbf{A} = \begin{pmatrix} 2 & 5 & -1 \\ -3 & 2 & 6 \\ 9 & -4 & 5 \end{pmatrix} \quad$ and $\quad \mathbf{B} = \begin{pmatrix} 0 & 1 & 6 \\ -7 & 2 & 1 \\ 4 & -2 & 0 \end{pmatrix}$

find:

12. $\mathbf{A} - 4\mathbf{B}$ **13.** $3\mathbf{A} + \mathbf{B}$ **14.** $2\mathbf{A} + 2\mathbf{B}$

15. Show that $2(\mathbf{A} + \mathbf{B}) = 2\mathbf{A} + 2\mathbf{B}$, thus demonstrating the distributive law (Eq. 85).

Scalar Product of Two Vectors

Multiply each pair of vectors.

16. $(6 \quad -2)\begin{pmatrix} -1 \\ 7 \end{pmatrix}$

17. $(5 \quad 3 \quad 7)\begin{pmatrix} 2 \\ 6 \\ 1 \end{pmatrix}$

18. $(-3 \quad 6 \quad -9)\begin{pmatrix} 8 \\ -3 \\ 4 \end{pmatrix}$

19. $(-4 \quad 3 \quad 8 \quad -5)\begin{pmatrix} 7 \\ -6 \\ 0 \\ 3 \end{pmatrix}$

Product of a Row Vector and a Matrix

Multiply each row vector and matrix.

20. $(4 \quad -2)\begin{pmatrix} 3 & 6 \\ -1 & 5 \end{pmatrix}$

21. $(3 \quad -1)\begin{pmatrix} 4 & 7 & -2 & 4 & 0 \\ 2 & -6 & 8 & -3 & 7 \end{pmatrix}$

22. $(2 \quad 8 \quad 1)\begin{pmatrix} 5 & 6 \\ 3 & 1 \\ 1 & 0 \end{pmatrix}$

23. $(-3 \quad 6 \quad -1)\begin{pmatrix} 5 & -2 & 7 \\ -6 & 2 & 5 \\ 9 & 0 & -1 \end{pmatrix}$

24. $(9 \quad 1 \quad 4)\begin{pmatrix} 6 & 2 & 1 & 5 & -8 \\ 7 & 1 & -3 & 0 & 3 \\ 1 & -5 & 0 & 3 & 2 \end{pmatrix}$

25. $(2 \quad 4 \quad 3 \quad -1 \quad 0)\begin{pmatrix} 4 & 3 & 5 & -1 & 0 \\ 1 & 3 & 5 & -2 & 6 \\ 2 & -4 & 3 & 6 & 5 \\ 3 & 4 & -1 & 6 & 5 \\ 2 & 3 & 1 & 4 & -6 \end{pmatrix}$

Product of Two Matrices

Multiply each pair of matrices.

26. $\begin{pmatrix} 7 & 2 \\ 1 & 3 \end{pmatrix}\begin{pmatrix} 4 & 1 & 2 \\ 3 & 2 & 5 \end{pmatrix}$

27. $\begin{pmatrix} 3 & 1 & 4 \\ 1 & -3 & 5 \end{pmatrix}\begin{pmatrix} 4 & 2 \\ -1 & 5 \\ 2 & -6 \end{pmatrix}$

28. $\begin{pmatrix} 4 & 2 & -1 \\ -2 & 1 & 6 \end{pmatrix}\begin{pmatrix} 5 & -1 & 2 & 3 \\ 1 & 3 & 5 & 2 \\ 0 & 1 & -2 & 4 \end{pmatrix}$ **29.** $\begin{pmatrix} 5 & 1 \\ -2 & 0 \\ 1 & 3 \end{pmatrix}\begin{pmatrix} -4 & 1 \\ 0 & 5 \end{pmatrix}$

30. $\begin{pmatrix} 2 & 4 \\ 0 & -1 \\ 2 & 5 \end{pmatrix}\begin{pmatrix} 0 & -2 & 3 & -2 \\ 1 & 3 & -4 & 1 \end{pmatrix}$

31. $\begin{pmatrix} 4 & 1 & -2 & 3 \\ 0 & 2 & 1 & 5 \end{pmatrix}\begin{pmatrix} 3 & -1 \\ 0 & 2 \\ 3 & 1 \\ 0 & -2 \end{pmatrix}$

32. $\begin{pmatrix} -1 & 0 & 3 & 1 \\ 2 & 1 & 0 & -3 \end{pmatrix}\begin{pmatrix} 1 & 2 & 3 & 0 \\ 3 & 0 & -1 & 2 \\ -1 & 4 & 3 & 0 \\ 2 & 0 & -2 & 1 \end{pmatrix}$

33. $\begin{pmatrix} 3 & 1 \\ -2 & 0 \\ 1 & -3 \\ 5 & 0 \end{pmatrix}\begin{pmatrix} -1 & 0 \\ 3 & 2 \end{pmatrix}$

34. $\begin{pmatrix} 1 & 0 & -2 \\ 2 & 4 & 1 \\ 0 & -1 & 3 \end{pmatrix}\begin{pmatrix} 4 & 0 & 1 & -2 \\ 0 & 2 & 1 & 3 \\ 1 & 0 & -3 & 2 \end{pmatrix}$

35. $\begin{pmatrix} 2 & 1 & 0 & -1 \\ 1 & 2 & -1 & 1 \\ 0 & -2 & 4 & 0 \end{pmatrix}\begin{pmatrix} 1 & 2 & 0 & -1 \\ 3 & 1 & -1 & 3 \\ 2 & 1 & 0 & 3 \\ 3 & 5 & 1 & 0 \end{pmatrix}$

Product of Square Matrices

Find the product **AB** and the product **BA** for each pair of square matrices.

36. $\mathbf{A} = \begin{pmatrix} 2 & 3 \\ 5 & 1 \end{pmatrix}$ $\mathbf{B} = \begin{pmatrix} 4 & 6 \\ 7 & 9 \end{pmatrix}$

37. $\mathbf{A} = \begin{pmatrix} 2 & -1 & 0 \\ 1 & 0 & 2 \\ -2 & 1 & 0 \end{pmatrix}$ $\mathbf{B} = \begin{pmatrix} 2 & 1 & 0 \\ 3 & 0 & 1 \\ -2 & 4 & 1 \end{pmatrix}$

Using the matrices in Problem 36, find

38. $\mathbf{A}^2$ **39.** $\mathbf{B}^3$

Product of a Matrix and a Column Vector

Multiply each matrix and column vector.

40. $\begin{pmatrix} 2 & 1 \\ 0 & 3 \end{pmatrix}\begin{pmatrix} 3 \\ 1 \end{pmatrix}$

41. $\begin{pmatrix} 2 & 0 & 1 \\ 1 & 5 & 2 \end{pmatrix}\begin{pmatrix} 3 \\ 0 \\ -1 \end{pmatrix}$

42. $\begin{pmatrix} 2 & 1 & 0 \\ 1 & 0 & -2 \\ 3 & 5 & 0 \\ 0 & -1 & 3 \end{pmatrix}\begin{pmatrix} 3 \\ 0 \\ -1 \end{pmatrix}$

43. $\begin{pmatrix} 0 & 2 & -1 & 4 \\ 1 & 5 & 3 & 0 \\ -2 & 0 & 1 & 5 \end{pmatrix}\begin{pmatrix} 2 \\ 0 \\ -1 \\ 3 \end{pmatrix}$

44. The unit matrix **I** is a square matrix that has 1s on the main diagonal and 0s elsewhere. Show that the product of **I** and another square matrix **A** is simply **A**.

Multiplying by the Unit Matrix	$\mathbf{AI = IA = A}$	94

Graphics Calculator

45. To add, subtract, or multiply two matrices on the TI graphics calculators, first enter the matrices as shown in Exercise 1. Then simply type the two matrices with the proper sign of operation between them. Thus, to add matrices **A** and **B**, type

$$\boxed{A}\ \boxed{+}\ \boxed{B}$$

Pressing $\boxed{\text{ENTER}}$ will display the sum of the two matrices. Similarly,

$$3\ \boxed{\text{2nd}}\ \boxed{A}$$

will multiply matrix **A** by the scalar 3.

   Use a graphics calculator to do any of the matrix operations in this exercise.

Computer

Write a *Basic* program or use a spreadsheet to:

46. Add two matrices.
47. Multiply a matrix by a scalar.
48. Multiply two matrices.

Test your programs on any of the above problems.

49. Matrix operations are easy to do on a computer algebra system. For adding or subtracting matrices, *Derive* and *Mathematica* use the + and − signs, and *Maple* uses **add(A,B);** to combine the matrices **A** and **B**. For multiplying two matrices, *Derive* and *Mathematica* both use the multiplication dot, while *Maple* uses the **&*** operator.

   Use a computer algebra system for any of the matrix operations in this exercise.

50. Some spreadsheets have built-in commands for matrix operations. *Lotus 123*, for example, can do matrix multiplication. Enter the elements of each matrix into the cells of the spreadsheet in rows and columns, just as they appear in the matrix itself. Then select

/Data Matrix Multiply

You will be prompted to identify the first matrix, then the second matrix, and finally the location where you want the product matrix. Try this for any of the multiplications in this exercise.

The Inverse of a Matrix

Inverse of a Square Matrix

12•3

Recall from Section 12•1 that the unit matrix **I** is a square matrix which has 1s along its main diagonal and zeros elsewhere:

$$\mathbf{I} = \begin{pmatrix} 1 & 0 & 0 & 0 \\ 0 & 1 & 0 & 0 \\ 0 & 0 & 1 & 0 \\ 0 & 0 & 0 & 1 \end{pmatrix}$$

Not every matrix has an inverse. The inverse exists only for a *nonsingular* matrix, that is, one whose determinant is not zero. Such a matrix is said to be *invertible*.

We now define the *inverse* of any given matrix **A** as another matrix $\mathbf{A}^{-1}$ such that the product of the matrix and its inverse is equal to the unit matrix.

Product of a Matrix and Its Inverse	$\mathbf{A}\mathbf{A}^{-1} = \mathbf{A}^{-1}\mathbf{A} = \mathbf{I}$	93

The product of a matrix and its inverse is the unit matrix.

In *ordinary* algebra, if b is some nonzero quantity, then

$$b\left(\frac{1}{b}\right) = bb^{-1} = 1$$

In *matrix* algebra, the unit matrix **I** has properties similar to the number 1, and the inverse of a matrix has properties similar to the *reciprocal* in ordinary algebra.

■ **Example 28:** The inverse of the matrix

$$\mathbf{A} = \begin{pmatrix} 1 & 0 \\ 2 & 0.5 \end{pmatrix} \quad \text{is} \quad \mathbf{A}^{-1} = \begin{pmatrix} 1 & 0 \\ -4 & 2 \end{pmatrix}$$

because

$$\mathbf{A}\mathbf{A}^{-1} = \begin{pmatrix} 1 & 0 \\ 2 & 0.5 \end{pmatrix}\begin{pmatrix} 1 & 0 \\ -4 & 2 \end{pmatrix} = \begin{pmatrix} 1(1) + 0(-4) & 1(0) + 0(2) \\ 2(1) + 0.5(-4) & 2(0) + 0.5(2) \end{pmatrix}$$

$$= \begin{pmatrix} 1 & 0 \\ 0 & 1 \end{pmatrix}$$

and

$$\mathbf{A}^{-1}\mathbf{A} = \begin{pmatrix} 1 & 0 \\ -4 & 2 \end{pmatrix}\begin{pmatrix} 1 & 0 \\ 2 & 0.5 \end{pmatrix} = \begin{pmatrix} 1(1) + 0(2) & 1(0) + 0(0.5) \\ -4(1) + 2(2) & -4(0) + 2(0.5) \end{pmatrix}$$

$$= \begin{pmatrix} 1 & 0 \\ 0 & 1 \end{pmatrix}$$

■

Finding the Inverse of a Matrix

When we solved sets of linear equations in Chapter 10, we were able to:

1. Interchange two equations.
2. Multiply an equation by a nonzero constant.
3. Add a constant multiple of one equation to another equation.

Thus, for a matrix that represents such a system of equations, we may perform the following transformations without altering the meaning of a matrix.

Elementary Transformations of a Matrix	1. Interchange any rows. 2. Multiply a row by a nonzero constant. 3. Add a constant multiple of one row to another row.	96

One method to find the inverse of a matrix is to apply the rules of matrix transformation to transform the given matrix into a unit matrix, while at the same time performing the same operations on a unit matrix. The unit matrix, after the transformations, becomes the inverse of the original matrix.

We will not try to prove the method here, but only show its use.

━ **Example 29:** Find the inverse of the matrix of Example 28,

$$\mathbf{A} = \begin{pmatrix} 1 & 0 \\ 2 & 0.5 \end{pmatrix}$$

Solution: To the given matrix **A**, we append a unit matrix,

$$\begin{pmatrix} 1 & 0 & | & 1 & 0 \\ 2 & 0.5 & | & 0 & 1 \end{pmatrix}$$

obtaining a *double-square* matrix. We then double the first row and subtract it from the second:

$$\begin{pmatrix} 1 & 0 & | & 1 & 0 \\ 0 & 0.5 & | & -2 & 1 \end{pmatrix}$$

We now double the second row:

$$\begin{pmatrix} 1 & 0 & | & 1 & 0 \\ 0 & 1 & | & -4 & 2 \end{pmatrix}$$

*Our original matrix **A** is now the unit matrix, and the original unit matrix is now the inverse of **A**.*

$$\mathbf{A}^{-1} = \begin{pmatrix} 1 & 0 \\ -4 & 2 \end{pmatrix}$$

━

━ **Example 30:** Find the inverse of the matrix

$$\mathbf{A} = \begin{pmatrix} a_1 & b_1 \\ a_2 & b_2 \end{pmatrix}$$

Solution: We append the unit matrix

$$\begin{pmatrix} a_1 & b_1 & | & 1 & 0 \\ a_2 & b_2 & | & 0 & 1 \end{pmatrix}$$

Then we multiply the first row by b_2 and the second by b_1, and subtract the second from the first:

$$\begin{pmatrix} a_1b_2 - a_2b_1 & 0 & | & b_2 & -b_2 \\ a_2b_1 & b_1b_2 & | & 0 & b_1 \end{pmatrix}$$

We now divide the first row by $a_1b_2 - a_2b_1$:

$$\begin{pmatrix} 1 & 0 & | & \dfrac{b_2}{a_1b_2 - a_2b_1} & \dfrac{-b_1}{a_1b_2 - a_2b_1} \\ a_2b_1 & b_1b_2 & | & 0 & b_1 \end{pmatrix}$$

Then we multiply the first row by a_2b_1 and subtract it from the second. After combining fractions, we get

$$\begin{pmatrix} 1 & 0 & | & \dfrac{b_2}{a_1b_2 - a_2b_1} & \dfrac{-b_1}{a_1b_2 - a_2b_1} \\ 0 & b_1b_2 & | & \dfrac{-a_2b_1b_2}{a_1b_2 - a_2b_1} & \dfrac{a_1b_1b_2}{a_1b_2 - a_2b_1} \end{pmatrix}$$

We then divide the second row by b_1b_2:

$$\begin{pmatrix} 1 & 0 & | & \dfrac{b_2}{a_1b_2 - a_2b_1} & \dfrac{-b_1}{a_1b_2 - a_2b_1} \\ 0 & 1 & | & \dfrac{-a_2}{a_1b_2 - a_2b_1} & \dfrac{a_1}{a_1b_2 - a_2b_1} \end{pmatrix}$$

The inverse of our matrix is then

$$\mathbf{A}^{-1} = \frac{1}{a_1b_2 - a_2b_1} \begin{pmatrix} b_2 & -b_1 \\ -a_2 & a_1 \end{pmatrix}$$

after factoring out $1/(a_1b_2 - a_2b_1)$.

Comparing this result with the original matrix, we see that:

1. The elements on the main diagonal are interchanged.
2. The elements on the secondary diagonal have reversed sign.
3. The original matrix is divided by its determinant. ▬

Shortcut for Finding the Inverse of a 2 × 2 Matrix

The results of Example 30 provide us with a way to write the inverse of a 2 × 2 matrix quickly. We obtain the inverse of a 2 × 2 matrix by:

1. Interchanging the elements on the main diagonal
2. Reversing the signs of the elements on the secondary diagonal
3. Dividing by the determinant of the original matrix

▬ **Example 31:** Find the inverse of

$$\mathbf{A} = \begin{pmatrix} 5 & -2 \\ 1 & 3 \end{pmatrix}$$

Solution: We interchange the 5 and the 3, and reverse the signs of the −2 and 1:

$$\begin{pmatrix} 3 & 2 \\ -1 & 5 \end{pmatrix}$$

and divide by the determinant of the original matrix:

$$5(3) - (-2)(1) = 17$$

So

$$\mathbf{A}^{-1} = \frac{1}{17}\begin{pmatrix} 3 & 2 \\ -1 & 5 \end{pmatrix}$$

Exercise 3 The Inverse of a Matrix

Find the inverse of each matrix.

1. $\begin{pmatrix} 4 & 8 \\ -5 & 0 \end{pmatrix}$
    2. $\begin{pmatrix} -2 & 4 \\ 3 & 1 \end{pmatrix}$

3. $\begin{pmatrix} 8 & -3 \\ 1 & 6 \end{pmatrix}$
    4. $\begin{pmatrix} 1 & 5 & 3 \\ 2 & 3 & 0 \\ 6 & 8 & 1 \end{pmatrix}$

5. $\begin{pmatrix} -1 & 3 & 7 \\ 4 & -2 & 0 \\ 7 & 2 & -9 \end{pmatrix}$
    6. $\begin{pmatrix} 18 & 23 & 71 \\ 82 & 49 & 28 \\ 36 & 19 & 84 \end{pmatrix}$

7. $\begin{pmatrix} 9 & 1 & 0 & 3 \\ 4 & 3 & 5 & 2 \\ 7 & 1 & 0 & 3 \\ 1 & 4 & 2 & 7 \end{pmatrix}$
    8. $\begin{pmatrix} -2 & 1 & 5 & -6 \\ 7 & -3 & 2 & -6 \\ -3 & 2 & 6 & 1 \\ 5 & 2 & 7 & 5 \end{pmatrix}$

Graphics Calculator

9. To invert a square matrix on the TI graphics calculators, first define the matrix as was shown in Exercise 1. Then type

$$\boxed{\text{A}}\ \boxed{\text{x}^{-1}}\ \boxed{\text{ENTER}}$$

and the inverse of matrix **A** will be displayed. Try this on any of the matrices above.

Computer

10. Write a *Basic* program to find and print the inverse of a matrix. Test your program by finding the inverse of some matrices given above.

11. A computer algebra system can be used to invert a matrix. In *Derive*, enter the matrix as was shown in Exercise 1. Then raise the matrix to the −1 power. In *Maple* and *Mathematica*, use the command **Inverse** to take the inverse of the matrix. Consult your manual for the exact format to use. Use a CAS to invert any of the matrices above.

12. Some spreadsheets have a command to invert a matrix. In *Lotus 123*, for example, you would enter the matrix in rows and columns in the spreadsheet. Then select

/Data Matrix Invert

You will be prompted to highlight the matrix to be inverted and to indicate where the inverted matrix is to be placed. Try this on any of the matrices in this exercise.

12·4 Solving a System of Linear Equations by Matrix Inversion

Representing a System of Equations by Matrices

Suppose that we have the set of equations

$$2x + y + 2z = 10$$
$$x + 2y + 3z = 14$$
$$3x + 4y - 3z = 2$$

The left sides of these equations can be represented by the product of a square matrix **A** made up of the coefficients, called the *coefficient matrix*, and a column vector **X** made up of the unknowns. If

$$\mathbf{A} = \begin{pmatrix} 2 & 1 & 2 \\ 1 & 2 & 3 \\ 3 & 4 & -3 \end{pmatrix} \quad \text{and} \quad \mathbf{X} = \begin{pmatrix} x \\ y \\ z \end{pmatrix}$$

then

$$\mathbf{A} = \begin{pmatrix} 2 & 1 & 2 \\ 1 & 2 & 3 \\ 3 & 4 & -3 \end{pmatrix} \begin{pmatrix} x \\ y \\ z \end{pmatrix} = \begin{pmatrix} 2x + y + 2z \\ x + 2y + 3z \\ 2x + 4y - 3z \end{pmatrix}$$

Note that our product is a column vector having *three* elements. The expression $(2x + y + 2z)$ is a *single element* in that vector.

If we now represent the constants in our set of equations by the column vector

$$\mathbf{B} = \begin{pmatrix} 10 \\ 14 \\ 2 \end{pmatrix}$$

our system of equations can be written, using matrices, as

$$\begin{pmatrix} 2 & 1 & 2 \\ 1 & 2 & 3 \\ 3 & 4 & -3 \end{pmatrix} \begin{pmatrix} x \\ y \\ z \end{pmatrix} = \begin{pmatrix} 10 \\ 14 \\ 2 \end{pmatrix}$$

or in the more compact form

Matrix Form for a System of Equations	$\mathbf{AX} = \mathbf{B}$	95

Solving Systems of Equations by Matrix Inversion

Suppose that we have a system of equations, which we represent in matrix form as

$$\mathbf{AX} = \mathbf{B}$$

where **A** is the coefficient matrix, **X** is the column vector of the unknowns, and **B** is the column of constants. Multiplying both sides by $\mathbf{A}^{-1}$, the inverse of **A**,

$$\mathbf{A}^{-1}\mathbf{AX} = \mathbf{A}^{-1}\mathbf{B}$$

or

$$\mathbf{IX} = \mathbf{A}^{-1}\mathbf{B}$$

since $\mathbf{A}^{-1}\mathbf{A} = \mathbf{I}$. But, by Eq. 94, $\mathbf{IX} = \mathbf{X}$, so

Solving a Set of Equations Using the Inverse	$\mathbf{X} = \mathbf{A}^{-1}\mathbf{B}$	98

There are several other methods for using matrices to solve a system of equations, including *Gauss Elimination* and the *Unit Matrix* method.

The matrix inversion method is one that is built into many calculators and computer programs.

The solutions to a set of equations can be obtained by multiplying the column of constants by the inverse of the coefficient matrix.

This is called the *matrix inversion* method. To use this method, set up the equations in standard form. Write **A**, the matrix of the coefficients. Then find $\mathbf{A}^{-1}$ by matrix inversion or by the shortcut method (for a 2×2 matrix). Finally, multiply $\mathbf{A}^{-1}$ by the column of constants **B** to get the solution.

■ **Example 32:** Solve the system of equations

$$x - 2y = -3$$
$$3x + y = 5$$

by the matrix inversion method.

Solution: The coefficient matrix **A** is

$$\mathbf{A} = \begin{pmatrix} 1 & -2 \\ 3 & 1 \end{pmatrix}$$

We could have used the shortcut method here, since this is a 2×2 matrix. We have, however, used the longer general method to give another example of its use.

We now find the inverse, $\mathbf{A}^{-1}$, of **A**. We append the unit matrix:

$$\begin{pmatrix} 1 & -2 & 1 & 0 \\ 3 & 1 & 0 & 1 \end{pmatrix}$$

and then multiply the first row by -3 and add the result to the second row.

$$\begin{pmatrix} 1 & -2 & 1 & 0 \\ 0 & 7 & -3 & 1 \end{pmatrix}$$

Then we multiply the second row by 2/7 and add the result to the first row:

$$\begin{pmatrix} 1 & 1 & 1/7 & 2/7 \\ 0 & 7 & -3 & 1 \end{pmatrix}$$

Finally, we divide the second row by 7.

$$\begin{pmatrix} 1 & 0 & 1/7 & 2/7 \\ 0 & 1 & -3/7 & 1/7 \end{pmatrix}$$

Thus the inverse of our coefficient matrix **A** is

$$\mathbf{A}^{-1} = \begin{pmatrix} 1/7 & 2/7 \\ -3/7 & 1/7 \end{pmatrix}$$

We then get our solution by multiplying the inverse $\mathbf{A}^{-1}$ by the column of constants, $\mathbf{B}$:

$$\begin{array}{ccc} \mathbf{A}^{-1} & \mathbf{B} & = & \mathbf{X} \end{array}$$

$$\begin{pmatrix} 1/7 & 2/7 \\ -3/7 & 1/7 \end{pmatrix}\begin{pmatrix} -3 \\ 5 \end{pmatrix} = \begin{pmatrix} -3/7 + 10/7 \\ 9/7 + 5/7 \end{pmatrix} = \begin{pmatrix} 1 \\ 2 \end{pmatrix}$$

so $x = 1$ and $y = 2$. ▬

We see that, even for a system of only two equations, manual solution by matrix inversion is a lot of work. Our main reason for covering it is for its wide use in computer solutions of sets of equations.

▬ **Example 33:** Solve the general system of two equations

$$a_1 x + b_1 y = c_1$$

$$a_2 x + b_2 y = c_2$$

by matrix inversion.

Solution: We write the coefficient matrix

$$\mathbf{A} = \begin{pmatrix} a_1 & b_1 \\ a_2 & b_2 \end{pmatrix}$$

The inverse of our coefficient matrix has already been found in Example 30. It is

$$\mathbf{A}^{-1} = \frac{1}{a_1 b_2 - a_2 b_1}\begin{pmatrix} b_2 & -b_1 \\ -a_2 & a_1 \end{pmatrix}$$

By Eq. 98 we now get the column of unknowns by multiplying the inverse by the column of coefficients

$$\mathbf{X} = \mathbf{A}^{-1}\mathbf{B}$$

$$= \frac{1}{a_1 b_2 - a_2 b_1}\begin{pmatrix} b_2 & -b_1 \\ -a_2 & a_1 \end{pmatrix}\begin{pmatrix} c_1 \\ c_2 \end{pmatrix}$$

$$= \begin{pmatrix} \dfrac{b_2 c_1 - b_1 c_2}{a_1 b_2 - a_2 b_1} \\ \dfrac{a_1 c_2 - a_2 c_1}{a_1 b_2 - a_2 b_1} \end{pmatrix}$$

Thus we again get the now familiar equations,

$x = \dfrac{b_2 c_1 - b_1 c_2}{a_1 b_2 - a_2 b_1} \qquad y = \dfrac{a_1 c_2 - a_2 c_1}{a_1 b_2 - a_2 b_1}$	**63**

▬

Exercise 4 Solving a System of Linear Equations by Matrix Inversion

1. Solve any of the sets of equations in Chapters 10 and 11 by matrix inversion.

Graphics Calculator

2. We showed how to invert a square matrix on the graphics calculator in Exercise 3, and how to multiply matrices in Exercise 2. Now, to solve a system of equations, simply enter the coefficient matrix, invert it, and multiply it by the column of constants. If the coefficient matrix is **A** and the column of constants is **B**, we would enter

and the solution would be displayed. Try this on any system of equations.

Computer

3. We showed how to invert a square matrix using a CAS in Exercise 3, and how to multiply matrices in Exercise 2. Now we can solve a system of equations by entering the coefficient matrix, inverting it, and multiplying it by the column of constants. Try this on any system of equations in Chapter 10 or 11.

4. We showed how to invert a square matrix in *Lotus 123* in Exercise 3 using

/Data Matrix Invert

and how to multiply matrices in Exercise 2 using

/Data Matrix Multiply

Now combine the two to solve a system of equations by entering the coefficient matrix, inverting it, and multiplying it by the column of constants. Try this on any system of equations.

CHAPTER 12 REVIEW PROBLEMS

1. Combine.

$$(4 \quad 9 \quad -2 \quad 6) + (2 \quad 4 \quad 9 \quad -1) - (4 \quad 1 \quad -3 \quad 7)$$

2. Multiply.

$$\begin{pmatrix} 8 & 4 \\ 9 & -5 \end{pmatrix} \begin{pmatrix} 3 & 7 \\ -3 & 6 \end{pmatrix}$$

3. Multiply.

$$(7 \quad -2 \quad 5) \begin{pmatrix} 6 \\ -2 \\ 8 \end{pmatrix}$$

4. Find the inverse.

$$\begin{pmatrix} 5 & -2 & 5 & 1 \\ 2 & 8 & -3 & -1 \\ -4 & 2 & 7 & 5 \\ 9 & 2 & 5 & 3 \end{pmatrix}$$

5. Find the inverse.

$$\begin{pmatrix} 4 & -4 \\ 3 & 1 \end{pmatrix}$$

6. Combine.

$$\begin{pmatrix} 5 & 9 \\ -4 & 7 \end{pmatrix} + \begin{pmatrix} -2 & 6 \\ 3 & 8 \end{pmatrix}$$

7. Multiply.

$$\begin{pmatrix} 1 & 2 \\ 0 & 3 \end{pmatrix} \begin{pmatrix} 1 & 2 & 4 \\ 3 & 0 & 1 \end{pmatrix}$$

8. Multiply.

$$\begin{pmatrix} 8 & 2 & 6 & 1 \\ 9 & 0 & 1 & 4 \\ 1 & 6 & 9 & 3 \\ 6 & 9 & 3 & 5 \end{pmatrix} \begin{pmatrix} 5 \\ 3 \\ 2 \\ 8 \end{pmatrix}$$

9. Solve.

$$\begin{aligned} x + \ y + \quad z + \quad w &= -4 \\ x + 2y + \ 3z + \ 4w &= \ 0 \\ x + 3y + \ 6z + 10w &= \ 9 \\ x + 4y + 10z + 20w &= 24 \end{aligned}$$

10. Multiply,

$$7\begin{pmatrix} 5 & -3 \\ -4 & 8 \end{pmatrix}$$

11. Solve.

$$5x + 3y - 2z = 5$$
$$3x - 4y + 3z = 13$$
$$x + 6y - 4z = -8$$

12. Find the inverse.

$$\begin{pmatrix} 5 & 1 & 4 \\ -2 & 6 & 9 \\ 4 & -1 & 0 \end{pmatrix}$$

13. Solve.

$$4x + 3y = 27$$
$$2x - 5y = -19$$

14. Multiply.

$$9(6 \quad 3 \quad -2 \quad 8)$$

15. The four loop currents (mA) in a certain circuit satisfy the equations

$$376I_1 + 374I_2 - 364I_3 - 255I_4 = 284$$
$$898I_1 - 263I_2 + 229I_3 + 274I_4 = -847$$
$$364I_1 + 285I_2 - 857I_3 - 226I_4 = 746$$
$$937I_1 + 645I_2 - 387I_3 + 847I_4 = -254$$

Solve this matrix to obtain the value of the four currents.

Writing

16. Suppose you have submitted a lab report in which you stated that you have used matrix inversion to solve some sets of equations. The report was rejected because you failed to say anything about that method.

Write one paragraph explaining matrix inversion to be inserted into the next draft of your report. Start by telling what matrix inversion is, and then go on to say how it works.

13

Exponents and Radicals

When you have completed this chapter, you should be able to:

- Use the laws of exponents to simplify and combine expressions having integral exponents.
- Simplify radicals by removing perfect powers, by rationalizing the denominator, and by reducing the index.
- Add, subtract, multiply, and divide radicals.
- Solve radical equations.

When we introduced algebra in Chapter 2, we studied expressions with integral exponents and derived some laws of exponents. We expand upon that work in this chapter, using the laws of exponents and our additional skills of factoring and manipulation of fractions to simplify more complex expressions.

We also give meaning to a fractional exponent, which we'll see is another way of writing a radical. We had a brief look at radicals in Chapter 1, where we computed roots by calculator. There, all the problems were numerical, but here we will have letter quantities under the radical sign. We will learn each operation first with numbers, because they are familiar, and then go on to letters. However, if you simply want the decimal value of a radical containing only numbers, you would use your calculator as was shown in Chapter 1.

In this chapter, we shall simplify, add, subtract, multiply, and divide radicals and solve some simple radical equations. We must postpone the harder radical equations until we can solve quadratic equations (Chapter 14).

13•1 Integral Exponents

Continuing the study of exponents started in Section 2•3, we repeat the laws of exponents derived there, and use them to simplify harder expressions than before. You should glance back at that section before starting this section.

Negative Exponents and Zero Exponents

The two laws that apply are given again here.

Negative Exponent	$x^{-a} = \dfrac{1}{x^a}$ $(x \neq 0)$	35

*When taking the reciprocal of a base raised to a power, **change the sign of the exponent.***

and

Zero Exponent	$x^0 = 1$ $(x \neq 0)$	34

Any quantity (except 0) raised to the zero power equals 1.

We use these laws to rewrite expressions so that they contain no negative or zero exponents.

■ **Example 1:**

(a) $xy^{-1} = \dfrac{x}{y}$

(b) $\dfrac{ab^{-2}}{c^{-3}d} = \dfrac{ac^3}{b^2 d}$

(c) $x^2 y^0 z = x^2 z$

(d) $(abc)^0 = 1$

(e) $\left(\dfrac{a}{b}\right)^{-1} = \dfrac{b}{a}$

■

We'll use these laws frequently in the examples to come.

Common Error	$x^{-a} \neq x^{\frac{1}{a}}$

Power Raised to a Power

Another law we derived in Chapter 1 is for raising a power to a power.

Powers	$(x^a)^b = x^{ab}$	31

*When raising a power to a power, keep the same base and **multiply the exponents**.*

■ **Example 2:**

(a) $(a^2)^3 = a^6$

(b) $(z^{-3})^{-2} = z^6$

(c) $(x^5)^{-2} = x^{-10} = \dfrac{1}{x^{10}}$

■

Products

The two laws of exponents that apply to products are given here again.

Products	$x^a \cdot x^b = x^{a+b}$	29

*When multiplying powers of the same base, keep the same base and **add the exponent.***

and

Product Raised to a Power	$(xy)^n = x^n y^n$	32

*When a product is raised to a power, each factor may be **separately** raised to the power.*

■ **Example 3:**
(a) $2axy^3z(3a^2xyz^3) = 6a^3x^2y^4z^4$ (b) $(3bx^3y^2)^3 = 27b^3x^9y^6$

(c) $\left(\dfrac{xy^2}{3}\right)^2 = \dfrac{x^2y^4}{9}$ ■

	Parentheses are important when raising products to a power.
Common Error	$(2x)^0 = 1$ but $2x^0 = 2(1) = 2$ $(4x)^{-1} = \dfrac{1}{4x}$ but $4x^{-1} = \dfrac{4}{x}$

We try to leave our expressions without zero or negative exponents.

■ **Example 4:**

(a) $3p^3q^2r^{-4}(4p^{-5}qr^4) = 12p^{-2}q^3r^0 = \dfrac{12q^3}{p^2}$

(b) $(2m^2n^3x^{-2})^{-3} = 2^{-3}m^{-6}n^{-9}x^6 = \dfrac{x^6}{8m^6n^9}$ ■

Of course, our old rules for multiplying multinomials still apply.

■ **Example 5:**
(a) $3x^{-2}y^3(2ax^3 - x^2y + ax^4y^{-3})$
     $= 6axy^3 - 3x^0y^4 + 3ax^2y^0 = 6axy^3 - 3y^4 + 3ax^2$
(b) $(p^2x - q^2y^{-2})(p^{-2} - q^{-2}y^2)$
     $= p^0x - p^2q^{-2}xy^2 - p^{-2}q^2y^{-2} + q^0y^0$

     $= x - \dfrac{p^2xy^2}{q^2} - \dfrac{q^2}{p^2y^2} + 1$ ■

Letters in the exponents are handled just as if they were numbers.

■ **Example 6:**

$$x^{n+1}y^{1-n}(x^{2n-3}y^{n-1}) = x^{n+1+2n-3}y^{1-n+n-1}$$
$$= x^{3n-2}y^0 = x^{3n-2}$$

■

Quotients

Our two laws of exponents that apply to quotients are repeated here.

Quotients	$\dfrac{x^a}{x^b} = x^{a-b}$ $(x \neq 0)$	30

*When dividing powers of the same base, keep the same base and **subtract the exponents.***

and

Quotient Raised to a Power	$\left(\dfrac{x}{y}\right)^n = \dfrac{x^n}{y^n}$ $(y \neq 0)$	33

*When a quotient is raised to a power, the numerator and denominator may be **separately** raised to the power.*

■ **Example 7:**

(a) $\dfrac{x^5}{x^3} = x^2$

(b) $\dfrac{16p^5q^{-3}}{8p^2q^{-5}} = 2p^3q^2$

(c) $\dfrac{x^{2p-1}y^2}{x^{p+4}y^{1-p}} = x^{2p-1-p-4}y^{2-1+p} = x^{p-5}y^{1+p}$

(d) $\left(\dfrac{x^3y^2}{p^2q}\right)^3 = \dfrac{x^9y^6}{p^6q^3}$

■

As before, we try to leave our expressions without zero or negative exponents.

■ **Example 8:**

(a) $\dfrac{8a^3b^{-5}c^3}{4a^5b^{-1}c^3} = 2a^{-2}b^{-4}c^0 = \dfrac{2}{a^2b^4}$

(b) $\left(\dfrac{a}{b}\right)^{-2} = \dfrac{a^{-2}}{b^{-2}} = \dfrac{b^2}{a^2} = \left(\dfrac{b}{a}\right)^2$

■

Note in Example 8(b) how the negative exponent had the effect of inverting the fraction.

Don't forget our hard-won skills of factoring, of combining fractions over a common denominator, and of simplifying complex fractions. Use them where needed.

■ **Example 9:**

(a) $\dfrac{1}{(5a)^2} + \dfrac{1}{(2a^2b^{-4})^2} = \dfrac{1}{25a^2} + \dfrac{1}{\dfrac{4a^4}{b^8}}$

We simplify the compound fraction and combine the two fractions over a common denominator, getting

$$\frac{1}{25a^2} + \frac{b^8}{4a^4} = \frac{4a^2}{100a^4} + \frac{25b^8}{100a^4}$$

$$= \frac{4a^2 + 25b^8}{100a^4}$$

(b) $(x^{-2} - 3y)^{-2} = \dfrac{1}{(x^{-2} - 3y)^2} = \dfrac{1}{\left(\dfrac{1}{x^2} - 3y\right)^2}$

$$= \dfrac{1}{\left(\dfrac{1 - 3x^2y}{x^2}\right)^2}$$

$$= \dfrac{x^4}{(1 - 3x^2y)^2}$$

(c) $\dfrac{p^{4m} - q^{2n}}{p^{2m} + q^n} = \dfrac{(p^{2m})^2 - (q^n)^2}{p^{2m} + q^n}$

Factoring the difference of two squares in the numerator and cancelling gives us

$$\frac{(p^{2m} + q^n)(p^{2m} - q^n)}{p^{2m} + q^n} = p^{2m} - q^n \qquad \blacksquare$$

Exercise 1 Integral Exponents

Simplify, and write without negative exponents.

1. $3x^{-1}$
2. $4a^{-2}$
3. $2p^0$
4. $(3m)^{-1}$
5. $a(2b)^{-2}$
6. x^2y^{-1}
7. a^3b^{-2}
8. m^2n^{-3}
9. p^3q^{-1}
10. $(2x^2y^3z^4)^{-1}$
11. $(3m^3n^2p)^0$
12. $(5p^2q^2r^2)^3$
13. $(4a^3b^2c^6)^{-2}$
14. $(a^p - b^q)^2$
15. $(x + y)^{-1}$
16. $(2a + 3b)^{-1}$
17. $(m^{-2} - 6n)^{-2}$
18. $(4p^2 + 5q^{-4})^{-2}$
19. $2x^{-1} + y^{-2}$
20. $p^{-1} - 3q^{-2}$
21. $(3m)^{-3} - 2n^{-2}$
22. $(5a)^{-2} + (2a^2b^{-4})^{-2}$
23. $(x^n + y^m)^2$
24. $(x^{a-1} + y^{a-2})(x^a + y^{a-1})$
25. $(16x^6y^0 \div 8x^4y) \div 4xy^6$
26. $(a^{n-1} + b^{n-2})(a^n + b^{n-1})$
27. $(72p^6q^7 \div 9p^4q) \div 8pq^6$

28. $\dfrac{(p^2 - pq)^8}{(p - q)^4}$
29. $\left(\dfrac{x^{m+n}}{x^n}\right)^m$

30. $\dfrac{27x^{3n} + 8y^{3n}}{3x^n + 2y^n}$
31. $\left(\dfrac{3}{b}\right)^{-1}$

32. $\left(\dfrac{x}{4}\right)^{-1}$
33. $\left(\dfrac{2x}{3y}\right)^{-2}$

34. $\left(\dfrac{3p}{4y}\right)^{-1}$

35. $\left(\dfrac{2px}{3qy}\right)^{-3}$

36. $\left(\dfrac{p^2}{q^0}\right)^{-1}$

37. $\left(\dfrac{3a^4b^3}{5x^2y}\right)^2$

38. $\left(\dfrac{x^2}{y}\right)^{-3}$

39. $\left(\dfrac{-2a^3x^3}{3b^2y}\right)^{2n}$

40. $\left(\dfrac{3p^2y^3}{4qx^4}\right)^{-2}$

41. $\left(\dfrac{2p^{-2}z^3}{3q^{-2}x^{-4}}\right)^{-1}$

42. $\left(\dfrac{9m^4n^3}{3p^3q}\right)^3$

43. $\left(\dfrac{5w^2}{2z}\right)^p$

44. $\left(\dfrac{5a^5b^3}{2x^2y}\right)^{3n}$

45. $\left(\dfrac{3n^{-2}y^3}{5m^{-3}x^4}\right)^{-2}$

46. $\left(\dfrac{z^0z^{2n-2}}{z^n}\right)^3$

47. $\left(\dfrac{1+a}{1+b}\right)^3 \div \dfrac{1+a^3}{b^2-1}$

48. $\left(\dfrac{p^2-q^2}{p+q}\right)^2 \cdot \dfrac{(p^3+q^3)^2}{(p+q)^2}$

49. $\dfrac{(x^2-xy)^7}{(x-y)^5}$

50. $\dfrac{(a^n)^{2n}-(b^{2n})^n}{(a^n)^n+(b^n)^n}$

51. $\dfrac{27a^{3n}-8b^{3n}}{3a^n-2b^n}$

52. $\left(\dfrac{a^2a^{2n-2}}{a^n}\right)^2$

53. $\left(\dfrac{x+1}{y+1}\right)^3 \div \dfrac{x^3+1}{y^2-1}$

54. $\left(\dfrac{a^2-b^2}{x+y}\right)^2 \cdot \dfrac{(x^3+y^3)^2}{(a+b)^2}$

55. $\left(\dfrac{7x^3}{15y^3a^{m-1}} \div \dfrac{x^{n+1}}{a^{m+n}}\right)\dfrac{y^n}{a^{m-1}}$

56. $\dfrac{a^7b^8c^9+a^6b^7c^8-3a^5b^6c^7}{a^5b^6c^7}$

57. $\dfrac{128a^4b^3-48a^5b^2-40a^6b+15a^7}{3a^2-8ab}$

58. $\left(\dfrac{x^{m+n}}{x^n}\right)^m \div \left(\dfrac{x^n}{x^{m+n}}\right)^{n+m}$

59. $\left(\dfrac{5a^3}{25b^3a^{m-1}} \div \dfrac{a^{n+1}}{a^{m+n}}\right)\dfrac{b^n}{a^{m-1}}$

60. $\dfrac{p^4q^8r^9-p^6q^4r^8+3p^5q^6r^4}{p^3q^2r^4}$

61. $\dfrac{3x^4y^3+4x^5y^2+3x^6y+4x^7}{4x^2+3xy}$

62. $\left(\dfrac{p^n}{p^{m+n}}\right)^{n-m} \div \left(\dfrac{p^{m+n}}{p^n}\right)^m$

63. $\dfrac{a^{-1}+b^{-1}}{a^{-1}-b^{-1}} \cdot \dfrac{a^{-2}-b^{-2}}{a^{-2}+b^{-2}} \cdot \dfrac{1}{\left(1+\dfrac{b}{a}\right)^{-2}+\left(1+\dfrac{a}{b}\right)^{-2}}$

13•2

Unless otherwise stated, we'll assume that, when the index is even, the radicand is *positive*. We'll consider square roots and fourth roots of negative numbers when we take up imaginary numbers in Chapter 21.

Simplification of Radicals

Relation between Fractional Exponents and Radicals

A quantity raised to a *fractional exponent* can also be written as a *radical*. A radical consists of a *radical sign*, a quantity under the radical sign called the *radicand*, and the *index* of the radical. A radical is written:

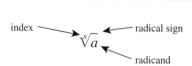

where n is an integer. An index of 2, for a square root, is usually not written.

■ **Example 10:**

$$x^{1/2} = \sqrt{x} \qquad y^{1/4} = \sqrt[4]{y} \qquad w^{-1/2} = \frac{1}{\sqrt{w}}$$

In general,

Relation between Exponents and Radicals	$a^{1/n} = \sqrt[n]{a}$	**36**

If a quantity is raised to a fractional exponent m/n (where m and n are integers), we have

$$a^{m/n} = (a^m)^{1/n} = \sqrt[n]{a^m}$$

Further,

$$a^{m/n} = (a^{1/n})^m = \left(\sqrt[n]{a}\right)^m$$

So,

	$a^{m/n} = \sqrt[n]{a^m} = \left(\sqrt[n]{a}\right)^m$	**37**

We use these definitions to switch between *exponential form* and *radical form*.

■ **Example 11:** Express $x^{1/2}y^{-1/3}$ in radical form.

Solution:

$$x^{1/2}y^{-1/3} = \frac{x^{1/2}}{y^{1/3}} = \frac{\sqrt{x}}{\sqrt[3]{y}}$$

■ **Example 12:** Express $\sqrt[3]{y^2}$ in exponential form.

Solution:

$$\sqrt[3]{y^2} = (y^2)^{1/3} = y^{2/3}$$

■ **Example 13:** Find the value of $\sqrt[4]{(81)^3}$ without using a calculator.

Solution: Instead of cubing 81 and then taking the fourth root, let us take the fourth root first.

$$\sqrt[4]{(81)^3} = \left(\sqrt[4]{81}\right)^3 = (3)^3 = 27 \qquad ■$$

Common Error	Don't confuse the **coefficient** of a radical with the **index** of a radical: $$3\sqrt{x} \neq \sqrt[3]{x}$$

Root of a Product

We have several *rules of radicals*, which are similar to the laws of exponents, and, in fact, are derived from them. The first rule is for products. By our definition of a radical,

$$\sqrt[n]{ab} = (ab)^{1/n}$$

Using the law of exponents for a product and then returning to radical form,

$$(ab)^{1/n} = a^{1/n}b^{1/n} = \sqrt[n]{a}\sqrt[n]{b}$$

So our first rule of radicals is

Root of a Product	$\sqrt[n]{ab} = \sqrt[n]{a}\sqrt[n]{b}$	**38**

The root of a product equals the product of the roots of the factors.

■ **Example 14:** We may split the radical $\sqrt{9x}$ into two radicals,

$$\sqrt{9x} = \sqrt{9}\sqrt{x} = 3\sqrt{x}$$

since $\sqrt{9} = 3$. ■

■ **Example 15:** Write $\sqrt{7}\sqrt{2}\sqrt{x}$ as a single radical.

Solution: By Eq. 38,

$$\sqrt{7}\sqrt{2}\sqrt{x} = \sqrt{7(2)x} = \sqrt{14x} \qquad ■$$

Common Error	There is no similar rule for the root of a sum: $$\sqrt[n]{a+b} \neq \sqrt[n]{a} + \sqrt[n]{b}$$

■ **Example 16:** $\sqrt{9} + \sqrt{16}$ does *not* equal $\sqrt{25}$. ■

Common Error	Equation 38 does not hold when a and b are both *negative* and the index is even.

■ **Example 17:**

$$\left(\sqrt{-4}\right)^2 = \sqrt{-4}\sqrt{-4} \ne \sqrt{(-4)(-4)}$$
$$\ne \sqrt{16} = +4$$

Instead, we convert to *imaginary numbers*, as we will show in Section 21•1.

■

Root of a Quotient

Just as the root of a product can be split up into the roots of the factors, the root of a quotient can be expressed as the root of the numerator divided by the root of the denominator. We first write the quotient in exponential form:

$$\sqrt[n]{\frac{a}{b}} = \left(\frac{a}{b}\right)^{1/n} = \frac{a^{1/n}}{b^{1/n}}$$

by the law of exponents for quotients. Returning to radical form, we have

Root of a Quotient	$\sqrt[n]{\dfrac{a}{b}} = \dfrac{\sqrt[n]{a}}{\sqrt[n]{b}}$	39

The root of a quotient equals the quotient of the roots of numerator and denominator.

■ **Example 18:** The radical $\sqrt{\dfrac{w}{25}}$ can be written $\sqrt{\dfrac{w}{25}}$ or $\dfrac{\sqrt{w}}{5}$. ■

Simplest Form for a Radical

Rather than "simplifying," we are actually putting radicals into a *standard form*, so that they may be combined or compared.

A radical is said to be in *simplest form* when:

1. The radicand has been reduced as much as is possible.
2. There are no radicals in the denominator and no fractional radicands.
3. The index has been made as small as is possible.

Removing Factors from the Radicand

Remember that we are doing numerical problems as a way of learning the rules. If you simply want the decimal value of a radical expression containing only numbers, use your calculator.

Using the fact that

$$\sqrt{x^2} = x, \qquad \sqrt[3]{x^3} = x, \dots, \qquad \text{and } \sqrt[n]{x^n} = x$$

try to factor the radicand so that one or more of the factors is a perfect *n*th power (where *n* is the index of the radical). Then use Eq. 38 to split the radical into two or more radicals, some of which can then be reduced.

■ **Example 19:**

$$\sqrt{50} = \sqrt{(25)(2)} = \sqrt{25}\sqrt{2} = 5\sqrt{2}$$

■

■ **Example 20:**

$$\sqrt{x^3} = \sqrt{x^2 x} = \sqrt{x^2}\sqrt{x} = x\sqrt{x}$$

■

■ **Example 21:** Simplify $\sqrt{50x^3}$.

Solution: We factor the radicand so that some factors are perfect squares

$$\sqrt{50x^3} = \sqrt{(25)(2)x^2x}$$

Then, by Eq. 38:

$$= \sqrt{25}\sqrt{x^2}\sqrt{2x} = 5x\sqrt{2x}$$ ■

■ **Example 22:** Simplify $\sqrt{24y^5}$.

Solution: We look for factors of the radicand that are perfect squares.

$$\sqrt{24y^5} = \sqrt{4(6)y^4y} = 2y^2\sqrt{6y}$$ ■

■ **Example 23:**

$$\sqrt[4]{24y^5} = \sqrt[4]{24y^4y} = y\sqrt[4]{24y}$$ ■

■ **Example 24:** Simplify $\sqrt[3]{24y^5}$.

Solution: We look for factors of the radicand that are perfect cubes.

$$\sqrt[3]{24y^5} = \sqrt[3]{8(3)y^3y^2}$$
$$= \sqrt[3]{8y^3}\sqrt[3]{3y^2} = 2y\sqrt[3]{3y^2}$$ ■

When the radicand contains more than one term, try to *factor out* a perfect n^{th} power (where n is the index).

■ **Example 25:** Simplify $\sqrt{4x^2y + 12x^4z}$.

Solution: We factor $4x^2$ from the radicand, and then remove it from under the radical sign.

$$\sqrt{4x^2y + 12x^4z} = \sqrt{4x^2(y + 3x^2z)}$$
$$= 2x\sqrt{y + 3x^2z}$$ ■

Rationalizing the Denominator

An expression is considered to be in simpler form when its denominators contain no radicals. To put it into this form is called *rationalizing* the denominator. We will show how to rationalize the denominator when it is a square root, a cube root, or a root with any index, and where it has more than one term.

If the denominator is a square root, multiply the numerator and denominator of the fraction by a quantity that will make the radicand in the denominator a perfect square. Note that we are eliminating radicals from the *denominator*, and that the numerator may still contain radicals. Further, even though we call this process *simplifying*, the resulting radical may look more complicated than the original.

■ **Example 26:**

$$\frac{5}{\sqrt{2}} = \frac{5}{\sqrt{2}} \cdot \frac{\sqrt{2}}{\sqrt{2}} = \frac{5\sqrt{2}}{\sqrt{4}} = \frac{5\sqrt{2}}{2}$$ ■

When the *entire* fraction is under the radical sign, we make the denominator of that fraction a perfect square and remove it from the radical sign.

■ **Example 27:**

$$\sqrt{\frac{3x}{2y}} = \sqrt{\frac{3x(2y)}{2y(2y)}} = \sqrt{\frac{6xy}{4y^2}} = \frac{\sqrt{6xy}}{2y}$$

If the denominator is a *cube* root, we must multiply numerator and denominator by a quantity that will make the quantity under the radical sign a perfect cube.

■ **Example 28:** Simplify

$$\frac{7}{\sqrt[3]{4}}$$

Solution: To rationalize the denominator $\sqrt[3]{4}$, we multiply numerator and denominator of the fraction by $\sqrt[3]{2}$. We chose this as the factor because it results in a perfect cube (8) under the radical sign.

$$\frac{7}{\sqrt[3]{4}} = \frac{7}{\sqrt[3]{4}} \cdot \frac{\sqrt[3]{2}}{\sqrt[3]{2}} = \frac{7\sqrt[3]{2}}{\sqrt[3]{8}} = \frac{7\sqrt[3]{2}}{2}$$

The same principle applies regardless of the index. In general, if the index is n, we must make the quantity under the radical sign (in the denominator) a perfect n^{th} power

■ **Example 29:**

$$\frac{2y}{3\sqrt[5]{x}} = \frac{2y}{3\sqrt[5]{x}} \cdot \frac{\sqrt[5]{x^4}}{\sqrt[5]{x^4}} = \frac{2y\sqrt[5]{x^4}}{3\sqrt[5]{x^5}} = \frac{2y\sqrt[5]{x^4}}{3x}$$

Sometimes the denominator will have more than one term.

■ **Example 30:**

$$\sqrt{\frac{a}{a^2 + b^2}} = \sqrt{\frac{a}{a^2 + b^2} \cdot \frac{a^2 + b^2}{a^2 + b^2}} = \frac{\sqrt{a(a^2 + b^2)}}{a^2 + b^2}$$

Reducing the Index

We can sometimes reduce the index by writing the radical in exponential form and then reducing the fractional exponent, as in the next example.

■ **Example 31:**

(a) $\sqrt[6]{x^3} = x^{3/6} = x^{1/2} = \sqrt{x}$

(b) $\sqrt[4]{4x^2y^2} = \sqrt[4]{(2xy)^2}$

$$= (2xy)^{2/4} = (2xy)^{1/2}$$

$$= \sqrt{2xy}$$

Exercise 2 Simplification of Radicals

Exponential and Radical Form

Express in radical form.

1. $a^{1/4}$ **2.** $x^{1/2}$ **3.** $z^{3/4}$

4. $a^{1/2}b^{1/4}$ **5.** $(m - n)^{1/2}$ **6.** $(x^2y)^{-1/2}$

7. $\left(\dfrac{x}{y}\right)^{-1/3}$ **8.** $a^0b^{-3/4}$

Express in exponential form.

9. $\sqrt{b}$ **10.** $\sqrt[3]{x}$ **11.** $\sqrt{y^2}$

12. $4\sqrt[3]{xy}$ **13.** $\sqrt[n]{a+b}$ **14.** $\sqrt[n]{x^m}$

15. $\sqrt{x^2y^2}$ **16.** $\sqrt[n]{a^n b^{3n}}$

Simplifying Radicals

Write in simplest form.

> Do not use your calculator for any of these numerical problems. Leave the answers in radical form.

17. $\sqrt{18}$ **18.** $\sqrt{75}$ **19.** $\sqrt{63}$

20. $\sqrt[3]{16}$ **21.** $\sqrt[3]{-56}$ **22.** $\sqrt[4]{48}$

23. $\sqrt{a^3}$ **24.** $3\sqrt{50x^5}$ **25.** $\sqrt{36x^2y}$

26. $\sqrt[3]{x^2y^5}$ **27.** $x\sqrt[3]{16x^3y}$ **28.** $\sqrt[4]{64m^2n^4}$

29. $3\sqrt[5]{32xy^{11}}$ **30.** $6\sqrt[3]{16x^4}$

31. $\sqrt{a^3 - a^2b}$ **32.** $x\sqrt{x^4 - x^3y^2}$

33. $\sqrt{9m^3 + 18n}$ **34.** $\sqrt{2x^3 + x^4y}$

35. $\sqrt[3]{x^4 - a^2x^3}$ **36.** $x\sqrt{a^3 + 2a^2b + ab^2}$

37. $(a + b)\sqrt{a^3 - 2a^2b + ab^2}$ **38.** $\sqrt{\dfrac{2}{5}}$

39. $\sqrt{\dfrac{3}{7}}$ **40.** $\sqrt{\dfrac{2}{3}}$

41. $\sqrt[3]{\dfrac{1}{4}}$ **42.** $\sqrt{\dfrac{5}{8}}$

43. $\sqrt[3]{\dfrac{2}{9}}$ **44.** $\sqrt[4]{\dfrac{7}{8}}$

45. $\sqrt{\dfrac{1}{2x}}$ **46.** $\sqrt{\dfrac{5m}{7n}}$

47. $\sqrt{\dfrac{3a^3}{5b}}$ **48.** $\sqrt{\dfrac{5ab}{6xy}}$

49. $\sqrt[3]{\dfrac{1}{x^2}}$ **50.** $\sqrt[3]{\dfrac{81x^4}{16yz^2}}$

51. $\sqrt[6]{\dfrac{4x^6}{9}}$ **52.** $\sqrt{x^2 - \left(\dfrac{x}{2}\right)^2}$

> In these more complicated types, you should start by simplifying the expression under the radical sign.

53. $(x^2 - y^2)\sqrt{\dfrac{x}{x+y}}$ **54.** $\sqrt{a^3 + \left(\dfrac{a^3}{2}\right)^3}$

55. $(m + n)\sqrt{\dfrac{m}{m-n}}$ **56.** $\sqrt{\left(\dfrac{x+1}{2}\right)^2 - x}$

57. $\sqrt{\dfrac{8a^2 - 48a + 72}{3a}}$

58. A stone is thrown upward with a horizontal velocity of 12 m/s and an upward velocity of 21 m/s. At t seconds it will have a horizontal displacement H equal to $12t$ and a vertical displacement V equal to $21t - 4.9t^2$. The straight-line distance S from the stone to the launch point is found by the Pythagorean theorem. Write an equation for S in terms of t, and simplify.

Computer

59. You can, of course, use a computer algebra system to simplify radicals. Just type in the radical expression and use the command SIMPLIFY. Try it with any of the expressions in this exercise.

13•3

One reason we learned to put radicals into a standard form is to combine them.

Operations with Radicals

Adding and Subtracting Radicals

Radicals are called *similar* if they have the same index and the same radicand, such as $5\sqrt[3]{2x}$ and $3\sqrt[3]{2x}$. We add and subtract radicals by *combining similar radicals*.

■ **Example 32:**

$$5\sqrt{y} + 2\sqrt{y} - 4\sqrt{y} = 3\sqrt{y}$$

■

Radicals that may look similar at first glance may not actually be similar.

■ **Example 33:** The radicals

$$\sqrt{2x} \qquad \text{and} \qquad \sqrt{3x}$$

are *not* similar.

■

Common Error	Do not try to combine radicals that are not similar. $$\sqrt{2x} + \sqrt{3x} \neq \sqrt{5x}$$

Radicals that do not appear to be similar at first may turn out to be so after simplification.

■ **Example 34:**
(a) $\sqrt{18x} - \sqrt{8x} = 3\sqrt{2x} - 2\sqrt{2x} = \sqrt{2x}$
(b) $\sqrt[3]{24y^4} + \sqrt[3]{81x^3y} = 2y\sqrt[3]{3y} + 3x\sqrt[3]{3y}$
  Factoring, $= (2y + 3x)\sqrt[3]{3y}$
(c) $5y\sqrt{\dfrac{x}{y}} - \sqrt{xy} + \sqrt{\dfrac{y}{x}}$

  $= 5y\sqrt{\dfrac{xy}{y^2}} - 2\sqrt{xy} + x\sqrt{\dfrac{xy}{x^2}}$

  $= 5\sqrt{xy} - 2\sqrt{xy} + \sqrt{xy} = 4\sqrt{xy}$

■

Multiplying Radicals

Radicals having the *same index* can be multiplied as in Eq. 38:

$$\sqrt[n]{a}\sqrt[n]{b} = \sqrt[n]{ab}$$

■ **Example 35:**
(a) $\sqrt{x}\sqrt{2y} = \sqrt{2xy}$
(b) $\left(5\sqrt[3]{3a}\right)\left(2\sqrt[3]{4b}\right) = 10\sqrt[3]{12ab}$
(c) $\left(2\sqrt{m}\right)\left(5\sqrt{n}\right)\left(3\sqrt{mn}\right) = 30\sqrt{m^2n^2} = 30\ mn$

(d) $\sqrt{2x}\sqrt{3x} = \sqrt{6x^2} = x\sqrt{6}$
(e) $\sqrt{3x}\sqrt{3x} = \sqrt{3x}$
(f) $\sqrt[3]{2x}\sqrt[3]{4x^2} = \sqrt[3]{8x^3} = 2x$ ▬

    Radicals having *different indices* are multiplied by first going to exponential form, then multiplying using Eq. 29 ($x^a x^b = x^{a+b}$), and finally returning to radical form.

▬ **Example 36:**

$$\sqrt{a}\sqrt[4]{b} = a^{1/2}b^{1/4}$$
$$= a^{2/4}b^{1/4} = (a^2 b)^{1/4}$$

or, in radical form,

$$= \sqrt[4]{a^2 b}$$ ▬

When the radicands are the same, the work is even easier.

▬ **Example 37:** Multiply $\sqrt[3]{x}$ by $\sqrt[6]{x}$

    Solution:

$$\sqrt[3]{x}\sqrt[6]{x} = x^{1/3}x^{1/6} = x^{2/6}x^{1/6}$$

By Eq. 29,
$$= x^{3/6} = x^{1/2}$$
$$= \sqrt{x}$$ ▬

Multinomials containing radicals are multiplied in the way we learned in Section 2•4.

▬ **Example 38:**
(a) $(3 + \sqrt{x})(2\sqrt{x} - 4\sqrt{y}) = 3(2\sqrt{x}) - 3(4\sqrt{y}) + 2\sqrt{x}\sqrt{x} - 4\sqrt{x}\sqrt{y}$
$$= 6\sqrt{x} - 12\sqrt{y} + 2x - 4\sqrt{xy}$$
(b) $\sqrt{50x}(\sqrt{2x} - \sqrt{xy}) = \sqrt{100x^2} - \sqrt{50x^2 y}$
$$= 10x - 5x\sqrt{2y}$$
(c) $(\sqrt{x} - \sqrt{y})(\sqrt{x} + \sqrt{y}) = \sqrt{x^2} + \sqrt{xy} - \sqrt{xy} - \sqrt{y^2}$
$$= \sqrt{x^2} - \sqrt{y^2}$$
$$= x - y$$ ▬

To raise a radical to a *power*, we simply multiply the radical by itself the proper number of times.

▬ **Example 39:** Cube the expression

$$2x\sqrt{y}$$

    Solution:

$$(2x\sqrt{y})^3 = (2x\sqrt{y})(2x\sqrt{y})(2x\sqrt{y})$$
$$= 2^3 x^3 (\sqrt{y})^3$$
$$= 8x^3\sqrt{y^3} = 8x^3 y\sqrt{y}$$ ▬

Dividing Radicals

Radicals having the same indices can be divided using Eq. 39,

$$\frac{\sqrt[n]{a}}{\sqrt[n]{b}} = \sqrt[n]{\frac{a}{b}}$$

━ **Example 40:**

(a) $\dfrac{\sqrt{4x^5}}{\sqrt{2x}} = \sqrt{\dfrac{4x^5}{2x}} = \sqrt{2x^4} = x^2\sqrt{2}$

(b) $\dfrac{\sqrt{3a^7} + \sqrt{12a^5} - \sqrt{6a^3}}{\sqrt{3a}} = \sqrt{\dfrac{3a^7}{3a}} + \sqrt{\dfrac{12a^5}{3a}} - \sqrt{\dfrac{6a^3}{3a}}$

$$= \sqrt{a^6} + \sqrt{4a^4} - \sqrt{2a^2}$$

$$= a^3 + 2a^2 - \sqrt{2a}$$

━

It is a common practice to rationalize the denominator after division.

━ **Example 41:**

$$\dfrac{\sqrt{10x}}{\sqrt{5y}} = \sqrt{\dfrac{10x}{5y}} = \sqrt{\dfrac{2x}{y}}$$

Rationalizing the denominator,

$$\sqrt{\dfrac{2x}{y}} = \sqrt{\dfrac{2x}{y} \cdot \dfrac{y}{y}} = \dfrac{\sqrt{2xy}}{y}$$

━

If the indices are different, we go to exponential form, as we did for multiplication. Divide using Eq. 30 and then return to radical form.

━ **Example 42:**

$$\dfrac{\sqrt[3]{a}}{\sqrt[4]{b}} = \dfrac{a^{1/3}}{b^{1/4}} = \dfrac{a^{4/12}}{b^{3/12}} = \left(\dfrac{a^4}{b^3}\right)^{1/12}$$

Returning to radical form, we obtain

$$\left(\dfrac{a^4}{b^3}\right)^{1/12} = \sqrt[12]{\dfrac{a^4}{b^3}}$$

$$= \sqrt[12]{\dfrac{a^4}{b^3} \cdot \dfrac{b^9}{b^9}}$$

$$= \sqrt[12]{\dfrac{a^4 b^9}{b^{12}}}$$

$$= \dfrac{1}{b}\sqrt[12]{a^4 b^9}$$

━

Thus, the conjugate of the binomial $a + b$ is $a - b$. The conjugate of $x - y$ is $x + y$.

When dividing by a binomial containing *square* roots, multiply the divisor and the dividend by the *conjugate* of that binomial (a binomial that differs from the original dividend only in the sign of one term).

Remember that when we multiply a binomial, say, $(a + b)$, by its conjugate $(a - b)$,

$$(a + b)(a - b) = a^2 - ab + ab - b^2$$

$$= a^2 - b^2$$

we get an expression where the cross-product terms ab and $-ab$ drop out, and the remaining terms are both squares. Thus, if a and b were square roots, our final expression would have no square roots.

We use the operation to remove square roots from the denominator, as shown in the following example.

■ **Example 43:** Divide $(3 + \sqrt{x})$ by $(2 - \sqrt{x})$.

Solution: The conjugate of the divisor $2 - \sqrt{x}$ is $2 + \sqrt{x}$. Multiplying divisor and dividend by $2 + \sqrt{x}$, we get

$$\frac{3 + \sqrt{x}}{2 - \sqrt{x}} = \frac{3 + \sqrt{x}}{2 - \sqrt{x}} \cdot \frac{2 + \sqrt{x}}{2 + \sqrt{x}}$$

$$= \frac{6 + 3\sqrt{x} + 2\sqrt{x} + \sqrt{x}\sqrt{x}}{4 + 2\sqrt{x} - 2\sqrt{x} - \sqrt{x}\sqrt{x}}$$

$$= \frac{6 + 5\sqrt{x} + x}{4 - x}$$

As in Exercise 2, do not use your calculator for any of these numerical problems. Leave the answers in radical form.

Exercise 3 Operations with Radicals

Additions and Subtraction of Radicals

Combine as indicated.

1. $2\sqrt{24} - \sqrt{54}$

2. $\sqrt{300} + \sqrt{108} - \sqrt{243}$

3. $\sqrt{24} - \sqrt{96} + \sqrt{54}$

4. $\sqrt{128} - \sqrt{18} + \sqrt{32}$

5. $2\sqrt{50} + \sqrt{72} + 3\sqrt{18}$

6. $\sqrt[3]{384} - \sqrt[3]{162} + \sqrt[3]{750}$

7. $2\sqrt[3]{2} - 3\sqrt[3]{16} + \sqrt[3]{-54}$

8. $3\sqrt[3]{108} + 2\sqrt[3]{32} - \sqrt[3]{256}$

9. $\sqrt[3]{625} - 2\sqrt[3]{135} - \sqrt[3]{320}$

10. $5\sqrt[3]{320} + 2\sqrt[3]{40} - 4\sqrt[3]{135}$

11. $\sqrt[4]{768} - \sqrt[4]{48} - \sqrt[4]{243}$

12. $3\sqrt{\dfrac{5}{3}} + 2\sqrt{45}$

13. $\sqrt{128x^2y} - \sqrt{98x^2y} + \sqrt{162x^2y}$

14. $3\sqrt{\dfrac{1}{3}} - 2\sqrt{\dfrac{3}{4}} + 4\sqrt{3}$

15. $7\sqrt{\dfrac{27}{50}} - 3\sqrt{\dfrac{2}{3}}$

16. $4\sqrt{50} - 2\sqrt{72} + \dfrac{3}{\sqrt{2}}$

17. $\sqrt{a^2x} + \sqrt{b^2x}$

18. $\sqrt{2b^2xy} - \sqrt{2a^2xy}$

19. $\sqrt{x^2y} - \sqrt{4a^2y}$

20. $\sqrt{80a^3} - 3\sqrt{20a^3} - 2\sqrt{45a^3}$

21. $4\sqrt{3a^2x} - 2a\sqrt{48x}$

22. $\sqrt[3]{125x^2} - 2\sqrt[3]{8x^2}$

23. $\sqrt[5]{1250a^3b} + \sqrt[3]{270c^3b}$

24. $2\sqrt[3]{ab^7} + 3\sqrt[3]{a^7b} + 2\sqrt[3]{8a^4b^4}$

25. $\sqrt[5]{a^{13}b^{11}c^{12}} - 2\sqrt[5]{a^8bc^2} + \sqrt[5]{a^3b^6c^7}$

26. $\sqrt{\dfrac{9x}{16}} - \dfrac{3\sqrt{x}}{4}$

27. $\sqrt[6]{8x^3} - 2\sqrt[4]{\dfrac{x^2}{4}} + 3\sqrt{8x}$

28. $\sqrt{\dfrac{x}{a^2}} + 2\sqrt{\dfrac{x}{b^2}} - 3\sqrt{\dfrac{x}{c^2}}$

29. $3\sqrt{\dfrac{3x}{4y^2}} + 2\sqrt{\dfrac{x}{27y^2}} - \sqrt{\dfrac{x}{3y^2}}$

30. $\sqrt{(a + b)^2x} + \sqrt{(a - b)^2x}$

Multiplication of Radicals

Multiply.

31. $3\sqrt{3}$ by $5\sqrt{3}$

32. $2\sqrt{3}$ by $3\sqrt{8}$

33. $\sqrt{8}$ by $\sqrt{160}$

34. $\sqrt{\dfrac{5}{8}}$ by $\sqrt{\dfrac{3}{4}}$

35. $4\sqrt[3]{45}$ by $2\sqrt[3]{3}$

36. $3\sqrt{3}$ by $2\sqrt{2}$

37. $3\sqrt{2}$ by $2\sqrt[3]{3}$

38. $2\sqrt{3}$ by $\sqrt[4]{5}$

39. $2\sqrt[3]{3}$ by $5\sqrt[4]{4}$

40. $2\sqrt[3]{24}$ by $\sqrt[9]{\dfrac{8}{27}}$

41. $2x\sqrt{3a}$ by $3\sqrt{y}$

42. $3\sqrt[3]{9a^2}$ by $\sqrt[3]{3abc}$

43. $\sqrt[5]{4xy^2}$ by $\sqrt[5]{8x^2y}$

44. $\sqrt{\dfrac{a}{b}}$ by $\sqrt{\dfrac{c}{d}}$

45. $\sqrt{a}$ by $\sqrt[4]{b}$

46. $\sqrt[3]{x}$ by $\sqrt{y}$

47. $\sqrt{xy}$ by $2\sqrt{xz}$ and $\sqrt[3]{x^2y^2}$

48. $\sqrt[3]{a^2b}$ by $\sqrt[3]{2a^2b^2}$ and $\sqrt{3a^3b^2}$

49. $\left(\sqrt{5} - \sqrt{3}\right)$ by $2\sqrt{3}$

50. $\left(x + \sqrt{y}\right)$ by $\sqrt{y}$

51. $\sqrt{x^3 - x^4y}$ by $\sqrt{x}$

52. $\left(\sqrt{x} - \sqrt{2}\right)$ by $\left(2\sqrt{x} + \sqrt{2}\right)$

53. $\left(a + \sqrt{b}\right)$ by $\left(a - \sqrt{b}\right)$

54. $\left(\sqrt{x} + \sqrt{y}\right)$ by $\left(\sqrt{x} + \sqrt{y}\right)$

55. $\left(4\sqrt{x} + 2\sqrt{y}\right)$ by $\left(4\sqrt{x} - 5\sqrt{y}\right)$

56. $\left(x + \sqrt{xy}\right)$ by $\left(\sqrt{x} - \sqrt{y}\right)$

Powers

Square the following expressions.

57. $3\sqrt{y}$

58. $4\sqrt[3]{4x^2}$

59. $3x\sqrt[3]{2x^2}$

60. $5 + 4\sqrt{x}$

61. $3 - 5\sqrt{a}$

62. $\sqrt{a} + 5a\sqrt{b}$

Cube the following radicals.

63. $5\sqrt{2x}$

64. $2x\sqrt{3x}$

65. $5\sqrt[3]{2ax}$

Division of Radicals

Divide.

66. $8 \div 3\sqrt{2}$

67. $6\sqrt{72} \div 12\sqrt{32}$

68. $\left(4\sqrt[3]{3} - 3\sqrt[3]{2}\right) \div \sqrt[3]{2}$

69. $5\sqrt[3]{12} \div 10\sqrt{8}$

70. $9\sqrt[3]{18} \div 3\sqrt{6}$

71. $12\sqrt[3]{4a^3} \div 4\sqrt[3]{2a^5}$

72. $12\sqrt{256} \div 18\sqrt{2}$

73. $\left(4\sqrt[3]{4} + 2\sqrt[3]{3} + 3\sqrt[3]{6}\right) \div \sqrt[3]{6}$

74. $2 \div \sqrt[3]{6}$

75. $\sqrt{72} \div 2\sqrt[4]{64}$

76. $8 \div 2\sqrt[3]{4}$

77. $8\sqrt[3]{ab} \div 4\sqrt{ac}$

78. $\sqrt[3]{4ab} \div \sqrt[4]{2ab}$

79. $2\sqrt[4]{a^2b^3c^2} \div 4\sqrt[3]{ab^2c^2}$

80. $6\sqrt[3]{x^4y^7z} \div \sqrt[4]{xy}$

81. $\left(3 + \sqrt{2}\right) \div \left(2 - \sqrt{2}\right)$

82. $5 \div \sqrt{3x}$

83. $4\sqrt{x} \div \sqrt{a}$

84. $10 \div \sqrt[3]{9x^2}$

85. $12 \div \sqrt[3]{4x^2}$

86. $5\sqrt{a^2b} \div 3\sqrt[3]{a^2b^2}$

87. $\left(10\sqrt{6} - 3\sqrt{5}\right) \div \left(2\sqrt{6} - 4\sqrt{5}\right)$

88. $\sqrt{x} \div \left(\sqrt{x} + \sqrt{y}\right)$

89. $a \div \left(a + \sqrt{b}\right)$

90. $\left(a + \sqrt{b}\right) \div \left(a - \sqrt{b}\right)$

91. $\left(\sqrt{x} - \sqrt{y}\right) \div \left(\sqrt{x} + \sqrt{y}\right)$

92. $\left(3\sqrt{m} - \sqrt{2n}\right) \div \left(\sqrt{3n} + \sqrt{m}\right)$

93. $\left(5\sqrt{x} + \sqrt{2y}\right) \div \left(2\sqrt{3x} + 2\sqrt{y}\right)$

94. $\left(5\sqrt{2p} - 3\sqrt{3q}\right) \div \left(3\sqrt{3p} + 2\sqrt{5q}\right)$

95. $\left(2\sqrt{3a} + 4\sqrt{5b}\right) \div \left(3\sqrt{2a} + 4\sqrt{b}\right)$

Computer

96. Use a computer algebra system for any of the problems in this exercise. Simply enter the entire expression and give the command SIMPLIFY.

13·4

Radical Equations

An equation in which the unknown is under a radical sign is called a *radical equation*. To solve a radical equation, it is necessary to isolate the radical term on one side of the equal sign and then to raise both sides to whatever power will eliminate the radical.

We will do more difficult radical equations in Chapter 14.

■ **Example 44:** Solve for x:

$$\sqrt{x - 5} - 4 = 0$$

Solution: Rearranging yields

$$\sqrt{x - 5} = 4$$

Squaring both sides:

$$x - 5 = 16$$

$$x = 21$$

Check:

$$\sqrt{21 - 5} - 4 \overset{?}{=} 0$$

$$\sqrt{16} - 4 \overset{?}{=} 0$$

$$4 - 4 = 0 \qquad \text{checks} \qquad ■$$

■ **Example 45:** Solve for x:

$$\sqrt{x^2 - 6x} = x - 9$$

Remember that we take only the principal (positive) root.

Solution: Squaring, we obtain

$$x^2 - 6x = x^2 - 18x + 81$$

$$12x = 81$$

$$x = \frac{81}{12} = \frac{27}{4}$$

Check:

$$\sqrt{\left(\frac{27}{4}\right)^2 - 6\left(\frac{27}{4}\right)} \overset{?}{=} \frac{27}{4} - 9$$

$$\sqrt{\frac{729}{16} - \frac{162}{4}} \overset{?}{=} \frac{27}{4} - \frac{36}{4}$$

$$\sqrt{\frac{81}{16}} = \frac{9}{4} \neq -\frac{9}{4} \qquad \text{does not check}$$

The given equation has no solution. ■

Common Error	The squaring process often introduces *extraneous roots*. These are discarded because they do not satisfy the original equation. Check your answer in the original equation.

If the equation has more than one radical, isolate one at a time and square both sides, as in the following example.

■ **Example 46:** Solve for x:

$$\sqrt{x - 32} + \sqrt{x} = 16$$

Solution: Rearranging gives

$$\sqrt{x - 32} = 16 - \sqrt{x}$$

Squaring yields

$$x - 32 = (16)^2 - 32\sqrt{x} + x$$

We rearrange again to isolate the radical,

$$32\sqrt{x} = 256 + 32 = 288$$
$$\sqrt{x} = 9$$

Squaring again, we obtain

$$x = 81$$

Check:

$$\sqrt{81 - 32} + \sqrt{81} \stackrel{?}{=} 16$$
$$\sqrt{49} + 9 \stackrel{?}{=} 16$$
$$7 + 9 = 16 \qquad \text{checks} \qquad \blacksquare$$

> *Tip*: It is usually better to isolate and square the *most complicated* radical first.

If a radical equation contains a fraction, we proceed as we did with other fractional equations and multiply both sides by the least common denominator.

■ **Example 47:** Solve:

$$\sqrt{x - 3} + \frac{1}{\sqrt{x - 3}} = \sqrt{x}$$

Solution: Multiplying both sides by $\sqrt{x - 3}$ gives

$$x - 3 + 1 = \sqrt{x}\sqrt{x - 3}$$
$$x - 2 = \sqrt{x^2 - 3x}$$

Squaring both sides yields

$$x^2 - 4x + 4 = x^2 - 3x$$
$$x = 4$$

Check:

$$\sqrt{4 - 3} + \frac{1}{\sqrt{4 - 3}} \stackrel{?}{=} \sqrt{4}$$

$$1 + \frac{1}{1} = 2 \qquad \text{checks} \qquad \blacksquare$$

Radical equations having indices other than 2 are solved in a similar way.

■ **Example 48:** Solve for x:

$$\sqrt[3]{x - 5} = 2$$

Solution: Cubing both sides, we obtain

$$x - 5 = 8$$

$$x = 13$$

Check:

$$\sqrt[3]{13 - 5} \overset{?}{=} 2$$

$$\sqrt[3]{8} = 2 \qquad \text{checks}$$

Approximate Solution of Radical Equations by Graphing

We learned how to find the approximate solution of equations by graphics utility in Section 5•6. Recall that we moved all terms of the given equation to one side, and graphed that expression. Then by zooming in and using TRACE we were able to find the value of x at which the curve crossed the x axis to any precision we wanted. That method works for any equation, and we use it here to solve a radical equation.

Example 49: Find an approximate solution to the equation given in Example 48.

Solution: Rearranging the equation gives

$$\sqrt[3]{x - 5} - 2 = 0$$

So we graph the function

$$y = \sqrt[3]{x - 5} - 2$$

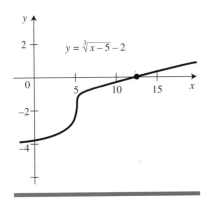

as shown in Fig. 13•1. Using TRACE and ZOOM, we verify that the root is at $x = 13$.

FIGURE 13•1

Exercise 4   Radical Equations

Radical Equations

Solve for x and check.

1. $\sqrt{x} = 6$

2. $\sqrt{x} + 5 = 9$

3. $\sqrt{7x + 8} = 6$

4. $\sqrt{3x - 2} = 5$

5. $\sqrt{2.95x - 1.84} = 6.23$

6. $\sqrt{5.88x + 4.92} = 7.72$

7. $\sqrt{x + 1} = \sqrt{2x - 7}$

8. $2 = \sqrt[4]{1 + 3x}$

9. $\sqrt{3x + 1} = 5$

10. $\sqrt[3]{2x} = 4$

11. $\sqrt{x - 3} = \dfrac{4}{\sqrt{x - 3}}$

12. $x + 2 = \sqrt{x^2 + 6}$

13. $\sqrt{x^2 - 7.25} = 8.75 - x$

14. $\sqrt{x - 15.5} = 5.85 - \sqrt{x}$

15. $\dfrac{6}{\sqrt{3 + x}} = \sqrt{x + 3}$

16. $\sqrt{12 + x} = 2 + \sqrt{x}$

17. $\sqrt[5]{x - 7} = 1$

18. $\sqrt{x^2 - 2x} - \sqrt{1 - x} = 1 - x$

19. $\sqrt{1.25x} - \sqrt{1.25x + 14.3} + 3.18 = 0$

20. $2.10x + \sqrt{4.41x^2 - 8.36} = 9.37$

FIGURE 13·2

FIGURE 13·3

21. $\sqrt{x-2} - \sqrt{x} = \dfrac{1}{\sqrt{x-2}}$ **22.** $\sqrt{\dfrac{1}{x}} - \sqrt{x} = \sqrt{1+x}$

23. $\sqrt{5x-19} - \sqrt{5x+14} = -3$ **24.** $\sqrt[3]{x-3} = 2$

Applications

25. A right triangle, Figure 13·2, has one side equal to 253 mm and a perimeter of 684 mm, so

$$x + 253 + \sqrt{x^2 + (253)^2} = 684$$

Solve this equation for x and for the hypotenuse.

26. Find the missing side and hypotenuse of a right triangle that has one side equal to 293 mm and a perimeter of 994 mm.

27. Find the side and hypotenuse of a right triangle that has a side of 2.73 m and a perimeter of 11.4 m.

28. The natural frequency f_n of a body under simple harmonic motion (Fig. 13·3) is found from Eqs. A37 and A38:

$$f_n = \frac{1}{2\pi}\sqrt{\frac{ka}{M}}$$

where a is the gravitational constant, k is a constant, and M is the mass. Solve for M.

29. The magnitude Z of the impedance in an *RLC* circuit (Fig. 13·4) having a resistance R, an inductance L, and a capacitance C, to which is applied a voltage of frequency ω, is given by Eq. A99:

$$Z = \sqrt{R^2 + \left(\omega L - \frac{1}{\omega C}\right)^2}$$

Solve for C.

30. The resonant frequency ω_n for the circuit shown in Figure 13·4 is given by Eq. A91

$$\omega_n = \sqrt{\frac{1}{LC}}$$

Solve for L.

FIGURE 13·4

Graphics Calculator

31. Use your graphics calculator to solve approximately any of the above equations, to three significant digits

Computer

32. Use your computer algebra system to solve any of the above equations. Enter the equation and give the command SOLVE.

33. If you have written a program to solve equations by the *midpoint method,* as suggested in Section 5·6, use your program to solve any of the radical equations above. If not, you may want to write that program now, for it will be very useful in later chapters as well.

CHAPTER 13   REVIEW PROBLEMS

Simplify

1. $\sqrt{52}$

2. $\sqrt{108}$

3. $\sqrt[3]{162}$

4. $\sqrt[4]{9}$

5. $\sqrt[6]{4}$

6. $\sqrt{81a^2x^3y}$

7. $3\sqrt[4]{81x^5}$

8. $\sqrt{ab^2 - b^3}$

9. $\sqrt[3]{(a - b^5)x^4}$

10. $5\sqrt{\dfrac{7x}{12y}}$

11. $\sqrt{\dfrac{a - 2}{a + 2}}$

Perform the indicated operations and simplify. Don't use a calculator.

12. $4b\sqrt{3y} \cdot 5\sqrt{x}$

13. $\sqrt{x} \cdot \sqrt{x^3 - x^4y}$

14. $(\sqrt{x} + \sqrt{y})(\sqrt{x} - \sqrt{y})$

15. $\dfrac{3 - 2\sqrt{3}}{2 - 5\sqrt{2}}$

16. $\dfrac{\sqrt{x} - \sqrt{y}}{\sqrt{x} + \sqrt{y}}$

17. $\dfrac{x + \sqrt{x^2 - y^2}}{x - \sqrt{x^2 - y^2}}$

18. $\sqrt{98x^2y^2} - \sqrt{128x^2y^2}$

19. $4\sqrt[3]{125x^2} + 3\sqrt[3]{8x^2}$

20. $3\sqrt{x^2 - y^2} - 2\sqrt{\dfrac{x + y}{x - y}}$

21. $\sqrt{a}\sqrt[3]{b}$

22. $\sqrt[3]{2abc^2} \cdot \sqrt{abc}$

23. $\left(3 + 2\sqrt{x}\right)^2$

24. $\left(4x\sqrt{2x}\right)^3$

25. $3\sqrt{50} - 2\sqrt{32}$

26. $3\sqrt{72} - 4\sqrt{8} + \sqrt{128}$

27. $5\sqrt{\dfrac{9}{8}} - 2\sqrt{\dfrac{25}{18}}$

28. $2\sqrt{2} \div \sqrt[3]{2}$

29. $\sqrt{2ab} \div \sqrt{4ab^2}$

30. $9 \div \sqrt[3]{7x^2}$

31. $3\sqrt{9} \cdot 4\sqrt{8}$

Solve for x and check.

32. $\dfrac{\sqrt{x} - 8}{\sqrt{x} - 6} = \dfrac{\sqrt{x} - 4}{\sqrt{x} + 2}$

33. $\sqrt{x + 6} = 4$

34. $\sqrt{2x - 7} = \sqrt{x - 3}$

35. $\sqrt[5]{2x + 4} = 2$

36. $\sqrt{4x^2 - 3} = 2x - 1$

37. $\sqrt{x} + \sqrt{x - 9.75} = 6.23$

38. $\sqrt[3]{21.5x} = 2.33$

Simplify, and write without negative exponents.

39. $(x^{n-1} + y^{n-2})(x^n + y^{n-1})$

40. $(72a^6b^7 \div 9a^4b) \div 8ab^6$

41. $\left(\dfrac{9x^4y^3}{6x^3y}\right)^3$

42. $\left(\dfrac{5w^2}{2x}\right)^n$

43. $\left(\dfrac{2x^5y^3}{x^2y}\right)^3$

44. $5a^{-1}$

45. $3w^{-2}$

46. $2r^0$

47. $(3x)^{-1}$

48. $2a^{-1} + b^{-2}$

49. $x^{-1} - 2y^{-2}$

50. $(5a)^{-3} - 3b^{-2}$

51. $(3x)^{-2} + (2x^2y^{-4})^{-2}$

52. $(a^n + b^m)^2$

53. $(p^{a-1} + q^{a-2})(p^a + q^{a-1})$

54. $(16a^6b^0 \div 8a^4b) \div 4ab^6$

55. p^2q^{-1}

56. x^3y^{-2}

57. r^2s^{-3}

58. a^3b^{-1}

59. $(3x^3y^2z)^0$

60. $(5a^2b^2c^2)^3$

Writing

61. Explain how exponents and radicals are really two different ways of writing the same expression. Also explain why, if they are the same, we need both.

14

Quadratic Equations

O B J E C T I V E S

When you have completed this chapter, you should be able to:

- Solve quadratic equations by factoring, by completing the square, and by quadratic formula.
- Solve literal and fractional quadratic equations.
- Solve radical equations that lead to quadratics.
- Solve word problems that result in quadratic equations.
- Graph quadratic equations, and solve them graphically.
- Solve polynomial equations of higher degree by factoring.
- Solve equations by the numerical method of simple iteration.
- Solve systems of two quadratic equations.

So far we have learned how to solve linear (first-degree) equations, and sets of first-degree equations. But many technical problems require us to solve more complicated equations than that. In this chapter we study second-degree equations (quadratics), and later we cover logarithmic, exponential, and trigonometric equations. That does not include every equation type that exists, but many of the common types.

Quadratic equations arise in many technical problems, such as the simple falling-body problem: "An object is thrown downward with a speed of 15 m/s. How long will it take to fall 100 m?"

The displacement s of a freely falling body is given by $s = v_0 t + \frac{1}{2} at^2$, and if we substitute $s = 100$, $v_0 = 15$, and $a = 9.8$ m/s^2, we get

$$100 = 15t + 10t^2$$

Now how do we solve that equation? How shall we find the values of t that will make the equation balance? Even this simple problem requires us to solve a quadratic equation.

Let us leave this problem and return to it after we have learned how to solve quadratics. Before we start, you might want to leaf through Chapter 8 if you have become rusty on factoring. Look especially at the sections on common factors, trinomials, and the perfect square trinomial.

14•1

Recall that, in a polynomial, all the powers of x are *positive integers*.

Solving Quadratics by Factoring

Terminology

A polynomial equation of second degree is called a *quadratic equation*. It is common practice to refer to it simply as a *quadratic*.

■ **Example 1:** The equations
(a) $4x^2 - 5x + 2 = 0$
(b) $x^2 = 58$
(c) $9x^2 - 5x = 0$
(d) $2x^2 - 7 = 0$
are quadratic equations. Equation (a) is called a *complete* quadratic, (b) and (d), which have no x terms, are called *pure* quadratics, and (c), which has no constant term, is called an *incomplete* quadratic. ■

A quadratic is in *general form* when it is written in the form

General Form of a Quadratic	$ax^2 + bx + c = 0$	**99**

where a, b, and c are constants.

■ **Example 2:** Write the quadratic equation

$$7 - 4x = \frac{5x^2}{3}$$

in general form, and identify a, b, and c.

Solution: Subtracting $5x^2/3$ from both sides and writing the terms in descending order of the exponents, we obtain

$$-\frac{5x^2}{3} - 4x + 7 = 0$$

Quadratics in general form are usually written without fractions and with the first term positive. Multiplying by -3, we get

$$5x^2 + 12x - 21 = 0$$

The equation is now in general form, with $a = 5$, $b = 12$, and $c = -21$. ■

Number of Roots

We'll see later in this chapter that the maximum number of roots that certain types of equations may have is equal to the degree of the equation. Thus, a quadratic equation, being of degree 2, has *two solutions* or roots. The two roots are sometimes equal, or they may be imaginary or complex numbers. However, in applications, we'll see that one of the two roots must sometimes be discarded.

■ **Example 3:** The quadratic equation

$$x^2 = 4$$

has the two roots, $x = 2$ and $x = -2$. ■

Solving Pure Quadratics

We simply isolate the x^2 term and then take the square root of both sides, as in the following example.

■ **Example 4:** Solve $3x^2 - 75 = 0$.

Solution: Adding 75 to both sides and dividing by 3, we obtain

$$3x^2 = 75$$
$$x^2 = 25$$

Taking the square root yields

$$x = \pm\sqrt{25} = \pm 5$$

Check: We check our solution the same way as for other equations, by substituting back into the original equation. Now, however, we must check two solutions.

Substitute $+5$: $\qquad\qquad 3(5)^2 - 75 = 0$

$$75 - 75 = 0 \qquad \text{checks}$$

Substitute -5: $\qquad\qquad 3(-5)^2 - 75 = 0$

$$75 - 75 = 0 \qquad \text{checks} \qquad\blacksquare$$

> When taking the square root, be sure to keep both the plus *and* the minus values. *Both* will satisfy the equation.

At this point students usually grumble: "First we're told that $\sqrt{4} = +2$ only, not ± 2 (Sec. 1•5). *Now* we're told to keep both plus and minus. What's going on here?" Here's the difference. When we solve a quadratic, we know that it must have two roots, so we keep both values. When we evaluate a square root, such as $\sqrt{4}$, which is not the solution of a quadratic, we agree to take only the positive value to avoid ambiguity.

The roots might sometimes be irrational, as in the following example.

■ **Example 5:** Solve $4x^2 - 15 = 0$.

Solution: Following the same steps as before, we get

$$4x^2 = 15$$

$$x^2 = \frac{15}{4}$$

$$x = \pm\sqrt{\frac{15}{4}} = \pm\frac{\sqrt{15}}{2} \qquad\blacksquare$$

Solving Incomplete Quadratics

To solve an incomplete quadratic, remove the common factor x from each term, and set each factor equal to zero.

■ **Example 6:** Solve

$$x^2 + 5x = 0$$

Solution: Factoring yields

$$x(x + 5) = 0$$

Note that this expression will be true if either or both of the two factors equals zero. We therefore set each factor in turn equal to zero.

$$x = 0, \quad x + 5 = 0$$
$$x = -5$$

The two solutions are thus $x = 0$ and $x = -5$. ■

> We use this idea often in this chapter. If we have the product of two quantities, a and b, set equal to zero, $ab = 0$, this equation will be true if $a = 0$ ($0 \cdot b = 0$) or if $b = 0$ ($a \cdot 0 = 0$), or if both are zero ($0 \cdot 0 = 0$).

	Do not cancel an x from the terms of an incomplete quadratic. That will cause a root to be lost. If, in the last example, we had said
	$$x^2 = -5x$$
Common Error	and had divided by x,
	$$x = -5$$
	we would have obtained the correct root $x = -5$ but would have lost the root $x = 0$.

Solving the Complete Quadratic

We now consider a quadratic that has all its terms in place, the complete quadratic.

General Form	$ax^2 + bx + c = 0$	**99**

First write the quadratic in general form, Eq. 99. Factor the trinomial (if possible) by the methods of Chapter 8 and set each factor equal to zero.

■ **Example 7:** Solve by factoring:

$$x^2 - x - 6 = 0$$

Solution: Factoring gives

$$(x - 3)(x + 2) = 0$$

This equation will be satisfied if either or both of the two factors $(x - 3)$ and $(x + 2)$ are zero. We therefore set each factor in turn to equal zero.

$$x - 3 = 0 \qquad x + 2 = 0$$

so the roots are

$$x = 3 \quad \text{and} \quad x = -2$$ ■

Common Error	When the product of two quantities is zero, as in $$(x - 3)(x + 2) = 0$$ we can set each factor equal to zero, getting $x - 3 = 0$ and $x + 2 = 0$. But *this is valid only when the product is zero.* Thus if $$(x - 3)(x + 2) = 5$$ we *cannot* say that $x - 3 = 5$ and $x + 2 = 5$.

Often an equation must first be simplified before factoring.

■ **Example 8:** Solve for x,

$$x(x - 8) = 2x(x - 1) + 9$$

Solution: Removing parentheses gives

$$x^2 - 8x = 2x^2 - 2x + 9$$

Collecting terms, we get

$$x^2 + 6x + 9 = 0$$

Factoring yields

$$(x + 3)(x + 3) = 0$$

which gives the double root,

$$x = -3$$

Sometimes an equation will not look like a quadratic, at first glance. The following example shows a fractional equation which, after simplification, turns out to be a quadratic.

■ **Example 9:** Solve for x,

$$\frac{3x - 1}{4x + 7} = \frac{x + 1}{x + 7}$$

Solution: We start by multiplying both sides by the LCD, $(4x + 7)(x + 7)$. We get

$$(3x - 1)(x + 7) = (x + 1)(4x + 7)$$

or

$$3x^2 + 20x - 7 = 4x^2 + 11x + 7$$

Collecting terms gives

$$x^2 - 9x + 14 = 0$$

Factoring yields

$$(x - 7)(x - 2) = 0$$

so $x = 7$ and $x = 2$. ■

Writing the Equation When the Roots Are Known

Given the roots, we simply reverse the process to find the equation.

▬ **Example 10:** Write the quadratic equation that has the roots $x = 2$ and $x = -5$.

    Solution: If the roots are 2 and -5, we know that the factors of the equation must be $(x - 2)$ and $(x + 5)$. So

$$(x - 2)(x + 5) = 0$$

Multiplying gives us

$$x^2 + 5x - 2x - 10 = 0$$

So

$$x^2 + 3x - 10 = 0$$

is the original equation.   ▬

Solving Radical Equations

In Chapter 13 we solved simple radical equations. We isolated a radical on one side of the equation and then squared both sides. Here we solve equations in which this squaring operation results in a quadratic equation.

▬ **Example 11:** Solve for x:

$$3\sqrt{x - 1} - \frac{4}{\sqrt{x - 1}} = 4$$

    Solution: We clear fractions by multiplying through by $\sqrt{x - 1}$.

$$3(x - 1) - 4 = 4\sqrt{x - 1}$$

$$3x - 7 = 4\sqrt{x - 1}$$

Squaring both sides yields

$$9x^2 - 42x + 49 = 16(x - 1)$$

Removing parentheses and collecting terms gives

$$9x^2 - 58x + 65 = 0$$

Factoring gives

$$(x - 5)(9x - 13) = 0$$

$$x = 5 \quad \text{and} \quad x = \frac{13}{9}$$

Check: When $x = 5$,

$$3\sqrt{5 - 1} - \frac{4}{\sqrt{5 - 1}} \stackrel{?}{=} 4$$

$$3(2) - \frac{4}{2} = 4 \qquad \text{checks}$$

When $x = \dfrac{13}{9}$,

$$\sqrt{\dfrac{13}{9} - 1} = \sqrt{\dfrac{4}{9}} = \dfrac{2}{3}$$

So

$$3 \cdot \dfrac{2}{3} - \dfrac{4}{\dfrac{2}{3}} \overset{?}{=} 4$$

$$2 - 6 \neq 4 \qquad \text{does not check}$$

Our solution is then $x = 5$.

> Remember that the squaring operation sometimes gives an extraneous root that will not check.

Exercise 1 Solving Quadratics by Factoring

> There are no applications in the first few exercises. These will come a little later.

Pure and Incomplete Quadratics

Solve for x.

1. $2x = 5x^2$
2. $2x - 40x^2 = 0$
3. $3x(x - 2) = x(x + 3)$
4. $2x^2 - 6 = 66$
5. $5x^2 - 3 = 2x^2 + 24$
6. $7x^2 + 4 = 3x^2 + 40$
7. $(x + 2)^2 = 4x + 5$
8. $5x^2 - 2 = 3x^2 + 6$
9. $8.25x^2 - 2.93x = 0$
10. $284x = 827x^2$

Complete Quadratics

Solve for x.

11. $x^2 + 2x - 15 = 0$
12. $x^2 + 6x - 16 = 0$
13. $x^2 - x - 20 = 0$
14. $x^2 + 13x + 42 = 0$
15. $x^2 - x - 2 = 0$
16. $x^2 + 7x + 12 = 0$
17. $x^2 + 3x + 2 = 0$
18. $x^2 - 4x - 21 = 0$
19. $x^2 - 7x - 18 = 0$
20. $x^2 + 6x + 8 = 0$
21. $x^2 + 12x + 32 = 0$
22. $x^2 - 10x - 39 = 0$
23. $x^2 - 12x - 64 = 0$
24. $x^2 + 14x + 33 = 0$
25. $2x^2 - 3x - 5 = 0$
26. $4x^2 - 10x + 6 = 0$
27. $2x^2 + 5x - 12 = 0$
28. $3x^2 - x - 2 = 0$
29. $5x^2 + 14x - 3 = 0$
30. $5x^2 + 3x - 2 = 0$
31. $2 + x - x^2 = 0$
32. $20 + 19x - 6x^2 = 0$
33. $-26x + 5 - 24x^2 = 0$
34. $15x^2 = 8 + 14x$
35. $2x^3 + x^2 - 18 = x(2x^2 + 3)$
36. $\dfrac{x}{2} + \dfrac{2}{x} - \dfrac{5}{2} = 0$
37. $\dfrac{2 - x}{3} = 2x^2$
38. $(x - 6)(x + 6) = 5x$
39. $x(x - 5) = 36$
40. $(2x - 3)^2 = 2x - x^2$
41. $x^2 - \dfrac{5}{6}x = \dfrac{1}{6}$
42. $\dfrac{7}{x + 4} - \dfrac{1}{4 - x} = \dfrac{2}{3}$
43. $\dfrac{2x - 1}{x + 3} = \dfrac{x + 3}{2x - 1}$
44. $1 - \dfrac{x}{2} = 5 - \dfrac{36}{x + 2}$
45. $3 - x^2 = \dfrac{2x - 76}{3}$
46. $\dfrac{x}{x - 1} - \dfrac{x - 1}{x} = \dfrac{3}{2}$

47. $\dfrac{2x}{3} - \dfrac{5}{4x} = \dfrac{7x}{9} - \dfrac{21}{4x}$

48. $\dfrac{2x + 5}{2x - 5} = \dfrac{7x - 5}{2x}$

49. $x^2 + \dfrac{x}{2} = \dfrac{2x^2}{5} - \dfrac{x}{5} + \dfrac{13}{10}$

50. $\dfrac{2x - 1}{x - 1} + \dfrac{1}{6} = \dfrac{2x - 3}{x - 2}$

Literal Equations

Solve for x.

51. $4x^2 + 16ax + 12a^2 = 0$
52. $14x^2 - 23ax + 3a^2 = 0$
53. $9x^2 + 30bx + 24b^2 = 0$
54. $24x^2 - 17xy + 3y^2 = 0$
55. $21x^2 + 23xy^2 + 6y^4 = 0$
56. $28x^2 - mx - 2m^2 = 0$

Writing the Equation from the Roots

Write the quadratic equations that have the following roots.

57. $x = 4$ and $x = 7$
58. $x = -3$ and $x = -5$
59. $x = \frac{2}{3}$ and $x = \frac{3}{5}$
60. $x = p$ and $x = q$
61. $x = -\frac{5}{3}$ and $x = -\frac{7}{2}$
62. $x = 3 + \sqrt{2}$ and $x = 3 - \sqrt{2}$
63. $x = 1 + \sqrt{5}$ and $x = 1 - \sqrt{5}$
64. $x = a$ and $x = a - b$

Radical Equations

Solve each radical equation for x and check.

65. $\sqrt{5x^2 - 3x - 41} = 3x - 7$

66. $3\sqrt{x - 1} - \dfrac{4}{\sqrt{x - 1}} = 4$

67. $\sqrt{x + 5} = \dfrac{12}{\sqrt{x + 12}}$

68. $\sqrt{7x + 8} - \sqrt{5x - 4} = 2$

69. $2x + \sqrt{4x^2 - 7} = \dfrac{21}{\sqrt{4x^2 - 7}}$

Computer

70. Use your program for solving equations by the midpoint method (Section 5•6) to find the roots of any of the quadratics in this exercise.

71. If you have a computer algebra system, use it to solve any of the equations in this exercise.

14·2

Solving Quadratics by Completing the Square

If a quadratic equation is not factorable, it is possible to manipulate it into factorable form by a procedure called *completing the square*. The form into which we shall put our expression is the *perfect square trinomial*, Eqs. 47 and 48, that we studied in Section 8·6.

If you recall the perfect square trinomial,

1. The first and last terms were perfect squares.

2. The middle term was twice the product of the square roots of the outer terms.

To complete the square, we manipulate our given expression so that these two conditions are met. This is best shown by an example.

The method of completing the square is really too cumbersome to be a practical tool for solving quadratics. The main reason we learn it is to derive the quadratic formula. Furthermore, the method of *completing the square* is a useful technique that we'll use again in later chapters.

■ **Example 12:** Solve the quadratic $x^2 - 8x + 6 = 0$ by completing the square.

Solution: Subtracting 6 from both sides, we obtain

$$x^2 - 8x = -6$$

We complete the square by *adding the square of half the coefficient of the x term* to both sides. The coefficient of x is -8. We take half of -8 and square it, getting $(-4)^2$ or 16. Adding 16 to both sides,

$$x^2 - 8x + 16 = -6 + 16 = 10$$

Some computer algebra systems can automatically complete the square. *Maple*, for example, uses the complete square ( ) command.

Factoring,

$$(x - 4)^2 = 10$$

Taking the square root of both sides,

$$x - 4 = \pm\sqrt{10}$$

Finally, adding 4 to both sides,

$$x = 4 \pm\sqrt{10}$$

$$\cong 7.16 \quad \text{or} \quad 0.838$$

	When adding to the left-hand side the quantity needed to complete the square, it is easy to forget to add the same quantity to the right-hand side.
Common Error	$x^2 - 8x \boxed{+16} = -6 \boxed{+16}$ ⬆ ————don't forget

If the x^2 term has a coefficient other than 1, divide through by this coefficient *before* completing the square.

■ **Example 13:** Solve

$$2x^2 + 4x - 3 = 0$$

Solution: Rearranging and dividing by 2 gives

$$x^2 + 2x = \frac{3}{2}$$

Completing the square by adding 1 (half the coefficient of the x term, squared) to both sides of the equation,

$$x^2 + 2x + 1 = \frac{3}{2} + 1$$

$$(x + 1)^2 = \frac{5}{2}$$

$$x + 1 = \pm\sqrt{\frac{5}{2}} = \frac{\pm\sqrt{10}}{2}$$

$$x = -1 \pm \frac{1}{2}\sqrt{10}$$

Common Error	Don't forget to divide through by the coefficient of the x^2 term *before* completing the square.

Exercise 2 Solving Quadratics by Completing the Square

Quadratics having noninteger coefficients can also be solved by completing the square. The method is exactly the same, although the work is harder.

Solve each quadratic by completing the square.

1. $x^2 - 8x + 2 = 0$ **2.** $x^2 + 4x - 9 = 0$
3. $x^2 + 7x - 3 = 0$ **4.** $x^2 - 3x - 5 = 0$
5. $4x^2 - 3x - 5 = 0$ **6.** $2x^2 + 3x - 3 = 0$
7. $3x^2 + 6x - 4 = 0$ **8.** $5x^2 - 2x - 1 = 0$
9. $4x^2 + 7x - 5 = 0$ **10.** $8x^2 - 4x - 3 = 0$
11. $x^2 + 6.25x - 3.27 = 0$ **12.** $2.45x^2 + 6.88x - 4.17 = 0$

Computer

13. If you have a computer algebra system, use it to solve any of the equations in this exercise.

14·3 Solving Quadratics by Formula

Of the several methods we have for solving quadratics, the most useful is the quadratic formula. It will work for any quadratic, regardless of the type of roots, and can easily be programmed for the computer.

Derivation of the Quadratic Formula

We wish to find the roots of the equation

$$ax^2 + bx + c = 0$$

by completing the square. We start by subtracting c from both sides and dividing by a:

We're assuming here that the coefficient *a* is not zero.

$$x^2 + \frac{b}{a}x = -\frac{c}{a}$$

Completing the square gives

$$x^2 + \frac{b}{a}x + \left(\frac{b}{2a}\right)^2 = \frac{b^2}{4a^2} - \frac{c}{a}$$

Factoring, we obtain

$$\left(x + \frac{b}{2a}\right)^2 = \frac{b^2 - 4ac}{4a^2}$$

Taking the square root yields

$$x + \frac{b}{2a} = \pm\frac{\sqrt{b^2 - 4ac}}{2a}$$

Rearranging, we get the well-known formula for finding the roots of the quadratic equation, $ax^2 + bx + c = 0$.

Quadratic Formula	$x = \dfrac{-b \pm \sqrt{b^2 - 4ac}}{2a}$	**100**

Using the Quadratic Formula

Simply put the given equation into general form (Eq. 99); list a, b, and c; and substitute them into the formula.

■ **Example 14:** Solve $2x^2 - 5x - 3 = 0$ by the quadratic formula.

Solution: The equation is already in the general form, with

$$a = 2 \quad b = -5 \quad c = -3$$

Substituting into Eq. 100, we obtain

$$x = \frac{-(-5) \pm \sqrt{(-5)^2 - 4(2)(-3)}}{2(2)}$$

$$= \frac{5 \pm \sqrt{25 + 24}}{4}$$

$$= \frac{5 \pm \sqrt{49}}{4} = \frac{5 \pm 7}{4}$$

$$= 3 \quad \text{and} \quad -\frac{1}{2}$$

Common Error	Always rewrite a quadratic in general form before trying to use the quadratic formula.

■ **Example 15:** Solve the equation $5.25x - 2.94x^2 + 6.13 = 0$ by the quadratic formula.

Solution: The constants a, b, and c are *not* 5.25, -2.94, and 6.13, as you might think at first glance. We must rearrange the terms.

$$-2.94x^2 + 5.25x + 6.13 = 0$$

Although not a necessary step, dividing through by the coefficient of x^2 simplifies the work a bit:

$$x^2 - 1.79x - 2.09 = 0$$

Substituting into the quadratic formula with $a = 1$, $b = -1.79$, and $c = -2.09$,

$$x = \frac{1.79 \pm \sqrt{(1.79)^2 - 4(1)(-2.09)}}{2(1)}$$

$$= 2.59 \quad \text{and} \quad -0.805 \qquad \blacksquare$$

We now have the tools to finish the falling-body problem started in the introduction to this chapter.

■ **Example 16:** Solve the equation

$$1\overline{0}0 = 15t + 4.9t^2$$

(where t is in seconds), to two significant digits.

Solution: We first go to general form,

$$4.9t^2 + 15t - 100 = 0$$

Substituting into the quadratic formula gives us

$$t = \frac{-15 \pm \sqrt{225 - 4(16)(-100)}}{2(16)}$$

$$= \frac{-15 \pm \sqrt{2185}}{9.8} = \frac{-15 \pm 47}{9.8}$$

$$= 3.2 \text{ s} \quad \text{or} \quad -6.3 \text{ s}$$

In this problem, a negative elapsed time makes no sense, so we discard the negative root. Thus it will take 3.2 s for an object to fall 100 m when thrown downward with a speed of 15 m/s. ■

Nonreal Roots

See Chapter 21 for a complete discussion of imaginary and complex numbers.

Quadratics resulting from practical problems will usually yield real roots if the equation is properly set up. Other quadratics, however, could give nonreal roots, as shown in the next example.

■ **Example 17:** Solve

$$x^2 + 2x + 5 = 0$$

Solution: From Eq. 100,

$$x = \frac{-2 \pm \sqrt{4 - 4(1)(5)}}{2} = \frac{-2 \pm \sqrt{-16}}{2}$$

The expression $\sqrt{-16}$ can be written $\sqrt{-1}\sqrt{16}$ or $j4$, where $j = \sqrt{-1}$. So

$$x = \frac{-2 \pm j4}{2} = -1 \pm j2$$ ▬

Predicting the Nature of the Roots

As seen from the preceding example, when the quantity in Eq. 100 under the radical sign ($b^2 - 4ac$) is negative, the roots are not real. It should also be evident that, if $b^2 - 4ac$ is zero, the roots will be equal. The quantity $b^2 - 4ac$, called the *discriminant*, can thus be used to predict what kind of roots an equation will give, without having actually to find the roots.

Do not lose too much sleep over the discriminant. If you need to know the nature of the roots of a quadratic and cannot remember Eq. 101, all you have to do is calculate the roots themselves. This is not much more work than finding the discriminant.

The Discriminant	If a, b, and c are real, and $b^2 - 4ac > 0$, the roots are real and unequal. $b^2 - 4ac = 0$, the roots are real and equal. $b^2 - 4ac < 0$, the roots are not real.	101

▬ **Example 18:** What sort of roots can you expect from the equation

$$3x^2 - 5x + 7 = 0?$$

Solution: Computing the discriminant, we obtain

$$b^2 - 4ac = (-5)^2 - 4(3)(7) = 25 - 84 = -59$$

A negative discriminant tells us that the roots are not real. ▬

Exercise 3 Solving Quadratics by Formula

Solve by quadratic formula, to three significant digits.

1. $x^2 - 12x + 28 = 0$
2. $x^2 - 6x + 7 = 0$
3. $x^2 + x - 19 = 0$
4. $x^2 - x - 13 = 0$
5. $3x^2 + 12x - 35 = 0$
6. $29.4x^2 - 48.2x - 17.4 = 0$
7. $36x^2 + 3x - 7 = 0$
8. $28x^2 + 29x + 7 = 0$
9. $49x^2 + 21x - 5 = 0$
10. $16x^2 - 16x + 1 = 0$
11. $3x^2 - 10x + 4 = 0$
12. $x^2 - 34x + 22 = 0$
13. $3x^2 + 5x = 7$
14. $4x + 5 = x^2 + 2x$
15. $x^2 - 4 = 4x + 7$
16. $x^2 - 6x - 14 = 3$
17. $6x - 300 = 205 - 3x^2$
18. $3x^2 - 25x = 5x - 73$
19. $2x^2 + 100 = 32x - 11$
20. $33 - 3x^2 - 10x = 0$
21. $x(2x - 3) = 3x(x + 4) - 2$

22. $2.95(x^2 + 8.27x) = 7.24x(4.82x - 2.47) + 8.73$
23. $(4.2x - 5.8)(7.2x - 9.2) = 8.2x + 9.9$
24. $(2x - 1)^2 + 6 = 6(2x - 1)$

Nature of the Roots

Determine whether the roots of each quadratic are real or nonreal, and whether they are equal or unequal.

25. $x^2 - 5x - 11 = 0$ **26.** $x^2 - 6x + 15 = 0$
27. $2x^2 - 4x + 7 = 0$ **28.** $2x^2 + 3x - 2 = 0$
29. $3x^2 - 3x + 5 = 0$ **30.** $4x^2 + 4x + 1 = 0$

Computer

31. Write a program or use a spreadsheet to compute and print the roots of any quadratic once the constants a, b, and c are entered. Have the computer evaluate the discriminant before computing the roots. If the discriminant is negative, have the run stop. This will prevent the program from crashing when the computer tries to take the square root of a negative number.
32. Use your program for solving equations by the midpoint method (Section 5•6) to find the roots of any of the quadratics in this exercise.
33. If you have a computer algebra system, use it to solve any of the equations in this exercise.

14•4

Applications and Word Problems

Now that we have the tools to solve any quadratic, let us go on to problems from technology that require us to solve these equations. At this point you might want to take a quick look at Chapter 3 and review some of the suggestions for setting up and solving word problems. You should set up these problems just as you did then.

When you solve the resulting quadratic you will get two roots, of course. If one of the roots does not make sense in the physical problem (like a beam having a length of -200 m), throw it away. But do not be too hasty. Often a second root will give an unexpected but equally good answer.

■ **Example 19:** The angle iron in Figure 14•1 has a cross-sectional area of 5340 mm². Find the thickness x.

Estimate: Let's assume that we have two rectangles of width x, with lengths of 156 mm and 104 mm. Setting their combined area equal to 5340 mm²,

$$x(156 + 104) = 5340$$

we get the approximation, $x \approx 20.5$ mm. But since our assumed lengths were too great, because we have counted the small square in the corner twice, our estimated value of x must be too small. We thus conclude that $x > 20.5$ mm.

Solution: We divide the area into two rectangles, as shown by the dashed line. One rectangle has an area of $104x$ and the other has an area of $(156 - x)x$. Since the sum of these areas must be 5340 mm²,

$$104x + (156 - x)x = 5340$$

FIGURE 14•1

Putting this equation into standard form, we get

$$104x + 156x - x^2 = 5340$$

$$x^2 - 260x + 5340 = 0$$

By the quadratic formula,

$$x = \frac{260 \pm \sqrt{67600 - 4(5340)}}{2} = \frac{260 \pm 215}{2}$$

So

$$x = \frac{260 - 215}{2} = 22.5 \text{ mm}$$

and

$$x = \frac{260 + 215}{2} = 238 \text{ mm}$$

We discard 238 mm because it is an impossible solution in this problem.

Check: Does our answer meet the requirements of the original statement? Let us compute the area of the angle iron using our value of 22.5 mm for the thickness. We get

$$\text{area} = 22.5(133.5) + 22.5(104)$$

$$= 3000 + 2340 = 5340 \text{ mm}^2$$

which is the required area. Our answer is also a little bigger than our 20.5 mm estimate, as expected. ■

■ **Example 20:** A certain train is to be replaced with a "bullet" train that goes 64.0 km/h faster than the old train and will make the 1400-km run in 3.00 h less time. Find the speed of each train.

Solution: Let

$$x = \text{rate of old train, km/h}$$

Then

$$x + 64 = \text{rate of bullet train, km/h}$$

The time it takes the old train to travel 1400 km at x km/h is, by Eq. A17,

$$(\text{time} =) \frac{\text{distance}}{\text{rate}} = \frac{1400}{x} \text{ h}$$

The time for the bullet train is then $(1400/x - 3.00)$ h. Applying Eq. A17 for the bullet train gives us

$$(\text{rate} \times \text{time} = \text{distance})$$

$$(x + 64)\left(\frac{1400}{x} - 3.00\right) = 1400$$

Removing parentheses, we have

$$1400 - 3.00x + \frac{89\,600}{x} - 192 = 1400$$

Collecting terms and multiplying through by x gives

$$-3.00x^2 + 89\,600 - 192x = 0$$

or

$$x^2 + 64x - 29\,900 = 0$$

Solving for x by the quadratic formula yields

$$x = \frac{-64.0 \pm \sqrt{4096 - 4(-29\,900)}}{2}$$

If we drop the negative root, we get

$$x = \frac{-64.0 + 352}{2} = 144 \text{ km/h} = \text{speed of old train}$$

and

$$x + 64 = 208 \text{ km/h} = \text{speed of bullet train} \qquad \blacksquare$$

Check: Old train takes $\dfrac{1400}{144}$ h $= 9.72$ h

Bullet train takes $\dfrac{1400}{208 \text{ h}} = 6.73$ h

The difference is 3 h.

Exercise 4 Applications and Word Problems

Number Problems

1. What fraction added to its reciprocal gives $2\frac{1}{6}$?
2. Find three consecutive numbers such that the sum of their squares will be 434.
3. Find two numbers whose difference is 7 and the difference of whose cubes is 1267.
4. Find two numbers whose sum is 11 and whose product is 30.
5. Find two numbers whose difference is 10 and the sum of whose squares is 250.
6. A number increased by its square is equal to 9 times the next higher number. Find the number.

The "numbers" in Problems 2 to 6 are all positive integers.

Geometry Problems

7. A rectangle is to be 2 m longer than it is wide and have an area of 24 m². Find its dimensions.
8. One leg of a right triangle is 30 mm greater than the other leg, and the hypotenuse is 150 mm. Find the legs of the triangle.
9. A rectangular sheet of brass is twice as long as it is wide. A square 30 mm × 30 mm is cut from each corner (Fig. 14•2), and the ends are turned up to form an open box having a volume of 648 000 mm³. What are the dimensions of the original sheet of brass?
10. The length, width, and height of a cubical shipping container are all decreased by 1.0 m, thereby decreasing the volume of the cube by 37 m³. What was the volume of the original container?
11. Find the dimensions of a rectangular field that has a perimeter of 724 m and an area of 32 400 m².
12. A flat of width w is to be cut on a bar of radius r (Fig. 14•3). Show that the required depth of cut x is given by the formula

$$x = r \pm \sqrt{r^2 - \frac{w^2}{4}}$$

30 mm

30 mm

FIGURE 14•2

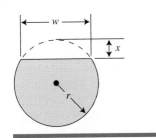

w

x

r

FIGURE 14•3

FIGURE 14·4

FIGURE 14·5

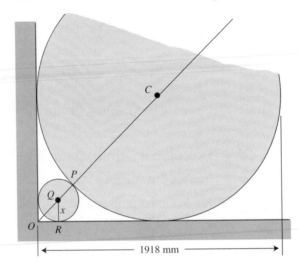

13. A casting in the shape of a cube is seen to shrink 4.45 mm on a side, with a reduction in volume of 40 640 mm³. Find the original dimensions of the cube.

14. The cylinder in Figure 14·4 has a surface area of 84 600 mm², including the ends. Find its radius.

15. A cylindrical tank having a diameter of 1918 mm is placed so that it touches a wall, as in Figure 14·5. Find the radius x of the largest pipe that can fit into the space between the tank, the wall, and the floor. *Hint:* First use the Pythagorean theorem to show that $OC = 1356$ mm and that $OP = 397.0$ mm. Then in triangle OQR, $(OP - x)^2 = x^2 + x^2$.

Uniform Motion

16. A truck travels 562 km to a delivery point, unloads, and, now empty, returns to the starting point at a speed 12.8 km/h greater than on the outward trip. What was the speed of the outward trip if the total round-trip driving time was 14.4 h?

17. An airplane flies $58\overline{0}$ km to Sydney. Then, with better winds, it continues on to Melbourne, $72\overline{0}$ km from Sydney, at a speed 25.0 km/h greater than on the first leg of the trip. The total flying time was 5.20 h. Find the speed at which the plane traveled to Sydney.

18. An express bus travels a certain $40\overline{0}$ km route in 1.0 h less time than it takes a local bus to travel a 380 km route. Find the speed of each bus if the speed of the local bus is 16 km/h less than that of the express.

19. A trucker calculates that, if he increases his average speed by 20 km/h, he could travel his 800-km route in 2.0 h less time than usual. Find his usual speed.

20. A boat sails 30 km at a uniform rate. If the rate had been 1 km/h more, the time of the sailing would have been 1 h less. Find the rate of travel.

Work Problems

21. A certain punch press requires 3 h longer to stamp a box of parts than does a newer-model punch press. After the older press has been punching a box of parts for 5 h, it is joined by the newer machine. Together, they finish the box of parts in 3 additional hours. How long does it take each machine, working alone, to punch a box of parts?

Load, w N/m

FIGURE 14·6 Simply supported beam
with a uniformly distributed load

22. Two water pipes together can fill a certain tank in 8.40 h. The smaller pipe alone takes 2.50 h longer than the larger pipe to fill that same tank. How long would it take the larger pipe alone to fill the tank?

23. A laborer built 35 m of stone wall. If she had built 2 m less each day, it would have taken her 2 days longer. How many metres did she build each day, working at her usual rate?

24. A woman worked a certain number of days, receiving for her pay $1800. If she had received $10 per day less than she did, she would have had to work 3 days longer to earn the same sum. How many days did she work?

Simply Supported Beam

25. For a simply supported beam of length l having a distributed load of w N/m (Figure 14·6), the bending moment M at any distance x from one end is given by

$$M = \frac{1}{2}\,wlx - \frac{1}{2}\,wx^2$$

Find the locations on the beam where the bending moment is zero.

26. A simply supported beam, 7.60 m long, carries a distributed load of 7.00 kN/m. At what distance from an end of the beam will the bending moment be 48 300 N·m? (Use the equation from Problem 25.)

Use $s = v_0 t + \frac{1}{2}\,at^2$, Eq. A18, for these falling-body problems, but be careful of the signs. If you take the upward direction as positive, a will be *negative*.

Freely Falling Body

27. An object is thrown upward with a velocity of 44.0 m/s. When will it be 26.0 m above its initial position?

28. An object is thrown upward with an initial speed of $12\overline{0}$ m/s. Find the time required for it to return to its starting point.

In series

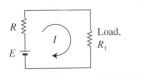

In parallel

FIGURE 14·7

Electrical Problems

29. What two resistances (Fig. 14·7) will give a total resistance of 780 Ω when wired in series and 105 Ω when wired in parallel? (See Eq. A63 and A64.)

30. Find two resistances that will give an equivalent resistance of 9070 Ω in series and 1070 Ω in parallel.

31. In the circuit of Figure 14·8 the power P dissipated in the load resistor R_1 is

$$P = EI - I^2 R$$

If the voltage E is 115 V, and $R = 105$ Ω, find the current I needed to produce a power of 29.3 W in the load.

32. The reactance X of a capacitance C and an inductance L in series (Fig. 14·9) is

$$X = \omega L - \frac{1}{\omega C}$$

FIGURE 14·8

FIGURE 14·9

where ω is the angular frequency in rad/s, L is in henries, and C is in farads. Find the angular frequency needed to make the reactance equal 1500 Ω, if $L = 0.5$ henry, and $C = 0.2 \times 10^{-6}$ farad (0.2 microfarad).

FIGURE 14•10

FIGURE 14•11 *N-channel JFET*

33. Figure 14•10 shows two currents flowing in a single resistor R. The total current in the resistor will be $I_1 + I_2$, so the power dissipated is

$$P = (I_1 + I_2)^2 R$$

If $R = 110\ \Omega$ and $I_2 = 0.2$ A, find the current I_1 needed to produce a power of 9.0 W.

34. A *square-law device* is one whose output is proportional to the square of the input. A junction field-effect transistor (JFET) (Fig. 14•11) is such a device. The current I that will flow through an n-channel JFET when a voltage V is applied is

$$I = A\left(1 - \frac{V}{B}\right)^2$$

where A is the drain saturation current and B is the gate source pinch-off voltage. Solve this equation for V.

35. A certain JFET has a drain saturation current of 4.8 mA and a gate source pinch-off voltage of -2.5 V. What input voltage is needed to produce a current of 1.5 mA?

14•5   Graphing the Quadratic Function

Quadratic Function

A *quadratic function* is one whose highest-degree term is of second degree.

■ **Example 21:** The functions
(a) $f(x) = 5x^2 - 3x + 2$ (b) $f(x) = 9 - 3x^2$
(c) $f(x) = x(x + 7)$ (d) $f(x) = x - 4 - 3x^2$
are quadratic functions. ■

The parabola is one of the four *conic sections* (the curves obtained when a cone is intersected by a plane, at various angles), and it has many interesting properties and applications. We take only a very brief look at the parabola here, with the main treatment saved for our study of the conic sections.

The Parabola

When we plot a quadratic function, we get the well-known and extremely useful curve called the *parabola*.

■ **Example 22:** Plot the quadratic function $y = x^2 + x - 3$, for $x = -3$ to 3.

Solution: We can graph the function using a graphics calculator or graphing software on a computer, or by computing a table of point pairs as was shown in Section 5•2.

x	-3	-2	-1	0	1	2
y	3	-1	-3	-3	-1	3

We plot these points (Fig. 14•12) and connect them with a smooth curve, a parabola.

FIGURE 14•12 A parabola

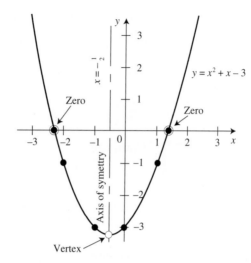

Note that the curve in this example is symmetrical about the line $x = -\frac{1}{2}$. This line is called the axis of symmetry. The point where the parabola crosses the axis of symmetry is called the *vertex*.

Recall that in Chapter 5 we said that a low point in a curve is called a *minimum point*, and that a high point is called a *maximum point*. Thus the vertex of this parabola is also a minimum point.   ▬

Solving Quadratics Graphically

This, of course, is not a practical way to solve a quadratic. It is much faster and more accurate to use the formula. However, the same method is valuable for finding the roots of other equations that cannot be as easily solved algebraically.

In Section 4•5 we saw that a graphical solution to the equation

$$f(x) = 0$$

could be obtained by plotting the function

$$y = f(x)$$

and locating the points where the curve crosses the x axis. These points are called the zeros of the function. They are the solution, or roots, of the equation. Notice that in Figure 14•12 there are two zeros, corresponding to the two roots of the equation.

▬ **Example 23:** Graphically find the approximate roots of the equation

$$x^2 + x - 3 = 0$$

Solution: The function

$$y = x^2 + x - 3$$

is already plotted in Figure 14•12. Reading the x intercepts as accurately as possible, we get for the roots

$$x \simeq -2.3 \quad \text{and} \quad x \simeq 1.3$$

If we were using a graphics utility, we could use TRACE and ZOOM to get the roots to whatever accuracy we wanted.   ▬

Exercise 5 Graphing the Quadratic Function

Plot the following quadratic functions. Use a graphics utility or a point-by-point plot, as directed by your instructor. Label the vertex, any zeros, and the axis of symmetry.

1. $y = x^2 + 3x - 15$ **2.** $y = 5x^2 + 14x - 3$
3. $y = 8x^2 - 6x + 1$ **4.** $y = 2.74x^2 - 3.12x + 5.38$

Computer

5. If you have graphing software, use it to make any of the graphs in this exercise. If you have written a program for generating a table of point pairs (see Chapter 5, Exercise 2), use it to compute the points needed to graph any of these equations.

Parabolic Arch

6. The parabolic arch is often used in construction because of its great strength. The equation of the bridge arch in Figure 14•13 is $y = -0.0625x^2 + 5x - 100$. Find the distances a, b, c, and d.

FIGURE 14•13 A parabolic bridge arch. Note that the *y* axis is positive downward.

7. Plot the parabolic arch of Problem 6, taking values of x every 10.0 m.

Parabolic Reflector

8. The parabolic solar collector in Figure 14•14 has the equation $x^2 = 125y$. Plot the curve, taking values of x every 10 mm.

FIGURE 14•14

A parabolic surface has the property that all the incoming rays that are parallel to the axis of symmetry, after being reflected from the surface of the parabola, will converge to a single point called the *focus*. This property is used in optical and radio telescopes, solar collectors, searchlights, microwave and radar antennas, and other devices.

9. Find the depth d of the collector of Problem 8 at its center.

Vertical Highway Curves

Where there is a change in the slope of a highway surface, such as at the top of a hill or the bottom of a dip, the roadway is often made parabolic in shape to provide a smooth transition between the two different grades.

To construct a vertical highway curve (Fig. 14•15) we make use of the following property of the parabola:

The offset C from a tangent to a parabola is proportional to the square of the distance x from the point of tangency.

or $C = kx^2$, where k is a constant of proportionality, found from a known offset.

FIGURE 14•15 A dip in a highway

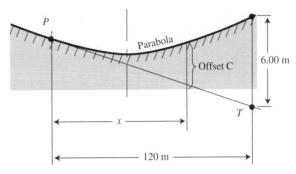

10. If the offset is 6.00 m at a point $12\overline{0}$ m from the point of tangency, find the constant of proportionality k.

11. For the highway curve of Problem 10, find the offset at a point 68.0 m from the point of tangency.

Square-Law Devices

12. For the *n*-channel JFET of Exercise 4, Problem 35, plot the curve of current *I* versus applied voltage *V*, the vertical axis for current, and the horizontal axis for voltage. Compute *I* for values of V from -2.5 V to 0 V. (The curve obtained is a parabola and is called the *transconductance curve*.) Graphically determine the voltage needed to produce a current of 1.0 mA.

14•6

Equations of Quadratic Type

Recognition of Form

The general quadratic, Eq. 99, can be written

$$a(x)^2 + b(x) + c = 0$$

The form of this equation obviously does not change if we put a different symbol in the parentheses, as long as we put the same one in both places. The equations

$$a(Q)^2 + b(Q) + c = 0$$

and

$$a(\$)^2 + b(\$) + c = 0$$

are still quadratics. The form still does not change if we put more complicated expressions in the parentheses, such as

$$a(x^2)^2 + b(x^2) + c = 0$$

or

$$a\left(\sqrt{x}\right)^2 + b\left(\sqrt{x}\right) + c = 0$$

or

$$a(x^{-1/3})^2 + b(x^{-1/3}) + c = 0$$

The preceding three equations can no longer be called quadratics, however, because they are no longer of second degree. They are called *equations of quadratic type*. They can be easily recognized because the power of x in one term is always twice the power of x in another term (and there are no other terms containing powers of x).

Solving Equations of Quadratic Type

The solution of these equations is best shown by examples.

■ **Example 24:** Solve

$$x^4 - 5x^2 + 4 = 0$$

Solution: We see that the power of x in the first term (4) is twice the power of x in the second term (2). Make the substitution; let $w = x^2$. The original equation then becomes the quadratic,

$$w^2 - 5w + 4 = 0$$

Factoring yields

$$(w - 1)(w - 4) = 0$$

So

$$w = 1 \quad \text{and} \quad w = 4$$

but

$$w = x^2 = 1 \quad \text{and} \quad w = x^2 = 4$$

So

$$x = \pm 1 \quad \text{and} \quad x = \pm 2$$

Check: The four values, 1, −1, 2, and −2, each satisfy the original equation (work not shown). ■

■ **Example 25:** Solve the equation

$$2x^{-1/3} + x^{-2/3} + 1 = 0$$

Solution: Inspecting the powers of x, we see that one of them, $-\frac{2}{3}$, is twice the other, $-\frac{1}{3}$. We make the substitution,

$$w = x^{-1/3}$$

and our equation becomes

$$2w + w^2 + 1 = 0$$

or

$$w^2 + 2w + 1 = 0$$

which factors into

$$(w + 1)(w + 1) = 0$$

Setting each factor equal to zero yields

$$w + 1 = 0 \quad \text{and} \quad w + 1 = 0$$

So

$$w = -1 = x^{-1/3}$$

Cubing both sides, we get

$$x^{-1} = (-1)^3 = -1$$

$$x^{-1} = \frac{1}{x} = -1$$

So

$$x = \frac{1}{-1} = -1$$

Check: $\qquad 2(-1)^{-1/3} + (-1)^{-2/3} + 1 \overset{?}{=} 0$

$$2(-1) \quad + (1) \quad + 1 = 0$$

$$0 = 0 \qquad \text{checks} \qquad \blacksquare$$

Exercise 6 Equations of Quadratic Type

Solve for all real values of x.

1. $x^6 - 6x^3 + 8 = 0$ **2.** $x^4 - 10x^2 + 9 = 0$
3. $x^{-1} - 2x^{-1/2} + 1 = 0$ **4.** $9x^4 - 6x^2 + 1 = 0$
5. $x^{-2/3} - x^{-1/3} = 0$ **6.** $x^{-6} + 19x^{-3} = 216$
7. $x^{-10/3} + 244x^{-5/3} + 243 = 0$ **8.** $x^6 - 7x^3 = 8$
9. $x^{2/3} + 3x^{1/3} = 4$ **10.** $64 + 63x^{-3/2} - x^{-3} = 0$
11. $81x^{-3/4} - 308 - 64x^{3/4} = 0$ **12.** $27x^6 + 46x^3 = 16$
13. $x^{1/2} - x^{1/4} = 20$ **14.** $3x^{-2} + 14x^{-1} = 5$
15. $2.35x^{1/2} - 1.82x^{1/4} = 43.8$ **16.** $1.72x^{-2} + 4.75x^{-1} = 2.24$

Computer

17. Use your program for finding roots of equations from Section 5•6 to solve any of the equations in this exercise.
18. A computer is especially useful for solving the complex equations in this section and in the one to follow. Some mathematical software, such as *MathCAD*, will give the approximate values of the roots using the ROOT command. A computer algebra system will give exact roots when it can; otherwise, it will give approximate roots. *Derive*, for example, must be put into APPROXIMATE mode for most of the equations in this exercise and those following, for it cannot solve them in EXACT mode. In approximate mode we must enter the range of x values between which we want the computer to search for a root. The simplest way to get these ranges is to have the computer graph the equation and to note where the graph crosses the x axis.
    Use a computer to solve any of the equations in this exercise.

14•7

Simple Equations of Higher Degree

Polynomial of Degree n

In Section 13•1, we used factoring to find the roots of a quadratic equation. We now expand this idea to include polynomials of higher degree. A polynomial, remember, has exponents that are all positive integers.

Polynomial of Degree n	$a_0x^n + a_1x^{n-1} + \cdots + a_{n-1}x + a_n$	**102**

The Factor Theorem

For example, in Section 14•1 the expression

$$x^2 - x - 6 = 0$$

factored into

$$(x - 3)(x + 2) = 0$$

and hence had the roots

$$x = 3 \quad \text{and} \quad x = -2$$

In a similar way, the cubic equation

$$x^3 - 7x - 6 = 0$$

has the factors

$$(x + 1)(x - 3)(x + 2) = 0$$

and hence has the roots

$$x = -1 \qquad x = 3 \qquad x = -2$$

In general,

Factor Theorem	If a polynomial equation $f(x) = 0$ has a root of r, then $(x - r)$ is a factor of the polynomial $f(x)$. Conversely, if $(x - r)$ is a factor of a polynomial $f(x)$, then r is a root of $f(x) = 0$.	**103**

Number of Roots

A polynomial equation of degree n *has* n *and only* n *roots*. Two or more of the roots may be equal, however, and some may be nonreal, giving the appearance of fewer than n roots; but there can never be *more* than n roots.

Solving Polynomial Equations

A graph of the function is very helpful in finding the roots.

If the expression cannot be factored directly, we proceed largely by trial and error to obtain one root. Once a root r is obtained (and verified by substituting in the equation), we obtain a *reduced* or *depressed* equation by dividing the original equation by $(x - r)$. The process is then repeated.

■ **Example 26:** A graph, Figure 14•16, shows that one root of the cubic equation $16x^3 - 13x + 3 = 0$ is $x = -1$. Find the other roots.

Solution: For a cubic, we expect a maximum of three roots. By the factor theorem, since $x = -1$ is a root, then $(x + 1)$ must be a factor of the given equation. Thus

$$(x + 1)(\text{other factor}) = 0$$

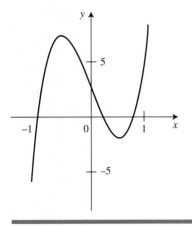

FIGURE 14·16 Graph of
$y = 16x^3 = 13x + 3$

We obtain the "other factor" by dividing the given equation by $(x + 1)$, getting $16x^2 - 16x + 3$ (work not shown). The "other factor," or reduced equation, is then the quadratic,

$$16x^2 - 16x + 3 = 0$$

By the quadratic formula,

$$x = \frac{16 \pm \sqrt{16^2 - 4(16)(3)}}{2(16)} = \frac{1}{4} \quad \text{and} \quad \frac{3}{4}$$

Our three roots are therefore $x = -1$, $x = \dfrac{1}{4}$, and $x = \dfrac{3}{4}$.

Solution of Equations by Approximate Methods

To solve an equation by the factor theorem, the equation must, of course, be factorable. This requirement severely limits the use of this method for practical problems.

Fortunately, we have several ways to solve nonfactorable equations approximately. That the solution is "approximate" is usually not a difficulty, because these methods allow us to obtain as many significant digits as we want.

We have already described:

1. Graphical solution of equations, with or without the graphics calculator, Section 5·5
2. Computer solution of equations by the midpoint method, Section 5·5
3. The use of commercially available computer software, such as *MathCAD*, *Derive*, *Maple*, *Mathematica*, and so forth

Here we give another computer method.

Simple Iteration: A Computer Method

This is also known as the *method of Picard*, after Charles Émile Picard, 1856–1941.

We already have the midpoint method for computer solution of equations, and now we learn the method of *simple iteration*.

With this method, we split the given equation into two or more terms, one of which is the unknown itself, and move the unknown to the left side of the equation. We then guess the value of x and substitute it into the right side of the equation to obtain another value of x, which is then substituted into the equation, and so on, until our values converge on the correct value of x.

■ **Example 27:** Find one root of the equation from Example 26,

$$16x^3 - 13x + 3 = 0$$

by simple iteration. Assume that there is a root somewhere near $x = 1$.

Solution: The equation contains an x in both the first and second terms. Either can be chosen to isolate on the left side of the equation. Let us choose the first term. Rearranging yields

$$16x^3 = 13x - 3$$

Dividing gives

$$x^3 = 0.8125x - 0.1875$$

if we work to four significant digits. Taking the cube root of both sides, we get

$$x = (0.8125x - 0.1875)^{1/3} \tag{1}$$

Note that we have not *solved* the equation, because there is still an x on the right side of the equation.

For a first approximation, let $x = 1$. Substituting into the right side of equation (1) gives

$$x = (0.8125 - 0.1875)^{1/3}$$

$$= 0.8550$$

This, of course, is not a root, but only a *second approximation* to a root. We now take the value 0.8550 and substitute it into the right side of equation (1).

$$x = [0.8125(0.8550) - 0.1875]^{1/3}$$

$$= 0.7975$$

This third approximation is substituted into (1), giving

$$x = [0.8125(0.7975) - 0.1875]1/3$$

$$= 0.7722$$

We continue, getting the following table of values:

0.8550
0.7975
0.7722
0.7605
0.7550
0.7524
0.7512
0.7506
0.7503

If the computation diverges instead of converging, we split the equation in a different way and try again. In the example here, we would isolate the x in the middle term, rather than the one in the first term.

Notice that we are converging on the value

$$x = 0.750$$

which is one of the roots found in Example 26. With a different first guess, we can usually make the computation converge on one of the other roots.

Exercise 7 Simple Equations of Higher Degree

Find the remaining roots of each polynomial, given one root.

1. $x^3 + x^2 - 17x + 15 = 0$		$x = 1$
2. $x^3 + 9x^2 + 2x - 48 = 0$		$x = 2$
3. $x^3 - 2x^2 - x + 2 = 0$		$x = 1$
4. $x^3 + 9x^2 + 26x + 24 = 0$		$x = -2$
5. $2x^3 + 7x^2 - 7x - 12 = 0$		$x = -1$
6. $3x^3 - 7x^2 + 4 = 0$		$x = 1$
7. $9x^3 + 21x^2 - 20x - 32 = 0$		$x = -1$
8. $16x^4 - 32x^3 - 13x^2 + 29x - 6 = 0$		$x = -1$

Graphics Calculator and Computer

9. Use a graphics calculator to find the roots of the above equations to three significant digits, using the TRACE and ZOOM features.

10. Use mathematical computation software or a computer algebra system to find the roots of any of the above equations, to three significant digits. You will have to be in APPROXIMATE mode, and will need to enter the values of x between which the root is located.

11. Write a program or use a spreadsheet for solving equations by simple iteration. Use it to find the roots of any of the above equations, to three significant digits.

12. Use your program for finding roots by the midpoint method to find the roots of any of the above equations, to three significant digits.

Find the roots of the following equations, to three significant digits. Use a graphics calculator, mathematical software, simple iteration, or the midpoint method.

13. $15.2x^3 - 11.3x + 1.72 = 0$
14. $1.26x^3 - 1.83x + 1.03 = 0$
15. $8.62x^3 - 6.27x + 1.62 = 0$
16. $3.92x^4 - 3.84x - 6.26 = 0$
17. $4.82x^4 - 16.1x^3 + 3.25 = 0$
18. $8.33x^4 + 3.95x^3 - 2.25x - 9.02 = 0$

14·8   Systems of Quadratic Equations

In Chapter 10 we solved systems of *linear* equations. We now use the same techniques, substitution or addition–subtraction, to solve sets of two equations in two unknowns, where one or both equations are of second degree.

One Equation Linear and One Quadratic

These are best done by substitution.

━ **Example 28:** Solve for x and y, to two decimal places.

$$2x + y = 5$$
$$2x^2 + y^2 = 17$$

Solution: From the first equation,

$$x = \frac{5 - y}{2}$$

Squaring gives

$$x^2 = \frac{25 - 10y + y^2}{4}$$

Substituting into the second equation yields

$$\frac{2(25 - 10y + y^2)}{4} + y^2 = 17$$
$$25 - 10y + y^2 + 2y^2 = 34$$

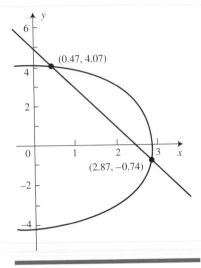

FIGURE 14•17

We get the quadratic

$$3y^2 - 10y - 9 = 0$$

which, by quadratic formula, gives

$$y = 4.07 \quad \text{and} \quad y = -0.74$$

Substituting back for x gives

$$x = \frac{5 - 4.07}{2} = 0.47 \quad \text{and} \quad x = \frac{5 - (-0.74)}{2} = 2.87$$

So our two solutions are (0.47, 4.07) and (2.87, −0.74). The graphs (Fig. 14•17) of the two given equations show points of intersection at those coordinates. ▬

▬ **Example 29:** Solve for x and y.

$$x + y = 2$$
$$xy + 15 = 0$$

Solution: From the first equation,

$$y = 2 - x$$

Substituting into the second equation, we have

$$x(2 - x) + 15 = 0$$

from which

$$x^2 - 2x - 15 = 0$$

Factoring gives

$$(x - 5)(x + 3) = 0$$
$$x = 5 \quad \text{and} \quad x = -3$$

Substituting back yields

$$y = 2 - 5 = -3$$

and

$$y = 2 - (-3) = 5$$

so the solutions are

$$x = 5, y = -3 \quad \text{and} \quad x = -3, y = 5$$

See Figure 14•18. ▬

Both Equations Quadratic

These may be solved either by substitution or by addition–subtraction.

▬ **Example 30:** Solve for x and y:

$$3x^2 - 4y = 47$$
$$7x^2 + 6y = 33$$

FIGURE 14·18

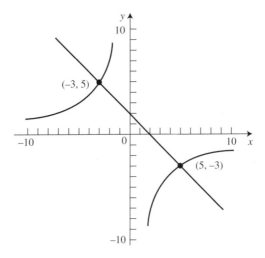

Solution: We multiply the first equation by 3 and the second by 2:

$$9x^2 - 12y = 141$$
$$14x^2 + 12y = 66$$

Add:
$$23x^2 = 207$$
$$x^2 = 9$$
$$x = \pm 3$$

Substituting back, we get $y = -5$ for both $x = 3$ and $x = -3$. A plot of the given curves (Fig. 14·19) clearly shows the points of intersection $(3, -5)$ and $(-3, -5)$.

FIGURE 14·19 Intersection of two parabolas. This is a good way to get an approximate solution to any pair of equations that can readily be graphed.

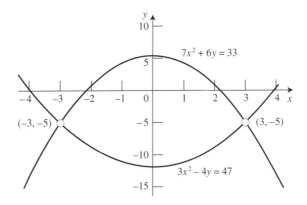

The graphs of the equations in the preceding examples intersected at two points. However, the graphs of two second-degree equations can sometimes intersect at as many as four points.

■ **Example 31:** Solve for x and y:

$$3x^2 + 4y^2 = 76$$

$$-11x^2 + 3y^2 = 4$$

Solution: We multiply the first equation by 3 and the second by -4.

$$9x^2 + 12y^2 = 228$$
$$\underline{44x^2 - 12y^2 = -16}$$

Add: $\qquad\qquad\quad 53x^2 = 212$

$$x^2 = 4$$
$$x = \pm 2$$

From the first equation, when x is either $+2$ or -2,

$$4y^2 = 76 - 12 = 64$$
$$y = \pm 4$$

So our solutions are

$x = 2$	$x = 2$	$x = -2$	$x = -2$
$y = 4$	$y = -4$	$y = 4$	$y = -4$

Sometimes we can eliminate the squared terms from a pair of equations, and obtain a linear equation. This linear equation can then be solved simultaneously with one of the original equations.

— **Example 32:** Solve for x and y:

$$x^2 + y^2 - 3y = 4$$
$$x^2 + y^2 + 2x - 5y = 2$$

Solution: Subtracting the second equation from the first gives

$$-2x + 2y = 2$$

or

$$y = x + 1$$

Substituting $x + 1$ for y in the first equation gives

$$x^2 + (x + 1)^2 - 3(x + 1) = 4$$
$$2x^2 - x - 6 = 0$$

Factoring yields

$$(x - 2)(2x + 3) = 0$$

From which

$$x = 2 \quad \text{and} \quad x = -3/2$$

Substituting $x = 2$ into both original equations gives

$$y = 0, y = 2, y = 3$$

Substituting $x = -3/2$ into both original equation gives

$$y = 7/2, y = 11/2, y = -1/2$$

We now have solutions of $(2, 3)$, $(-3/2, -1/2)$, $(2, 0)$, $(2, 2)$, $(-3/2, 7/2)$, and $(-3/2, 11/2)$. Only two of these,

$$(2, 3) \quad \text{and} \quad (-3/2, -1/2)$$

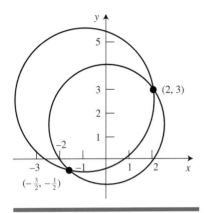

FIGURE 14·20

check in both original equations. Figure 14·20 shows plots of the two original equations, which graph as circles. The points found are the coordinates of the points of intersection of the two circles.

Solution by Graphics Calculator or Computer

In Section 10·1 we showed how to use a graphics calculator or graphing software on a computer to solve a system of linear equations. We simply graphed the two lines and found the coordinates of the point of intersection. Then, using the TRACE and ZOOM features, we could obtain the coordinates with any degree of accuracy that we wanted.

The procedure here is the same, except now there will usually be more than one point of intersection. Also, since the calculator or computer requires the equations to be in *explicit form*, we must solve each equation for y.

■ **Example 33:** Use a graphics utility to solve the system of equations

$$2.74x + 1.04y = 4.88$$

$$2.03x^2 + 1.63y^2 = 15.3$$

to three significant digits.

Solution: We first solve each equation for y. The first equation gives

$$y = \frac{4.88 - 2.74x}{1.04}$$

and from the second original equation we get

$$y = \pm\sqrt{\frac{15.3 - 2.03x^2}{1.63}}$$

We need both the plus and minus in this equation, to get both the upper and lower portions of the curve, so in our graphics calculator or computer program we enter the equations

$$Y_1 = (4.88 - 2.74x)/1.04$$

$$Y_2 = ((15.3 - 2.03x\char`\^2)/1.63)\char`\^(1/2)$$

$$Y_3 = -((15.3 - 2.03x\char`\^2)/1.63\char`\^(1/2)$$

We get the graph shown in Figure 14·21. Using TRACE, we read the coordinates of one of the points of intersection. We then zoom in repeatedly, until our reading of the coordinates no longer changes in the third digit. We then repeat this operation for the other point. Doing this, we get the points

$$(0.651, 2.98) \quad \text{and} \quad (2.37, -1.55)$$

The approximate solution to our set of equations, to three significant digits, is then,

$$x = 0.651, y = 2.98 \quad \text{and} \quad x - 2.37, y = -1.55$$ ■

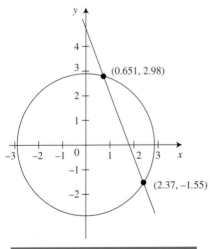

FIGURE 14·21

Exercise 8 Systems of Quadratic Equations

Solve for x and y.

1. $x - y = 4$
$x^2 - y^2 = 32$

2. $x + y = 5$
$x^2 + y^2 = 13$

3. $x + 2y = 7$
$2x^2 - y^2 = 14$

4. $x - y = 15$
$x = 2y^2$

5. $4y + x = 14$
$y^2 - 2y + 4x = 11$

6. $x^2 + y = 3$
$x^2 - y = 4$

7. $2x^2 + 3y = 10$
$x^2 - y = 8$

8. $2x^2 - 3y = 15$
$5x^2 + 2y = 12$

9. $x + 3y^2 = 7$
$2x - y^2 = 9$

10. $x^2 - y^2 = 3$
$x^2 + 3y^2 = 7$

11. $x - y = 11$
$xy + 28 = 0$

12. $x^2 + y^2 - 8x - 4y + 16 = 0$
$x^2 + y^2 - 4x - 8y + 16 = 0$

Graphics Calculator and Computer

Use a graphics calculator or graphing software on a computer to find an approximate graphical solution to any of the above problems. Also use either device to solve the following, to three significant digits.

13. $3.52x^2 + 4.82y^2 = 34.2$
$5.92x - 3.72y = 4.58$

14. $15.1x^2 + 8.23y^2 = 23.2$
$9.22x - 5.47y = 2.84$

15. $7.15x^2 - 6.68y = 4.27$
$4.83x - 3.75y^2 = 1.83$

16. $11.2x - 14.2y^2 + 13.6 = 0$
$15.9x^2 - 13.7y = 14.8$

CHAPTER 14   REVIEW PROBLEMS

Solve each equation for any real roots.

1. $y^2 - 5y - 6 = 0$
2. $2x^2 - 5x = 2$
3. $x^4 - 13x^2 + 36 = 0$
4. $(a + b)x^2 + 2(a + b)x = -a$
5. $w^2 - 5w = 0$
6. $x(x - 2) = 2(-2 - x + x^2)$
7. $\dfrac{r}{3} = \dfrac{r}{r + 5}$
8. $6y^2 + y - 2 = 0$
9. $3t^2 - 10 = 13t$
10. $2.73x^2 + 1.47x - 5.72 = 0$
11. $\dfrac{1}{t^2} + 2 = \dfrac{3}{t}$
12. $3w^2 + 2w - 11 = 0$
13. $9 - x^2 = 0$

14. $\dfrac{2y}{3} = \dfrac{3}{5} + \dfrac{2}{y}$
15. $2x(x + 2) = x(x + 3) + 5$
16. $\dfrac{ax^2}{b} + \dfrac{bx}{c} + \dfrac{c}{a} = 0$
17. $y + 6 = 5y^{1/2}$
18. $18 + w^2 + 11w = 0$
19. $9y^2 + y = 5$
20. $\dfrac{5}{w} - \dfrac{4}{w^2} = \dfrac{3}{5}$
21. $\dfrac{z}{2} = \dfrac{5}{z}$
22. $3x - 6 = \dfrac{5x + 2}{4x}$
23. $2x^2 + 3x = 2$
24. $x^2 + Rx - R^2 = 0$

25. $27x = 3x^2$

26. $\dfrac{n}{n + 1} = \dfrac{2}{n + 3} - 1$

27. $z^{2/3} + 8 = 9z^{1/3}$

28. $6w^2 + 13w + 6 = 0$

29. $5y^2 = 125$

30. $\dfrac{t + 2}{t} = \dfrac{4t}{3}$

31. $1.26x^2 - 11.8 = 1.13x$

32. $2.62z^2 + 4.73z - 5.82 = 0$

33. $5.12y^2 + 8.76y - 9.89 = 0$

34. $3w^2 + 2w^4 - 2 = 0$

35. $27.2w^2 + 43.6w = 45.2$

36. $2.35x^{-2} + 4.26x^{-1} - 5.57 = 0$

37. $3.21z^6 - 21.3 = 4.23z^3$

38. If one root is $x = 1$, find the other roots of the equation

$$x^3 + x^2 - 5x + 3$$

39. Solve for x and y.

$$x^2 + y^2 = 55$$
$$x + y = 7$$

40. Solve for x and y.

$$x - y^2 = 1$$
$$x^2 + 3y^2 = 7$$

41. If one root is $x = -1$, find the other roots of the equation

$$x^4 - 2x^3 - 13x^2 + 14x + 24 = 0$$

42. Plot the parabola $y = 3x^2 + 2x - 6$. Label the vertex, the axis of symmetry, and any zeros.

43. Solve for x and y.

$$x + 2y = 4$$
$$2x^2 - 4y = 1$$

44. Solve for x and y.

$$2x + y = 5$$
$$2x^2 + y = 8$$

45. A person purchased some bags of insulation for $1000. If she had purchased 5 more bags for the same sum, they would have cost 12 cents less per bag. How many did she buy?

46. The perimeter of a rectangular field is 56 m and its area 180 m². Find its dimensions.

47. A rectangular yard (Fig. 14•22) is to be enclosed by fence on three sides, and an existing wall is to form the fourth side. The area of the yard is to be 450 m², and the length is to be twice its width. Find the dimensions of the yard.

Existing wall

450 m²

Fence

FIGURE 14•22

48. A fast train runs 12.8 km/h faster than a slow train, and takes 3.00 h less to travel 460 km. Find the rates of the trains.

49. A man started to walk 5.00 km, intending to arrive at a certain time. After walking 2.00 km he was detained 10.0 min and had to walk the rest of the way 1.60 km/h faster in order to arrive at the intended time. What was his original speed?

50. A rectangular field is 12 m longer than it is wide and contains 448 m². What are the lengths of its sides?

51. A tractor wheel, 4.60 m in circumference, revolves in a certain number of seconds. If it revolved in a time longer by 1.0 s, the tractor would travel 4390 m less in 1.0 h. In how many seconds does it revolve?

52. The iron counterweight in Figure 14•23 is to have its weight increased by 50% by bolting plates of iron along the top and one side (but not at the ends). The top plate and the side plate have the same thickness. Find their thickness.

53. A 660-mm-wide strip of steel is to have its edges bent up at right angles to form an open trough, as in Figure 14•24. The cross-sectional area is to be 51 600 mm². Disregarding the thickness of the steel sheet, find the width and depth of the trough.

54. A boat sails 48 km at a uniform rate. If the rate had been 2.0 km/h less, the time of the sailing would have been 1 h more. Find the rate of travel.

55. In a certain number of hours a woman traveled 36.0 km. If she had traveled 1.50 km more per hour, it would have taken her 3.00 h less to make

FIGURE 14·23

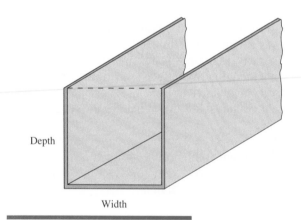

FIGURE 14·24

57. The area of an initially square plate will double if its dimensions are increased by 1.8 m along one side and 1.2 m along the other. Find its dimensions.

58. A mirror 460 mm by 320 mm is to be set in a frame of uniform width, and the area of the frame is to be equal to that of the glass. Find the width of the frame.

59. A heating element of 2.0-Ω resistance gives a power output of 16.0 kW when the supply voltage is increased by 35.0 V. Using Equations A66 and A67, find the original voltage.

60. The power in a circuit is given by $P = I^2R$. An increase of 1.80 A in the current produces a power of 312 W. Find the original current if the circuit resistance is 9.50 Ω.

Writing

61. As in Chapter 3, our writing assignment is to make up a word problem, but now we want a word problem that leads to a quadratic equation. As before, swap with a classmate, solve each other's problem, note anything unclear, unrealistic, or ambiguous, and then rewrite your problem if needed.

Team Project

62. In Exercise 4, Problem 25, we used a formula for the bending moment for a simply supported beam carrying a distributed load w (Fig. 14·6).

$$M = \frac{1}{2}wlx - \frac{1}{2}wx^2$$

The bending moment curve is therefore a parabola. Plot the curve of M against values of x for a 3.00-m-long beam carrying a load of 1360 N/m. Take 0.25 m intervals along the beam. Graphically locate **(a)** the points of zero bending moment, and **(b)** the point of maximum bending moment.

the journey. How many kilometres did she travel per hour?

56. The length of a rectangular court exceeds its width by 2 m. If the length and width were each increased by 3 m, the area of the court would be 80 m². Find the dimensions of the court.

15

Oblique Triangles and Vectors

OBJECTIVES

When you have completed this chapter, you should be able to:

- Identify the algebraic sign of a given trigonometric function for an angle in any quadrant.
- Write the trigonometric function of an angle given a point on the terminal side.
- Determine the reference angle for a given angle.
- Find a trigonometric function for any angle using a calculator.
- Determine the angle(s) given the value of a trigonometric function.
- Solve oblique triangles using the law of sines.
- Solve oblique triangles using the law of cosines.
- Solve applied problems requiring oblique triangles.
- Determine the resultant of two or more vectors.
- Resolve a vector into its components.
- Solve applied problems requiring vectors.

In Chapter 7 we defined the trigonometric functions for angles of any size, but used them only for acute angles. Here we learn how to find the trigonometric functions of obtuse angles, negative angles, angles greater than one revolution, and angles with terminal sides on the coordinate axes. We need the trigonometric functions of obtuse angles to solve oblique triangles, and the trigonometric functions of angles larger than 180° for vectors and other applications.

An *oblique triangle* is one that does not contain a right angle. In this chapter we derive two new formulas, the *law of sines* and the *law of cosines*, to enable us to solve oblique triangles quickly. We cannot, of course, use the methods we derived for solving right triangles (the Pythagorean theorem or the six trigonometric functions) to solve oblique triangles, although we will use these relationships to derive the law of sines and law of cosines.

We also continue our study of vectors in this chapter. In Chapter 7 we dealt with vectors at right angles to each other; here we consider vectors at any angle.

Trigonometric Functions of Any Angle

Definition of the Trigonometric Functions

We defined the trigonometric functions of any angle in Section 7•2 but have so far solved problems containing only acute angles. We turn now to larger angles.

Figure 15•1(a)–(c) shows angles in the second, third, and fourth quadrants, and Figure 15•1(d) shows an angle greater than 360°. The trigonometric functions of any of these angles are defined exactly as for an acute angle in quadrant I. From any point P on the terminal side of the angle we drop a perpendicular to the *x* axis, forming a right triangle with legs *x* and *y* and with a hypotenuse *r*. The six trigonometric ratios are then given by Eqs. 146 to 151, just as before, except that some of the ratios might now be negative.

FIGURE 15•1

(a)

(b)

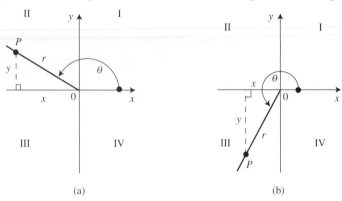

(c)   (d)

■ **Example 1:** A point on the terminal side of angle θ has the coordinates $(-3, -5)$. Write the six trigonometric functions of θ to three significant digits.

Solution: We sketch the angle (Fig. 15•2) and see that it lies in the third quadrant. We find distance *r* by the Pythagorean theorem:

$$r^2 = (-3)^2 + (-5)^2 = 9 + 25 = 34$$

$$r = 5.83$$

Then by Eqs. 146 to 151, with $x = -3$, $y = -5$, and $r = 5.83$,

$$\sin \theta = \frac{y}{r} = \frac{-5}{5.83} = -0.858$$

FIGURE 15•2

$$\cos \theta = \frac{x}{r} = \frac{-3}{5.83} = -0.515$$

$$\tan \theta = \frac{y}{x} = \frac{-5}{-3} = 1.67$$

$$\cot \theta = \frac{x}{y} = \frac{-3}{-5} = 0.600$$

$$\sec \theta = \frac{r}{x} = \frac{5.83}{-3} = -1.94$$

$$\csc \theta = \frac{r}{y} = \frac{5.83}{-5} = -1.17$$

Algebraic Signs of the Trigonometric Functions

Why bother learning the signs when a calculator gives them to us automatically? One reason is that you will need them when using a calculator to find the *inverse* of a function, as discussed later.

We saw in Chapter 7 that the trigonometric functions of first quadrant angles were always positive. From the preceding example, it is clear that some of the trigonometric functions of angles in the second, third, and fourth quadrants are negative, because x or y can be negative (r is always positive). Figure 15•3 shows the signs of the trigonometric functions in each quadrant.

Instead of trying to remember which trigonometric functions are negative in which quadrants, just sketch the angle and note whether x or y is negative. From this you can figure out whether the function you want is positive or negative.

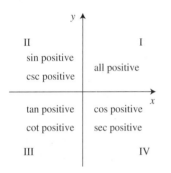

FIGURE 15•3

■ **Example 2:** What is the algebraic sign of $\csc 315°$?

Solution: We make a sketch, such as in Figure 15•4. It is not necessary to draw the angle accurately, but it must be shown in the proper quadrant, quadrant IV in this case. We note that y is negative and that r is (always) positive. So

$$\csc 315° = \frac{r}{y} = \frac{(+)}{(-)} = \text{negative}$$

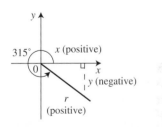

FIGURE 15•4

Trigonometric Functions of Any Angle by Calculator

In Section 7•2 we learned how to find the six trigonometric functions of an acute angle. Now we will find the trigonometric functions of any angle, acute or obtuse, positive or negative, less than or greater than 360°.

The keystrokes are exactly the same as we used for acute angles, and the calculator will automatically give the correct algebraic sign. On some calculators we enter the angle first, and then press the proper trigonometric key. On other calculators we press the trigonometric key first, and then enter the angle. Refer to your manual to see which way your calculator works.

For either type of calculator, you must put it into the proper mode, degree or radian, before doing the calculation. Use your calculator to verify the calculations in the following example, to four significant digits.

■ **Example 3:**
(a) $\sin 212° = -0.5299$
(b) $\cos 163° = -0.9563$
(c) $\tan 314° = -1.036$

As before, to find the cotangent, secant, and cosecant, we use the reciprocal relations:

Reciprocal Relationships	$\cot \theta = \dfrac{1}{\tan \theta}$ $\sec \theta = \dfrac{1}{\cos \theta}$ $\csc \theta = \dfrac{1}{\sin \theta}$	**152**

Verify the calculations in Examples 4, 5, and 6, to four significant digits.

■ **Example 4:**
(a) $\cot 101° = -0.1944$
(b) $\sec 213° = -1.192$
(c) $\csc 294° = -1.095$ ▬

Negative angles are entered directly on some calculators using the $\boxed{(-)}$ key. On other calculators, the positive angle is entered and its sign changed to negative using a change-sign key. Again, see your manual. Try the following.

■ **Example 5:**
(a) $\tan(-35.0°) = -0.7002$
(b) $\sec(-125°) = -1.743$ ▬

Angles greater than 360° are handled in the same manner as any other angle.

■ **Example 6:**
(a) $\cos 412° = 0.6157$
(b) $\csc 555° = -3.864$ ▬

Evaluating Trigonometric Expressions

In Section 7•2 we evaluated some simple trigonometric expressions. Here we will evaluate some that are slightly more complicated, and some that contain obtuse angles.

■ **Example 7:** Evaluate the expression

$$(\sin^2 48° + \cos 62°)^3$$

to four significant digits.

Solution: The notation $\sin^2 48°$ is the same as $(\sin 48°)^2$. Let us carry five digits and round to four in the last step.

$$(\sin^2 48° + \cos 62°)^3 = [(0.74314)^2 + 0.46947]^3$$
$$= (1.0217)^3 = 1.067 \qquad ▬$$

■ **Example 8:** Evaluate the expression

$$\cos 123.5° - \sin^2 242.7°$$

to four significant digits.

Solution: Since

$$\cos 123.5° = -0.55194$$

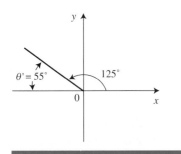

FIGURE 15·5 Reference angle θ'. It is also called the working angle.

and

$$\sin 242.7° = -0.88862$$

we get

$$\cos 123.5° - \sin^2 242.7° = -0.55194 - (-0.88862)^2$$
$$= -1.342$$

rounded to four digits. ▬

Common Error	Do not confuse an exponent that is on the angle with one that is on the entire function. $$(\sin \theta)^2 = \sin^2 \theta \neq \sin \theta^2$$

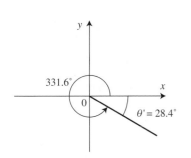

FIGURE 15·6

Reference Angle

Finding the trigonometric function of any angle by calculator is no problem—the calculator does all the thinking. This is not the case, however, when we are given the function and asked to find the angle, or when we have to find trigonometric functions in a table. For both these operations we will make use of the *reference angle*.

For an angle in standard position on coordinate axes, the *acute* angle that its terminal side makes with the *x* axis is called the *reference angle*.

▬ **Example 9:** The reference angle θ' for an angle of 125° is

$$\theta' = 180° - 125° = 55°$$

as in Figure 15·5. ▬

▬ **Example 10:** The reference angle θ' for an angle of 236° is

$$\theta' = 236° - 180° = 56°$$

as in Figure 15·6. ▬

We treat the quadrantal angles, 180° and 360°, as *exact* numbers. Thus the rounding of our answer is determined by the significant digits in the given angle.

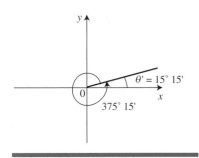

FIGURE 15·7

▬ **Example 11:** The reference angle θ' for an angle of 331.6° (Fig. 15·7) is

$$\theta' = 360° - 331.6° = 28.4°$$ ▬

▬ **Example 12:** The reference angle θ' for an angle of 375°15′ is

$$\theta' = 375°15' - 360° = 15°15'$$

as in Figure 15·8. ▬

Common Error	The reference angle is always measured from the *x* axis, and never measured from the *y* axis.

FIGURE 15·8

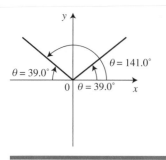

FIGURE 15•9

It may be helpful to remember that for an acute angle θ'

$$180° - \theta' \quad \text{is in quadrant II}$$
$$180° + \theta' \quad \text{is in quadrant III}$$
$$360° - \theta' \quad \text{is in quadrant IV}$$

Finding the Angle When the Function Is Given

We use the same procedure as was given for acute angles. However, a calculator gives us just *one* angle, when we enter the value of a trigonometric function. We know that there are infinitely many angles that have the same value of that trigonometric function. We must use the angle given by calculator to determine the reference angle, which is then used to compute as many larger angles as we wish having the same trigonometric ratio. Usually, we want only the two positive angles less than 360° that have the required trigonometric function.

■ **Example 13:** If $\sin \theta = 0.6293$, find two positive values of θ less than 360°. Work to the nearest tenth of a degree.

Solution: We use the $\boxed{\sin^{-1}}$ key (or the $\boxed{\text{arc}}$ $\boxed{\text{sin}}$ or $\boxed{\text{inv}}$ $\boxed{\text{sin}}$ keys) and get,

$$\theta' = 39.0°$$

Check your work by taking the sine. In this case, sin 141.0° = 0.6293. This checks.

The sine is positive in the first and second quadrants. Our first quadrant angle is 39.0° (Fig. 15•9), and our second quadrant angle is, taking 39.0° as the reference angle,

$$\theta = 180° - 39.0° = 141.0°$$ ■

■ **Example 14:** Find, to the nearest tenth of a degree, the two positive angles less than 360° that have a tangent of -2.25.

Solution: From the calculator, $\tan^{-1}(-2.25) = -66.0°$, so our reference angle is 66°. The tangent is negative in the second and fourth quadrants. Our second quadrant angle is

$$180° - 66.0° = 114.0°$$

and our fourth quadrant angle is (Fig. 15•10)

$$360° - 66.0° = 294.0°$$ ■

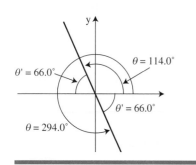

FIGURE 15•10

■ **Example 15:** Find $\cos^{-1} 0.575$, to the nearest tenth of a degree.

Solution: From the calculator,

$$\cos^{-1} 0.575 = 54.9°$$

The cosine is positive in the first and fourth quadrants. Our fourth quadrant angle is

$$360° - 54.9° = 305.1°$$ ■

Common Error	Do not confuse the *inverse* with the *reciprocal*. $$\underbrace{\sin^{-1}\theta}_{inverse} \ne \underbrace{(\sin\theta)^{-1}}_{reciprocal} = \cfrac{1}{\sin\theta}$$

When the cotangent, secant, or cosecant is given, we make use of the reciprocal relationships (Eqs. 152) as in the following example.

■ **Example 16:** Find two positive angles less than 360° that have a secant of −4.22. Work to the nearest tenth of a degree.

Solution: If we let the angle be θ, then, by Eq. 152(b),

$$\cos\theta = \frac{1}{\sec\theta} = \frac{1}{-4.22} = -0.237$$

By calculator,

$$\theta = 103.7° \qquad ■$$

The secant is also negative in the third quadrant. Our reference angle (Fig. 15•11) is

$$\theta' = 180° - 103.7° = 76.3°$$

so the third quadrant angle is

$$\theta' = 180° + 76.3° = 256.3° \qquad ■$$

■ **Example 17:** Evaluate arcsin (−0.528), to the nearest tenth of a degree.

Solution: As before, we seek only two positive angles less than 360°. By calculator,

$$\text{arcsin } (-0.528) = -31.9°$$

which is a fourth-quadrant angle. As a positive angle, it is

$$\theta = 360° - 31.9° = 328.1° \qquad ■$$

The sine is also negative in the third quadrant. Using 31.9° as our reference angle,

$$\theta = 180° + 31.9° = 211.9° \qquad ■$$

Special Angles

The angles in the following table appear so frequently in problems that it is convenient to be able to write their trigonometric functions from memory.

The angles 0°, 90°, 180°, and 360° are called *quadrantal* angles because the terminal side of each of them lies along one of the coordinate axes.

Notice that the tangent is undefined for 90° and 270°, angles whose terminal side is on the *y* axis. This is because, for any point (x, y) on the *y* axis, the value of *x* is zero. Since the tangent is equal to y/x, we have division by zero, which is not defined.

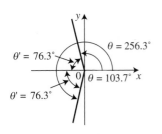

FIGURE 15•11

ANGLE	SINE	COSINE	TANGENT
0	0	1	0
30	$\frac{1}{2}$	$\sqrt{3}/2$ (or 0.8660)	$\sqrt{3}/3$ (or 0.5774)
45	$\sqrt{2}/2$ (or 0.7071)	$\sqrt{2}/2$ (or 0.7071)	1
60	$\sqrt{3}/2$ (or 0.8660)	$\frac{1}{2}$	$\sqrt{3}$ (or 1.732)
90	1	0	undefined
180	0	-1	0
270	-1	0	undefined
360	0	1	0

Exercise 1 Trigonometric Functions of Any Angle

Signs of the Trigonometric Functions

Assume all angles in this exercise to be in standard position.

State in what quadrant or quadrants the terminal side of θ can lie if:

1. $\theta = 123°$ **2.** $\theta = 272°$

3. $\theta = -47°$ **4.** $\theta = -216°$

5. $\theta = 415°$ **6.** $\theta = -415°$

7. $\theta = 845°$ **8.** $\sin \theta$ is positive

9. $\cos \theta$ is negative   **10.** $\sec \theta$ is positive

11. $\cos \theta$ is positive and $\sin \theta$ is negative

12. $\sin \theta$ and $\cos \theta$ are both negative

13. $\tan \theta$ is positive and $\csc \theta$ is negative

State whether the following expressions are positive or negative. Do not use your calculator, and try not to refer to your book.

14. $\sin 174°$ **15.** $\cos 329°$ **16.** $\tan 227°$

17. $\sec 332°$ **18.** $\cot 206°$ **19.** $\csc 125°$

20. $\sin(-47°)$ **21.** $\tan(-200°)$ **22.** $\cos 400°$

Give the algebraic signs of the sine, cosine, and tangent of:

23. $110°$ **24.** $206°$ **25.** $335°$

26. $-48°$ **27.** $500°$

Trigonometric Functions

Sketch the angle and write the six trigonometric functions if the terminal side of the angle passes through the point:

28. $(3, 5)$ **29.** $(-4, 12)$ **30.** $(24, -7)$

31. $(-15, -8)$ **32.** $(0, -3)$ **33.** $(5, 0)$

Write the sine, cosine, and tangent of θ if:

Leave your answers for this set in fractional or radical form.

34. $\sin \theta = -\frac{3}{5}$ and $\tan \theta$ is positive.

35. $\cos \theta = -\frac{4}{5}$ and θ is in the third quadrant.

36. $\csc \theta = -\frac{25}{7}$ and $\cos \theta$ is negative.

37. $\tan \theta = 2$ and θ is not in the first quadrant.

38. $\cot \theta = -\frac{4}{3}$ and $\sin \theta$ is positive.

39. $\sin \theta = \frac{2}{3}$ and θ is not in the first quadrant.

40. $\cos \theta = -\frac{7}{9}$ and $\tan \theta$ is negative.

Write, to four significant digits, the sine, cosine, and tangent of each angle.

41. 101°	**42.** 216°	**43.** 331°
44. 125.8°	**45.** −62.85°	**46.** −227.4°
47. 486°	**48.** −527°	**49.** 114°23′
50. 264°15′45″	**51.** −166°55′	**52.** 1.15°
53. −11°18′	**54.** 412°	**55.** 238°

Evaluating Trigonometric Expressions

Find the numerical value of each expression to four significant digits.

56. $\sin 35° + \cos 35°$

57. $\sin 125° \tan 225°$

58. $\cos 270° \cos 150° + \sin 270° \sin 150°$

59. $\dfrac{\sin^2 155°}{1 + \cos 155°}$

60. $\sin^2 75°$

61. $\tan^2 125° - \cos^2 125°$

62. $(\cos^2 206° + \sin 206°)^2$

63. $\sqrt{\sin^2 112° - \cos 112°}$

Inverse Trigonometric Functions

Find, to the nearest tenth of a degree, all positive angles less than 360° whose trigonometric function is:

64. $\sin \theta = \frac{1}{2}$	**65.** $\tan \theta = -1$
66. $\cot \theta = -\sqrt{3}$	**67.** $\cos \theta = 0.8372$
68. $\csc \theta = -3.85$	**69.** $\tan \theta = 6.372$
70. $\cos \theta = -\frac{1}{2}$	**71.** $\cot \theta = 0$
72. $\cos \theta = -1$	**73.** $\sin \theta = -0.6358$
74. $\cot \theta = -2.8458$	**75.** $\tan \theta = 1.7361$
76. $\cos \theta = 0.3759$	

Evaluate, to the nearest tenth of a degree.

77. arcsin(−0.736)	**78.** arcsec 2.85
79. $\cos^{-1} 0.827$	**80.** arccot 5.22
81. arctan(−4.48)	**82.** $\csc^{-1} 5.02$

Evaluate from memory. Do not use a calculator.

83. $\sin 30°$	**84.** $\cos 45°$	**85.** $\tan 180°$
86. $\sin 360°$	**87.** $\tan 45°$	**88.** $\cos 30°$
89. $\sin 180°$	**90.** $\cos 360°$	**91.** $\tan 0°$
92. $\sin 90°$	**93.** $\cos 180°$	**94.** $\sin 45°$
95. $\tan 360°$	**96.** $\cos 270°$	**97.** $\cos 60°$
98. $\sin 60°$	**99.** $\cos 0°$	**100.** $\tan 90°$
101. $\cos 90°$		

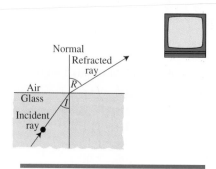

FIGURE 15•12 Refraction of light

Computer

102. Figure 15•12 shows a ray of light passing from glass to air. The angle of refraction R is related to the angle of incidence I by Snell's law,

$$\frac{\sin R}{\sin I} = \text{constant}$$

Using a value for the constant (called the index of refraction) of 1.5, write a program or use a spreadsheet that will compute and print angle R for values of I from 0 to 90°. Have the computer inspect $\sin R$ each time it is computed, and when its value exceeds 1.00, stop the computation and print "TOTAL INTERNAL REFLECTION."

15•2

Law of Sines

Derivation

We first derive the law of sines for an oblique triangle in which all three angles are acute, such as in Figure 15•13. We start by breaking the given triangle into two right triangles by drawing altitude h to side AB.

In right triangle ACD,

$$\sin A = \frac{h}{b} \qquad \text{or} \qquad h = b \sin A$$

In right triangle BCD,

$$\sin B = \frac{h}{a} \qquad \text{or} \qquad h = a \sin B$$

So

$$b \sin A = a \sin B$$

Dividing by $\sin A \sin B$, we have

$$\frac{a}{\sin A} = \frac{b}{\sin B}$$

Similarly, drawing altitude j to side AC, and using triangles BEC and AEB, we get

$$j = a \sin C = c \sin A$$

or

$$\frac{a}{\sin A} = \frac{c}{\sin C}$$

Combining this with the previous result, we obtain

FIGURE 15•13 Derivation of the law of sines

Law of Sines	$\dfrac{a}{\sin A} = \dfrac{b}{\sin B} = \dfrac{c}{\sin C}$	**140**

The sides of a triangle are proportional to the sines of the opposite angles.

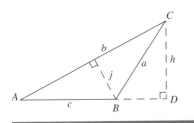

FIGURE 15·14

When one of the angles of the triangle is obtuse, as in Figure 15•14, the derivation is nearly the same. We draw an altitude h to the extension of side AB.

In right triangle ACD: $\sin A = \dfrac{h}{b}$ or $h = b \sin A$

In right triangle BDC: $\sin(180° - B) = \dfrac{h}{a}$

but $\sin (180° - B) = \sin B$, so

$$h = a \sin B$$

The derivation then proceeds exactly as before.

Solving a Triangle When Two Angles and One Side Are Given (AAS) or (ASA)

Recall that "solving a triangle" means to find all missing sides and angles. Here we use the law of sines to solve an oblique triangle. To do this, we must have *a known side opposite to a known angle*, as well as another angle.

■ **Example 18:** Solve triangle ABC where $A = 32.5°$, $B = 49.7°$, and $a = 226$.

Solution: We want to find the unknown angle C and sides b and c. We sketch the triangle (Fig. 15•15). The missing angle is found by Eq. 139:

$$C = 180 - 32.5 - 49.7 = 97.8°$$

Then, by the law of sines,

$$\frac{a}{\sin A} = \frac{b}{\sin B}$$

$$\frac{226}{\sin 32.5°} = \frac{b}{\sin 49.7°}$$

Solving for b, we get

$$b = \frac{226 \sin 49.7°}{\sin 32.5°} = 321$$

Again using the law of sines,

$$\frac{a}{\sin A} = \frac{c}{\sin C}$$

$$\frac{226}{\sin 32.5°} = \frac{c}{\sin 97.8°}$$

So

$$c = \frac{226 \sin 97.8°}{\sin 32.5°} = 417$$

FIGURE 15•15

A diagram drawn more or less to scale can serve as a good check of your work and reveal inconsistencies in the given data. As another rough check, see that the longest side is opposite the largest angle and that the shortest side is opposite the smallest angle.

Notice that, if two angles are given, the third can easily be found, since all angles of a triangle must have a sum of 180°. This means that if two angles and an included side are given (ASA), the problem can be solved as shown above for AAS.

Solving a Triangle When Two Sides and One Angle Are Given (SSA): The Ambiguous Case

In Example 18, *two angles* and *one side* were given. We can also use the law of sines when *one angle* and *two sides* are given, provided that the given angle is opposite one of the given sides. But we must be careful here, because we can sometimes get *two solutions*, as in the following example.

■ **Example 19:** Solve triangle *ABC* where *A* = 27.6°, *a* = 112, and *c* = 165.

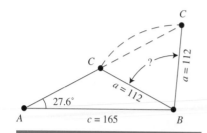

FIGURE 15·16 The ambiguous case

Solution: We want to find the unknown angles *B* and *C*, and side *b*. When we draw the triangle (Fig. 15·16) we see that there are two possible positions for side *a*, both of which satisfy the given data. We will solve both cases. By the law of sines,

$$\frac{\sin C}{165} = \frac{\sin 27.6°}{112}$$

$$\sin C = \frac{165 \sin 27.6°}{112} = 0.6825$$

$$C = 43.0°$$

This is *one* of the possible values for *C*. The other is

$$C = 180° - 43.0° = 137.0°$$

We now find the two corresponding values for side *b* and angle *B*.
When *C* = 43.0°,

$$B = 180° - 27.6° - 43.0° = 109.4°$$

So

$$\frac{b}{\sin 109.4°} = \frac{112}{\sin 27.6°}$$

from which *b* = 228.
When *C* = 137.0°:

$$B = 180° - 27.6° - 137.0° = 15.4°$$

So

$$\frac{b}{\sin 15.4°} = \frac{112}{\sin 27.6°}$$

from which *b* = 64.2. So our two solutions are:

Recall from Section 15·1 that there are two angles less than 180° for which the sine is positive. One of them, *θ*, is in the first quadrant, and the other, 180° − *θ*, is in the second quadrant.

	A	B	C	a	b	c
1.	27.6°	109.4°	43.0°	112	228	165
2.	27.6°	15.4°	137.0°	112	64.2	165

Common Error	In a problem like the preceding one, it is easy to forget the second possible solution ($C = 137.0°$), especially since a calculator will give only the acute angle when computing the arc sine.

Not every SSA problem has two solutions, as we'll see in the following example.

■ **Example 20:** Solve triangle *ABC* if $A = 35.2°$, $a = 525$, and $c = 412$.

Solution: When we sketch the triangle (Fig. 15•17) we see that the given information allows us to draw the triangle in only one way. We will get a unique solution. By the law of sines,

FIGURE 15•17

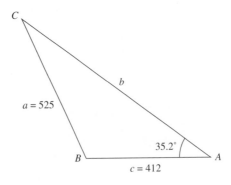

$$\frac{\sin C}{412} = \frac{\sin 35.2°}{525}$$

$$\sin C = \frac{412 \sin 35.2°}{525} = 0.4524$$

Thus the two possible values for *C* are

$$C = 26.9° \quad \text{and} \quad C = 180° - 26.9° = 153.1°$$

Our sketch, even if crudely drawn, shows that *C* cannot be obtuse, so we discard the 153.1° value. Then, by Eq. 139,

$$B = 180° - 35.2° - 26.9° = 117.9°$$

It is sometimes convenient, as in this problem, to use the *reciprocals* of the expressions in the law of sines.

Using the law of sines once again, we get

$$\frac{b}{\sin 117.9°} = \frac{525}{\sin 35.2°}$$

$$b = \frac{525 \sin 117.9°}{\sin 35.2°} = 805$$

■

Exercise 2 Law of Sines

Sets of data for triangle ABC are given in the following table. Solve for the missing parts.

| | ANGLES | | | SIDES | | |
	A	B	C	a	b	c
1.		46.3°		228	304	
2.		65.9°			1.59	1.46
3.			43.0°		15.0	21.0
4.	21.45°	35.17°		276.0		
5.	61.9°		47.0°	7.65		
6.	126°	27.0°			119	
7.		31.6°	44.8°		11.7	
8.	15.0°		72.0°			375
9.		125°	32.0°			58.0
10.	24.14°	38.27°		5562		
11.		55.38°	18.20°		77.85	
12.	44.47°		63.88°			1.065
13.	18.0°	12.0°		50.7		
14.			45.55°		1137	1010

Computer

15. Write a program to solve a triangle by the law of sines. Have it *menu-driven* with the following choices:

   1. Two angles and an opposite side given (AAS)
   2. Two sides and one angle given (SSA)
   3. Two angles and the included side given (ASA)

These triangles are shown in Figure 15•20 (page 430). For each, have the program ask for the given sides and angles, and then compute and print the missing sides and angles.

15•3 Law of Cosines

Derivation

Consider an oblique triangle ABC as in Figure 15•18. As we did for the law of sines, we start by dividing the triangle into two right triangles by drawing an altitude h to side AC.

    In right triangle ABD,

$$c^2 = h^2 + (AD)^2$$

But $AD = b - CD$. Substituting, we get

$$c^2 = h^2 + (b - CD)^2 \qquad (1)$$

Now, in right triangle BCD, by Eq. 147,

$$\frac{CD}{a} = \cos C$$

FIGURE 15•18 Derivation of law of cosines

or

$$CD = a \cos C$$

Substituting $a \cos C$ for CD in (1) yields

$$c^2 = h^2 + (b - a \cos C)^2$$

Expanding $(b - a \cos C)^2$ we have

$$c^2 = h^2 + b^2 - 2ab \cos C + a^2 \cos^2 C \qquad (2)$$

Let us leave this expression for the moment, and write the Pythagorean theorem for the same triangle BCD:

$$h^2 = a^2 - (CD)^2$$

Again, substituting $a \cos C$ for CD, we obtain

$$h^2 = a^2 - (a \cos C)^2$$
$$= a^2 - a^2 \cos^2 C$$

Substituting this expression for h^2 back into (2), we get

$$c^2 = a^2 - a^2 \cos^2 C + b^2 - 2ab \cos C + a^2 \cos^2 C$$

Collecting terms we get the law of cosines,

$$c^2 = a^2 + b^2 - 2ab \cos C$$

We can repeat the derivation, with perpendiculars drawn to side AB and to side BC, and get two more forms of the law of cosines:

Law of Cosines	$a^2 = b^2 + c^2 - 2bc \cos A$ $b^2 = a^2 + c^2 - 2ac \cos B$ $c^2 = a^2 + b^2 - 2ab \cos C$	**141**

The square of any side equals the sum of the squares of the other two sides minus twice the product of the other sides and the cosine of the opposite angle.

■ **Example 21:** Find side x, Figure 15•19.

Solution: By the law of cosines,

$$x^2 = (1.24)^2 + (1.87)^2 - 2(1.24)(1.87) \cos 42.8°$$
$$= 5.03 - 4.64(0.7337) = 1.63$$
$$x = 1.28 \text{ m}$$

Most students find it easier to think of the law of cosines in terms of the parts of the triangle, the given angle, the side opposite to the given angle, and the sides adjacent to the given angle, rather than by letters of the alphabet.

Notice that, when the angle in these equations is 90°, the law of cosines reduces to the Pythagorean theorem.

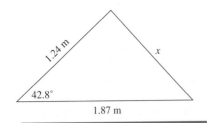

FIGURE 15•19

When to Use the Law of Sines or Law of Cosines

It is sometimes not clear whether to use the law of sines or the law of cosines to solve a triangle. We use the law of sines when we have *a known side opposite a known angle, together with another known angle or side.* We use the law of cosines only when the law of sines does not work. In Figure 15•20, the blue lines and angles indicate the known information and may help in choosing the proper law.

FIGURE 15·20 When to use the law of sines or law of cosines

Use law of sines

Use law of cosines

Using the Cosine Law When Two Sides and the Included Angle Are Known

We can solve triangles by the law of cosines if we know *two sides and the angle between them*, or if we know *three sides*. We consider the first of these in the following example.

■ **Example 22:** Solve triangle *ABC* where $a = 184$, $b = 125$, and $C = 27.2°$.

Solution: We make a sketch (Fig. 15·21). Then, by the law of cosines,

$$c^2 = a^2 + b^2 - 2ab \cos C$$

$$= (184)^2 + (125)^2 - 2(184)(125) \cos 27.2°$$

$$c = \sqrt{(184)^2 + (125)^2 - 2(184)(125) \cos 27.2°}$$

$$= 92.6$$

Notice that we cannot initially use the law of sines because we do not have a known side opposite a known angle.

Now that we have a known side opposite a known angle, we can use the law of sines to find angle *A* or angle *B*. Which shall we find first?

Use the law of sines *to find the acute angle first* (angle *B* in this example). If, instead, you solve for the obtuse angle first, you may forget to subtract the angle obtained from the calculator from 180°. Further, if one of the angles is so close to 90° that you cannot tell them from your sketch if it is acute or obtuse, find the other angle first and then subtract the two known angles from 180° to obtain the third angle.

By the law of sines,

$$\frac{\sin B}{125} = \frac{\sin 27.2°}{92.6}$$

$$\sin B = \frac{125 \sin 27.2°}{92.6} = 0.617$$

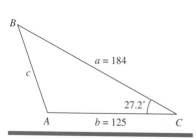

FIGURE 15·21

$$B = 38.1° \quad \text{and} \quad B = 180 - 38.1 = 141.9°$$

We drop the larger value because our sketch shows us that B must be acute. Then, by Eq. 139,

$$A = 180° - 27.2° - 38.1° = 114.7°$$ ▬

In our next example, the given angle is *obtuse*.

▬ **Example 23:** Solve triangle ABC where $b = 16.4$, $c = 10.6$, and $A = 128.5°$.

Solution: We make a sketch (Fig. 15•22). Then, by the law of cosines,

$$a^2 = (16.4)^2 + (10.6)^2 - 2(16.4)(10.6) \cos 128.5°$$

FIGURE 15•22

	The cosine of an obtuse angle is *negative*. Be sure to use
Common Error	the proper algebraic sign when applying the law of cosines to an obtuse angle.

In our example,

$$\cos 128.5° = -0.6225$$

So

$$a = \sqrt{(16.4)^2 + (10.6)^2 - 2(16.4)(10.6)(-0.6225)} = 24.4$$

By the law of sines,

$$\frac{\sin B}{16.4} = \frac{\sin 128.5°}{24.4}$$

$$\sin B = \frac{16.4 \sin 128.5°}{24.4} = 0.526$$

$$B = 31.7° \quad \text{and} \quad B = 180 - 31.7 = 148.3°$$

We drop the larger value because our sketch shows us that B must be acute. Then, by Eq. 139,

$$C = 180° - 31.7° - 128.5° = 19.8°$$ ▬

Using the Cosine Law When Three Sides Are Known

When three sides of an oblique triangle are known, we can use the law of cosines to solve for one of the angles. A second angle is found using the law of sines, and the third angle is found by subtracting the other two from 180°.

▬ **Example 24:** Solve triangle ABC in Figure 15•23, where $a = 128$, $b = 146$, and $c = 222$.

FIGURE 15•23

Solution: We start by writing the law of cosines for any of the three angles. A good way to avoid ambiguity is to find the largest angle first (the law of cosines will tell us if it is acute or obtuse) and then we are sure that the other two angles are acute.

Writing the law of cosines for angle C gives

$$(222)^2 = (128)^2 + (146)^2 - 2(128)(146) \cos C$$

Solving for $\cos C$:

$$\cos C = -0.3099$$

Since the cosine is negative, C must be obtuse, so

$$C = 108.1°$$

Then by the law of sines

$$\frac{\sin A}{128} = \frac{\sin 108.1°}{222}$$

from which $\sin A = 0.5482$. Since we know that A is acute, we get

$$A = 33.2°$$

Finally,

$$B = 180° - 108.1° - 33.2° = 38.7°$$ ▬

Exercise 3 Law of Cosines

Sets of data for triangle ABC are given in the following table. Solve for the missing parts.

| | ANGLES | | | SIDES | | |
	A	B	C	a	b	c
1.			106.0°	15.7	11.2	
2.		51.4°		1.95		1.46
3.	68.3°				18.3	21.7
4.				728	906	663
5.			27.3°	128	152	
6.		128°		1.16		1.95
7.	135°				275	214
8.			35.2°	77.3	81.4	
9.				11.3	15.6	12.8
10.		41.7°		199		202
11.	115°				46.8	51.3
12.				1.475	1.836	2.017
13.			67.0°	9.08	6.75	
14.		129°		186		179
15.	158°				1.77	1.99
16.				41.8	57.2	36.7
17.			41.77°	1445	1502	
18.		108.8°		7.286		6.187
19.				97.3	81.4	88.5
20.	36.29°				47.28	51.36

Computer

21. Write a program to solve a triangle by the law of cosines. Have it *menu-driven* with the following choices:

  1. Two sides and the included angle given (SAS)
  2. Three sides given (SSS)

These triangles are shown in Figure 15•20. For each, have the program ask for the given sides and angles, and then compute and print the missing sides and angles.

15•4 Applications

As with right triangles, oblique triangles have many applications in technology, as you will see in the exercises for this section. Follow the same procedures for setting up these problems as we used for other word problems, and solve the resulting triangle by the law of sines or the law of cosines, or both.

If an *area* of an oblique triangle is needed, either compute all the sides and use Hero's formula (Eq. 138) or find an altitude with right triangle trigonometry and use Eq. 137.

■ **Example 25:** Find the area of the gusset in Figure 15•24(a).

Solution: We first find θ:

$$\theta = 90° + 35.0° = 125.0°$$

We now know two sides and the angle between them, so can find side x by the law of cosines:

$$x^2 = (460)^2 + (510)^2 - 2(460)(510) \cos 125° = 741\ 000$$

$$x = 860 \text{ mm}$$

FIGURE 15•24

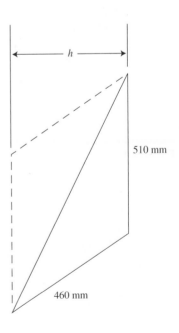

(a)

(b)

We find the area of the gusset by Hero's formula (Eq. 138),

$$s = \tfrac{1}{2}(460 + 510 + 860) = 915$$

$$\text{Area} = \sqrt{915(915 - 460)(915 - 510)(915 - 860)}$$

$$= 96\ 300 \text{ mm}^2$$

Does the answer look reasonable? Let's place the gusset inside the parallelogram, Figure 15•24(b), and estimate the height h by eye at about 380 mm. Thus the area of the parallelogram would by 380×510, or 194 000 mm², just over double that found for the triangle. ▬

▬ **Example 26:** A ship takes a sighting on two buoys. At a certain instant the bearing of buoy A is N 44.23°W and of buoy B is N 62.17° E. The distance between the buoys is 3.60 km and the bearing of B from A is N 87.87°E. Find the distance of the ship from each buoy.

Estimate: Let us draw the figure with a ruler and protractor, as in Figure 15•25. Notice how the compass directions are laid out, starting from north and turning in the indicated direction. Measuring, we get $SA = 1.7$ units and $SB = 2.8$ units. If you try it you will probably get slightly different values.

Solution: Calculating the angles of triangle ABS gives,

$$\theta = 44.23° + 62.17° = 106.40°$$

Since angle SAC is 44.23°,

$$\alpha = 180° - 87.87° - 44.23° = 47.90°$$

and

$$\beta = 180° - 106.40° - 47.90° = 25.70°$$

From the law of sines,

$$\frac{SA}{\sin 25.70°} = \frac{SB}{\sin 47.90°} = \frac{3.60}{\sin 106.40°}$$

from which

$$SA = \frac{3.60 \sin 25.70°}{\sin 106.40°} = 1.63 \text{ km}$$

FIGURE 15•25

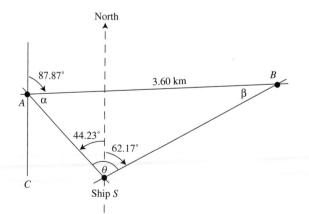

and

$$SB = \frac{3.60 \sin 47.90°}{\sin 106.40°} = 2.78 \text{ km}$$

which agree with our estimated values.

Exercise 4 Applications

Determining Inaccessible Distances

This set of problems contains no vectors, which are covered in the next section.

1. Two stakes, *A* and *B*, are 88.6 m apart. From a third stake *C*, the angle *ACB* is 85.4°, and, from *A*, the angle *BAC* is 74.3°. Find the distance from *C* to each of the other stakes.

2. From a point on level ground, the angles of elevation of the top and the bottom of an antenna standing on top of a building are 32.6° and 27.8°, respectively. If the building is 38.0 m high, how tall is the antenna?

Remember that angles of elevation or depression are always measured from the horizontal.

3. A triangular lot measures 115 m, 187 m, and 215 m along its sides. Find the angles between the sides.

4. Two boats are 45.5 km apart. Both are traveling toward the same point, which is 87.6 km from one of them and 77.8 km from the other. Find the angle at which their paths intersect.

Navigation

Hint: Draw your diagram after *t* hours have elapsed.

5. A ship is moving at 15.0 km/h in the direction N 15.0° W. A helicopter with a speed of 22.0 km/h is due east of the ship. In what direction should the helicopter travel if it is to meet the ship?

6. A jet flies from Caracas (Venezuela) S 24.0° E to Rio de Janeiro (Brazil). The flight then proceeds to Lima (Peru) flying W 10.0° N. The jet returns to Caracas by the flight path N 11.0° E. The distance from Lima to Caracas is $270\overline{0}$ km. Find the distance between Caracas and Rio and between Rio and Lima.

7. A ship is moving in a direction S 24.25° W at a rate of 13.7 km/h. If a launch that travels at 24.6 km/h is due west of the ship, in what direction should it travel in order to meet the ship?

8. A ship is 9.50 km directly east of a port. If the ship sails southeast for 2.50 km, how far will it be from the port?

9. From a plane flying due east, the bearing of a radio station is S 31.0° E at 1 P.M. and S 11.0° E at 1:20 P.M. The ground speed of the plane is 625 km/h. Find the distance of the plane from the station at 1 P.M.

Structures

10. A tower stands vertically on sloping ground whose inclination with the horizontal is 11.6°. From a point 42.0 m downhill from the tower (measured along the slope), the angle of elevation of the top of the tower is 18.8°. How tall is the tower?

11. A vertical antenna stands on a slope that makes an angle of 8.70° with the horizontal. From a point directly uphill from the antenna the angle of elevation of its top is 61.0°. From a point 16.0 m farther up the slope (measured along the slope) the angle of elevation of its top is 38.0°. How tall is the antenna?

12. A power pole on level ground is supported by two wires that run from the top of the pole to the ground (Fig. 15•26). One wire is 18.5 m long

FIGURE 15•26

and makes an angle of 55.6° with the ground, and the other wire is 17.8 m long. Find the angle the second wire makes with the ground.

13. A 71.6-m-high antenna mast (Fig. 15•27) is to be placed on sloping ground with the cables making an angle of 42.5° with the top of the mast. Find the lengths of the two cables.

FIGURE 15•27

14. In the roof truss in Figure 15•28, find the lengths of members *AB*, *BD*, *AC*, and *AD*.

FIGURE 15•28 Roof truss

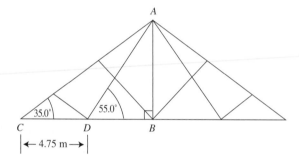

15. From a point on level ground between two power poles of the same height, cables are stretched to the top of each pole. One cable is 16.0 m long, the other is 20.5 m long, and the angle of intersection between the two cables is 125°. Find the distance between the poles.

16. A pole standing on level ground makes an angle of 85.5° with the horizontal. The pole is supported by a 6.7 m prop whose base is 3.8 m from the base of the pole. Find the angle made by the prop with the horizontal.

Mechanisms

17. In the slider crank mechanism shown in Figure 15•29, find the distance *x* between the wrist pin *W* and the crank center *C*, when $\theta = 35.7°$.

FIGURE 15•29

18. In the four-bar linkage of Figure 15•30, find angle θ when angle *BAD* is 41.5°.

FIGURE 15•30

19. Two links, *AC* and *BC* (Fig. 15•31), are pivoted at *C*. How far apart are *A* and *B* when angle *ACB* is 66.3°?

FIGURE 15•31

FIGURE 15•32

Geometry

20. Find angles *A*, *B*, and *C* in the quadrilateral in Figure 15•32.

21. Find side *AB* in the quadrilateral in Figure 15•33.

FIGURE 15•33

22. Two sides of a parallelogram are 22.8 and 37.8 m and one of the diagonals is 42.7 m. Find the angles of the parallelogram.

23. Find the lengths of the sides of a parallelogram if a diagonal, which is 125 mm long, makes angles with the sides of 22.7° and 15.4°.

A *median* of a triangle is a line joining a vertex to the midpoint of the opposite side.

24. Find the lengths of the diagonals of a parallelogram, two of whose sides are 3.75 m and 1.26 m; their included angle is 68.4°.

25. In triangle *ABC*, *A* = 62.3°, *b* = 112, and the median from *C* to the midpoint of *c* is 186. Find *c*.

26. The sides of a triangle are 124, 175, 208. Find the length of the median drawn to the longest side.

27. The angles of a triangle are in the ratio 3:4:5 and the shortest side is 994. Solve the triangle.

28. The sides of a triangle are in the ratio 2:3:4. Find the cosine of the largest angle.

29. Two solar panels are to be placed as shown in Figure 15•34. Find the minimum distance x so that the first panel will not cast a shadow on the second when the angle of elevation of the sun is 18.5°.

FIGURE 15•34 Solar panels

Window ⟶

FIGURE 15•35

30. Find the overhang x so that the window in Figure 15•35 will be in complete shade when the sun is 60° above the horizontal.

Computer

31. Combine your triangle-solving programs from Exercises 2 and 3 into a single program to solve any triangle. The menu should contain the five options shown in Figure 15•20 (page 430). Also compute the area of the triangle by Hero's formula.

32. For the slider crank mechanism of Figure 15•29 (page 436), compute and print the position x of the wrist pin for values of θ from 0° to 180°, in 15° steps.

15•5

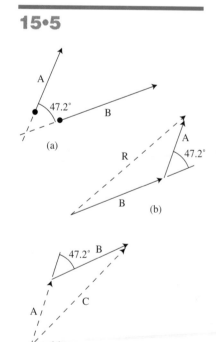

FIGURE 15•36 Addition of vectors

Addition of Vectors

In Section 7•6 we added two or more nonperpendicular vectors by first resolving each into components, then adding the components, and finally resolving the components into a single resultant. Now, by using the law of sines and the law of cosines, we can combine two nonperpendicular vectors directly, with much less time and effort. However, when more than two vectors must be added, it is faster to resolve each into its x and y components, combine the x components and the y components, and then find the resultant of those two perpendicular vectors. In this section we show both methods.

Vector Diagram

We can illustrate the resultant, or vector sum, of two vectors by means of a diagram. Suppose that we wish to add the vectors **A** and **B** [Fig. 15•36(a)]. If we draw the two vectors tip to tail, as in Figure 15•36(b), the resultant **R** will be the vector that will complete the triangle when drawn from the tail of the first vector to the tip of the second vector. It does not matter whether vector **A** or vector **B** is drawn first; the same resultant will be obtained either way, as shown in Figure 15•36(c).

The *parallelogram method* will give the same result. To add the same two vectors **A** and **B** as before, we first draw the given vectors *tail to tail* (Fig. 15•37) and complete a parallelogram by drawing lines from the tips of the given vectors, parallel to the given vectors. The resultant **R** is then the diagonal of the parallelogram drawn from the intersections of the tails of the original vectors.

Finding the Resultant of Two Nonperpendicular Vectors

Whichever method we use for drawing the two vectors, *the resultant is one side of an oblique triangle.* To find the length of the resultant and the angle it makes with one of the original vectors, we simply solve the oblique triangle by the methods we learned earlier in this chapter.

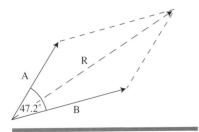

FIGURE 15·37 Parallelogram method

■ **Example 27:** Two vectors, **A** and **B**, make an angle of 47.2° with each other (Fig. 15·37). If their magnitudes are $A = 125$ and $B = 146$, find the magnitude of the resultant **R** and the angle **R** makes with vector **B**.

Solution: We make a vector diagram, either tip to tail or by the parallelogram method. Either way, we must solve the oblique triangle in Figure 15·38 for R and ϕ. Finding θ yields

$$(\theta =) \; 180° - 47.2° = 132.8°$$

By the law of cosines,

$$R^2 = (125)^2 + (146)^2 - 2(125)(146) \cos 132.8° = 61\,740$$

$$R = 248$$

FIGURE 15·38

Then, by the law of sines,

$$\frac{\sin \phi}{125} = \frac{\sin 132.8}{248}$$

$$\sin \phi = \frac{125 \sin 132.8}{248} = 0.3698$$

$$\phi = 21.7°$$ ■

Addition of Several Vectors

The law of sines and the law of cosines are good for adding *two* nonperpendicular vectors. However, when several vectors are to be added, we usually break each into its x and y components and combine them, as in the following example.

■ **Example 28:** Find the resultant of the vectors shown in Figure 15·39(a).

Solution: The x component of a vector of magnitude **V** at any angle θ is

$$\mathbf{V} \cos \theta$$

and the y component is

$$\mathbf{V} \sin \theta$$

These equations apply for an angle in any quadrant. We compute and tabulate the x and y components of each original vector, and find the sum of each.

VECTOR	x COMPONENT	y COMPONENT
A	42.0 cos 58.0° = 22.3	42.0 sin 58.0° = 35.6
B	56.1 cos 148° = −47.6	56.1 sin 148° = 29.7
C	52.7 cos 232° = −32.4	52.7 sin 232° = −41.5
D	45.3 cos 291° = 16.2	45.3 sin 291° = −42.3
R	$R_x = -41.5$	$R_y = -18.5$

The two vectors $\mathbf{R}_x$ and $\mathbf{R}_y$ are shown in Figure 15•39(b). We find their resultant $\mathbf{R}$ by the Pythagorean theorem:

$$R^2 = (-41.5)^2 + (-18.5)^2 = 2065$$

$$R = 45.4$$

and the angle θ by

$$\theta = \arctan \frac{R_y}{R_x}$$

$$= \arctan \frac{-18.5}{-41.5}$$

$$= 24.0° \text{ or } 204°$$

Since our resultant is in the third quadrant, we drop the 24.0° value. Thus, the resultant has a magnitude of 45.4 and a direction of 204°. This is often written in the form

$$R = 45.4\underline{/204°}$$

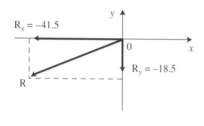

(b)

FIGURE 15•39

This is called *polar form*, which we'll cover in Chapter 17.

Exercise 5 Addition of Vectors

The magnitudes of vectors **A** and **B** are given in the table below, as well as the angle between each pair of vectors. For each, find the magnitude R of the resultant and the angle that the resultant makes with vector **B**.

	MAGNITUDES		
	A	B	ANGLE
1.	244	287	21.8°
2.	1.85	2.06	136°
3.	55.9	42.3	55.5°
4.	1.006	1.745	148.4°
5.	4483	5829	100.0°
6.	35.2	23.8	146°

Force Vectors

In Section 7•7 we gave examples of applications of force vectors, velocity vectors, and impedance vectors. You might want to review that section before trying the applications here. These problems are set up in exactly the same way, only now they will require the solution of an oblique triangle rather than a right triangle.

7. Two forces of 18.6 N and 21.7 N are applied to a point on a body. The angle between the forces is 44.6°. Find the magnitude of the resultant and the angle it makes with the larger force.

8. Two forces whose magnitudes are 832 N and 917 N act on an object. The angle between the forces is 88.4°. Find the magnitude of the resultant force.

9. A force of 125 N pulls due west on a body, and a second force pulls N 28.7° W. The resultant force is 212 N. Find the second force and the direction of the resultant.

10. Forces of 2900 N and 3700 N act on a body. The smaller force acts due north; the larger force acts N 52.3° E. Find the direction and magnitude of the resultant.

11. Two forces, of 925 N and 1130 N, act on an object. Their lines of action make an angle of 67.2° with each other. Find the magnitude and direction of their resultant.

12. Two forces, of 606 N and 1120 N, act on an object, with an angle of 53.9° between their lines of action. Find the magnitude of their resultant and its direction.

13. The resultant of two forces of 1120 N and 2210 N is 2870 N. What angle does the resultant make with each of the two forces?

14. Three forces are in equilibrium: 212 N, 325 N, and 408 N. Find the angles between their lines of action.

Velocity Vectors

See Figure 7•42 for definitions of the flight terms used in these problems.

15. As an airplane heads west with an air speed of 520 km/h, a wind with a speed of 56 km/h causes the plane to travel slightly south of west with a ground speed of 490 km/h. In what direction is the wind blowing? In what direction does the plane travel?

16. A boat heads S 15.0° E on a river that flows due west. The boat travels S 11.0° W with a speed of 25.0 km/h. Find the speed of the current and the speed of the boat in still water.

17. A pilot wishes to fly in the direction N 45.0° E. The wind is from the west at 36.0 km/h and the plane's speed in still air is 388 km/h. Find the heading and the ground speed.

18. The heading of a plane is N 27.7° E, and its air speed is 410 km/h. If the wind is blowing from the south with a velocity of 68 km/h, find the actual direction of travel of the plane and its ground speed.

19. A plane flies with a heading of N 48.0° W and an air speed of 584 km/h. It is driven from its course by a wind of 58.0 km/h from S 12.0° E. Find the ground speed and the drift angle of the plane.

Current and Voltage Vectors

20. We will see later that it is possible to represent an alternating current or voltage by a vector whose length is equal to the maximum amplitude of the current or voltage, placed at an angle that we later define as the *phase angle*. Then to add two alternating currents or voltages, we *add the vectors* representing those voltages or currents in the same way that we add force or velocity vectors.

    A current I_1 is represented by a vector of magnitude 12.5 A at an angle of 15.6°, and a second current I_2 is represented by a vector of magnitude 7.38 A at an angle of 132°, as in Figure 15•40. Find the magnitude and direction of the sum of these currents, represented by the vector I.

21. Figure 15•41 shows two impedances in parallel, with the currents represented by

$$I_1 = 18.4 \underline{/51.5°} \text{ A}$$

and

$$I_2 = 11.3 \underline{/0° } \text{ A}$$

FIGURE 15•40

FIGURE 15•41

FIGURE 15·42

The current **I** will be the vector sum of I_1 and I_2. Find the magnitude and direction of the vector representing **I**.

22. Figure 15·42 shows two impedances in series, with the voltage drop V_1 equal to 92.4 V at 71.5° and V_2 equal to 44.2 V at −53.8°. Find the magnitude and direction of the vector representing the total drop **V**.

Addition of Several Vectors

Find the resultant of each of the following vectors:

23. $273/34.0°$ $179/143°$ $203/225°$ $138/314°$

24. $72.5/284°$ $28.5/331°$ $88.2/104°$ $38.9/146°$

Computer

25. Write a program or use a spreadsheet that will accept as input the magnitude and direction of any number of vectors. Have the computer resolve each vector into x and y components, combine these components into a single x component and y component, and compute and print the magnitude and direction of the resultant. Try your program on Problems 23 and 24.

26. A certain airplane has an air speed of 225 km/h, and the wind is from the northeast at 45.0 km/h. Write a program or use a spreadsheet to compute and print the groundspeed and actual direction of travel of the plane, for headings that vary from due north completely around the compass in steps of 15°.

CHAPTER 15   REVIEW PROBLEMS

Solve oblique triangle ABC, if:

1. $C = 135°$ $a = 44.9$ $b = 39.1$
2. $A = 92.4°$ $a = 129$ $c = 83.6$
3. $B = 38.4°$ $a = 1.84$ $c = 2.06$
4. $B = 22.6°$ $a = 2840$ $b = 1170$
5. $A = 132°$ $b = 38.2$ $c = 51.8$

In what quadrant(s) will the terminal side of θ lie if:

6. $\theta = 227°$ **7.** $\theta = -45°$
8. $\theta = 126°$ **9.** $\theta = 170°$
10. tan θ is negative

Without using book or calculator, state the algebraic sign of:

11. tan 275°   **12.** sec(−58°)
13. cos 183°   **14.** cos 45°
15. sin 300°

Write the sin, cos, and tan, to three significant digits, for the angle whose terminal side passes through the point:

16. (−2, 5)
17. (−3, −4)
18. (5, −1)

*In each set of data below, two vectors of magnitudes A and B are separated by an angle θ. Find the resultant and the angle the resultant makes with vector **B**.*

19. $A = 837$ $B = 527$ $\theta = 58.2°$
20. $A = 2.58$ $B = 4.82$ $\theta = 82.7°$
21. $A = 44.9$ $B = 29.4$ $\theta = 155°$
22. $A = 8374$ $B = 6926$ $\theta = 115.4°$

23. From a ship sailing north at the rate of 18.0 km/h, the bearing of a lighthouse is N 18°15′ E. Ten minutes later the bearing is N 75°46′ E. How far is the ship from the lighthouse at the time of the second observation?

Write the sin, cos, and tan, to four decimal places, of:

24. 273°
25. 175°
26. 334°36′
27. 127°22′
28. 114°

Evaluate to four significant digits the expression

29. sin 35° cos 35°
30. tan² 68°
31. (cos 14° + sin 14°)²

32. What angle does the slope of a hill make with the horizontal if a vertical tower 18.5 m tall, located on the slope of the hill, is found to subtend an angle of 25.5° from a point 35.0 m directly downhill from the foot of the tower, measured along the slope?

33. Three forces are in equilibrium. One force of 457 N acts in the direction N 28.0° W. The second force acts N 37.0° E. Find the direction of the third force of magnitude 638 N.

Find to the nearest tenth of a degree all nonnegative values of θ less than 360°.

34. cos θ = 0.736
35. tan θ = −1.16
36. sin θ = 0.774

Evaluate to the nearest tenth of a degree.

37. arcsin 0.737
38. tan⁻¹ 4.37
39. cos⁻¹ 0.174

40. A ship wishes to travel in the direction N 38.0° W. The current is from due east at 6.70 km/h and the speed of the ship in still water is 29.6 km/h. Find the direction in which the ship should head, and the speed of the ship in the actual direction of travel.

41. Two forces, of 4830 N and 2730 N act on a body. The angle between the lines of action of these forces is 48.2°. Find the magnitude of the resultant and the angle it makes with the 4830 N force.

42. Find the vector sum of two voltages, $\mathbf{V}_1 = 134\underline{/24.5°}$ and $\mathbf{V}_2 = 204\underline{/85.7°}$.

43. A point on a rotating wheel has a tangential velocity of 5230 mm/s. Find the *x* and *y* components of the velocity when the point is in the position shown in Figure 15·43.

FIGURE 15·43

44. A voltage $V = 100v \angle 0°$ is to be added to $V_1 = 200v \angle 120°$ and $V_2 = 80v \angle 230°$. Find the resultant voltage vector in both magnitude and direction.

45. A reactance of a capacitor is given as 2800 Ω and it is combined with an inductive reactance of 1300 Ω and a resistance of 1200 Ω. Find the resulting impedance of the circuit.

Writing

46. Suppose that you have analyzed a complex bridge truss made up of many triangles, sometimes using the law of sines and sometimes the more time-consuming law of cosines. Your client's accountant, angry over the size of your bill, has attacked your report for often using the longer law when it is clear to him that the shorter law of sines is also "good for solving triangles." Write a letter to your client explaining why you sometimes had to use one law and sometimes the other.

Team Project

47. Four mutually tangent circles are shown in Figure 15·44. Find the radius of the shaded circle.

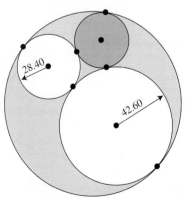

FIGURE 15·44

16

Radian Measure, Arc Length, and Rotation

O B J E C T I V E S

When you have completed this chapter, you should be able to:
- Convert angles between radians, degrees, and revolutions.
- Write the trigonometric functions of an angle given in radians.
- Compute arc length, radius, or central angle.
- Compute the angular velocity of a rotating body.
- Compute the linear speed of a point on a rotating body.
- Solve applied problems involving arc length or rotation.

Until now we usually have been expressing the measures of angles in degrees or in revolutions. Another angular measure, much more useful in many cases, is the *radian*. The radian is not an arbitrarily chosen unit like the degree or grad, but uses a part of the circle itself (the radius) as a unit.

Here we review how to convert between radians, degrees, and revolutions. We go on to study two important uses for the radian. We find arc lengths, and then study the rotation of rigid bodies.

Radian Measure

A *central angle* (Fig. 16•1) is one whose vertex is at the center of the circle. An *arc* is a portion of the circle. In Chapter 6 we introduced the *radian*: If an arc is laid off along a circle with a length equal to the radius of the circle, the central angle subtended by this arc is defined as *one radian* (Fig. 16•2).

Angle Conversion

An arc having a length equal to the radius of the circle subtends a central angle of one radian, and an arc having a length of twice the radius subtends a central angle of two radians, and so on. Thus an arc with a length of 2π times the radius (the entire circumference) subtends a central angle of 2π radians.

16•1

FIGURE 16•1

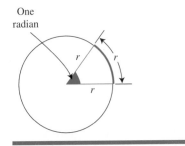

One
radian

FIGURE 16·2

If we divide 360° by 2π we get

1 rad ≈ 57.3°

Therefore, 2π radians is equal to 1 revolution, or to 360°. This gives us the following conversions for angular measure:

Angle Conversions	1 rev = 360° = 2π rad	**117**

We convert angular units in the same way that we converted other units in Chapter 1.

■ **Example 1:** Convert 47.6° to radians and revolutions.

Solution: By Eq. 117,

$$47.6 \text{ deg} \left(\frac{2\pi \text{ rad}}{360 \text{ deg}} \right) = 0.831 \text{ rad}$$

Note that 2π and 360° are exact numbers, so we keep the same number of digits in our answer as in the given angle. Now, converting to revolutions, we obtain

$$47.6 \text{ deg} \left(\frac{1 \text{ rev}}{360 \text{ deg}} \right) = 0.132 \text{ rev}$$

■ **Example 2:** Convert 1.8473 rad to degrees and revolutions.

Solution: By Eq. 117,

$$1.8473 \text{ rad} \left(\frac{360 \text{ deg}}{2\pi \text{ rad}} \right) = 105.84°$$

and

$$1.8473 \text{ rad} \left(\frac{1 \text{ rev}}{2\pi \text{ rad}} \right) = 0.29401 \text{ rev}$$

■ **Example 3:** Convert 1.837520 rad to degrees, minutes, and seconds.

Solution: We first convert to decimal°.

$$1.837520 \text{ rad} \left(\frac{360°}{2\pi \text{ rad}} \right) = 105.2821°$$

Converting the decimal part (0.2821°) to minutes,

$$0.2821° \left(\frac{60'}{1 \text{ deg}} \right) = 16.93'$$

Converting the decimal part of 16.93′ to seconds,

$$0.93' \left(\frac{60''}{1 \text{min}} \right) = 56$$

So 1.837520 rad = 105°16′56″.

Radian Measure in Terms of π

Not only is it common to express radians in decimal form, but it is also very common to express radian measure in terms of π. We know that 180° equals π radians, so

$$90° = \frac{\pi}{2} \text{ rad}$$

$$45° = \frac{\pi}{4} \text{ rad}$$

$$15° = \frac{\pi}{12} \text{ rad}$$

and so on. Thus, to convert an angle from degrees to radians in terms of π, multiply the angle by (π rad/180°) and reduce to lowest terms.

■ **Example 4:** Express 135° in radian measure in terms of π.

Solution:

$$135° \left(\frac{\pi \text{ rad}}{180°} \right) = \frac{135\pi}{180} \text{ rad} = \frac{3\pi}{4} \text{ rad}$$ ■

Common Error	Students sometimes confuse the decimal value of π with the degree equivalent of π radians. What is the value of π? 180 or 3.1416 . . . ? Remember that the approximate decimal value of π is always $$\pi \simeq 3.1416$$ but that when converting π radians to degrees, $$\pi \text{ radians} = 180 \text{ degrees}$$ Note that we write "radians" or "rad" after π when referring to the angle, but not when referring to the decimal value.

To convert an angle from radians to degrees, multiply the angle by (180°/π rad).

■ **Example 5:** Convert $7\pi/9$ rad to degrees.

Solution:

$$\frac{7\pi}{9} \text{ rad} \left(\frac{180°}{\pi \text{ rad}} \right) = \frac{7(180)}{9} \text{ deg} = 140°$$ ■

Trigonometric Functions of Angles in Radians

We use a calculator to find the trigonometric functions of angles in radians just as we did for angles in degrees. However, we first *switch the calculator into radian mode.* Consult your calculator manual on how to do this. Many calculators will display an R or the word RAD when in radian mode.

On some calculators you enter the angle and then press the required trigonometric function key. On other calculators you must press the trigonometric function key *first* and then enter the angle. Be sure you know which way your own calculator works.

■ **Example 6:** Use your calculator to verify the following, to four decimal places:
(a) $\sin 2.83 \text{ rad} = 0.3066$
(b) $\cos 1.52 \text{ rad} = 0.0508$
(c) $\tan 0.463 \text{ rad} = 0.4992$ ■

To find the cotangent, secant, or cosecant, we make use of the reciprocal relations, just as when working in degrees.

■ **Example 7:** Find $\sec 0.733 \text{ rad}$ to three decimal places.

   Solution: We put the calculator into radian mode. The reciprocal of the secant is the cosine, so we take the cosine of 0.733 rad and get,

$$\cos 0.733 \text{ rad} = 0.7432$$

Then taking the reciprocal of 0.7432 gives

$$\sec 0.733 = \frac{1}{\cos 0.733} = \frac{1}{0.7432} = 1.346 \quad ■$$

■ **Example 8:** Use your calculator to verify the following, to four decimal places.
(a) $\csc 1.33 \text{ rad} = 1.0297$
(b) $\cot 1.22 \text{ rad} = 0.3659$
(c) $\sec 0.726 \text{ rad} = 1.3372$ ■

The Inverse Trigonometric Functions

Remember that the inverse trigonometric function can be written in two different ways. Thus the inverse sine can be written

$$\arcsin \theta \quad \text{or} \quad \sin^{-1} \theta$$

Also recall that there are infinitely many angles that have a particular value of a trigonometric function. Of these, we are finding just the smallest positive angle.

The inverse trigonometric functions are found the same way as when working in degrees. Just be sure that your calculator is in radian mode.
   As with the trigonometric functions, some calculators require that you press the function key before entering the number, and some require it to be pressed after entering the number.

■ **Example 9:** Use your calculator to verify the following, in radians, to four decimal places:
(a) $\arcsin 0.2373 = 0.2396 \text{ rad}$
(b) $\cos^{-1} 0.5152 = 1.0296 \text{ rad}$
(c) $\arctan 3.246 = 1.2720 \text{ rad}$ ■

To find the arccot, arcsec, and arccsc, we first take the reciprocal of the given function, and then find the inverse function, as shown in the following example.

■ **Example 10:** If $\theta = \cot^{-1} 2.745$, find θ in radians to four decimal places.

   Solution: If the cotangent of θ is 2.745, then

$$\cot \theta = 2.745$$

so

$$\frac{1}{\tan \theta} = 2.745$$

Taking the reciprocal of each side gives

$$\tan \theta = \frac{1}{2.745} = 0.3643$$

So,

$$\theta = \tan^{-1} 0.3643 = 0.3494$$ ▬

To find the trigonometric function of an angle in radians expressed in terms of π using the calculator, it is necessary first to convert the angle to decimal form.

▬ **Example 11:** Find $\cos (5\pi/12)$ to four significant digits.

Solution: Converting $5(\pi)/12$ to decimal form,

$$5(\pi)/12 = 1.3090$$

With our calculator in radian mode, we then take the cosine:

$$\cos 1.3090 = 0.2588$$ ▬

▬ **Example 12:** Evaluate to four significant digits,

$$5 \cos (2\pi/5) + 4 \sin^2 (3\pi/7)$$

Solution: From the calculator,

$$\cos \frac{2\pi}{5} = 0.30902 \quad \text{and} \quad \sin \frac{3\pi}{7} = 0.97493$$

so

$$5 \cos \frac{2\pi}{5} + 4 \sin^2 \frac{3\pi}{7} = 5(0.30902) + 4(0.97493)^2$$
$$= 5.347$$ ▬

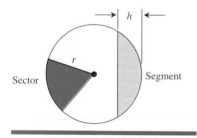

FIGURE 16•3 Segment and sector of a circle

Areas of Sectors and Segments

Sectors and segments of a circle (Fig. 16•3) were defined in Section 6•4. Now we will compute their areas.

The area of a circle of radius r is given by πr^2, so the area of a semicircle is $\pi r^2/2$, the area of a quarter circle is $\pi r^2/4$, and so on. The segment area is the same fractional part of the whole area as the central angle is of the whole.

Thus, if the central angle is 1/4 revolution, the sector area is also 1/4 of the total circle area.

If the central angle (in radians) is $\theta/2\pi$ of a revolution, the sector area is also $\theta/2\pi$ of the total circle area. So,

$$\text{area of sector} = \pi r^2 \left(\frac{\theta}{2\pi} \right)$$

or

Area of a Sector	$A = \dfrac{r^2 \theta}{2}$	**116**

■ **Example 13:** Find the area of a sector having a radius of 8.25 m and a central angle of 46.8°.

Solution: We first convert the central angle to radians.

$$46.8° \ (\pi \ \text{rad}/180°) = 0.8168 \ \text{rad}$$

Then, by Eq. 116,

$$\text{area} = \frac{(8.25)^2(0.8168)}{2} = 27.8 \ \text{m}^2 \qquad \blacksquare$$

The area of a *segment* of a circle (Fig. 16•3) is

$$(\text{area of segment} =) \ r^2 \arccos \frac{r-h}{r} - (r-h)\sqrt{2rh - h^2}$$

where $\arccos \dfrac{r-h}{r}$ is in radians.

■ **Example 14:** Compute the area of a segment having a height of 10.0 cm in a circle of radius 25.0 cm.

Solution: Substituting into the given equation gives

$$\text{area} = (25.0)^2 \arccos \frac{25.0 - 10.0}{25.0} - (25.0 - 10.0)\sqrt{2(25.0)(10.0) - (10.0)^2}$$

$$= 625 \arccos 0.600 - 15.0\sqrt{500 - 100}$$

$$= 625(0.9273) - 15.0(20.0) = 280 \ \text{cm}^2 \qquad \blacksquare$$

Exercise 1 Radian Measure

Convert to radians.

1. 47.8°	**2.** 18.7°	**3.** 35°15′
4. 0.370 rev	**5.** 1.55 rev	**6.** 1.27 rev

Convert to revolutions.

7. 1.75 rad	**8.** 2.30 rad	**9.** 3.12 rad
10. 0.0633 rad	**11.** 1.12 rad	**12.** 0.766 rad

Convert to degrees (decimal).

13. 2.83 rad	**14.** 4.275 rad	**15.** 0.372 rad
16. 0.236 rad	**17.** 1.14 rad	**18.** 0.116 rad

Convert each angle given in degrees to radian measure in terms of π.

19. 60°	**20.** 130°	**21.** 66°
22. 240°	**23.** 126°	**24.** 105°
25. 78°	**26.** 305°	**27.** 400°
28. 150°	**29.** 81°	**30.** 189°

Convert each angle given in radian measure to degrees.

31. $\dfrac{\pi}{8}$ **32.** $\dfrac{2\pi}{3}$ **33.** $\dfrac{9\pi}{11}$

34. $\dfrac{3\pi}{5}$ **35.** $\dfrac{\pi}{9}$ **36.** $\dfrac{4\pi}{5}$

37. $\dfrac{7\pi}{8}$ **38.** $\dfrac{5\pi}{9}$ **39.** $\dfrac{2\pi}{15}$

40. $\dfrac{6\pi}{7}$ **41.** $\dfrac{\pi}{12}$ **42.** $\dfrac{8\pi}{9}$

Use a calculator to evaluate to four significant digits.

43. $\sin\dfrac{\pi}{3}$ **44.** $\tan 0.442$ **45.** $\cos 1.063$

46. $\tan\left(-\dfrac{2\pi}{3}\right)$ **47.** $\cos\dfrac{3\pi}{5}$ **48.** $\sin\left(-\dfrac{7\pi}{8}\right)$

49. $\sec 0.355$ **50.** $\csc\dfrac{4\pi}{3}$ **51.** $\cot\dfrac{8\pi}{9}$

52. $\tan\dfrac{9\pi}{11}$ **53.** $\cos\left(-\dfrac{6\pi}{5}\right)$ **54.** $\sin 1.075$

55. $\cos 1.832$ **56.** $\cot 2.846$ **57.** $\sin 0.6254$

58. $\csc 0.8163$ **59.** $\arcsin 0.7263$ **60.** $\arccos 0.6243$

61. $\cos^{-1} 0.2320$ **62.** $\text{arccot } 1.546$ **63.** $\sin^{-1} 0.265$

64. $\csc^{-1} 2.6263$ **65.** $\arctan 3.7253$ **66.** $\text{arcsec } 2.848$

67. $\sin^2\dfrac{\pi}{6} + \cos\dfrac{\pi}{6}$ **68.** $7\tan^2\dfrac{\pi}{9}$ **69.** $\cos^2\dfrac{3\pi}{4}$

70. $\dfrac{\pi}{6}\sin\dfrac{\pi}{6}$ **71.** $\sin\dfrac{\pi}{8}\tan\dfrac{\pi}{8}$ **72.** $3\sin\dfrac{\pi}{9}\cos^2\dfrac{\pi}{9}$

73. Find the area of a sector having a radius of $15\overline{0}$ mm and a central angle of 62.5°.

74. Find the area of a sector having a radius of 3.15 m and a central angle of 28.3°.

75. Find the area of a segment of height 124 mm in a circle of radius 384 mm.

76. Find the area of a segment of height 1400 mm in a circle of radius 3100 mm.

77. A mass bouncing on the end of a spring moves with *simple harmonic motion* according to the equation $y = 60.0 \cos 25t$, where y is in millimetres. Find the displacement y when $t = 2.00$ s. (In this equation, the angle $25t$ must be in radians.)

78. The angle D (measured at the earth's center) between two points on the earth's surface is found by

$$\cos D = \sin L_1 \sin L_2 + \cos L_1 \cos L_2 \cos (M_1 - M_2)$$

where L_1 and M_1 are the latitude and longitude, respectively, of one point and L_2 and M_2 are the latitude and longitude of the second point.

Find the angle between Ottawa (latitude 45°N, longitude 75°W) and Miami (latitude 26°N, longitude 80°W) by substituting into this equation.

16•2

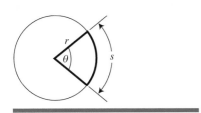

FIGURE 16•4 Relationship between arc length, radius, and central angle

Arc Length

We have seen that arc length, radius, and central angle are related to each other. In Figure 16•4, if the arc length s is equal to the radius r, we have θ equal to 1 radian. For other lengths s, the angle θ is equal to the ratio of s to r.

Central Angle	$\theta = \dfrac{s}{r}$ (θ must be in radians)	115

The central angle in a circle (in radians) is equal to the ratio of the intercepted arc and the radius of the circle.

When dividing s by r to obtain θ, s and r must have the same unit. The units cancel, *leaving θ as a dimensionless ratio* of two lengths. Thus the radian is not a unit of measure like the degree or metre, although we usually carry it along as if it were.

We can use Eq. 115 to find any of the quantities θ, r, or s, when the other two are known.

■ **Example 15:** Find the angle that would intercept an arc of 8.30 m in a circle of radius 6.40 m.

Solution: From Eq. 115,

$$\theta = \frac{s}{r} = \frac{8.30 \text{ m}}{6.40 \text{ m}} = 1.29 \text{ rad}$$ ■

■ **Example 16:** Find the arc length intercepted by a central angle of 62.5° in a 1041-mm-radius circle.

Solution: Converting the angle to radians, we get

$$62.5°\left(\frac{\pi \text{ rad}}{180°}\right) = 1.09 \text{ rad}$$

By Eq. 115,
$$s = r\theta = 104 \text{ mm } (1.09) = 113 \text{ mm}$$ ■

■ **Example 17:** Find the radius of a circle in which an angle of 2.06 rad intercepts an arc of 35.0 m.

Solution: By Eq. 115,

$$r = \frac{s}{\theta} = \frac{35.0 \text{ } m}{2.06} = 17.0 \text{ m}$$ ■

Common Error	Be sure that r and s have the same unit. Convert if necessary.

Pitch diameter = 22.5 mm

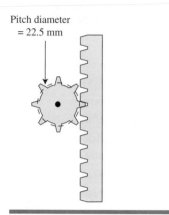

FIGURE 16•5 Rack and pinion

■ **Example 18:** Find the angle that intercepts a 906-mm arc in a circle of radius 492 mm.

Solution: We divide s by r, and convert units at the same time.

$$\theta = \frac{s}{r} = \frac{906 \text{ mm}}{492 \text{ mm}} = 1.84 \text{ rad} \qquad ■$$

■ **Example 19:** How far will the rack in Figure 16•5 move when the pinion rotates 300.0°?

Estimate: 5/6 revolution $\times \pi \times 22 \cong 57$ mm (low)

Solution: Converting to radians gives us

$$\theta = 300.0° \left(\frac{\pi \text{ rad}}{180°} \right) = 5.236 \text{ rad}$$

Then, by Eq. 115,

$$s = r\theta = 11.25 \text{ mm} (5.236) = 58.91 \text{ mm}$$

As a rough check, we note that the pinion rotates 5/6 of a revolution, so the rack will travel a distance less than the circumference of the pinion. This circumference is about 22π. So our answer of 58.91 mm seems reasonable. ■

■ **Example 20:** How many kilometres north of the equator is a town of latitude 43.6° N. Assume the earth is a sphere of radius 6340 km and refer to the definitions of latitude and longitude shown in Figure 16•6.

FIGURE 16•6 *Latitude* is the angle (measured at the earth's center) between a point on the earth and the equator. *Longitude* is the angle between the meridian passing through a point on the earth, and the principal (or prime) meridian passing through Greenwich, England.

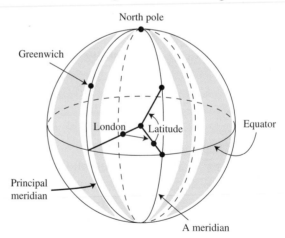

Assume the earth to be a sphere with a radius of 6342 km. Actually, the distance from pole to pole is about 43 km less than the diameter at the equator.

Estimate: Our given latitude angle is about 1/8 of a circle, so the required distance must be about 1/8 of the earth's circumference (12 680π or 13 000 $\times$ 3 = 39 000 km). Thus, the required distance is about 5000 km (which is *high*).

Solution: The latitude angle, in radians, is

$$\theta = 43.6° \left(\frac{\pi \text{ rad}}{180°} \right) = 0.761 \text{ rad}$$

Then, by Eq. 115,

$$s = r\theta = 6340 \text{ km} (0.761) = 4820 \text{ km} \qquad ■$$

Exercise 2 Arc Length

In the following table, s is the length of arc subtended by a central angle θ in a circle of radius r. Fill in the missing values.

	r	θ	s
1.	4.83 m	$\dfrac{2\pi}{5}$	
2.	115 mm	1.36 rad	
3.	284 m	46°24′	
4.	2.87 m	1.55 rad	
5.	64.8 mm	38.5°	
6.	28.3 m		32.5 m
7.	263 mm		582 mm
8.	21.5 m		18.2 m
9.	3.87 m		15.8 m
10.		$\dfrac{\pi}{12}$	88.1 mm
11.		77.2°	12.0 mm
12.		2.08 rad	3.84 m
13.		12°55′	28.2 m
14.		$\dfrac{5\pi}{6}$	125 mm

FIGURE 16·7

FIGURE 16·8 Belt and pulley

FIGURE 16·9 Brake drum

Applications

15. A certain town is at a latitude of 35.2°N. Find the distance in km from the town to the north pole.

16. The hour hand of a clock is 85.5 mm long. How far does the tip of the hand travel between 1:00 A.M. and 11:00 A.M.?

17. Find the radius of a circular railroad track that will cause a train to change direction by 17.5° in a distance of 182 m.

18. The pulley attached to the tuning knob of a radio (Fig. 16·7) has a radius of 35.00 mm. How far will the needle move if the knob is turned a quarter of a revolution?

19. Find the length of contact ABC between the belt and pulley in Fig. 16·8.

20. One circular "track" on a magnetic disk used for computer data storage is located at a radius of 155 mm from the center of the disk. If 10 bits of data can be stored in 1.00 mm of track, how many bits can be stored in the length of track subtending an angle of $\pi/12$ rad?

21. If we assume the earth's orbit around the sun to be circular, with a radius of 150 million kilometres, how many kilometres does the earth travel (around the sun) in 125 days ?

22. Find the latitude of a city that is 1265 km from the equator.

23. A 1.25-m-long pendulum swings 5.75° on each side of the vertical. Find the length of arc traveled by the end of the pendulum.

24. A brake band is wrapped around a drum (Fig. 16·9). If the band has a width of 92.0 mm, find the area of contact between the band and the drum.

FIGURE 16•10

(a)   (b)

25. Sheet metal is to be cut from the pattern of Figure 16•10(a) and bent to form the frustum of a cone [Fig. 16•10(b)], with top and bottom open. Find the dimensions r and R and the angle θ in degrees.

26. An isosceles triangle is to be inscribed in a circle of radius 1.000. Find the angles of the triangle if its base subtends an arc of length 1.437.

27. A satellite is in a circular orbit $36\overline{0}$ km above the equator of the earth. How many kilometres must it travel for its longitude to change by $85.0°$?

28. City B is due north of city A. City A has a latitude of $14°37'$N and city B has a latitude of $47°12'$N. Find the distance in kilometres between the cities.

FIGURE 16•11

29. The link AB in the mechanism of Figure 16•11 rotates through an angle of $28.3°$. Find the distance traveled by point A.

30. Find the radius R of the sector gear of Fig. 16•12.

31. A circular highway curve has a radius of 99.20 m and a central angle of $15°25'15''$ measured to the centerline of the road. Find the length of the curve.

FIGURE 16•12 Sector gear

32. When bending metal (Fig. 16•13), the amount s that must be allowed for the bend is called the *bending allowance*. If we assume that the neutral axis (the line at which there is no stretching or compression of the metal) is at a distance from the inside of the bend equal to four-tenths of the metal thickness t: **(a)** show that the bending allowance is

$$s = \frac{A(r + 0.4t)\pi}{180}$$

where A is the angle of bend in degrees; and **(b)** find the bending allowance for a $60°$ bend in 8.0-mm-thick steel with a radius of 38 mm.

FIGURE 16•13 Bending allowance

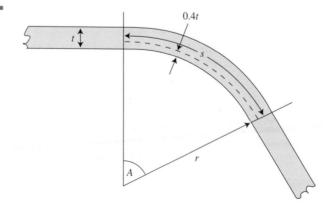

33. In Section 16•1 we gave the formula for the area of a circular sector of radius r and central angle θ, area $= r^2\theta/2$ (Eq. 116). Using Eq. 115, $\theta = s/r$, show that the area of a sector is also equal to $rs/2$, where s is the length of the arc intercepted by the central angle.

34. Find the area of a sector having a radius of 348 mm and an arc length of 147 mm.

Computer

35. For the angles from 0° to 10°, with steps every $\frac{1}{2}$ degree, compute and print the angle in radians, the sine of the angle, and the tangent of the angle. What do you notice about these three columns of figures? What is the largest angle for which the sine and tangent are equal to the angle in radians, to three significant digits?

16•3

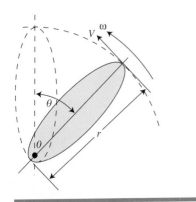

FIGURE 16•14 Rotating body. The symbol ω is a lower case Greek omega. It is not a letter w.

Formula A26 is similar to our old formula (distance = rate × time) for linear motion.

Uniform Circular Motion

Angular Velocity

Let us consider a rigid body (Fig. 16•14) that is rotating about a point O. The *angular velocity* ω is a measure of the *rate* at which the object rotates. The motion is called *uniform* when the angular velocity is constant. The units of angular velocity are degrees, radians, or revolutions, per unit time.

Angular Displacement

The angle θ through which the body rotates in time t is called the *angular displacement*. It is related to ω and t by

Angular Displacement	$\theta = \omega t$	**A26**

The angular displacement is the product of the angular velocity and the elapsed time.

■ Example 21: A wheel is rotating with an angular velocity of 1800 rev/min. How many revolutions does the wheel make in 1.50 s?

Solution: We first make the units of time consistent. Converting yields

$$\omega = \frac{1800 \text{ rev}}{\text{min}} \cdot \frac{1 \text{ min}}{60 \text{ s}} = 30 \text{ rev/s}$$

Then, by Eq. A26,

$$\theta = \omega t = \frac{30 \text{ rev}}{\text{s}}(1.5\text{s}) = 45 \text{ rev}$$ ■

■ Example 22: Find the angular velocity in revolutions per minute of a pulley that rotates 275° in 0.75 s.

Solution: By Eq. A26,

$$\omega = \frac{\theta}{t} = \frac{275°}{0.750 \text{ s}} = 367 \text{ deg/s}$$

Converting to rev/min, we obtain

$$\omega = \frac{367 \text{ deg}}{\text{s}} \cdot \frac{60 \text{ s}}{\text{min}} \cdot \frac{1 \text{ rev}}{360 \text{ deg}} = 61.2 \text{ rev/min}$$

■ **Example 23:** How long will it take a spindle rotating at 3.55 rad/s to make 1000 revolutions?

Solution: Converting revolutions to radians, we get

$$\theta = 1000 \text{ rev} \cdot \frac{2\pi \text{ rad}}{1 \text{ rev}} = 6280 \text{ rad}$$

Then, by Eq. A26,

$$t = \frac{\theta}{\omega} = \frac{6280 \text{ rad}}{3.55 \text{ rad/s}} = 1770 \text{ s} = 29.5 \text{ min}$$

Linear Speed

For any point on the rotating body, the linear displacement per unit time along the circular path is called the *linear speed*. The linear speed is zero for a point at the center of rotation and is directly proportional to the distance r from the point to the center of rotation. If ω is expressed in radians per unit time, the linear speed v is

Linear Speed	$v = \omega r$	A27

The linear speed of a point on a rotating body is proportional to the distance from the center of rotation.

■ **Example 24:** A wheel is rotating at 2450 rev/min. Find the linear speed of a point 352 mm from the center.

Solution: We first express the angular velocity in terms of radians:

$$\omega = \frac{2450 \text{ rev}}{\text{min}} \cdot \frac{2\pi \text{ rad}}{\text{rev}} = 15\,400 \text{ rad/min}$$

Then, by Eq. A27,

$$v = \omega r = \frac{15\,400 \text{ rad}}{\text{min}} (352 \text{ mm}) = 5\,420\,000 \text{ mm/min}$$

$$= 90.3 \text{ m/s}$$

What became of "radians" in our answer? Shouldn't the final units be rad mm/min? No. Remember that radians is a dimensionless ratio; it is the ratio of two lengths (arc length and radius) whose units cancel.

Common Error	Remember when using Eq. A27 that the angular velocity must be expressed in *radians* per unit time.

■ **Example 25:** A belt having a speed of 22 480 mm/min turns a 317.0-mm-radius pulley. Find the angular velocity of the pulley in rad/s.

Solution: By Eq. A27,

$$\omega = \frac{v}{r} = \frac{22\,480 \text{ mm}}{\text{m}} \div 317.0 \text{ mm} = 70.91 \text{ rad/m}$$

Converting yields

$$\omega = \frac{70.91 \text{ rad}}{60 \text{ s}} = 1.18 \text{ rad/s}$$

Exercise 3   Uniform Circular Motion

Angular Velocity

Fill in the missing values in this table.

	rev/min	rad/s	deg/s
1.	1850		
2.		5.85	
3.			77.2
4.		$3\pi/5$	
5.			48.1
6.	22 600		

7. A flywheel makes 725 revolutions in a minute. How many degrees does it rotate in 1.00 s?

8. A propeller on a wind generator rotates 60.0° in 1.00 s. Find the angular velocity of the propeller in revolutions per minute.

9. A gear is rotating at 2550 rev/min. How many seconds will it take to rotate through an angle of 2.00 rad?

Linear Speed

10. A milling machine cutter has a diameter of 75.0 mm and is rotating at 56.5 rev/min. What is the linear speed at the edge of the cutter?

11. A sprocket 75 mm in diameter is driven by a chain that moves at a speed of 1400 mm/s. Find the angular velocity of the sprocket in rev/min.

12. A capstan on a magnetic tape drive rotates at 3610 rad/min and drives the tape at a speed of 45.0 m/min. Find the diameter of the capstan in millimetres.

13. A blade on a water turbine turns 155° in 1.25 s. Find the linear speed of a point on the tip of the blade 0.75 m from the axis of rotation.

14. A steel bar 165.0 mm in diameter is being turned in a lathe. The surface speed of the bar is 16.76 m/min. How many revolutions will the bar make in 10.00 s?

15. Assuming the earth to be a sphere 12 680 km in diameter, calculate the linear speed, in kilometres per hour, of a point on the equator which is due to the rotation of the earth about its axis.

16. Assuming the earth's orbit about the sun to be a circle with a radius of $15\overline{0} \times 10^6$ km, calculate the linear speed of the earth around the sun.

17. A car is traveling at a rate of 65.5 km/h and has tires that have a radius of 316 mm. Find the angular velocity of the wheels of the car.

18. A wind generator has a propeller 6.60 m in diameter, and the gearbox between the propeller and the generator has a gear ratio of 1:44 (with the generator shaft rotating faster than the propeller). Find the tip speed of the propeller when the generator is rotating at 1800 rev/min.

CHAPTER 16   REVIEW PROBLEMS

Convert to degrees.

1. $\dfrac{3\pi}{7}$ 2. $\dfrac{9\pi}{4}$ 3. $\dfrac{\pi}{9}$

4. $\dfrac{2\pi}{5}$ 5. $\dfrac{11\pi}{12}$

6. Find the central angle in radians that would intercept an arc of 5.83 m in a circle of radius 7.29 m.
7. Find the angular velocity in rad/s of a wheel that rotates 33.5 revolutions in 1.45 min.
8. A wind generator has blades 3.50 m long. Find the tip speed when the blades are rotating at 35 rev/min.

Convert to radians in terms of π.

9. 300°   10. 150°
11. 230°   12. 145°

Evaluate to four significant digits.

13. $\sin \dfrac{\pi}{9}$ 14. $\cos^2 \dfrac{\pi}{8}$

15. $\sin \left(\dfrac{2\pi}{5}\right)^2$ 16. $3 \tan \dfrac{3\pi}{7} - 2 \sin \dfrac{3\pi}{7}$

17. $4 \sin^2 \dfrac{\pi}{9} - 4 \sin \left(\dfrac{\pi}{9}\right)^2$

18. What arc length is subtended by a central angle of 63.4° in a circle of radius 124 mm?
19. A winch has a drum $30\overline{0}$ mm in diameter. The steel cable wrapped around the drum is to be pulled in at a rate of 2.40 m/s. Ignoring the thickness of the cable, find the angular speed of the drum, in revolutions per minute.
20. Find the linear velocity of the tip of a 140-mm-long minute hand of a clock.
21. A satellite has a circular orbit around the earth with a radius of $68\overline{0}0$ km. The satellite makes a complete orbit of the earth in 3 days, 7h, and 35 min. Find the linear speed of the satellite.

Evaluate to four decimal places. (Angles are in radians.)

22. $\cos 1.83$ 23. $\tan 0.837$
24. $\csc 2.94$ 25. $\sin 4.22$
26. $\cot 0.371$ 27. $\sec 3.38$
28. $\cos^2 1.74$ 29. $\sin(2.84)^2$
30. $(\tan 0.475)^2$ 31. $\sin^2(2.24)^2$
32. Find the area of a sector with a central angle of 29.3° and a radius of 945 mm.
33. Find the radius of a circle in which an arc of length 384 mm intercepts a central angle of 1.73 rad.
34. Find the arc length intercepted in a circle of radius 3.85 m by a central angle of 1.84 rad.

Writing

35. When we multiply an angular velocity in radians per second by a length in metres, we get a linear speed in metres per second. Explain why radians do not appear in the units for linear speed.

Team project

36. The kinetic energy of a rotating body is given by

$$E = \tfrac{1}{2} mk^2\omega^2 \text{ joules}$$

where m is the mass in kilograms, ω is the angular velocity in radians/s, and k is the radius of gyration in metres, which for a sphere of radius r is $\sqrt{2/5}\, r$.

Your team should determine the mass and dimensions of a golf ball, a billiard ball, a baseball, a softball, and a basketball. Then compute the kinetic energy of rotation for each, assuming that it is spinning at a rate of 3.0 revolutions per second.

17

Graphs of the Trigonometric Functions

When you have completed this chapter, you should be able to:

- Find the amplitude, period, frequency, and phase shift for a sine wave or a cosine wave.
- Graph the sine function, cosine function, or tangent function.
- Write a sine function or cosine function, given the amplitude, period, and phase shift.
- Graph composite functions.
- Graph the sine or cosine wave as a function of time.
- Convert between polar and rectangular coordinates.
- Graph points and equations in polar coordinates.
- Graph parametric equations in polar coordinates.

Here we apply the graphing techniques of Chapter 5 to graph some *periodic* functions—the sine, cosine, and tangent—and we'll see how the constants in the equation for each affect the shape and position of the curves. We define some terms that will be applicable to the study of periodic functions in general, such as *cycle, period,* and *frequency*. This material has applications to such fields as alternating current, sound waves, mechanical vibrations, reciprocating machinery such as a gasoline or steam engine, and so on.

Finally, we introduce a second coordinate system (we already have rectangular coordinates) called the *polar coordinate system*, and learn how to make transformations from one system to the other.

17•1

The Sine Curve

Periodic Functions

A curve that repeats its shape over and over is called a *periodic* curve or *periodic waveform*, as in Figure 17•1. The function that has this graph is thus called a *periodic function*. Each repeated portion of the curve is called a *cycle*.

459

FIGURE 17•1 A periodic waveform

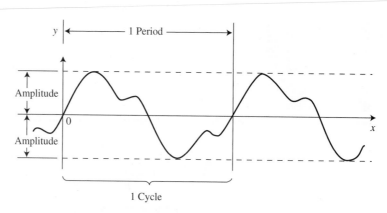

The *x* axis represents either *an angle* (in degrees or radians) or *time* (usually seconds or milliseconds).

Recall that a *complete graph* of a function is one that contains all the features of interest: intercepts, maximum and minimum points, and so forth. Thus a complete graph of a periodic waveform must contain at least one cycle.

The *period* is the *x* distance taken for one cycle. Depending on the units on the *x* axis, the period is expressed in degrees per cycle, radians per cycle, or seconds per cycle.

The *frequency* of a periodic waveform is the number of cycles that will fit into one unit (degree, radian, or second) along the *x* axis. It is the reciprocal of the period:

$$\text{frequency} = \frac{1}{\text{period}}$$

Units of frequency are cycles/degree, cycles/radian, or, most commonly, cycles/second (called *hertz*), depending on the units of the period.

The *amplitude* is half the difference between the greatest and least value of a waveform (Fig. 17•1). The peak-to-peak value of a curve is equal to twice the amplitude.

The *instantaneous value* of a waveform is its *y* value at any given *x*.

■ **Example 1:** For the voltage curve in Figure 17•2, find the period, frequency, amplitude, and peak-to-peak value, and the instantaneous value of *y* when *x* is 50 ms.

Solution: By observation of Figure 17•2,

$$\text{period} = 200 \text{ ms/cycle}$$

FIGURE 17•2

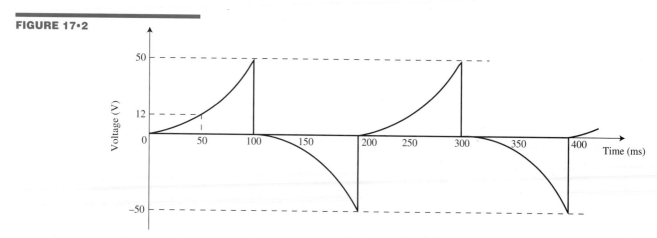

$$\text{frequency} = \frac{1 \text{ cycle}}{200 \times 10^{-3} \text{ s}}$$

$$= 5 \text{ cycles/s} = 5 \text{ hertz (Hz)}$$

$$\text{amplitude} = 50 \text{ V}$$

$$\text{peak-to-peak value} = 100 \text{ V}$$

$$\text{instantaneous value when } x \text{ is 50 ms} = 12 \text{ V}$$ ▬

Graph of the Sine Function, $y = \sin x$

> The sine curve or sine wave is also called a *sinusoid*.

We will graph the sine curve just as we graphed other functions in Section 5•2. We choose values of x and substitute them into the equation to get corresponding values of y, and then plot the resulting table of point pairs.

The units of angular measure used for the x axis are sometimes degrees and sometimes radians. We will show examples of each.

▬ **Example 2:** Plot the sine curve $y = \sin x$, for values of x from 0° to 360°.

Solution: Let us choose 30° intervals and make a table of point pairs.

x	0	30°	60°	90°	120°	150°	180°	210°	240°	270°	300°	330°	360°
y	0	0.5	0.866	1	0.866	0.5	0	−0.5	−0.866	−1	−0.866	−0.5	0

Plotting these points gives the periodic curve shown in Figure 17•3. If we had plotted points from $x = 360°$ to 720°, we would have obtained another cycle of the sine curve, identical to the one just plotted. We see then that the sine curve is periodic, requiring 360° for each cycle. Thus the period is equal to 360°.

> **FIGURE 17•3** $y = \sin x$ (x is in degrees)

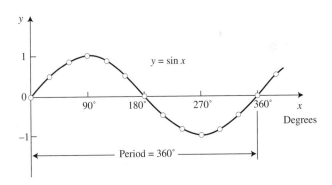

We'll now do an example using radians.

▬ **Example 3:** Plot $y = \sin x$ for values of x from 0 rad to 2π rad.

> It is not easy to work in radian measure when we are used to thinking of angles in degrees. You might want to glance back at Section 16•1.

Solution: We could choose integer values for x, such as 1, 2, 3, . . . and so on, or follow the usual practice of using multiples and fractions of π. This will give us points at the peaks and valleys of the curve, and where the curve crosses the x axis. We shall take intervals of $\pi/6$ and produce the following table of point pairs.

x(rad)	0	$\frac{\pi}{6}$	$\frac{\pi}{3}$	$\frac{\pi}{2}$	$\frac{2\pi}{3}$	$\frac{5\pi}{6}$	π	$\frac{7\pi}{6}$	$\frac{4\pi}{3}$	$\frac{3\pi}{2}$	$\frac{5\pi}{3}$	$\frac{11\pi}{6}$	2π
y	0	0.5	0.866	1	0.866	0.5	0	−0.5	−0.866	−1	−0.866	−0.5	0

Our curve (Fig. 17•4) is the same as before, except for the x-axis scale. Here we show both integer values of x and multiples of π.

FIGURE 17•4 $y = \sin x$ (x is in radians)

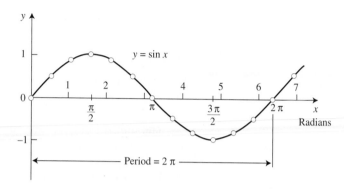

Figure 17•5 shows the same curve with both radian and degree scales on the x axis. Notice that one cycle of the curve fits into a rectangle whose height is twice the amplitude of the sine curve and whose width is equal to the period. We use this later for rapid sketching of periodic curves.

FIGURE 17•5 The sine curve (x is in degrees and radians)

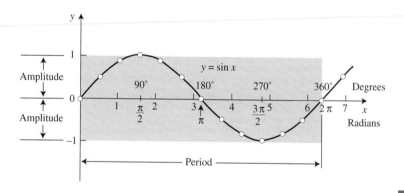

Graphing the Sine Function with a Graphics Calculator

The graphics calculator makes it easy to graph the trigonometric functions, and also to explore how the constants in the equation affect the graph. We will do the simplest case here, and more complicated ones later.

■ **Example 4:** Use the graphics calculator to graph $y = \sin x$, for x from −30° to 400°.

Solution: We put the calculator in degree mode and set the range,

$$\text{Xmin} = -30 \qquad \text{Xmax} = 400 \qquad \text{Xscl} = 30$$

You may recall that the sine of an angle varies between 1 and −1, so let us set the y range as follows:

$$\text{Ymin} = -1.5 \qquad \text{Ymax} = 1.5 \qquad \text{Yscl} = 1$$

Once you have the graph, use the TRACE feature to find the coordinates of zeros, and of the maximum and minimum points.

We enter the equation Y1 = sin x, and press GRAPH, and get the display shown in figure 17•6.

The graphics calculator will not show labels on the axes. We include them for clarity.

FIGURE 17•6 Graph of y = sin x

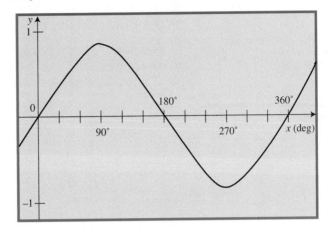

We'll now do an example using radians.

■ **Example 5:** Use the graphics calculator to graph y = sin x, for x from −4 radians to 4 radians.

Solution: We put the calculator into radian mode and set the range:

Xmin = −4   Xmax = 4   Xscl = 0.7854   (π/4)

Ymin = −1.5   Ymax = 1.5   Yscl = 1

Again we enter the equation Y1 = sin x, and press GRAPH, and get the display shown in Figure 17•7.

FIGURE 17•7 Graph of y = sin x

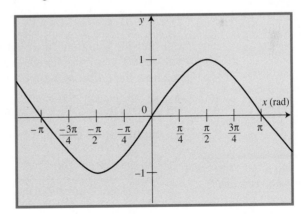

Graph of y = a sin x

We'll now see that the constant a in our sine wave is the *amplitude* of the wave. In the preceding examples, the constant a was equal to 1, and we got sine waves with amplitudes of 1. In examples that follow, a will have other values.

When stating the value of amplitude, we always give the absolute value, amplitude = $|a|$. If the value for amplitude is $|-a|$, the equation is of the form

$$y = -a \sin (bx + c)$$

■ **Example 6:** Plot the sine curve $y = 3 \sin x$ for $x = 0$ to 2π.

Solution: When we make a table of point pairs, it becomes apparent that all the y values will be three times as large as the ones in the preceding example. These points are plotted in Figure 17•8.

FIGURE 17•8 Graph of $y = 3 \sin x$

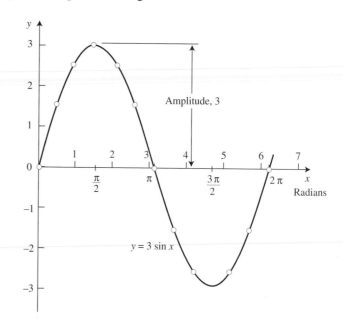

Use your graphics calculator to plot

$$y = \sin x$$

and

$$y = 3 \sin x$$

in the same viewing rectangle. Work either in degrees or radians. How do the two graphs differ?

The sine wave $y = \sin x$ is sometimes called the *fundamental*, and the sine waves

$$y = \sin bx, \text{ where } b = 1, 2, 3, \dots$$

are called the *harmonics*. Thus

$$y = \sin 2x \text{ is the } second \text{ harmonic.}$$

Graph of $y = a \sin bx$

For the sine function $y = a \sin x$, we saw that the curve repeated in an interval of 360° (or 2π radians). We called this interval the *period*. Now we will see how the constant b affects the graph of the equation.

■ **Example 7:** Plot $y = \sin 2x$ for $x = 0°$ to 360°.

Solution: As before, we make a table of point pairs, taking 30° intervals.

x	0	30°	60°	90°	120°	150°	180°	210°	240°	270°	300°	330°	360°
y	0	0.866	0.866	0	−0.866	−0.866	0	0.866	0.866	0	−0.866	−0.866	0

Plotting these points and connecting them with a smooth curve gives the graph shown in Figure 17•9. Notice that the curve repeats twice in the 360° interval, instead of just once as it did before. In other words, the period is half that of $y = \sin x$.

FIGURE 17·9

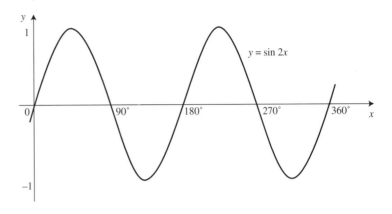

In general,

$$y = a \sin bx$$

will have a period of $\dfrac{360°}{b}$, if x is in degrees, or $\dfrac{2\pi}{b}$ radians, if x is in radians.

Period	$P = \dfrac{360}{b}$ degrees/cycle $= \dfrac{2\pi}{b}$ radians/cycle	**211**

■ **Example 8:** Find the period for the sine curve $y = \sin 4x$ in degrees and also in radians per cycle.

Solution:

$$P = \frac{360°}{4} = 90°/\text{cycle}$$

or

$$P = \frac{2\pi}{4} = \frac{\pi}{2} \quad \text{radians/cycle}$$ ■

The *frequency f* is the reciprocal of the period.

Frequency	$f = \dfrac{b}{360}$ cycles/degree $= \dfrac{b}{2\pi}$ cycles/radian	**212**

■ **Example 9:** Determine the amplitude, period, and frequency of the sine curve $y = 2 \sin(\pi x/2)$, where x is in radians, and graph one cycle of the curve.

FIGURE 17•10 Graph of
$y = 2 \sin (\pi x/2)$.

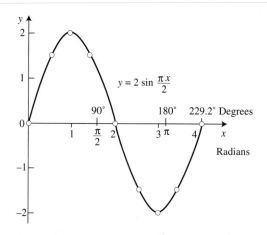

Solution: Here $a = 2$ and $b = \pi/2$, so the amplitude is 2 and the period is

$$P = \frac{2\pi}{\pi/2} = 4 \text{ rad/cycle}$$

or, in degrees,

$$P = \frac{360°}{\pi/2} = 229.2°/\text{cycle}$$

We make a table of point pairs for $x = 0$ to 4 rad.

x(rad)	0	$\frac{1}{2}$	1	$\frac{3}{2}$	2	$\frac{5}{2}$	3	$\frac{7}{2}$	4
y	0	1.41	2	1.41	0	-1.41	-2	-1.41	0

These points are plotted in Fig. 17•10. The frequency is

$$f = \frac{1}{P} = \frac{1}{4} \text{ cycle/rad}$$

In degrees,

$$f = \frac{1}{229.2°} = 0.00436 \text{ cycle/deg}$$

■ **Example 10:** Use the graphics calculator to graph, in the same viewing window,

$$y = \sin x, \quad y = \sin 2x, \quad \text{and} \quad y = \sin 0.5x$$

for x from $-30°$ to $400°$

Solution: We put the calculator in degree mode and set the range,

$$\text{Xmin} = -30 \qquad \text{Xmax} = 400 \qquad \text{Xscl} = 45$$

$$\text{Ymin} = -1.5 \qquad \text{Ymax} = 1.5 \qquad \text{Yscl} = 1$$

We enter the equations and press GRAPH , and get the display shown in Figure 17•11.

Notice that the graph of $y = \sin 2x$ completes two cycles in the same interval that $y = \sin x$ completes in one cycle. This is not surprising, because $2x$ is twice as large as x, $2x$ will reach the value of 360° (a full cycle) twice as soon as x.

FIGURE 17·11

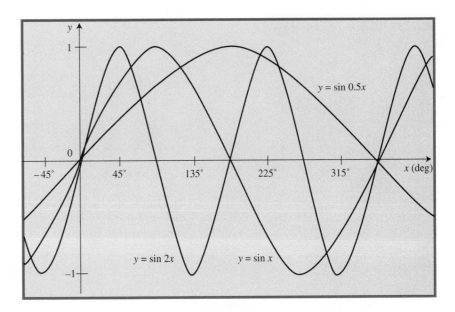

Similarly, 0.5x will reach 360° half as soon as x will, so y = sin 0.5x completes only half a cycle in the same interval in which y = sin x completes a full cycle.　■

Graph of the General Sine Function
y = a sin (bx + c)

The graph of y = a sin bx, we have seen, passes through the origin. However, the graph of the general sine function,

General Sine Curve	$y = a \sin(bx + c)$	**210**

will be shifted in the x direction by an amount called the *phase displacement*, or *phase shift*.

■ **Example 11:** Graph y = sin(3x − 90°).

Solution: Since a = 1 and b = 3, we expect an amplitude of 1 and a period of 360/b = 120°. The effect that the constant c has on the curve will be clearer if we put the given expression into the form

$$y = a \sin b(x + c/b)$$

by factoring. Thus our equation becomes

$$y = \sin 3(x - 30°)$$

We make a table of point pairs and plot each point (Fig. 17·12).

x	0	15°	30°	45°	60°	75°	90°	105°	120°	135°	150°
y	−1	−0.707	0	0.707	1	0.707	0	−0.707	−1	−0.707	0

Our curve, unlike those plotted earlier, does not pass through the origin.

■

FIGURE 17•12 Sine curve with phase shift

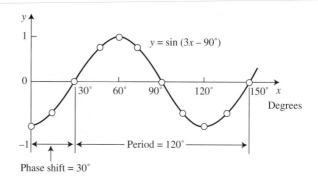

We see from Figure 17•12 that the phase shift is that x distance from the origin at which the positive half-cycle of the sine wave starts. To find this value for the general sine function $y = a\sin(bx + c)$ we set $y = 0$ and solve for x.

$$y = a\sin(bx + c) = 0$$

$$\sin(bx + c) = 0$$

$$bx + c = 0°, 180°, \dots$$

We discard $180°$ because that is the start of the negative half-cycle. So $bx + c = 0$ and

$$x = -\frac{c}{b}$$

or

Phase Shift	Phase shift $= -\dfrac{c}{b}$	213

The phase shift will have the same units, radians or degrees as the constant c. Where no units are indicated for c, assume it to be in radians. If the phase shift is *negative*, it means that the positive half-cycle starts at a point to the left of the origin, so *the curve is shifted to the left*. Conversely, a *positive* phase shift means that the curve is shifted to the *right*.

You will see, when you study *translation of axes* in analytic geometry, that replacing x in a function by $(x - h)$, where h is a constant, causes the graph of the function to be shifted h units in the x direction.

■ **Example 12:** For the sine function $y = \sin(x + 45°)$

$$a = 1, \quad b = 1, \quad \text{and} \quad c = 45°$$

$$\text{Phase shift} = -\frac{c}{b} = -45°$$

so the curve is shifted $45°$ to the left [Fig. 17•13(b)]. For comparison, Figure 17•13 also shows (a) the unshifted sine wave and (c) the wave shifted $45°$ to the right. ■

■ **Example 13:** For the sine function $y = 3\sin(4x - 2)$, we have

$$a = 3, \quad b = 4, \quad \text{and} \quad c = -2$$

so

$$\text{phase shift} = -\frac{c}{b} = -\left(\frac{-2}{4}\right) = \frac{1}{2}\text{ rad}$$

The curve is thus shifted $\frac{1}{2}$ rad to the right (Fig. 17•14). ■

FIGURE 17·13

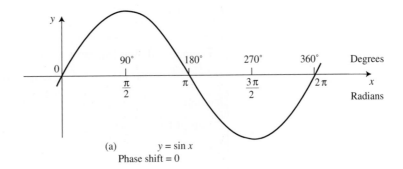

(a) $y = \sin x$
Phase shift = 0

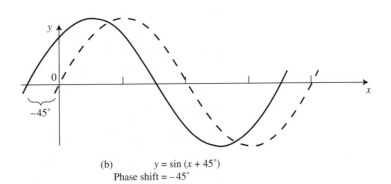

(b) $y = \sin (x + 45°)$
Phase shift = $-45°$

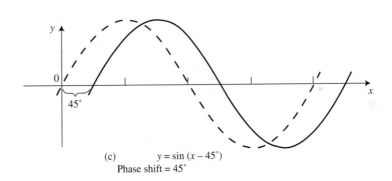

(c) $y = \sin (x - 45°)$
Phase shift = $45°$

FIGURE 17·14

To summarize,

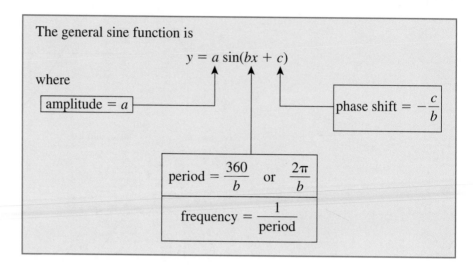

The general sine function is

$$y = a \sin(bx + c)$$

where

amplitude $= a$

phase shift $= -\dfrac{c}{b}$

period $= \dfrac{360}{b}$ or $\dfrac{2\pi}{b}$

frequency $= \dfrac{1}{\text{period}}$

Quick Sketching of the Sine Curve

We can plot any curve, as in the preceding examples, by computing and plotting a set of point pairs, but a faster way to get a sketch is to draw a rectangle of width P and height $2a$, and then sketch the sine curve (whose *shape* does not vary) within that box. First determine the amplitude, period, and phase shift. Then:

1. Draw two horizontal lines, each at a distance a from x axis.
2. Draw a vertical line at a distance P from the origin.
3. Subdivide the period P into four equal parts. Label the x axis at these points and draw vertical lines through them.
4. Lightly sketch in the sine curve.
5. Shift the curve by the amount of the phase shift.

━ **Example 14:** Make a quick sketch of $y = 2 \sin (3x + 60°)$.

Solution: We have $a = 2$, $b = 3$, and $c = 60°$. From Eq. 211, the period is

$$P = \frac{360°}{3} = 120°$$

and, by Eq. 213,

$$\text{phase shift} = -\frac{60°}{3} = -20°$$

The steps for sketching the curve are shown in Figure 17•15. ━

The graphics calculator can, of course, easily graph the general sine function. It can also be used to illustrate the effect of phase shift, as in the following example.

FIGURE 17·15 Quick sketching of the sine curve

(a) Draw horizontals 2 units above and below *x* axis.

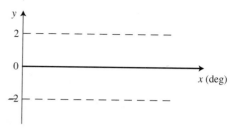

(b) Draw a vertical at a distance *P* (120°) from the origin.

(c) Divide the period into 4 equal parts.

(d) Sketch the curve lightly.

(e) Shift the curve by an amount of the phase shift (20°), right for a positive phase shift and left for a negative one.

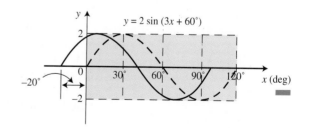

■ **Example 15:** Use the graphics calculator to graph, in the same viewing window,

$$y = 2 \sin 3x \quad \text{and} \quad y = 2 \sin(3x + 45°)$$

for *x* from −30° to 135°.

Solution: We put the calculator in degree mode and set the range:

$$\text{Xmin} = -30 \qquad \text{Xmax} = 135 \qquad \text{Xscl} = 45$$

$$\text{Ymin} = -2.5 \qquad \text{Ymax} = 2.5 \qquad \text{Yscl} = 1$$

We enter the equations and press $\boxed{\text{GRAPH}}$, and get the display shown in Figure 17•16. Notice that $-c/b = -45/3 = -15°$, so that the curve $y = 2 \sin(2x + 45°)$ is shifted 15° to the left.

FIGURE 17•16

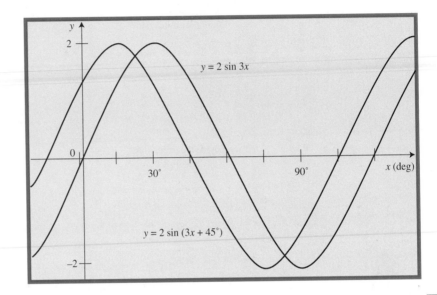

Example 16: Use the graphics calculator to make a complete graph of

$$y = -3.24 \sin(1.22x - 0.526)$$

in radians. Then use the TRACE and ZOOM features to find the coordinates of the intercepts and the maximum and minimum points, to three significant digits.

Solution: We put the calculator in radian mode and enter the equation. We note that the amplitude is 3.24, so let us set the Ymax to 4 and Ymin to -4, with Yscl equal to 1. We can set the X range either by first calculating the period, or by using trial and error with the ZOOM feature. Either way we get a complete graph, with a little to spare, with the X range set approximately to the following values:

$$\text{Xmin} = -3 \qquad \text{Xmax} = 4 \qquad \text{Xscl} = 1$$

$$\text{Ymin} = -4 \qquad \text{Ymax} = 4 \qquad \text{Yscl} = 1$$

The coordinates of the points of interest are shown in Figure 17•17.

FIGURE 17•17

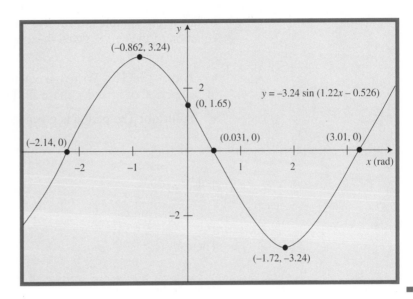

We shall now produce a sketch using radians as our units.

■ **Example 17:** Make a quick sketch of

$$y = 1.5 \sin (5x - 2)$$

Solution: From the given equation,

$$a = 1.5, \quad b = 5, \quad \text{and} \quad c = -2 \text{ rad}$$

so

$$P = \frac{2\pi}{5} = 1.26 \text{ rad}$$

and

$$\text{phase shift} = -\left(\frac{-2}{5}\right) = 0.4 \text{ rad}$$

We draw a rectangle [Fig. 17•18(a)] whose height is $2 \times 1.5 = 3$ units, and whose width is 1.26 rad, and then draw three verticals spaced at intervals of $1.26/4 = 0.315$ rad. We sketch a sine wave (shown dashed) into this rectangle, and then shift it 0.4 rad to the right to produce the final curve [Fig. 17•18(b)].

FIGURE 17•18

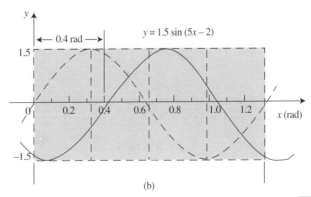

In our next example we reverse the procedure. We show how to write the equation of the curve, given the amplitude, period, and phase shift.

━━ **Example 18:** Write the equation of a sine curve having an amplitude of 5, a period of π, and a phase shift of -0.5 rad.

Solution: The period is given as π, so

$$P = \pi = \frac{2\pi}{b}$$

and

$$b = \frac{2\pi}{\pi} = 2$$

Then

$$\text{phase shift} = -0.5 = -\frac{c}{b}$$

Since $b = 2$, we get

$$c = -2(-0.5) = 1$$

Substituting into the general equation of the sine function

$$y = a \sin(bx + c)$$

with $a = 5$, $b = 2$, and $c = 1$ gives

$$y = 5 \sin(2x + 1)$$

━━

Exercise 1 The Sine Curve

Periodic Waveforms

Find the period, frequency, and amplitude for each period waveform.

1. Figure 17•19(a).
2. Figure 17•19(b).

FIGURE 17•19

(a)

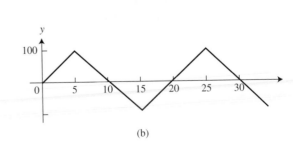

(b)

The Sine Function

Graph each function below. Find the amplitude, period, and phase shift. Do a point-by-point or a quick plot, as directed by your instructor

3. $y = 2 \sin x$

4. $y = 1.5 \sin x$

5. $y = -3 \sin x$

6. $y = 4.25 \sin x$

7. $y = \sin 2x$

8. $y = \sin \dfrac{x}{3}$

9. $y = 4 \sin(x - 180°)$

10. $y = -2 \sin(x + 90°)$

11. $y = \sin(x + 90°)$

12. $y = 20 \sin(2x - 45°)$

13. $y = 0.5 \sin 2x$

14. $y = 100 \sin \dfrac{3x}{2}$

15. $y = 2 \sin 3x$

16. $y = \sin \pi x$

17. $y = \sin 3\pi x$

18. $y = -3 \sin \pi x$

19. $y = \sin(x - 1)$

20. $y = 0.5 \sin\left(\dfrac{x}{2} - 1\right)$

21. $y = \sin\left(x + \dfrac{\pi}{2}\right)$

22. $y = \sin\left(x + \dfrac{\pi}{8}\right)$

23. Write the equations of the sine curves in Figure 17•20.

FIGURE 17•20

(a)

(b)

(c)

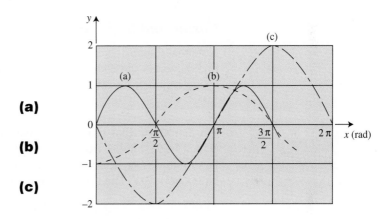

24. Write the equation of a sine curve that has an amplitude of 3, a period of 4π, and a phase shift of zero.

25. Write the equation of a sine curve having an amplitude of $|-2|$, a period of 6π, and a phase shift of $-\pi/4$.

Graphics Calculator or Computer

Use a graphics calculator or a graphics program on the computer to plot any of the equations in this exercise. Also use it to graph the following:

26. $y = 2.63 \sin(1.63x - 0.823)$

27. $y = 45.3 \sin(4.22x + 0.372)$

28. $y = -5.21 \sin(0.234x + 1.35)$

29. $y = 3.82 \sin(2.33x + 24.6°)$

30. $y = 25.6 \sin(4.42x - 45.2°)$

31. $y = -61.3 \sin(3.27x - 58.2°)$

17•2

Graphs of More Trigonometric Functions

Graph of the Cosine Function, y = cos x

Let us graph one cycle of function $y = \cos x$. We make a table of point pairs, and plot each point. The graph of the cosine function is shown in Figure 17•21.

x	0	$\frac{\pi}{6}$	$\frac{\pi}{3}$	$\frac{\pi}{2}$	$\frac{2\pi}{3}$	$\frac{5\pi}{6}$	π	$\frac{7\pi}{6}$	$\frac{4\pi}{3}$	$\frac{3\pi}{2}$	$\frac{5\pi}{3}$	$\frac{11\pi}{6}$	2π
y	1	0.866	0.5	0	−0.5	−0.866	−1	−0.866	−0.5	0	0.5	0.866	1

FIGURE 17•21 $y = \cos x$

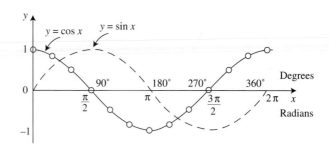

Cosine and Sine Curves Related

Note that the cosine curve (Fig. 17•21) and the sine curve, shown as a dashed line, have the same shape. In fact, the cosine curve appears to be identical to a sine curve shifted 90° to the left, or that

$$\cos \theta = \sin(\theta + 90°) \qquad (1)$$

Since the sine and cosine curves are identical except for phase shift, we can use either one to describe periodically varying quantities.

We can show that (1) is true. We lay out the two angles θ and $\theta + 90°$ (Fig. 17•22), choose points P and Q so that $OP = OQ$, and drop perpendiculars PR and QS to the x axis. Since triangles OPR and OQS are congruent, we have $OR = QS$. The cosine of θ is then

$$\cos \theta \frac{OR}{OP} = \frac{QS}{OQ} = \sin(\theta + 90°)$$

which verifies (1).

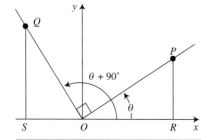

FIGURE 17•22

Graph of the General Cosine Function, y = a cos(bx + c)

The equation for the general cosine function is

$$y = a \cos(bx + c)$$

The amplitude, period, frequency, and phase shift are found the same way as for the sine curve, and, of course, the quick plotting method works here, too.

■ **Example 19:** Find the amplitude, period, frequency, and phase shift for the curve $y = 3 \cos(4x - 120°)$ and make a graph.

Solution: From the equation, a = amplitude = 3. Since $b = 4$,

$$\text{period} = \frac{360°}{4} = 90°/\text{cycle}$$

and

$$\text{frequency} = \frac{1}{P} = 0.0111 \text{ cycle/degree}$$

Since $c = -120°$,

$$\text{phase shift} = -\frac{c}{b} = -\frac{-120°}{4} = 30°$$

so we expect the curve to be shifted 30° to the right. For a quick plot, we draw a rectangle with height twice the amplitude and a length of one period (Fig. 17•23). We sketch in the cosine curve, shown as a dashed line, and then shift it 30° to the right to obtain the final curve, shown as a solid line.

FIGURE 17•23

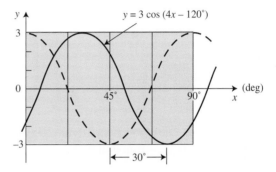

Graph of the Tangent Function, y = tan x

We now plot the function $y = \tan x$. As usual, we make a table of point pairs.

x	0	30°	60°	90°	120°	150°	180°	210°	240°	270°	300°	330°	360°
y	0	0.577	1.73	—	−1.73	−0.577	0	0.577	1.73	—	−1.73	−0.577	0

The tangent is not defined at 90° (or 270°), as we saw in Section 15•1. But for angles slightly less than 90° (or 270°) the tangent is large and grows larger the closer the angle gets to 90° (for example, tan 89.9° = 573, tan 89.99° = 5730, and so on). The same thing happens for angles slightly larger than 90° (or 270°) except that the tangent is now negative (tan 90.1° = −573, tan 90.01° = −5730, and so on). With this information, we graph the tangent curve in Figure 17•24.

The terms "period" and "frequency" have the same meaning as before, but *amplitude* is not used in connection with the tangent function, as the curve extends to infinity in the positive and negative directions.

The vertical lines at $x = 90°$ and 270° that the tangent graph approaches but never touches are called *asymptotes*.

As with the sine and cosine functions, the tangent function may also take the form

$$y = a \tan(bx + c)$$

where the constants, a, b, and c, affect the shape, period, and phase angle of the function.

FIGURE 17·24

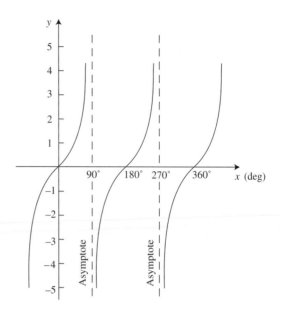

■ **Example 20:** Use a graphics calculator to graph two cycles of the function

$$y = 3 \tan (2x - 40°)$$

Solution: We put the calculator into degree mode and enter the equation. By trial and error we quickly find that the range settings that give us two cycles are approximately

$$\text{Xmin} = -30 \qquad \text{Xmax} = 170 \qquad \text{Xscl} = 20$$

$$\text{Ymin} = -10 \qquad \text{Ymax} = 10 \qquad \text{Yscl} = 1$$

We get the graph shown in Figure 17·25.

FIGURE 17·25

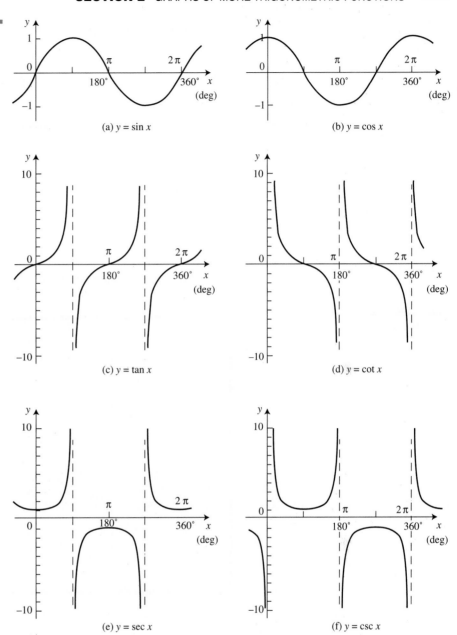

(a) $y = \sin x$

(b) $y = \cos x$

(c) $y = \tan x$

(d) $y = \cot x$

(e) $y = \sec x$

(f) $y = \csc x$

Graphs of Cotangent, Secant, and Cosecant Functions

For completeness, the graphs of all six trigonometric functions are shown in Figure 17•26. To make them easier to compare, the same horizontal scale is used for each curve. Only the sine and cosine curves find much use in technology. Notice that, of the six, they are the only curves that have no "gaps" or "breaks." They are called *continuous* curves, while the others are called *discontinuous*.

If the need should arise to graph a cotangent, secant, or cosecant function, simply make a table of point pairs and plot them, or use a graphics calculator or graphing utility on a computer. With the calculator or computer you will need to use the reciprocal relations.

■ **Example 21:** To graph the function

$$y = 3 \sec(2x - 1)$$

for $x = -2$ to 3 radians, we set the calculator in radian mode and set the x range:

$$\text{Xmin} = -2 \qquad \text{Xmax} = 3 \qquad \text{Xscl} = .5$$

We enter the function

$$\text{Y1} = 3/\cos(2x - 1)$$

and press ⎡GRAPH⎤. We find a suitable y scale by trial and error. Some values that work well are

$$\text{Ymin} = -10 \qquad \text{Ymax} = 10 \qquad \text{Yscl} = 2.5$$

The resulting graph is shown in Figure 17•27.

FIGURE 17•27

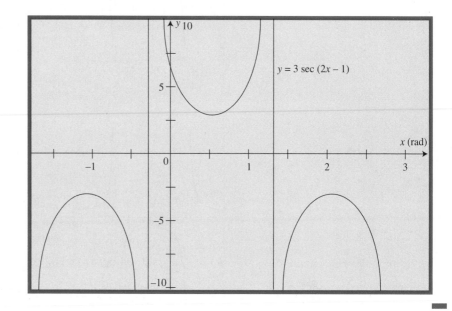

Composite Curves

One way to graph a function containing several terms is to graph each term separately, and then add (or subtract) them on the graph paper. This is called the method of *addition of ordinates*. It is especially useful when at least one term of the expression to be graphed is a trigonometric function.

■ **Example 22:** Graph the function $y = 8/x + \cos x$, where x is in radians, from $x = 0$ to 12 rad

Solution: We separately graph $y_1 = 8/x$ and $y_2 = \cos x$, shown as a dashed line in Figure 17•28. We add the ordinates graphically to get the composite curve, shown as a solid line.

FIGURE 17·28 Graphing by addition of ordinates

Exercise 2 More Trigonometric Functions

The Cosine Curve

Make a complete graph of each function. Find the amplitude, period, and phase shift.

1. $y = 3 \cos x$ **2.** $y = \cos 2x$ **3.** $y = 2 \cos 3x$

4. $y = \cos(x + 2)$ **5.** $y = 3 \cos\left(x - \dfrac{\pi}{4}\right)$ **6.** $y = 2 \cos(3x + 1)$

The Tangent Curve

Make a complete graph of each function.

7. $y = 2 \tan x$ **8.** $y = \tan 4x$ **9.** $y = 3 \tan 2x$

10. $y = \tan\left(x - \dfrac{\pi}{2}\right)$ **11.** $y = 2 \tan(3x - 2)$ **12.** $y = 4 \tan\left(x + \dfrac{\pi}{6}\right)$

Cotangent, Secant, and Cosecant Curves

Make a complete graph of each function.

13. $y = 2 \cot 2x$ **14.** $y = 3 \sec 4x$ **15.** $y = \csc 3x$
16. $y = \cot(x - 1)$ **17.** $y = 2 \sec(3x + 1)$ **18.** $y = \csc(2x + 0.5)$

Composite Curves

Graph by addition of ordinates (x is in radians).

19. $y = x + \sin x$ **20.** $y = \cos x - x$

21. $y = \dfrac{2}{x} - \sin x$ **22.** $y = 2x + 5 \cos x$

23. $y = \sin x + \cos 2x$

24. $y = \sin x + \sqrt{x}$

25. $y = 2 \sin 2x - \cos 3x$

26. $y = 3 \cos 3x + 2 \sin 4x$

Graphics Calculator or Computer

Use a graphics calculator or a graphing program on a computer to graph any of the above functions. Also use it to make a complete graph of the following.

27. $y = 3.72 \cos(1.39x + 0.836)$

28. $y = 23.1 \tan(2.24x + 35.2°)$

29. $y = 0.723 \cot(3.82x + 12.2°)$

30. $y = 4.82 \sec(4.19x + 1.36)$

17·3

The Sine Wave as a Function of Time

The sine curve can be generated in a simple geometric way. Figure 17·29 shows a vector OP rotating with a constant angular velocity ω. A rotating vector is called a *phasor*. Its angular velocity ω is given in radians per second (rad/s).

If the length of the phasor is a, then its projection on the y axis is

$$y = a \sin \theta$$

but, since by Eq. A26 the angle θ at any instant of time t is equal to ωt,

$$y = a \sin \omega t$$

Further, if the phasor does not start from the x axis but has some phase *angle* φ, we get

$$y = a \sin(\omega t + \phi)$$

FIGURE 17·29 The sine curve generated by a rotating vector

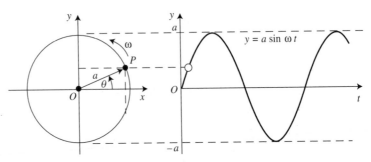

Notice in this equation that y *is a function of time* rather than of an angle.

We'll soon see that a sine wave that is a function of time is more appropriate for representing alternating current than a sine wave that is a function of an angle.

▬ **Example 23:** Write the equation for a sine wave generated by a phasor of length 8 rotating with an angular velocity of 300 rad/s, and with a phase angle φ = 0.

Solution: Substituting, with $a = 8$, $\omega = 300$ rad/s, and φ = 0,

$$y = 8 \sin 300t$$

▬

Period

Recall that the period was defined as the distance along the x axis taken by one cycle of the waveform. When the units on the x axis represented an angle, the period was in radians or degrees. Now that the x axis shows time, the period will be in seconds. From Eq. 211,

$$P = \frac{2\pi}{b}$$

But, in the equation $y = a \sin \omega t$, $b = \omega$, so

Period of a Sine Wave	$P = \dfrac{2\pi}{\omega}$	**A77**

where P is in seconds and ω is in rad/s.

■ **Example 24:** Find the period and amplitude of the sine wave $y = 6 \sin 10t$ and make a graph with time t shown on the horizontal axis.

FIGURE 17·30

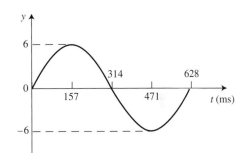

Solution: The period, from Eq. A77, is

$$(P =) \frac{2\pi}{\omega} = \frac{2(3.142)}{10} = 0.628 \text{ s}$$

Thus, it takes 628 ms for a full cycle, 314 ms for a half cycle, 157 ms for a quarter cycle, and so forth. This sine wave, with amplitude 6, is plotted in Figure 17·30. ■

Common Error	Don't confuse the function $y = \sin bx$ with the function $y = \sin \omega t$ In the first case, y is a function of an angle x, and b is a coefficient that has no units. In the second case, y is a function of time, t, and ω is an angular velocity in radians per second.

Frequency

From Eq. 212, we see that the frequency f of a periodic waveform is equal to the reciprocal of the period P. So, for the sine wave,

Frequency of a Sine Wave	$f = \dfrac{1}{P} = \dfrac{\omega}{2\pi}$	**A78**

where P is in seconds and ω is in rad/s.

The unit of frequency is therefore cycles/s, or *hertz* (Hz):

$$1 \text{ Hz} = 1 \text{ cycle/s}$$

Higher frequencies are often expressed in kilohertz (kHz), where

$$1 \text{ kHz} = 10^3 \text{ Hz}$$

or in megahertz (MHz), where

$$1 \text{ MHz} = 10^6 \text{ Hz}$$ ▬

▬ **Example 25:** The frequency of the sine wave of Example 24 is

$$f = \frac{1}{P} = \frac{1}{0.628} = 1.59 \text{ Hz}$$ ▬

When the period P is not wanted, the angular velocity can be obtained directly from Eq. A78 by noting that $\omega = 2\pi f$.

▬ **Example 26:** Find the angular velocity of a 1000-Hz source.

Solution: from Eq. A78,

$$\omega = 2\pi f = 2(3.14)(1000) = 6280 \text{ rad/s}$$ ▬

A sine wave as a function of time can also have a phase shift, expressed either in degrees or radians, as in the following example.

▬ **Example 27:** Given the sine wave $y = 5.83 \sin(114t + 15°)$, find (a) the amplitude, (b) the angular velocity, (c) the period, (d) the frequency, and (e) the phase angle, and (f) make a graph.

Solution:
(a) The amplitude is 5.83 units.
(b) The angular velocity is $\omega = 114$ rad/s.
(c) From Eq. A77, the period is

$$P = \frac{2\pi}{\omega} = \frac{2\pi}{114} = 0.0551 \text{ s} = 55.1 \text{ ms}$$

(d) From Eq. A78, the frequency is

$$f = \frac{1}{P} = \frac{1}{0.0551} = 18.1 \text{ Hz}$$

Even though it is often done, some object to mixing degrees and radians in the same equation. If you do this, work with extra care.

(e) The phase angle is 15°. It is not unusual to see a sine wave given with ωt in radians and the phase angle in degrees. We get the phase shift, in units of time, the same way we got the phase shift for the general sine function in Section 17•1. We find the value of t at which the positive half-cycle starts. As before, we set y equal to zero and solve for t.

$$y = \sin(\omega t + \phi) = 0$$

$$\omega t = -\phi$$

$$t = -\frac{\phi}{\omega} = \text{phase shift}$$

Substituting our values for ω and ϕ (which we first convert to 0.262 radians) gives

$$\text{phase shift} = -\frac{0.262 \text{ rad}}{114 \text{ rad/s}} = -0.00230 \text{ s}$$

so our curve is shifted 2.30 milliseconds to the left.

(f) This sine wave is graphed in Figure 17·31. We draw a rectangle of height 2(5.83) and width 55.1 ms. We subdivide the rectangle into four rectangles of equal width and sketch in the sine wave, shown as a dashed line. We then shift the sine wave 2.30 ms to the left to get the final (solid) curve.

FIGURE 17·31

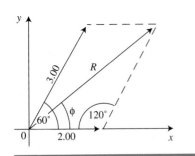

	It's easy to get confused about in which direction to shift
Common Error	the curve. Check your work by substituting the value of an x intercept (such as -0.00230 s in the above example) back into the original equation. You should get a value of zero for y.

Adding Sine Waves of the Same Frequency

We have seen that $A \sin \omega t$ is the y component of a phasor of magnitude A rotating at angular velocity ω. Similarly, $B \sin(\omega t + \theta)$ is the y component of a phasor of magnitude B rotating at the same angular velocity ω, but with a phase angle ϕ between A and B. Since each is the y component of a phasor, their sum is equal to the sum of the y components of the two phasors, in other words, simply the y component of the resultant of those phasors.

Thus, to add two sine waves of the same frequency, we simply *find the resultant of the phasors representing those sine waves.*

■ **Example 28:** Express $y = 2.00 \sin \omega t + 3.00 \sin (\omega t + 60°)$ as a single sine wave.

Solution: We represent $2.00 \sin \omega t$ by a phasor of length 2.00, and we represent $3.00 \sin (\omega t + 60°)$ as a phasor of length 3.00, at an angle of 60°. These phasors are shown in Figure 17·32. We wish to add $y = 2.00 \sin \omega t$ and $y = 3.00 \sin(\omega t + 60°)$. By the law of cosines,

$$R = \sqrt{2.00^2 + 3.00^2 - 2(2.00)(3.00) \cos 120°} = 4.36$$

Then by the law of sines,

FIGURE 17·32

$$\frac{\sin \phi}{3.00} = \frac{\sin 120}{4.36}$$

$$\sin \phi = 0.596$$

$$\phi = 36.6°$$

Thus

$$y = 2.00 \sin \omega t + 3.00 \sin(\omega t + 60°)$$

$$= 4.36 \sin(\omega t + 36.6°)$$

Figure 17·33 shows the two original sine waves as well as a graph of $4.36 \sin (\omega t + 36.6°)$. Note that the sum of the ordinates of the original waves, at any value of ωt, is equal to the ordinate of the final wave.

FIGURE 17·33

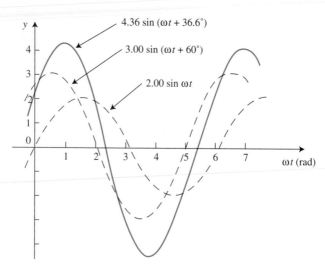

Use a graphics calculator or computer to graph the original function and the final one, on the same axes. The two curves should be identical.

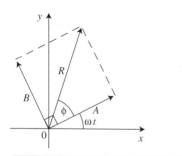

FIGURE 17·34

In Section 18·2 we will derive this same equation using the trigonometric identities.

Adding Sine and Cosine Waves of the Same Frequency

In Section 17·2 we verified that

$$\cos \omega t = \sin(\omega t + 90°)$$

and saw that a cosine wave A cos ωt is identical to the sine wave A sin ωt, except for a phase difference of 90° between the two curves (see Fig. 17·21). Thus we can find the sum (A sin ωt + B cos ωt) of a sine and a cosine wave the same way that we added two sine waves in the preceding section, by finding the resultant of the phasors representing each sine wave. Since the angle between the two phasors is 90° (Fig. 17·34), the resultant has a magnitude

$$R = \sqrt{A^2 + B^2}$$

and is at an angle

$$\phi = \arctan \frac{B}{A}$$

So

Addition of a Sine Wave and a Cosine Wave	$A \sin \omega t + B \cos \omega t = R \sin(\omega t + \phi)$ where $R = \sqrt{A^2 + B^2}$ and $\phi = \arctan \dfrac{B}{A}$	214

Thus we can represent the sum of a sine and a cosine function by a single sine function.

■ **Example 29:** Express $y = 274 \sin \omega t + 371 \cos \omega t$ as a single sine function.

Solution: The magnitude of the resultant is

$$R = \sqrt{(274)^2 + (371)^2} = 461$$

and the phase angle is

$$\phi = \arctan \frac{371}{274} = \arctan 1.354 = 53.6°$$

Note that you can use the rectangular to polar conversion keys on your calculator to do this calculation.

so

$$y = 274 \sin \omega t + 371 \cos \omega t$$
$$= 461 \sin(\omega t + 53.6°)$$

FIGURE 17·35

Figure 17·35 shows the original sine and cosine functions, and a graph of $y = 461 \sin(\omega t + 53.6°)$. Note that the sum of the ordinates of the original waves equals the ordinate of the computed wave at any abscissa.   ■

Alternating Current

When a loop of wire rotates in a magnetic field, any portion of the wire cuts the field while traveling first in one direction and then in the other direction. Since the polarity of the voltage induced in the wire depends on the direction in which the field is cut, the induced current will travel first in one direction and then in the other. It *alternates*.

The same is true for a wire-wound armature, a more complex form of the simple loop. We get an *alternating current*. Just as the rotating phasor in Figure 17·29 generated a sine wave, the current induced in the rotating armature will be sinusoidal.

The sinusoidal voltage or current can be described by the equation

$$y = a \sin(\omega t + \phi)$$

We have given the phase angle ϕ subscripts because, in a given circuit, the current and voltage waves will usually have different phase angles.

or, in electrical terms,

$$i = I_m \sin(\omega t + \phi_2) \tag{A76}$$

where i is the current at time t, I_m the maximum current (the amplitude), and ϕ_2 the phase angle. If we let V_m stand for the amplitude of the voltage wave, the instantaneous voltage v becomes

$$v = V_\mathrm{m} \sin(\omega t + \phi_1) \qquad \text{(A75)}$$

Equations A77 and A78 still apply here.

$$\text{Period} = \frac{2\pi}{\omega}\ \text{s}$$

$$\text{Frequency} = \frac{\omega}{2\pi}\ \text{Hz} \qquad \blacksquare$$

■ **Example 30:** Utilities in Canada supply alternating current at a frequency of 60Hz. Find the angular velocity and the period P.

Solution: By Eq. A78,

$$P = \frac{1}{f} = \frac{1}{60} = 0.0167\ \text{s}$$

and, by Eq. A77,

$$\omega = \frac{2\pi}{P} = \frac{2\pi}{0.0167} = 377\ \text{rad/s}$$

These are good numbers to remember.　　　　　　　　　　　　　■

■ **Example 31:** A certain alternating current has an amplitude of 1.5 A and a frequency of 60 Hz (cycles/s). Taking the phase angle as zero, write the equation for the current as a function of time, find the period, and find the current at $t = 0.01$ s.

Solution: From Example 30,

$$P = 0.0167\ \text{s} \quad \text{and} \quad \omega = 377\ \text{rad/s}$$

so the equation is

$$i = 1.5 \sin(377t)$$

When $t = 0.01$ s,

$$i = 1.5 \sin(377)(0.01) = -0.882\ \text{A}$$

as shown in Figure 17•36.　　　　　　　　　　　　　　　　■

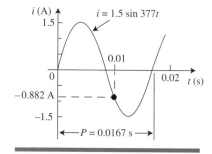

FIGURE 17•36

Phase Shift

When writing the equation of a single alternating voltage or current, we are usually free to choose the origin anywhere along the time axis, and thus we can place it so as to make the phase angle equal to zero. However, when there are *two* curves on the same graph that are *out of phase*, we usually locate the origin so that the phase angle of one curve is zero.

If the difference in phase between two sine waves is t seconds, then we often say that one curve *leads* the other by t seconds. Conversely, we could say that one curve *lags* the other by t seconds.

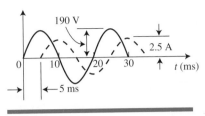

FIGURE 17·37

■ **Example 32:** Figure 17·37 shows voltage and current waves, with the voltage wave leading the current wave by 5 ms. Write the equations for the two waves.

Solution: For the voltage wave,

$$V_m = 190, \quad \phi = 0, \quad \text{and} \quad P = 0.02 \text{ s}$$

By Eq. A77,

$$\omega = \frac{2\pi}{0.02} = 100\pi = 314 \text{ rad/s}$$

so

$$v = 190 \sin 314t$$

where v is expressed in volts. For the current wave, $I_m = 2.5$ A. Since the curve is shifted to the right by 5 ms,

$$\text{phase shift} = 0.005 \text{ s} = -\frac{\phi}{\omega}$$

so the phase angle ϕ is

$$(\phi =) -(0.005 \text{ s})(100\pi \text{ rad/s}) = -\frac{\pi}{2} \text{ rad} = -90°$$

The angular frequency is the same as before, so,

$$i = 2.5 \sin(314t - 90°)$$

where i is expressed in amperes. With ϕ in radians,

$$i = 2.5 \sin\left(314t - \frac{\pi}{2}\right)$$

where i is expressed in amperes.   ■

Exercise 3   The Sine Wave as a Function of Time

Find the period and angular velocity of a repeating waveform that has a frequency of:

1. 68 Hz   **2.** 10 Hz   **3.** 5000 Hz

Find the frequency (in hertz) and angular velocity of a repeating waveform whose period is:

4. 1 s   **5.** $\frac{1}{8}$ s   **6.** 95 ms

7. If a periodic waveform has a frequency of 60 Hz, how many seconds will it take to complete 200 cycles?

8. Find the frequency in hertz for a wave that completes 150 cycles in 10 s.

Find the period and frequency of a sine wave that has an angular velocity of:

9. 455 rad/s   **10.** 2.58 rad/s   **11.** 500 rad/s

Find the period, amplitude, and phase angle for:

12. The sine wave shown in Figure 17·38(a)
13. The sine wave shown in Figure 17·38(b)

14. Write an equation for a sine wave generated by a phasor of length 5, rotating with an angular velocity of 750 rad/s, with a phase angle of 0°.
15. Repeat Problem 14, with a phase angle of 15°.

FIGURE 17·38

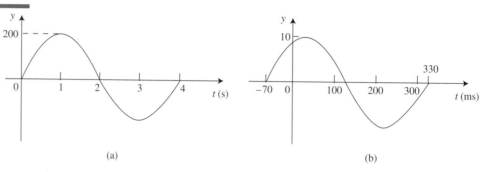

(a)   (b)

Plot each sine wave.

16. $y = \sin t$

17. $y = 3 \sin 377t$

18. $y = 54 \sin(83t - 20°)$

19. $y = 375 \sin\left(55t + \dfrac{\pi}{4}\right)$

Adding Sine Waves and Cosine Waves

Express as a single sine wave.

20. $y = 3.00 \sin \omega t + 5.50 \sin(\omega t + 30°)$
21. $y = 18.3 \sin \omega t + 26.3 \sin(\omega t + 75°)$
22. $y = 2.47 \sin \omega t + 1.83 \sin(\omega t - 24°)$
23. $y = 384 \sin \omega t + 536 \sin(\omega t - 48°)$
24. $y = 8370 \sin \omega t + 7570 \cos \omega t$
25. $y = 7.37 \cos \omega t + 5.83 \sin \omega t$
26. $y = 74.2 \sin \omega t + 69.3 \cos \omega t$
27. $y = 364 \sin \omega t + 550 \cos \omega t$

Alternating Current

28. An alternating current has the equation

$$i = 25 \sin(635t - 18°)$$

where i is given in amperes. Find the maximum current, the period, the frequency, the phase angle, and the instantaneous current at $t = 0.01$ s.

29. Given an alternating voltage $v = 4.27 \sin(463t + 27°)$, find the maximum voltage, period, frequency, phase angle, and the instantaneous voltage at $t = 0.12$ s.

30. Write an equation of an alternating voltage that has a peak value of 155 V, a frequency of 60 Hz, and a phase angle of 22°.

31. Write an equation for an alternating current that has a peak amplitude of 49.2 mA, a frequency of 35 Hz, and a phase angle of 63.2°.

17·4

Polar Coordinates

The Polar Coordinate System

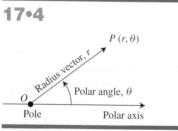

FIGURE 17·39 Polar coordinates

The *polar coordinate system* (Fig. 17·39) consists of a *polar axis*, passing through point O, which is called the *pole*. The location of a point P is given by its distance r from the origin, called the *radius vector*, and by the angle θ, called the *polar angle* (sometimes called the vectorial angle or reference angle). The polar angle is called positive when measured counterclockwise from the polar axis, and negative when measured clockwise.

The *polar coordinates* of a point P are thus r and θ, usually written in the form $P(r, \theta)$, or as $r\underline{/\theta}$ (read r at an angle of θ).

■ **Example 33:** A point at a distance 5 from the origin with a polar angle of 28° can be written

$$P(5, 28°) \quad \text{or} \quad 5\underline{/28°}$$ ■

Most of our graphing will continue to be in rectangular coordinates, but in some cases polar coordinates will be more convenient.

Plotting Points in Polar Coordinates

For plotting in polar coordinates it is convenient, although not essential, to have *polar coordinate paper* (Fig. 17•40). This paper has concentric circles, equally spaced, and an angular scale in degrees or radians.

FIGURE 17•40

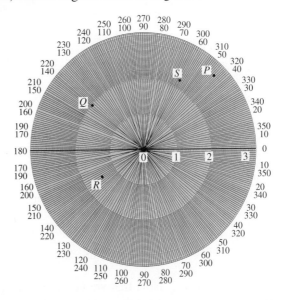

■ **Example 34:** The points $P(3, 45°)$, $Q(-2, 320°)$, $R(1.5, 7\pi/6$, and $S(2.5, -\frac{5\pi}{3})$ are plotted in Figure 17•40.

Notice that to plot $Q(-2, 320°)$, which has a negative value for r, we first locate $(2, 320°)$ and then find the corresponding point along the diameter and in the opposite quadrant. ■

Graphing Equations in Polar Coordinates

To graph a function $r = f(\theta)$, simply assign convenient values to θ and compute the corresponding value for r. Then plot the resulting table of point pairs.

■ **Example 35:** Graph the function $r = \cos \theta$.

Solution: Let us take values for θ every 30° and make a table.

θ	0	30°	60°	90°	120°	150°	180°	210°	240°	270°	300°	330°	360°
n	1	0.87	0.5	0	−0.5	−0.87	−1	0.87	−0.5	0	0.5	0.87	1

Plotting these points, we get a circle (Fig. 17•41). ■

In Chapters 5 and 14 we graphed a parabola in rectangular coordinates. We now graph an equation in polar coordinates that also results in a parabola.

FIGURE 17•41 Graph of $r = \cos \theta$. The polar equation of a circle that passes through the pole and has its center at (c, α) is $r = 2c \cos (\theta - \alpha)$.

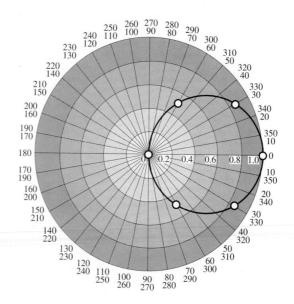

━━ **Example 36:** Graph the parabola

$$r = \frac{p}{1 - \cos \theta}$$

with $p = 1$.

Solution: As before, we compute r for selected values of θ.

θ	0	30°	60°	90°	120°	150°	180°	210°	240°	270°	300°	330°	360°
n	—	7.46	2.00	1.00	0.667	0.536	0.500	0.536	0.667	1.00	2.00	7.46	—

Note that we get division by zero at $\theta = 0°$ and $360°$, so the curve does not exist there. Plotting these points (except for 7.46, which is off the graph), we get the parabola shown in Figure 17•42.

FIGURE 17•42

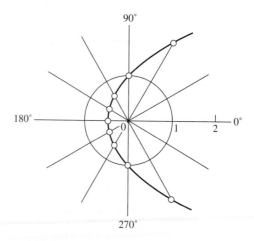

Some of the more interesting curves in polar coordinates are shown in Figure 17•43.

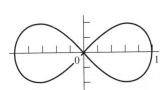

Lemniscate of Bernoulli
$r = a \cos 2\theta$

Bifolium
$r = a \sin \theta \cos^2 \theta$

Three-leaved rose
$r = a \cos 3\theta$

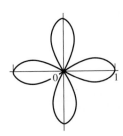

Four-leaved rose
$r = a \cos 2\theta$

Four-leaved rose
$r = a \sin 2\theta$

Cardioid
$r = a(1 - \cos \theta)$

Limaçon of Pascal
$r = b - a \cos \theta$
(graphed with $a = 3$, $b = 2$)

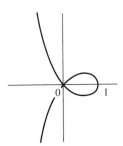

Strophoid
$r = a \cos 2\theta \sec \theta$

Cissoid of Diocles
$r = a(\sec \theta - \cos \theta)$

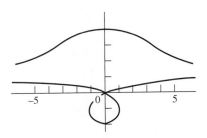

Conchoid of Nicodemus
$r = a \csc \theta + b$
(graphed with $a = 1$, $b = 3$)

Spiral of Archimedes
$r = a\theta$

Hyperbolic spiral
$r = a/\theta$

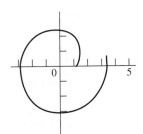

Parabolic spiral
$r = a\sqrt{\theta} + b$
(graphed with $a - b = 1$)

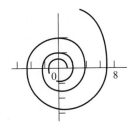

Logarithmic spiral
$r = e^{a\theta}$
(graphed with $a = 0.1$)

FIGURE 17·43 Some curves in polar coordinates. Unless otherwise noted, the curves were graphed with $a = 1$.

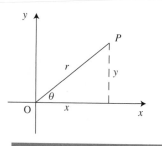

FIGURE 17·44 Rectangular and polar coordinates of a point

Transforming between Polar and Rectangular Coordinates

The relationships between rectangular coordinates and polar coordinates are easily seen when we put both systems on a single diagram (Fig. 17·44). Using the trigonometric functions and the Pythagorean theorem, we get

Rectangular Coordinates	$x = r \cos \theta$	158
	$y = r \sin \theta$	159
Polar Coordinates	$r = \sqrt{x^2 + y^2}$	160
	$\theta = \arctan \dfrac{y}{x}$	161

Some calculators have special keys for converting between polar and rectangular coordinates. Check your manual.

■ **Example 37:** What are the polar coordinates of $P(3, 4)$?

Solution:

$$r = \sqrt{3^2 + 4^2} = 5$$

$$\theta = \arctan \frac{4}{3} = 53.1°$$

So the polar coordinates of P are $(5, 53.1°)$. ■

■ **Example 38:** The polar coordinates of a point are $(8, 125°)$. What are the rectangular coordinates?

Solution:

$$x = 8 \cos 125° = -4.59$$
$$y = 8 \sin 125° = 6.55$$

So the rectangular coordinates are $(-4.59, 6.55)$. ■

We may also use Eqs. 158 to 161 to transform *equations* from one system of coordinates to the other.

■ **Example 39:** Transform the polar equation $r = \cos \theta$ to rectangular coordinates.

Solution: Multiplying both sides by r yields

$$r^2 = r \cos \theta$$

Then by Eqs. 158 and 160,

$$x^2 + y^2 = x$$ ■

■ **Example 40:** Transform the rectangular equation $2x + 3y = 5$ into polar form.

Solution: By Eqs. 158 and 160,

$$2r \cos \theta + 3r \sin \theta = 5$$

or

$$r(2 \cos \theta + 3 \sin \theta) = 5$$

$$r = \frac{5}{2 \cos \theta + 3 \sin \theta}$$ ▬

Exercise 4 Polar Coordinates

Plot each point in polar coordinates:

1. $(4, 35°)$ **2.** $(3, 120°)$ **3.** $(2.5, 215°)$

4. $(3.8, 345°)$ **5.** $\left(2.7, \dfrac{\pi}{6}\right)$ **6.** $\left(3.9, \dfrac{7\pi}{8}\right)$

7. $\left(-3, \dfrac{\pi}{2}\right)$ **8.** $\left(4.2, \dfrac{2\pi}{5}\right)$ **9.** $(3.6, -20°)$

10. $(-2.5, -35°)$ **11.** $\left(-1.8, -\dfrac{\pi}{6}\right)$ **12.** $\left(-3.7, -\dfrac{3\pi}{5}\right)$

Graph the following curves from Figure 17•43.

13. The lemniscate of Bernoulli   **14.** The bifolium
15. The three-leaved rose   **16.** The four-leaved rose,
                        $r = a \cos 2\theta$
17. The cardioid   **18.** The limaçon of Pascal
19. The strophoid   **20.** The cissoid of Diocles
21. The conchoid of Nicodemus   **22.** The spiral of Archimedes
23. The hyperbolic spiral   **24.** The parabolic spiral
25. The logarithmic spiral

Graph each function in polar coordinates.

26. $r = 2 \cos \theta$ **27.** $r = 3 \sin \theta$
28. $r = 3 \sin \theta + 3$ **29.** $r = 2 \cos \theta - 1$
30. $r = 3 \cos 2\theta$ **31.** $r = 2 \sin 3\theta$
32. $r = \sin 2\theta - 1$ **33.** $r = 2 + \cos 3\theta$

Write the polar coordinates of each point.

34. $(2.00, 5.00)$ **35.** $(3.00, 6.00)$
36. $(1.00, 4.00)$ **37.** $(4.00, 3.00)$
38. $(2.70, -1.80)$ **39.** $(-4.80, -5.90)$
40. $(207, 186)$ **41.** $(-312, -509)$
42. $(1.08, -2.15)$

Write the rectangular coordinates of each point.

43. $(5.00, 47.0°)$ **44.** $(6.30, 227°)$

45. $(445, 312°)$ **46.** $\left(3.60, \dfrac{\pi}{5}\right)$

47. $\left(-4.00, \dfrac{3\pi}{4}\right)$ **48.** $\left(18.3, \dfrac{2\pi}{3}\right)$

49. $(15.0, -35.0°)$ **50.** $(-12.0, -48.0°)$

51. $\left(-9.80, -\dfrac{\pi}{5}\right)$

Write each polar equation in rectangular form.

52. $r = 6$ **53.** $r = 2 \sin \theta$
54. $r = \sec \theta$ **55.** $r^2 = 1 - \tan \theta$
56. $r(1 - \cos \theta) = 1$ **57.** $r^2 = 4 - r \cos \theta$

Write each rectangular equation in polar form.

58. $x = 2$ **59.** $y = -3$
60. $x = 3 - 4y$ **61.** $x^2 + y^2 = 1$
62. $3x - 2y = 1$ **63.** $y = x^2$

Graphics Calculator and Computer

Some graphics calculators, and some computer software such as *Derive*, allow the plotting of polar equations. If you are able, use your calculator or computer to plot any of the polar equations in this exercise. Also plot the following, taking a large enough range for θ to give a complete graph.

64. $r = 1.42 \cos 2\theta$
65. $r = 2.53 \sin 2\theta + 4.23$
66. $r = 1.55 \sin^2 2\theta$
67. $r = 2.35 \sin^2 \theta + 2.94 \cos^2 \theta$

Some calculators require that a polar equation first be transformed into a pair of parametric equations before they can be graphed. We show how to do this in the next section.

17·5   Graphing Parametric Equations

Parametric Equations with Trigonometric Functions

In Chapter 5 we discussed parametric equations of the form

$$x = g(t)$$

and

$$y = h(t)$$

where x and y are expressed in terms of a third variable t, called the *parameter*. There we graphed parametric equations in which the $h(t)$ and $g(t)$ were *algebraic* functions; here we graph some parametric equations in which the functions are *trigonometric*.

The procedure is the same. We assign values to the parameter (which will now be θ) and compute x and y for each θ. The table of (x, y) pairs is then plotted in rectangular coordinates.

━ **Example 41:** Plot the parametric equations

$$x = 3 \cos \theta$$

$$y = 2 \sin 2\theta$$

Solution: We select values for θ and compute x and y.

θ	0	$\frac{\pi}{4}$	$\frac{\pi}{2}$	$\frac{3\pi}{4}$	π	$\frac{5\pi}{4}$	$\frac{3\pi}{2}$	$\frac{7\pi}{4}$	2π
x	3	2.12	0	-2.12	-3	-2.12	0	2.12	3
y	0	2	0	-2	0	2	0	-2	0

Each (x, y) pair is plotted in Figure 17•45.

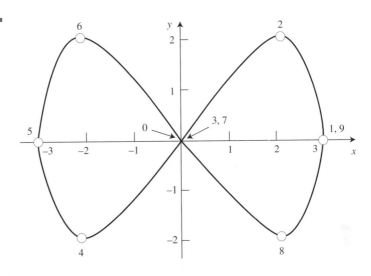

FIGURE 17•45 Patterns of this sort can be obtained by applying AC voltages to both the horizontal and vertical deflection plates of an oscilloscope. Called *Lissajous figures*, they can indicate the relative amplitudes, frequencies, and phase angles of the two applied voltages.

Note that these parametric equations are graphed in *rectangular coordinates*, not in polar coordinates.

The graphs of some common parametric equations in which the functions are trigonometric are given in Figure 17•46.

Converting a Polar Equation to Parametric Form

Some graphics calculators cannot graph a polar equation directly. It is first necessary to convert the polar equation to a pair of parametric equations, and then plot those.

To convert the polar equation

$$r = f(\theta)$$

to the parametric equations

$$x = g(\theta) \quad \text{and} \quad y = h(\theta)$$

we make use of Eqs. 158 and 159. Thus,

$$x = r \cos \theta = f(\theta) \cos \theta$$

and

$$y = r \sin \theta = f(\theta) \sin \theta$$

■ **Example 42:** Write the polar equation $r = 3 \sin 2\theta$ in parametric form, and plot, using a graphics calculator.

Solution: Here, $f(\theta) = 3 \sin 2\theta$, so

$$x = f(\theta) \cos \theta = 3 \sin 2\theta \cos \theta$$

FIGURE 17•46 Graphs of some parametric equations. Unless otherwise noted, the curves were graphed with $a = 1$.

Cycloid
$$x = a(\theta - \sin \theta)$$
$$y = a(1 - \cos \theta)$$

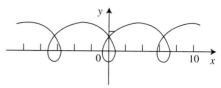

Prolate cycloid
$$x = a\theta - b \sin \theta$$
$$y = a - b \cos \theta$$
(graphed with $a = 1, b = 2$)

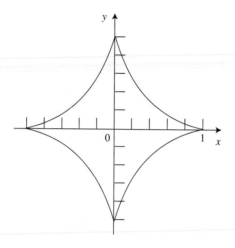

Hypocycloid of four cusps
or Astroid
$$x = a \cos^3 \theta$$
$$y = a \sin^3 \theta$$

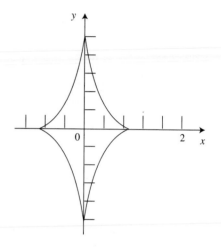

Evolute of ellipse
$$x = a \cos^3 \theta$$
$$y = b \sin^3 \theta$$
(graphed with $a = 1, b = 2$)

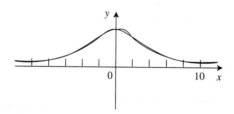

Witch of Agnesi
$$x = a \cot \theta$$
$$y = a \sin^2 \theta$$
(graphied with $a = 2$)

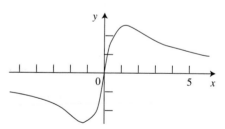

Serpentine
$$x = a \cot \theta$$
$$y = b \sin \theta \cos \theta$$
(graphed with $a = 1, b = 5$)

and

$$y = f(\theta) \sin \theta = 3 \sin 2\theta \sin \theta$$

We put the calculator into radian and parametric mode. We then enter the equations (using T instead of θ).

$$X1t = 3 \sin 2T \cos T$$

$$Y1t = 3 \sin 2T \sin T$$

We set the range:

$$T:\ 0 \text{ to } 2\pi$$
$$X:\ -4 \text{ to } 4$$
$$Y:\ -4 \text{ to } 4$$

and get the four-leaved rose shown in Figure 17•43.

Exercise 5 Parametric Equations

Graph the following curves from Figure 17•46.

1. The cycloid
2. The prolate cycloid
3. The hypocycloid of four cusps
4. The evolute of ellipse
5. The witch of Agnesi
6. The serpentine

Graph each pair of parametric equations.

7. $x = \sin \theta$
$y = \sin \theta$
8. $x = \sin \theta$
$y = 2 \sin \theta$
9. $x = \sin \theta$
$y = \sin 2\theta$
10. $x = \sin 2\theta$
$y = \sin 3\theta$
11. $x = \sin \theta$
$y = \sin (\theta + \pi/4)$
12. $x = \sin \theta$
$y = \sin (2\theta - \pi/6)$

Rewrite each polar equation in parametric form and graph.

13. $r = 3 \cos \theta$
14. $r = 2 \sin \theta$
15. $r = 2 \cos 3\theta$
16. $r = 3 \sin 4\theta$
17. $r = 3 \sin 3\theta - 2$
18. $r = 4 + \cos 2\theta$

Graphics Calculator or Computer

Use your graphics calculator or a graphing program on a computer to graph any of the parametric equations in this exercise. Also use one of these approaches to graph the following. Take a large enough range for θ to get a complete graph.

19. $x = \sin 2\theta$
$y = \sin 3\theta$
20. $x = \sin \theta$
$y = 1.32 \sin 2\theta$
21. $x = 5.83 \sin 2\theta$
$y = 4.24 \sin \theta$
22. $x = 6.27 \sin \theta$
$y = 4.83 \sin (\theta + 0.527)$

CHAPTER 17 REVIEW PROBLEMS

Graph one cycle of each curve and find the period, amplitude, and phase shift.

1. $y = 3 \sin 2x$
2. $y = 5 \cos 3x$
3. $y = 1.5 \sin \left(3x + \dfrac{\pi}{2}\right)$
4. $y = -5 \cos \left(x - \dfrac{\pi}{6}\right)$

5. $y = 2.5 \sin \left(4x + \dfrac{2\pi}{9}\right)$
6. $y = 4 \tan x$
7. Write the equation of a sine curve that has an amplitude of 5, a period of 3π, and a phase shift of $\dfrac{-\pi}{6}$

Graph by addition of ordinates.

8. $y = \sin x + \cos 2x$
9. $y = x + \cos x$

10. $y = 2 \sin x - \dfrac{1}{x}$

Plot each point in polar coordinates.

11. $(3.4, 125°)$ **12.** $(-2.5, 228°)$

13. $\left(1.7, -\dfrac{\pi}{6}\right)$

Graph each equation in polar coordinates.

14. $r^2 = \cos 2\theta$ **15.** $r + 2 \cos \theta = 1$

Write the polar coordinates of each point.

16. $(7, 3)$ **17.** $(-5.30, 3.80)$
18. $(-24, -52)$

Write the rectangular coordinates of each point.

19. $(3.80, 48.0°)$ **20.** $\left(-65, \dfrac{\pi}{9}\right)$

21. $(3.80, -44.0°)$

Transform into rectangular form.

22. $r(1 - \cos \theta) = 2$
23. $r = 2 \cos \theta$

Transform into polar form.

24. $x - 3y = 2$
25. $5x + 2y = 1$

26. Find the frequency and angular velocity of a sine wave that has a period of 2.5 s.
27. Find the period and angular velocity of a cosine wave that has a frequency of 120 Hz.
28. Find the period and frequency of a sine wave that has an angular velocity of 44.8 rad/s.
29. If a sine wave has a frequency of 30 Hz, how many seconds will it take to complete 100 cycles?
30. What frequency must a sine wave have in order to complete 500 cycles in 2 s?
31. Graph the parametric equations $x = 2 \sin \theta$ and $y = 3 \sin 4\theta$.
32. Write an equation for an alternating current that has a peak amplitude of 92.6 mA, a frequency of 82 Hz, and a phase angle of 28.3°.
33. Write as a single sine wave:
   (a) $y = 63.7 \sin \omega t + 42.9 \sin (\omega t - 38°)$
   (b) $y = 1.73 \sin \omega t + 2.64 \cos \omega t$

34. Given an alternating voltage $v = 27.4 \sin(736t + 37°)$, find the maximum voltage, period, frequency, phase angle, and the instantaneous voltage at $t = 0.25$ s.

Convert to parametric form and plot.

35. $r = 2 \cos 3\theta$ **36.** $r = 3 \sin 4\theta$

Writing

37. Given the general sine wave, $y = a \sin(bx + c)$, explain in your own words how a change in one of the constants (a, b, or c) will affect the appearance of the sine wave.

Team Projects

38. A force F (Fig. 17•47) pulls a mass (m) along a horizontal surface. If f is the coefficient of friction, then

$$F = \frac{f \cdot m \cdot a}{f \sin \theta + \cos \theta}$$

where $a = 9.8$ m/s²

FIGURE 17.47

Graphically find the value of θ, to two significant digits, so that the least force is required. Do this for values of f of 0.50, 0.60, and 0.70.

39. Graph the function that is the sum of the following four functions:

$$y = \sin x$$
$$y = (1/3) \sin 3x$$
$$y = (1/5) \sin 5x$$
$$y = (1/7) \sin 7x$$

Use a graphics calculator or computer, or manual addition of ordinates on graph paper.

What can you say about the shape of the composite curve? What do you think would happen if you added in more sine waves, $y = (1/9) \sin 9x$ and so on?

18

Trigonometric Identities and Equations

O B J E C T I V E S

When you have completed this chapter, you should be able to:

- Write a trigonometric expression in terms of the sine and cosine.
- Simplify a trigonometric expression using the fundamental identities.
- Prove trigonometric identities using the fundamental identities.
- Simplify expressions or prove identities using the sum or difference formulas, the double-angle formulas, or the half-angle formulas.
- Solve trigonometric equations.
- Add a sine wave and a cosine wave of the same frequency.
- Evaluate inverse trigonometric functions.

In Section 3•1 we said that an *identity* is an equation that is true for *all* meaningful values of the variables, as contrasted with a conditional equation, which is true only for certain values of the variables. Thus $(x + 2)(x - 2) = x^2 - 4$ is true for every value of x. A *trigonometric identity* is one that contains one or more trigonometric functions. We have already seen that $\sin \theta = 1/\csc \theta$ for any angle θ (except, of course, for values of θ for which $\csc \theta = 0$).

We derive some new identities in this chapter, which we can then use to simplify trigonometric expressions, to verify other identities, and to aid in the solution of trigonometric equations.

18•1   Fundamental Identities

Reciprocal Relations

We have already encountered the reciprocal relations in Section 7•2, and we repeat them here.

Reciprocal Relations	$\sin \theta = \dfrac{1}{\csc \theta}$ or $\csc \theta = \dfrac{1}{\sin \theta}$ or $\sin \theta \csc \theta = 1$	**152(a)**
	$\cos \theta = \dfrac{1}{\sec \theta}$ or $\sec \theta = \dfrac{1}{\cos \theta}$ or $\cos \theta \sec \theta = 1$	**152(b)**
	$\tan \theta = \dfrac{1}{\cot \theta}$ or $\cot \theta = \dfrac{1}{\tan \theta}$ or $\tan \theta \cot \theta = 1$	**152(c)**

■ **Example 1:** Simplify $\dfrac{\cos \theta}{\sec^2 \theta}$.

Solution: Using Eq. 152(b) gives us

$$\frac{\cos \theta}{\sec^2 \theta} = \cos \theta(\cos^2 \theta) = \cos^3 \theta$$

■

Quotient Relations

Figure 18•1 shows an angle θ in standard position, as when we first defined the trigonometric functions in Section 7•2. We see that

$$\sin \theta = \frac{y}{r} \quad \text{and} \quad \cos \theta = \frac{x}{r}$$

Dividing yields

$$\frac{\sin \theta}{\cos \theta} = \frac{\dfrac{y}{r}}{\dfrac{x}{r}} = \frac{y}{x}$$

But $y/x = \tan \theta$, so

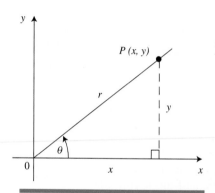

FIGURE 18•1 Angle in standard position

Quotient Relations	$\tan \theta = \dfrac{\sin \theta}{\cos \theta}$	**162**
	$\cot \theta = \dfrac{\cos \theta}{\sin \theta}$	**163**

where $\cot \theta$ is found by taking the reciprocal of $\tan \theta$.

■ **Example 2:** Rewrite the expression

$$\frac{\cot \theta}{\csc \theta} - \frac{\tan \theta}{\sec \theta}$$

so that it contains only the sine and cosine, and simplify.

Solution:

$$\frac{\cot \theta}{\csc \theta} - \frac{\tan \theta}{\sec \theta} = \frac{\cos \theta}{\sin \theta} \cdot \frac{\sin \theta}{1} - \frac{\sin \theta}{\cos \theta} \cdot \frac{\cos \theta}{1}$$

$$= \cos \theta - \sin \theta$$

■

Pythagorean Relations

We can get three more relations by applying the Pythagorean theorem to the triangle in Figure 18•1.

$$x^2 + y^2 = r^2$$

Dividing through by r^2, we get

$$\frac{x^2}{r^2} + \frac{y^2}{r^2} = 1$$

or

$$\left(\frac{x}{r}\right)^2 + \left(\frac{y}{r}\right)^2 = 1$$

but $x/r = \cos\theta$ and $y/r = \sin\theta$, so

Recall that $\sin^2\theta$ is a short way of writing $(\sin\theta)^2$.

Pythagorean Relation	$\sin^2\theta + \cos^2\theta = 1$	**164**

Returning to equation $x^2 + y^2 = r^2$, we now divide through by x^2,

$$1 + \frac{y^2}{x^2} = \frac{r^2}{x^2}$$

But $y/x = \tan\theta$ and $r/x = \sec\theta$, so

Pythagorean Relation	$1 + \tan^2\theta = \sec^2\theta$	**165**

Now dividing $x^2 + y^2 = r^2$ by y^2,

$$\frac{x^2}{y^2} + 1 = \frac{r^2}{y^2}$$

But $x/y = \cot\theta$ and $r/y = \csc\theta$, so

Pythagorean Relation	$1 + \cot^2\theta = \csc^2\theta$	**166**

■ **Example 3:** Simplify

$$\sin^2\theta - \csc^2\theta - \tan^2\theta + \cot^2\theta + \cos^2\theta + \sec^2\theta$$

Solution: By the Pythagorean relations,

$$\sin^2\theta - \csc^2\theta - \tan^2\theta + \cot^2\theta + \cos^2\theta + \sec^2\theta$$
$$= (\sin^2\theta + \cos^2\theta) - (\tan^2\theta - \sec^2\theta) + (\cot^2\theta - \csc^2\theta)$$
$$= 1 - (-1) + (-1) = 1$$

■

Simplification of Trigonometric Expressions

One use of the trigonometric identities is the simplification of expressions, as in the preceding example. We now give a few more examples.

■ **Example 4:** Simplify $(\cot^2 \theta + 1)(\sec^2 \theta - 1)$.

Solution: By Eqs. 165 and 166,

$$(\cot^2 \theta + 1)(\sec^2 \theta - 1) = \csc^2 \theta \tan^2 \theta$$

and by Eqs. 152(a) and 162,

$$= \frac{1}{\sin^2 \theta} \cdot \frac{\sin^2 \theta}{\cos^2 \theta}$$

$$= \frac{1}{\cos^2 \theta}$$

and by Eq. 152(b),

$$= \sec^2 \theta \qquad ■$$

■ **Example 5:** Simplify $\dfrac{1 - \sin^2 \theta}{\sin \theta + 1}$.

> Students tend to forget the rules of *algebraic operations* when working trigonometric expressions. We still need to factor, to combine fractions over a common denominator, and so on.

Solution: Factoring the difference of two squares in the numerator gives

$$\frac{1 - \sin^2 \theta}{\sin \theta + 1} = \frac{(1 - \sin \theta)(1 + \sin \theta)}{\sin \theta + 1} = 1 - \sin \theta \qquad ■$$

■ **Example 6:** Simplify $\dfrac{\cos \theta}{1 - \sin \theta} + \dfrac{\sin \theta - 1}{\cos \theta}$.

Solution: Combining the two fractions over a common denominator, we have

$$\frac{\cos \theta}{1 - \sin \theta} + \frac{\sin \theta - 1}{\cos \theta} = \frac{\cos^2 \theta + (\sin \theta - 1)(1 - \sin \theta)}{(1 - \sin \theta) \cos \theta}$$

$$= \frac{\cos^2 \theta + \sin \theta - \sin^2 \theta - 1 + \sin \theta}{(1 - \sin \theta) \cos \theta}$$

From Eq. 164:

$$= \frac{-\sin^2 \theta - \sin^2 \theta + 2 \sin \theta}{(1 - \sin \theta) \cos \theta}$$

$$= \frac{-2 \sin^2 \theta + 2 \sin \theta}{(1 - \sin \theta) \cos \theta}$$

Factor the numerator:

$$= \frac{2 \sin \theta(-\sin \theta + 1)}{(1 - \sin \theta) \cos \theta}$$

$$= \frac{2 \sin \theta}{\cos \theta}$$

By Eq. 162:

$$= 2 \tan \theta \qquad ■$$

Trigonometric Identities

We know that an *identity* is an equation that is true for any set of values of the unknowns, and we have presented eight trigonometric identities so far in this chapter. We now use these eight identities to *verify* or *prove* whether a given identity is true. We do this by trying to transform one side of the identity (usually the more complicated side) until it is identical to the other side.

A good way to start is to rewrite each side so that it contains only sines and cosines.

Proving identities is *not easy*. It takes a good knowledge of the fundamental identities, lots of practice, and often several false starts. Do not be discouraged if you fail to get them right away.

■ **Example 7:** Prove the identity $\sec \theta \csc \theta = \tan \theta + \cot \theta$

Solution: Expressing the given identity in terms of sines and cosines gives

$$\sec \theta \csc \theta = \tan \theta + \cot \theta$$

$$\frac{1}{\cos \theta} \cdot \frac{1}{\sin \theta} = \frac{\sin \theta}{\cos \theta} + \frac{\cos \theta}{\sin \theta}$$

If we are to make one side identical to the other, each must finally have the same number of terms. But the left side now has one term and the right has two, so we combine the two fractions on the right over a common denominator.

$$\frac{1}{\sin \theta \cos \theta} = \frac{\sin^2 \theta + \cos^2 \theta}{\sin \theta \cos \theta}$$

By Eq. 164:

$$\frac{1}{\sin \theta \cos \theta} = \frac{1}{\sin \theta \cos \theta} \qquad ■$$

Common Error	Each side of an identity must be worked *separately*; we cannot transpose, or multiply both sides by the same thing, the way we do with equations. The reason for this is that we do not yet know if the two sides are in fact equal; that is what we are trying to prove.

■ **Example 8:** Prove the identity $\csc x + \tan x = \dfrac{\cot x + \sin x}{\cos x}$

Solution: As in Example 7, we have a single term on one side of the equal sign, and two terms on the other. Now, however, it may be easier to split the single term into two, rather than combine the two terms into one, as we did before,

$$\csc x + \tan x = \frac{\cot x}{\cos x} + \frac{\sin x}{\cos x}$$

Switching to sines and cosines yields

$$\frac{1}{\sin x} + \frac{\sin x}{\cos x} = \frac{\dfrac{\cos x}{\sin x}}{\cos x} + \frac{\sin x}{\cos x}$$

$$= \frac{1}{\sin x} + \frac{\sin x}{\cos x}$$

—

Using the Graphics Calculator for Trigonometric Identities

Some computer algebra systems such as *Derive* are able to simplify, expand, and otherwise manipulate trigonometric expressions.

We can use a graphics calculator or a graphing utility on the computer to plot each side of a trigonometric identity. If the two graphs are not identical, we can be sure that we do not have an identity. If the two graphs appear to be identical, we probably have an identity, although this does not constitute a proof.

— **Example 9:** Graphically verify the identity

$$\tan x \sec x = \sin x$$

Solution: In the same viewing window we graph

$$Y_1 = \tan x(1/\cos x)$$

and

$$Y_2 = \sin x$$

The two graphs, Figure 18•2, are different, so we do not have an identity.

FIGURE 18•2

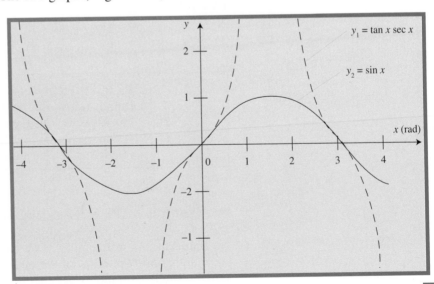

— **Example 10:** Graphically verify the identity

$$\cot x = \cot x \sec^2 x - \tan x$$

Solution: We graph

$$Y_1 = 1/\tan x$$

FIGURE 18·3

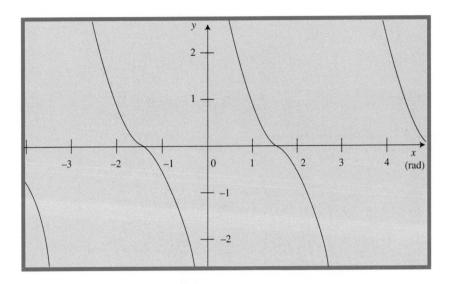

and

$$Y_2 = (1/\tan x)(1/\cos x)^2 - \tan x$$

in the same viewing window, Figure 18·3. We get a single curve, strongly indicating, but not proving, that our given relation is an identity. ▬

Exercise 1 Fundamental Identities

Change to an expression containing only sin and cos:

1. $\tan x - \sec x$

2. $\cot x + \csc x$

3. $\tan \theta \csc \theta$

4. $\sec \theta - \tan \theta \sin \theta$

5. $\dfrac{\tan \theta}{\csc \theta} + \dfrac{\sin \theta}{\tan \theta}$

6. $\cot x + \tan x$

Simplify:

7. $1 - \sec^2 x$

8. $\dfrac{\csc \theta}{\sin \theta}$

9. $\dfrac{\cos \theta}{\cot \theta}$

10. $\sin \theta \csc \theta$

11. $\tan \theta \csc \theta$

12. $\dfrac{\sin \theta}{\csc \theta}$

13. $\sec x \sin x$

14. $\sec x \sin x \cot x$

15. $\csc \theta \tan \theta - \tan \theta \sin \theta$

16. $\dfrac{\cos x}{\cot x \sin x}$

17. $\cot \theta \tan^2 \theta \cos \theta$

18. $\dfrac{\tan x(\csc^2 x - 1)}{\sin x + \cot x \cos x}$

19. $\dfrac{\sin \theta}{\cos \theta \tan \theta}$

20. $\dfrac{\sin^2 x + \cos^2 x}{1 - \cos^2 x}$

21. $\dfrac{1}{\sec^2 x} + \dfrac{1}{\csc^2 x}$

22. $\sin \theta (\csc \theta + \cot \theta)$

23. $\csc x - \cot x \cos x$

24. $1 + \dfrac{\tan^2 \theta}{1 + \sec \theta}$

25. $\dfrac{\sec x - \csc x}{1 - \cot x}$

26. $\dfrac{1}{1 + \sin x} + \dfrac{1}{1 - \sin x}$

27. $\sec^2 x(1 - \cos^2 x)$

28. $\tan x + \dfrac{\cos x}{\sin x + 1}$

29. $\cos \theta \sec \theta - \dfrac{\sec \theta}{\cos \theta}$

30. $\cot^2 x \sin^2 x + \tan^2 x \cos^2 x$

All identities in this chapter *can* be proven.

Prove each identity:

31. $\tan x \cos x = \sin x$

32. $\tan x = \dfrac{\sec x}{\csc x}$

33. $\dfrac{\sin x}{\csc x} + \dfrac{\cos x}{\sec x} = 1$

34. $\sin \theta = \dfrac{1}{\cot \theta \sec \theta}$

35. $(\cos^2 \theta + \sin^2 \theta)^2 = 1$

36. $\tan x = \dfrac{\tan x - 1}{1 - \cot x}$

37. $\dfrac{\csc \theta}{\sec \theta} = \cot \theta$

38. $\cot^2 x = \dfrac{\cos x}{\tan x \sin x}$

39. $\cos x + 1 = \dfrac{\sin^2 x}{1 - \cos x}$

40. $\csc x - \sin x = \cot x \cos x$

41. $\cot^2 x - \cos^2 x = \cos^2 x \cot^2 x$

42. $\csc x = \cos x \cot x + \sin x$

43. $1 = (\csc x - \cot x)(\csc x + \cot x)$

44. $\tan x = \dfrac{\tan x + \sin x}{1 + \cos x}$

45. $\dfrac{\tan x + 1}{1 - \tan x} = \dfrac{\sin x + \cos x}{\cos x - \sin x}$

46. $\cot x = \cot x \sec^2 x - \tan x$

47. $\dfrac{\sin \theta + 1}{1 - \sin \theta} = (\tan \theta + \sec \theta)^2$

48. $\dfrac{1 + \sin \theta}{1 - \sin \theta} = \dfrac{1 + \csc \theta}{\csc \theta - 1}$

49. $(\sec \theta - \tan \theta)(\tan \theta + \sec \theta) = 1$

50. $\dfrac{1 + \cot \theta}{\csc \theta} = \dfrac{\tan \theta + 1}{\sec \theta}$

Graphics Calculator or Computer

51. Use a graphics calculator or a graphing utility on a computer to graphically verify any of the identities in this exercise. You may also use the same method to check your answers in Problems 1 to 30.

52. Graph the expression

$$\sin^2 x + \cos^2 x$$

How do you interpret your resulting graph?

Also graph

$$\sec^2 x - \tan^2 x$$

and

$$\csc^2 x - \cot^2 x$$

and interpret the results.

53. Use a computer algebra system to simplify any of the above expressions, or to aid in proving the above identities.

Sum or Difference of Two Angles

The Sine of the Sum of Two Angles

We wish now to derive a formula for the sine of the sum of two angles, say α and β. For example, is it true that

$$\sin 20° + \sin 30° = \sin 50°?$$

Try it on your calculator—you will see that it is not true.

We start by drawing two positive acute angles α and β (Fig. 18·4), small enough that their sum $(\alpha + \beta)$ is also acute. From any point P on the

FIGURE 18·4

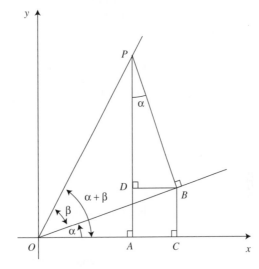

terminal side of β we draw perpendicular AP to the x axis, and draw perpendicular BP to line OB. Since the angle between two lines equals the angle between the perpendiculars to those lines, we note that angle APB is equal to α. Then

$$\sin(\alpha + \beta) = \frac{AP}{OP} = \frac{AD + PD}{OP} = \frac{BC + PD}{OP}$$

$$= \frac{BC}{OP} + \frac{PD}{OP}$$

But in triangle OBC,

$$BC = OB \sin \alpha$$

and in triangle PBD,

$$PD = PB \cos \alpha$$

Substituting, we obtain

$$\sin(\alpha + \beta) = \frac{OB \sin \alpha}{OP} + \frac{PB \cos \alpha}{OP}$$

But in triangle OPB,

$$\frac{OB}{OP} = \cos \beta$$

and

$$\frac{PB}{OP} = \sin \beta$$

So

We have proven this true for acute angles whose sum is also acute. These identities are, in fact, true for any size angles, positive or negative, although we will not take the space to prove this.

$$\sin(\alpha + \beta) = \sin \alpha \cos \beta + \cos \alpha \sin \beta$$

Common Error	The sine of the sum of two angles is *not* the sum of the sines of the two angles. $$\sin(\alpha + \beta) \neq \sin \alpha + \sin \beta$$

Cosine of the Sum of Two Angles

Using the same figure, we can derive an expression for $\cos(\alpha + \beta)$. From Eq. 147,

$$\cos(\alpha + \beta) = \frac{OA}{OP} = \frac{OC - AC}{OP} = \frac{OC - BD}{OP}$$

$$= \frac{OC}{OP} - \frac{BD}{OP}$$

Now in triangle *OBC*,

$$OC = OB \cos \alpha$$

and in triangle *PDB*,

$$BD = PB \sin \alpha$$

Substituting, we obtain

$$\cos(\alpha + \beta) = \frac{OB \cos \alpha}{OP} - \frac{PB \sin \alpha}{OP}$$

As before,

$$\frac{OB}{OP} = \cos \beta \quad \text{and} \quad \frac{PB}{OP} = \sin \beta$$

So

$$\cos(\alpha + \beta) = \cos \alpha \cos \beta - \sin \alpha \sin \beta$$

The Difference of Two Angles

We can obtain a formula for the sine of the difference of two angles merely by substituting $-\beta$ for β in the equation previously derived for $\sin(\alpha + \beta)$.

$$\sin[\alpha + (-\beta)] = \sin \alpha \cos(-\beta) + \cos \alpha \sin(-\beta)$$

But for β in the first quadrant, $(-\beta)$ is in the fourth, so

$$\cos(-\beta) = \cos \beta \quad \text{and} \quad \sin(-\beta) = -\sin \beta$$

Therefore,

$$\sin(\alpha - \beta) = \sin \alpha \cos \beta + \cos \alpha(-\sin \beta)$$

or

$$\sin(\alpha - \beta) = \sin \alpha \cos \beta - \cos \alpha \sin \beta$$

When the double signs are used, it is understood that the upper signs correspond and the lower signs correspond.

We see that the result is identical to the formula for sin $(\alpha + \beta)$ except for a change in sign. This enables us to write the two identities in a single expression using the $\pm$ sign:

Sine of Sum or Difference of Two Angles	$\sin(\alpha \pm \beta) = \sin \alpha \cos \beta \pm \cos \alpha \sin \beta$	**167**

Similarly, finding cos $(\alpha - \beta)$, we have

$$\cos[\alpha + (-\beta)] = \cos \alpha \cos(-\beta) - \sin \alpha \sin(-\beta)$$

So

$$\cos(\alpha - \beta) = \cos \alpha \cos \beta + \sin \alpha \sin \beta$$

or

Cosine of Sum or Difference of Two Angles	$\cos(\alpha \pm \beta) = \cos \alpha \cos \beta \mp \sin \alpha \sin \beta$	**168**

▬ **Example 11:** Expand the expression sin$(x + 3y)$.

Solution: By Eq. 167,

$$\sin(x + 3y) = \sin x \cos 3y + \cos x \sin 3y$$ ▬

▬ **Example 12:** Simplify

$$\cos 5x \cos 3x - \sin 5x \sin 3x$$

Solution: We see that this has a form similar to Eq. 168, with $\alpha = 5x$ and $\beta = 3x$, so

$$\cos 5x \cos 3x - \sin 5x \sin 3x = \cos(5x + 3x)$$
$$= \cos 8x$$ ▬

▬ **Example 13:** Prove that

$$\cos(180° - \theta) = -\cos \theta$$

Solution: Expanding the left side by means of Eq. 168, we get

$$\cos (180° - \theta) = \cos 180° \cos \theta + \sin 180° \sin \theta$$

But $\cos 180° = -1$ and $\sin 180° = 0$, so

$$\cos(180° - \theta) = (-1)\cos\theta + (0)\sin\theta = -\cos\theta \qquad \blacksquare$$

■ **Example 14:** Prove $\dfrac{\tan x - \tan y}{\tan x + \tan y} = \dfrac{\sin(x - y)}{\sin(x + y)}$.

Solution: The right side contains functions of the sum of two angles, but the left side contains functions of single angles. We thus start by expanding the right side by using Eq. 167,

$$\frac{\sin(x - y)}{\sin(x + y)} = \frac{\sin x \cos y - \cos x \sin y}{\sin x \cos y + \cos x \sin y}$$

Our expression now contains $\sin x$, $\sin y$, $\cos x$, and $\cos y$, but we want an expression containing only $\tan x$ and $\tan y$.

To have $\tan x$ instead of $\sin x$, we can divide numerator and denominator by $\cos x$. Similarly, to obtain $\tan y$ instead of $\sin y$, we can divide by $\cos y$. We thus divide numerator and denominator by $\cos x \cos y$.

$$\frac{\sin x \cos y - \cos x \sin y}{\sin x \cos y + \cos x \sin y} = \frac{\dfrac{\sin x \cos y}{\cos x \cos y} - \dfrac{\cos x \sin y}{\cos x \cos y}}{\dfrac{\sin x \cos y}{\cos x \cos y} + \dfrac{\cos x \sin y}{\cos x \cos y}}$$

Then, by Eq. 162,

$$= \frac{\tan x - \tan y}{\tan x + \tan y} \qquad \blacksquare$$

Tangent of the Sum or Difference of Two Angles

Since, by Eq. 162,

$$\tan\theta = \frac{\sin\theta}{\cos\theta}$$

we simply divide Eq. 167 by Eq. 168,

$$\tan(\alpha + \beta) = \frac{\sin(\alpha + \beta)}{\cos(\alpha + \beta)} = \frac{\sin\alpha\cos\beta + \cos\alpha\sin\beta}{\cos\alpha\cos\beta - \sin\alpha\sin\beta}$$

Dividing numerator and denominator by $\cos\alpha\cos\beta$ yields

$$\tan(\alpha + \beta) = \frac{\dfrac{\sin\alpha}{\cos\alpha} + \dfrac{\sin\beta}{\cos\beta}}{1 - \dfrac{\sin\alpha}{\cos\alpha}\cdot\dfrac{\sin\beta}{\cos\beta}}$$

Applying Eq. 162 again, we get

$$\tan(\alpha + \beta) = \frac{\tan\alpha + \tan\beta}{1 - \tan\alpha\tan\beta}$$

A similar derivation (which we will not do) will show that $\tan(\alpha - \beta)$ is identical to the expression just derived, except for, as we might expect, a reversal of signs. We combine the two expressions using double signs:

Tangent of Sum or Difference of Two Angles	$\tan(\alpha \pm \beta) = \dfrac{\tan \alpha \pm \tan \beta}{1 \mp \tan \alpha \tan \beta}$	**169**

■ **Example 15:** Simplify

$$\frac{\tan 3x + \tan 2x}{\tan 2x \tan 3x - 1}$$

Solution: This can be put into the form of Eq. 169 if we factor (-1) from the denominator,

$$\frac{\tan 3x + \tan 2x}{\tan 2x \tan 3x - 1} = \frac{\tan 3x + \tan 2x}{-(-\tan 2x \tan 3x + 1)}$$

$$= -\frac{\tan 3x + \tan 2x}{1 - \tan 3x \tan 2x}$$

$$= -\tan(3x + 2x)$$

$$= -\tan 5x$$ ■

■ **Example 16:** Prove that

$$\tan(45° + x) = \frac{1 + \tan x}{1 - \tan x}$$

Solution: Expanding the left side by Eq. 169, we get

$$\tan(45° + x) = \frac{\tan 45° + \tan x}{1 - \tan 45° \tan x}$$

But $\tan 45° = 1$, so

$$\tan(45° + x) = \frac{1 + \tan x}{1 - \tan x}$$ ■

■ **Example 17:** Prove

$$\frac{\cot y - \cot x}{\cot x \cot y + 1} = \tan(x - y)$$

Solution: Using Eq. 152(c) on the left side yields

$$\frac{\dfrac{1}{\tan y} - \dfrac{1}{\tan x}}{\dfrac{1}{\tan x} \cdot \dfrac{1}{\tan y} + 1} = \tan(x - y)$$

Multiply numerator and denominator by $\tan x \tan y$:

$$\frac{\tan x - \tan y}{1 + \tan x \tan y} = \tan(x - y)$$

Then by Eq. 169:

$$\tan(x - y) = \tan(x - y)$$ ■

Adding a Sine Wave and a Cosine Wave of the Same Frequency

In Section 17•3, we used vectors to show that the sum of a sine wave and a cosine wave of the same frequency could be written as a single sine wave, at the original frequency, but with some phase angle. The resulting equation is useful in electrical applications. Here we use the formula for the sum or difference of two angles to derive that equation.

Let $A \sin \omega t$ be a sine wave of amplitude A, and $B \cos \omega t$ be a cosine wave of amplitude B, each of frequency $\omega/2\pi$. If we draw a right triangle (Fig. 18•5) with sides A and B and hypotenuse R, then

$$A = R \cos \phi \quad \text{and} \quad B = R \sin \phi$$

The sum of the sine wave and the cosine wave is then

$$A \sin \omega t + B \cos \omega t = R \sin \omega t \cos \phi + R \cos \omega t \sin \phi$$

$$= R(\sin \omega t \cos \phi + \cos \omega t \sin \phi)$$

The expression on the right will be familiar. It is the relationship of the sine of the *sum* of two quantities, ωt and ϕ. Continuing, we have

$$A \sin \omega t + B \cos \omega t = R(\sin \omega t \cos \phi + \cos \omega t \sin \phi)$$

$$= R \sin(\omega t + \phi)$$

by Eq. 167. Thus,

FIGURE 18•5

Addition of a Sine Wave and a Cosine Wave	$A \sin \omega t + B \cos \omega t = R \sin (\omega t + \phi)$ where $R = \sqrt{A^2 + B^2}$ and $\phi = \arctan \dfrac{B}{A}$	**214**

This is sometimes referred to as *magnitude and phase* form. As we mentioned in Section 17•3, this calculation can be done using the rectangular to polar conversion keys on the calculator. Enter the rectangular coordinates A and B and read the polar coordinates R and θ.

■ **Example 18:** Express as a single sine function

$$y = 3.46 \sin \omega t + 2.28 \cos \omega t$$

Solution: The magnitude of the resultant is

$$R = \sqrt{(3.46)^2 + (2.28)^2} = 4.14$$

and the phase angle is

$$\phi = \arctan \frac{2.28}{3.46} = \arctan 0.659 = 33.4°$$

So

$$y = 3.46 \sin \omega t + 2.28 \cos \omega t$$

$$= 4.14 \sin(\omega t + 33.4°)$$ ■

Exercise 2   Sum or Difference of Two Angles

Expand by means of the addition and subtraction formulas and simplify:

1. $\sin(\theta + 30°)$
2. $\cos(45° - x)$
3. $\sin(x + 60°)$

4. $\tan(\pi + \theta)$

5. $\cos\left(x + \dfrac{\pi}{2}\right)$

6. $\tan(2x + y)$

7. $\sin(\theta + 2\phi)$

8. $\cos(\alpha + \beta)$

9. $\tan(2\theta - 3\alpha)$

Simplify:

10. $\cos 2x \cos 9x + \sin 2x \sin 9x$

11. $\cos(\pi + \theta) + \sin(\pi + \theta)$

12. $\sin 3\theta \cos 2\theta - \cos 3\theta \sin 2\theta$

13. $\sin\left(\dfrac{\pi}{3} - x\right) - \cos\left(\dfrac{\pi}{6} - x\right)$

Prove each identity:

14. $\cos x = \sin(x + 90°)$

15. $\sin(30° - x) + \cos(60° - x) = \cos x$

16. $2 \sin \alpha \cos \beta = \sin(\alpha + \beta) + \sin(\alpha - \beta)$

17. $\sin(\theta + 60°) + \cos(\theta + 30°) = \sqrt{3} \cos \theta$

18. $\cos(2\pi - x) = \cos x$

19. $\sin \alpha = \cos (30° - \alpha) - \sin(60° - \alpha)$

20. $\cos(x + y) + \cos(x - y) = 2 \cos x \cos y$

21. $\cos x = \sin\left(x + \dfrac{\pi}{6}\right) - \sin\left(x - \dfrac{\pi}{6}\right)$

22. $\tan(360° - \beta) = -\tan \beta$

23. $\cos(60° + \alpha) + \sin(330° + \alpha) = 0$

24. $\sin 5x \sec x \csc x = \dfrac{\sin 4x}{\sin x} + \dfrac{\cos 4x}{\cos x}$

25. $\dfrac{\sin(x - y)}{\sin(x + y)} = \dfrac{\tan x - \tan y}{\tan x + \tan y}$

26. $\cos(x + 60°) + \cos(60° - x) = \cos x$

27. $\dfrac{\cos(x - y)}{\sin x \cos y} = \tan y + \cot x$

28. $\cot\left(x + \dfrac{\pi}{4}\right) + \tan\left(x - \dfrac{\pi}{4}\right) = 0$

29. $\tan(\alpha + 45°) = \dfrac{\cos \alpha + \sin \alpha}{\cos \alpha - \sin \alpha}$

30. $\dfrac{\cot \alpha \cot \beta - 1}{\cot \alpha + \cot \beta} = \cot (\alpha + \beta)$

31. $\dfrac{1 + \tan x}{1 - \tan x} = \tan\left(\dfrac{\pi}{4} + x\right)$

Express as a single sine function:

32. $y = 47.2 \sin \omega t + 64.9 \cos \omega t$
33. $y = 8470 \sin \omega t + 7360 \cos \omega t$
34. $y = 1.83 \sin \omega t + 2.74 \cos \omega t$
35. $y = 84.2 \sin \omega t + 74.2 \cos \omega t$

Graphics Calculator or Computer

36. Use a graphics calculator or a graphing utility on a computer to verify any of the expansions, simplifications, or identities in this exercise.

18·3   Functions of Double Angles

Sine of 2α

An equation for the sine of 2α is easily derived by setting $\beta = \alpha$ in Eq. 167,

$$\sin(\alpha + \beta) = \sin(\alpha + \alpha) = \sin\alpha\cos\alpha + \cos\alpha\sin\alpha$$

or

Sine of Twice an Angle	$\sin 2\alpha = 2\sin\alpha\cos\alpha$	**170**

Cosine of 2α

Similarly, setting $\beta = \alpha$ in Eq. 168, we have

$$\cos(\alpha + \alpha) = \cos\alpha\cos\alpha - \sin\alpha\sin\alpha$$

or

Cosine of Twice an Angle	$\cos 2\alpha = \cos^2\alpha - \sin^2\alpha$	**171(a)**

There are two alternative forms for Eq. 171(a). From Eq. 164,

$$\cos^2\alpha = 1 - \sin^2\alpha$$

Substituting into Eq. 171(a) yields

$$\cos 2\alpha = 1 - \sin^2\alpha - \sin^2\alpha$$

Cosine of Twice an Angle	$\cos 2\alpha = 1 - 2\sin^2\alpha$	**171(b)**

We can similarly use Equation 164 to eliminate the $\sin^2\alpha$ term:

$$\cos 2\alpha = \cos^2\alpha - (1 - \cos^2\alpha)$$

So

Cosine of Twice an Angle	$\cos 2\alpha = 2\cos^2\alpha - 1$	**171(c)**

■ **Example 19:** Express $\sin 3x$ in terms of the single angle x.

Solution: We can consider $3x$ to be $x + 2x$, and, using Eq. 167, we have

$$\sin 3x = \sin(x + 2x) = \sin x \cos 2x + \cos x \sin 2x$$

We now replace $\cos 2x$ by $\cos^2 x - \sin^2 x$ and $\sin 2x$ by $2 \sin x \cos x$:

$$\sin 3x = \sin x(\cos^2 x - \sin^2 x) + \cos x(2 \sin x \cos x)$$
$$= \sin x \cos^2 x - \sin^3 x + 2 \sin x \cos^2 x$$
$$= 3 \sin x \cos^2 x - \sin^3 x$$

■

■ **Example 20:** Prove that

$$\cos 2A + \sin(A - B) = 0$$

where A and B are the two acute angles of a right triangle.

Solution: By Eqs. 171(a) and 167,

$$\cos 2A + \sin(A - B) = \cos^2 A - \sin^2 A + \sin A \cos B - \cos A \sin B$$

but by the cofunctions, Eq. 154,

$$\cos B = \sin A \quad \text{and} \quad \sin B = \cos A$$

Thus

$$\cos 2A + \sin(A - B) = \cos^2 A - \sin^2 A + \sin A \sin A - \cos A \cos A$$
$$= \cos^2 A - \sin^2 A + \sin^2 A - \cos^2 A = 0$$

■

■ **Example 21:** Simplify the expression

$$\frac{\sin 2x}{1 + \cos 2x}$$

Solution: By Eqs. 170 and 171(c),

$$\frac{\sin 2x}{1 + \cos 2x} = \frac{2 \sin x \cos x}{1 + 2 \cos^2 x - 1}$$
$$= \frac{2 \sin x \cos x}{2 \cos^2 x}$$
$$= \frac{\sin x}{\cos x} = \tan x$$

■

Tangent of 2α

Setting $\beta = \alpha$ in Eq. 169 gives

$$\tan(\alpha + \alpha) = \frac{\tan \alpha + \tan \alpha}{1 - \tan \alpha \tan \alpha}$$

Thus

Tangent of Twice an Angle	$\tan 2\alpha = \dfrac{2 \tan \alpha}{1 - \tan^2 \alpha}$	172

■ **Example 22:** Prove

$$\frac{2 \cot x}{\csc^2 x - 2} = \tan 2x$$

Solution: By Eq. 172,

$$\tan 2x = \frac{2 \tan x}{1 - \tan^2 x}$$

and, by Eq. 152(c),

$$= \frac{\dfrac{2}{\cot x}}{1 - \dfrac{1}{\cot^2 x}}$$

Multiply numerator and denominator by $\cot^2 x$:

$$= \frac{2 \cot x}{\cot^2 x - 1}$$

Then by Eq. 166:

$$= \frac{2 \cot x}{(\csc^2 x - 1) - 1} = \frac{2 \cot x}{\csc^2 x - 2}$$ ■

Common Error	The sine of twice an angle is not twice the sine of the angle. Nor is the cosine (or tangent) of twice an angle equal to twice the cosine (or tangent) of that angle. Remember to use the formulas from this section for all the trigonometric functions of double angles.

Exercise 3 Functions of Double Angles

Simplify:

1. $2 \sin^2 x + \cos 2x$ **2.** $2 \sin 2\theta \cos 2\theta$ **3.** $\dfrac{2 \tan x}{1 + \tan^2 x}$

4. $\dfrac{2 - \sec^2 x}{\sec^2 x}$ **5.** $\dfrac{\sin 6x}{\sin 2x} - \dfrac{\cos 6x}{\cos 2x}$

Prove:

6. $\dfrac{2 \tan \theta}{1 - \tan^2 \theta} = \tan 2\theta$ **7.** $\dfrac{1 - \tan^2 x}{1 + \tan^2 x} = \cos 2x$

8. $2 \csc 2\theta = \tan \theta + \cot \theta$ **9.** $2 \cot 2x = \cot x - \tan x$

10. $\sec 2x = \dfrac{1 + \cot^2 x}{\cot^2 x - 1}$ **11.** $\dfrac{1 - \tan x}{\tan x + 1} = \dfrac{\cos 2x}{\sin 2x + 1}$

12. $\dfrac{\sin 2\theta + \sin \theta}{1 + \cos \theta + \cos 2\theta} = \tan \theta$ **13.** $1 + \cot x = \dfrac{2 \cos 2x}{\sin 2x - 2 \sin^2 x}$

14. $4 \cos^3 x - 3 \cos x = \cos 3x$ **15.** $\sin \alpha + \cos \alpha = \dfrac{\sin 2\alpha + 1}{\cos \alpha + \sin \alpha}$

16. $\dfrac{\cot^2 x - 1}{2 \cot x} = \cot 2x$

If A and B are the two acute angles in a right triangle, show that:

17. $\sin 2A = \sin 2B$

18. $\tan(A - B) = -\cot 2A$

19. $\sin 2A = \cos(A - B)$

Graphics Calculator or Computer

20. Use a graphics calculator or a graphing utility on a computer to verify any of the simplifications or identities in this exercise.

18·4

Functions of Half-Angles

Sine of α/2

The double-angle formulas derived in Section 18·3 can also be regarded as half-angle formulas, because if one angle is double another, the second angle must be half the first.

Starting with Eq. 171(b), we obtain

$$\cos 2\theta = 1 - 2\sin^2\theta$$

We solve for $\sin \theta$:

$$2\sin^2\theta = 1 - \cos 2\theta$$

$$\sin \theta = \pm\sqrt{\frac{1 - \cos 2\theta}{2}}$$

FIGURE 18·6

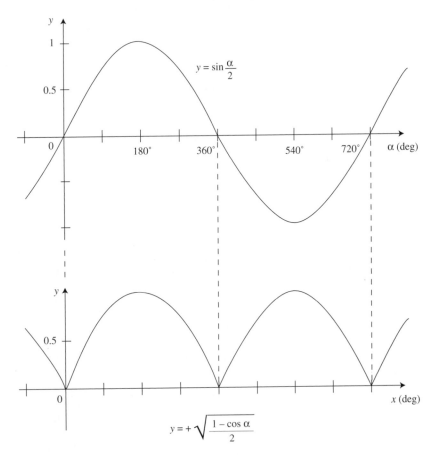

For emphasis, we replace θ by $\alpha/2$.

Sine of Half an Angle	$\sin\dfrac{\alpha}{2} = \pm\sqrt{\dfrac{1 - \cos\alpha}{2}}$	173

The $\pm$ sign in Eq. 173 (and in Eqs. 174 and 175(c) as well) is to be read as plus *or* minus, but *not both*. This is different from the $\pm$ sign in the quadratic formula, for example, where we took both the positive and the negative values.

The reason for this is clear from Figure 18·6, which shows a graph of $\sin \alpha/2$ and a graph of $+\sqrt{(1 - \cos\alpha)/2}$. Note that the two curves are the same only when $\sin \alpha/2$ is positive. When $\sin \alpha/2$ is negative, it is necessary to use the negative of $\sqrt{(1 - \cos\alpha)/2}$. This occurs when $\alpha/2$ is in the third or fourth quadrant. Thus we choose the plus or the minus according to in which quadrant $\alpha/2$ is located.

■ **Example 23:** Given that $\cos 200° = -0.9397$, find $\sin 100°$.

Solution: From Eq. 173,

$$\sin\frac{200°}{2} = \pm\sqrt{\frac{1 - \cos 200°}{2}} = \pm\sqrt{\frac{1 - (-0.9397)}{2}} = \pm0.9848$$

Since $100°$ is in the second quadrant, the sine is positive, so we drop the minus sign and get

$$\sin 100° = 0.9848$$

■

Cosine of $\alpha/2$

Similarly, starting with Eq. 171(c), we have

$$\cos 2\theta = 2\cos^2\theta - 1$$

Then we solve for $\cos \theta$,

$$2\cos^2\theta = 1 + \cos 2\theta$$

$$\cos \theta = \pm\sqrt{\frac{1 + \cos 2\theta}{2}}$$

and replace θ by $\alpha/2$.

Here, also, we choose the plus *or* the minus according to in which quadrant $\alpha/2$ is located.

Cosine of Half an Angle	$\cos\dfrac{\alpha}{2} = \pm\sqrt{\dfrac{1 + \cos\alpha}{2}}$	174

Tangent of $\alpha/2$

There are three formulas for the tangent of a half-angle; we will show the derivation of each in turn. From Eq. 162,

$$\tan\frac{\alpha}{2} = \frac{\sin\dfrac{\alpha}{2}}{\cos\dfrac{\alpha}{2}}$$

Multiply numerator and denominator by 2 sin(α/2):

$$= \frac{2 \sin^2\frac{\alpha}{2}}{2 \sin\frac{\alpha}{2} \cos\frac{\alpha}{2}}$$

Then by Eqs. 171(b) and 170,

Tangent of Half an Angle	$\tan\dfrac{\alpha}{2} = \dfrac{1 - \cos \alpha}{\sin \alpha}$	**175(a)**

Another form of this identity is obtained by multiplying numerator and denominator by $1 + \cos \alpha$:

$$\tan\frac{\alpha}{2} = \frac{1 - \cos \alpha}{\sin \alpha} \cdot \frac{1 + \cos \alpha}{1 + \cos \alpha}$$

$$= \frac{1 - \cos^2\alpha}{\sin \alpha(1 + \cos \alpha)} = \frac{\sin^2\alpha}{\sin \alpha(1 + \cos \alpha)}$$

or

Tangent of Half an Angle	$\tan\dfrac{\alpha}{2} = \dfrac{\sin \alpha}{1 + \cos \alpha}$	**175(b)**

We can obtain a third formula for the tangent by dividing Eq. 173 by Eq. 174:

$$\tan \frac{\alpha}{2} = \frac{\sin\frac{\alpha}{2}}{\cos\frac{\alpha}{2}} = \frac{\pm\sqrt{\dfrac{1 - \cos \alpha}{2}}}{\pm\sqrt{\dfrac{1 + \cos \alpha}{2}}}$$

Tangent of Half an Angle	$\tan\dfrac{\alpha}{2} = \pm\sqrt{\dfrac{1 - \cos \alpha}{1 + \cos \alpha}}$	**175(c)**

━━ **Example 24:** Prove

$$\frac{1 + \sin^2\frac{\theta}{2}}{1 + \cos^2\frac{\theta}{2}} = \frac{3 - \cos \theta}{3 + \cos \theta}$$

Solution: By Eqs 173 and 174,

$$\frac{1 + \sin^2\frac{\theta}{2}}{1 + \cos^2\frac{\theta}{2}} = \frac{1 + \dfrac{1 - \cos \theta}{2}}{1 + \dfrac{1 + \cos \theta}{2}}$$

Multiply numerator and
denominator by 2:

$$= \frac{2 + 1 - \cos \theta}{2 + 1 + \cos \theta}$$

$$= \frac{3 - \cos \theta}{3 + \cos \theta}$$

Exercise 4 Functions of Half-Angles

Prove each identity:

1. $2 \sin^2 \dfrac{\theta}{2} + \cos \theta = 1$

2. $4 \cos^2 \dfrac{x}{2} \sin^2 \dfrac{x}{2} = 1 - \cos^2 x$

3. $2 \cos^2 \dfrac{x}{2} = \dfrac{\sec x + 1}{\sec x}$

4. $\cot \dfrac{\theta}{2} = \csc \theta + \cot \theta$

5. $\dfrac{\sin \alpha}{\cos \alpha + 1} = \sin\dfrac{\alpha}{2} \sec\dfrac{\alpha}{2}$

6. $\dfrac{\cos^2 \dfrac{\theta}{2} - \cos \theta}{\sin^2 \dfrac{\theta}{2}} = 1$

7. $\sec \theta = \tan \dfrac{\theta}{2} \tan \theta + 1$

8. $\sin x + 1 = \left(\cos\dfrac{x}{2} + \sin\dfrac{x}{2} \right)^2$

9. $2 \sin \alpha + \sin 2\alpha = 4 \sin \alpha \cos^2\dfrac{\alpha}{2}$

10. $\dfrac{1 - \cos x}{\sin x} = \tan\dfrac{x}{2}$

11. $\dfrac{1 - \tan^2 \dfrac{\theta}{2}}{1 + \tan^2 \dfrac{\theta}{2}} = \cos \theta$

In right triangle ABC, show that:

12. $\tan\dfrac{A}{2} = \dfrac{a}{b + c}$

13. $\sin\dfrac{A}{2} = \sqrt{\dfrac{c - b}{2c}}$

Graphics Calculator or Computer

14. Use a graphics calculator or a graphing utility on a computer to verify any of the identities in this exercise.

18·5

Trigonometric Equations

Solving Trigonometric Equations

One use for the trigonometric identities we have just studied is in the solution of trigonometric equations.

A trigonometric equation will usually have an infinite number of roots. However, it is customary to list only *nonnegative values less than 360°* that satisfy the equation.

▬ **Example 25:** Solve the equation $\sin \theta = \frac{1}{2}$.

Solution: Even though there are infinitely many values of θ,

$$\theta = 30°, 150°, 390°, 510°, \ldots$$

whose sine is $\frac{1}{2}$, we will follow the common practice of listing only the non-negative values less than 360°, and give as our solution

$$\theta = 30°, 150°$$

The solution could also be expressed in radian measure: $\theta = \pi/6, \frac{5}{6}\pi$ radians.

Graphical Solution of Trigonometric Equations

In Section 5•6 we used a graphics calculator or a graphing utility on the computer to get an approximate solution to an algebraic equation. Here we use exactly the same procedure to solve a trigonometric equation.

We put the given equation into the form $f(\theta) = 0$ and then graph $y = f(\theta)$. We then use the TRACE and ZOOM features to locate the zeros as accurately as we wish.

■ **Example 26:** Find, to the nearest tenth of a degree, any nonnegative values less than 360° of the zeros of the equation in Example 25,

$$\sin \theta = \tfrac{1}{2}$$

Solution: We rewrite the given equation in the form

$$\sin \theta - \tfrac{1}{2} = 0$$

FIGURE 18•7 Graph of $y = \sin \theta - \frac{1}{2}$

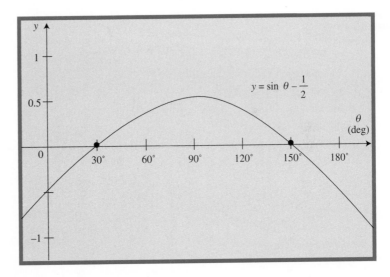

and graph the function $y = \sin \theta - \frac{1}{2}$ (Fig. 18•7). We see zeros at about 30° and 150°. Using TRACE and ZOOM at each zero, we get

$$\theta = 30.0° \text{ and } 150°$$

to the nearest tenth of a degree.

It is difficult to give general rules for solving the great variety of possible trigonometric equations, but a study of the following examples should be helpful.

Equations Containing a Single Trigonometric Function and a Single Angle

We start with the simplest type. These equations contain, after simplification, only one trigonometric function (only sine, or only cosine, for example) and have only one angle, as in Example 25. If an equation does not *appear* to be of this type, simplify it first. Then isolate the trigonometric function on one side of the equation and find the angles.

■ **Example 27:** Solve the equation $\dfrac{2.73 \sec \theta}{\csc \theta} + \dfrac{1.57}{\cos \theta} = 0$.

Solution: As with identities, it is helpful to rewrite the given expression with only sines and cosines. Thus

$$\frac{2.73 \sin \theta}{\cos \theta} + \frac{1.57}{\cos \theta} = 0$$

Multiplying by $\cos \theta$ and rearranging gives an expression with only one function, sine.

$$\sin \theta = -\frac{1.57}{2.73} = -0.575$$

Our reference angle is arcsin(0.575) or 35.1°. The sine is negative in the third and fourth quadrants, so we give the third and fourth quadrant values for θ:

$$\theta = 180° + 35.1° = 215.1°$$

FIGURE 18•8

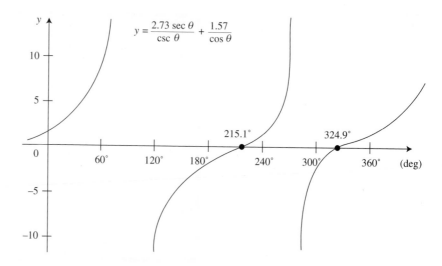

$$y = \frac{2.73 \sec \theta}{\csc \theta} + \frac{1.57}{\cos \theta}$$

and

$$\theta = 360° - 35.1° = 324.9°$$

Figure 18•8 shows a graph of the function and its zeros.

Our next example contains a double angle.

■ **Example 28:** Solve the equation $2 \cos 2\theta - 1 = 0$.

Solution: Rearranging and dividing, we have

$$\cos 2\theta = \tfrac{1}{2}$$

$$2\theta = 60°, 300°, 420°, 660°, \text{ and so on}$$

$$\theta = 30°, 150°, 210°, \text{ and } 330°$$

Note that, although this problem contained a double angle, *we did not need the double-angle formula*. It would have been needed, however, if the same problem contained both a double angle *and* a single angle.

if we limit our solution to angles less than 360°. Figure 18•9 shows a graph of the function $y = 2 \cos 2\theta - 1$ and its zeros.

FIGURE 18•9

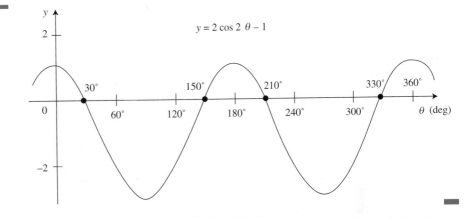

<table>
<tr><td>Common Error</td><td>It is easy to forget to find *all the angles* less than 360°, especially when the given equation contains a double angle, such as in Example 28.</td></tr>
</table>

If one of the functions is *squared*, we may have an equation in *quadratic form*, which can be solved by the methods of Chapter 14.

■ **Example 29:** Solve the equation $\sec^2\theta = 4$.

Solution: Taking the square root of each side gives us

$$\sec \theta = \pm\sqrt{4} = \pm 2$$

We thus have two solutions. By the reciprocal relations, we get

$$\frac{1}{\cos \theta} = 2 \qquad \text{and} \qquad \frac{1}{\cos \theta} = -2$$

$$\cos \theta = \tfrac{1}{2} \qquad \text{and} \qquad \cos \theta = -\tfrac{1}{2}$$

$$\theta = 60°, 300° \qquad \text{and} \qquad \theta = 120°, 240°$$

Our solution is then

$$\theta = 60°, 120°, 240°, 300°$$

Figure 18•10 shows a graph of the function $y = \sec^2\theta - 4$ and its zeros.

FIGURE 18·10

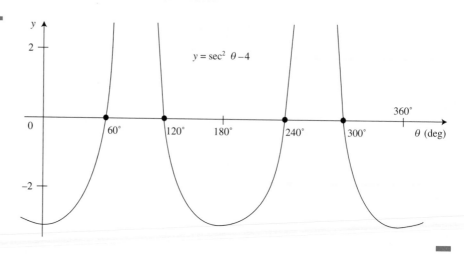

■ **Example 30:** Solve the equation $2 \sin^2\theta - \sin \theta = 0$.

Solution: This is an *incomplete quadratic* in sin θ. Factoring, we obtain

$$\sin \theta(2 \sin \theta - 1) = 0$$

Setting each factor equal to zero yields

$\sin \theta = 0$	$2 \sin \theta - 1 = 0$
$\theta = 0°, 180°$	$\sin \theta = \frac{1}{2}$
	Since sine is positive in the first and second quadrants,
	$\theta = 30°, 150°$

Figure 18·11 shows a graph of the function $y = 2 \sin^2\theta - \sin \theta$ and its zeros.

FIGURE 18·11

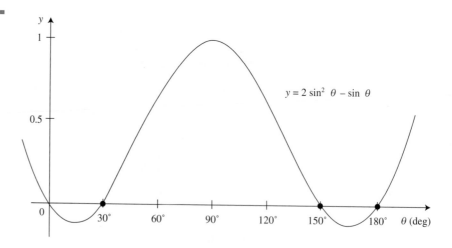

If the equation is in the form of a quadratic that cannot be factored, use the quadratic formula.

■ **Example 31:** Solve the equation $\cos^2\theta = 3 + 5\cos\theta$.

Solution: Rearranging into standard quadratic form, we have

$$\cos^2\theta - 5\cos\theta - 3 = 0$$

This cannot be factored, so we use the quadratic formula,

$$\cos\theta = \frac{5 \pm \sqrt{25 - 4(-3)}}{2}$$

There are two values for $\cos\theta$:

$\cos\theta = 5.54$	$\cos\theta = -0.541$
(not possible)	Since cosine is negative in the second and third quadrants,
	$\theta = 123°, 237°$

Figure 18•12 shows a graph of the function $y = \cos^2\theta - 3 - 5\cos\theta$ and its zeros.

FIGURE 18•12

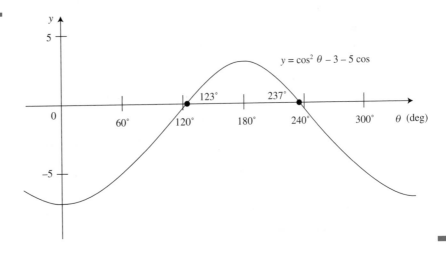

Equations with One Angle But More Than One Function

If the equation contains two or more trigonometric functions of the same angle, first transpose all the terms to one side and try to factor that side into factors, *each containing only a single function*, and proceed as above.

■ **Example 32:** Solve $\sin\theta\sec\theta - 2\sin\theta = 0$.

Solution: Factoring,

$$\sin\theta(\sec\theta - 2) = 0$$

$\sin\theta = 0$	$\sec\theta = 2$
	$\cos\theta = \frac{1}{2}$

FIGURE 18·13

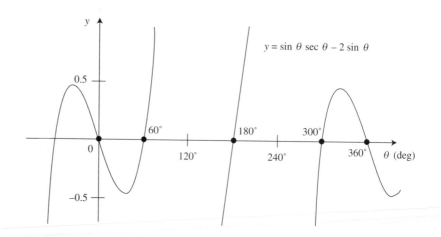

$$y = \sin \theta \sec \theta - 2 \sin \theta$$

	Since cosine is positive in the first and fourth quadrants,
$\theta = 0°, 180°$	$\theta = 60°, 300°$

Figure 18·13 shows a graph of the function $y = \sin \theta \sec \theta - 2 \sin \theta$ and its zeros.

If the expression is *not factorable* at first, use the fundamental identities to *express everything in terms of a single trigonometric function* and proceed as above.

■ **Example 33:** Solve $\sin^2\theta + \cos \theta = 1$.

Solution: By Eq. 164, $\sin^2\theta = 1 - \cos^2\theta$. Substituting gives

$$1 - \cos^2\theta + \cos \theta = 1$$
$$\cos \theta - \cos^2\theta = 0$$

FIGURE 18·14

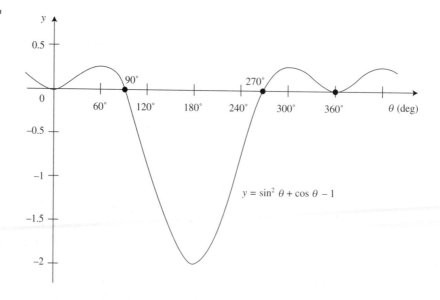

$$y = \sin^2 \theta + \cos \theta - 1$$

Factoring, we obtain

$$\cos\theta(1 - \cos\theta) = 0$$

$$\cos\theta = 0 \quad | \quad \cos\theta = 1$$

$$\theta = 90°, 270° \quad | \quad \theta = 0°$$

Figure 18·14 shows a graph of the function $y = \sin^2\theta + \cos^2\theta - 1$ and its zeros. ◼

In order to simplify an equation using the Pythagorean relations, it is sometimes necessary to *square both sides*.

◼ **Example 34:** Solve $\sec\theta + \tan\theta = 1$.

Solution: We have no identity that enables us to write $\sec\theta$ in terms of $\tan\theta$, but we do have an identity for $\sec^2\theta$. We rearrange and square both sides, getting

$$\sec\theta = 1 - \tan\theta$$

$$\sec^2\theta = 1 - 2\tan\theta + \tan^2\theta$$

Replacing $\sec^2\theta$ by $1 + \tan^2\theta$ yields

$$1 + \tan^2\theta = 1 - 2\tan\theta + \tan^2\theta$$

$$\tan\theta = 0$$

$$\theta = 0, 180°$$

Since squaring can introduce extraneous roots that do not satisfy the original equation, we substitute back to check our answers. We find that the only angle that satisfies the given equation is $\theta = 0°$. Figure 18·15 shows a graph of the function and the zeros.

A computer algebra system can be used to solve trigonometric equations. Use the same commands as for solving an algebraic equation, such as soLve in *Derive*.

FIGURE 18·15

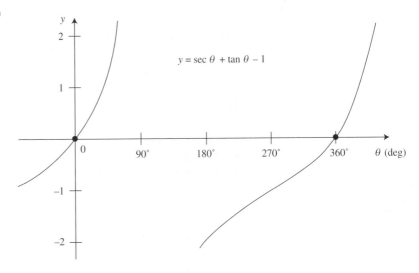

$$y = \sec\theta + \tan\theta - 1$$

For our final example, let us find the roots of a trigonometric equation that would be difficult or impossible to solve exactly. We will do an approximate graphical solution.

FIGURE 18•16 Graph of $y = 2.43$ $\sin^3(1.89\theta) - 1.74 \cos(1.12\theta) + 1.15$

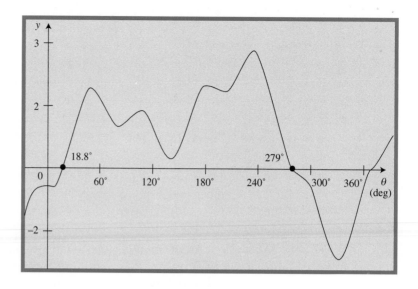

■ **Example 35:** Find, to the nearest tenth of a degree, any nonnegative values less than 360°, and also the zeros of

$$2.43 \sin^3(1.89\theta) = 1.74 \cos(1.12\theta) - 1.15$$

Solution: The graph of the function

$$f(\theta) = 2.43 \sin^3(1.89\theta) - 1.74 \cos(1.120\theta) + 1.15$$

is shown in Figure 18•16. We see zeros at about 20° and 280°. Using TRACE and ZOOM at each zero, we get

$$\theta = 18.8° \quad \text{and} \quad 279.0°$$

to the nearest tenth of a degree. ■

Exercise 5 Trigonometric Equations

Solve each equation for all nonnegative values of θ less than 360°.

1. $\sin \theta = \frac{1}{2}$
2. $2 \cos \theta - \sqrt{3} = 0$
3. $1 - \tan \theta = 0$
4. $\sin \theta = \sqrt{3} \cos \theta$
5. $4 \sin^2\theta = 3$
6. $2 \sin 3\theta = \frac{1}{2}$
7. $3 \sin \theta - 1 = 2 \sin \theta$
8. $\csc^2\theta = 4$
9. $2 \cos^2\theta = 1 + 2 \sin^2\theta$
10. $2 \sec \theta = -3 - \cos \theta$
11. $4 \sin^4\theta = 1$
12. $2 \csc \theta - \cot \theta = \tan \theta$
13. $1 + \tan \theta = \sec^2\theta$
14. $1 + \cot^2\theta = \sec^2\theta$
15. $3 \cot \theta = \tan \theta$

16. $\sin^2\theta = 1 - 6 \sin\theta$
17. $3 \sin(\theta/2) - 1 = 2 \sin^2(\theta/2)$
18. $\sin\theta = \cos\theta$
19. $4 \cos^2\theta + 4 \cos\theta = -1$
20. $1 + \sin\theta = \sin\theta \cos\theta + \cos\theta$
21. $3 \tan\theta = 4 \sin^2\theta \tan\theta$
22. $3 \sin\theta \tan\theta + 2 \tan\theta = 0$
23. $\sec\theta = -\csc\theta$
24. $\sin\theta = 2 \cos(\theta/2)$
25. $\sin\theta = 2 \sin\theta \cos\theta$
26. $\cos\theta \sin 2\theta = 0$

Graphics Calculator and Computer

27. Use your program for solving equations by the midpoint method (Sec. 5•6) to find the roots of any of the trigonometric equations in this exercise.
28. Use a graphics calculator or a graphing utility on a computer to graphically locate the roots of any of the above equations.
29. Use a computer algebra system to solve any of the above equations.

18•6

Glance back at what we have already said about inverse trigonometric functions in Chapters 7 and 15.

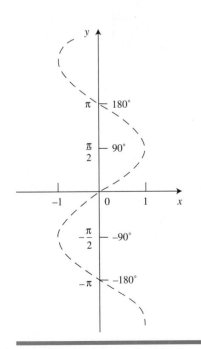

FIGURE 18•17 Graph of arcsin x

Inverse Trigonometric Functions

Inverse of the Sine Function: The Arc Sine

Recall from Section 4•3 that to find the inverse of a function $y = f(x)$, we

1. Solve the given equation for x, and
2. Interchange x and y.

Thus, starting with the sine function,

$$y = \sin x$$

we solve for x and get

$$x = \arcsin y$$

Now we interchange x and y so that y is, as usual, the dependent variable. The inverse of $y = \sin x$ is thus

$$y = \arcsin x$$

The graph of $y = \arcsin x$ is shown in Figure 18•17. Note that it is identical to the graph of the sine function but with the x and y axes interchanged.

Recalling the distinction between a relation and a function from Section 4•1, we see that $y = \arcsin x$ is a relation, but not a function, because for a single x there may be more than one y. For this relation to be a function also, we must limit the range so that repeated values of y are not encountered.

The arc sine, for example, is customarily limited to the interval between $-\pi/2$ and $\pi/2$ (or $-90°$ to $90°$), as shown in Figure 18•18. The numbers within this interval are called the *principal values* of the arc sine. It is also, of course, the *range* of arcsin x.

Given these limits, our relation $y = \arcsin x$ now becomes a *function*. The first letter of the function is sometimes capitalized. Thus, $y = \arcsin x$ would be the relation and $y = \text{Arcsin } x$ would be the function. (This practice has not been used throughout this text.)

FIGURE 18·18 Principal values

Arc Cosine and Arc Tangent

In a similar way, the inverse of the cosine and tangent functions are limited to principal values, as shown by the solid lines in Figures 18·19 and 18·20.

The numerical values of any of the arc functions are found by calculator, as was shown in Sections 7·3 and 15·1.

To summarize, if *x is positive*, then arcsin *x* is an angle between 0 and 90°, and hence lies in quadrant I. The same is true of arccos *x* and arctan *x*. If *x is negative*, then arcsin *x* is an angle between −90° and 0° and hence is in quadrant IV. The same is true of arctan *x*. However, arccos *x* is in quadrant II when *x* is negative. These facts are summarized in the table on page 533:

FIGURE 18·19

FIGURE 18•20

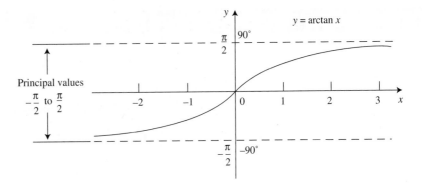

X	ARCSIN X	ARCCOS X	ARCTAN X
Positive	Quadrant I	Quadrant I	Quadrant I
Negative	Quadrant IV	Quadrant II	Quadrant IV

Most calculators will give the principal value directly, for first- and second-quadrant angles, and as a negative angle for fourth-quadrant angles. Try your calculator to see what it does.

■ **Example 36:** Find (a) arcsin 0.638, (b) $\tan^{-1}(-1.63)$, and (c) arcsec(-2.34). Give your answer in degrees, to one decimal place.

Solution: (a) By calculator,

$$\text{arcsin } 0.638 = 39.6°$$

(b) By calculator,

$$\tan^{-1}(-1.63) = -58.5°$$

(c) Using the reciprocal relations we get,

$$\text{arcsec}(-2.34) = \arccos\frac{1}{-2.34} = \arccos(-0.427)$$

$$= 115.3° \quad ■$$

Exercise 6 Inverse Trigonometric Functions

Evaluate each expression, giving your answer in degrees to one decimal place:

1. arcsin 0.374 **2.** arccos 0.826 **3.** arctan(-4.92)
4. $\cos^{-1}0.449$ **5.** $\tan^{-1}6.92$ **6.** $\sin^{-1}(-0.822)$
7. arcsec 3.96 **8.** $\cot^{-1}4.97$ **9.** $\csc^{-1}1.824$
10. $\sec^{-1}2.89$

Graphics Calculator and Computer

Use a graphics calculator or a graphing utility on a computer to graph the following functions.

11. $y = \arcsin x$ **12.** $y = \arccos x$ **13.** $y = \arctan x$
14. $y = 2 \arcsin x$ **15.** $y = \arccos 2x$ **16.** $y = 3 \arctan 2x$

CHAPTER 18   REVIEW PROBLEMS

Prove:

1. $\sec^2\theta + \tan^2\theta = \sec^4\theta - \tan^4\theta$

2. $\dfrac{1 + \csc\theta}{\cot\theta} = \dfrac{\cot\theta}{\csc\theta - 1}$

3. $\tan^2\theta \sin^2\theta = \tan^2\theta - \sin^2\theta$

4. $\cot\theta + \csc\theta = \dfrac{1}{\csc\theta - \cot\theta}$

5. $\sin(45° + \theta) - \sin(45° - \theta) = \sqrt{2}\,\sin\theta$

6. $\dfrac{\cot\alpha\cot\beta + 1}{\cot\beta - \cot\alpha} = \cot(\alpha - \beta)$

7. $\dfrac{\sin^3\theta + \cos^3\theta}{\sin\theta + \cos\theta} = 1 - \dfrac{\sin 2\theta}{2}$

8. $\dfrac{1 + \tan\theta}{1 - \tan\theta} = \sec 2\theta + \tan 2\theta$

9. $\sin\theta\cot\dfrac{\theta}{2} = \cos\theta + 1$

10. $\sin^4\theta + 2\sin^2\theta\cos^2\theta + \cos^4\theta = 1$

11. $\cot\alpha\cot\beta = \dfrac{\csc\beta + \cot\alpha}{\tan\alpha\sec\beta + \tan\beta}$

12. $\cos\theta\cot\theta = \dfrac{\cos\theta + \cot\theta}{\tan\theta + \sec\theta}$

Simplify:

13. $\dfrac{\sin\theta\sec\theta}{\tan\theta}$

14. $\sec^2\theta - \sin^2\theta\sec^2\theta$

15. $\dfrac{\sec\theta}{\sec\theta - 1} + \dfrac{\sec\theta}{\sec\theta + 1}$

16. $\dfrac{\sin^3\theta + \cos^3\theta}{\sin\theta + \cos\theta}$

17. $\cos\theta\tan\theta\csc\theta$

18. $(\sec\theta - 1)(\sec\theta + 1)$

19. $\dfrac{\cot\theta}{1 + \cot^2\theta} \cdot \dfrac{\tan^2\theta + 1}{\tan\theta}$

20. $\dfrac{\cos\theta}{1 - \tan\theta} + \dfrac{\sin\theta}{1 - \cot\theta}$

21. $(1 - \sin^2\theta)\sec^2\theta$

22. $\tan^2\theta\,(1 + \cot^2\theta)$

23. $\dfrac{\sin\theta - 2\sin\theta\cos\theta}{2 - 2\sin^2\theta - \cos\theta}$

Solve for all positive values of θ less than 360°:

24. $1 + 2\sin^2\theta = 3\sin\theta$

25. $3 + 5\cos\theta = 2\cos^2\theta$

26. $\cos\theta - 2\cos^3\theta = 0$

27. $\tan\theta = 2 - \cot\theta$

28. $\sin 3\theta - \sin 6\theta = 0$

29. $\cot 2\theta - 2\cos 2\theta = 0$

30. $\sin\theta + \cos 2\theta = 1$

31. $\sin\theta = 1 - 3\cos\theta$

32. $5\tan\theta = 6 + \tan^2\theta$

33. $\sin^2\theta = 1 + 6\sin\theta$

34. $\tan^2 2\theta = 1 + \sec 2\theta$

35. $16\cos^4\dfrac{\theta}{2} = 9$

36. $\tan^2\theta + 1 = \sec\theta$

Evaluate:

37. $\arcsin 0.825$

38. $\cos^{-1} 0.232$

39. $\arctan 3.55$

Express as a single sine function:

40. $y = 1.84\sin\omega t + 2.18\cos\omega t$

41. $y = 47.6\sin\omega t + 62.1\cos\omega t$

Team Project

42. Several sections of rail were welded together to form a continuous straight rail 78.00 metres long. It was installed when the temperature was 0° C, the crew neglecting to allow a gap for thermal expansion. The ends of the rail are fixed so that they cannot move outward, so the rail took the shape shown in Fig. 18•21 when the temperature rose to 32°C. Assuming the curve to be circular, find the height x at the midpoint of the track.

The coefficient of linear expansion is

$$\mu = 11.7 \times 10^{-6}/°C.$$

FIGURE 18•21

19

Ratio, Proportion, and Variation

When you have completed this chapter, you should be able to:

- Set up and solve a proportion for a missing quantity.
- Solve applied problems using proportions.
- Set up and solve problems involving direct variation, inverse variation, joint variation, and combined variation.
- Solve applied problems involving variation.
- Set up and solve power function problems.
- Find dimensions, areas, and volumes of similar geometric figures.

In Chapter 9, we introduced the idea of a *ratio* as the quotient of two quantities. Here we expand upon that idea, and also do problems where two ratios are set equal to each other, that is, problems involving *proportions*. The computations will be no different, but we will learn another way of looking at problems involving fractions.

When two quantities, say x and y, are connected by some functional relation, $y = f(x)$, some variation in the independent variable x will imply a variation in the dependent variable y. Under the heading of *functional variation*, we study the changes in y brought about by changes in x, for several simple functions. We often want to know the amount by which y will change when we make a certain change in x. The quantities x and y will not be abstract quantities but quantities we care about, such as: By how much will the deflection y of a beam increase when we decrease the beam thickness x by 50%? We shall see that the methods of this chapter give us another powerful tool for making *estimates*.

We have, in fact, already studied some aspects of functional variation—first when we substituted numerical values for x into a function and computed corresponding values of y and later when we graphed functions in Chapter 5. We do some graphing here, too, and also learn some better techniques for solving numerical problems.

19•1

Ratio and Proportion

Ratio

In our work so far we have often dealt with expressions of the form

$$\frac{a}{b}$$

There are several different ways of looking at such an expression. We can say that a/b is

- A *fraction*, with a numerator a and a denominator b
- A *quotient*, where a is *divided* by b
- The *ratio* of a to b

Thus a ratio can be thought of as a fraction, or as the quotient of two quantities. For a ratio of two physical quantities, it is usual to express the numerator and denominator *in the same units*, so that they cancel and leave the ratio *dimensionless*. The quantities a and b are called the *terms* of the ratio.

━ **Example 1:** A corridor is 3.00 m wide and 10.0 m long. Find the ratio of length to width.

The ratio of length to width is

$$\frac{10}{3} = \frac{a}{b} = 3.33$$ ━

Another way of writing a ratio is with the colon (:). The ratio of a to b is

$$\frac{a}{b} = a : b$$

In Example 1 we could write that the ratio of length to width is 10 : 3.

Dimensionless ratios are handy because you do not have to worry about units, and are often used in technology. Some examples are:

Poisson's ratio	*fuel–air ratio*	*turn ratio*
endurance ratio	*load ratio*	*gear ratio*
radian measure of angles	*pi*	*trigonometric ratio*

The word *specific* is often used to denote a ratio when there is a standard unit to which a given quantity is being compared under standard conditions. A few such ratios are:

specific heat	*specific volume*	*specific conductivity*
specific density	*specific speed*	

For example, the specific density of a solid or liquid is the ratio of the density of the substance to the density of water, at a standard temperature.

━ **Example 2:** Aluminum has a density of 2770 kg/m^3 and water has a density of $100\overline{0}$ kg/m^3. Find the specific density of aluminum.

Solution: Dividing gives

$$SG = \frac{2770 \text{ kg/m}^3}{1000 \text{ kg/m}^3} = 2.77$$

Note that specific density is a *dimensionless ratio*.

Proportion

A *proportion* is an equation obtained when two ratios are set equal to each other. If the ratio $a : b$ is equal to the ratio $c : d$, we have the proportion

$$a : b = c : d$$

which reads "the ratio of a to b equals the ratio of c to d" or "a is to b as c is to d." We will often write such a proportion in the form

This can also be written $a : b :: c : d$.

$$\frac{a}{b} = \frac{c}{d}$$

The two inside terms of a proportion are called the *means*, and the two outside terms are the *extremes*:

$$\overbrace{a : b}^{\text{extremes}} = \underbrace{c : d}_{\text{means}}$$

Finding a Missing Term

Solve a proportion just as you would any other fractional equation.

■ **Example 3:** Find x if $\dfrac{3}{x} = \dfrac{7}{9}$.

Solution: Multiplying both sides by the LCD, $9x$, we obtain

$$27 = 7x$$

$$x = \frac{27}{7}$$

■ **Example 4:** Find x if $\dfrac{x + 2}{3} = \dfrac{x - 1}{5}$.

Solution: Multiplying through by 15 gives

$$5(x + 2) = 3(x - 1)$$

$$5x + 10 = 3x - 3$$

$$2x = -13$$

$$x = -\frac{13}{2}$$

■ **Example 5:** Insert the missing quantity:

$$\frac{x - 3}{2x} = \frac{?}{4x^2}$$

Solution: Replacing the question mark with a variable, say z, and solving for z gives us

$$z = \frac{4x^2(x - 3)}{2x}$$
$$= 2x(x - 3)$$

■

Mean Proportional

When the means (the two inside terms) of a proportion are equal, as in

$$a : b = b : c$$

the term b is called the *mean proportional* between a and c. Solving for b, we get

$$b^2 = ac$$

Mean Proportional	$b = \pm\sqrt{ac}$	**59**

The mean proportional *b* is also called the *geometric mean* between *a* and *c*, because *a*, *b*, and *c* form a *geometric progression* (a series of numbers in which each term is obtained by multiplying the previous term by the same quantity).

Some books define *b* as positive if both *a* and *c* are positive. Here, we'll show both values.

■ **Example 6:** Find the mean proportional between 3 and 12.

Solution: From Eq. 59,

$$b = \pm\sqrt{3(12)} = \pm 6$$

■

Applications

Use the same guidelines for setting up these word problems as were given in Section 3•2 for any word problem. Just be careful not to reverse the terms in the proportion. Match the first item in the verbal statement with the first number in the ratio, and the second with the second.

■ **Example 7:** A man is 25 years old and his brother is 15. In how many years will their ages be in the ratio 5 : 4?

Solution: Let x = required number of years. After x years, the man's age will be

$$25 + x$$

and the brother's age will be

$$15 + x$$

Forming a proportion, we have

$$\frac{25 + x}{15 + x} = \frac{5}{4}$$

Multiplying by $4(15 + x)$, we obtain

$$4(25 + x) = 5(15 + x)$$
$$100 + 4x = 75 + 5x$$
$$x = 25 \text{ years} \qquad \blacksquare$$

Exercise 1 Ratio and Proportion

Find the value of x:

1. $3 : x = 4 : 6$ **2.** $x : 5 = 3 : 10$
3. $4 : 6 = x : 4$ **4.** $3 : x = x : 12$
5. $x : (14 - x) = 4 : 3$ **6.** $x : 12 = (x - 12) : 3$
7. $x : 6 = (x + 6) : 10\frac{1}{2}$ **8.** $(x - 7) : (x + 7) = 2 : 9$

Insert the missing quantity:

9. $\dfrac{x}{3} = \dfrac{?}{9}$ **10.** $\dfrac{?}{4x} = \dfrac{7}{16x}$

11. $\dfrac{5a}{7b} = \dfrac{?}{-7b}$ **12.** $\dfrac{a - b}{c - d} = \dfrac{b - a}{?}$

13. $\dfrac{x + 2}{5x} = \dfrac{?}{5}$

Find the mean proportional between:

14. 2 and 50   **15.** 3 and 48   **16.** 6 and 150
17. 5 and 45   **18.** 4 and 36

Applications

19. Find two numbers that are to each other as $5 : 7$ and whose sum is 72.
20. Separate $150 into two parts so that the smaller may be to the greater as 7 is to 8.
21. Into what two parts may the number 56 be separated so that one may be to the other as 3 is to 4?
22. The difference between two numbers is 12 and the larger is to the smaller as 11 is to 7. What are the numbers?
23. An estate of $75 000 was divided between two heirs so that the elder's share was to the younger's as 8 is to 7. What was the share of each?
24. Two partners jointly bought some stock. The first put in $400 more than the second, and the stock of the first was to that of the second as 5 is to 4. How much money did each invest?
25. The sum of two numbers is 20 and their sum is to their difference as 10 is to 1. What are the numbers?
26. The sum of two numbers is a and their sum is to their difference as m is to n. What are the numbers?
27. For the transformer shown in Figure 19•1, the ratio of the number of turns in the secondary winding to the number of turns in the primary winding is 15. The primary winding has 4500 turns. Find the number of turns in the secondary.

FIGURE 19•1 A transformer

FIGURE 19•2 A line subdivided by the golden ratio

28. A line, as in Figure 19•2, is subdivided into two segments a and b such that the ratio of the smaller segment a to the larger segment b equals the ratio of the larger segment b to the whole $(a + b)$. The ratio a/b is called the *golden ratio* or *golden section*. Set up a proportion, based on the above definition, and compute the numerical value of this ratio.

Direct Variation

Constant of proportionality

If two variables are related by an equation of the form

Direct Variation	$y = kx$	**60**

where k is a constant, we say that y *varies directly* as x, or that y is *directly proportional* to x. The constant k is called the *constant* of *proportionality*. Direct variation may also be written using the special symbol $\propto$:

$$y \propto x$$

It is read "y varies directly as x" or "y is directly proportional to x."

Solving Variation Problems

Variation problems can be solved with or without evaluating the constant of proportionality. We first show a solution in which the constant *is* found by substituting the given values into Eq. 60.

━ **Example 8:** If y is directly proportional to x, and y is 27 when x is 3, find y when x is 6.

Solution: Since y varies directly as x, we use Eq. 60:

$$y = kx$$

To find the constant of proportionality, we substitute the given values for x and y, 3 and 27:

$$27 = k(3)$$

$$k = 9$$

Our equation is then

$$y = 9x$$

19•2

Glance back at Section 5•3 where we plotted the equation (Eq. 289) of the straight line

$$y = mx + b$$

We see that Eq. 60 is the equation of a straight line with a slope of k and a y intercept of zero.

When $x = 6$,

$$y = 9(6) = 54$$ ▬

We now show how to solve such a problem without finding the constant of proportionality.

▬ **Example 9:** Solve Example 8 *without* finding the constant of proportionality.

Solution: When quantities vary directly with each other, we can set up a proportion and solve it. Let us represent the initial values of x and y by x_1 and y_1, and the second set of values by x_2 and y_2. Substituting each set of values into Eq. 60 gives us

$$y_1 = kx_1$$

and

$$y_2 = kx_2$$

We divide the second equation by the first, and k cancels.

$$\frac{y_2}{y_1} = \frac{x_2}{x_1}$$

The proportion says: The new y is to the old y as the new x is to the old x. We now substitute the old x and y (3 and 27), as well as the new x (6).

$$\frac{y_2}{27} = \frac{6}{3}$$

Solving yields

$$y_2 = 27\left(\frac{6}{3}\right) = 54$$

as before. ▬

> Of course, the same proportion can also be written in the form $y_1/x_1 = y_2/x_2$. Two other forms are also possible:
>
> $$\frac{x_1}{y_1} = \frac{x_2}{y_2}$$
>
> and
>
> $$\frac{x_1}{x_2} = \frac{y_1}{y_2}.$$

▬ **Example 10:** If y varies directly as x, fill in the missing numbers in the table of values.

x	1	2		5	
y			16	20	28

Solution: We find the constant of proportionality from the given pair of values (5, 20). Starting with Eq. 60, we have

$$y = kx$$

and substituting gives

$$20 = k(5)$$

$$k = 4$$

So

$$y = 4x$$

With this equation we find the missing values.

When $x = 1$: $y = 4$

When $x = 2$: $y = 8$

When $y = 16$: $x = \dfrac{16}{4} = 4$

When $y = 28$: $x = \dfrac{28}{4} = 7$

So the completed table is

x	1	2	4	5	7
y	4	8	16	20	28

Applications

Many practical problems can be solved using the idea of direct variation. Once you know that two quantities are directly proportional, you may assume an equation of the form of Eq. 60. Substitute the two given values to obtain the constant of proportionality, which you then put back into Eq. 60 to obtain the complete equation. From it you may find any other corresponding values.

Alternatively, you may decide not to find k, but to form a proportion in which three values will be known, enabling you to find the fourth.

■ **Example 11:** The force F needed to stretch a spring (Fig. 19•3) is directly proportional to the distance x stretched. If it takes 15 N to stretch a certain spring 280 mm how much force is needed to stretch it 340 mm?

Estimate: We see that 15 N will stretch the spring 280 mm, or the stretch is about 20 mm/N. Thus a stretch of 340 mm should take about $340 \div 20$ or 17 N.

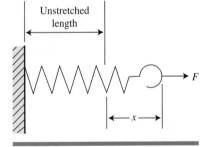

Unstretched length

FIGURE 19•3

Solution: Assuming an equation of the form

$$F = kx$$

and substituting the first set of values, we have

$$15 = k(280)$$

$$k = \frac{15}{280}$$

So the equation is $F = \dfrac{15}{280}x$.

When $x = 340$

$$F = \left(\frac{15}{280}\right)340 = 18 \text{ N} \quad \text{(rounded)}$$

which is close to our estimated value of 17 N.

Exercise 2 Direct Variation

1. If y varies as x, and y is 56 when x is 21, find y when x is 74.

2. If w is directly proportional to z, and w has a value of 136 when z is 10.8, find w when z is 37.3.

3. If p varies directly as q, and p is 846 when q is 135, find q when p is 448.

4. If y is directly proportional to x, and y has a value of 88.4 when x is 23.8:
(a) Find the constant of proportionality. **(b)** Write the equation $y = f(x)$. **(c)** Find y when $x = 68.3$. **(d)** Find x when $y = 164$.

Assuming that y varies directly as x, fill in the missing values in each table of ordered pairs:

5.

x	9	11	
y	45		75

6.

x	3.40	7.20		12.3
y		50.4	68.6	

7.

x	115	125		154
y			167	187

8. Graph the linear function $y = 2x$ for values of x from -5 to 5.

Applications

9. The distance between two cities is 828 km and they are 295 mm apart on a map. Find the distance between two points 156 mm apart on the same map.

10. If the mass of 2500 steel balls is 3.65 kg, find the number of balls in 10.0 kg.

11. If 80 transformer laminations make a stack 17.5 mm thick, how many laminations are contained in a stack 30 mm thick?

12. If your car now uses 10 L/100 km of gas and you can go 460 km on a tank of gasoline, how far could you drive with the same amount of gasoline with a car that uses 8 L/100 km?

13. A certain automobile engine delivers 40 kW and has a displacement (the total volume swept out by the pistons) of 3.0 L. If the power is directly proportional to the displacement, what power would you expect from a similar engine that has a displacement of 3.8 L.

14. The resistance of a conductor is directly proportional to its length. If the resistance of 4.2 km of a certain transmission line is 155 Ω, find the resistance of 120 km of that line.

15. The resistance of a certain spool of wire is 1120 Ω. A piece 10.0 m long is found to have a resistance of 12.3 Ω. Find the length of wire on the spool.

16. If a certain machine can make 1850 parts in 55 min, how many parts can it make in 7.5 h? Work to the nearest part.

17. In Figure 19•4, the constant force on the plunger keeps the pressure of the gas in the cylinder constant. The piston raises when the gas is heated and falls when the gas is cooled. if the volume of the gas is 1.53 m³ when the temperature is 302°K, find the volume when the temperature is 358°K.

18. If the power generated by a hydroelectric plant is directly proportional to the flow rate through the turbines, and a flow rate of 24 750 L of water per minute produces 41.2 MW, how much power would you expect when a drought reduces the flow to 22 150 L/m?

For Problem 17, use Charles's law: *The volume of a gas at constant pressure is directly proportional to its absolute temperature.* K is the abbreviation for kelvin, the SI absolute temperature scale. Add 273°C to Celsius temperatures to obtain temperatures on the kelvin scale.

FIGURE 19•4 Absolute temperature °K (degrees kelvin)

$$°K = x°C + 273°C$$

Absolute temperature value must be used in thermodynamic problems.

Graphics Calculator or Computer

19. Use a graphics calculator or a graphing utility on a computer to graph, on the same axes, the *family of curves*

$$y_1 = x \qquad\qquad y_2 = 2x$$
$$y_3 = 3x \qquad\qquad y_4 = \tfrac{1}{2}x$$

for $x = -1$ to 5. In what way do the four curves differ? What quantity in the equations causes the difference?

19·3 The Power Function

Power Function

In Section 19•2, we saw that we could represent the statement "y varies directly as x" by Eq. 60,

$$y = kx$$

Similarly, if y varies directly as the *square* of x, we have

$$y = kx^2$$

or if y varies directly as the *square root* of x,

$$y = k\sqrt{x} = kx^{1/2}$$

These are all examples of the *power function*:

Power Function	$y = kx^n$	**196**

The constants can, of course, be represented by any letter. Appendix A shows *a* instead of *k*.

where the constants k and n can be any positive or negative number. This simple function gives us a great variety of relations useful in technology whose forms depend on the value of the exponent, n. A few of these are shown in the following table.

For exponents of 4 and 5, we have the *quartic* and *quintic* functions, respectively.

WHEN	WE GET THE		WHOSE GRAPH IS A
$n = 1$	Linear function	$y = kx$ (direct variation)	Straight line
$n = 2$	Quadratic function	$y = kx^2$	Parabola
$n = 3$	Cubic function	$y = kx^3$	Cubical parabola
$n = -1$		$y = \dfrac{k}{x}$ (inverse variation)	Hyperbola

The first three of these are special cases of the *general polynomial function of degree n*,

$y = a_0 x^n + a_1 x^{n-1} + \cdots + a_{n-3}x^3 + a_{n-2}x^2 + a_{n-1}x + a_n$	**102**

where n is a positive integer and the as are constants. For example, the quadratic function $y = kx^2$ is a polynomial function of second degree, where $a_{n-2} = k$ and all the other as are zeros. It is called *incomplete* because it is lacking an x term and a constant term.

We also consider power functions that are not polynomials; those with noninteger positive powers will be covered in this section and those with negative exponents in the following section on inverse variation.

Graph of the Power Function

The graph of a power function varies greatly, depending on the exponent. We first show some power functions with positive, integral exponents.

■ **Example 12:** Graph the power functions $y = x^2$ and $y = x^3$ for a range of x from -3 to $+3$.

You can, of course, use a graphics calculator or computer to do this graph and the later ones, instead of doing a point-by-point plot.

Solution: Make a table of values.

x	-3	-2	-1	0	1	2	3
$y = x^2$	9	4	1	0	1	4	9
$y = x^3$	-27	-8	-1	0	1	8	27

The graph of $y = kx^3$ is sometimes called a *cubical parabola*.

The curves $y = x^2$ and $y = x^3$ (shown as a dashed line) are plotted in Figure 19•5. Notice that the plot of $y = x^2$ has no negative values of y. This is typi-

FIGURE 19•5

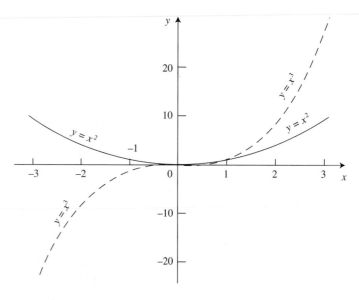

cal of power functions that have *even* positive integers for exponents. The plot of $y = x^3$ does have negative ys for negative values of x. The shape of this curve is typical of a power function that has an *odd* positive integer as exponent. ■

When graphing a power function with a *fractional* exponent, the curve may not exist for negative values of x.

■ **Example 13:** Graph the function $y = x^{1/2}$ for $x = -9$ to 9.

Solution: We see that for negative values of x there are no real number values of y. For the nonnegative values, we get

x	0	1	2	3	4	5	6	7	8	9
y	0	1	1.41	1.73	2.00	2.24	2.45	2.65	2.83	3.00

which are plotted in Figure 19•6.

FIGURE 19•6

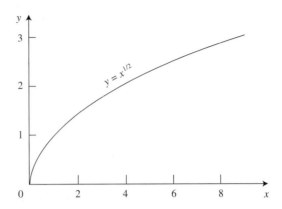

Solving Power Function Problems

As with direct variation (and with inverse variation and combined variation treated later), we can solve problems involving the power function with or without finding the constant of proportionality. The following example will illustrate both methods.

■ **Example 14:** If y varies directly as the $\frac{3}{2}$ power of x, and y is 54 when x is 9, find y when x is 25.

Solution by Solving for the Constant of Proportionality: Here we set up an equation with k, and solve for the constant of proportionality. We let the exponent n in Eq. 196 be equal to $\frac{3}{2}$.

$$y = kx^{3/2}$$

As before, we evaluate the constant of proportionality by substituting the known values into the equation. Using $x = 9$ and $y = 54$, we obtain

$$54 = k(9)^{3/2} = k(27)$$

so $k = 2$. Our power function is then

$$y = 2x^{3/2}$$

This equation can then be used to find other pairs of corresponding values. For example, when $x = 25$,

$$y = 2(25)^{3/2}$$
$$= 2\left(\sqrt{25}\right)^3$$
$$= 2(5)^3 = 250$$

Solution by Setting Up a Proportion: Here we set up a proportion. Three values are known, and we then solve for the fourth. If

$$y_1 = kx_1^{3/2}$$

and

$$y_2 = kx_2^{3/2}$$

then y_2 is to y_1 as $kx_2^{3/2}$ is to $kx_1^{3/2}$:

$$\frac{y_2}{y_1} = \left(\frac{x_2}{x_1}\right)^{3/2}$$

Substituting $y_1 = 54$, $x_1 = 9$, and $x_2 = 25$ yields

$$\frac{y_2}{54} = \left(\frac{25}{9}\right)^{3/2}$$

from which

$$y_2 = 54\left(\frac{25}{9}\right)^{3/2} = 250$$

— **Example 15:** The horizontal distance S traveled by a projectile is directly proportional to the square of its initial velocity V. If the distance traveled is 1250 m when the initial velocity is 190 m/s, find the distance traveled when the initial velocity is 250 m/s.

Solution: The problem statement implies a power function of the form $S = kV^2$. Substituting the initial set of values gives us

$$1250 = k(190)^2$$

$$k = \frac{1250}{(190)^2} = 0.03463$$

So our relationship is

$$S = 0.03463\ V^2$$

When $V = 250$ m/s,

$$S = 0.03463(250)^2 = 2160 \text{ m}$$

Check: We use our graphics calculator to plot $S = 0.03463V^2$, as in Figure 19•7. Using the TRACE feature, we check that $S = 2160$ when $V = 250$, that $S = 1250$ when $V = 190$, and also that $S = 0$ when $V = 0$.

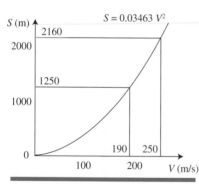

FIGURE 19•7

Some problems may contain no numerical values at all, as in the following example.

— **Example 16:** If y varies directly as the cube of x, by what factor will y change if x is increased by 25%?

Solution: The relationship between x and y is

$$y = kx^3$$

If we give subscript 1 to the initial values and subscript 2 to the final values, we may write the proportion

$$\frac{y_2}{y_1} = \frac{k(x_2)^3}{k(x_1)^3} = \left(\frac{x_2}{x_1}\right)^3$$

If the new x is 25% greater than the old x, then $x_2 = x_1 + 0.25x_1$ or $1.25x_1$. We thus substitute

$$x_2 = 1.25x_1$$

so

$$\frac{y_2}{y_1} = \left(\frac{1.25x_1}{x_1}\right)^3 = \left(\frac{1.25}{1}\right)^3 = 1.95$$

or

$$y_2 = 1.95y_1$$

So y has increased by a factor of 1.95. ▬

Similar Figures

We are using the term *dimension* to refer only to linear dimensions, such as lengths of sides or perimeters. It does not refer to angles, areas, or volumes.

We considered similar triangles in Chapter 6, and said that corresponding sides were in proportion. We now expand the idea to cover similar plane figures of *any* shape, and also similar *solids*. Similar figures (plane or solid) are those in which the distance between any two points on one of the figures is a *constant multiple* of the distance between two corresponding points on the other figure. In other words, if two corresponding dimensions are in the ratio of, say, 2 : 1, all other corresponding dimensions must be in the ratio of 2 : 1. In other words,

Dimensions of Similar Figures	Corresponding dimensions of plane or solid similar figures are in proportion.	**134**

▬ **Example 17:** Two similar solids are shown in Figure 19•8. Find the hole diameter D of the larger solid.

FIGURE 19•8 Similar solids

Solution: By Statement 134,

$$\frac{D}{22.5} = \frac{134}{80.0}$$

$$D = \frac{22.5(134)}{80.0} = 37.7 \text{ mm} \quad ▬$$

FIGURE 19•9 We can, in our minds, make the squares so small that they completely fill any irregular area. We use a similar idea in calculus when finding areas by integration.

Areas of Similar Figures

The area of a square of side s is equal to the square of one side, that is, $s \times s$ or s^2. Thus, if a side is multiplied by a factor k, the area of the larger square is $(ks) \times (ks)$ or k^2s^2. We see that the area has increased by a factor of k^2.

The area of a shape (Fig 19•9) more complicated than a square can be thought of as made up of many small squares. Then if a dimension of that area is multiplied by k, the area of each small square increases by a factor of k^2, and hence the entire are of the figure increases by a factor of k^2. Thus

Areas of Similar Figures	Areas of similar plane or solid figures are to each other as the *squares* of any two corresponding dimensions.	**135**

Thus if a figure has its sides doubled, the new area would be *four* times the original area. This relationship is valid not only for plane areas and for surface areas of solids, but also for cross-sectional areas of solids.

■ **Example 18:** The triangular top surface of the smaller solid shown in Figure 19•8 has an area of 3120 mm^2. Find the area A of the corresponding surface on the larger solid.

Estimate: To set limits for our answer, note that if the dimensions of the larger solid were double those of the smaller solid, the area of the top would be greater by a factor of 4, or about 12 480 mm^2. But the larger dimensions are less than double, so the area will be less than 12 480 mm^2. Therefore, we expect the area to be between 3200 mm^2 and 12 480 mm^2.

Solution: By Statement 135, the area A is to 3120 mm as the *square* of the ratio of 134 to 80.0.

$$\frac{A}{3120} = \left(\frac{134}{80.0}\right)^2$$

$$A = 3120\left(\frac{134}{80.0}\right)^2 = 8750 \text{ mm}^2$$ ■

Volumes of Similar Solids

A cube of side s has volume s^3. We can think of any solid as being made up of many tiny cubes, each of which has a volume equal to the cube of its side. Thus if the dimensions of the solid are multiplied by a factor of k, the volume of each cube (and hence the entire solid) will increase by a factor of k^3.

Volumes of Similar Figures	Volumes of similar solid figures are to each other as the *cubes* of any two corresponding dimensions.	**136**

The units of measure for volume are cubic metres (m^3) and cubic millimetres (mm^3), depending on the units used for the sides of the solid figure.

■ **Example 19:** If the volume of the smaller solid in Figure 19•8 is 256 000 mm^3, find the volume V of the larger solid.

Note that we know very little about the size and shape of these solids, yet we are able to compute the volume of the larger solid. The methods of this chapter give us another powerful tool for making *estimates.*

Solution: By statement 136, the volume V is to 256 000 as the *cube* of the ratio 134 to 80.0:

$$\frac{V}{256\ 000} = \left(\frac{134}{80.0}\right)^3$$

$$V = 256\ 000\left(\frac{134}{80.0}\right)^3 = 429\ 000 \text{ mm}^3$$

Common Error	Students often forget to *square* corresponding dimensions when finding areas, and to *cube* corresponding dimensions when finding volumes.

Scale drawings

An important application of similar figures is in the use of *scale drawings,* such as maps, engineering drawings, surveying layouts, and so on. The ratio of distances on the drawing to corresponding distances on the actual object is called the *scale* of the drawing. Use Statement 135 to convert between the areas on the drawing and areas on the actual object.

— **Example 20:** A certain map has a scale of 1 : 5000. How many hectares on the land are represented by 109 000 mm² on the map (1 hectare = 10 000 m²)?

Solution: If A = the area on the land, then by Statement 135,

$$\frac{A}{109\ 000} = \left(\frac{5000}{1}\right)^2 = 25\ 000\ 000$$

$$A = 109\ 000(25\ 000\ 000) = (2.73 \times 10^{12} \text{ mm}^2)$$

Converting to hectares, we have

$$A = \frac{2.73 \times 10^{12} \text{ mm}^2}{1000 \times 1000} = 2.73 \times 10^6 \text{ m}^2$$

$$A = \frac{2.73 \times 10^6 \text{ m}^2}{10\ 000 \text{ m}^2/\text{hectare}}$$

$$= 2.73 \times 10^2 \text{ hectares}$$

$$= 273 \text{ hectares}$$

Exercise 3 The Power Function

1. If y varies directly as the square of x, and y is 726 when x is 163, find y when x is 274.

2. If y is directly proportional to the square of x, and y is 5570 when x is 172, find y when x is 382.

3. If y varies directly as the cube of x, and y is 4.83 when x is 1.33, find y when x is 3.38.

4. If y is directly proportional to the cube of x, and y is 27.2 when x is 11.4, find y when x is 24.9.

5. If y varies directly as the square of x, and y is 285.0 when x is 112.0, find y when x is 351.0.

6. If y varies directly as the square root of x, and y is 11.8 when x is 342, find y when x is 288.
7. If y is directly proportional to the cube of x, and y is 638 when x is 145, find y when x is 68.3.
8. If y is directly proportional to the five-halves power of x, and y has the value 55.3 when x is 17.3: **(a)** find the constant of proportionality; **(b)** write the equation $y = f(x)$; **(c)** find y when $x = 27.4$; **(d)** find x when $y = 83.6$.
9. If y varies directly as the fourth power of x, fill in the missing values in the following table of ordered pairs.

x	18.2	75.6	
y	29.7		154

10. If y is directly proportional to the $\frac{3}{2}$ power of x, fill in the missing values in the following table of ordered pairs.

x	1.054	1.135	
y		4.872	6.774

11. If y varies directly as the cube root of x, fill in the missing values in the following table of ordered pairs.

x	315		782
y		148	275

12. Graph the power function $y = 1.04x^2$ for $x = -5$ to 5.
13. Graph the power function $y = 0.553x^5$ for $x = -3$ to 3.
14. Graph the power function $y = 1.25x^{3/2}$ for $x = 0$ to 5.

Freely Falling Body

From Eq. A18, we see that the distance fallen by a body (from rest) varies directly as the square of the elapsed time. Assume an initial velocity of zero for each of these problems.

15. If a body falls 176 m in 6.00 s, how far will it fall in 9.00 s?
16. If a body falls 4.90 m during the first second, how far will it fall during the third second?
17. If a body falls 19.6 m in 2.00 s, how many seconds will it take to fall 162 m?
18. If a body falls 44.2 m in 3.00 s, how far will it fall in 6.00 s?

Power in a Resistor

The power dissipated in a resistor varies directly as the square of the current in the resistor (Eq. A67).

19. If the power dissipated in a resistor is 486 W when the current is 2.75 A, find the power when the current is 3.45 A.
20. If the current through a resistor is increased by 28%, by what percentage will the power increase?
21. By what factor must the current in an electric heating coil be increased to triple the power consumed by the heater?

Photographic Exposures

The exposure time for a photograph is directly proportional to the square of the f stop. (The f stop of a lens is its focal length divided by its diameter.)

22. A certain photograph will be correctly exposed at a shutter speed of 1/100 s with a lens opening of f5.6. What shutter speed is required if the lens opening is changed to f8?
23. For the photograph in Problem 22, what lens opening is needed for a shutter speed of 1/200 s?

Photographer's rule of thumb: *Double the exposure time for each increase in f stop.*

24. Most cameras have the following f stops: f2.8, f4, f5.6, f8, f11, and f16. To keep the same correct exposure, by what factor must the shutter speed be increased when the lens is opened one stop?

25. A certain enlargement requires an exposure time of 24 s when the enlarger's lens is set at f22. What lens opening is needed to reduce the exposure time to 6 s?

Similar Figures

26. A container for storing propane gas is 0.755 m high and contains 20.0 L. How high would a container of similar shape have to be to have a volume of 40.0 L?

27. A certain wood stove has a firebox volume of 70 $\overline{0}$00 mm³. What firebox volume would be expected if all dimensions of the stove are increased by a factor of 1.25?

28. If the stove in Problem 27 has a mass of 148 kg, what mass would we expect for the larger stove?

29. A certain solar house stores heat in 155 tonnes of stones which are in a chamber beneath the house. Another solar house is to have a chamber of similar shape but with all dimensions increased by 15%. How many tonnes of stone will it hold?

30. Each side of a square is increased by 15.0 mm and the area is seen to increase by 2450 mm². What were the dimensions of the original square?

31. The floor plan of a certain building has a scale of 5 mm = 300 mm and shows a room having an area of 25 860 mm². What is the actual room area in square metres?

32. The area of a window of a car is 11 800 mm² on a drawing having a scale of 1 : 4. Find the actual window area in square metres.

Assume that the amount of flow through a pipe is proportional to its cross-sectional area.

33. A pipe 76.0 mm in diameter discharges 50$\overline{0}$0 L of water in a certain time. What must be the diameter of a pipe that will discharge 75$\overline{0}$0 L in the same time?

34. If it cost $756 to put a fence around a circular pond, what will it cost to enclose another pond having $\frac{1}{5}$ the area?

35. A triangular field whose base is 215 m contains 12 400 m². Find the area of a field of similar form whose base is 328 m.

Graphics Calculator Computer

36. The power function $y = 11.9x^{2.32}$ has been proposed as an equation to fit the following data:

x	1	2	3	4	5	6	7	8	9	10
y	11.9	59.4	152	292	496	754	1097	1503	1901	2433

Write a program or use a spreadsheet that will compute and print for each given x: **(a)** the value of y from the formula; **(b)** the difference between the value of y from the table and that obtained from the formula. This is called a *residual*.

37. Use your graphics calculator or a computer to graph the family of curves

$$y = x \qquad\qquad y = x^2$$
$$y = x^3 \qquad\qquad y = x^4$$

in the same viewing window.

19•4

Inverse Variation

Inverse Variation

When we say that "y varies inversely as x" or that "y is inversely proportional to x," we mean that x and y are related by the following equation, where, as before, k is a constant of proportionality.

We could also say that we have inverse variation when the product of x and y is a constant, that is, when $xy = k$.

Inverse Variation	$y = \dfrac{k}{x}$	61

The Hyperbola

The graph of the function $y = k/x$ is called a *hyperbola*. It is one of the *conic sections*, which you will study in more detail when you take analytic geometry.

■ **Example 21:** Graph the function $y = 2/x$ from $x = 0$ to $x = 5$.

Solution: Make a table of point pairs:

x	0	$\frac{1}{2}$	1	2	3	4	5
y	Not defined	4	2	1	$\frac{2}{3}$	$\frac{1}{2}$	$\frac{2}{5}$

Do not confuse inverse variation with the inverse of a function.

These points are graphed in Figure 19•10. Note that as x takes on smaller and smaller values, y gets larger and larger; and as x gets very large, y gets smaller and smaller but never reaches zero. Thus the curve gets ever closer to the x and y axes, but never touches them. The x and y axes are *asymptotes* for this curve.

FIGURE 19•10 A hyperbola

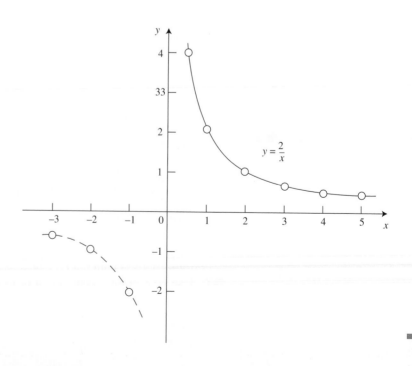

We did not plot the curve for negative values of x, but if we had, we would have obtained the second branch of the hyperbola, shown as a dashed line in the figure.

Power Function with Negative Exponent

Suppose, for example, that y varies inversely as the cube of x. This would be written

$$y = \frac{k}{x^3}$$

This is the same as

$$y = kx^{-3}$$

The equation is seen to be a power function with a negative exponent. Such power functions are sometimes referred to as *hyperbolic*.

Solving Inverse Variation Problems

Inverse variation problems are solved by the same methods as for any other power function. As before, we can work these problems with or without finding the constant of proportionality.

■ **Example 22:** If y is inversely proportional to x, and y is 8 when x is 3, find y when x is 12.

Solution: x and y are related by $y = k/x$. We find the constant of proportionality by substituting the given values of x and y, 3 and 8.

$$8 = \frac{k}{3}$$

$$k = 3(8) = 24$$

so

$$y = 24/x$$

When $x = 12$,

$$y = \frac{24}{12} = 2$$ ■

■ **Example 23:** If y is inversely proportional to the square of x, by what factor will y change if x is tripled?

Solution: From the problem statement we know that $y = k/x^2$ or $k = x^2 y$. If we use the subscript 1 for the original values and 2 for the new values, we can write

$$k = (x_1)^2 y_1 = (x_2)^2 y_2$$

Since the new x is triple the old, we substitute $3x_1$ for x_2,

$$(x_1)^2 y_1 = (3x_1)^2 y_2$$

$$= 9(x_1)^2 y_2$$

$$y_1 = 9y_2$$

or

$$y_2 = \frac{y_1}{9}$$

So the new y is one ninth of its initial value.

■ **Example 24:** If y varies inversely as x, fill in the missing values in the table:

x	1			9	12
y			12	4	

Solution: Substituting the ordered pair (9, 4) into Eq. 61,

$$4 = \frac{k}{9}$$

$$k = 36$$

So

$$y = \frac{36}{x}$$

Filling in the table, we have

x	1	3	9	12
y	36	12	4	3

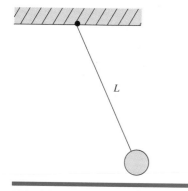

FIGURE 19•11 A simple pendulum

■ **Example 25:** The number of oscillations N that a pendulum (Fig. 19•11) makes per unit time is inversely proportional to the square root of the length L of the pendulum, and $N = 2.00$ oscillations per second when $L = 85\overline{0}$ mm. (a) Write the equation $N = f(L)$, and (b) find N when $L = 1150$ mm.

Solution: (a) The equation will be of the form

$$N = \frac{k}{\sqrt{L}}$$

Substituting $N = 2.00$ and $L = 850$ gives us

$$2.00 = \frac{k}{\sqrt{850}}$$

$$k = 2.00\sqrt{850} = 58.3$$

So the equation is

$$N = \frac{58.3}{\sqrt{L}}$$

(b) When $L = 1150$

$$N = \frac{58.3}{\sqrt{1150}} = 1.72 \text{ oscillations per second}$$

Check: Does the answer seem reasonable? We see that N has decreased, which we expect with a longer pendulum, but it has not decreased by much. As a check, we note that L has increased by a factor of $1150 \div 850$ or 1.35

so we expect N to decrease by a factor of $\sqrt{1.35}$ or 1.16. Dividing, $2.00 \div 1.72 = 1.16$, so the answer checks. ▬

Exercise 4 Inverse Variation

1. If y varies inversely as x, and y is 385 when x is 832, find y when x is 226.
2. If y is inversely proportional to the square of x, and y has the value 1.55 when x is 7.38, find y when x is 44.2.
3. If y is inversely proportional to x, how does y change when x is doubled?
4. If y varies inversely as x, and y has the value of 104 when x is 532: **(a)** find the constant of proportionality; **(b)** write the equation $y = f(x)$; **(c)** find y when x is 668; and **(d)** find x when y is 226.
5. If y is inversely proportional to x, fill in the missing values.

x	306	622	
y	125		418

6. Fill in the missing values, assuming that y is inversely proportional to the square of x.

x	2.69		7.83
y		1.16	1.52

7. If y varies inversely as the square root of x, fill in the missing values.

x		3567	5725
y	1136	1828	

8. If y is inversely proportional to the cube root of x, by what factor will y change when x is tripled?
9. If y is inversely proportional to the square root of x, by what percentage will y change when x is decreased by 50%?
10. Plot the curve $y = 5/x^2$ for the domain 0 to 5.
11. Plot the function $y = 1/x$ for the domain 0 to 10.

Boyle's Law

Boyle's law states that, for a confined gas at a constant temperature, the product of the pressure and the volume is a constant. Another way of stating this is that the pressure is inversely proportional to the volume, or that the volume is inversely proportional to the pressure. Assume a constant temperature in the following problems.

The *Pascal* (Pa) is the SI unit of pressure. It equals one newton per square metre.

12. A certain quantity of gas, when compressed to a volume of 2.50 m³, has a pressure of 184 kPa. Find the pressure resulting when that gas is further compressed to 1.60 m³.
13. The air in the cylinder in Figure 19•4 (page 544) is at a pressure of 101.3 kPa and occupies a volume of 2.87×10^{-3} m³. Find the pressure when it is compressed to 4.10×10^{-4} m³.
14. A balloon contains 320 m³ of gas at a pressure of 140 kPa. What would be the volume if the same quantity of gas were at a pressure of 250 kPa?

Gravitational Attraction

Newton's law of gravitation states that any two bodies attract each other with a force that is inversely proportional to the square of the distance between them.

Force = mass × acceleration

Force = (m)kg × 9.81 m/s² (N)

15. The force of attraction between two certain steel spheres is 3.75×10^{-5} dynes when the spheres are placed 180 mm apart. Find the force of attraction when they are 520 mm apart.

16. How far apart must the spheres in Problem 15 be placed to cause the force of attraction between them to be 3.00×10^{-5} dynes?

17. The law of gravitation states that the force of a body of mass m is inversely proportional to the square of its distance from the center of the earth. If an individual having a mass of 68.0 kg creates a force of 667 N at the earth's surface, what force of attraction will that person have at an altitude of 2460 km above the earth's surface? (Assume the distance from the center of the earth to the surface to be 6340 km.)

18. What force of attraction will a satellite have when in an orbit of 252 km above the earth's surface, if the force at the earth's surface is measured as 1.24 kN?

Illumination

For a surface illuminated by a light source, the *inverse square law* states that the intensity of illumination on the surface is inversely proportional to the *square* of the distance between the source and the surface.

19. A certain light source produces an illumination of 800 lux (a lux is 1 lumen per square metre) on a surface. Find the illumination on that surface if the distance to the light source is doubled.

20. A light source located 2.75 m from a surface produces an illumination of 528 lux on that surface. Find the illumination if the distance is changed to 1.55 m.

21. A light source 7.50 m from a surface produces an illumination of 426 lux on that surface. At what distance must that light source be placed to give an illumination of 854 lux?

22. When photographing a document on a certain copy stand, an exposure time of $\frac{1}{25}$ s is needed with the light source 0.750 m from the document. At what distance must the light be located to reduce the exposure time to $\frac{1}{100}$ s?

Electrical

23. The current in a resistor is inversely proportional to the resistance. By what factor will the current change if a resistor increases 10% because of heating?

24. The resistance of a wire is inversely proportional to the square of its diameter. If an AWG size 12 conductor (2.05 mm diameter) has a resistance of 14.8 Ω, what will be the resistance of an AWG size 10 conductor (2.59 mm diameter) of the same length and material?

25. The capacitive reactance X_c of a circuit varies inversely as the capacitance C of the circuit. If the capacitance of a certain circuit is decreased by 25%, by what percentage will X_c change?

Graphics Calculator or Computer

26. Use a graphics calculator or a computer to graph

$$y = 1/x \quad \text{and} \quad y = 1/x^2$$

in the same viewing window, from $x = -4$ to 4. How do you explain the different behavior of the two functions for negative values of x?

19·5

Functions of More than One Variable

Joint Variation

So far in this chapter we have considered only cases where y was a function of a *single* variable x. In functional notation, this is represented by $y = f(x)$. In this section we cover functions of two or more variables, such as

$$y = f(x, w)$$

$$y = f(x, w, z)$$

and so forth. When y varies directly as x and w, we say that y varies *jointly* as x and w. The three variables are related by the following equation, where, as before, k is a constant of proportionality.

Joint Variation	$y = kxw$	**62**

■ **Example 26:** If y varies jointly as x and w, how will y change when x is doubled and w is one fourth of its original value?

Solution: Let y' be the new value of y obtained when x is replaced by $2x$ and w is replaced by $w/4$, while the constant of proportionality k, of course, does not change. Substituting in Eq. 62, we obtain

$$y' = k(2x)\left(\frac{w}{4}\right)$$

$$= \frac{kxw}{2}$$

but, since $kxw = y$, then

$$y' = \frac{y}{2}$$

So the new y is half as large as its former value. ■

Combined Variation

When one variable varies with two or more variables in ways that are more complex than in Eq. 62, the variation is referred to as *combined*. This term is applied to many different kinds of relationships, so a formula cannot be given that will cover all types. You must carefully read the problem statement in order to write the equation. Once you have the equation, the solution of combined variation problems is no different than for other types of variation.

■ **Example 27:** If y varies directly as the cube of x and inversely as the square of z, we write

$$y = \frac{kx^3}{z^2}$$ ■

■ **Example 28:** If y is directly proportional to x and the square root of w, and inversely proportional to the square of z, we write

$$y = \frac{kx\sqrt{w}}{z^2}$$

■ **Example 29:** If y varies directly as the square root of x and inversely as the square of w, by what factor will y change when x is made four times larger and w is tripled?

Solution: First write the equation linking y to x and w, including a constant of proportionality k:

$$y = \frac{k\sqrt{x}}{w^2}$$

When x is replaced by $4x$ and w is replaced by $3w$, we get a new value for y; let's call it y'.

$$y' = \frac{k\sqrt{4x}}{(3w)^2} = k\frac{2\sqrt{x}}{9w^2}$$

$$= \frac{2}{9}\left(\frac{k\sqrt{x}}{w^2}\right) = \frac{2}{9}y$$

We see that y' is $\frac{2}{9}$ the size of the original y.

■ **Example 30:** If y varies directly as the square of w and inversely as the cube root of x and $y = 225$ when $w = 103$ and $x = 157$, find y when $w = 126$ and $x = 212$.

Solution: From the problem statement,

$$y = k\frac{w^2}{\sqrt[3]{x}}$$

Solving for k, we have

$$225 = k\frac{(103)^2}{\sqrt[3]{157}} = 1967k$$

or

$$k = 0.1144. \text{ So}$$

$$y = \frac{0.1144w^2}{\sqrt[3]{x}}$$

When $w = 349$ and $x = 212$,

$$y = \frac{0.1144(126)^2}{\sqrt[3]{212}} = 305$$

■ **Example 31:** The value of y is directly proportional to the square of x and inversely proportional to the cube of w. By what factor will y change if x is increased by 15% and w is decreased by 20%?

Solution: The relationship between x, y, and w is

$$y = k\frac{x^2}{w^3}$$

so we can write the proportion

$$\frac{y_2}{y_1} = \frac{k\dfrac{x_2^2}{w_2^3}}{k\dfrac{x_1^2}{w_1^3}} = \frac{x_2^2}{w_2^3} \cdot \frac{w_1^3}{x_1^2} = \left(\frac{x_2}{x_1}\right)^2 \left(\frac{w_1}{w_2}\right)^3$$

We replace x_2 with $1.15x_1$ and replace w_2 with $0.8w_1$:

$$\frac{y_2}{y_1} = \left(\frac{1.15x_1}{x_1}\right)^2 \left(\frac{w_1}{0.8w_1}\right)^3 = \frac{(1.15)^2}{(0.8)^3} = 2.58$$

Now y will increase by a factor of 2.58.   ▬

Exercise 5 Functions of More than One Variable

Joint Variation

1. If y varies jointly as w and x, and y is 483 when x is 742 and w is 383, find y when x is 274 and w is 756.
2. If y varies jointly as x and w, by what factor will y change if x is tripled and w is halved?
3. If y varies jointly as w and x, by what percentage will y change if w is increased by 12% and x is decreased by 7.0%?
4. If y varies jointly as w and x, and y is 3.85 when w is 8.36 and x is 11.6, evaluate the constant of proportionality and write the complete expression for y in terms of w and x.
5. If y varies jointly as w and x, fill in the missing values.

w	x	y
46.2	18.3	127
19.5	41.2	
	8.86	155
12.2		79.8

Combined Variation

6. If y is directly proportional to the square of x and inversely proportional to the cube of w, and y is 11.6 when x is 84.2 and w is 28.4, find y when x is 5.38 and w is 2.28.
7. If y varies directly as the square root of w and inversely as the cube of x, by what factor will y change if w is tripled and x is halved?
8. If y is directly proportional to the cube root of x and to the square root of w, by what percentage will y change if x and w are both increased by 7.0%?
9. If y is directly proportional to the $\frac{3}{2}$ power of x and inversely proportional to w, and y is 284 when x is 858 and w is 361, evaluate the constant of proportionality and write the complete equation for y in terms of x and w.
10. If y varies directly as the cube of x and inversely as the square root of w, fill in the missing values in the table.

w	x	y
1.27		3.05
	5.66	1.93
4.66	2.75	3.87
7.07	1.56	

Geometry

11. The area of a triangle varies jointly as its base and altitude. By what percentage will the area change if the base is increased by 15% and the altitude decreased by 25%?

12. If the base and altitude of a triangle are both halved, by what factor will the area change?

Electrical Applications

13. When an electric current flows through a wire, the resistance to the flow varies directly as the length and inversely as the cross-sectional area of the wire. If the length and the diameter are both tripled, by what factor will the resistance change?

14. If 755 m of 3.00-mm-diameter wire has a resistance of 27.6 Ω, what length of similar wire 5.00 mm in diameter will have the same resistance?

Gravitation

15. Newton's law of gravitation states that every body in the universe attracts every other body with a force that varies directly as the product of their masses and inversely as the square of the distance between them. By what factor will the force change when the distance is doubled and each mass is tripled?

16. If both masses are increased by 60% and the distance between them is halved, by what percentage will the force of attraction increase?

Illumination

17. The intensity of illumination at a given point is directly proportional to the intensity of the light source and inversely proportional to the square of the distance from the light source. If a desk is properly illuminated by a 75.0 W lamp 2.44 m from the desk, what size lamp will be needed to provide the same lighting at a distance of 3.66 m?

18. How far from a 150-candela light source would a picture have to be placed to receive the same illumination as when it is placed 12 m from an 85-candela source?

Gas Laws

19. The volume of a given weight of gas varies directly as the absolute temperature t and inversely as the pressure p. If the volume is 4.45 m³ when $p = 225$ kilopascals (kPa) and $t = 305°$K, find the volume when $p = 325$ kPa and $t = 354°$K.

20. If the volume of a gas is 3.54 m³, find its volume when the absolute temperature is increased 10% and the pressure is doubled.

Work

21. The amount paid to a work crew varies jointly as the number of persons working and the length of time worked. If five workers earn $5123.73 in three weeks, in how many weeks will six workers earn a total of $6148.48?

22. If five bricklayers take six days to finish a certain job, how long would it take seven bricklayers to finish a similar job requiring four times the number of bricks?

Strength of Materials

23. The maximum safe load of a rectangular beam (Fig. 19•12) varies jointly as the width and the square of the depth, and inversely as the length of the beam. If a beam $20\overline{0}$ mm wide, $29\overline{0}$ mm deep, and 4.87 m long can safely support 66.8 kN, find the safe load for a beam 165 mm wide, 340 mm deep, and 6.40 m long made of the same material.

FIGURE 19•12 A rectangular beam

24. If the width of a rectangular beam is increased by 11%, the depth decreased by 8%, and the length increased by 6%, by what percentage will the safe load change?

Mechanics

FIGURE 19•13 A stretched wire

25. The number of vibrations per second made when a stretched wire (Fig. 19•13) is plucked varies directly as the square root of the tension in the wire, and inversely as the length. If a 1.00-m-long wire will vibrate 325 times a second when the tension is 115 N, find the frequency of vibration if the wire is shortened to 0.750 m and the tension is decreased to 95.0 N.

26. The kinetic energy of a moving body is directly proportional to its mass and the square of its speed. If the mass of a bullet is halved, by what factor must its speed be increased to have the same kinetic energy as before?

Fluid Flow

FIGURE 19•14 A vertical cylindrical tank

27. The time needed to empty a vertical cylindrical tank (Fig. 19•14) varies directly as the square root of the height of the tank and the square of the radius. By what factor will the emptying time change if the height is doubled and the radius increased by 25%?

28. The power available in a jet of liquid is directly proportional to the cross-sectional area of the jet and to the cube of the velocity. By what factor will the power increase if the area and velocity are both increased 50%?

CHAPTER 19 REVIEW PROBLEMS

1. If y varies inversely as x, and y is 736 when x is 822, find y when x is 583.

2. If y is directly proportional to the $\frac{5}{2}$ power of x, by what factor will y change when x is tripled?

3. If y varies jointly as x and z, by what percentage will y change when x is increased by 15% and z is decreased by 4%?

4. The braking distance of an automobile varies directly as the square of the speed. If the braking distance of a certain automobile is 10.4 m at 40.0 km/h, find the braking distance at 90.0 km/h.

5. The rate of flow of liquid from a hole in the bottom of a tank is directly proportional to the square root of the liquid depth. If the flow rate is 225 litres/minute when the depth is 3.46 m, find the flow rate when the depth is 1.00 m.

6. If the power needed to drive a ship varies directly as the cube of the speed of the ship and a 58-kW engine will drive a certain ship at 11.2 knots, find the power needed to propel that ship at 18.0 knots.

7. If the tensile strength of a cylindrical steel bar varies as the square of its diameter, by what factor must the diameter be increased to triple the strength of the bar?

8. If the life of an incandescent lamp varies inversely as the 12th power of the applied voltage and the light output varies directly as the 3.5th power of the applied voltage, by what factor will the life increase if the voltage is lowered by an amount that will decrease the light output by 10%?

9. One of Kepler's laws states that the time for a planet to orbit the sun varies directly as the $\frac{3}{2}$ power of its distance from the sun. How many years will it take for Saturn, which is about $9\frac{1}{2}$ times as far from the sun as is the earth, to orbit the sun?

10. The volume of a cone varies directly as the square of the base radius and as the altitude. By what factor will the volume change if the altitude is doubled and the base radius is halved?

11. The number of oscillations made by a pendulum in a given time is inversely proportional to the length of the pendulum. A certain clock with a 760-mm-long pendulum is losing 15.00 minutes/day. Should the pendulum be lengthened or shortened, and by how much?

12. A trucker usually makes a trip in 18.0 h at an average speed of 100.0 km/h. Find the travelling time if the speed is reduced to 80.00 km/h.

13. The force on the vane of a wind generator varies directly as the area of the vane and the square of the wind velocity. By what factor must the area of a vane be increased so that the wind force on it will be the same in a 12-km/h wind as it was in a 35 km/h wind?

14. The maximum deflection of a rectangular beam varies inversely as the product of the width and the cube of the depth. If the deflection of a beam having a width of 150 mm and a depth of 350 mm is 7.5 mm, find the deflection if the width is made $2\overline{0}0$ mm and the depth 450 mm.

15. When an object moves at a constant speed, the travel time is inversely proportional to the speed. If a satellite now circles the earth in 26 h 18 min, how long will it take if booster rockets increase the speed of the satellite by 15%?

16. The life of an incandescent lamp is inversely proportional to the 12th power of the applied voltage. If a lamp has a life of 2500 h when run at 115 V, what would be its life expectancy when run at $11\overline{0}$ V?

17. How far from the earth will a spacecraft be equally attracted by the earth and the moon? The distance from the earth to the moon is approximately 382 000 km, and the mass of the earth is about 82 times that of the moon.

18. Ohm's law states that the electric current flowing in a circuit varies directly as the applied voltage and inversely as the resistance. By what percentage will the current change when the voltage is increased by 25% and the resistance increased by 15%?

19. The allowable strength F of a column varies directly as its length L and inversely as its radius of gyration r. If $F = 350$ N when L is 12 m and r is 36 mm, find F when L is 18 m and r is 45 mm.

20. The time it takes a pendulum to go through one complete oscillation (the *period*) is directly proportional to the square root of its length. If the period of a 1.0-m pendulum is 1.25 s, how long must the pendulum be to have a period of 2.50 s?

21. If the maximum safe current in a wire is directly proportional to the $\frac{3}{2}$ power of the wire diameter, by what factor will the safe current increase when the wire diameter is doubled?

22. Four workers take ten 6-h days to finish a job. How many workers are needed to finish a similar job which is three times as large, in five 8-h days?

23. When a jet of water strikes the vane of a water turbine and is deflected through an angle θ, the force on the vane varies directly as the square of

the jet velocity and the sine of $\theta/2$. If θ is decreased from 55° to 40° and the jet velocity increases by 40%, by what percentage will the force change?

24. By what factor will the kinetic energy change if the speed of a projectile is doubled and its mass is halved? Use the fact that the kinetic energy of a moving body is directly proportional to the product of the mass and the square of the velocity of the body.

25. The fuel consumption for a ship is directly proportional to the cube of the ship's speed. If a certain tanker uses 6985 L of diesel fuel on a certain run at 15.0 knots, how much fuel would it use for the same run when the speed is reduced to 10.0 knots? A *knot* is equal to one nautical mile per hour. (1 nautical mile = 1.854 kilometres)

26. The diagonal of a certain square is doubled. By what factor does the area change?

27. A certain parachute is made from 52.0 m² of fabric. If all its dimensions are increased by a factor of 1.40, how many square metres of fabric will be needed?

28. The rudder of a certain airplane has an area of 0.7 m³. By what factor must the dimensions be scaled up to triple the area?

29. A 38.0-mm-diameter pipe fills a cistern in 5.0 h. Find the diameter of a pipe that will fill the same cistern in 9.0 h.

30. If 315.0 m of fence will enclose a circular field containing 0.792 hectares, what length will enclose 1.988 hectares?

31. The surface area of a one-quarter model of an automobile measures 1.10 m². Find the surface area of the full-sized car.

32. A certain water tank is 7.60 m high and holds 20 0$\overline{0}$0 L. How much would a 10.7-m-high tank of similar shape hold?

33. A certain square water tank has a mass of 5.80 tonnes. If all its dimensions were scaled up by a factor of 1.30, what would be the mass of the larger tank?

34. If a trough 1.50 m long holds 12 pailfuls of water, how many pailfuls will a similar trough hold that is 2.44 m long?

35. A sphere 114 mm in diameter has a mass of 2.85 kg. What is the mass of another sphere of the same density that is 235 mm in diameter?

36. A ball 108 mm in diameter has a mass of 1.26 kg. What is the diameter of a similar ball of mass 16.0 kg?

37. A worker's contract has a cost-of-living clause that requires that his salary be proportional to the cost-of-living index. If he earned $450 per week when the index was 9.40, how much should he earn when the index is 12.7?

38. A woodsman pays a landowner $8.00 for each cord of wood he cuts on the landowner's property, and sells the wood for $75 per cord. When the price of firewood rose to $95, the landowner asked for a proportional share of the price. How much should he get per cord?

39. The series of numbers 3.5, 5.25, 7.875, . . . form a *geometric progression*, where the ratio of any term to the one preceding it is a constant. This is called the *common ratio*. Find this ratio.

40. The *specific density* of a solid or liquid is the ratio of the density of the substance to the density of water, at a standard temperature, Eq. A45.

Taking the density of water as 100$\overline{0}$ kg/m³, find the density of copper having a specific density of 8.89.

41. An iron casting having a surface area of 746 300-mm² is heated so that its length increases by 1.0%. Find the new area.

42. A certain boiler pipe will permit a flow of 156 litres/minute. Buildup of scale inside the pipe eventually reduces its diameter to three-fourths of its previous value. Assuming that the flow rate is proportional to the cross-sectional area, find the new flow rate for the pipe.

Writing

43. Suppose your company makes plastic trays and is planning new ones with dimensions double those now being made. Your company president is convinced that they will need only twice as much plastic as the older version. "Twice the size, twice the plastic," he proclaims, and no one is willing to challenge him. Your job is to make a presentation to the president where you tactfully point out that he is wrong and where you explain that the new trays will require eight times as much plastic. Write your presentation.

Specific Density	Specific density = $\dfrac{\text{density of substance}}{\text{density of water}}$	**A45**

20

Exponential and Logarithmic Functions

O B J E C T I V E S

When you have completed this chapter, you should be able to:

- Graph the exponential function.
- Solve exponential growth and decay problems by formula or by the universal growth and decay curves.
- Convert expressions between exponential and logarithmic form.
- Evaluate common and natural logarithms and antilogarithms.
- Evaluate, manipulate, and simplify logarithmic expressions.
- Solve exponential and logarithmic equations.
- Solve applied problems involving exponential or logarithmic equations.
- Make graphs on logarithmic or semilogarithmic paper.
- Graph empirical data and determine an approximate equation describing the data.

You may have heard the story about the inventor of chess, who asked that the reward for his invention be a grain of wheat on the first square of the chessboard, two grains on the second square, four on the third, and so on, each square getting double the amount on the previous square. It turns out that he would receive more wheat than has been grown by man during all history, an illustration of the remarkable properties of the exponential function, which we study in this chapter.

We also study the logarithmic function and show how it is related to the exponential function, and do a few logarithmic computations. We then solve exponential and logarithmic equations and use them in some interesting applications, and do some graphing on logarithmic and semilogarithmic paper.

20·1

The Exponential Function

Definition

An *exponential function* is one in which the independent variable appears in the exponent. The quantity that is raised to the power is called the *base*.

■ **Example 1:**

$$y = 5^x \qquad y = b^x \qquad y = e^x \qquad y = 10^x$$

$$y = 3a^x \qquad y = 7^{x-3} \qquad y = 5e^{-2x}$$

are exponential functions if a, b, and e represent positive constants. ■

Realize that these are different from the *power function, $y = ax^n$*. Here the unknown is *in the exponent*.

We shall see that e, like π, has a specific value that we will discuss later in this chapter.

Graph of the Exponential Function

We may make a graph of an exponential function in the same way as we graphed other functions in Chapter 5. Choose values of the independent variable x throughout the region of interest, and for each x compute the corresponding value of the dependent variable y. Plot the resulting table of ordered pairs and connect with a smooth curve.

■ **Example 2:** Graph the exponential function $y = 2^x$ from $x = -4$ to $x = +3$. For comparison, plot the power function $y = x^2$ on the same axes.

Solution: We make our graphs, Figure 20·1, using a graphics calculator or a computer, or by computing and plotting point pairs.

Note that the graph of the exponential function is completely different from the graph of the power function whose graph is a parabola. For the exponential function, note that as x increases, y increases faster, and that the curve gets steeper and steeper. This is a characteristic of *exponential growth*,

FIGURE 20·1

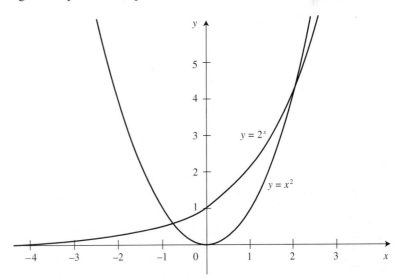

which we cover more fully later. Also note that the y intercept is 1 and that there is no x intercept, the x axis being an asymptote. Finally, note that each successive y value is two times the previous one. We say that y *increases geometrically*. ▬

Sometimes the exponent of an exponential function is negative. We will see in the following example what effect a negative exponent has on the graph of the function.

▬ **Example 3:** Graph the exponential functions $y = 2^x$ and $y = 2^{-x}$, for $x = -4$ to 4, on the same axes.

Solution: We have already graphed $y = 2^x$ in the preceding example, and now we add the graph of $y = 2^{-x}$, Figure 20•2.

FIGURE 20•2

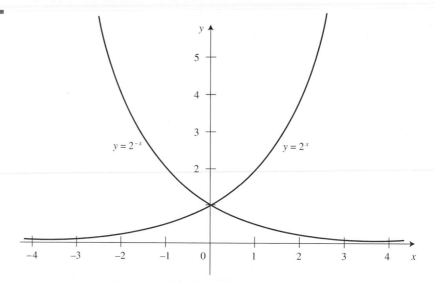

Note that when the exponent is *positive*, the graph *increases exponentially*, and that when the exponent is *negative*, the graph *decreases exponentially*. Also notice that neither curve reaches the x axis. Thus for the exponential functions $y = 2^x$ and $y = 2^{-x}$, y cannot equal zero. ▬

Exponential functions often have the irrational number e as the base. We shall see why in the following section. For now, we shall treat it like any other number, using $e \approx 2.718$ for its approximate value.

▬ **Example 4:** Graph the exponential function $y = 1.85e^{-x/2}$, for $x = -4$ to 4, if e equals 2.718.

Solution: Scientific calculators have a key, marked $\boxed{e^x}$, for raising e to any power. On some calculators you press the $\boxed{e^x}$ key and then enter the exponent; on other calculators you enter the exponent and then press the $\boxed{e^x}$ key. With the aid of that key, we make our graph, Figure 20•3, using a graphing utility, or by making a table of point pairs.

Note that the negative sign in the exponent has made the graph *decrease exponentially* as x increases, and that the curve approaches the x axis as an asymptote. The shape of the curve, however, is that of an exponential function.

FIGURE 20·3

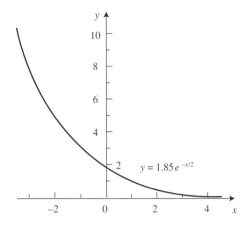

$$y = 1.85\,e^{-x/2}$$

Compound Interest

In this and the next few sections, we will see some problems that require exponential equations for their solution.

When an amount of money a (called the *principal*) is invested at an interest rate n (expressed as a decimal), it will earn an amount of interest $a \times n$ at the end of the first interest period. If this interest is then added to the principal and both continue to earn interest, we have what is called *compound interest*, the type of interest commonly given on bank accounts.

Suppose that the interest rate is 5% (0.05). As the balance increases, the interest received for the current period (5% of a or $0.05a$) is added to the previous balance (100% of a or $1.00a$) to give a new total of $1.05a$. So we could say we multiply a by $(1 + 0.05)$ or 1.05.

Similarly, for an interest rate of n, the balance y_t at the end of any period t is obtained by multiplying the preceding balance y_{t-1} by $(1 + n)$.

Recursion Relation for Compound Interest	$y_t = y_{t-1}(1 + n)$	**A10(b)**

This equation is called a *recursion relation*, from which each term in a series of numbers may be found from the term immediately preceding it. We'll do more with recursion relations in Chapter 25, but now we will use Eq. A10(b) to make a table showing the balance at the end of a number of interest periods.

PERIOD	BALANCE y AT END OF PERIOD
1	$a(1 + n)$
2	$a(1 + n)^2$
3	$a(1 + n)^3$
4	$a(1 + n)^4$
.	.
.	.
t	$a(1 + n)^t$

We thus get the following exponential function, with a equal to the principal, n equal to the rate of interest, and t the number of interest periods.

Compound Interest Computed Once per Period	$y = a(1 + n)^t$	**A10(a)**

■ **Example 5:** To what amount (to the nearest cent) will an initial deposit of $500 accumulate if invested at a compound interest rate of $6\frac{1}{2}\%$ per year for 8 years?

Solution: We are given

Principal $a = \$500$
Interest rate $n = 0.065$, expressed in decimal form
Number of interest periods $t = 8$

Substituting into Eq. A10(a) gives

$$y = \$500(1 + 0.065)^8$$

$$= \$827.50$$ ■

Compound Interest Computed m Times per Period

We can use Eq. A10(a) to compute interest on a savings account for which the interest is computed once a year. But what if the interest is computed more often, as is done on many bank accounts, either monthly, weekly, or even daily?

Let us modify the compound interest formula. Instead of computing interest *once* per period, let us compute it *m times* per period. The exponent in Eq. A10(a) thus becomes mt. The interest rate n, however, has to be reduced to $(1/m)$th of its old value, that is, to n/m.

In Section 20•2, we will use this equation to derive an equation for exponential (continuous) growth.

Compound Interest Computed m Times per Period	$y = a\left(1 + \dfrac{n}{m}\right)^{mt}$	**A11**

■ **Example 6:** Repeat the computation of Example 5 with the interest computed monthly rather than annually.

Solution: As in Example 5, $a = \$500$, annual interest rate $n = 0.065$, and $t = 8$. But n is an annual rate, so we must use Eq. A11, with $m = 12$:

$$y = \$500\left(1 + \frac{0.065}{12}\right)^{12(8)} = \$500(1.00542)^{96}$$

$$= \$839.83$$

or $12.33 more than in Example 5. ■

Exercise 1 The Exponential Function

Exponential Function

Graph each exponential function over the given domains of x, taking $e = 2.718$:

1. $y = 0.2(3.2)^x$ $(x = -4$ to $+4)$ **2.** $y = 3(1.5)^{-2x}$ $(x = 0$ to $5)$

3. $y = 5(1 - e^{-x})$ $(x = 0$ to $10)$ **4.** $y = 4e^{x/2}$ $(x = 0$ to $4)$

5. A rope or chain between two points hangs in the shape of a curve called a *catenary* (Fig. 20·4). Its equation is

$$y = \frac{a(e^{x/a} + e^{-x/a})}{2}$$

Using values of $a = 2.5$ and $e = 2.718$, plot y for $x = -5$ to 5.

FIGURE 20·4 A rope or chain hangs in the shape of a catenary. Mount your finished graph for Problem 5 vertically on a wall or board and hang a fine chain from the endpoints. Does the shape of the chain (after you have adjusted its length) match that of your graph?

Compound Interest

6. Find the amount to which $500 will accumulate in six years at a compound interest rate of 6% per year, compounded annually.

7. If our compound interest formula, Eq. A10(a), is solved for a, we get

$$a = \frac{y}{(1 + n)^t}$$

The amount a is called the *present worth* of the future amount y. This formula, and the three that follow, are standard formulas used in business and finance.

where a is the amount that must be deposited now at interest rate n to produce an amount y in t years. How much money would have to be invested with a yearly interest rate of $7\frac{1}{2}$% to accumulate to $10 000 in 10 years?

8. What annual compound interest rate (compounded annually) is needed to enable an investment of $5000 to accumulate to $10 000 in 12 years?

9. Using Eq. A11, find the amount to which $1 will accumulate in 20 years at a compound interest rate of 10% per year **(a)** compounded annually; **(b)** compounded monthly; **(c)** compounded daily.

A series of annual payments such as these is called an *annuity*.

10. If an amount of money R is deposited *every year* for t years at a compound interest rate n, it will accumulate to an amount y, where

$$y = R\left[\frac{(1 + n)^t - 1}{n}\right]$$

If a worker pays $2000 per year into a retirement plan yielding 6% annual interest, what will be the value of this retirement plan after 25 years?

This is called a *sinking fund*.

11. If the equation for the retirement plan in Problem 10 is solved for R, we get

$$R = \frac{ny}{(1 + n)^t - 1}$$

where R is the annual deposit required to produce a total amount y at the end of t years. How much would the worker in Problem 10 have to deposit each year (at 6% per year) to have a total of $100 000 after 25 years?

This is called *capital recovery*.

12. The yearly payment R that can be obtained for t years from a present investment a is

$$R = a\left[\frac{n}{(1 + n)^t - 1} + n\right]$$

If a person has $85 000 in a retirement fund, how much can be withdrawn each year so that the fund will be exhausted in 20 years if the amount remaining in the fund is earning $6\frac{1}{4}$% per year?

20·2

Exponential Growth and Decay

Exponential Growth

Equation A11, $y = a(1 + n/m)^{mt}$, allows us to compute the amount obtained, with interest compounded any number of times per period that we choose. We could use this formula to compute the interest if it were compounded every week, or every day, or every second. But what about *continuous* compounding, or continuous growth? What would happen to Eq. A11 if m got very, very large, in fact, infinite? Let us make m increase to large values, but first, to simplify the work, we make the substitution; let

$$k = \frac{m}{n}$$

Equation A11 then becomes

$$y = a\left(1 + \frac{1}{k}\right)^{knt}$$

which can be written

$$y = a\left[\left(1 + \frac{1}{k}\right)^k\right]^{nt}$$

Then as m grows large, so will k. Let us try some values on the calculator, and evaluate only the quantity in the square brackets, to four decimal places.

k	$\left(1 + \frac{1}{k}\right)^k$
1	2
10	2.5937 . . .
100	2.7048 . . .
1 000	2.7169 . . .
10 000	2.7181 . . .
100 000	2.7183 . . .
1 000 000	2.7183 . . .

We get the surprising result that as m (and k) continue to grow infinitely large, the value of $(1 + 1/k)^k$ does not grow without limit, but approaches a specific, well-known value, the value 2.7183. . . . . This important number is given the special symbol e. We can express the same idea in *limit notation*, by writing

<table>
<tr><td>We will not study limits here. They are covered in detail in calculus.</td><td>Definition of e</td><td>$\lim_{k \to \infty}\left(1 + \frac{1}{k}\right)^k = e$</td><td>**185**</td></tr>
</table>

As k grows without bound, the value of $(1 + 1/k)^k$ approaches e ($\approx 2.7183 . . .$).

The number e is named after a Swiss mathematician, Leonhard Euler (1707–1783). Its value has been computed to thousands of decimal places. In Exercise 2, Problem 19, we show how to find e using a particular series, and in Problem 21 we show how to find the value of e graphically.

Thus, when m gets infinitely large, the quantity $(1 + 1/k)^k$ approaches e, and the formula for continuous growth becomes

Exponential Growth	$y = ae^{nt}$	**199**

Banks that offer "continuous compounding" of your account use Eq. 199.

■ **Example 7:** Repeat the computation of Example 5 if the interest were compounded *continuously* rather than monthly.

Solution: From Eq. 199,

$$y = \$500e^{0.065(8)}$$

$$= \$500e^{0.52}$$

$$= \$841.01$$

or $1.18 more than when compounded monthly. ■

Common Error	When using Eq. 199, the time units of n and t *must agree*.

■ **Example 8:** A quantity grows exponentially at the rate of 2% per minute. By how many times will it have increased after 4 h?

Solution: The units of n and t do *not* agree:

$$n = 2\% \text{ per } minute \quad \text{and} \quad t = 4 \text{ } hours$$

So we convert one of them to agree with the other.

$$t = 4 \text{ h} = 240 \text{ min}$$

Using Eq. 199,

$$y = ae^{nt} = ae^{0.02(240)}$$

We can find the ratio of y to a by dividing both sides by a:

$$\frac{y}{a} = e^{0.02(240)} = e^{4.8} = 122$$

So the final amount is 122 times as great as the initial amount. ■

Exponential Decay

When a quantity *decreases* so that the amount of decrease is proportional to the present amount, we have what is called *exponential decay*. Take, for example, a piece of steel just removed from a furnace. The amount of heat leaving the steel depends upon its initial temperature; the hotter it is, the faster heat will leave, and the faster it will cool. So, as the steel cools, its lowering temperature causes slower heat loss. Slower heat loss causes slower rate of temperature drop, and so on. The result is the typical exponential decay curve shown in Figure 20·5. Finally, the temperature is said to *asymptotically approach* the outside (room) temperature.

The equation for exponential decay is the same as for exponential growth, except that the exponent is negative.

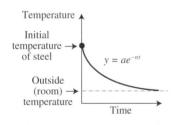

FIGURE 20·5 Exponential decrease in temperature. This is called *Newton's law of cooling.*

Exponential Decay	$y = ae^{-nt}$	**201**

■ **Example 9:** A room initially 27.00°C above the outside temperature cools exponentially at the rate of 25% per hour. Find the temperature of the room (above the outside temperature) at the end of 135 minutes.

Solution: We first make the units consistent: 135 m = 2.25 h. Then by Eq. 201,

$$y = 27.00e^{-0.25(2.25)} = 15.38°C \qquad \rule[0.5ex]{1em}{0.4ex}$$

Exponential Growth to an Upper Limit

Suppose that the bucket in Figure 20·6 initially contains a litres of water. Then assume that y_1, the amount remaining in the bucket, decreases exponentially. By Eq. 201,

$$y_1 = ae^{-nt}$$

The amount of water in bucket 2 thus increases from zero to a final amount a. The amount y in bucket 2 at any instant is equal to the amount that has left bucket 1, or

$$y = a - y_1$$
$$= a - ae^{-nt}$$

or

FIGURE 20·6 The amount in bucket 2 grows exponentially to an upper limit a.

Exponential Growth to an Upper Limit	$y = a(1 - e^{-nt})$	**202**

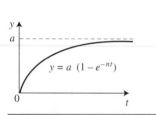

FIGURE 20·7 Exponential growth to an upper limit

So the equation for this type of growth to an upper limit is exponential, where a equals the upper limit quantity, n is equal to the rate of growth, and t represents time (see Fig. 20·7).

$\rule[0.5ex]{1em}{0.4ex}$ **Example 10:** The voltage (v) across a certain capacitor grows exponentially from 0.00 V to a maximum of 75.0 V, at a rate of 7.00% per second. Write the equation for the voltage at any instant, and find the voltage at 2.0 s.

Solution: From Eq. 202, with $a = 75.0$ and $n = 0.070$,

$$v = 75.0(1 - e^{-0.0700t})$$

where v represents the instantaneous voltage. When $t = 2.00$ s,

$$v = 75(1 - e^{-0.140})$$
$$= 9.80 \text{ V} \qquad \rule[0.5ex]{1em}{0.4ex}$$

Time Constant

Our equations for exponential growth and decay all contained a rate of growth n. Often it is more convenient to work with the *reciprocal* of n, rather than n itself. This reciprocal is called the *time constant, T*.

Time Constant	$T = \dfrac{1}{n}$	**203**

■ **Example 11:** If a quantity decays exponentially at a rate of 25.0% per second, what is the time constant?

Solution:

$$T = \frac{1}{0.25} = 4.00 \text{ s}$$

Notice that the time constant has the units of *time*. ■

Universal Growth and Decay Curves

If we replace n by $1/T$ in Eq. 201, we get

$$y = ae^{-t/T}$$

and then divide both sides by a,

$$\frac{y}{a} = e^{-t/T}$$

We plot this curve (Fig. 20•8) with the dimensionless ratio t/T for our horizontal axis and the dimensionless ratio y/a for the vertical axis. Thus the horizontal axis is *the number of time constants* that have elapsed, and the vertical axis is *the ratio of the final amount to the initial amount*. It is called the *universal decay curve*.

FIGURE 20•8 Universal growth and decay curves

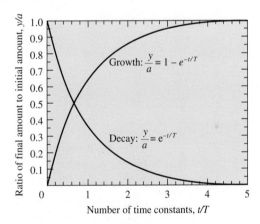

We can use the universal decay curve to obtain *graphical solutions* to exponential decay problems.

■ **Example 12:** A current decays from an initial value of $3\overline{0}0$ mA, at an exponential rate of 20% per second. Find the current after 7 s graphically, using the universal decay curve.

Solution: We have $n = 0.20$, so the time constant is

$$T = \frac{1}{n} = \frac{1}{0.20} = 5 \text{ s}$$

Our given time $t = 7$ s is then equivalent to

$$\frac{t}{T} = \frac{7}{5} = 1.4 \text{ time constants}$$

From the universal decay curve, at $t/T = 1.4$, we read

$$\frac{y}{a} = 0.25$$

Since $a = 300$ mA,

$$y = 300(0.25) = 75 \text{ mA}$$

Figure 20·8 also shows the *universal growth curve*,

$$\frac{y}{a} = 1 - e^{-t/T}$$

It is used in the same way as the universal decay curve,

A Recursion Relation for Exponential Growth

We have found that an amount a will grow to an amount y in t periods of time (Eq. 199):

$$y = ae^{nt}$$

where n is the rate of growth. Computing y for different values of t gives

t	y
0	$y_0 = ae^0 = a$
1	$y_1 = ae^n = y_0 e^n$
2	$y_2 = ae^{2n} = (e^n)(ae^n) = e^n y_1$
3	$y_3 = ae^{3n} = (e^n)(ae^{2n}) = e^n y_2$
.	.
.	.
t	$y_t = e^n y_{t-1}$

Thus, each value y_1 may be obtained by multiplying the preceding value y_{t-1} by the constant e^n. If we replace e^n by a constant B (sometimes called the *birthrate*), we have the recursion relation,

Recursion Relation for Exponential Growth	$y_t = B\, y_{t-1}$	**204**

■ Example 13: Compute and graph values of y versus t using a starting value of 1 and a birthrate of 2, for five time periods.

Solution: We get each new y by multiplying the preceding y by 2.

t	0	1	2	3	4	5
y	1	2	4	8	16	32

The graph of y versus t, Figure 20·9, is a typical exponential growth curve.

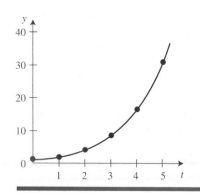

FIGURE 20·9

Nonlinear Growth Equation

Equations 199 and 204 represent a population which can grow without being limited by shortage of food or space, predators, and so forth. This is rarely the case, so biologists have modified the equation to take these limiting factors into account. One model of the growth equation that takes these limits into account is obtained by multiplying the right side of Eq. 204 by the factor $(1 - y_{t-1})$.

Nonlinear Growth Equation	$y_t = B\,y_{t-1}(1 - y_{t-1})$	**205**

This equation is one form of what is called the *Logistic Function*, or the *Verhulst Population Model*. As y_{t-1} gets larger, the factor $(1 - y_{t-1})$ gets smaller. This equation will cause the predicted population y to stabilize at some value, for a range of values of the birthrate B from 1 to 3, regardless of the starting value for y.

■ **Example 14:** Compute the population for 20 time periods using the nonlinear growth equation. Use a starting population of 0.8 and a birthrate of 2.

Solution: Making a table of values,

The population of 0.8 is a *normalized* population, considered to be 80% of some reference value.

t	POPULATION y
0	0.8
1	2(0.8)(1 − 0.8) = 0.32
2	2(0.32)(1 − 0.32) = 0.44
3	2(0.44)(1 − 0.44) = 0.49
4	2(0.49)(1 − 0.49) = 0.50
5	2(0.50)(1 − 0.50) = 0.50
.	.
.	.
.	.
20	2(0.50)(1 − 0.50) = 0.50

We see that the population y stabilizes at a value of 0.50 [Fig. 20•10(b)] ■

For a birthrate less than 1, the nonlinear growth equation predicts that the population eventually dies out [Fig. 20•10(a)]. For a birthrate between 1 and 3, the population y will stabilize at some value between 0 and 0.667, but for a birthrate of 3 or greater, strange things start to happen.

■ **Example 15:** Repeat the computation of Example 14 with a birthrate of 3.

Solution: Again using a starting value of 0.8 and $B = 3$, we get the results shown in the table on page 578.

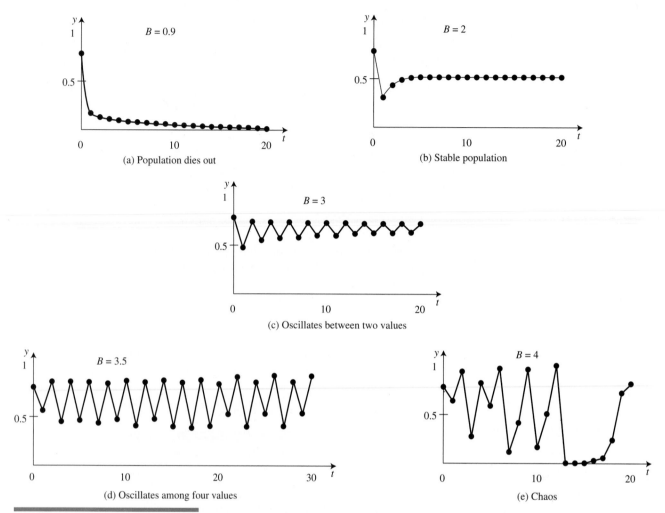

(a) Population dies out

(b) Stable population

(c) Oscillates between two values

(d) Oscillates among four values

(e) Chaos

FIGURE 20·10

t	y	t	y
0	0.8	.	.
1	0.48	.	.
2	0.75	.	.
3	0.56	17	0.62
4	0.74	18	0.71
5	0.58	19	0.62
		20	0.71

We see that the value *y oscillates* between two different values [Fig. 20·10(c)]. We have what is called *period doubling* or *bifurcation*.

Chaos

For *B* between 3.4495 and 3.56, the population has been found to oscillate among *four* different values. Figure 20·10(d), or *B* = 3.5, shows oscillation among values of 0.38, 0.5, 0.83, and 0.87. At higher values of *B*, the population oscillates among eight values, then sixteen. Above *B* = 3.57 the population jumps around in a way that is not predictable at all.

■ **Example 16:** Figure 20•10(e) shows the first 20 values of y using $B = 4$ and an initial y of 0.8. Note that the values do not repeat. The same simple equation that gave us predictable populations for certain values of B now gives us *chaos* when we increase the value of B above a certain level.   ■

Exercise 2 Exponential Growth and Decay

Exponential Growth

Use either the formulas or the universal growth and decay curves, as directed by your instructor.

1. A quantity grows exponentially at the rate of 5.00% per year for seven years. Find the final amount if the initial amount is $20\overline{0}$ units.

2. A yeast manufacturer finds that the yeast will grow exponentially at a rate of 15.0% per hour. How many kilograms of yeast must they start with to obtain $50\overline{0}$ kg at the end of 8.00 h?

3. If the population of a country was 11.4 million in 1995, and grows at an annual rate of 1.63%, find the population by the year 2000.

4. If the rate of inflation is 12.0% per year, how much would a camera that now costs $225 be expected to cost five years from now?

5. If the oil consumption of a certain country was 12.0 million barrels in 1995, and grew at an annual rate of 8.30%, what would the oil consumption be by the year 2000.

6. A pharmaceutical company makes a vaccine that grows at a rate of 2.5% per hour. How many units of this organism must they have initially to have $1\overline{0}00$ units after five days?

Exponential Growth to an Upper Limit

7. A steel casting initially at 0°C is placed in a furnace at $80\overline{0}$°C. If it increases in temperature at the rate of 5.0% per minute, find its temperature after 20.0 min.

8. Equation 202 approximately describes the hardening of concrete, where y is the compressive strength in (MPa) t days after pouring. Using values of $a = 12.0$ MPa and $n = 0.0696$ in the equation, find the compressive strength after 14 days.

9. When the switch in Figure 20•11 is closed, the current i will grow exponentially according to the equation

FIGURE 20•11

Inductor Current When Charging	$i = \dfrac{E}{R}(1 - e^{-Rt/L})$ amperes	**A88**

where L is the inductance in henries and R is the resistance in ohms. Find the current at 0.0750 s if $R = 6.25$ Ω, $L = 186$ henries, and $E = 25\overline{0}$ V.

Exponential Decay

10. A flywheel is rotating at a speed of $18\overline{0}0$ rev/m. When the power is disconnected, the speed decreases exponentially at the rate of 32.0% per minute. Find the speed after 10.0 m.

11. A steel forging is 815°C above room temperature. If it cools exponentially at the rate of 2.00% per minute, how much will its temperature drop in 1 hour?

12. As light passes through glass or water, its intensity decreases exponentially according to the equation

$$I = I_0 e^{-kx}$$

where I is the intensity at a depth x and I_0 is the intensity before entering the glass or water. If, for a certain filter glass, $k = 0.050$/mm (which means that each millimetre of filter thickness removes half the light reaching it), find the fraction of the original intensity that will pass through a filter glass 20.0 mm thick.

13. The atmospheric pressure p decreases exponentially with the height h (km) above the earth according to the function $p = 1200e^{-h/5}$ mm of mercury. Find the pressure at a height of 9150 m.

14. A certain radioactive material loses its radioactivity at the rate of $2\frac{1}{2}\%$ per year. What fraction of its initial radioactivity will remain after 10.0 years?

15. When a capacitor C, charged to a voltage E, is discharged through a resistor R (Fig. 20•12) the current i will decay exponentially according to the equation

FIGURE 20•12

Capacitor Current When Charging or Discharging	$i = \dfrac{E}{R}e^{-t/RC}$ amperes	**A83**

Find the current after 45 ms (0.045 s) in a circuit where $E = 220$ V, $C = 130$ microfarads (130×10^{-6} farad), and $R = 2700\ \Omega$.

16. When a fully discharged capacitor C (Fig. 20•13) is connected across a battery, the current i flowing into the capacitor will decay exponentially according to Equation A83. If $E = 115$ V, $R = 35\overline{0}\ \Omega$, and $C = 0.000750$ F, find the current after 75.0 ms.

FIGURE 20•13

17. In a certain fabric mill, cloth is removed from a dye bath and is then observed to dry exponentially at the rate of 24% per hour. What percentage of the original moisture will still be present after 5 h?

Computer

18. Program a computer to print a two-column table, the first column giving the value of k and the second column the value of $(1 + 1/k)^k$. Take a starting value for k equal to 1 and increase it each time by a factor of 10. Stop the run when $1/k$ is less than 0.00001. Does the value of $(1 + 1/k)^k$ seem to be converging on some value? If not, why not?

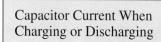

Series Approximation for e	$e = 2 + \dfrac{1}{2!} + \dfrac{1}{3!} + \dfrac{1}{4!} + \dots$	**206**

19. We can get an approximate value for e from the infinite series where $4!$ (read 4 *factorial*) is $4(3)(2)(1) = 24$. Write a program to compute e using the first five terms of the series.

20. The infinite series often used to calculate e^x is

Series Approximation for e^x	$e^x = 1 + x + \dfrac{x^2}{2!} + \dfrac{x^3}{3!} + \dfrac{x^4}{4!} + \ldots$	**207**

Write a program to compute e^x by using the first 15 terms of this series, and use it to find e^5.

Graphics Utility

21. Use a graphics calculator or a graphing utility on a computer to plot $y = (1 + 1/x)^x$. What happens to the value of y as x increases? Use TRACE to find the coordinates of points on the curve as x increases from zero to, say, 100.

20·3

Logarithms

In Section 20·1 we studied the exponential function

$$y = b^x$$

Given b and x, we know how to find y. Thus if $b = 2.48$ and $x = 3.50$, then, by calculator,

$$y = 2.48^{3.50} = 24.0$$

We are also able, given y and x, to find b. For example, if y were 24.0 and x were 3.50,

$$24.0 = b^{3.50}$$

$$b = 24.0^{1/3.50} = 2.48$$

We will finish this problem in Section 20·5.

Suppose, now, that we have y and b and want to find x. Say that $y = 24.0$ when $b = 2.48$:

$$24.0 = 2.48^x$$

Try it. You will find that none of the math we have learned so far will allow us to find x. To solve this and similar problems, we need *logarithms*, which are explained in this section.

We have the same relationship between the same quantities as we had before but a different way of expressing it. We have a similar situation in ordinary language. Take "Mary is John's *sister*." If we had only the word *sister* (and not *brother*) to describe the relationship between children, we would have to say something like "John is the person whom Mary is the *sister of*." That is as awkward as "the exponent to which the base must be raised to obtain the number." So we introduce new words, such as *brother* and *logarithm*.

Definition of a Logarithm

The logarithm of some positive number y is *the exponent* to which a base b must be raised to obtain y.

■ **Example 17:** Since $10^2 = 100$, we say that "2 is the logarithm of 100, to the base 10" because 2 is the exponent to which the base 10 must be raised to obtain 100. The logarithm is written

$$\log_{10} 100 = 2$$

Notice that the base is written in small numerals below the word "log." The statement is read: "log of 100 (to the base 10) is 2." This means that

2 is an exponent because *a logarithm is an exponent.* The result of raising the base to that power is 100. So these two expressions are equivalent:

$$10^2 = 100$$

$$\log_{10} 100 = 2$$

Given the exponential function $y = bx$, we say that "x is the logarithm of y, to the base b" because x is the exponent to which the base b must be raised to obtain y.

So, in general,

Definition of a Logarithm	If $\quad y = b^x \quad (y > 0,\ b > 0,\ b \neq 1)$ then $\quad x = log_b\, y$ (x is the logarithm of y to the base of b.)	**186**

In practice, the base b is taken as either 10 for common logarithms, or e for natural logarithms. If "log" is written without a base, the base is assumed to be 10.

■ **Example 18:**

$$\log 5 \equiv \log_{10} 5$$

Converting between Logarithmic and Exponential Form

In working with logarithmic and exponential expressions, we often have to switch between exponential and logarithmic form. When converting from one form to the other, remember that (1) the base in exponential form is also the base in logarithmic form, and (2) "the *log* is the *exponent.*"

■ **Example 19:** Change the exponential expression $3^2 = 9$ to logarithmic form.

Solution: The base (3) in the exponential expression remains the base in the logarithmic expression:

$$3^2 \quad = 9$$
$$\downarrow$$
$$\log_3(\ \ ) = (\ \ )$$

The log is the exponent

$$3^2 \quad = 9$$
$$\log_3(\ \ ) = 2$$

and 9 the number

So our expression is

$$\log_3 9 = 2$$

> We could also write the same expression in *radical form*, $\sqrt{9} = 3$.

This is read "the log *of* 9 (to the base 3) *is* 2."

■ **Example 20:** Change $\log_e x = 3$ to exponential form.

Solution:

$$\log_e x = 3$$
$$e^3 = x$$

■

■ **Example 21:** Change $10^3 = 1000$ to logarithmic form.

Solution:

$$\log_{10} 1000 = 3$$

■

Common Logarithms

Also called *Briggs' logarithms*, after Henry Briggs (1561–1630)

Although we may write logarithms to any base, there are only two bases in regular use, the base 10 and the base e. Logarithms to the base e, called *natural* logarithms, are discussed later. In this section we study logarithms to the base 10, called *common* logarithms.

Common Logarithms by Calculator

We use the calculator key marked $\boxed{\log}$ to find common logarithms. On some calculators we press $\boxed{\log}$, and then enter the number of which we wish to take the log (called the *argument*), and then press $\boxed{\text{ENTER}}$. On other calculators we enter the argument first and then press $\boxed{\log}$.

■ **Example 22:** Verify the following common logarithms, found to five significant digits.
(a) $\log 74.82 = 1.8740$
(b) $\log 0.03755 = -1.4254$

■

■ **Example 23:** Try to take the common logarithm of -2. You should get an error indication. We cannot take the logarithm of a negative number.

■

Antilogarithms by Calculator

Suppose that we have the logarithm of a number, and want to find the number itself: say, $\log x = 1.852$. This process is known as finding the antilogarithm (antilog) of 1.852. First we switch to exponential form,

$$x = 10^{1.852}$$

Some calculators use $\boxed{\text{INV}}$ $\boxed{\text{LOG}}$ to find antilogarithms.

This quantity can be found using the $\boxed{10^x}$ key on the calculator. On some calculators, press $\boxed{10^x}$ and then enter the number. On other calculators, enter the number first and then press $\boxed{10^x}$.

■ **Example 24:** Verify the following antilogarithms, found to four significant digits.
(a) The antilog of 1.852 is 71.12.
(b) The antilog of -1.738 is 0.01828.

■

■ **Example 25:** Find x to four significant digits, if log $x = 2.74$.

Solution: By calculator,

$$x = 10^{2.74} = 549.5$$

■

The Logarithmic Function

We wish to graph the logarithmic function $x = \log_b y$, but first let us follow the usual convention of calling the dependent variable y and the independent variable x. Our function then becomes

Logarithmic Function	$y = \log_b x$ $(x > 0, b > 0, b \neq 1)$	**208**

■ **Example 26:** Graph the logarithmic function $y = \log x$, for $x = -1$ to 14.

Solution: We use a graphing utility or make a table of point pairs, getting the values of y by using the common $\boxed{\log}$ key on the calculator.

x	-1	0	1	2	3	4	5	6	7	8	9	10	11	12	13	14
y	—	—	0	0.30	0.48	0.60	0.70	0.78	0.85	0.90	0.95	1.00	1.04	1.08	1.11	1.15

First we notice that, when x is negative or zero, our calculator gives an error indication. In other words, the domain of x is the positive numbers only. *We cannot take the common logarithm of a negative number or zero.* We'll see that this is true for logarithms to other bases as well.

If we try a value of x between zero and 1, say, $x = 0.5$, we get a negative y (-0.3 in this case). Plotting our point pairs gives the curve in Figure 20•14.

FIGURE 20•14

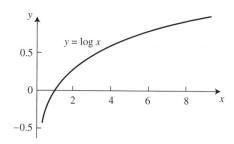

Natural Logarithms

Also called *Napierian logarithms*, after John Napier (1550–1617), who first wrote logarithms.

You may want to refer to Section 20•2 for our earlier discussion of the number e (2.718 approximately). After we have defined e, we can use it as a base; logarithms using e as a base are called *natural* logarithms. They are written ln x. Thus ln x is understood to mean $\log_e x$.

Natural Logarithms by Calculator

To find the natural logarithm of a (positive) number by calculator, we use the $\boxed{\text{ln}}$ key. As with common logarithms, you must check your calculator to see if the number whose logarithm you want is to be entered before or after pressing the $\boxed{\text{ln}}$ key.

■ **Example 27:** Find ln 19.3 to four significant digits.

   Solution: Enter 19.3. Press $\boxed{\text{ln}}$. Read 2.960 (rounded).

or

   Press $\boxed{\text{ln}}$. Enter 19.3. Press $\boxed{\text{ENTER}}$.   ■

■ **Example 28:** Verify the following, found to four significant digits:
(a) ln 25.4 = 3.235
(b) ln 0.826 = −0.1912
(c) ln (−3) gives an error indication.   ■

Antilogarithms by Calculator

Some calculators do not have an $\boxed{e^x}$ key. Instead, use $\boxed{\text{inv}}$ $\boxed{\text{ln}}$ or $\boxed{\text{2nd}}$ $\boxed{\text{ln}}$

If the natural logarithm of a number is known, we can find the number itself by using the $\boxed{e^x}$ key. Again, some calculators require entering the number before pressing the $\boxed{e^x}$ key, and some after.

■ **Example 29:** Find x to four significant digits if ln x = 3.825.

   Solution: Rewriting the expression ln x = 3.825 in exponential form, we have by calculator

$$x = e^{3.825} = 45.83$$

   ■

Exercise 3   Logarithms

Converting between Logarithmic and Exponential Form

Convert to logarithmic form:

1. $3^4 = 81$ **2.** $5^3 = 125$
3. $4^6 = 4096$ **4.** $7^3 = 343$
5. $x^5 = 995$ **6.** $a^3 = 6.83$

Convert to exponential form:

7. $\log_{10} 100 = 2$ **8.** $\log_2 16 = 4$
9. $\log_5 125 = 3$ **10.** $\log_4 1024 = 5$
11. $\log_3 x = 57$ **12.** $\log_x 54 = 285$
13. $\log_5 x = y$ **14.** $\log_w 3 = z$

Logarithmic Function

Graph each logarithmic function from $x = \frac{1}{2}$ to $x = 4$:

15. $y = \log_e x$ **16.** $y = \log_{10} x$

Common Logarithms

Find the common logarithm of each number to four decimal places:

17. 27.6	**18.** 4.83	**19.** 5.93
20. 9.26	**21.** 48.3	**22.** 385
23. 836	**24.** 1.03	**25.** 27.4
26. 0.0573	**27.** 0.00737	**28.** 9738
29. 34 970	**30.** 5.28×10^6	

Find x to three significant digits if the common logarithm of x is equal to:

31. 1.584	**32.** 2.957	**33.** 5.273
34. 0.886	**35.** -2.857	**36.** 0.366
37. -2.227	**38.** 4.973	**39.** 3.979
40. 1.295	**41.** -3.972	**42.** -0.8835

Natural Logarithms

Find the natural logarithm of each number to four decimal places:

43. 48.3	**44.** 846	**45.** 2365
46. 1.005	**47.** 0.845	**48.** 4.97
49. 0.00836	**50.** 45 900	**51.** 0.0000462
52. 82 900	**53.** 3.84×10^4	**54.** 8.24×10^{-3}

Find to four significant digits the number whose natural logarithm is:

55. 2.846	**56.** 4.263	**57.** 0.879
58. -2.846	**59.** -0.365	**60.** 5.937
61. 0.936	**62.** -4.97	**63.** 15.84
64. -9.47	**65.** -18.36	**66.** 21.83

Computer

67. The series approximation for the natural logarithm of a positive number x is

Series Approximation	$$\ln x = 2a + \frac{2a^3}{3} + \frac{2a^5}{5} + \frac{2a^7}{7} + \ldots$$ where $$a = \frac{x-1}{x+1}$$	**209**

   Write a program to compute $\ln x$ using the first 10 terms of the series.

68. The series expansion for b^x is

Series Approximation for b^x	$$b^x = 1 + x \ln b + \frac{(x \ln b)^2}{2!} + \frac{(x \ln b)^3}{3!} + \ldots$$ $$(b > 0)$$	**198**

   Write a program to compute b^x using the first 20 terms of the series.

69. To enter a logarithm when using a computer algebra system, use the following commands.

	Natural Log	*Log to base b*
Derive	LN(x)	LOG(x, b)
Maple	ln(x)	ln(x)/ln(b)
Mathematica	Log[x]	Log[b, x]

To find the antilogarithm of y, simply raise the base, e or b, to the power y. Use exp(y) if y is a natural logarithm, and $b \wedge y$ if y is a logarithm to the base b. Try your CAS on any of the problems in this exercise.

20•4

Properties of Logarithms

In this section we use the properties of logarithms, together with the conversion between exponential and logarithmic forms.

Here, $b > 0$, $b \neq 1$.

Products

We wish to write an expression for the log of the product of two positive numbers, say, M and N.

$$\log_b MN = ?$$

Let us substitute $M = b^c$ and $N = b^d$. Then

$$MN = b^c b^d = b^{c+d}$$

by the laws of exponents. Writing this expression in logarithmic form,

$$\log_b MN = c + d$$

but, since $b^c = M$, $c = \log_b M$. Similarly, $d = \log_b N$. Substituting, we get

Log of a Product	$\log_b MN = \log_b M + \log_b N$	**187**

The log of a product equals the sum of the logs of the factors.

■ **Example 30:**
(a) $\log 7x = \log 7 + \log x$
(b) $\log 3 + \log x + \log y = \log 3xy$ ■

Common Errors	The log of a sum is *not* equal to the sum of the logs: $$\log_b(M + N) \neq \log_b M + \log_b N$$
	The product of two logs is *not* equal to the sum of the logs: $$(\log_b M)(\log_b N) \neq \log_b M + \log_b N$$

We shall not pretend that this is a practical problem, now that we have calculators, but we recommend doing a few logarithmic computations to practice using the properties of logarithms, which we'll need later to solve logarithmic and exponential equations.

■ **Example 31:** Multiply $(2.947)(9.362)$ by logarithms.

Solution: We take the log of the product

$$\log(2.947 \times 9.362) = \log 2.947 + \log 9.362$$
$$= 0.46938 + 0.97137 = 1.44075$$

This gives us the logarithm of the product. To get the product itself, we take the antilog,

$$(2.947)(9.362) = 10^{1.44075} = 27.59$$ ■

Quotients

Let us now consider the quotient M divided by N. Using the same substitution as above,

$$\frac{M}{N} = \frac{b^c}{b^d} = b^{c-d}$$

Going to logarithmic form,

$$\log_b \frac{M}{N} = c - d$$

Finally, substituting back,

Log of a Quotient	$\log_b \dfrac{M}{N} = \log_b M - \log_b N$	**188**

The log of a quotient equals the log of the dividend minus the log of the divisor.

■ **Example 32:**

$$\log \frac{3}{4} = \log 3 - \log 4$$ ■

■ **Example 33:** Express as the sum or difference of two or more logarithms,

$$\log \frac{ab}{xy}$$

Solution: By Eq. 188,

$$\log \frac{ab}{xy} = \log ab - \log xy$$

and by Eq. 187,

$$\log ab - \log xy = \log a + \log b - (\log x + \log y)$$

$$= \log a + \log b - \log x - \log y$$ ■

■ **Example 34:** The expression $\log 10x^2 - \log 5x$ can be expressed as a single logarithm,

$$\log \frac{10x^2}{5x} \quad \text{or} \quad \log 2x$$ ■

Common Error	Similar errors are made with quotients as with products. $$\log_b(M - N) \neq \log_b M - \log_b N$$ $$\frac{\log_b M}{\log_b N} \neq \log_b M - \log_b N$$

■ **Example 35:** Divide, using logarithms:

$$28.47 \div 1.883$$

Solution: By Eq. 188,

$$\log \frac{28.47}{1.883} = \log 28.47 - \log 1.883$$

$$= 1.4544 - 0.2749 = 1.1795$$

This gives us the logarithm of the quotient. To get the quotient itself, we take the antilog,

$$28.47 \div 1.883 = 10^{1.1795} = 15.12 \qquad ■$$

Powers

Consider now the quantity M raised to a power p. Substituting b^c for M, as before,

$$M^p = (b^c)^p = b^{cp}$$

In logarithmic form,

$$\log_b M^p = cp$$

Substituting back, we get

Log of a Power	$\log_b M^p = p \log_b M$	**189**

The log of a number raised to a power equals the power times the log of the number.

■ **Example 36:**

$$\log 3.85^{1.4} = 1.4 \log 3.85 \qquad ■$$

■ **Example 37:** The expression $7 \log x$ can be expressed as a single logarithm with a coefficient of 1, as

$$\log x^7 \qquad ■$$

■ **Example 38:** Express $2 \log 5 + 3 \log 2 - 4 \log 1$ as a single logarithm.

Solution:

$$2 \log 5 + 3 \log 2 - 4 \log 1 = \log 5^2 + \log 2^3 - \log 1^4$$

$$= \log \frac{25(8)}{1} = \log 200 \qquad ■$$

■ **Example 39:** Express as a single logarithm with a coefficient of 1:

$$2 \log \frac{2}{3} + 4 \log \frac{a}{b} - 3 \log \frac{x}{y}$$

Solution:

$$2 \log \frac{2}{3} + 4 \log \frac{a}{b} - 3 \log \frac{x}{y} = \log \frac{2^2}{3^2} + \log \frac{a^4}{b^4} - \log \frac{x^3}{y^3}$$

$$= \log \frac{4a^4 y^3}{9b^4 x^3}$$ ▬

▬ **Example 40:** Rewrite without logarithms, the equation

$$\log(a^2 - b^2) + 2 \log a = \log(a - b) + 3 \log b$$

Solution: We first try to combine all the logarithms into a single logarithm. Rearranging gives

$$\log(a^2 - b^2) - \log(a - b) + 2 \log a - 3 \log b = 0$$

By the properties of logarithms,

$$\log \frac{a^2 - b^2}{a - b} + \log \frac{a^2}{b^3} = 0$$

or

$$\log \frac{a^2(a - b)(a + b)}{b^3(a - b)} = 0$$

Simplifying yields

$$\log \frac{a^2(a + b)}{b^3} = 0$$

We then rewrite without logarithms, by going from logarithmic to exponential form:

$$\frac{a^2(a + b)}{b^3} = 10^0 = 1$$

or

$$a^2(a + b) = b^3$$ ▬

▬ **Example 41:** Find $35.82^{1.4}$ by logarithms to four significant digits.

Solution: By Eq. 189,

$$\log 35.82^{1.4} = 1.4 \log 35.82$$

$$= 1.4(1.5541) = 2.1758$$

Taking the antilog yields

$$35.82^{1.4} = 10^{2.1758} = 149.9$$ ▬

Roots

We can write a given radical expression in exponential form, and then use the rule for powers. Thus, by Eq. 36,

$$\sqrt[q]{M} = M^{1/q}$$

Taking the logarithm of each side, we obtain

$$\log_b \sqrt[q]{M} = \log_b M^{1/q}$$

We may take the logarithm of each side of an equation, just as we took the square root of each side of an equation, or took the sine of each side of an equation.

Then, by Eq. 189,

Log of a Root	$\log_b \sqrt[q]{M} = \dfrac{1}{q} \log_b M$	**190**

The log of the root of a number equals the log of the number divided by the index of the root.

■ **Example 42:**

(a) $\log \sqrt[5]{8} = \dfrac{1}{5} \log 8 = \dfrac{1}{5} (0.9031) = 0.1806$

(b) $\dfrac{\log x}{2} + \dfrac{\log z}{4} = \log \sqrt{x} + \log \sqrt[4]{z}$ ▬

■ **Example 43:** Find $\sqrt[5]{3824}$ by logarithms.

Solution: By Eq. 190,

$$\log \sqrt[5]{3824} = \frac{1}{5} \log 3824 = \frac{3.5825}{5}$$

$$= 0.7165$$

Taking the antilog gives us

$$\sqrt[5]{3824} = 10^{0.7165} = 5.206$$ ▬

Log of 1

Let us take the log to the base b of 1, and call it x:

$$x = \log_b 1$$

Switching to exponential form, we have

$$b^x = 1$$

This equation is satisfied, for any positive b, by $x = 0$. Therefore,

Log of 1	$\log_b 1 = 0$	**191**

The log of 1 is zero.

Log of the Base

We now take the $\log_b$ of its own base b; let us call this quantity x:

$$\log_b b = x$$

Going to exponential form gives us

$$b^x = b$$

So x must equal 1.

Log of the Base	$\log_b b = 1$	192

The log (to the base b) of b is equal to 1.

■ **Example 44:**

(a) $\log 1 = 0$ (b) $\ln 1 = 0$ (c) $\log_5 5 = 1$
(d) $\log 10 = 1$ (e) $\ln e = 1$ ■

Log of the Base Raised to a Power

Consider the expression $\log_b b^n$. *We set this expression equal to x, and, as before, go to exponential form:*

$$\log_b b^n = x$$
$$b^x = b^n$$
$$x = n$$

Therefore,

Log of the Base Raised to a Power	$\log_b b^n = n$	193

The log (to the base b) of b raised to a power is equal to the power.

■ **Example 45:**

(a) $\log_2 2^{4.83} = 4.83$
(b) $\log_e e^{2x} = 2x$
(c) $\log_{10} 0.0001 = \log_{10} 10^{-4} = -4$ ■

Base Raised to a Logarithm of the Same Base

We want to evaluate an expression of the form

$$b^{\log_b x}$$

Setting this expression equal to y and taking the logarithms of both sides gives us

$$y = b^{\log_b x}$$

$$\log_b y = \log_b b^{\log_b x} = \log_b x \log_b b$$

Since $\log_b b = 1$, we have $\log_b y = \log_b x$. Taking the antilog of both sides,

$$x = y = b^{\log_b x}$$

Thus,

Base Raised to a Logarithm of the Same Base	$b^{\log_b x} = x$	194

■ **Example 46:**

(a) $10^{\log w} = w$ (b) $e^{\log_e 3x} = 3x$ ■

Change of Base

We can convert between natural logarithms and common logarithms (or between logarithms to any base) by the following procedure. Suppose that $\log N$ is the common logarithm of some number N. We set it equal to x,

$$\log N = x$$

Going to exponential form, we obtain

$$10^x = N$$

Now we take the natural log of each side:

$$\ln 10x = \ln N$$

By Eq. 189,

$$x \ln 10 = \ln N$$

$$x = \frac{\ln N}{\ln 10}$$

But $x = \log N$, so

<table>
<tr><td rowspan="2">Change of Base</td><td colspan="2">$\log N = \dfrac{\ln N}{\ln 10}$</td><td rowspan="2">195</td></tr>
<tr><td>where</td><td>$\ln 10 \simeq 2.3026$</td></tr>
</table>

Some computer languages enable us to find the natural log but not the common log. This equation lets us convert from one to the other.

The common logarithm of a number is equal to the natural log of that number divided by the natural log of 10.

━ **Example 47:** Find $\log N$ if $\ln N = 5.824$.

Solution: By Eq. 195,

$$\log N = \frac{5.824}{2.3026} = 2.529$$ ━

━ **Example 48:** What is $\ln N$ if $\log N = 3.825$?

Solution: By Eq. 195,

$$\ln N = \ln 10 \, (\log N)$$
$$= 2.3026(3.825) = 8.807$$ ━

Exercise 4 Properties of Logarithms

Write as the sum or difference of two or more logarithms:

1. $\log \frac{2}{3}$ **2.** $\log 4x$

3. $\log ab$ **4.** $\log \dfrac{x}{2}$

5. $\log xyz$ **6.** $\log 2ax$

7. $\log \dfrac{3x}{4}$

8. $\log \dfrac{5}{xy}$

9. $\log \dfrac{1}{2x}$

10. $\log \dfrac{2x}{3y}$

11. $\log \dfrac{abc}{d}$

12. $\log \dfrac{x}{2ab}$

Express as a single logarithm with a coefficient of 1, assuming that the logarithms in each problem have the same base:

13. $\log 3 + \log 4$
14. $\log 7 - \log 5$
15. $\log 2 + \log 3 - \log 4$
16. $3 \log 2$
17. $4 \log 2 + 3 \log 3 - 2 \log 4$
18. $\log x + \log y + \log z$
19. $3 \log a - 2 \log b + 4 \log c$

20. $\dfrac{\log x}{3} + \dfrac{\log y}{2}$

21. $\log \dfrac{x}{a} + 2 \log \dfrac{y}{b} + 3 \log \dfrac{z}{c}$

22. $2 \log x + \log(a + b) - \frac{1}{2} \log(a + bx)$
23. $\frac{1}{2} \log (x + 2) + \log(x - 2)$

Rewrite each equation or expression so that it contains no logarithms:

24. $\log x + 3 \log y = 0$
25. $\log_2 x + 2 \log_2 y = x$
26. $2 \log (x - 1) = 5 \log(y + 2)$
27. $\log_2 (a^2 + b^2) + 1 = 2 \log_2 a$
28. $\log (x + y) - \log 2 = \log x + \log(x^2 - y^2)$
29. $\log (p^2 - q^2) - \log(p + q) = 2$
30. $\log_2 2$
31. $\log_e e$
32. $\log_{10} 10$
33. $\log_3 3^2$
34. $\log_e e^x$
35. $\log_{10} 10^x$
36. $e^{\log_e x}$
37. $2^{\log_2 3y}$
38. $10^{\log x^2}$

This may not seem very exciting in the age of calculators and computers, but the use of logarithms revolutionized computation in its time. The French mathematician Laplace wrote: "The method of logarithms, by reducing to a few days the labor of many months, doubles, as it were, the life of the astronomer, besides freeing him from the errors and disgust inseparable from long calculation."

Logarithmic Computation

Evaluate, using logarithms:

39. 5.937×92.47
40. 6923×0.003846
41. $3.97 \times 8.25 \times 9.82$
42. $88.25 \div 42.94$
43. $\sqrt[9]{8563}$
44. $4.836^{3.970}$
45. $83.62^{0.5720}$
46. $\sqrt[3]{587}$
47. $\sqrt[7]{8364}$
48. $\sqrt[4]{62.4}$

Change of Base

Find the common logarithm of the number whose natural logarithm is:

49. 8.36
50. -3.846
51. 3.775
52. 15.36
53. 5.26
54. -0.638

Find the natural logarithm of the number whose common logarithm is:

55. 84.9
56. 2.476
57. -3.82
58. 73.9
59. 2.37
60. -2.63

Graphics Calculator

61. Use a graphing utility to separately graph each side of the equation

$$\log 2x = \log 2 + \log x$$

from $x = 0$ to 10. Then graph both sides of

$$\log (2 + x) = \log 2 + \log x$$

and

$$(\log 2)(\log x) = \log 2 + \log x$$

What do your graphs tell you about these three expressions?

Computer

62. A computer algebra system can simplify or manipulate logarithmic expressions. Enter the logarithms as was shown in Exercise 3 and use the SIMPLIFY and EXPAND commands to change the form of the expression. Use your CAS to try to simplify any of the expressions in this exercise. You may find some expressions that the computer cannot simplify.

20•5

Exponential Equations

Solving Exponential Equations

We return now to the problem we started in Section 20•3 but could not finish, that of finding the *exponent* when the other quantities in an exponential equation were known. We tried to solve the equation

$$24.0 = 2.48^x$$

The key to solving exponential equations is to *take the logarithms of both sides*. This enables us to use Eq. 189 to extract the unknown from the exponent. Taking the logarithm of both sides gives

$$\log 24.0 = \log 2.48^x$$

By Eq. 189,

$$\log 24.0 = x \log 2.48$$

$$x = \frac{\log 24.0}{\log 2.48} = \frac{1.380}{0.3945} = 3.50$$

In this example we took *common* logarithms, but *natural* logarithms would have worked just as well.

■ **Example 49:** Solve for x to three significant digits:

$$3.25^{x+2} = 1.44^{3x-1}$$

Solution: We take the log of both sides. This time choosing to use natural logs, we get

$$(x + 2) \ln 3.25 = (3x - 1) \ln 1.44$$

$$\frac{\ln 3.25}{\ln 1.44} (x + 2) = 3x - 1$$

By calculator,

$$3.232(x + 2) = 3x - 1$$

Removing parentheses and collecting terms yields

$$0.232x = -7.464$$

$$x = -32.2$$

Solving Exponential Equations with Base e

If the exponential equation contains the base e, taking *natural* logarithms rather than common logarithms will simplify the work.

Example 50: Solve for x:

$$157 = 112e^{3x+2}$$

Solution: Dividing each side by 112 gives

$$1.402 = e^{3x+2}$$

Taking natural logs gives us

$$\ln 1.402 = \ln e^{3x+2}$$

By Eq. 189,

$$\ln 1.402 = (3x + 2) \ln e$$

But $\ln e = 1$, so

$$\ln 1.402 = 3x + 2$$

$$x = \frac{\ln 1.402 - 2}{3} = -0.554$$

Example 51: Solve for x to three significant digits:

$$3e^x + 2e^{-x} = 4(e^x - e^{-x})$$

Solution: Removing parentheses gives

$$3e^x + 2e^{-x} = 4e^x - 4e^{-x}$$

Combining like terms yields

$$e^x - 6e^{-x} = 0$$

Factoring gives

$$e^{-x}(e^{2x} - 6) = 0$$

This equation will be satisfied if either of the two factors is equal to zero, so we set each factor equal to zero (just as when solving a quadratic by factoring) and get

$$e^{-x} = 0 \quad \text{and} \quad e^{2x} = 6$$

There is no value of x that will make e^{-x} equal to zero, so we get no root from that equation. We solve the other equation by taking the natural logarithm of each side,

$$2x \ln e = \ln 6 = 1.792$$

$$x = 0.896$$

If our exponential equation is of *quadratic type*, it can be solved by substitution, which we did in Chapter 14.

■ **Example 52:** Solve for x to three significant digits:

$$3e^{2x} - 2e^x - 5 = 0$$

Solution: If we substitute

$$w = e^x$$

our equation becomes the quadratic

$$3w^2 - 2w - 5 = 0$$

By the quadratic formula,

$$w = \frac{2 \pm \sqrt{4 - 4(3)(-5)}}{6} = -1 \quad \text{and} \quad \frac{5}{3}$$

Substituting back, we have

$$e^x = -1 \quad \text{and} \quad e^x = \frac{5}{3}$$

So, $x = \ln(-1)$, which we discard, and

$$x = \ln \frac{5}{3} = 0.511$$

■

Solving Exponential Equations with Base 10

If the equation contains 10 as a base, the work will be simplified by taking *common* logarithms.

■ **Example 53:** Solve $10^{5x} = 2(10^{2x})$, to three significant digits.

Solution: Taking common logarithms of both sides gives us

$$\log 10^{5x} = \log[2(10^{2x})]$$

By Eqs. 187 and 189,

$$5x \log 10 = \log 2 + 2x \log 10$$

By Eq. 192, $\log 10 = 1$, so

$$5x = \log 2 + 2x$$

$$3x = \log 2$$

$$x = \frac{\log 2}{3} = 0.100$$

■

Doubling Time

Being able to solve an exponential equation for the exponent allows us to return to the formulas for exponential growth and decay (Section 20•2) and derive two interesting quantities: doubling time and half-life.

If a quantity grows exponentially according to the function

Exponential Growth	$y = ae^{nt}$	**199**

it will eventually double (y would be twice a). Setting $y = 2a$, we get

$$2a = ae^{nt}$$

or $2 = e^{nt}$. Taking natural logs, we have

$$\ln 2 = \ln e^{nt} = nt \ \ln e = nt$$

or

Doubling Time	$t = \dfrac{\ln 2}{n}$	**200**

■ **Example 54:** In how many years will a quantity double if it grows at the rate of 5.0% per year?

Solution:

$$\begin{aligned}
\text{Doubling time} &= \frac{\ln 2}{0.050} \\
&= \frac{0.693}{0.050} \\
&= 14 \text{ years}
\end{aligned}$$

■

Half-Life

When a material decays exponentially according to the function

Exponential Decay	$y = ae^{-nt}$	**201**

the time it takes for the material to be half gone is called the *half-life*. If we let $y = a/2$,

$$\frac{a}{2} = ae^{-nt}$$

$$\frac{1}{2} = e^{-nt} = \frac{1}{e^{nt}}$$

$$2 = e^{nt}$$

Taking natural logarithms gives us

$$\ln 2 = \ln e^{nt} = nt$$

Notice that the equation for half-life is the same as for doubling time. The rule of thumb is, of course, also the same. The rule of thumb gives us another valuable tool for *estimation*.

Half-Life	$t = \dfrac{\ln 2}{n}$	**200**

■ **Example 55:** Find the half-life of a radioactive material that decays exponentially at the rate of 2.0% per year.

Solution:

$$\text{Half-life} = \frac{\ln 2}{0.020} = 35 \text{ years}$$

■

Change of Base

If we have an exponential expression, such as 5^x, we can convert it to another exponential expression with base e, or any other base.

■ **Example 56:** Convert 5^x into an exponential expression with base e.

Solution: We write 5 as e raised to some power, say n.

$$5 = e^n$$

Taking the natural logarithm, we obtain

$$\ln 5 = \ln e^n = n$$

So $n = \ln 5 \simeq 1.61$, and $5 = e^{1.61}$. Then

$$5^x = (e^{1.61})^x = e^{1.61x} \qquad \blacksquare$$

■ **Example 57:** Convert 2^{4x} to an exponential expression with base e.

Solution: We first express 2 as e raised to some power.

$$2 = e^n$$

$$\ln 2 = \ln e^n = n$$

$$n = \ln 2 = 0.693$$

Then

$$2^{4x} = (e^{0.693})^{4x} = e^{2.773x} \qquad \blacksquare$$

■ **Example 58:** A bacteria sample contains 2850 bacteria and grows at a rate of 5.85% per hour. Assuming that the bacteria grow exponentially,
(a) write the equation for the number N of bacteria as a function of time, and
(b) find the time for the sample to grow to 10 000 bacteria.

Estimate: Note that the doubling time here is $\ln 2 \div 0.06$ or about 12 hours. To grow from 2850 to 10 000 will require nearly two doublings, or nearly 24 hours.

Solution:

(a) We substitute into the equation for exponential growth, $y = ae^{nt}$, with $y = N$, $a = 2850$, and $n = 0.0585$, getting

$$N = 2850\, e^{0.0585t}$$

(b) Setting $N = 10\ 000$ and solving for t,

$$10\ 000 = 2850\, e^{0.0585t}$$

$$e^{0.0585t} = 3.51$$

We take the natural log of both sides and set $\ln e = 1$,

$$0.0585t \ln e = \ln 3.51$$

$$t = \frac{\ln 3.51}{0.0585} = 21.5 \text{ h}$$

which agrees with our estimate. ■

Exercise 5 Exponential Equations

Solve for x to three significant digits:

1. $2^x = 7$

2. $(7.26)^x = 86.8$

3. $(1.15)^{x+2} = 12.5$

4. $(2.75)^x = (0.725)^{x^2}$

5. $(15.4)^{\sqrt{x}} = 72.8$

6. $e^{5x} = 125$

7. $5.62e^{3x} = 188$

8. $1.05e^{4x+1} = 5.96$

9. $e^{2x-1} = 3e^{x+3}$

10. $14.8e^{3x^2} = 144$

11. $5^{2x} = 7^{3x-2}$

12. $3^{x^2} = 175^{x-1}$

13. $10^{3x} = 3(10^x)$

14. $e^x + e^{-x} = 2(e^x - e^{-x})$

15. $2^{3x+1} = 3^{2x+1}$

16. $5^{2x} = 3^{3x+1}$

Hint: Problems 18 to 20 are *equations of quadratic type.*

17. $7e^{1.5x} = 2e^{2.4x}$

18. $e^{4x} - 2e^{2x} - 3 = 0$

19. $e^x + e^{-x} = 2$

20. $e^{6x} - e^{3x} - 2 = 0$

Convert to an exponential expression with base e:

21. $3(4^{3x})$

22. $4(2.2^{4x})$

Applications

23. The current i in a certain circuit is given by

$$i = 6.25e^{-125t} \quad \text{amperes}$$

where t is the time in seconds. At what time will the current be 1.00 A?

24. The cooling equation for an iron casting in still air is given as

$$T = 1080e^{-0.062t}$$

Find the time in seconds for the casting to cool from 1080°C to $26\overline{0}$°C.

25. A certain long pendulum, released from a height y_0 above its rest position, will be at a height

$$y = y_0 e^{-0.75t}$$

at t seconds. If the pendulum is released at a height of 150 mm, at what time will the height be $5\overline{0}$ mm?

26. A population growing at a rate of 2.0% per year from an initial population of $9\overline{0}00$ will grow in t years to an amount

$$P = 9000e^{0.02t}$$

How many years will it take for the population to triple?

27. The barometric pressure in mm of mercury at a height of h metres above sea level is

$$p = 760\, e^{-kh}$$

where $k = 1.3 \times 10^{-4}$. At what height will the pressure be 250 mm of mercury?

28. The approximate density of seawater in kg/m^3 at a depth of h km is

$$d = 100\overline{0}\, e^{.0042h}$$

Find the depth at which the density will be 1006 kg/m^3.

FIGURE 20·15

29. A rope passing over a rough cylindrical beam (Fig. 20·15) supports a mass. The force F_2 needed to hold the mass is given by $F_2 = F_1 e^{-\mu\theta}$, where μ is the coefficient of friction and θ is the angle of wrap of the rope around the cylindrical beam, in radians. If $\mu = 0.15$, what angle of wrap is needed for a force of 450 N to hold a mass of 62 kg ($a = 9.8$ kg·m/s²)

30. Using the formula for compound interest, Eq. A10, calculate the number of years it will take for a sum of money to triple when invested at a rate of 12% per year.

31. Using the formula for present worth, Exercise 1, Problem 7, in how many years will $50 000 accumulate to $70 000 at 15% interest?

32. Using the annuity formula, Exercise 1, Problem 10, find the number of years it will take a worker to accumulate $100 000 with an annual payment of $3000 if the interest rate is 8.0%.

33. Using the capital recovery formula from Exercise 1, Problem 12, calculate the number of years a person can withdraw $10 000/year from a retirement fund containing $60 000 if the rate of interest is $6\frac{3}{4}\%$.

34. Find the half-life of a material that decays exponentially at the rate of 3.50% per year.

35. How long will it take the Canadian annual oil consumption to double if it is increasing exponentially at a rate of 7.0% per year?

36. How long will it take the world population to double at an exponential growth rate of 1.64% per year?

37. What is the maximum annual growth in energy consumption permissible if the consumption is not to double in the next 20 years?

Computer

38. An iron ball with a mass of 1 kg is cut into two equal pieces. It is cut again, the second cut producing four equal pieces, the third cut making eight pieces, and so on. Write a program to compute the number of cuts needed to make each piece smaller than one atom (mass = 9.4×10^{-26} kg). Assume that no material is removed during cutting.

39. Assuming that the present annual world oil consumption is 17×10^9 barrels/year, that this rate of consumption is increasing at a rate of 5% per year, and that the total world oil reserves are 1700×10^9 barrels, compute and print the following table.

YEAR	ANNUAL CONSUMPTION	OIL REMAINING
0	17	1700
1	17.85	1682.15
.	.	.
.	.	.
.	.	.

Have the computation stop when the oil reserves are gone.

40. Use your program for finding roots of equations by simple iteration or the midpoint method to solve any of Problems 1 to 20.

41. Use a computer algebra system to solve any of the equations in Problems 1 to 20. Simply type in the equation and give the SOLVE command. Enter e^x by typing Exp(x) and b^x by typing $b \wedge x$. The computer may also give you some complex solutions, containing the imaginary number i, which we will not consider here.

Graphics Calculator

42. Use a graphics utility to get an approximate solution to any of the equations in this exercise. Recall that we first put the equation into the form $f(x) = 0$, then graph $y = f(x)$, and note where the curve crosses the x axis. We then use TRACE and ZOOM to find the roots to whatever accuracy we wish.

20·6 Logarithmic Equations

Often a logarithmic expression can be evaluated, or an equation containing logarithms can be solved, simply by rewriting it in exponential form.

■ **Example 59:** Evaluate $x = \log_5 25$.

Solution: Changing to exponential form, we have
$$5^x = 25 = 5^2$$
$$x = 2$$
Since $5^2 = 25$, the answer checks. ▬

■ **Example 60:** Solve for x:
$$\log_x 4 = \frac{1}{2}$$

Solution: Going to exponential form gives us
$$x^{1/2} = 4$$
Squaring both sides yields
$$x = 16$$
Since $16^{1/2} = 4$, the answer checks. ▬

■ **Example 61:** Solve for x:
$$\log_{25} x = -\frac{3}{2}$$

Solution: Writing the equation in exponential form, we obtain
$$25^{-3/2} = x$$
$$x = \frac{1}{25^{3/2}} = \frac{1}{5^3} = \frac{1}{125}$$
Since $25^{-3/2} = \dfrac{1}{125}$, the answer checks. ▬

■ **Example 62:** Evaluate $x = \log_{81} 27$.

Solution: Changing to exponential form yields
$$81^x = 27$$

But 81 and 27 are both powers of 3.

$$(3^4)^x = 3^3$$

$$3^{4x} = 3^3$$

$$4x = 3$$

$$x = 3/4$$

To check, we verify that $81^{3/4} = 3^3 = 27$.   ▬

If only one term in our equation contains a logarithm, we isolate that term on one side of the equation and then go to exponential form.

▬ **Example 63:** Solve for x to three significant digits:

$$3 \log(x^2 + 2) - 6 = 0$$

Solution: Rearranging and dividing by 3 gives

$$\log(x^2 + 2) = 2$$

Going to exponential form, we obtain

$$x^2 + 2 = 10^2 = 100$$

$$x^2 = 98$$

$$x = \pm 9.90$$ ▬

If every term contains "log," we use the properties of logarithms to combine those terms into a single logarithm on each side of the equation, and then take the antilog of each side.

▬ **Example 64:** Solve for x to three significant digits.

$$3 \log x - 2 \log 2x = 2 \log 5$$

Solution: Using the properties of logarithms gives

$$\log \frac{x^3}{(2x)^2} = \log 5^2$$

$$\log \frac{x}{4} = \log 25$$

Taking the antilog of each side, we have

$$\frac{x}{4} = 25$$

$$x = 100$$ ▬

If one or more terms do not contain a log, combine all the terms that do contain a log on one side of the equation. Then go to exponential form.

▬ **Example 65:** Solve for x:

$$\log(5x + 2) - 1 = \log(2x - 1)$$

Solution: Rearranging yields

$$\log(5x + 2) - \log(2x - 1) = 1$$

By Eq. 188,
$$\log \frac{5x + 2}{2x - 1} = 1$$

Expressing in exponential form gives

$$\frac{5x + 2}{2x - 1} = 10^1 = 10$$

Solving for x, we have

$$5x + 2 = 20x - 10$$
$$12 = 15x$$
$$x = \frac{4}{5}$$

■ **Example 66:** *The Richter Scale*: The Richter magnitude R, used to rate the intensity of an earthquake, is given by

$$R = \log \frac{a}{a_0}$$

where a and a_0 are the vertical amplitudes of the ground movement of the measured earthquake and of an earthquake taken as reference. If two earthquakes measure 4 and 5 on the Richter scale, by what factor is the amplitude of the stronger quake greater than that of the weaker?

Solution: Let us rewrite the equation for the Richter magnitude using the laws of logarithms:

$$R = \log a - \log a_0$$

Then, for the first earthquake,

$$4 = \log a_1 - \log a_0$$

and for the second,

$$5 = \log a_2 - \log a_0$$

Subtracting the first equation from the second gives

$$1 = \log a_2 - \log a_1 = (\log a_2/a_1)$$

Going to exponential form, we have

$$\frac{a_2}{a_1} = 10^1 = 10$$
$$a_2 = 10a_1$$

The second earthquake has ten times the amplitude of the first.

Check: Does this seem reasonable? From our study of logarithms, we know that as a number increases tenfold, its common logarithm increases only by 1. For example, $\log 45 = 1.65$ and $\log 450 = 2.65$. Since the Richter magnitude is proportional to the common log of the amplitude, it seems reasonable that a tenfold increase in amplitude increases the Richter magnitude by just one unit. ■

Exercise 6 Logarithmic Equations

Find the value of x in each expression.

1. $x = \log_3 9$ **2.** $x = \log_2 8$ **3.** $x = \log_8 2$
4. $x = \log_9 27$ **5.** $x = \log_{27} 9$ **6.** $x = \log_4 8$
7. $x = \log_8 4$ **8.** $x = \log_{27} 81$ **9.** $\log_x 8 = 3$
10. $\log_3 x = 4$ **11.** $\log_x 27 = 3$ **12.** $\log_x 16 = 4$
13. $\log_5 x = 2$ **14.** $\log_x 2 = \frac{1}{2}$ **15.** $\log_{36} x = \frac{1}{2}$
16. $\log_2 x = 3$ **17.** $x = \log_{25} 125$ **18.** $x = \log_5 125$

Solve for x to three significant digits. Check your answers.

19. $\log(2x + 5) = 2$ **20.** $2 \log(x + 1) = 3$
21. $\log(2x + x^2) = 2$ **22.** $\ln x - 2 \ln x = \ln 64$
23. $\ln 6 + \ln(x - 2) = \ln(3x - 2)$ **24.** $\ln(x + 2) - \ln 36 = \ln x$
25. $\ln(5x + 2) - \ln(x + 6) = \ln 4$ **26.** $\log x + \log 4x = 2$
27. $\ln x + \ln(x + 2) = 1$ **28.** $\log 8x^2 - \log 4x = 2.54$
29. $2 \log x - \log(1 - x) = 1$ **30.** $3 \log x - 1 = 3 \log(x - 1)$
31. $\log(x^2 - 4) - 1 = \log(x + 2)$ **32.** $2 \log x - 1 = \log(20 - 2x)$
33. $\log(x^2 - 1) - 2 = \log(x + 1)$ **34.** $\ln 2x - \ln 4 + \ln(x - 2) = 1$
35. $\log(4x - 3) + \log 5 = 6$

This equation is derived from the compound interest formula. The equations in the next two problems are obtained from the equations for an annuity and for capital recovery from Exercise 1. Can you see how they were derived?

Applications

36. An amount of money a invested at a compound interest rate of n per year will take t years to accumulate to an amount y, where

$$t = \frac{\log y - \log a}{\log(1 + n)} \text{ years}$$

How many years will it take for an investment to triple in value when deposited at 8.00% per year?

37. If an amount R is deposited once every year at a compound interest rate n, the number of years it will take to accumulate to an amount y is

$$t = \frac{\log\left[\dfrac{ny}{R} + 1\right]}{\log(1 + n)} \text{ years}$$

How many years will it take an annual payment of $1500 to accumulate to $13 800 at 9.0% per year?

38. If an amount a is invested at a compound interest rate n, it will be possible to withdraw a sum R at the end of every year for t years until the deposit is exhausted. The number of years is given by

$$t = \frac{\log\left[\dfrac{an}{R - an} + 1\right]}{\log(1 + n)} \text{ years}$$

If $200 000 is invested at 12% interest, for how many years can an annual withdrawal of $30 000 be made before the money is used up?

39. The *magnitude M* of a star of intensity I is

$$M = 2.5 \log \frac{I_1}{I} + 1$$

where I_1 is the intensity of a first-magnitude star. What is the magnitude of a star whose intensity is one-tenth that of a first-magnitude star?

40. The difference in elevation h (m) between two locations having barometer readings of B_1 and B_2 mm of mercury is given by the logarithmic equation $h = 15360 \log (B_2/B_1)$, where B_1 is the pressure at the *upper* station. Find the difference in elevation between two stations having barometer readings of 740.16 mm Hg at the lower station and 665.98 mm at the upper.

41. What will be the barometer reading 248 m above a station having a reading of 716.78 mm Hg?

Use the following information for Problems 42 to 45. If the power input to a network or device is P_1 and the power output is P_2, the number of decibels gained or lost in the device is given by the logarithmic equation

Decibels Gained or Lost	$G = 10 \log_{10} \dfrac{P_2}{P_1}$ dB	**A104**

42. A certain amplifier gives a power output of 1000 W for an input of 50 W. Find the dB gain.

43. A transmission line has a loss of 3.25 dB. Find the power transmitted for an input of 2750 kW.

44. What power input is needed to product a 250-W output with an amplifier having a 50 dB gain?

45. The output of a certain device is half the input. This is a loss of how many decibels?

FIGURE 20·16 An insulated pipe

46. The rate of heat loss $\dot{Q}$ per metre of cylindrical pipe insulation (Fig. 20·16) having an inside radius r_1 and outside radius r_2 is given by the logarithmic equation

$$\dot{Q} = \frac{2\pi k(t_1 - t_2)}{\ln (r_2/r_1)} \text{ joules/h}$$

where t_1 and t_2 are the inside and outside temperatures (°C) and k is the conductivity of the insulation. Find $\dot{Q}$ for a $10\overline{0}$-mm-thick insulation having a coefficient of thermal conductivity, k, of 0.036 W/m°K wrapped around a 228-mm-diameter pipe at 305°C if the surroundings are at 32.0°C.

47. If a resource is being used up at a rate that increases exponentially, the time it takes to exhaust the resource (called the exponential expiration time, EET) is

$$\text{EET} = \frac{1}{n} \ln \left(\frac{nR}{r} + 1 \right)$$

where n is the rate of increase in consumption, R the total amount of the resource, and r the initial rate of consumption. If we assume that the United States has oil reserves of 207×10^9 barrels and that their present rate of consumption is 6.00×10^9 barrels/year, how long will it take to exhaust these reserves if their consumption increases by 7.00% per year?

Use the following information for Problems 48 to 50. The pH value of a solution having a concentration C of hydrogen ions is

pH	$\text{pH} = -\log_{10} C$	**A49**

48. Find the concentration of hydrogen ions in a solution having a pH of 4.65.

49. A pH of 7 is considered *neutral*, while a lower pH is *acid* and a higher pH is *alkaline*. What is the hydrogen ion concentration at a pH of 7.0?

50. The acid rain during a certain storm had a pH of 3.5. Find the hydrogen ion concentration. How does it compare with that for a pH of 7.0? Show that **(a)** when the pH doubles, the hydrogen ion concentration is *squared*, and **(b)** when the pH increases by a factor of *n*, the hydrogen ion concentration is raised *to the nth power*.

51. Two earthquakes have Richter magnitudes of 4.6 and 6.2. By what factor is the amplitude of the stronger quake greater than that of the weaker? See Example 66 (page 604).

Computer

52. Use your program for solving equations by simple iteration or by the midpoint method to solve any of the Problems 19 to 35.

53. Use a computer algebra system to solve any of the equations in Problems 19 to 35. Simply type in the equation and give the SOLVE command.

Graphics Calculator

54. Use a graphics utility to get an approximate solution to any of the equations in this exercise. Recall that we first put the equation into the form $f(x) = 0$, then graph $y = f(x)$, and note where the curve crosses the *x* axis. We then use TRACE and ZOOM to find the roots to whatever accuracy we wish.

20•7

Graphs on Logarithmic and Semilogarithmic Paper

Logarithmic and Semilogarithmic Paper

Our graphing so far has all been done on ordinary graph paper, on which the lines are equally spaced. For some purposes, though, it is better to use *logarithmic* paper (Fig. 20•17), also called *log-log* paper, or *semilogarithmic* paper (Fig. 20•18), also called *semilog* paper. Looking at the logarithmic scales of these graphs, we note the following:

1. The lines are not equally spaced. The distance in millimetres from, say, 1 to 2, is equal to the distance from 2 to 4, which, in turn, is equal to the distance from 4 to 8.
2. Each tenfold increase in the scale, say from 1 to 10 or from 10 to 100, is called a *cycle*. Each cycle requires the same distance in millimetres along the scale.
3. The log scales do not include zero.

Looking at Figure 20•18, notice that, although the numbers on the vertical scale are in equal increments (1, 2, 3, . . . , 10), the spacing on that scale is proportional to the logarithms of those numbers. So the numeral 2 is placed at a position corresponding to log 2 (which is 0.3010, or about one third of the distance along the vertical), 4 is placed at log 4 (about 0.6 of the way), and 10 is at log 10 (which equals 1, at the top of the scale).

FIGURE 20·17 Logarithmic graph paper

FIGURE 20·18 Semilogarithmic graph paper

FIGURE 20·19 The power function and the exponential function, graphed on ordinary graph paper and log-log or semilog graph paper

When to Use Logarithmic or Semilog Paper

We use this special graph paper in the following situations:

1. When the range of the variables is too large for ordinary graph paper
2. When we want to graph a power function or an exponential function (Each of these will plot as a straight line on the appropriate graph paper, as shown in Figure 20·19.)
3. When we want to find an equation that will approximately represent a set of empirical data

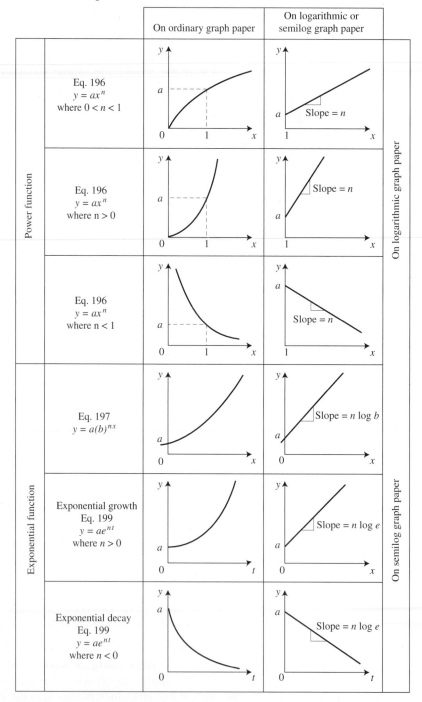

Graphing the Power Function

A *power function* is one whose equation is of the form

Power Function	$y = ax^n$	196

Recall that we studied the power function in Section 19·3.

where a and n are nonzero constants. This equation is nonlinear (except where $n = 1$), and the shape of its graph depends upon whether n is positive or negative, and whether n is greater than or less than 1. Figure 20·19 shows the shapes that this curve can have for various ranges of n. If we take the logarithm of each side of Eq. 196, we get

$$\log y = \log(ax^n)$$

$$= \log a + n \log x$$

If we now make the substitution $X = \log x$ and $Y = \log y$, our equation becomes

$$Y = nX + \log a$$

This equation *is* linear, and, on regular graph paper, graphs as a straight line with a slope of n and a y intercept of $\log a$ (Fig. 20·20). However, we do not have to make the substitutions shown above *if we use logarithmic paper*, where the scales are proportional to the logarithms of the variables x and y. We simply have to plot the original equation on log-log paper, and it will be a straight line with slope n, and which has a value of $y = a$ when $x = 1$ (see Fig. 20·19). This will be illustrated in the following example.

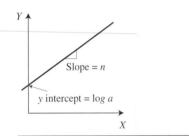

FIGURE 20·20 Graph of $y = ax^n$ on rectangular graph paper, where $X = \log x$ and $Y = \log y$

■ **Example 67:** Plot the equation $q = 2.5x^{1.4}$ for values of x from 1 to 10. Choose graph paper so that the equation plots as a straight line.

Solution: We make a table of point pairs. Since the graph will be a straight line we need only two points, with a third as a check. Here, we will plot four points to show that all points do lie on a straight line. We choose values of x and for each compute the value of y.

x	0	1	4	7	10
y	0	2.5	17.4	38.1	62.8

We choose log-log rather than semilog paper, because we are graphing a power function, which plots as a straight line on this paper (see Fig. 20·19).

We choose the number of cycles for each scale by looking at the range of values for x and y. Note that the logarithmic scales do not contain zero, so we cannot plot the point $(0, 0)$. Thus, on the x axis we need one cycle. On the y axis, we must go from 2.5 to 62.8. With two cycles we can span a range of 1 to 100. Thus we need log-log paper, one cycle by two cycles.

We mark the scales and plot the points as shown in Figure 20·21, and get a straight line as expected. We note that the value of y at $x = 1$ is equal to 2.5, and is the same as the coefficient of $x^{1.4}$ in the given equation.

We can get the slope of the straight line by measuring the rise and run with a scale, and dividing rise by run. We can, of course, use the values from the graph, but since the spacing on the graph really tells the logarithmic value of the position of the pictured points, we must remember to take the

FIGURE 20·21 Graph of $y = 2.5x^{1.4}$

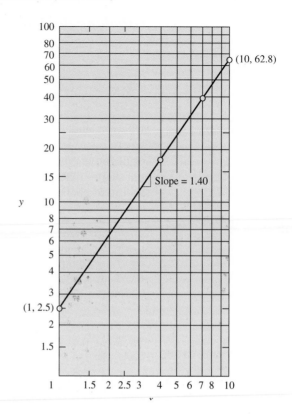

logarithm of those values. (Either common or natural will give the same result.) Thus

$$\text{slope} = \frac{\text{rise}}{\text{run}} = \frac{\ln 62.8 - \ln 2.5}{\ln 10 - \ln 1} = \frac{3.22}{2.30} = 1.40$$

The slope of the line is thus equal to the power of x, as expected from Figure 20·20. We will use these ideas later when we try to write an equation to fit a set of data. ▬

Common Error	Be sure to take the *logs* of the values on the x and y axes when computing the slope.

Graphing the Exponential Function

Consider the exponential function given by

Exponential Function	$y = a(b)^{nx}$	**197**

If we take the logarithms of both sides, we get

$$\log y = \log b^{nx} + \log a$$

$$\log y = (n \log b)x + \log a$$

FIGURE 20•22 Graph of
$y = 100e^{-0.2x}$

When computing the slope on semilog paper, we take the logarithms of the values on the log scale, but not on the linear scale. Computing the slope using common logs, we get

$$\text{slope} = n \log e$$

$$= \frac{\log 13.5 - \log 100}{10}$$

$$= -0.0870$$

$$n = \frac{-0.0870}{\log e} = -0.2$$

as we got using natural logs.

The process of fitting an approximate equation to fit a set of data points is called *curve fitting*. In statistics it is referred to as *regression*. Here we will do only some very simple cases.

TABLE 20•1

v(V)	1	2	3	4	5
i(A)	5.61	15.4	27.7	42.1	58.1

If we replace log y with Y, we get the linear equation

$$Y = (n \log b)x + \log a$$

If we graph the given equation on semilog paper with the logarithmic scale along the y axis, we get a straight line with a slope of $n \log b$ which cuts the y axis at a (Fig. 20•19). Also shown are the special cases where the base b is equal to e (2.718 . . .). Here, the independent variable is shown as t, because exponential growth and decay are usually functions of time.

■ **Example 68:** Plot the exponential function

$$y = 100 \, e^{-0.2x}$$

for values of x from 0 to 10.

Solution: We make a table of point pairs:

x	0	2	4	6	8	10
y	100	67.0	44.9	30.1	20.2	13.5

We choose semilog paper for graphing the exponential function, and use the linear scale for x. The range of y is from 13.5 to 100; thus we need *one cycle* of the logarithmic scale. The graph is shown in Figure 20•22. Note that the line obtained has a y intercept of 100. Also, the slope is equal to $n \log e$, or, if we use natural logs, is equal to n:

$$\text{slope} = n = \frac{\ln 13.5 - \ln 100}{10} = -0.2$$

This is the coefficient of x in our given equation. ■

Empirical Functions

We choose logarithmic or semilog paper to plot a set of empirical data when:

1. The range of values is too large for ordinary graph paper
2. We suspect that the relation between our variables may be a power function or an exponential function, and we want to find that function

We show the second case by means of an example.

■ **Example 69:** A test of a certain electronic device shows it to have an output current i versus input voltage v as in Table 20•1. Plot the given empirical data and try to find an approximate formula for y in terms of x.

Solution: We first make a graph on linear graph paper (Fig. 20•23) and get a curve that is concave upward. Comparing its shape with the curves in Figure 20•19 (page 608), we suspect that the equation of the curve (if we can find one at all) may be either a power function or an exponential function.

Next, we make a plot on semilog paper (Fig. 20•24) and do *not* get a straight line, but a plot on log-log paper (Fig. 20•25) is linear. We thus assume that our equation has the form

$$i = av^n \quad \text{or} \quad \ln i = n \ln v + \ln a$$

FIGURE 20•23 Plot of Table 20•1 on linear graph paper

FIGURE 20•24 Plot of Table 20•1 on semilog paper

FIGURE 20•25 Plot of Table 20•1 on log-log paper

Here our data plotted as a nice straight line on logarithmic paper, but with real data we are often unable to draw a straight line that passes through every point. The *method of least squares*, not shown here, is often used to draw a line that is considered the "best fit" for a scattering of data points

In Example 67 (page 609) we showed how to compute the slope of the line to get the exponent n, and also saw that the coefficient a was the value of the function at $x = 1$. Now we show a different method for finding a and n in Example 69, which can be used even if we do not have the y value at $x = 1$. We choose two points on the curve, say (5, 58.1) and (2, 15.4), and substitute each into

$$\ln i = n \ln v + \ln a$$

getting

$$\ln 58.1 = n \ln 5 + \ln a$$

and

$$\ln 15.4 = n \ln 2 + \ln a$$

A simultaneous solution, now shown, for n and a yields

$$n = 1.45 \quad \text{and} \quad a = 5.64$$

Our equation is then

$$i = 5.64 v^{1.45}$$

Finally, we test this formula by computing values of i and comparing them with the original data.

v	1	2	3	4	5
Original i	5.61	15.4	27.7	42.1	58.1
Calculated i	5.64	15.4	27.7	42.1	58.2

We get values very close to the original.

> Here, again, we could have used common logarithms and obtained the same result.

> The fitting of a power function to a set of data is called *power regression* in statistics. You may be able to do this on your graphics calculator. See Exercise 7, Problem 27.

Exercise 7 Graphs on Logarithmic and Semilogarithmic Paper

Graphing the Power Function

Graph each power function on log-log paper, for $x = 1$ to 10.

1. $y = 2x^3$ **2.** $y = 3x^4$ **3.** $y = x^5$
4. $y = x^{3/2}$ **5.** $y = 5\sqrt{x}$ **6.** $y = 2\sqrt[3]{x}$
7. $y = 1/x$ **8.** $y = 3/x^2$ **9.** $y = 2x^{2/3}$

Graph each set of data on log-log paper, determine the coefficients graphically, and write an approximate equation to fit the given data.

10.

x	2	4	6	8	10
y	3.48	12.1	25.2	42.2	63.1

11.

x	2	4	6	8	10
y	240	31.3	9.26	3.91	2.00

Graphing the Exponential Function

Graph each exponential function on semilog paper.

12. $y = 3^x$
13. $y = 5^x$
14. $y = e^x$
15. $y = e^{-x}$
16. $y = 4^{x/2}$
17. $y = 3^{x/4}$
18. $y = 3e^{2x/3}$
19. $y = 5e^{-x}$
20. $y = e^{x/2}$

Graphing Empirical Functions

You may be able to do this on your graphics calculator. See Problem 27.

Graph each set of data on log-log or semilog paper, determine the coefficients graphically, and write an approximate equation to fit the given data.

21.

x	0	1	2	3	4	5
y	1.00	2.50	6.25	15.6	39.0	97.7

22.

x	1	2	3	4
y	48.5	29.4	17.6	10.8

23. Current in a tungsten lamp, i, for various voltages, v

v (V)	2	8	25	50	100	150	200
i (mA)	24.6	56.9	113	172	261	330	387

24. Difference in temperature, T, between a cooling body and its surroundings at various times, t.

t (s)	0	3.51	10.9	19.0	29.0	39.0	54.0	71.0
T (°C)	20.0	19.0	17.0	15.0	13.0	11.0	8.50	6.90

25. Pressure, p, of 1 kg of saturated steam at various volumes, v

v (m³)	0.75	0.55	0.41	0.32	0.23
p (kPa)	101	142	196	267	357

26. Maximum height y reached by a long pendulum t seconds after being set in motion

t (s)	0	1	2	3	4	5
y (mm)	254	126	62.7	30.9	15.5	7.62

Graphics Calculator

27. Some graphics calculators can fit a straight line, a power function, an exponential function, or a logarithmic function to a given set of data points, and give the two constants in the function. Such fitting goes by the statistics name of *regression*. The TI-81, for example, can do linear, logarithmic, exponential, and power regression. You must enter the data points, then choose the type of function you think will fit, and the calculator will give the two constants. It will also give the *correlation coefficient*, which is a measure of goodness of fit. If this coefficient is close to 1 or -1, the fit is good; if close to 0, the fit is bad.

Study your calculator manual to learn how to do regression. Then use it for any of Problems 21 to 26 in this exercise.

CHAPTER 20 REVIEW PROBLEMS

Convert to logarithmic form.

1. $x^{5.2} = 352$
2. $4.8^x = 58$
3. $24^{1.4} = x$

Convert to exponential form.

4. $\log_3 56 = x$
5. $\log_x 5.2 = 124$
6. $\log_2 x = 48.2$

Solve for x.

7. $\log_{81} 27 = x$
8. $\log_3 x = 4$
9. $\log_x 32 = -\frac{5}{7}$

Write as the sum or difference of two or more logarithms.

10. $\log xy$

11. $\log \dfrac{3x}{z}$

12. $\log \dfrac{ab}{cd}$

Express as a single logarithm.

13. $\log 5 + \log 2$
14. $2 \log x - 3 \log y$
15. $\frac{1}{2} \log p - \frac{1}{4} \log q$

Find the common logarithm of each number to four decimal places.

16. 6.83
17. 364
18. 0.00638

Find x if log x is equal to:

19. 2.846
20. 1.884
21. -0.473

Evaluate, using logarithms.

22. 5.836×88.24

23. $\dfrac{8375}{2846}$

24. $(4.823)^{1.5}$

Find the natural logarithm of each number to four decimal places.

25. 84.72
26. 2846
27. 0.00873

Find the number whose natural logarithm is:

28. 5.273
29. 1.473
30. -4.837

Find log x if:

31. $\ln x = 4.837$
32. $\ln x = 8.352$

Find ln x if:

33. $\log x = 5.837$
34. $\log x = 7.264$

Solve for x, to three significant digits.

35. $(4.88)^x = 152$
36. $e^{2x+1} = 72.4$
37. $3 \log x - 3 = 2 \log x^2$
38. $\log (3x - 6) = 3$
39. A sum of $1500 is deposited at a compound interest rate of $6\frac{1}{2}\%$ compounded quarterly. How much will it accumulate to in five years?
40. A quantity grows exponentially at a rate of 2.00% per day for 10.0 weeks. Find the final amount if the initial amount is $50\overline{0}$ units.
41. A flywheel decreases in speed exponentially at the rate of 5.00% per minute. Find the speed after 20.0 m if the initial speed is 2250 rev/m.
42. Find the half-life of a radioactive substance that decays exponentially at the rate of 3.50% per year.
43. Find the doubling time for a population growing at the rate of 3.0% per year.
44. Graph the power function $y = 3x^{2/3}$ on log-log paper, for $x = 1$ to 6.
45. Graph the exponential function $y = e^{x/3}$ on semi-log paper, for $x = 0$ to 6.
46. Current and time readings from a circuit produced the results shown in the following table:

Current I (milliamps)	132	47.8	17.6	6.50	2.40	0.80
Time (s)	0	2	4	6	8	10

Plot the data and determine the law of this relationship.

Writing

47. In this chapter we have introduced two more kinds of equations, the exponential equation and the logarithmic equation. Earlier we have had five other types. List the seven types, give an example of each, and write one sentence for each telling how it differs from the others.

Team Project

48. The temperatures of a kettle of water, measured every minute during cooling from 100.0°C at $t = 0$ to a room temperature of 21.10°C, are as follows:

100.0	96.94	92.44	85.33
77.32	68.50	58.00	99.67
43.34	38.11	32.28	30.17
26.17	23.67	22.83	22.50
22.11	21.10	21.61	21.17

Write an equation for the kettle temperature as a function of time, with all constants evaluated.

21

Complex Numbers

O B J E C T I V E S

When you have completed this chapter, you should be able to:

- Simplify radicals having negative radicands.
- Write complex numbers in rectangular, polar, trigonometric, and exponential forms.
- Evaluate powers of j.
- Find the sums, differences, products, quotients, powers, and roots of complex numbers.
- Solve quadratic equations having complex roots.
- Factor polynomials that have complex factors.
- Add, subtract, multiply, and divide vectors using complex numbers.
- Solve alternating current problems using complex numbers.

So far we have dealt entirely with real numbers. Recall that these are all the numbers that correspond to points on the number line, that is, the rational and irrational numbers. These include integers, fractions, roots, and the negatives of these numbers. In this chapter we consider imaginary and complex numbers. We learn what they are, how to express them in several different forms, and how to perform the basic operations with them.

Why bother with a new type of number when, as we have seen, the real numbers can do so much? The complex number system is a natural extension of the real number system. We use complex numbers mainly to manipulate *vectors*, which are so important in many branches of technology. Complex numbers (despite their unfortunate name) really simplify computations with vectors.

21•1   Complex Numbers in Rectangular Form

The Imaginary Unit

Recall that, in the real number system, the equation

$$x^2 = -1$$

had no solution. This was because there was no real number such that its square was -1. Now we extend our number system to allow the quantity

The letter *i* is often used for the imaginary unit. In technical work, however, we save *i* for electric current. Further, *j* (or *i*) is sometimes written before the *b*, and sometimes after. So the number *j*5 may also be written 5*i*, 5*j*, or *i*5.

$\sqrt{-1}$ to have a meaning. We define the *imaginary unit* as the square root of -1, and represent it by the symbol *j*.

$$\text{Imaginary unit } j = \sqrt{-1}$$

Complex Numbers

A *complex number* is any number, real or imaginary, that can be written in the form

$$a + jb$$

where *a* and *b* are real numbers, and $j = \sqrt{-1}$ is the *imaginary unit*.

■ **Example 1:** The numbers

$$4 + j2 \qquad -7 + j8 \qquad 5.92 - j2.93 \qquad 83 \qquad j27$$

are complex numbers. ▬

Real and Imaginary Numbers

When $b = 0$ in a complex number $a + jb$, we have a *real number*. When $a = 0$, the number is called a *pure imaginary number*.

■ **Example 2:**
(a) The complex number 48 is also a real number.
(b) The complex number *j*9 is a pure imaginary number. ▬

The two parts of a complex number are called the *real part* and the *imaginary part*.

This is called the *rectangular form* of a complex number.

Complex Number	$a + jb$ real part ⬏ ⬏ imaginary part	**218**

Addition and Subtraction of Complex Numbers

To combine complex numbers, separately combine the real parts, and then the imaginary parts, and express the result in the form $a + jb$.

Addition of Complex Numbers	$(a + jb) + (c + jd) = (a + c) + j(b + d)$	**219**
Subtraction of Complex Numbers	$(a + jb) - (c + jd) = (a - c) + j(b - d)$	**220**

■ **Example 3:** Add or subtract, as indicated.
(a) $j3 + j5 = j8$
(b) $j2 + (6 - j5) = 6 - j3$
(c) $(2 - j5) + (-4 + j3) = (2 - 4) + j(-5 + 3) = -2 - j2$
(d) $(-6 + j2) - (4 - j) = (-6 - 4) + j[2 - (-1)] = -10 + j3$ ▬

Powers of j

We often have to evaluate powers of the imaginary unit, especially the square of j. Since

$$j = \sqrt{-1}$$
$$j^2 = \sqrt{-1}\sqrt{-1} = -1$$

Higher powers are easily found.

$$j^3 = j^2 j \ \ = (-1)j = -j$$
$$j^4 = (j^2)^2 = (-1)^2 = 1$$
$$j^5 = j^4 j \ \ = (1)j \ \ = j$$
$$j^6 = j^4 j^2 = (1)j^2 \ = -1$$

We see that the values are starting to repeat: $j^5 = j$, $j^6 = j^2$, and so on. The first four values keep repeating.

Note that when the exponent n is a multiple of 4, then $j^n = 1$.

Powers of j	$j = \sqrt{-1}, \quad j^2 = -1, \quad j^3 = -j,$ $j^4 = 1, \qquad j^5 = j, \qquad$ etc.	**217**

■ **Example 4:** Evaluate j^{17}.

Solution: Using the laws of exponents, we express j^{17} in terms of one of the first four powers of j.

$$j^{17} = j^{16}j = (j^4)^4 j = (1)^4 j = j \qquad ■$$

Multiplication of Imaginary Numbers

Multiply as with ordinary numbers, but use Eq. 217 to simplify any powers of j.

■ **Example 5:**
(a) $5 \times j3 = j15$
(b) $j2 \times j4 = j^2 8 = (-1)8 = -8$
(c) $3 \times j4 \times j5 \times j = j^3 60 = (-j)60 = -j60$
(d) $(j3)^2 = j^2 3^2 = (-1)9 = -9$ ■

Multiplication of Complex Numbers

Multiply complex numbers as you would any algebraic expressions, replace j^2 by -1, and put the expression into the form $a + jb$.

Multiplication of Complex Numbers	$(a + jb)(c + jd) = (ac - bd) + j(ad + bc)$	**221**

■ **Example 6:**

(a) $3(5 + j2) = 15 + j6$

(b) $(j3)(2 - j4) = j6 - j^2 12 = j6 - (-1)12 = 12 + j6$

(c) $(3 - j2)(-4 + j5) = 3(-4) + 3(j5) + (-j2)(-4) + (-j2)(j5)$
$$= -12 + j15 + j8 - j^2 10$$
$$= -12 + j15 + j8 - (-1)10$$
$$= -2 + j23$$

(d) $(3 - j5)^2 = (3 - j5)(3 - j5)$
$$= 9 - j15 - j15 + j^2 25 = 9 - j30 - 25$$
$$= -16 - j30$$ ■

To multiply radicals that contain negative quantities in the radicand, first express all quantities in terms of j. Then proceed to multiply. Always be sure to convert radicals to imaginary numbers *before* performing other operations, or contradictions may result.

We will see in the next section that multiplication and division are easier in *polar* form.

■ **Example 7:** Multiply $\sqrt{-4}$ by $\sqrt{-4}$.

Solution: We can write $\sqrt{-4}$ as $\sqrt{-1}\sqrt{4}$

Converting to imaginary numbers, we obtain
$$\sqrt{-4}\sqrt{-4} = (j2)(j2) = j^2 4$$

Since $j^2 = -1$,
$$j^2 4 = -4$$ ■

Common Error	It is *incorrect* to write $$\sqrt{-4}\sqrt{-4} = \sqrt{(-4)(-4)} = \sqrt{16} = +4$$ Our previous rule of $\sqrt{a} \cdot \sqrt{b} = \sqrt{ab}$ applied only to positive values of a and b.

The Conjugate of a Complex Number

A computer algebra system can find the conjugate of a complex number. See Exercise 1, Problem 68.

The *conjugate* of a complex number is obtained by changing the sign of its imaginary part.

■ **Example 8:**

(a) The conjugate of $2 + j3$ is $2 - j3$.

(b) The conjugate of $-5 - j4$ is $-5 + j4$.

(c) The conjugate of $a + jb$ is $a - jb$. ■

Multiplying any complex number by its conjugate will eliminate the j term.

This has the same form as the difference of two squares.

■ **Example 9:**
$$(2 + j3)(2 - j3) = 4 - j6 + j6 - j^2 9 = 4 - (-1)(9) = 13$$ ■

Division of Complex Numbers

Division involving single terms, real or imaginary, is shown by examples.

Example 10:
(a) $j8 \div 2 = j4$
(b) $j6 \div j3 = 2$
(c) $(4 - j6) \div 2 = 2 - j3$ ■

Example 11: Divide 6 by $j3$.

Solution:

$$\frac{6}{j3} = \frac{6}{j3} \times \frac{j3}{j3} = \frac{j18}{j^2 9} = \frac{j18}{-9} = -j2$$ ■

To divide by a complex number, multiply dividend and divisor by the conjugate of the divisor. This will make the divisor a real number, as in the following example.

Example 12: Divide $3 - j4$ by $2 + j$.

This is very similar to *rationalizing the denominator* of a fraction containing radicals (Sec. 13·2).

Solution: We multiply numerator and denominator by the conjugate $(2 - j)$ of the denominator.

$$\frac{3-j4}{2+j} = \frac{3 - j4}{2 + j} \cdot \frac{2 - j}{2 - j}$$

$$= \frac{6 - j3 - j8 + j^2 4}{4 + j2 - j2 - j^2}$$

$$= \frac{2 - j11}{5}$$

$$= \frac{2}{5} - j\frac{11}{5}$$ ■

In general,

Division of Complex Numbers	$\dfrac{a + jb}{c + jd} = \dfrac{ac + bd}{c^2 + d^2} + j\dfrac{bc - ad}{c^2 + d^2}$	**222**

Quadratics with Complex Roots

A computer algebra system will give complex roots of a quadratic equation. See Exercise 1, Problem 69 (page 624).

When we solved quadratic equations in Chapter 14, the roots were real numbers. Some quadratics, however, will yield complex roots, as in the following example.

Example 13: Solve for x to three significant digits,

$$2x^2 - 5x + 9 = 0$$

Solution: By the quadratic formula (Eq. 100),

$$x = \frac{5 \pm \sqrt{25 - 4(2)(9)}}{4} = \frac{5 \pm \sqrt{-47}}{4}$$

$$= \frac{5 \pm j6.86}{4} = 1.25 \pm j1.72$$

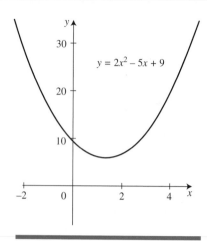

FIGURE 21·1

A computer algebra system can find complex factors. See Exercise 1, Problem 70 (page 624).

A graph of the function $y = 2x^2 - 5x + 9$ (Fig. 21·1) shows that the curve does not cross the x axis and hence has no real zeros. ▬

Complex Factors

It is sometimes necessary to factor an expression into *complex factors*, as shown in the following example.

▬ **Example 14:** Factor the expression $a^2 + 4$ into complex factors.

Solution:

$$a^2 + 4 = a^2 - j^2 4 = a^2 - (j2)^2$$
$$= (a - j2)(a + j2)$$ ▬

Exercise 1 Complex Numbers in Rectangular Form

Write as imaginary numbers:

1. $\sqrt{-9}$ **2.** $\sqrt{-81}$

3. $\sqrt{-\dfrac{4}{16}}$ **4.** $\sqrt{-\dfrac{1}{5}}$

Write as a complex number in rectangular form:

5. $4 + \sqrt{-4}$ **6.** $\sqrt{-25} + 3$

7. $\sqrt{-\dfrac{9}{4}} - 5$ **8.** $\sqrt{-\dfrac{1}{3}} + 2$

Combine and simplify:

9. $\sqrt{-9} + \sqrt{-4}$ **10.** $\sqrt{-4a^2} - a\sqrt{-25}$

11. $(3 - j2) + (-4 + j3)$ **12.** $(-1 - j2) - (j + 6)$

13. $(a - j3) + (a + j5)$ **14.** $(p + jq) + (q + jp)$

15. $\left(\dfrac{1}{2} + \dfrac{j}{3}\right) + \left(\dfrac{1}{4} - \dfrac{j}{6}\right)$ **16.** $(-84 + j91) - (28 + j72)$

17. $(2.28 - j1.46) + (1.75 + j2.66)$

Evaluate each power of j:

18. j^{11} **19.** j^5 **20.** j^{10}

21. j^{21} **22.** j^{14}

Multiply and simplify:

23. $7 \times j2$ **24.** $9 \times j3$

25. $j3 \times j5$ **26.** $j \times j4$

27. $4 \times j2 \times j3 \times j4$ **28.** $j \times 5 \times j4 \times j3 \times 5$

29. $(j5)^2$ **30.** $(j3)^2$

31. $2(3 - j4)$ **32.** $-3(7 + j5)$

33. $j4(5 - j2)$ **34.** $j5(2 + j3)$

35. $(3 - j5)(2 + j6)$
37. $(6 + j3)(3 - j8)$
39. $(5 - j2)^2$

36. $(5 + j4)(4 + j2)$
38. $(5 - j3)(8 + j2)$
40. $(3 + j6)^2$

Write the conjugate of each complex number:

41. $2 - j3$
43. $p + jq$
45. $-jm + n$

42. $-5 - j7$
44. $-j5 + 6$
46. $5 - j8$

Divide and simplify:

47. $j8 \div 4$
49. $j12 \div j6$
51. $(4 + j2) \div 2$
53. $(-2 + j3) \div (1 - j)$
55. $(j7 + 2) \div (j3 - 5)$

48. $9 \div j3$
50. $j44 \div j2$
52. $8 \div (4 - j)$
54. $(5 - j6) \div (-3 + j2)$
56. $(-9 + j3) \div (2 - j4)$

Quadratics with Complex Roots

Solve for x to three significant digits:

57. $3x^2 - 5x + 7 = 0$
59. $x^2 - 2x + 6 = 0$

58. $2x^2 + 3x + 5 = 0$
60. $4x^2 + x + 8 = 0$

Complex Factors

Factor each expression into complex factors:

61. $x^2 + 9$
63. $4y^2 + z^2$

62. $b^2 + 25$
64. $25a^2 + 9b^2$

Computer

65. Modify your program for solving quadratic equations (Chapter 14) so that the run will not end when the discriminant is negative, but will instead compute and print complex roots in the form $a + jb$.

66. To convert a number from radical to complex form in a computer algebra system, simply type it in and give the SIMPLIFY command. Thus,

$$\text{SQRT}(-4) \text{ simplifies to } j2$$

Different systems have different ways to display a complex number. (j is displayed as $\hat{\imath}$ in *Derive*, I in *Maple*, and I in *Mathematica*.) Use this to do any of Problems 1 to 10 in this exercise.

67. Complex expressions can be entered in a CAS by typing the imaginary unit j as #i in *Derive* or I in *Mathematica*. The command Simplify will then return the simplest form of the expression. Use this to do any of Problems 11 to 40 and 47 to 56 in this exercise.

68. A complex conjugate is obtained by the command CONJ( ) in *Derive* and Conjugate [ ] in *Mathematica*. Use this to do any of Problems 41 to 46 in this exercise.

69. To obtain complex roots of a quadratic in a CAS, simply enter the equation and give the SOLVE command. Use this to solve any of the quadratics in Problems 57 to 60.

70. To get complex factors of an expression in a CAS, first set the factoring level to COMPLEX. Then enter the expression and give the FACTOR command. Use this to factor any of the expressions in problems 61 to 64.

21·2

Graphing Complex Numbers

The Complex Plane

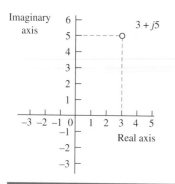

FIGURE 21·2 The complex plane

A complex number in rectangular form is made up of two parts: a real part a and an imaginary part jb. To graph a complex number we can use a rectangular coordinate system (Fig. 21·2) in which the horizontal axis is the *real* axis and the vertical axis is the *imaginary* axis. Such a coordinate system defines what is called the *complex plane*. Real numbers are graphed as points on the horizontal axis. Pure imaginary numbers are graphed as points on the vertical axis. Complex numbers, such as $3 + j5$ (Fig. 21·2), are graphed elsewhere within the plane.

Such a plot is called an *Argand diagram*, named for Jean Robert Argand (1768–1822).

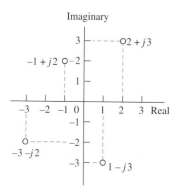

FIGURE 21·3

Graphing a Complex Number

To plot a complex number $a + jb$ in the complex plane, simply locate a point with a horizontal coordinate of a and a vertical coordinate of b.

■ **Example 15:** Plot the complex numbers $(2 + j3)$, $(-1 + j2)$, $(-3 - j2)$, and $(1 - j3)$.

Solution: The points are plotted in Fig. 21·3. ■

Exercise 2   Graphing Complex Numbers

Graph each complex number:

1. $2 + j5$
3. $3 - j2$
5. $j5$
7. $-2.7 - j3.4$
9. $1.46 - j2.45$

2. $-1 - j3$
4. $2 - j$
6. $2.25 - j3.62$
8. $5.02 + j$

21·3

In some books, the terms "polar form" and "trigonometric form" are used interchangeably. Here, we distinguish between them.

Complex Numbers in Trigonometric and Polar Forms

Polar Form

In Chapter 17 we saw that a point in a plane could be located by *polar coordinates*, as well as by rectangular coordinates, and we learned how to convert from one set of coordinates to the other. We will do the same thing now with complex numbers, converting between rectangular form and polar form.

In Figure 21·4, we plot a complex number $a + jb$. We connect that point to the origin with a line of length r at an angle of θ with the horizontal axis. Now, in addition to expressing the complex number in terms of a and b, we can express it in terms of r and θ:

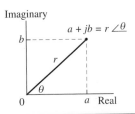

Imaginary

FIGURE 21·4 Polar form of a complex number shown on a complex plane

Polar Form	$a + jb = r\underline{/\theta}$	228

Since $\cos \theta = a/r$ and $\sin \theta = b/r$, we get

	$a = r \cos\ \theta$	224
	$b = r \sin\ \theta$	225

The radius r is called the *absolute value*. It can be found from the Pythagorean theorem:

	$r = \sqrt{a^2 + b^2}$	226

The angle θ is called the *argument* of the complex number. Since $\tan \theta = b/a$

	$\theta = \arctan \dfrac{b}{a}$	227

If your calculator has keys for converting between rectangular and polar coordinates, you can use these keys to convert complex numbers between rectangular and polar forms.

■ **Example 16:** Write the complex number $2 + j3$ in polar form.

Solution: The absolute value is

$$r = \sqrt{2^2 + 3^2} \cong 3.61$$

And the argument is found from

$$\tan \theta = \frac{3}{2}$$

$$\theta \approx 56.3°$$

So

$$2 + j3 = 3.61\underline{/56.3°}$$ ■

Trigonometric Form

The angle is sometimes written $\theta = \arg z$, which means "θ is the argument of the complex number z." Also, the expression in parentheses in Eq. 223 is sometimes abbreviated as cis θ, so cis $\theta = \cos \theta + j \sin \theta$.

If we substitute the values of a and b from Eqs. 224 and 225 into $a + jb$, we get

$$a + jb = (r \cos \theta) + j(r \sin \theta)$$

Factoring gives

Trigonometric Form	$a + jb = r(\cos \theta + j \sin \theta)$ rectangular form trigonometric form	223

■ **Example 17:** Write the complex number $2 + j3$ in polar and trigonometric form.

Solution: We already have r and θ from Example 16:

$$r = 3.61 \qquad \text{and} \qquad \theta = 56.3°$$

Therefore,

$$2 + j3 = 3.61\underline{/56.3°}$$

So by Eq. 224,

$$2 + j3 = 3.61(\cos 56.3° + j \sin 56.3°)$$

■

━ **Example 18:** Write the complex number $6(\cos 30° + j \sin 30°)$ in polar and rectangular form.

Solution: By inspection,

$$r = 6 \qquad \text{and} \qquad \theta = 30°$$

So

$$a = r \cos \theta = 6 \cos 30° = 5.20$$

and

$$b = r \sin \theta = 6 \sin 30° = 3.00$$

So our complex number, in rectangular form, is $5.20 + j3.00$, and in polar form, $6\underline{/30°}$.

■

Arithmetic Operations in Polar Form

It is common practice to switch back and forth between rectangular and polar forms during a computation, using that form in which a particular operation is easiest. We saw that addition and subtraction are fast and easy in rectangular form, and we now show that multiplication, division, and raising to a power are best done in polar form.

Products

We will use trigonometric form to work out the formula for multiplication and then express the result in the simpler polar form.
    Let us multiply $r(\cos \theta + j \sin \theta)$ by $r'(\cos \theta' + j \sin \theta')$.

$$[r(\cos \theta + j \sin \theta)][r'(\cos \theta' + j \sin \theta')]$$

$$= rr'\,(\cos \theta \cos \theta' + j \cos \theta \sin \theta' + j \sin \theta \cos \theta' + j^2 \sin \theta \sin \theta')$$

$$= rr'\,[(\cos \theta \cos \theta' - \sin \theta \sin \theta') + j(\sin \theta \cos \theta' + \cos \theta \sin \theta')]$$

However, by Eq. 168,

$$\cos \theta \cos \theta' - \sin \theta \sin \theta' = \cos(\theta + \theta')$$

and by Eq. 167,

$$\sin \theta \cos \theta' + \cos \theta \sin \theta' = \sin(\theta + \theta')$$

Therefore,

$$r(\cos \theta + j \sin \theta) \cdot r'(\cos \theta' + j \sin \theta') = rr'[\cos(\theta + \theta') + j \sin(\theta + \theta')]$$

Switching now to polar form, we get

Products	$r\underline{/\theta} \cdot r'\underline{/\theta'} = rr'\underline{/\theta + \theta'}$	**229**

The absolute value of the product of two complex numbers is the product of their absolute values, and the argument is the sum of the individual arguments.

■ **Example 19:** Multiply $5\underline{/30°}$ by $3\underline{/20°}$.

Solution: The absolute value of the product will be $5(3) = 15$ and the argument of the product will be $30° + 20° = 50°$, so

$$5\underline{/30°} \cdot 3\underline{/20°} = 15\underline{/50°}$$

■

The angle θ is not usually written greater than 360°. Subtract multiples of 360° if necessary.

■ **Example 20:** Multiply $6.27\underline{/300°}$ by $2.75\underline{/125°}$.

Solution:

$$6.27\underline{/300°} \times 2.75\underline{/125°} = (6.27)(2.75)\underline{/300° + 125°}$$
$$= 17.2\underline{/425°}$$
$$= 17.2\underline{/65°}$$

■

Quotients

The rule for division of complex numbers in trigonometric form is similar to that for multiplication:

You might try deriving this yourself.

Quotients	$\dfrac{r\underline{/\theta}}{r'\underline{/\theta'}} = \dfrac{r}{r'}\underline{/\theta - \theta'}$	**230**

The absolute value of the quotient of two complex numbers is the quotient of their absolute values; and the argument is the difference (numerator minus denominator) of their arguments.

■ **Example 21:**

$$\frac{6\underline{/70°}}{2\underline{/50°}} = 3\underline{/20°}$$

■

Powers

To raise a complex number to a power, we merely have to multiply it by itself the proper number of times, using Eq. 229,

$$\left(r\underline{/\theta}\right)^2 = r\underline{/\theta} \cdot r\underline{/\theta} = r \cdot r\underline{/\theta + \theta} = r^2\underline{/2\theta}$$
$$\left(r\underline{/\theta}\right)^3 = r\underline{/\theta} \cdot r^2\underline{/2\theta} = r \cdot r^2\underline{/\theta + 2\theta} = r^3\underline{/3\theta}$$

Do you see a pattern developing? In general, we get

After Abraham DeMoivre (1667–1754)

DeMoivre's Theorem	$\left(r\underline{/\theta}\right)^n = r^n\underline{/n\theta}$	**231**

When a complex number is raised to the nth power, the new absolute value is equal to the original absolute value raised to the nth power, and the new argument is n times the original argument.

■ **Example 22:**

$$\left(2\underline{/10°}\right)^5 = 2^5\underline{/5(10°)} = 32\underline{/50°}$$

■

Roots

We know that $1^4 = 1$, so, conversely, the fourth root of 1 is 1.

$$\sqrt[4]{1} = 1$$

But we have seen that $j^4 = 1$, so shouldn't it also be true that

$$\sqrt[4]{1} = j?$$

In fact, both 1 and j are fourth roots of 1, and there are two other roots as well. In this section we learn how to use DeMoivre's theorem to find all the roots of a number.

First we note that a complex number $r\underline{/\theta}$ in polar form is unchanged if we add multiples of 360° to the angle θ (in degrees). Thus

$$r\underline{/\theta} = r\underline{/\theta + 360°} = r\underline{/\theta + 720°} = r\underline{/\theta + 360k}$$

where k is an integer. Rewriting deMoivre's theorem with an exponent $1/p$ (where p is an integer), we get

$$\left(r\underline{/\theta}\right)^{1/p} = \left(r\underline{/\theta + 360k}\right)^{1/p} = r^{1/p}\underline{/(\theta + 360k)/p}$$

so

$$\left(r\underline{/\theta}\right)^{1/p} = r^{1/p}\underline{/(\theta + 360k)/p} \tag{1}$$

We use this equation to find all the roots of a complex number by letting k take on the values $k = 0, 1, 2, \ldots, (p - 1)$. We'll see in the following example that values of k greater than $(p - 1)$ will give duplicate roots.

■ **Example 23:** Find the fourth roots of 1.

Solution: We write the given number in polar form, thus $1 = 1\underline{/0°}$. Then, using (1) with $p = 4$,

$$1^{1/4} = \left(1\underline{/0°}\right)^{1/4} = 1^{1/4}\underline{/(0 + 360k°)/4} = 1\underline{/90k°}$$

We now let $k = 0, 1, 2, \ldots$:

	ROOT	
k	**POLAR FORM**	**RECTANGULAR FORM**
0	$1\underline{/0°}$	1
1	$1\underline{/90°}$	j
2	$1\underline{/180°}$	-1
3	$1\underline{/270°}$	$-j$
4	$1\underline{/360°}$	$1\underline{/0°} = 1$
5	$1\underline{/450°}$	$1\underline{/90°} = j$

Notice that the roots repeat for $k = 4$ and higher, so we look no further. Thus the fourth roots of 1 are $1, j, -1$, and $-j$. We check them by noting that each raised to the fourth power equals 1. ▬

Thus the number 1 has four fourth roots. In general, any number has two square roots, three cube roots, and so on.

> There are p pth roots of a complex number.

If a complex number is in rectangular form, we convert to polar form before taking the root.

▬ **Example 24:** Find $\sqrt[3]{256 + j192}$.

Solution: We convert the given complex number to polar form.

$$r = \sqrt{(256)^2 + (192)^2} = 320 \qquad \theta = \arctan(192/256) = 36.9°$$

Then, using Eq. (1), we have

$$\sqrt[3]{256 + j192} = (320\underline{/36.9°})^{1/3} = (320)^{1/3}\underline{/(36.9° + 360k)/3}$$
$$= 6.84\underline{/12.3° + 120k}$$

We let $k = 0, 1, 2$, to obtain the three roots.

	ROOT		
k	**POLAR FORM**		**RECTANGULAR FORM**
0	$6.84\underline{/12.3° + 0°}$	$= 6.84\underline{/12.3°}$	$6.68 + j1.46$
1	$6.84\underline{/12.3° + 120°}$	$= 6.84\underline{/132.3°}$	$-4.60 + j5.06$
2	$6.84\underline{/12.3° + 240°}$	$= 6.84\underline{/252.3°}$	$-2.08 + j6.52$

▬

Round to three significant digits, where necessary, in this exercise.

Exercise 3 Complex Numbers in Trigonometric and Polar Forms

Write each complex number in polar and trigonometric form:

1. $5 + j4$
2. $-3 - j7$
3. $4 - j3$
4. $8 + j4$
5. $-5 - j2$
6. $-4 + j7$

7. $-9 - j5$
8. $7 - j3$
9. $-4 - j7$

Write in rectangular form and in polar form:

10. $4(\cos 25° + j \sin 25°)$
11. $3(\cos 57° + j \sin 57°)$
12. $2(\cos 110° + j \sin 110°)$
13. $9(\cos 150° + j \sin 150°)$
14. $7(\cos 12° + j \sin 12°)$
15. $5.46(\cos 47.3° + j \sin 47.3°)$

Write in rectangular and trigonometric form:

16. $5\underline{/28°}$
17. $9\underline{/59°}$
18. $4\underline{/63°}$
19. $7\underline{/-53°}$
20. $6\underline{/-125°}$

Multiplication and Division

Multiply:

21. $3(\cos 12° + j \sin 12°)$ by $5(\cos 28° + j \sin 28°)$
22. $7(\cos 48° + j \sin 48°)$ by $4(\cos 72° + j \sin 72°)$
23. $5.82(\cos 44.8° + j \sin 44.8°)$ by $2.77(\cos 10.1° + j \sin 10.1°)$
24. $5\underline{/30°}$ by $2\underline{/10°}$
25. $8\underline{/45°}$ by $7\underline{/15°}$
26. $2.86\underline{/38.2°}$ by $1.55\underline{/21.1°}$

Divide:

27. $8(\cos 46° + j \sin 46°)$ by $4(\cos 21° + j \sin 21°)$
28. $49(\cos 27° + j \sin 27°)$ by $7(\cos 15° + j \sin 15°)$
29. $58.3(\cos 77.4° + j \sin 77.4°)$ by $12.4(\cos 27.2° + j \sin 27.2°)$
30. $24\underline{/50°}$ by $12\underline{/30°}$
31. $50\underline{/72°}$ by $5\underline{/12°}$
32. $71.4\underline{/56.4°}$ by $27.7\underline{/15.2°}$

Powers and Roots

Evaluate:

33. $[2(\cos 15° + j \sin 15°)]^3$
34. $[9(\cos 10° + j \sin 10°)]^2$
35. $(7\underline{/20°})^2$
36. $(1.55\underline{/15°})^3$
37. $\sqrt{57\underline{/52°}}$
38. $\sqrt{22\underline{/12°}}$
39. $\sqrt[3]{38\underline{/73°}}$

40. $\sqrt[3]{15/89°}$

41. $\sqrt{135 + j204}$

42. $\sqrt[3]{56.3 + j28.5}$

Calculator

43. Learn how to convert between rectangular and polar form on your calculator. Use these keys to aid you in doing Problems 1 to 20 in this exercise.

Computer

44. In *Derive*, the command ABS(z) will give the absolute value r of a complex number z, and the command PHASE(z) will give the argument θ of that complex number, in radians. Thus

$$ABS(3 + î4) \text{ gives the value } 5$$

and

$$PHASE(3 + î4) \text{ gives the value } 0.927$$

the radian equivalent of 53.1°. The equivalent commands in *Mathematica* are Abs[ ] and Arg[ ]. Thus these two commands can be used to convert a complex number from rectangular form to polar and trigonometric forms. Use them to do any of Problems 1 to 9 in this exercise.

45. To convert a complex number from trigonometric to rectangular form, enter the number and give the SIMPLIFY command. Use this to convert the numbers in Problems 10 to 15.

46. Algebraic operations on complex expressions in rectangular or trigonometric form are done by entering the expressions and giving the SIMPLIFY command. The result will be given in rectangular form. If polar form or trigonometric form is wanted, convert as shown in Problem 44 above. Use this to simplify any of the expressions in Problems 21 to 23, 27 to 29, 33, and 34.

21•4

Complex Numbers in Exponential Form

Euler's Formula

We have already expressed a complex number in *rectangular* form

$$a + jb$$

in *polar* form

$$r/\theta$$

and in *trigonometric* form

$$r(\cos \theta + j \sin \theta)$$

Our next (and final) form for a complex number is *exponential* form, given by Euler's formula.

Leonhard Euler (1707–1783). We give this formula without proof here.

Euler's Formula	$re^{j\theta} = r(\cos \theta + j \sin \theta)$	**232**

Here e is the base of natural logarithms (approximately 2.718), discussed in Chapter 20, and θ is the argument expressed in radians.

■ **Example 25:** Write the complex number $5(\cos 180° + j \sin 180°)$ in exponential form.

Solution: We first convert the angle to radians, $180° = \pi$ rad:

$$5(\cos \pi + j \sin \pi) = 5e^{j\pi}$$

■

Common Error	Make sure that θ is in *radians* when using Eq. 232.

■ **Example 26:** Write the complex number $3e^{j2}$ in rectangular, trigonometric, and polar forms.

Setting $\theta = \pi$ and $r = 1$ in Euler's formula gives

$$e^{j\pi} = \cos \pi + j \sin \pi$$
$$= -1 + j0$$
$$= -1$$

The constant e arises out of natural growth, j is the square root of -1, and π is the ratio of the circumference of a circle to its diameter. Thus we get the astounding result that the irrational number e raised to the product of the imaginary unit j and the irrational number π gives the integer -1.

Solution: Changing θ to degrees gives us

$$\theta = 2 \text{ rad} = 115°$$

and from Eq. 232,

$$r = 3$$

From Eq. 224,

$$a = r \cos \theta = 3 \cos 115° = -1.27$$

and from Eq. 225,

$$b = r \sin \theta = 3 \sin 115° = 2.72$$

So, in rectangular form,

$$3e^{j2} = -1.27 + j2.72$$

in polar form,

$$= 3\underline{/115°}$$

and in trigonometric form,

$$= 3(\cos 115° + j \sin 115°)$$

■

Products

We now find products, quotients, powers, and roots of complex numbers in exponential form. These operations are quite simple in this form, as we merely have to use the laws of exponents. Thus, by Eq. 29,

Products	$r_1 e^{j\theta_1} \cdot r_2 e^{j\theta_2} = r_1 r_2 e^{j(\theta_1 + \theta_2)}$	**233**

■ **Example 27:**
(a) $2e^{j3} \cdot 5e^{j4} = 10e^{j7}$ (b) $2.83e^{j2} \cdot 3.15e^{j4} = 8.91e^{j6}$
(c) $-13.5e^{-j3} \cdot 2.75e^{j5} = -37.1e^{j2}$

■

Quotients

By Eq. 30,

Quotients	$\dfrac{r_1 e^{j\theta_1}}{r_2 e^{j\theta_2}} = \dfrac{r_1}{r_2} e^{j(\theta_1 - \theta_2)}$	**234**

━ **Example 28:**

(a) $\dfrac{8e^{j5}}{4e^{j2}} = 2e^{j3}$

(b) $\dfrac{63.8e^{j2}}{13.7e^{j5}} = 4.66e^{-j3}$

(c) $\dfrac{5.82e^{-j4}}{9.83e^{-j7}} = 0.592e^{j3}$

━

Powers and Roots

By Eq. 31,

Powers and Roots	$(re^{j\theta})^n = r^n e^{jn\theta}$	**235**

━ **Example 29:**

(a) $(2e^{j3})^4 = 16e^{j12}$

(b) $(-3.85e^{-j2})^3 = -57.1e^{-j6}$

(c) $(0.223e^{-j3})^{-2} = \dfrac{e^{j6}}{(0.223)^2} = \dfrac{e^{j6}}{0.0497} = 20.1e^{j6}$

━

Exercise 4 Complex Numbers in Exponential Form

Express each complex number in exponential form:

1. $2 + j3$

2. $-1 + j2$

3. $3(\cos 50° + j \sin 50°)$

4. $12 \underline{/14°}$

5. $2.5 \underline{/\pi/6}$

6. $7\left(\cos \dfrac{\pi}{3} + j \sin \dfrac{\pi}{3}\right)$

7. $5.4 \underline{/\pi/12}$

8. $5 + j4$

Express in rectangular, polar, and trigonometric form:

9. $5e^{j3}$

10. $7e^{j5}$

11. $2.2e^{j1.5}$

12. $4e^{j2}$

Operations in Exponential Form

Multiply:

13. $9e^{j2} \cdot 2e^{j4}$

14. $8e^{j} \cdot 6e^{j3}$

15. $7e^{j} \cdot 3e^{j3}$

16. $6.2e^{j1.1} \cdot 5.8e^{j2.7}$

17. $1.7e^{j5} \cdot 2.1e^{j2}$

18. $4e^{j7} \cdot 3e^{j5}$

Divide:

19. $18e^{j6}$ by $6e^{j3}$
20. $45e^{j4}$ by $9e^{j2}$
21. $55e^{j9}$ by $5e^{j6}$
22. $123e^{j6}$ by $105e^{j2}$
23. $21e^{j2}$ by $7e^{j}$
24. $7.7e^{j4}$ by $2.3e^{j2}$

Evaluate:

25. $(3e^{j5})^2$
26. $(4e^{j2})^3$
27. $(2e^{j})^3$

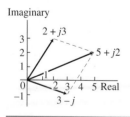

Computer

28. In Exercise 3, Problem 44 (page 631), we showed how to obtain the absolute value r of a complex number z, and the argument θ of that complex number, in radians. We used ABS( ) and PHASE( ) in *Derive* and Abs[ ] and Arg[ ] in *Mathematica*. We used these two commands to convert a complex number from rectangular form to polar and trigonometric forms, but we can also use them to convert to exponential form. Use them to do any of Problems 1 to 8 in this exercise.

29. When studying the exponential function, we showed how to enter the base e raised to a power in a CAS, using EXP( ). We enter a complex number in exponential form in the same way. The expression is then converted by the command SIMPLIFY. Use this to do Problems 9 to 12 in this exercise.

30. To do arithmetic operations on complex numbers in exponential form in a CAS, enter the expressions and give the SIMPLIFY command. Use this to do any of Problems 13 to 27.

21•5   Vector Operations Using Complex Numbers

Vectors Represented by Complex Numbers

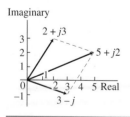

FIGURE 21•5 A vector represented by a complex number

One of the major uses of complex numbers is that they can represent vectors and, as we will soon see, enable us to manipulate them in ways that are easier than those we learned when studying oblique triangles.

Take the complex number $2 + j3$, for example, which is plotted in Figure 21•5. If we connect that point with a line to the origin, we can think of the complex number $2 + j3$ *as representing a vector* **R** *having a horizontal component of 2 units and a vertical component of 3 units.* The complex number used to represent a vector can, of course, be expressed in any of the forms of a complex number.

Vector Addition and Subtraction

FIGURE 21•6 Vector addition with complex numbers

Let us place a second vector on our diagram, represented by the complex number $3 - j$ (Fig. 21•6). We can add the two vectors graphically by the parallelogram method and we get a resultant $5 + j2$. But let us add the two original complex numbers, $2 + j3$ and $3 - j$:

$$(2 + j3) + (3 - j) = 5 + j2$$

This is the same as we obtained graphically. In other words, *the resultant of two vectors is equal to the sum of the complex numbers representing those vectors.*

■ **Example 30:** Subtract the vectors $25\underline{/48°} - 18\underline{/175°}$.

Solution: Vector addition and subtraction are best done in rectangular form. Converting the first vector,

$$a_1 = 25 \cos 48° = 16.7$$
$$b_1 = 25 \sin 48° = 18.6$$

so

$$25\underline{/48°} = 16.7 + j18.6$$

Similarly for the second vector,

$$a_2 = 18 \cos 175° = -17.9$$
$$b_2 = 18 \sin 175° = 1.57$$

so

$$18\underline{/175°} = -17.9 + j1.57$$

Combining, we have

$$(16.7 + j18.6) - (-17.9 + j1.57) = (16.7 + 17.9) + j(18.6 - 1.57)$$

$$= 34.6 + j17.0$$

These vectors are shown in Figure 21•7.

FIGURE 21•7

Multiplication and Division of Vectors

Multiplication or division is best done if the vectors are expressed as a complex numbers in polar form.

■ **Example 31:** Multiply the vectors $2\underline{/25°}$ and $3\underline{/15°}$.

Solution: By Eq. 229, the product vector will have a magnitude of $3(2) = 6$ and an angle of $25° + 15° = 40°$. The product is thus

$$6\underline{/40°}$$

■ **Example 32:** Divide the vector $8\underline{/44°}$ by $4\underline{/12°}$.

Solution: By Eq. 230,

$$(8\underline{/44°}) \div (4\underline{/12°}) = \frac{8}{4}\underline{/44° - 12°} = 2\underline{/32°}$$

━━ **Example 33:** If a certain current I is represented by the complex number $1.15\underline{/23.5°}$ amperes, and a complex impedance Z is represented by $24.6\underline{/14.8°}$ ohms, multiply I by Z to obtain the voltage V.

Solution:

$$V = IZ = \left(1.15\underline{/23.5°}\right)\left(24.6\underline{/14.8°}\right) = 28.3\underline{/38.3°}\ V$$

━━

The j Operator

Let us multiply a complex number $r\underline{/\theta}$ by j. First we must express j in polar form. By Eq. 224,

$$j = 0 + j1 = 1(\cos 90° + j \sin 90°) = 1\underline{/90°}$$

After multiplying by j, the new absolute value will be

$$r \cdot 1 = r$$

and the argument will be

$$\theta + 90°$$

So

$$r\underline{/\theta} \cdot j = r\underline{/\theta + 90°}$$

Thus, the only effect of multiplying our original complex number by j was to increase the angle by 90°. If our complex number represents a vector, *we may think of* j *as an operator that causes the vector to rotate through one-quarter revolution.*

Round to three significant digits, where needed, in this exercise.

Exercise 5 Vector Operations Using Complex Numbers

Express each vector in rectangular and polar form.

	MAGNITUDE	ANGLE			MAGNITUDE	ANGLE
1.	7.00	49.0°	**4.**		34.2	1.10 rad
2.	28.0	136°	**5.**		39.0	2.50 rad
3.	193	73.5°	**6.**		59.4	58.0°

Combine the vectors.

7. $(3 + j2) + (5 - j4)$ **8.** $(7 - j3) - (4 + j)$
9. $58\underline{/72°} + 21\underline{/14°}$ **10.** $8.60\underline{/58°} - 4.20\underline{/160°}$
11. $9(\cos 42° + j \sin 42°) + 2(\cos 8° + j \sin 8°)$
12. $8(\cos 15° + j \sin 15°) - 5(\cos 9° - j \sin 9°)$

Multiply the vectors.

13. $(7 + j3)(2 - j5)$ **14.** $\left(2.50\underline{/18°}\right)\left(3.70\underline{/48°}\right)$
15. $2(\cos 25° - j \sin 25°) \cdot 6(\cos 7° - j \sin 7°)$

Divide the vectors.

16. $(25 - j2) \div (3 + j4)$ **17.** $\left(7.70\underline{/47°}\right) \div \left(2.50\underline{/15°}\right)$
18. $5(\cos 72° + j \sin 72°) \div 3(\cos 31° + j \sin 31°)$

21•6

Glance back at Section 17•3 where we first introduced alternating current.

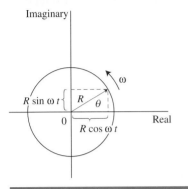

FIGURE 21•8

Alternating Current Applications

Rotating Vectors in the Complex Plane

We have already shown that a vector can be represented by a complex number, $r\underline{/\theta}$. For example, the complex number $5.00\underline{/28°}$ represents a vector of magnitude 5.00 at an angle of 28° with the real axis.

A phasor (a rotating vector) may also be represented by a complex number $R\underline{/\omega t}$ by replacing the angle θ by ωt, where ω is the angular velocity and t is time.

■ **Example 34:** The complex number

$$11\underline{/5t}$$

represents a phasor of magnitude 11 rotating with an angular velocity of 5 rad/s. ■

In Section 17•3 we showed that a phasor of magnitude R has a projection on the y axis of $R \sin \omega t$. Similarly, a phasor $R\underline{/\omega t}$ in the complex plane (Fig. 21•8) will have a projection on the imaginary axis of $R \sin \omega t$. Thus

$$R \sin \omega t = \text{imaginary part of } R\underline{/\omega t}$$

Similarly,

$$R \cos \omega t = \text{real part of } R\underline{/\omega t}$$

Thus either a sine or cosine wave can be represented by a complex number $R\underline{/\omega t}$, depending upon whether we project onto the imaginary or real axis. It does not usually matter which we choose, because the sine and the cosine functions are identical except for a phase difference of 90°. What does matter is that we are consistent. Here we will follow the convention of projecting the phasor onto the imaginary axis, and drop the phrase "imaginary part of." Thus we say that

$$R \sin \omega t = R\underline{/\omega t}$$

Similarly, if there is a phase angle ϕ,

$$R \sin(\omega t + \phi) = R\underline{/\omega t + \phi}$$

One final simplification: It is customary to draw phasors at $t = 0$, so that ωt vanishes from the expression. Thus we write

$$R \sin(\omega t + \phi) = R\underline{/\phi}$$

Effective or Root Mean Square (rms) Values

Before we write currents and voltages in complex form, we must define *effective value* of current and voltage. The power P delivered to a resistor by a direct current I is $P = I^2R$. We now define an effective current I_{eff} that delivers the same power from an alternating current as that delivered by a direct current of the same number of amperes:

$$P = I_{eff}{}^2 R$$

We get the effective value by taking the square root of the mean value squared; hence it is also called a *root mean squared value*. Thus, I_{eff} is often written I_{rms} instead.

Figure 21•9 shows an alternating current $i = I_m \sin \omega t$ and i^2, the square of that current. The mean value of this alternating quantity is found to deliver the same power in a resistor as a steady quantity of the same value.

$$P = I_{eff}{}^2 R = (\text{mean } i^2)R$$

But the mean value of i^2 is equal to $I_m{}^2/2$, half the peak value, so

$$I_{eff} = \sqrt{I_m{}^2/2} = I_m/\sqrt{2}$$

Thus *the effective current I_{eff} is equal to the peak current I_m divided by $\sqrt{2}$.* Similarly, *the effective voltage V_{eff} is equal to the peak voltage V_m divided by $\sqrt{2}$.*

FIGURE 21•9

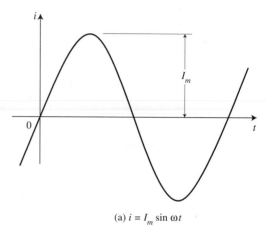

(a) $i = I_m \sin \omega t$

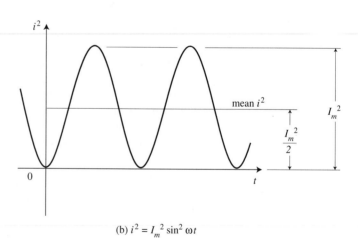

(b) $i^2 = I_m{}^2 \sin^2 \omega t$

■ **Example 35:** An alternating current has a peak value of 2.84 A. What is the effective current?

Solution:

$$I_{eff} = \frac{I_m}{\sqrt{2}} = \frac{2.84}{\sqrt{2}} = 2.01 \text{ A}$$ ■

Alternating Current and Voltage in Complex Form

Next we will write a sinusoidal current or voltage expression in the form of a complex number, because computations are easier in that form. At the same time we will express the magnitude of the current or voltage in terms of effective value. The effective current I_{eff} is the quantity that is always implied when a current is given, rather than the peak current I_m. It is the quantity that is read when using a meter. The same is true of effective voltage.

To write an alternating current in complex form, we give the effective value of the current and the phase angle. The current is written in boldface type, as **I**. Thus,

Complex Voltage and Current	The current is represented by $$i = I_m \sin(\omega t + \phi_2)$$ $$\mathbf{I} = I_{eff}\underline{/\phi_2} = \frac{I_m}{\sqrt{2}}\underline{/\phi_2}$$	**A76**
	Similarly, the voltage is represented by $$v = V_m \sin(\omega t + \phi_1)$$ $$\mathbf{V} = V_{eff}\underline{/\phi_1} = \frac{V_m}{\sqrt{2}}\underline{/\phi_1}$$	**A75**

The "complex" expressions are the simpler. This happy situation is made use of in the AC computations to follow, which are much more cumbersome without complex numbers.

Note that the complex expressions for voltage and current do not contain t. We say that the voltage and current have been converted from the *time domain* to the *phasor domain*.

■ **Example 36:** The complex expression for the alternating current

$$i = 2.84 \sin(\omega t + 33°) \text{ A}$$

is

$$\mathbf{I} = I_{eff}\underline{/33°} = \frac{2.84}{\sqrt{2}}\underline{/33°} \text{ A}$$

$$= 2.01\underline{/33°} \text{ A} \qquad ■$$

■ **Example 37:** The sinusoidal expression for the voltage

$$\mathbf{V} = 84.2\underline{/-49°} \text{ V}$$

is

$$v = 84.2\sqrt{2}\sin(\omega t - 49°)$$

$$= 119\sin(\omega t - 49°) \qquad ■$$

Complex Impedance

In Section 7·7 we drew a vector impedance diagram in which the impedance was the resultant of two perpendicular vectors, the resistance R along the horizontal axis and the reactance X along the vertical axis. If we now use the complex plane, and draw the resistance along the *real* axis and the reactance along the *imaginary* axis, we can represent impedance by a complex number.

Complex Impedance	$$\mathbf{Z} = R + jX = Z\underline{/\phi}$$	**A101**

(a)

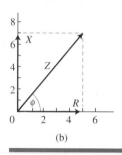

(b)

FIGURE 21•10

where

$$R = \text{circuit resistance}$$

$$X = \text{circuit reactance} = X_L - X_c \qquad \text{(A98)}$$

$$Z = \text{magnitude of impedance} = \sqrt{R^2 + X^2} \qquad \text{(A99)}$$

$$\phi = \text{phase angle} = \arctan \frac{X}{R} \qquad \text{(A100)}$$

■ **Example 38:** A circuit has a resistance of 5 Ω in series with a reactance of 7 Ω [Fig. 21•10(a)]. Represent the impedance by a complex number.

Solution: We draw the vector impedance diagram [Fig. 21•10(b)]. The impedance, in rectangular form, is

$$Z = 5 + j7$$

The magnitude of the impedance is

$$\sqrt{5^2 + 7^2} = 8.60$$

The phase angle is

$$\arctan \frac{7}{5} = 54.5°$$

Now so we can write the impedance as a complex number in polar form,

$$Z = 8.60 \underline{/54.5°} \qquad ■$$

Ohm's Law for AC

We stated at the beginning of this section that the use of complex numbers would make calculation with alternating current almost as easy as for direct current. We do this by means of the following relationship:

Ohm's Law for AC	$V = ZI$	**A103**

Note the similarity between this equation and Ohm's law, Eq. A62. It is used in the same way.

■ **Example 39:** A voltage of $142 \sin 200t$ is applied to the circuit of Figure 21•10(a). Write a sinusoidal expression for the current i.

Solution: We first write the voltage in complex form. By Eq. A75,

$$V = \frac{142}{\sqrt{2}} \underline{/0°} = 100 \underline{/0°}$$

Next we find the complex impedance Z. From Example 38,

$$Z = 8.60 \underline{/54.5°}$$

The complex current I, by Ohm's law for AC, is

$$I = \frac{V}{Z} = \frac{100 \underline{/0°}}{8.60 \underline{/54.5°}} = 11.6 \underline{/-54.5°}$$

Then the current in sinusoidal form is (Eq. A76)

$$i = 11.6 \sqrt{2} \sin(200t - 54.5°)$$

$$= 16.4 \sin(200t - 54.5°)$$

The current and voltage phasors are plotted in Figure 21•11, and the instantaneous current and voltage are plotted in Figure 21•12. Note the phase difference between the voltage and current waves. This phase difference, 54.5°, converted to time, is

$$54.5° = 0.951 \text{ rad} = 200t$$

FIGURE 21•11

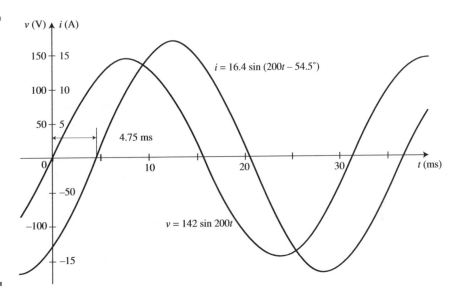

FIGURE 21•12

$$t = 0.951/200 = 0.00475 \text{ s} = 4.75 \text{ ms}$$

We say that the current lags the voltage by 54.5° or 4.75 ms.

Exercise 6 Alternating-Current Applications

Express each current or voltage in complex form:

1. $i = 250 \sin(\omega t + 25°)$ **2.** $v = 1.5 \sin(\omega t - 30°)$
3. $v = 57 \sin(\omega t - 90°)$ **4.** $i = 2.7 \sin \omega t$
5. $v = 144 \sin \omega t$ **6.** $i = 2.7 \sin(\omega t - 15°)$

Express each current or voltage in sinusoidal form:

7. $V = 150\underline{/0°}$ **8.** $V = 1.75\underline{/70°}$
9. $V = 300\underline{/-90°}$ **10.** $I = 25\underline{/30°}$
11. $I = 7.5\underline{/0°}$ **12.** $I = 15\underline{/-130°}$

Express the impedance of each circuit as a complex number in rectangular and in polar form:

13. Figure 21•13(a)
14. Figure 21•13(b)
15. Figure 21•13(c)

FIGURE 21•13

(d)   (e)

(f)

$R = 552\ \Omega$

$X_L = 148\ \Omega$

$X_c = 720\ \Omega$

(g)

FIGURE 21•13 (Continued)

16. Figure 21•13(d)
17. Figure 21•13(e)
18. Figure 21•13(f)
19. Figure 21•13(g)
20. Write a sinusoidal expression for the current i in each part of Figure 21•14.

(a)   (b)

FIGURE 21•14

21. Write a sinusoidal expression for the voltage v in each part of Figure 21•15.

(a)   (b)

FIGURE 21•15

22. Find the complex impedance **Z** in each part of Figure 21•16.

(a)   (b)

FIGURE 21•16

CHAPTER 21 REVIEW PROBLEMS

Express the following as complex numbers in rectangular, polar, trigonometric, and exponential forms:

1. $3 + \sqrt{-4}$
2. $-\sqrt{-9} - 5$
3. $-2 + \sqrt{-49}$
4. $3.25 + \sqrt{-11.6}$

Evaluate.

5. j^{17}
6. j^{25}

Combine the complex numbers below, leaving your answer in rectangular form:

7. $(7 - j3) + (2 + j5)$
8. $4.8\underline{/28°} - 2.4\underline{/72°}$
9. $52(\cos 50° + j \sin 50°) + 28(\cos 12° + j \sin 12°)$
10. $2.7e^{j7} - 4.3e^{j5}$

Multiply and leave your answer in the same form as the complex numbers below:

11. $(2 - j)(3 + j5)$
12. $\left(7.3\underline{/21°}\right)\left(2.1\underline{/156°}\right)$
13. $2(\cos 20° + j \sin 20°) \cdot 6(\cos 18° + j \sin 18°)$
14. $(93e^{j2})(5e^{j7})$

Divide and leave your answer in the same form as the complex numbers:

15. $(9 - j3) \div (4 + j)$
16. $\left(18\underline{/72°}\right) \div \left(6\underline{/22°}\right)$
17. $16(\cos 85° + j \sin 85°) \div 8(\cos 40° + j \sin 40°)$
18. $127e^{j8} \div 4.75e^{j5}$

Graph each complex number:

19. $7 + j4$
20. $2.75\underline{/44°}$
21. $6(\cos 135° + j \sin 135°)$
22. $4.75e^{j2.2}$

Evaluate each power:

23. $(-4 + j3)^2$
24. $(5\underline{/12°})^3$
25. $[5(\cos 10° + j \sin 10°)]^3$
26. $[2e^{j3}]^5$
27. Express in complex form, $i = 45 \sin(\omega t + 32°)$.
28. Express in sinusoidal form, $V = 283\underline{/-22°}$.
29. Write a complex expression for the current i in Figure 21•17.

Writing

30. Suppose you are completing a job application to an electronics company which asks you to "explain, in writing, how you would use complex numbers in an electrical calculation, and illustrate your explanation with an example." How would you respond?

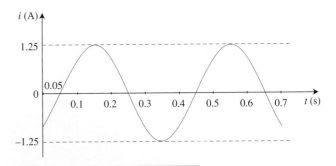

FIGURE 21•17

Team Project: The Mandelbrot Set

31. Figure 21•18 shows a plot of the Mandelbrot set in the complex plane. One way to define this set of numbers is: If we take a complex number, square it, add the original number, square the result, add the original number, square the result, and so forth for an infinite number of iterations, and the total does not grow without bound, then the original number is in the Mandelbrot set.

  This project is to write a computer program to plot the Mandelbrot set. Instead of an infinite number of iterations, we will do 50. Our test will be to see if the absolute value of $p^2 + q^2$ of each succeeding iteration $p + jq$ does not exceed 2.

  Your program should do the following:

(a) Choose a point (a, b) representing a complex number $a + jb$. Start with the point $(-2, 0)$ in the window, Figure 21•18, and proceed in steps of about 0.002 in both a and b until the opposite corner $(1, 1)$ is reached.
(b) Square the complex number.
(c) Add this square to the original number $a + jb$, getting a new complex number with real part p and imaginary part q.
(d) Test $p + jq$. If, at any point in this iteration, $p^2 + q^2$ gets larger than 4, go to step **(a)** and proceed to the next point.
(e) Repeat steps **(b)**, **(c)**, and **(d)** fifty times. If in those iterations the test in step **(d)** has not been failed, then the original number $a + jb$ is in the Mandelbrot set. Plot the point (a, b). Also plot its mirror image $(a - b)$.
(f) Go to step **(a)** and proceed to the next point.

Run your program on the fastest computer you have available. It may take hours to run.

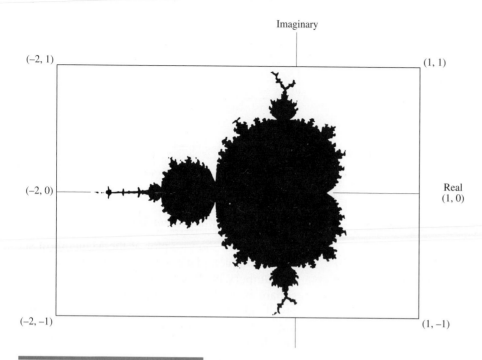

FIGURE 21•18 Plot of the
Mandelbrot set. Named for Benoit
Mandelbrot, who did much pioneering
work in the new field of Chaos and
Fractals

22

Analytic Geometry

When you have completed this chapter, you should be able to:

- Calculate the distance between two points.
- Determine the slope of a line, given two points on the line.
- Find the slope of a line given its angle of inclination, and vice versa.
- Determine the slope of a line perpendicular to a given line.
- Calculate the angle between two lines.
- Write the equation of a line using the slope-intercept form, the point-slope form, or the two-point form.
- Solve applied problems involving the straight line.
- Write the equation of a circle, an ellipse, a parabola, or a hyperbola from given information.
- Write an equation in standard form, given the equation of any of the conic sections.
- Determine all the features of interest from the standard equation of any conic section, and make a graph.
- Make a graph of any of the conic sections.
- Tell, by inspection, whether a given second-degree equation represents a circle, ellipse, parabola, or hyperbola.
- Write a new equation for a curve with the axes shifted when given the equation of that curve.
- Solve applied problems involving any of the conic sections.

This chapter begins our study of analytic geometry. The main idea in analytic geometry is to place geometric figures (points, lines, circles, and so forth) on coordinate axes, where they may be studied using the methods of algebra.

We start with the straight line, building on what we have already covered in Chapter 5. We study the idea of slope of a line and of a curve, an idea that will be crucial to our understanding of the derivative. Next come the *conic sections*, the circle, parabola, ellipse, and hyperbola. They are called *conic sections*, or just *conics*, because each can be obtained by passing a plane through a right circular cone, as shown in Figure 22•1.

When the plane is perpendicular to the cone's axis, it intercepts a *circle*. When the plane is tilted a bit, but not so much as to be parallel to an element (a line on the cone that passes through the vertex) of the cone, we get an

645

FIGURE 22•1 Conic sections

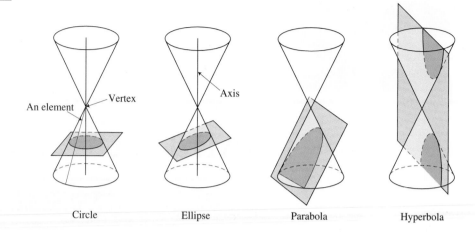

Circle Ellipse Parabola Hyperbola

ellipse. When the plane is parallel to an element of the cone, we get a *parabola*, and when the plane is steep enough to cut the upper nappe of the cone, we get the two branched *hyperbola*.

In this chapter we learn to write the equations of the straight line, and of the conics. These equations enable us to understand and to use these geometric figures in ways that are not possible without the equations. We also give some interesting applications for each curve.

22•1

The Straight Line

Length of a Line Segment Parallel to a Coordinate Axis

When we speak about the length of a line segment, or about the distance between two points, we usually mean the magnitude of that length or distance.

To find the magnitude of the length of a line segment lying on or parallel to the *x* (or *y*) axis, simply subtract the abscissa (or ordinate) of either endpoint from the abscissa (or ordinate) of the other endpoint, and take the absolute value of this result.

━━ **Example 1:** The magnitudes of the lengths of the lines in Figure 22•2 are
(a) $AB = |5 - 2| = 3$
(b) $PQ = |5 - (-2)| = 7$
(c) $RS = |-1 - (-5)| = 4$ ━━

Note that it doesn't matter if we reverse the order of the endpoints. We get the same result.

━━ **Example 2:** Repeating Example 1(a) with the endpoints reversed gives

$$AB = |2 - 5| = |-3| = 3$$

as before. ━━

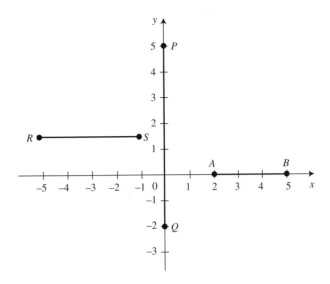

Directed Distance

Note that directed distance applies only to a line parallel to a coordinate axis.

Sometimes when speaking about the length of a line segment or the distance between two points, it is necessary to specify direction as well as magnitude. When we specify the directed distance AB, for example, we mean the distance *from A to B*. This is sometimes written $\overline{AB}$.

■ **Example 3:** Consider two points, $P(5, 2)$ and $Q(1, 2)$. The directed distance PQ is $PQ = 1 - 5 = -4$ and the directed distance QP is $QP = 5 - 1 = 4$. ■

Increments

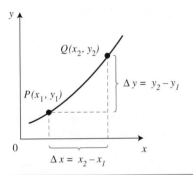

FIGURE 22•3 Increments

Let us say that a particle is moving along a curve (Fig. 22•3) from point P to point Q. In doing so, its abscissa changes from x_1 to x_2. We call this change an *increment* in x, and label it Δx (read *delta x*). Similarly, the ordinate changes from y_1 to y_2 and is labelled Δy. The increments are found simply by subtracting the coordinates at P from those at Q.

Increments	$\Delta x = x_2 - x_1 \quad \text{and} \quad \Delta y = y_2 - y_1$	**337**

Some calculators can automatically find the straight-line distance between two points on a straight line or a curve. Check your manual to see if you have such a feature.

■ **Example 4:** A particle moves from $P_1(2, 5)$ to $P_2(7, 3)$. The increments in its coordinates are

$$\Delta x = x_2 - x_1 = 7 - 2 = 5$$

and

$$\Delta y = y_2 - y_1 = 3 - 5 = -2$$ ■

Distance Formula

We now find the length of a line inclined at any angle, such as PQ in Figure 22•4. We first draw a horizontal line through P and drop a perpendicular from Q, forming a right triangle PQR. The sides of the triangle are d, Δx, and Δy. By the Pythagorean theorem,

FIGURE 22•4 Length of a line segment

$$d^2 = (\Delta x)^2 + (\Delta y)^2 = (x_2 - x_1)^2 + (y_2 - y_1)^2$$

Since we want the magnitude of the distance, we take only the positive root and get

Distance Formula	$d = \sqrt{(\Delta x)^2 + (\Delta y)^2}$ $= \sqrt{(x_2 - x_1)^2 + (y_2 - y_1)^2}$	**283**

■ **Example 5:** Find the length of the line segment with the endpoints $(3, -5)$ and $(-1, 6)$.

Solution: Let us give the first point $(3, -5)$ the subscripts 1, and the other point the subscripts 2 (it does not matter which we label 1). So

$$x_1 = 3, \quad y_1 = -5, \quad x_2 = -1, \quad y_2 = 6$$

Substituting into the distance formula, we obtain

$$d = \sqrt{(-1 - 3)^2 + [6 - (-5)]^2} = \sqrt{(-4)^2 + (11)^2} = 11.7 \quad \text{(rounded)} \quad ■$$

Common Error	Do not take the square root of each term separately. $d \neq \sqrt{(x_2 - x_1)^2} + \sqrt{(y_2 - y_1)^2}$

Slope and Angle of Inclination of a Straight Line

Recall from Section 5.4 that the slope of a straight line for which

$$\text{rise} = \Delta y = y_2 - y_1$$

$$\text{run} = \Delta x = x_2 - x_1$$

is given by

Slope	$m = \dfrac{\text{rise}}{\text{run}} = \dfrac{\Delta y}{\Delta x} = \dfrac{y_2 - y_1}{x_2 - x_1}$	**284**

The slope is equal to the rise divided by the run.

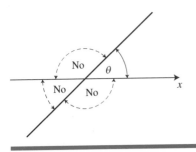

FIGURE 22·5 Angle of inclination, θ

FIGURE 22·6

FIGURE 22·7

FIGURE 22·8

We now relate the slope to the *angle of inclination*. The smallest positive angle that a line makes with the positive x direction is called the *angle of inclination* θ of the line (Fig. 22•5). A line parallel to the x axis has an angle of inclination of zero. Thus the angle of inclination can have values from 0° up to 180°. From Figure 22.4,

$$\tan \theta = \frac{\text{opposite side}}{\text{adjacent side}} = \frac{y_2 - y_1}{x_2 - x_1} = \frac{\text{rise}}{\text{run}} = \frac{\Delta y}{\Delta x}$$

But this is the slope m of the line, so

$m = \tan \theta$ $0° \leqq \theta < 180°$	**285**

The slope of a line is equal to the tangent of the angle of inclination θ (except when $\theta = 90°$).

■ **Example 6:** The slope of a line having an angle of inclination of 50° (Fig. 22•6) is, by Eq. 285,

$$m = \tan 50° = 1.192 \quad \text{(rounded)} \qquad ■$$

■ **Example 7:** Find the angle of inclination of a line (Fig. 22•7) having a slope of 3.

Solution: By Eq. 285, $\tan \theta = 3$, so

$$\theta = \arctan 3 = 71.6° \quad \text{(rounded)} \qquad ■$$

When the slope is negative, our calculator will give us a negative angle, which we then use to obtain a positive angle of inclination less than 180°.

■ **Example 8:** For a line having a slope of -2 (Fig. 22•8), arctan $(-2) = -63.4°$ (rounded), so

$$\theta = 180° - 63.4° = 116.6° \qquad ■$$

■ **Example 9:** Find the angle of inclination of the line passing through $(-2.47, 1.74)$ and $(3.63, -4.26)$ (Fig. 22•9).

Solution: The slope, from Eq. 285, is

$$m = \frac{-4.26 - 1.74}{3.63 - (-2.47)} = -0.984$$

from which $\theta = 135.5°$. ■

When *different scales* are used for the x and y axes, the angle of inclination *will appear distorted.*

■ **Example 10:** The angle of inclination of the line in Figure 22•10 is $\theta = \arctan 10 = 84.3°$. Notice that the angle in the graph appears much smaller than 84.3°, because of the different scales on the two axes.

FIGURE 22•9

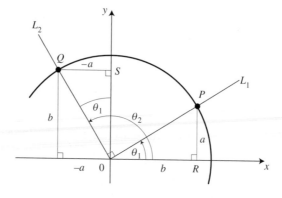

FIGURE 22•10

Slopes of Parallel and Perpendicular Lines

Parallel lines have, of course, *equal* slopes.

Slopes of Parallel Lines	$m_1 = m_2$	294

Parallel lines have equal slopes.

Now consider line L_1, with slope m_1 and angle of inclination θ_1, and line L_2 perpendicular to L_1, with slope m_2 and angle of inclination $\theta_2 = \theta_1 + 90°$ (Fig. 22•11). Note that $\angle QOS = \theta_2 - 90° = \theta_1 + 90° - 90° = \theta_1$, so right triangles OPR and OQS are congruent. Thus the magnitudes of their corresponding sides a and b are equal. The slope m_1 of L_1 is a/b, and the slope m_2 of L_2 is $-b/a$, so

Slopes of Perpendicular Lines	$m_1 = -\dfrac{1}{m_2}$	295

The slope of a line is the negative reciprocal of the slope of a perpendicular to that line.

FIGURE 22•11 Slopes of perpendicular lines

■ **Example 11:** Any line perpendicular to a line whose slope is 5 has a slope of $-\frac{1}{5}$. ■

Common Error	The minus sign in Eq. 295 is often forgotten. $$m_1 \neq \frac{1}{m_2}$$

■ **Example 12:** Is angle ACB (Fig. 22•12) a right angle?

FIGURE 22•12

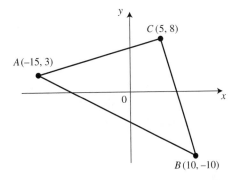

Solution: The slope of AC is

$$\frac{8-3}{5-(-15)} = \frac{5}{20} = \frac{1}{4}$$

To be perpendicular, BC must have a slope of -4. Its actual slope is

$$\frac{-10-8}{10-5} = \frac{-18}{5} = -3.6$$

Although lines AC and BC *appear* to be perpendicular, we have shown that they are not. Thus $\angle ACB$ is not a right angle. ■

Angle of Intersection between Two Lines

Figure 22•13 shows two lines L_1 and L_2 intersecting at an angle ϕ, measured counterclockwise from line L_1 to line L_2. We want a formula for ϕ in terms of the slopes m_1 and m_2 of the lines. By Eq. 142, θ_2 equals the sum of the angle of inclination θ_1 and the angle of intersection ϕ, so $\phi = \theta_2 - \theta_1$. Taking the tangents of both sides gives $\tan \phi = \tan(\theta_2 - \theta_1)$

FIGURE 22•13 Angle of intersection between two lines

or

$$\tan \phi = \frac{\tan \theta_2 - \tan \theta_1}{1 + \tan \theta_1 \tan \theta_2}$$

by the trigonometric identity for the tangent of the difference of two angles (Eq. 169). But the tangent of an angle of inclination is the slope, so

Angle between Two Lines	$$\tan \phi = \frac{m_2 - m_1}{1 + m_1 m_2}$$	**296**

FIGURE 22•14

■ **Example 13:** The tangent of the angle of intersection between line L_1 having a slope of 4, and line L_2 having a slope of -1, is

$$\tan \phi = \frac{-1 - 4}{1 + 4(-1)} = \frac{-5}{-3} = \frac{5}{3}$$

from which $\phi = \arctan \frac{5}{3} = 59.0°$ (rounded). This angle is measured counterclockwise from line L_1 to line L_2, as shown in Figure 22•14. ■

Tangents and Normals to Curves

We know what the tangent to a circle is, and probably have an intuitive idea of what the *tangent to a curve* is. We'll speak a lot about tangents, so let us try to get a clear idea of what one is.

To determine the tangent line at P (Fig. 22•15), we start by selecting a second point, Q, on the curve. As shown, Q can be on either side of P. The line PQ is called a *secant line*. We then let Q approach P (from either side). If the secant lines PQ approach a single line T as Q approaches P, then line T is called the tangent line at P.

FIGURE 22•15 A tangent line T at point P, here defined as the limiting position of a secant line PQ, as Q approaches P

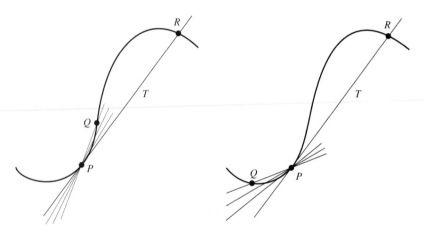

In calculus you will see that the slope gives the *rate of change* of the function, an extremely useful quantity to find. You will see that it is found by taking the *derivative* of the function.

Note that the tangent line can intersect the curve at more than one point, such as point R. However, at points "near" P, the tangent line intersects the curve just once while a secant line intersects the curve twice. The *slope of a curve* at some point P is defined as the *slope of the tangent* to the curve drawn through that point.

■ **Example 14:** Plot the curve $y = x^2$ for integer values of x from 0 to 4. By eye, draw the tangent to the curve at $x = 2$ and find the approximate value of the slope.

Solution: We make a table of point pairs:

x	0	1	2	3	4
y	0	1	4	9	16

The plot and the tangent line are shown in Figure 22•16. Using the scales on the x and y axes, we measure a rise of 12 units for the tangent line in a run of 3 units. The slope of the tangent line is then

$$m_1 \simeq \frac{12}{3} = 4$$

FIGURE 22·16 Slope of a curve

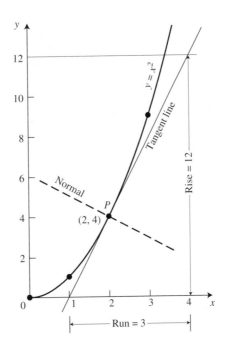

The notion of a tangent to a curve can be clearly demonstrated by using a graphics utility to zoom in on a portion of the curve.

■ **Example 15:** Zoom in on the curve of Example 14 at the point (2, 4), and estimate the slope of the tangent.

Solution: As we zoom in at (2, 4), the curve appears straighter and straighter. With a viewing window of $x = 1.9$ to 2.1 and $y = 3.9$ to 4.1, the curve appears as in Figure 22·17. Using TRACE, we get the coordinates of two points on the curve, (1.9873, 3.9494) and (2.0143, 4.0573). Calculating the slope gives

FIGURE 22·17

$$m = \frac{4.0573 - 3.9494}{2.0143 - 1.9873} = 3.996$$

which agrees with the value found in Example 14.

The *normal* to a curve at a given point is the line perpendicular to the tangent at that point, as in Figure 22·16. Its slope is the negative reciprocal of the slope of the tangent. For Example 14, $m_n = -\frac{1}{4}$.

Equation of a Straight Line

This is a good time to glance back at Section 5·4 and review some of the exercises there.

In Section 5·4 we introduced the *slope–intercept form*, the equation of a straight line. The equation for a line with a slope m and y intercept b is

Slope–Intercept Form	$y = mx + b$	**289**

Using this equation we can quickly write the equation of a straight line if we know the slope and the y intercept. However, we may have *other* information about the line, such as the coordinates of two points on that line, and want to write the equation using that information. To enable us to do this, we'll now derive several other forms for the straight-line equation.

General Form

The slope–intercept form is the equation of a straight line in *explicit* form, $y = f(x)$. We can also write the equation of a straight line in *implicit* form, $f(x, y) = 0$, simply by transposing all terms to one side of the equal sign and simplifying. We usually write the x term first, then the y term, and finally the constant term. This form is referred to as the *general form* of the equation of a straight line.

General Form	$Ax + By + C = 0$	286

where A, B, and C are constants.

You will see as we go along that there are several forms for the equation of a straight line, and we use the one that is most convenient in a particular problem. But to make it easy to compare answers, we usually rearrange the equation into general form.

■ **Example 16:** Change the equation $y = \frac{6}{7}x - 5$ from slope–intercept form to general form.

Solution: Subtracting y from both sides, we have

$$0 = \frac{6}{7}x - 5 - y$$

Multiplying by 7 and rearranging gives $6x - 7y - 35 = 0$.   ■

Point–Slope Form

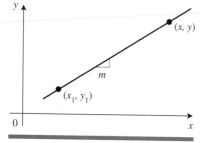

FIGURE 22·18

Let us write an equation for a line of slope m, which passes through a given point (x_1, y_1) which is *not*, in general, on either axis, as in Figure 22·18. Again using the definition of slope (Eq. 284), with a general point (x, y), we get the following form.

Point–Slope Form	$m = \dfrac{y - y_1}{x - x_1}$	291

This form of the equation of a straight line is most useful when we know the slope of a line and one point through which the line passes.

■ **Example 17:** Write the equation in general form of the line having a slope of 2 and passing through the point $(1, -3)$ (Fig. 22·19).

Solution: Substituting $m = 2$, $x_1 = 1$, $y_1 = -3$ into Eq. 291 gives us

$$2 = \frac{y - (-3)}{x - 1}$$

Multiplying by $x - 1$ yields

$$2x - 2 = y + 3$$

FIGURE 22·19

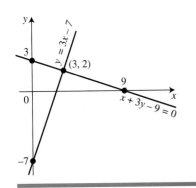

FIGURE 22·20

FIGURE 22·21

FIGURE 22·22

or, in general form,

$$2x - y - 5 = 0$$

■ **Example 18:** Write the equation in general form of the line passing through the point (3, 2) and perpendicular to the line $y = 3x - 7$ (Fig. 22·20).

Solution: The slope of the given line is 3, so the slope of our perpendicular line is $-\frac{1}{3}$. Using the point–slope form, we obtain

$$-\frac{1}{3} = \frac{y - 2}{x - 3}$$

Going to the general form, $x - 3 = -3y + 6$, or

$$x + 3y - 9 = 0$$

■ **Example 19:** Write the equation in general form of the line passing through the point (3.15, 5.88) and having an angle of inclination of 27.8° (Fig. 22·21).

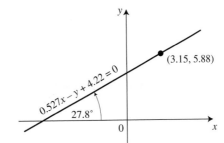

Solution: From Eq. 285, $m = \tan 27.8° = 0.527$. From Eq. 291,

$$0.527 = \frac{y - 5.88}{x - 3.15}$$

Changing to general form, $0.527x - 1.66 = y - 5.88$,

or

$$0.527x - y + 4.22 = 0$$

Two–Point Form

If two points on a line are known, the equation of the line is easily written using the two point form, which we now derive. In Figure 22·22, the slope of the line between the points P_1 and P_2 is

FIGURE 22•23

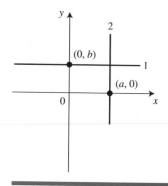

FIGURE 22•24

$$m = \frac{y_2 - y_1}{x_2 - x_1}$$

The slope of the line segment connecting P_1 with any other point P on the same line is

$$m = \frac{y - y_1}{x - x_1}$$

Since these slopes must be equal, we get

Two–Point Form	$\dfrac{y - y_1}{x - x_1} = \dfrac{y_2 - y_1}{x_2 - x_1}$	**290**

■ **Example 20:** Write the equation in general form of the line passing through the points $(1, -3)$ and $(-2, 5)$ (Fig. 22•23).

Solution: Calling the first given point P_1 and the second P_2 and substituting into Eq. 290, we have

$$\frac{y - (-3)}{x - 1} = \frac{5 - (-3)}{-2 - 1} = \frac{8}{-3}$$

$$\frac{y + 3}{x - 1} = -\frac{8}{3}$$

Putting the equation into general form, $3y + 9 = -8x + 8$, or

$$8x + 3y + 1 = 0$$ ■

Lines Parallel to the Coordinate Axes

Line 1 in Figure 22•24 is parallel to the x axis. Its slope is 0 and it cuts the y axis at $(0, b)$. From the point–slope form, $y - y_1 = m(x - x_1)$, we get $y - b = 0(x - 0)$, or

Line Parallel to x Axis	$y = b$	**287**

Line 2 has an undefined slope, but we get its equation by noting that $x = a$ at every point on the line, *regardless of the value of y*. Thus

Line Parallel to y Axis	$x = a$	**288**

■ **Example 21:**
(a) A line that passes through the point $(5, -2)$ and is parallel to the x axis has the equation $y = -2$.
(b) A line that passes through the point $(5, -2)$ and is parallel to the y axis has the equation $x = 5$. ■

Exercise 1 The Straight Line

Length of a Line Segment

Find the distance between the given points:

1. (5, 0) and (2, 0)
2. (0, 3) and (0, −5)
3. (−2, 0) and (7, 0)
4. (−4, 0) and (−6, 0)
5. (0, −2.74) and (0, 3.86)
6. (55.34, 0) and (25.38, 0)
7. (5.59, 3.25) and (8.93, 3.25)
8. (−2.06, −5.83) and (−2.06, −8.34)
9. (8.38, −3.95) and (2.25, −4.99)

Find the directed distance *AB*:

10. $A(3, 0)$; $B(5, 0)$
11. $A(3.95, -2.07)$; $B(-3.95, -2.07)$
12. $B(-8, -2)$; $A(-8, -5)$
13. $A(-9, -2)$; $B(17, -2)$
14. $B(-6, -6)$; $A(-6, -7)$
15. $B(11.5, 3.68)$; $A(11.5, -5.38)$

Slope and Angle of Inclination

Find the slope of the line having the given angle of inclination:

16. 38.2°   **17.** 77.9°   **18.** 1.83 rad
19. 58°14′   **20.** 156.3°   **21.** 132.8°

Find the angle of inclination, in decimal degrees to three significant digits, of a line having the given slope:

22. $m = 3$ **23.** $m = 1.84$ **24.** $m = -4$
25. $m = -2.75$ **26.** $m = 0$ **27.** $m = -15$

Find the slope of a line perpendicular to a line having the given slope:

28. $m = 5$ **29.** $m = 2$ **30.** $m = 4.8$
31. $m = -1.85$ **32.** $m = -2.85$ **33.** $m = -5.372$

Find the slope of a line perpendicular to a line having the given angle of inclination:

34. 58.2°   **35.** 1.84 rad   **36.** 136°44′

Find the angle of inclination, in decimal degrees to three significant digits, of a line passing through the given points:

37. (5, 2) and (−3, 4)   **38.** (−2.5, −3.1) and (5.8, 4.2)
39. (6, 3) and (−1, 5)   **40.** $(x, 3)$ and $(x + 5, 8)$

Angle between Two Lines

41. Find the angle of intersection between line L_1 having a slope of 1 and line L_2 having a slope of 6.

42. Find the angle of intersection between line L_1 having a slope of 3 and line L_2 having a slope of -2.

43. Find the angle of intersection between line L_1 having an angle of inclination of $35°$ and line L_2 having an angle of inclination of $160°$.

44. Find the angle of intersection between line L_1 having an angle of inclination of $22°$ and line L_2 having an angle of inclination of $86°$.

Tangents to Curves

Plot the functions below from $x = 0$ to $x = 4$. Graphically find the slope of the curve at $x = 2$.

45. $y = x^3$ **46.** $y = -x^2 + 3$ **47.** $y = \dfrac{x^2}{4}$

Equation of a Straight Line

Write the equation in general form of each line described below:

48. Slope = 4, y intercept = -3
49. Slope = 2.25, y intercept = -1.48
50. Passes through points $(3, 5)$ and $(-1, 2)$
51. Passes through points $(4.24, -1.25)$ and $(3.85, 4.27)$
52. Slope = -4, passes through $(-2, 5)$
53. Slope = -2, passes through $(-2, -3)$
54. x intercept = 5, y intercept = -3
55. x intercept = -2, y intercept = 6
56. y intercept = 3, parallel to $y = 5x - 2$
57. y intercept = -2.3, parallel to $2x - 3y + 1 = 0$
58. y intercept = -5, perpendicular to $y = 3x - 4$
59. y intercept = 2, perpendicular to $4x - 3y = 7$
60. Passing through $(-2, 5)$, parallel to $y = 5x - 1$
61. Passing through $(4, -1)$, parallel to $4x - y = -3$
62. Passing through $(-4, 2)$, perpendicular to $y = 5x - 3$
63. Passing through $(6, 1)$, perpendicular to $6y - 2x = 3$
64. y intercept = 4.0, angle of inclination = $48°$
65. y intercept = -3.52, angle of inclination = $154°44'$
66. Passing through $(4, -1)$, angle of inclination = $22.8°$
67. Passing through $(-2.24, 5.17)$, angle of inclination = $68°14'$
68. Passing through $(5, 2)$ and is parallel to the x axis.
69. Passing through $(-3, 6)$ and is parallel to the y axis.
70. Line A in Figure 22•25
71. Line B in Figure 22•25
72. Line C in Figure 22•25
73. Line D in Figure 22•25
74. Find the length of girder AB in Figure 22•26.
75. Find the distance between the centers of the holes in Figure 22•27.
76. A triangle has vertices at $(3, 5)$, $(-2, 4)$, and $(4, -3)$. Find the length of each side. Then compute the area using Hero's formula (Eq. 138). Work to three significant digits.

FIGURE 22·25

FIGURE 22·26

FIGURE 22·27

77. The distance between two stakes on a slope is taped at 626 m and the angle of the slope with the horizontal is 12.3°. Find the horizontal distance between the stakes.

78. What is the angle of inclination with the horizontal of a roadbed that rises 4.60 m in each 76.2 m measured horizontally?

79. Two stakes are positioned on a 7° slope with one above the other by a horizontal distance of 125 cm. How far apart are the two stakes when measured up the slope?

80. On a 5% road grade, at what angle is the road inclined to the horizontal? How far does one rise in travelling upward 152.4 m; measured along the road?

81. A straight tunnel under a river is $23\overline{0}$ m long and descends 3.66 m in this distance. What angle does the tunnel make with the horizontal?

82. A straight driveway slopes downward from a house to a road and is 28 m in length. If the angle of inclination from the road to the house is 3.6°, find the height of the house above the road.

83. An escalator is built so as to rise 2 m for each 3 m of horizontal travel. Find its angle of inclination.

84. A straight highway makes an angle of 4.5° with the horizontal. How much does the highway rise in a distance of 762 m measured along the road?

In some fields, such as highway work, the word *grade* is used instead of slope. It is usually expressed as a percentage:

$$percentage\ grade = 100 \times slope$$

Thus, a 5% grade rises 5 units for every 100 units of run.

FIGURE 22•28

Spring Constant

85. A spring whose length is L_0 with no force applied (Fig. 22•28) stretches an amount x with an applied force of F, where $F = kx$. The constant k is called the spring constant. Write an equation, in slope–intercept form, for F in terms of k, L, and L_0.

86. What force would be needed to stretch a spring ($k = 2.54$ N/mm) from an unstretched length of 216 mm to a length of 318 mm?

Velocity of Uniformly Accelerated Body

87. When a body moves with constant acceleration a (such as in free fall), its velocity v at any time t is given by $v = v_0 + at$, where v_0 is the initial velocity. Note that this is the equation of a straight line. If a body has a constant acceleration of 2.15 m/s² and has a velocity of 21.8 m/s at 5.25 s, find **(a)** the initial velocity and **(b)** the velocity at 25.0 s.

Resistance Change with Temperature

88. The resistance of metals is a linear function of the temperature (Fig. 22•29) for certain ranges of temperature. The slope of the line is $R_1\alpha$, where α is the temperature coefficient of resistance at temperature t_1. If R is the resistance of any temperature t, write an equation for R as a function of t.

89. Using a value for α of $1/(234.5t_1)$ (for copper), find the resistance of a copper conductor at 75.0°C if its resistance at 20.0°C is 148.4 Ω.

90. If the resistance of the copper conductor in Problem 89 is 1255 Ω at 20.0°C, at what temperature will the resistance be 1265 Ω?

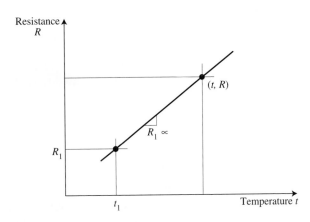

Thermal Expansion

91. When a bar is heated, its length will increase from an initial length L_0 at temperature t_0 to a new length L at temperature t. The plot of L versus t is a straight line (Fig 22·30) with a slope of $L_0\alpha$, where α is the coefficient of thermal expansion. Derive the equation $L = L_0(1 + \alpha \, \Delta t)$, where Δt is the change in temperature, $t - t_0$.

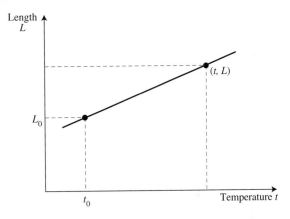

92. A steel pipe is 21.50 m long at 0°C. Find its length at 75.0°C if α for steel is 12.0×10^{-6} per Celsius degree.

Fluid Pressure

93. The pressure at a point located at a depth x m from the surface of the liquid varies directly as the depth. If the pressure at the surface is 103 kPa and increases by 12.4 kPa for every metre of depth, write an equation for P as a function of the depth x (in metres). At what depth will the pressure be 208 kPa?

94. A straight pipe slopes downward from a reservoir to a water turbine (Fig. 22·31). The pressure head at any point in the pipe, expressed in metres, is equal to the vertical distance between the point and the surface of the reservoir. If the reservoir surface is 7.62 m above the upper end of the pipe, write an expression for the head H as a function of the horizontal distance x. At what distance x will the head be 10.7 m?

FIGURE 22·31

Temperature Gradient

95. Figure 22·32 shows a uniform wall whose inside face is at temperature t_i and whose outside face is at t_o. The temperatures within the wall plot as a straight line connecting t_i and t_o. Write the equation $t = f(x)$ of that line, taking $x = 0$ at the inside face, if $t_i = 25.0°C$ and $t_o = -5.0°C$. At what x will the temperature be $0°C$? What is the slope of the line?

FIGURE 22·32 Temperature drop in a wall. The slope of the line (in °C/cm) is called the *temperature gradient*. The amount of heat flowing through the wall is proportional to the temperature gradient.

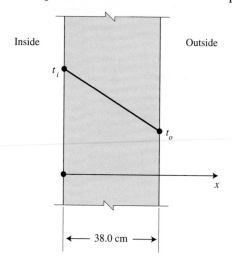

Hooke's Law

96. The increase in length of a wire in tension is directly proportional to the applied load P. Write an equation for the length L of a wire that has an initial length of 3.00 m and which stretches 1.00 mm for each 12.5 N. Find the length of the wire with a load of $75\overline{0}$ N.

Straight-Line Depreciation

97. The straight-line method is often used to depreciate a piece of equipment for tax purposes. Starting with the purchase price P, the item is assumed to drop in value the same amount each year (the annual depreciation) until the salvage value S is reached (Fig. 22·33). Write an expression for the book value y (the value at any time) as a function of the number of years t. For a lathe that cost \$15 428 and has a salvage value of \$2264, find the book value after 15 years if it is depreciated over a period of 20 years.

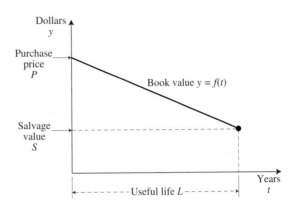

FIGURE 22·33 Straight-line depreciation

FIGURE 22·33 Straight-line depreciation

Computer

98. Write a program that will accept as input the coordinates of the vertices of a triangle, and then compute and print the length of each side and the area of the triangle.

Graphics Utility

99. Use a graphics calculator or a graphics utility on a computer to graph any of the straight lines in this exercise. The equation of the line must first be written in explicit form, that is, the slope–intercept form.

22·2

The Circle

Definition

Anyone who has drawn a circle using a compass will not be surprised by the following definition of the circle:

Definition	A *circle* is a plane curve all points of which are at a fixed distance (the *radius*) from a fixed point (the *center*).	**303**

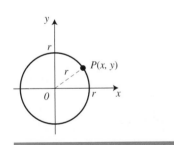

FIGURE 22·34 Circle with center at origin

Circle with Center at the Origin

We will now derive an equation for a circle of radius r, starting with the simplest case of a circle whose center is at the origin (Fig. 22·34). Let x and y be the coordinates of any point P on the circle. The equation we develop will give a relationship between x and y that will have two meanings: geometrically, (x, y) will represent a point on the circle, and, algebraically, the numbers corresponding to those points will satisfy that equation.

We observe that, by the definition of a circle, the distance OP must be constant and equal to r. But by the distance formula (Eq. 283),

$$OP = \sqrt{x^2 + y^2} = r$$

Squaring, we get a *standard equation of a circle* (also called *standard form* of the equation).

Standard Equation, Circle of Radius r: Center of Origin	$x^2 + y^2 = r^2$	**304**

■ **Example 22:** Write, in standard form, the equation of a circle of radius 3, whose center is at the origin.

Solution:

$$x^2 + y^2 = 3^2 = 9$$ ■

Note that both x^2 and y^2 have the same coefficient. Otherwise, the graph is not a circle.

Circle with Center Not at the Origin

Figure 22•35 shows a circle whose center has the coordinates (h, k). We can think of the difference between this circle and the one in Figure 22•34 as the location of the center. The circle in Figure 22•35 has had its center moved or *translated* h units to the right and k units upward. Our derivation is similar to the preceding one.

$$CP = r = \sqrt{(x - h)^2 + (y - k)^2}$$

Squaring, we get

Standard Equation, Circle of Radius r: Center at (h, k)	$(x - h)^2 + (y - k)^2 = r^2$	**305**

FIGURE 22•35 Circle with center at (h, k)

■ **Example 23:** Write, in standard form, the equation of a circle of radius 5 whose center is at $(3, -2)$.

Solution: We substitute into Eq. 305 with $r = 5$, $h = 3$, and $k = -2$:

$$(x - 3)^2 + [y - (-2)]^2 = 5^2$$
$$(x - 3)^2 + (y + 2)^2 = 25$$ ■

■ **Example 24:** Find the radius and the coordinates of the center of the circle $(x + 5)^2 + (y - 3)^2 = 16$.

Solution: We see that $r^2 = 16$, so the radius r is 4. Also, since

$$x - h = x + 5$$
$$h = -5$$

and since

$$y - k = y - 3$$
$$k = 3$$

so the center is at $(-5, 3)$ (Fig. 22•36). ■

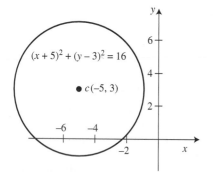

FIGURE 22•36

Common Error	It is easy to get the signs of h and k wrong. In the preceding example, do *not* take $$h = +5 \quad \text{and} \quad k = -3$$

Translation of Axes

We see that Eq. 305 for a circle with its center at (h, k) is almost identical to Eq. 304 for a circle with center at the origin, except that *x has been replaced by* $(x - h)$ *and y has been replaced by* $(y - k)$. This same substitution will, of course, work for curves other than the circle, and we will use it to translate or shift the axes for the other conic sections.

Translation of Axes	To translate or shift the axes of a curve to the left by a distance h and downward by a distance k, replace x by $(x - h)$ and y by $(y - k)$ in the equation of the curve.	**298**

General Equation of a Circle

A second-degree equation in x and y which has all possible terms would have an x^2 term, a y^2 term, an xy term, and all terms of lesser degree as well. The general second-degree equation is usually written with terms in the following order, where A, B, C, D, E, and F are constants.

There are six constants in this equation, but only five are independent. We can divide through by any constant and thus make it equal to 1.

General Second-Degree Equation	$Ax^2 + Bxy + Cy^2 + Dx + Ey + F = 0$	**297**

If we expand Eq. 305 we get

$$(x - h)^2 + (y - k)^2 = r^2$$

$$x^2 - 2hx + h^2 + y^2 - 2ky + k^2 = r^2$$

Rearranging gives $x^2 + y^2 - 2hx - 2ky + (h^2 + k^2 - r^2) = 0$, or an equation with D, E, and F as constants.

General Equation of a Circle	$x^2 + y^2 + Dx + Ey + F = 0$	**306**

Comparing this with the general second-degree equation, we see that the general second-degree equation

$$Ax^2 + Bxy + Cy^2 + Dx + Ey + F = 0$$

represents a circle if $B = 0$ and $A = C$.

■ **Example 25:** Write the equation of Example 24 in general form.

Solution: The equation, in standard form, was

$$(x + 5)^2 + (y - 3)^2 = 16$$

Expanding, we obtain

$$x^2 + 10x + 25 + y^2 - 6y + 9 = 16$$

or

$$x^2 + y^2 + 10x - 6y + 18 = 0$$

Some computer algebra systems have commands for completing the square. See Problem 35 in Exercise 2 (page 670).

Changing from General to Standard Form

When we want to go from general form to standard form, we must *complete the square*, both for x and for y.

■ **Example 26:** Write the equation $2x^2 + 2y^2 - 18x + 16y + 60 = 0$ in standard form. Find the radius and center, and plot the curve.

Solution: We first divide by 2:

$$x^2 + y^2 - 9x + 8y + 30 = 0$$

and separate the x and y terms:

$$(x^2 - 9x) + (y^2 + 8y) = -30$$

We complete the square for the x terms with $\frac{81}{4}$ because we take $\frac{1}{2}$ of (-9) and square it. Similarly, for completing the square for the y terms, $(\frac{1}{2} \times 8)^2 = 16$. Completing the square on the left and compensating on the right gives

$$\left(x^2 - 9x + \frac{81}{4}\right) + (y^2 + 8y + 16) = -30 + \frac{81}{4} + 16$$

Factoring each group of terms yields

$$\left(x - \frac{9}{2}\right)^2 + (y + 4)^2 = \left(\frac{5}{2}\right)^2$$

So

$$r = \frac{5}{2}, \quad h = \frac{9}{2}, \quad k = -4$$

The circle is shown in Figure 22·37.   ■

FIGURE 22·37

Graphics Utility

To use a graphics calculator or a graphics utility on the computer to graph a circle, we must first solve the equation of the circle for y,

$$y = k \pm \sqrt{r^2 - (x - h)^2}$$

and plot the two functions

$$y_1 = k + \sqrt{r^2 - (x - h)^2}$$

and

$$y_2 = k - \sqrt{r^2 - (x - h)^2}$$

Note that the graph may not *appear* circular on a particular grapher, but some have a provision for equalizing the vertical and horizontal scales so that circles do appear circular.

Applications

■ **Example 27:** Write an equation for the circle shown in Figure 22·38, and find the dimensions A and B produced by the circular cutting tool.

FIGURE 22·38

Estimate: The easiest way to get an estimate is to make a sketch and measure the distances. We get

$$A \approx 66 \text{ mm} \quad \text{and} \quad B \approx 69 \text{ mm}$$

Solution: In order to write an equation we must have coordinate axes; otherwise the quantities x and y in the equation will have no meaning. Since no axes are given we are free to draw them anywhere we please. Our first impulse might be to place the origin at the corner p, since most of the dimensions are referenced from that point, but our equation will be simpler if we place the origin at the center of the circle. Let us draw axes as shown, so that not all our numbers will be negative. The equation of the circle is then

$$x^2 + y^2 = (38.00 \text{ mm})^2$$

$$x^2 + y^2 = 1444 \text{ mm}$$

The distance from the y axis to the top edge of the block is (105.5 mm − 80.00 mm) = 25.54 mm. Substituting this value for x into the equation of the circle will give the corresponding value for y. When $x = 25.54$ mm,

$$y^2 = 1444 \text{ mm} - (25.54 \text{ mm})^2 = 791.86 \text{ mm}$$

$$y = 28.14 \text{ mm}$$

Similarly, the distance from the x axis to the right edge of the block is 105.5 mm − 94.36 mm = 11.14 mm. When $y = 11.14$ mm,

$$x^2 = 1444 \text{ mm} - (-11.14 \text{ mm})^2 = 1319.9 \text{ mm}$$

$$x = 36.33 \text{ mm}$$

Finally,

$$A = 94.36 \text{ mm} - 28.14 \text{ mm} = 66.22 \text{ mm}$$

and

$$B = 105.5 \text{ mm} - 36.33 \text{ mm} = 69.17 \text{ mm}$$

Exercise 2 The Circle

Equation of a Circle

Write the equation of each circle in standard form:

1. Center at $(0, 0)$, radius = 7
2. Center at $(0, 0)$, radius = 4.82
3. Center at $(2, 3)$, radius = 5
4. Center at $(5, 2)$, radius = 10
5. Center at $(5, -3)$, radius = 4
6. Center at $(-3, -2)$, radius = 11

Find the center and radius of each circle:

7. $x^2 + y^2 = 49$
8. $x^2 + y^2 = 64.8$
9. $(x - 2)^2 + (y + 4)^2 = 16$
10. $(x + 5)^2 + (y - 2)^2 = 49$
11. $(y + 5)^2 + (x - 3)^2 = 36$
12. $(x - 2.22)^2 + (y + 7.16)^2 = 5.93$
13. $x^2 + y^2 - 8x = 0$
14. $x^2 + y^2 - 2x - 4y = 0$
15. $x^2 + y^2 - 10x + 12y + 25 = 0$
16. $x^2 + y^2 - 4x + 2y = 36$
17. $x^2 + y^2 + 6x - 2y = 15$
18. $x^2 + y^2 - 2x - 6y = 39$

Write the equation of each circle in general form:

19. Center at $(1, 1)$, passes through $(4, -3)$
20. With diameter joining the points $(-2, 5)$ and $(6, -1)$

Tangent to a Circle

Write the equation of the tangent to each circle described below at the given point. (*Hint:* The slope of the tangent is the negative reciprocal of the slope of the radius to the given point.)

21. $x^2 + y^2 = 25$ at $(4, 3)$
22. $(x - 5)^2 + (y - 6)^2 = 100$ at $(11, 14)$
23. $x^2 + y^2 + 10y = 0$ at $(-4, -2)$

Intercepts

Find the x and y intercepts for each circle described below. (*Hint:* Set x and y, in turn, equal to zero to find the intercepts.)

24. $x^2 + y^2 - 6x + 4y + 4 = 0$
25. $x^2 + y^2 - 5x - 7y + 6 = 0$

Intersecting Circles

Find the point(s) of intersection of the pairs of circles below. (*Hint:* Solve each pair of equations simultaneously as we did in Chapter 14, Exercise 8.)

26. $x^2 + y^2 - 10x = 0$ and $x^2 + y^2 + 2x - 6y = 0$
27. $x^2 + y^2 - 3y - 4 = 0$ and $x^2 + y^2 + 2x - 5y - 2 = 0$
28. $x^2 + y^2 + 2x - 6y + 2 = 0$ and $x^2 + y^2 - 4x + 2 = 0$

Applications

Even though you may be able to solve some of these with only the Pythagorean theorem, we suggest that you use analytic geometry for the practice.

29. Prove that any angle inscribed in a semicircle is a right angle.

30. Write the equation of the circle in Figure 22•39, taking the axes as shown. Use your equation to find A and B.

FIGURE 22•39

31. Write the equation for each of the circular arches in Figure 22•40, taking the axes as shown. Solve simultaneously to get the point of intersection P, and compute the height L of the column.

FIGURE 22•40 Circular arches

32. Write the equation of the centerline of the circular street shown in Figure 22•41, taking the origin at the intersection 0. Use your equation to find the distance y.

FIGURE 22·41 Circular street

33. Each side of a Gothic arch is a portion of a circle. Write the equation of one side of the Gothic arch shown in Figure 22·42. Use the equation to find the width w of the arch at a height of $100\overline{0}$ mm.

FIGURE 22·42 Gothic arch

Graphics Utility

34. Use a graphics calculator or a graphics utility on the computer to graph any of the circles in this exercise.

Computer

35. Some computer algebra systems can complete the square. *Maple*, for example, uses the **completesquare** command. If the expression has two variables, however, it is necessary to complete the square in two separate operations, once for x and once for y. If you have such a system, use it to go from general to standard form whenever needed in this exercise.

22•3

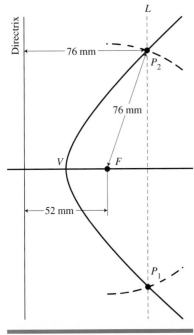

FIGURE 22•43 Construction of a parabola

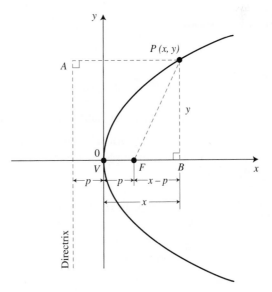

FIGURE 22•44 Parabola

FIGURE 22•45

The Parabola

Definition

A parabola has the following definition:

Definition	A *parabola* is the set of points in a plane each of which is equidistant from a fixed point, the *focus*, and a fixed line, the *directrix*.	**307**

■ **Example 28:** Use the definition above to construct a parabola for which the distance from focus to directrix is 51 mm.

Solution: We draw a line to represent the directrix, Figure 22•43, and indicate a focus 52 mm from that line. Then draw a line L parallel to the directrix at some arbitrary distance, say 76 mm. Then, with that same (76 mm) distance as radius and F as center, use a compass to draw arcs intersecting L at P_1 and P_2. Each of these points is now at the same distance (76 mm) from F and from the directrix, and is hence a point on the parabola. Repeat the construction with distances other than 76 mm to get more points on the parabola. ■

Figure 22•44 shows the typical shape of the parabola. The parabola has an *axis of symmetry* which intersects it at the *vertex*. The distance p from directrix to vertex is equal to the directed distance from the vertex to the focus.

Standard Equation of a Parabola with vertex at the origin

Let us place the parabola on coordinate axes with the vertex at the origin (Fig. 22•45) and with the axis of symmetry along the x axis. Choose any point P on the parabola. Then, by the definition of a parabola, $FP = AP$. But in right triangle FBP,

$$FP = \sqrt{(x - p)^2 + y^2}$$

and also,

$$AP = p + x$$

But since $FP = AP$,

$$\sqrt{(x - p)^2 + y^2} = p + x$$

Squaring both sides yields

$$(x - p)^2 + y^2 = p^2 + 2px + x^2$$

$$x^2 - 2px + p^2 + y^2 = p^2 + 2px + x^2$$

Collecting terms, we get the standard equation of a parabola with vertex at the origin.

Standard Equation of a Parabola: Vertex at Origin, Axis Horizontal		$y^2 = 4px$	**308**

We have defined p as the directed distance VF from the vertex V to the focus F. Thus, if p is positive, the focus must lie to the right of the vertex, and hence the parabola opens to the right. Conversely, if p is negative, the parabola opens to the left.

■ **Example 29:** Find the coordinates of the focus of the parabola $2y^2 + 7x = 0$.

Solution: Subtracting $7x$ from both sides and dividing by 2 gives us

$$y^2 = -3.5x$$

Thus $4p = -3.5$ and $p = -0.875$. Since p is negative, the parabola opens to the left. The focus is thus 0.875 unit to the left of the vertex (Fig. 22•46) and so has the coordinates $(-0.875, 0)$. ■

FIGURE 22•46

We have graphed the parabola before. Glance back at Section 5•2.

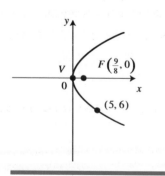

FIGURE 22•47

■ **Example 30:** Find the coordinates of the focus and write the equation of a parabola whose vertex is at the origin, that has a horizontal axis of symmetry, and that passes through the point $(5, -6)$.

Solution: Our given point must satisfy the equation $y^2 = 4px$. Substituting 5 for x and -6 for y gives

$$(-6)^2 = 4p(5)$$

Thus $4p = \frac{36}{5}$ and $p = \frac{9}{5}$. The equation of the parabola is, then, $y^2 = 36x/5$, or

$$5y^2 = 36x$$

Since the axis is horizontal and p is positive, the focus must be on the x axis and is a distance $p(\frac{9}{5})$ to the right of the origin. The coordinates of F are thus $(\frac{9}{5}, 0)$ (Fig. 22•47). ■

Standard Equation of a Parabola with Vertical Axis

The standard equation for a parabola having a vertical axis is obtained by switching the positions of x and y in Eq. 308,

Standard Equation of a Parabola: Vertex at Origin, Axis Vertical		$x^2 = 4py$	309

When p is positive, the parabola opens upward; when p is negative, it opens downward.

■ **Example 31:** A parabola has its vertex at the origin and passes through the points (3, 2) and (−3, 2). Write its equation and find the focus.

Solution: A sketch (Fig. 22•48) shows that the axis must be vertical, so our equation is of the form $x^2 = 4py$. Substituting 3 for x and 2 for y gives

$$3^2 = 4p(2)$$

from which $4p = \frac{9}{2}$ and $p = \frac{9}{8}$. Our equation is then $x^2 = 9y/2$ or $2x^2 = 9y$. The focus is on the y axis at a distance $p = \frac{9}{8}$ from the origin, so its coordinates are $(0, \frac{9}{8})$. ■

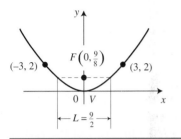

FIGURE 22•48

Focal Width of a Parabola

The *latus rectum* of a parabola is a line through the focus which is perpendicular to the axis of symmetry, such as line AB in Figure 22•49. The length of the latus rectum is also called the *focal width*. We will find the focal width, or length L of the latus rectum, by substituting the coordinates (p, h) of point A into Eq. 308:

$$h^2 = 4p(p) = 4p^2$$
$$h = \pm 2p$$

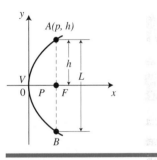

FIGURE 22•49

The focal width is twice h, so

Focal Width of a Parabola	$L = |4p|$	313

The focal width (length of the latus rectum) of a parabola is four times the distance from vertex to focus.

■ **Example 32:** The focal width for the parabola in Figure 22•48 is $\frac{9}{2}$, or 4.5 units. ■

Shift of Axes

As with the circle, when the vertex of the parabola is not at the origin but at (h, k), our equations will be similar to Eqs. 308 and 309, except that x is replaced with $x - h$ and y is replaced with $y - k$.

Standard Equations of a Parabola: Vertex at (h, k)	Axis Horizontal	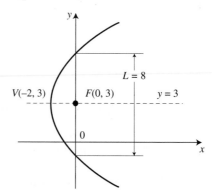	$(y - k)^2 = 4p(x - h)$	**310**
	Axis Vertical		$(x - h)^2 = 4p(y - k)$	**311**

■ **Example 33:** Find the vertex, focus, focal width, and equation of the axis for the parabola $(y - 3)^2 = 8(x + 2)$.

Solution: The given equation is of the same form as Eq. 310, so the axis is horizontal. Also, $h = -2$, $k = 3$, and $4p = 8$. So the vertex is at $V(-2, 3)$ (Fig. 22•50). Since $p = \frac{8}{4} = 2$, the focus is 2 units to the right of the vertex, at $F(0, 3)$. The focal width is $4p$, so $L = 8$. The axis is horizontal and 3 units from the x axis, so its equation is $y = 3$. ■

FIGURE 22•50

FIGURE 22•51

■ **Example 34:** Write the equation of a parabola that opens upward, with vertex at $(-1, 2)$, and which passes through the point $(1, 3)$ (Fig. 22•51). Find the focus and the focal width.

Solution: We substitute $h = -1$ and $k = 2$ into Eq. 311:

$$(x + 1)^2 = 4p(y - 2)$$

Now, since $(1, 3)$ is on the parabola, these coordinates must satisfy our equation. Substituting yields

$$(1 + 1)^2 = 4p(3 - 2)$$

Solving for p, we obtain $2^2 = 4p$, or $p = 1$. So the equation is

$$(x + 1)^2 = 4(y - 2)$$

The focus is p units above the vertex, at $(-1, 3)$. The focal width is, by Eq. 313,

$$L = |4p| = 4(1) = 4 \text{ units}$$ ■

General Equation of a Parabola

We get the general equation of the parabola by expanding the standard equation (Eq. 310):

$$(y - k)^2 = 4p(x - h)$$
$$y^2 - 2ky + k^2 = 4px - 4ph$$

or

$$y^2 - 4px - 2ky + (k^2 + 4ph) = 0$$

which is of the following general form (C, D, E, and F are constants).

Compare this with the general second-degree equation.

General Equation of a Parabola with Horizontal Axis	$Cy^2 + Dx + Ey + F = 0$	**312**

We see that the equation of a parabola having a horizontal axis of symmetry has a y^2 term but no x^2 term. Conversely, the equation for a parabola with vertical axis has an x^2 term but not a y^2 term. The parabola is the only conic for which there is only one variable squared.

If the coefficient B of the xy term in the general second-degree equation (Eq. 297) were not zero, it would indicate that the axis of symmetry was *rotated* by some amount and was no longer parallel to a coordinate axis. The presence of an xy term indicates rotation of the ellipse and also of a hyperbola.

Completing the square

As with the circle, we go from general to standard form by completing the square.

■ **Example 35:** Find the vertex, focus, and focal width for the parabola

$$x^2 + 6x + 8y + 1 = 0$$

Solution: Separating the x and y terms, we have

$$x^2 + 6x = -8y - 1$$

Completing the square by adding 9 to both sides, we obtain

$$x^2 + 6x + 9 = -8y - 1 + 9$$

Factoring yields

$$(x + 3)^2 = -8(y - 1)$$

which is the form of Eq. 311, with $h = -3$, $k = 1$, and $p = -2$.

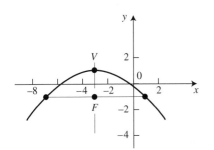

FIGURE 22·52

The vertex is $(-3, 1)$. Since the parabola opens downward (Fig. 22·52), the focus is 2 units below the vertex, at $(-3, -1)$. The focal width is $|4p|$ or 8 units. ■

Exercise 3 The Parabola

Parabola with Vertex at Origin

Find the focus and focal width of each parabola:

1. $y^2 = 8x$ **2.** $x^2 = 16y$
3. $7x^2 + 12y = 0$ **4.** $3y^2 + 5x = 0$

Write the equation of each parabola:

5. Focus at $(0, -2)$
6. Passes through $(25, 20)$, axis horizontal
7. Passes through $(3, 2)$ and $(3, -2)$
8. Passes through $(3, 4)$ and $(-3, 4)$

Parabola with Vertex Not at Origin

Find the vertex, the focus, the focal width, and the equation of the axis for each parabola:

9. $(y - 5)^2 = 12(x - 3)$
10. $(x + 2)^2 = 16(y - 6)$
11. $(x - 3)^2 = 24(y + 1)$
12. $(y + 3)^2 = 4(x + 5)$
13. $3x + 2y^2 + 4y - 4 = 0$
14. $y^2 + 8y + 4 - 6x = 0$
15. $y - 3x + x^2 + 1 = 0$
16. $x^2 + 4x - y - 6 = 0$

Write the equation, in general form, for each parabola:

17. Vertex at $(1, 2)$, $L = 8$, axis is $y = 2$, opens to the right
18. Axis is $y = 3$, passes through $(6, -1)$ and $(3, 1)$
19. Passes through $(-3, 3)$, $(-6, 5)$, and $(-11, 7)$, axis horizontal
20. Vertex $(0, 2)$, axis is $x = 0$, passes through $(-4, -2)$
21. Axis is $y = -1$, passes through $(-4, -2)$ and $(2, 1)$

Trajectories

22. A ball thrown into the air (Fig. 22•53) will, neglecting air resistance, follow a parabolic path. Write the equation of the path, taking axes as shown. Use your equation to find the height of the ball when it is at a horizontal distance of 29.00 m from O.

FIGURE 22•53 Ball thrown into the air

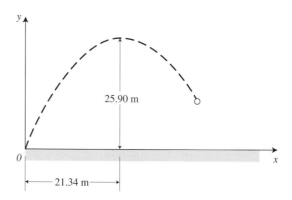

23. Some comets follow a parabolic orbit with the sun at the focal point (Fig. 22•54). Taking axes as shown, write the equation of the path if the distance p is 75 million kilometres.

FIGURE 22•54 Path of a comet

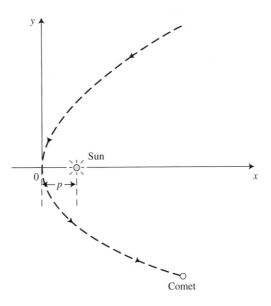

24. An object dropped from a moving aircraft (Fig. 22•55) will follow a parabolic path if air resistance is negligible. A weather instrument released at a height of 3520 m is observed to strike the water at a distance of 2150 m from the point of release. Write the equation of the path, taking axes as shown. Find the height of the instrument when x is $10\overline{0}0$ m.

FIGURE 22•55 Object dropped from an aircraft

Parabolic Arch

25. A 3.0-m-high truck passes under a parabolic arch (Fig. 22•56). Find the maximum distance x that the side of the truck can be from the center of the road.

26. Assuming the bridge cable *AB* (Fig. 22•57) to be a parabola, write its equation, taking axes as shown.

FIGURE 22•56 Parabolic arch

FIGURE 22•57 Parabolic bridge cable

A cable will hang in the shape of a parabola if the vertical load per horizontal metre is constant.

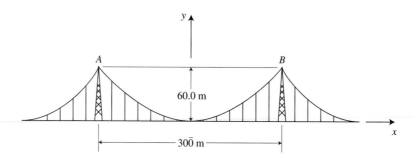

27. A parabolic arch supports a roadway (Fig. 22•58). Write the equation of the arch, taking axes as shown. Use your equation to find the vertical distance from the roadway to the arch at a horizontal distance of 50.0 m from the center.

FIGURE 22•58 Parabolic arch

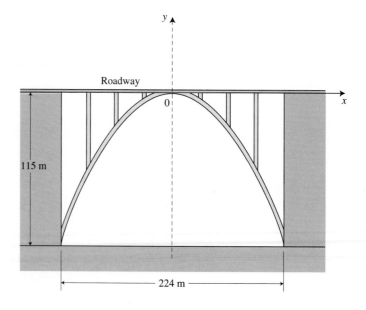

Parabolic Reflector

28. A certain solar collector consists of a long panel of polished steel bent into a parabolic shape (Fig. 22•59), which focuses sunlight onto a pipe P at the focal point of the parabola. At what distance x should the pipe be placed?

FIGURE 22•59 Parabolic solar collector

29. A parabolic collector for receiving television signals from a satellite is shown in Figure 22•60. The receiver R is at the focus, 1.00 m from the vertex. Find the depth d of the collector.

FIGURE 22•60 Parabolic antenna

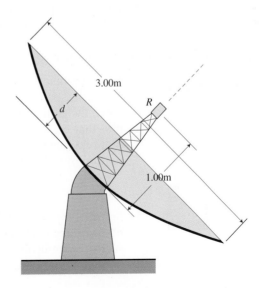

Vertical Highway Curves

30. A parabolic curve is to be used at a dip in a highway. The road dips 32.0 m in a horizontal distance of 125 m, and then rises to its previous height in another 125 m. Write the equation of the curve of the roadway, taking the origin at the bottom of the dip and the y axis vertical.

31. Write the equation of the vertical highway curve in Fig. 22•61, taking axes as shown.

FIGURE 22•61 Road over a hill

Beams

32. A simply supported beam with a concentrated load at its midspan (Fig. 22•62) will deflect in the shape of a parabola. If the deflection at the midspan is 25.4 mm, write the equation of the parabola (called the elastic curve), taking axes as shown.

FIGURE 22•62 Deflection of a beam

33. Using the equation found in Problem 32, find the deflection of the beam in Figure 22•62 at a distance of 3052 mm from the left end.

Graphics Utility

34. Use a graphics calculator or a graphics utility on a computer to graph any of the parabolas in this exercise. As with the circle, you must first solve the equation for y. For a parabola whose axis is vertical, simply plot that equation. For a parabola whose axis is horizontal, you must plot two functions, one for the upper portion and another for the lower portion of the curve.

Computer

35. Some computer algebra systems have commands, such as the **completesquare** command in *Maple*, to complete the square. If you have such a system, use it to go from general to standard form wherever needed in this exercise.

22•4

The Ellipse

Definition

The ellipse is defined in the following way:

Definition	An *ellipse* is the set of all points in a plane such that the sum of the distances from each point on the ellipse to two fixed points (called the *foci*) is constant.	**315**

One way to draw an ellipse that is true to its definition is to pass a loop of string around two tacks, pull the string taut with a pencil, and trace the curve (Fig. 22•63)

FIGURE 22•63 Construction of an ellipse

Figure 22•64 shows the typical shape of the ellipse. An ellipse has two axes of symmetry, the *major axis* and the *minor axis*, which intersect at the *center* of the ellipse. A *vertex* is a point where the ellipse crosses the major axis.

FIGURE 22•64 Ellipse

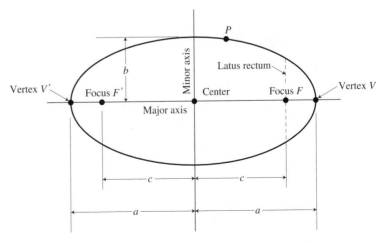

It is often convenient to speak of *half* the lengths of the major and minor axes, and these are called the *semimajor* and *semiminor* axes, whose lengths we label *a* and *b*, respectively. The distance from either focus to the center is labeled *c*.

Distance to Focus

Before deriving an equation for the ellipse, let us first write an expression for the distance *c* from the center to a focus, in terms of the semimajor axis *a* and the semiminor axis *b*.

From our definition of an ellipse, if *P* is any point on the ellipse, then

$$PF + PF' = k \tag{1}$$

where *k* is a constant. If *P* is taken at a vertex *V*, then (1) becomes

$$VF + VF' = k = 2a \tag{2}$$

because *VF* + *VF'* is equal to the length of the major axis. Substituting back into (1) gives us

$$PF + PF' = 2a \tag{3}$$

Figure 22•65 shows our point *P* moved to the intersection of the ellipse and the minor axis. Here *PF* and *PF'* are equal, but since their sum is 2*a*, *PF* and *PF'* must each equal *a*. By the Pythagorean theorem, $c^2 + b^2 = a^2$, or

$$c^2 = a^2 - b^2$$

Ellipse: Distance from Center to Focus	$c = \sqrt{a^2 - b^2}$	**321**

FIGURE 22•65

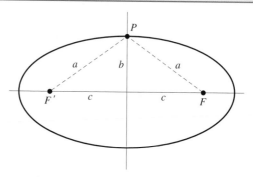

Ellipse with Center at the Origin, Major Axis Horizontal

Let us place an ellipse on coordinate axes with its center at the origin and major axis along the *x* axis, as in Figure 22•66. If *P*(*x*, *y*) is any point on the ellipse, then by the definition of the ellipse,

$$PF + PF' = 2a$$

A line from a focus to a point on the ellipse is called a *focal radius*.

To get *PF* and *PF'* in terms of *x* and *y*, we first drop a perpendicular from *P* to the *x* axis. Then, in triangle *PQF*,

$$PF = \sqrt{(c - x)^2 + y^2}$$

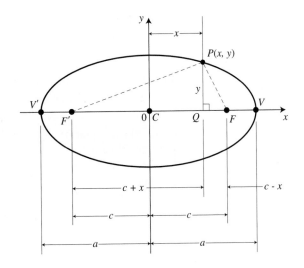

and in triangle PQF',

$$PF' = \sqrt{(c + x)^2 + y^2}$$

Substituting yields

$$PF + PF' = \sqrt{(c - x)^2 + y^2} + \sqrt{(c + x)^2 + y^2} = 2a$$

Rearranging, we obtain

$$\sqrt{(c + x)^2 + y^2} = 2a - \sqrt{(c - x)^2 + y^2}$$

Squaring, and expanding the binomials gives

$$x^2 + 2cx + c^2 + y^2 = 4a^2 - 4a\sqrt{(c - x)^2 + y^2} + c^2 - 2cx + x^2 + y^2$$

Collecting terms, we get

$$cx = a^2 - a\sqrt{(c - x)^2 + y^2}$$

Dividing by a and rearranging, we have

$$a - \frac{cx}{a} = \sqrt{(c - x)^2 + y^2}$$

Squaring both sides again yields

$$a^2 - 2cx + \frac{c^2 x^2}{a^2} = c^2 - 2cx + x^2 + y^2$$

Collecting terms gives

$$a^2 + \frac{c^2 x^2}{a^2} = c^2 + x^2 + y^2$$

But $c = \sqrt{a^2 - b^2}$. Substituting, we have

$$a^2 + \frac{x^2}{a^2}(a^2 - b^2) = a^2 - b^2 + x^2 + y^2$$

or

$$a^2 + x^2 - \frac{b^2 x^2}{a^2} = a^2 - b^2 + x^2 + y^2$$

Collecting terms and rearranging gives us

$$\frac{b^2x^2}{a^2} + y^2 = b^2$$

Finally, dividing through by b^2, we get the standard form of the equation of an ellipse with center at origin.

Standard Equation of an Ellipse: Center at Origin, Major Axis Horizontal	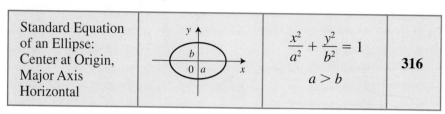	$\dfrac{x^2}{a^2} + \dfrac{y^2}{b^2} = 1$ $a > b$	316

Here a is half the length of the major axis, and b is half the length of the minor axis.

■ **Example 36:** Find the vertices and foci for the ellipse

$$16x^2 + 36y^2 = 576.$$

Solution: To be in standard form, our equation must have 1 (unity) on the right side. Dividing by 576 and simplifying gives us

$$\frac{x^2}{36} + \frac{y^2}{16} = 1$$

from which $a = 6$ and $b = 4$. The vertices are then $V(6, 0)$ and $V'(-6, 0)$ (Fig. 22•67). The distance c from the center to a focus is

$$c = \sqrt{6^2 - 4^2} = \sqrt{20} \approx 4.47$$

FIGURE 22•67

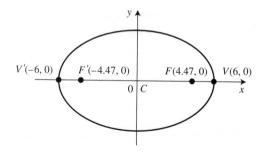

so the foci are $F(4.47, 0)$ and $F'(-4.47, 0)$. ■

Ellipse with Center at Origin, Major Axis Vertical

When the major axis is vertical rather than horizontal, the only effect on the standard equation is to interchange the positions of x and y.

Standard Equation of an Ellipse: Center at Origin, Major Axis Vertical	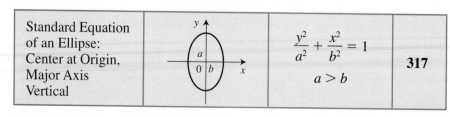	$\dfrac{y^2}{a^2} + \dfrac{x^2}{b^2} = 1$ $a > b$	317

Notice that the quantities a and b are dimensions of the semimajor and semi-minor axes and remain so as the ellipse is turned or shifted. Therefore, for an ellipse in any position, the distance c from center to focus is found in the same way as before.

■ **Example 37:** Find the lengths of the major and minor axes and the distance from center to focus for the ellipse

$$\frac{x^2}{16} + \frac{y^2}{49} = 1$$

Solution: How can we tell which denominator is a^2 and which is b^2? It is easy: a is always greater than b. So $a = 7$ and $b = 4$. Thus the major and minor axes are 14 units and 8 units long (Fig. 22•68). From Eq. 321,

$$c = \sqrt{a^2 - b^2} = \sqrt{49 - 16} = \sqrt{33}$$ ■

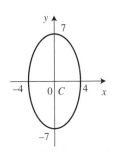

FIGURE 22•68

■ **Example 38:** Write the equation of an ellipse with center at the origin, whose major axis is 12 units on the y axis, and whose minor axis is 10 units (Fig. 22•69).

Solution: Substituting into Eq. 317, with $a = 6$ and $b = 5$, we obtain

$$\frac{y^2}{36} + \frac{x^2}{25} = 1$$ ■

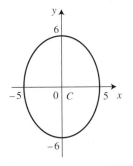

FIGURE 22•69

■ **Example 39:** An ellipse whose center is at the origin and whose major axis is on the x axis has a minor axis of 10 units and passes through the point $(6, 4)$ (Fig. 22•70). Write the equation of the ellipse in standard form.

Solution: Our equation will have the form of Eq. 316. Substituting, with $b = 5$, we have

$$\frac{x^2}{a^2} + \frac{y^2}{25} = 1$$

Since the ellipse passes through $(6, 4)$, these coordinates must satisfy our equation. Substituting yields

$$\frac{36}{a^2} + \frac{16}{25} = 1$$

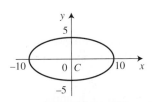

FIGURE 22•70

Solving for a^2, we multiply by the LCD, $25a^2$:

$$36(25) + 16a^2 = 25a^2$$
$$9a^2 = 36(25)$$
$$a^2 = 100$$

So our final equation is

$$\frac{x^2}{100} + \frac{y^2}{25} = 1$$ ■

Common Error	Do not confuse a and b in the ellipse equations. The *larger* denominator is always a^2. Also, the variable (x or y) in the same term with a^2 tells the direction of the major axis.

Shift of Axes

Now consider an ellipse whose center is not at the origin, but at (h, k). The equation for such an ellipse will be the same as before, except that x is replaced by $x - h$ and y is replaced by $y - k$.

Standard Equations of an Ellipse: Center at (h, k)	Major Axis Horizontal		$\dfrac{(x - h)^2}{a^2} + \dfrac{(y - k)^2}{b^2} = 1$ $a > b$	**318**
	Major Axis Vertical		$\dfrac{(y - k)^2}{a^2} + \dfrac{(x - h)^2}{b^2} = 1$ $a > b$	**319**

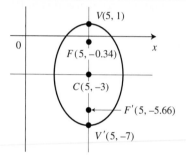

FIGURE 22•71

■ **Example 40:** Find the center, vertices, and foci for the ellipse

$$\frac{(x - 5)^2}{9} + \frac{(y + 3)^2}{16} = 1$$

Solution: From the given equation, $h = 5$ and $k = -3$, the center is $C(5, -3)$ (Fig. 22•71). Also, $a = 4$ and $b = 3$, and the major axis is vertical because a is with the y term. By setting $x = 5$ in the equation of the ellipse, the vertices are $V(5, 1)$ and $V'(5, -7)$. The distance c to the foci is

$$c = \sqrt{4^2 - 3^2} = \sqrt{7} \cong 2.66$$

so the foci are $F(5, -0.34)$ and $F'(5, -5.66)$. ■

■ **Example 41:** Write in standard form the equation of an ellipse with a vertical major axis 10 units long, center at $(3, 5)$, and the distance between focal points of 8 units (Fig. 22•72).

Solution: From the information given, $h = 3$, $k = 5$, $a = 5$, and $c = 4$. By Eq. 321,

$$b = \sqrt{a^2 - c^2} = \sqrt{25 - 16} = 3 \text{ units}$$

Substituting into Eq. 319, we get

$$\frac{(y - 5)^2}{25} + \frac{(x - 3)^2}{9} = 1$$ ■

Yes, Eq. 321 still applies here.

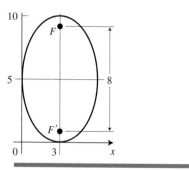

FIGURE 22•72

General Equation of an Ellipse

As we did with the circle, we now expand the standard equation for the ellipse to get the general equation. Starting with Eq. 318,

$$\frac{(x - h)^2}{a^2} + \frac{(y - k)^2}{b^2} = 1$$

we multiply through by a^2b^2, and expand the binomials:

$$b^2(x^2 - 2hx + h^2) + a^2(y^2 - 2ky + k^2) = a^2b^2$$

$$b^2x^2 - 2b^2hx + b^2h^2 + a^2y^2 - 2a^2ky + a^2k^2 - a^2b^2 = 0$$

or

$$b^2x^2 + a^2y^2 - 2b^2hx - 2a^2ky + (b^2h^2 + a^2k^2 - a^2b^2) = 0$$

which is of the following general form.

General Equation of an Ellipse	$Ax^2 + Cy^2 + Dx + Ey + F = 0$	**320**

Comparing this with the general equation of the second degree, we see that the general equation represents an ellipse with axes parallel to the coordinate axes if $B = 0$, and if A and C are different but have the same sign.

Completing the Square

As before, we go from general to standard form by completing the square.

■ **Example 42:** Find the center, foci, vertices, and major and minor axes for the ellipse $9x^2 + 25y^2 + 18x - 50y - 191 = 0$.

Solution: Grouping the x terms and the y terms gives us

$$(9x^2 + 18x) + (25y^2 - 50y) = 191$$

Factoring yields

$$9(x^2 + 2x \quad) + 25(y^2 - 2y \quad) = 191$$

Completing the square, we obtain

$$9(x^2 + 2x + 1) + 25(y^2 - 2y + 1) = 191 + 9 + 25$$

Factoring gives us

$$9(x + 1)^2 + 25(y - 1)^2 = 225$$

Finally, dividing by 225, we have

$$\frac{(x + 1)^2}{25} + \frac{(y - 1)^2}{9} = 1$$

We see that $h = -1$ and $k = 1$, so the center is at $(-1, 1)$. Also, $a = 5$, so the major axis is 10 units and is horizontal, and $b = 3$, so the minor axis is 6 units. A vertex is located 5 units to the right of the center, at $(4, 1)$, and 5 units to the left, at $(-6, 1)$. From Eq. 321,

$$c = \sqrt{a^2 - b^2}$$
$$= \sqrt{25 - 9}$$
$$= 4$$

So the foci are at $(3, 1)$ and $(-5, 1)$. This ellipse is shown in Figure 22·73.

Common Error	In Example 42 we needed 1 to complete the square on x but added 9 to the right side, because the expression containing the 1 was multiplied by a factor of 9. Similarly, for y, we needed 1 on the left but added 25 to the right. It is very easy to forget to multiply by those factors.

FIGURE 22·73

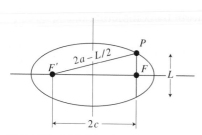

FIGURE 22·74 Derivation of focal width

Focal Width of an Ellipse

The focal width L, or length of the latus rectum, is the width of the ellipse through the focus (Fig. 22·74). The sum of the focal radii PF and PF' from a point P at one end of the latus rectum must equal $2a$, by the definition of an ellipse, so $PF' = 2a - PF$, or, since $L/2 = PF$, $PF' = 2a - L/2$. Squaring both sides, we have

$$(PF')^2 = 4a^2 - 2aL + \frac{L^2}{4} \tag{1}$$

However, in right triangle PFF',

$$(PF')^2 = \left(\frac{L}{2}\right)^2 + (2c)^2 = \frac{L^2}{4} + 4c^2 = \frac{L^2}{4} + 4a^2 - 4b^2 \tag{2}$$

since $c^2 = a^2 - b^2$. Equating (1) and (2) and collecting terms gives $2aL = 4b^2$, or

As with the parabola, the main use for L is in the quick sketching of the ellipse.

Focal Width of an Ellipse	$L = \dfrac{2b^2}{a}$	**322**

The focal width of an ellipse is twice the square of the semiminor axis, divided by the semimajor axis.

■ **Example 43:** The focal width of an ellipse that is 25 m long and 10 m wide is

$$L = \frac{2(5^2)}{12.5} = \frac{50}{12.5} = 4 \text{ m}$$
■

Exercise 4 The Ellipse

Ellipse with Center at Origin

Find the coordinates of the vertices and foci for each ellipse:

1. $\dfrac{x^2}{25} + \dfrac{y^2}{16} = 1$

2. $\dfrac{x^2}{49} + \dfrac{y^2}{36} = 1$

3. $3x^2 + 4y^2 = 12$

4. $64x^2 + 15y^2 = 960$

5. $4x^2 + 3y^2 = 48$

6. $8x^2 + 25y^2 = 200$

Write the equation of each ellipse in standard form.

7. Vertices at $(\pm 5, 0)$, foci at $(\pm 4, 0)$
8. Vertical major axis 8 units long, a focus at $(0, 2)$
9. Horizontal major axis 12 units long, passes through $\left(3, \sqrt{3}\right)$
10. Passes through $(4, 6)$ and $\left(2, 3\sqrt{5}\right)$
11. Horizontal major axis 26 units long, distance between foci $= 24$
12. Vertical minor axis 10 units long, distance from focus to vertex $= 1$
13. Passes through $(1, 4)$ and $(-6, 1)$
14. Distance between foci $= 18$, sum of axes $= 54$, horizontal major axis

Ellipse with Center Not at Origin

Find the coordinates of the center, vertices, and foci for each ellipse, rounding to three significant digits where needed:

15. $\dfrac{(x - 2)^2}{16} + \dfrac{(y + 2)^2}{9} = 1$

16. $\dfrac{(x + 5)^2}{25} + \dfrac{(y - 3)^2}{49} = 1$

17. $5x^2 + 20x + 9y^2 - 54y + 56 = 0$
18. $16x^2 - 128x + 7y^2 + 42y = 129$
19. $7x^2 - 14x + 16y^2 + 32y = 89$
20. $3x^2 - 6x + 4y^2 + 32y + 55 = 0$
21. $25x^2 + 150x + 9y^2 - 36y + 36 = 0$

Write the equation of each ellipse:

22. Minor axis $= 10$, foci at $(13, 2)$ and $(-11, 2)$
23. Center at $(0, 3)$, vertical major axis $= 12$, length of minor axis $= 6$
24. Center at $(2, -1)$, a vertex at $(2, 5)$, length of minor axis $= 3$
25. Center at $(-2, -3)$, a vertex at $(-2, 1)$, a focus halfway between vertex and center

Intersections of Curves

Solve simultaneously to find the points of intersection of each ellipse with the given curve:

26. $3x^2 + 6y^2 = 11$ with $y = x + 1$
27. $2x^2 + 3y^2 = 14$ with $y^2 = 4x$
28. $x^2 + 7y^2 = 16$ with $x^2 + y^2 = 10$

Construction of an Ellipse

29. Draw an ellipse using tacks and string, as shown in Figure 22•63 (page 681), with major axis of $84\overline{0}$ mm and minor axis of $58\overline{0}$ mm. How far apart must the tacks be placed?

Applications

For Problems 30–33, first write the equation for each ellipse.

30. A certain bridge arch is in the shape of half an ellipse 36.0 m wide and 10.0 m high. At what horizontal distance from the center of the arch is the height equal to 4.57 m?

31. A curved mirror in the shape of an ellipse will reflect all rays of light coming from one focus onto the other focus (Fig. 22•75). A certain spot heater is to be made with a heating element at A and the part to be heated at B, contained within an ellipsoid (a solid obtained by rotating an ellipse about one axis). Find the width x of the chamber if its length is 250 mm and the distance from A to B is 150 mm.

FIGURE 22•75 Focusing property of the ellipse

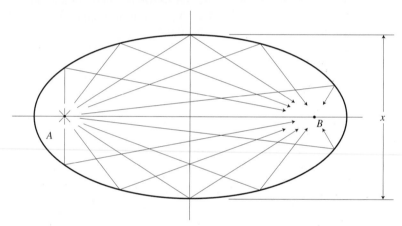

An *astronomical unit*, AU, is the distance between the earth and the sun, about 148 million kilometres.

32. The paths of the planets and certain comets are ellipses, with the sun at one focal point. The path of Halley's comet is an ellipse with a major axis of 36.18 AU and a minor axis of 9.12 AU. What is the greatest distance that Halley's comet gets from the sun?

33. An elliptical culvert (Fig. 22•76) is filled with water to a depth of $30\overline{0}$ mm. Find the width w of the stream.

FIGURE 22•76

Graphics Utility

34. Use a graphics calculator or a graphics utility in a computer to graph any of the ellipses in this exercise. As before, you must first solve the equation for *y* and then plot two functions, one for the upper portion and another for the lower portion of the curve.

35. Find a graphical solution to Problems 26 to 28 by graphing each pair of curves, and then using TRACE and ZOOM to find the coordinates of the points of intersection.

Computer

36. Use a computer algebra system to complete the square in Problems 17 to 21, to put those equations into standard form.

22·5

The Hyperbola

Definition	A *hyperbola* is the set of all points in a plane such that the distances from each point to two fixed points, the *foci*, have a constant difference.	**325**

Figure 22•77 shows the typical shape of the hyperbola. The point midway between the foci is called the *center* of the hyperbola. The line passing through the foci and the center is one *axis* of the hyperbola. The hyperbola crosses the axis at points called the *vertices*. The line segment connecting the vertices is called the *transverse axis*. A second axis of the hyperbola passes through the center and is perpendicular to the transverse axis. The segment of this axis within the square shown in Figure 22•77 is called the *conjugate axis*. Half the lengths of the transverse and conjugate axes are the *semitransverse* and *semiconjugate* axes, respectively. They are also referred to as *semiaxes*.

FIGURE 22•77 Hyperbola

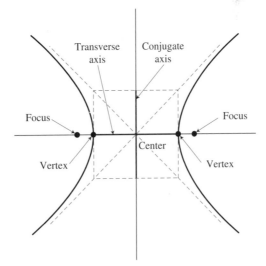

FIGURE 22·78 Hyperbola with center at origin

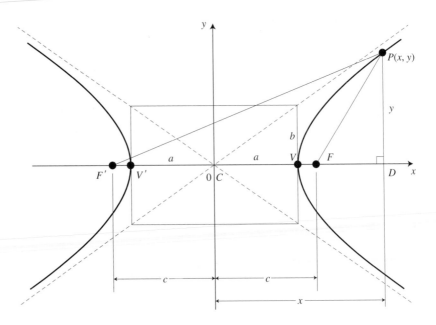

Standard Equations of a Hyperbola with Center at Origin

We place the hyperbola on coordinate axes, with its center at the origin and its transverse axis on the x axis (Fig. 22·78). Let a be half the transverse axis, and let c be half the distance between the foci. Now take any point P on the hyperbola and draw the focal radii PF and PF'. Then, by the definition of a hyperbola, $|PF' - PF| = $ constant. The constant can be found by moving P to the vertex V, where

$$|PF' - PF| = VF' - VF$$
$$= 2a + V'F' - VF$$
$$= 2a$$

since $V'F'$ and VF are equal, so $|PF' - PF| = 2a$. But in right triangle $PF'D$,

$$PF' = \sqrt{(x + c)^2 + y^2}$$

and in right triangle PFD,

$$PF = \sqrt{(x - c)^2 + y^2}$$

Thus

$$\sqrt{(x + c)^2 + y^2} - \sqrt{(x - c)^2 + y^2} = 2a$$

Notice that this equation is almost identical to the one we had when deriving the equation for the ellipse in Section 22·4, and the derivation is almost identical as well. However, to eliminate c from our equation, we define a new quantity b, such that $b^2 = c^2 - a^2$. We'll soon give a geometric meaning to the quantity b.

The remainder of the derivation is left as an exercise. The resulting equations are very similar to those for the ellipse.

Try to derive these equations. Follow the same steps we used for the ellipse.

Standard Equations of a Hyperbola: Center at Origin	Transverse Axis Horizontal		$\dfrac{x^2}{a^2} - \dfrac{y^2}{b^2} = 1$	**326**
	Transverse Axis Vertical		$\dfrac{y^2}{a^2} - \dfrac{x^2}{b^2} = 1$	**327**

Asymptotes of a Hyperbola

In Figure 22•78, the dashed diagonal lines are asymptotes of the hyperbola. (The two branches of the hyperbola approach, but do not intersect, the asymptotes.)

We find the slopes of these asymptotes from the equation of the hyperbola. Solving Eq. 326 for y gives $y^2 = b^2(x^2/a^2 - 1)$, or

$$y = \pm b\sqrt{\frac{x^2}{a^2} - 1}$$

As x gets large, the 1 under the radical sign becomes insignificant in comparison with x^2/a^2, and the equation for y becomes

$$y = \pm\frac{b}{a}x$$

This is the equation of a straight line having a slope of b/a. Thus, as x increases, the branches of the hyperbola more closely approach straight lines having slopes of $+b/a$ and $-b/a$.

In general, if the distance from a point P on a curve to some line L approaches zero as the distance from P to the origin increases without bound, then L is an *asymptote*. The hyperbola has two such asymptotes, with slopes $+b/a$ and $-b/a$.

For a hyperbola whose transverse axis is *vertical*, the slopes of the asymptotes can be shown to be $+a/b$ and $-a/b$.

Slope of the Asymptotes of a Hyperbola	Transverse Axis Horizontal	Slope $= +\dfrac{b}{a}$ and $-\dfrac{b}{a}$	**332**
	Transverse Axis Vertical	Slope $= +\dfrac{a}{b}$ and $-\dfrac{a}{b}$	**333**

Common Error	The asymptotes are not (usually) perpendicular to each other. The slope of one is **not** the negative reciprocal of the other.

Looking back at Figure 22•78, we can now give meaning to the quantity b. If an asymptote has a slope b/a, it must have a rise of b in a run equal to a. Thus b is the distance, perpendicular to the transverse axis, from vertex to asymptote. It is half the length of the conjugate axis.

Hyperbola: Distance from Center to Focus	$c = \sqrt{a^2 + b^2}$	**331**

■ **Example 44:** Find a, b, and c, the coordinates of the center, the vertices, and the foci, and the slope of the asymptotes for the hyperbola

$$\frac{x^2}{25} - \frac{y^2}{36} = 1$$

Solution: This equation is of the same form as Eq. 326, so we know that the center is at the origin and that the transverse axis is on the x axis. Also, $a^2 = 25$ and $b^2 = 36$, so

$$a = 5 \quad \text{and} \quad b = 6$$

The vertices then have the coordinates

$$V(5, 0) \quad \text{and} \quad V'(-5, 0)$$

Then, from Eq. 331,

$$c^2 = a^2 + b^2 = 25 + 36 = 61$$

so $c = \sqrt{61} \cong 7.81$. The coordinates of the foci are then,

$$F(7.81, 0) \quad \text{and} \quad F'(-7.81, 0)$$

The slopes of the asymptotes are

$$+\frac{a}{b} = +\frac{6}{5} \quad \text{and} \quad -\frac{a}{b} = -\frac{6}{5}$$

This hyperbola is shown in Fig. 22•79. In the following section we show how to make such a graph. ■

FIGURE 22•79 Graph of
$$\frac{x^2}{25} - \frac{y^2}{36} = 1$$

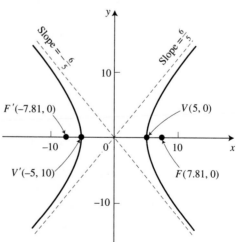

Graphing a Hyperbola

A good way to start a sketch of the hyperbola is to draw a rectangle whose dimension along the transverse axis is $2a$ and whose dimension along the conjugate axis is $2b$. The asymptotes are then drawn along the diagonals of this rectangle. Half the diagonal of the rectangle has a length $\sqrt{a^2 + b^2}$, which is equal to c, the distance to the foci. Thus an arc of radius c will cut the transverse axes at the focal points.

As with the parabola and ellipse, a perpendicular through a focus connecting two points on the hyperbola is called a *latus rectum*. Its length, called the focal width, is $2b^2/a$, the same as for the ellipse.

■ **Example 45:** Find the vertices, foci, semiaxes, slope of the asymptotes, and focal width, and graph the hyperbola $64x^2 - 49y^2 = 3136$.

Solution: We write the equation in standard form by dividing by 3136,

$$\frac{x^2}{49} - \frac{y^2}{64} = 1$$

This is the form of Eq. 326, so the transverse axis is horizontal, with $a = 7$ and $b = 8$. We draw a rectangle of width 14 and height 16 (shown shaded in Fig. 22•80), thus locating the vertices at $(\pm 7, 0)$. Diagonals through the rectangle give us the asymptotes of slopes $\pm \frac{8}{7}$. We locate the foci by swinging an arc of radius c, equal to half the diagonal of the rectangle. Thus

$$c = \sqrt{7^2 + 8^2} = \sqrt{113} \simeq 10.6$$

The foci then are at $(\pm 10.6, 0)$. We obtain a few more points by computing the focal width,

$$L = \frac{2b^2}{a} = \frac{2(64)}{7} \simeq 18.3$$

This gives us the additional points $(10.6, 9.15)$, $(10.6, -9.15)$, $(-10.6, 9.15)$, and $(-10.6, -9.15)$. ■

FIGURE 22•80

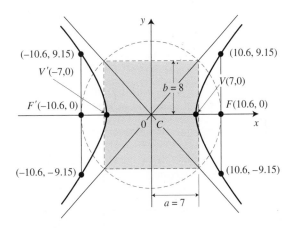

■ **Example 46:** A hyperbola whose center is at the origin has a focus at $(0, -5)$ and a transverse axis 8 units long (Fig. 22•81). Write the standard equation of the hyperbola and find the slope of the asymptotes.

Solution: The transverse axis is 8, so $a = 4$. A focus is 5 units below the origin, so the transverse axis must be vertical, and $c = 5$. From Eq. 331,

$$b = \sqrt{c^2 - a^2} = \sqrt{25 - 16} = 3$$

Substituting into Eq. 327 gives us

$$\frac{y^2}{16} - \frac{x^2}{9} = 1$$

FIGURE 22·81

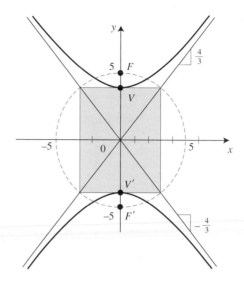

and, from Eq. 333, the slopes of the asymptotes are $+\dfrac{a}{b} = +\dfrac{4}{3}$ and $-\dfrac{a}{b} = -\dfrac{4}{3}$

Common Error	Be sure that you know the direction of the transverse axis before computing the slopes of the asymptotes, which are $+b/a$ and $-b/a$ when the axis is horizontal, but $+a/b$ and $-a/b$ when the axis is vertical.

Shift of Axes

As with the other conics, we shift the axes by replacing x by $(x - h)$ and y by $(y - k)$ in Eqs. 326 and 327.

Standard Equations of a Hyperbola: Center at (h, k)	Transverse Axis Horizontal		$\dfrac{(x - h)^2}{a^2} - \dfrac{(y - k)^2}{b^2} = 1$	**328**
	Transverse Axis Vertical		$\dfrac{(y - k)^2}{a^2} - \dfrac{(x - h)^2}{b^2} = 1$	**329**

The equations for c and for the slope of the asymptotes are still valid for these cases.

Common Error	Do not confuse these equations with those for the ellipse. Here the terms have **opposite signs**. Also, a^2 is always the denominator of the **positive** term, even though it may be smaller than b^2. As with the ellipse, the variable in the same term as a^2 tells the direction of the transverse axis.

■ **Example 47:** A certain hyperbola has a focus at $(1, 0)$, passes through the origin, has its transverse axis on the x axis, and has a distance of 10 between its focal points. Write its standard equation.

Solution: In Figure 22•82 we plot the given focus $F(1, 0)$. Since the hyperbola passes through the origin, and the transverse axis also passes through the origin, a vertex must be at the origin as well. Then, since $c = 5$, we go 5 units to the left of F and plot the center, $(-4, 0)$. Thus $a = 4$ units from center to vertex. Then, by Eq. 331,

$$b = \sqrt{c^2 - a^2}$$
$$= \sqrt{25 - 16} = 3$$

Substituting into Eq. 328 with $h = -4$, $k = 0$, $a = 4$, and $b = 3$ we get

$$\frac{(x + 4)^2}{16} - \frac{y^2}{9} = 1$$

as the required equation.   ■

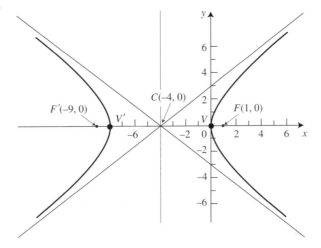

General Equation of a Hyperbola

Since the standard equations for the ellipse and hyperbola are identical except for the minus sign, it is not surprising that their general equations should be identical except for a minus sign. The general second-degree equations for an ellipse or a hyperbola is

General Equation of a Hyperbola	$Ax^2 + Cy^2 + Dx + Ey + F = 0$	**330**

For the ellipse, A and C have like signs; for the hyperbola, they have opposite signs.

As before, we complete the square to go from general form to standard form.

■ **Example 48:** Write the equation $x^2 - 4y^2 - 6x + 8y - 11 = 0$ in standard form. Find the center, vertices, foci, and asymptotes.

Solution: Rearranging gives us

$$(x^2 - 6x \quad) - 4(y^2 - 2y \quad) = 11$$

Completing the square and factoring yields

$$(x^2 - 6x + 9) - 4(y^2 - 2y + 1) = 11 + 9 - 4$$

$$(x - 3)^2 - 4(y - 1)^2 = 16$$

(Take care, when completing the square, to add -4 to the right side to compensate for 1×-4 added on the left.) Dividing by 16 gives us

$$\frac{(x - 3)^2}{16} - \frac{(y - 1)^2}{4} = 1$$

from which $a = 4$, $b = 2$, $h = 3$, and $k = 1$.

From Eq. 331, $c = \sqrt{a^2 + b^2} = \sqrt{16 + 4} \approx 4.47$, and, from Eq. 332,

$$\text{slope of asymptotes} = \frac{b}{a} = \frac{1}{2} \quad \text{and} \quad -\frac{b}{a} = -\frac{1}{2}$$

This hyperbola is plotted in Figure 22•83.

FIGURE 22•83

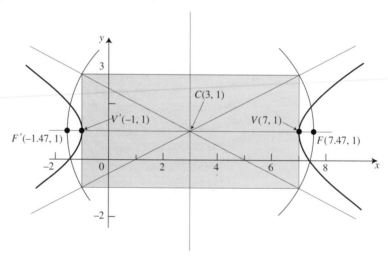

Hyperbola Whose Asymptotes Are the Coordinate Axes

The graph of an equation of the form

$$xy = k$$

where k is a constant, is a hyperbola similar to those we have studied in this section, but rotated so that the coordinate axes are now the asymptotes, and the transverse and conjugate axes are at $45°$.

Hyperbola: Axes Rotated 45°	$xy = k$	335

Example 49: Plot the equation $xy = -4$.

Solution: We select values for x and evaluate $y = -4/x$:

x	-4	-3	-2	-1	0	1	2	3	4
y	1	$\frac{4}{3}$	2	4	—	-4	-2	$-\frac{4}{3}$	-1

The graph (Fig. 22•84) shows vertices at $(-2, 2)$ and $(2, -2)$. We see from the graph that a and b are equal, and that each is the hypotenuse of a right triangle of side 2. Therefore,

$$a = b = \sqrt{2^2 + 2^2} = \sqrt{8}$$

and, from Eq. 331,

$$c = \sqrt{a^2 + b^2} = \sqrt{16} = 4$$

FIGURE 22•84 Hyperbola whose asymptotes are the coordinate axis

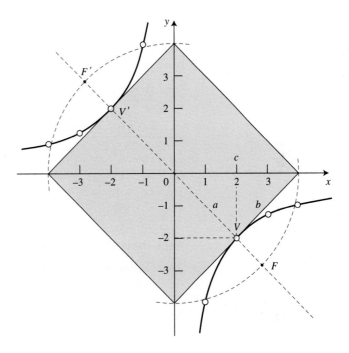

When the constant k in Eq. 335 is negative, the hyperbola lies in the second and fourth quadrants, as in Example 49. When k is positive, the hyperbola lies in the first and third quadrants.

Exercise 5 The Hyperbola

Hyperbola with Center at Origin

Find the vertices, foci, the lengths a and b of the semiaxes, and the slope of the asymptotes for each hyperbola:

1. $\dfrac{x^2}{16} - \dfrac{y^2}{25} = 1$

2. $\dfrac{y^2}{25} - \dfrac{x^2}{49} = 1$

3. $16x^2 - 9y^2 = 144$

4. $9x^2 - 16y^2 = 144$

5. $x^2 - 4y^2 = 16$ **6.** $3x^2 - y^2 + 3 = 0$

Write the equation of each hyperbola in standard form:

7. Vertices at $(\pm 5, 0)$, foci at $(\pm 13, 0)$
8. Vertices at $(0, \pm 7)$, foci at $(0, \pm 10)$
9. Distance between foci = 8, transverse axis = 6 and is horizontal
10. Conjugate axis = 4, foci at $(\pm 2.5, 0)$
11. Transverse and conjugate axes equal, passes through $(3, 5)$, transverse axis vertical
12. Transverse axis = 16 and is horizontal, conjugate axis = 14
13. Transverse axis = 10 and is vertical, curve passes through $(8, 10)$
14. Transverse axis = 8 and is horizontal, curve passes through $(5, 6)$

Hyperbola with Center Not at Origin

Find the center, lengths of the semiaxes, foci, slope of the asymptotes, and vertices for each hyperbola:

15. $\dfrac{(x - 2)^2}{25} - \dfrac{(y + 1)^2}{16} = 1$

16. $\dfrac{(y + 3)^2}{25} - \dfrac{(x - 2)^2}{49} = 1$
17. $16x^2 - 64x - 9y^2 - 54y = 161$
18. $16x^2 + 32x - 9y^2 + 592 = 0$
19. $4x^2 + 8x - 5y^2 - 10y + 19 = 0$
20. $y^2 - 6y - 3x^2 - 12x = 12$

Write the equation of each hyperbola in standard form:

21. Center at $(3, 2)$, length of the transverse axis = 8 and is vertical, length of the conjugate axis = 4
22. Foci at $(-1, -1)$ and $(-5, -1)$, $a = b$
23. Foci at $(5, -2)$ and $(-3, -2)$, vertex halfway between center and focus
24. Length of the conjugate axis = 8 and is horizontal, center at $(-1, -1)$, length of the transverse axis = 16

Hyperbola Whose Asymptotes Are Coordinate Axes

25. Write the equation of a hyperbola with center at the origin and with asymptotes on the coordinate axes, whose vertex is at $(6, 6)$.
26. Write the equation of a hyperbola with center at the origin and with asymptotes on the coordinate axes, and which passes through the point $(-9, 2)$.

Applications

27. A hyperbolic mirror (Fig. 22·85) has the property that a ray of light directed at one focus will be reflected so as to pass through the other focus. Write the equation of the mirror shown, taking the axes as indicated.

FIGURE 22•85 Hyperbolic mirror.
This type of mirror is used in the
Cassegrain form of reflecting telescope.

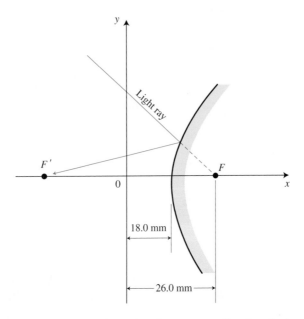

28. A ship (Fig. 22•86) receives simultaneous radio signals from stations P and Q, on the shore. The signal from station P is found to arrive 375 microseconds (μs) later than that from Q. Assuming that the signals travel at a rate of 298 m/μs, find the distance from the ship to each station. (*Hint:* The ship will be on one branch of a hyperbola H whose foci are at P and Q. Write the equation of this hyerbola, taking axes as shown, and then substitute $12\overline{0}$ km for y to obtain the distance x.)

FIGURE 22•86

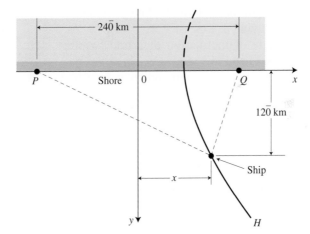

29. Boyle's law states that, under certain conditions, the product of the pressure and volume of a gas is constant, or $pv = c$. This equation has the same form as the hyperbola (Eq. 335). If a certain gas has a pressure of 174 kPa at a volume of 0.0164 m³, write Boyle's law for this gas and make a graph of pressure versus volume.

Computer

30. Write a program that will accept as input the constants A, B, and C in the general second-degree equation (Eq. 297), and then identify and print the type of conic represented.

31. Some computer algebra systems have commands, such as the **completesquare** command in *Maple*, to complete the square. If you have such a system, use it to go from general to standard form wherever needed in this exercise.

Graphics Utility

32. Use a graphics calculator or a graphics utility on the computer to graph any of the hyperbolas in this exercise. As for the circle, you must first solve the equation for y, and you must plot two functions, one for the upper portion and another for the lower portion of the curve.

CHAPTER 22   REVIEW PROBLEMS

1. Find the distance between the points $(3, 0)$ and $(7, 0)$.

2. Find the distance between the points $(4, -4)$ and $(1, -7)$.

3. Find the slope of the line perpendicular to a line that has an angle of inclination of $34.8°$.

4. Find the angle of inclination in degrees of a line with a slope of -3.

5. Find the angle of inclination of a line perpendicular to a line having a slope of 1.55.

6. Find the angle of inclination of a line passing through $(-3, 5)$ and $(5, -6)$.

7. Find the slope of a line perpendicular to a line having a slope of $a/2b$.

8. Write the equation of a line having a slope of -2 and a y intercept of 5.

9. Find the slope and y intercept of the line $2y - 5 = 3(x - 4)$.

10. Write the equation of a line having a slope of $2p$ and a y intercept of $p - 3q$.

11. Write the equation of the line passing through $(-5, -1)$ and $(-2, 6)$.

12. Write the equation of the line passing through $(-r, s)$ and $(2r, -s)$.

13. Write the equation of the line having a slope of 5 and passing through the point $(-4, 7)$.

14. Write the equation of the line having a slope of $3c$ and passing through the point $(2c, c - 1)$.

15. Write the equation of the line having an x intercept of -3 and a y intercept of 7.

16. Find the acute angle between two lines, if one line has a slope of 1.50, and the other has a slope of 3.40.

17. Write the equation of the line that passes through $(2, 5)$ and is parallel to the x axis.

18. Find the angle of intersection between line L_1 having a slope of 2 and line L_2 having a slope of 7.

19. Find the directed distance AB between the points $A(-2, 0)$ and $B(-5, 0)$.

20. Find the angle of intersection between line L_1 having an angle of inclination of $18°$ and line L_2 having an angle of inclination of $75°$.

21. Write the equation of the line that passes through $(-3, 6)$ and is parallel to the y axis.

22. Find the increments in the coordinates of a particle that moves along a curve from $(3, 4)$ to $(5, 5)$.

23. Find the area of a triangle with vertices at $(6, 4)$, $(5, -2)$, and $(-3, -4)$.

In Problems 24 to 33, a tangent T, of slope m, and a normal N are drawn to a curve at the point $P(x_1, y_1)$ (Fig. 22•87). Show the following:

24. The equation of the tangent is $y - y_1 = m(x - x_1)$.

25. The equation of the normal is
$$x - x_1 + m(y - y_1) = 0$$

26. The x intercept A of the tangent is $x_1 - y_1/m$.

27. The y intercept B of the tangent is $y_1 - mx_1$.

28. The length of the tangent from P to the x axis is
$$PA = \frac{y_1}{m}\sqrt{1 + m^2}.$$

29. The length of the tangent from P to the y axis is $PB = x_1\sqrt{1 + m^2}$.

30. The x intercept C of the normal is $x_1 + my_1$.

31. The y intercept D of the normal is $y_1 + x_1/m$.

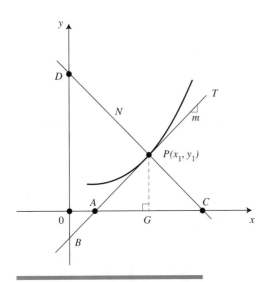

FIGURE 22·87 Tangent and normal to a curve

32. The length of the normal from P to the x axis is $PC = y_1\sqrt{1 + m^2}$.

33. The length of the normal from P to the y axis is

$$PD = \frac{x_1}{m}\sqrt{1 + m^2}.$$

Identify the curve represented by each equation below. Find, where applicable, the center, vertices, foci, radius, semi-axes, and so on.

34. $x^2 - 2x - 4y^2 + 16y = 19$
35. $x^2 + 6x + 4y = 3$
36. $x^2 + y^2 = 8y$
37. $25x^2 - 200x + 9y^2 - 90y = 275$
38. $16x^2 - 9y^2 = 144$
39. $x^2 + y^2 = 9$
40. Write the equation for an ellipse whose center is at the origin, whose major axis ($2a$) is 20 and is horizontal, and whose minor axis ($2b$) equals the distance ($2c$) between the foci.
41. Write an equation for the circle passing through $(0, 0)$, $(8, 0)$, and $(0, -6)$.
42. Write the equation for a parabola whose vertex is at the origin and whose focus is $(-4.25, 0)$.
43. Write an equation for a hyperbola whose transverse axis is horizontal, with center at $(1, 1)$ and which passes through $(6, 2)$ and $(-3, 1)$.
44. Write the equation of a circle whose center is $(-5, 0)$ and whose radius is 5.
45. Write the equation of a hyperbola whose center is at the origin, whose transverse axis $= 8$ and is horizontal, and which passes through $(10, 25)$.

46. Write the equation of an ellipse whose foci are at $(2, 1)$ and $(-6, 1)$, and the sum of the focal radii is 10.
47. Write the equation of a parabola whose axis is the line $y = -7$, whose vertex is 3 units to the right of the y axis, and which passes through $(4, -5)$.
48. Find the intercepts of the curve $y^2 + 4x - 6y = 16$.
49. Find the points of intersection of $x^2 + y^2 + 2x + 2y = 2$ and $3x^2 + 3y^2 + 5x + 5y = 10$.
50. A stone bridge arch is in the shape of half an ellipse and is 15.0 m wide and 5.00 m high. Find the height of the arch at a distance of 6.00 m from its center.
51. Write the equation of a hyperbola centered at the origin, where the conjugate axis $= 12$ and is vertical, and the distance between foci is 13.
52. A parabolic arch is 5.00 m high and 6.00 m wide at the base. Find the width of the arch at a height of 2.00 m above the base.
53. A stone thrown in the air follows a parabolic path, and reaches a maximum height of 17.0 m in a horizontal distance of 14.6 m. At what horizontal distances from the launch point will the height be 7.62 m.

Writing

54. Write a short paragraph explaining, in your own words, what is meant by the slope of a curve.
55. Suppose that, the day before your visit to your former high school math class, the teacher unexpectedly asks you to explain how that day's topic, the conic sections, got that name. Write a paragraph on what you will tell the class about how the circle, ellipse, parabola, and hyperbola (and the point and straight line, too) can be formed by intersecting a plane and a cone. You may plan to illustrate your talk with a clay model or a piece of cardboard rolled into a cone. You will probably be asked what the conic sections are good for, so include at least one use for each curve.

Team Project

56. There is an infinite number of number pairs p and q (such as 3 and 1.5) whose product equals their sum. Write an expression for q as a function of p, and make a graph of p versus q for all the real numbers, not just integer values, from -5 to 5. With a suitable shift of axes, show that the graph is a hyperbola of the form $y = 1/x$.

23

Binary, Hexadecimal, Octal, and BCD Numbers

O B J E C T I V E S

When you have completed this chapter, you should be able to:

- Convert between binary and decimal numbers.
- Convert between decimal and binary fractions.
- Convert between binary and hexadecimal numbers.
- Convert between decimal and hexadecimal numbers.
- Convert between binary and octal numbers.
- Convert between binary and 8421 BCD numbers.

The decimal number system of Chapter 1 is fine for calculations done by humans, but it is not the easiest system for a computer to use. A digital computer contains elements that can be in either of two states: on or off, magnetized or not magnetized, and so on. For such devices, calculations are most conveniently done using *binary numbers*. In this chapter we learn what binary numbers are and how to convert between binary and decimal numbers.

Binary numbers are useful in a computer, where each binary digit (bit) can be represented by one state of a "binary switch" that is either on or off, but they are hard to read, partly because of their great length. To represent a nine-digit social security number, for example, requires a binary number *29 bits long*. So, in addition to binary numbers, we also study other ways in which numbers can be represented. *Hexadecimal*, *octal*, and *binary-coded decimal* systems allow us to express binary numbers more compactly, and make the transfer of data between computers and people much easier. Here we learn how to convert numbers between these systems, and between decimal and binary as well.

23·1

The Binary Number System

Binary Numbers

A *binary number* is a sequence of the digits 0 and 1, such as

$$1101001$$

The number shown has no fractional part, and so is called a *binary integer*. A binary number having a fractional part contains a *binary point* (also called a *radix point*), as in the number

$$1001.01$$

Base or Radix

The *base* of a number system (also called the *radix*) is equal to the number of digits used in the system.

■ **Example 1:**
(a) The decimal system uses the ten digits

$$0 \quad 1 \quad 2 \quad 3 \quad 4 \quad 5 \quad 6 \quad 7 \quad 8 \quad 9$$

and has a base of 10.
(b) The binary system uses the two digits

$$0 \quad 1$$

and has a base of 2.   ■

Bits, Bytes, and Words

Each of the digits is called a *bit*, from

$$\text{Binary digIT}$$

A *byte* is a group of 8 bits, and a *word* is the largest string of bits that a computer can handle in one operation. The number of bits in a word is called the *word length*. Different computers have different word lengths, with 8, 16, or 32 bits being common for desktop or personal computers. The longer words are often broken down into bytes for easier handling. Half a byte (4 bits) is called a *nibble*.

A *kilobyte* (Kbyte or KB) is 1024 (2^{10}) bytes, and a *megabyte* (Mbyte or MB) is 1 048 575 (2^{20}) bytes.

> Note that this is different from the usual meaning of these prefixes, where kilo means 1000 and mega means 1 000 000.

Writing Binary Numbers

A binary number is sometimes written with a subscript 2 when there is a chance that the binary number would otherwise be mistaken for a decimal number.

■ **Example 2:** The binary number 110 could easily be mistaken for the decimal number 110, unless we write it

$$110_2$$

Similarly, a decimal number that may be mistaken for binary is often written with a subscript 10, as in

$$101_{10}$$ ▬

Long binary numbers are sometimes written with their bits in groups of four for easier reading.

▬ **Example 3:** The number 100100010100.001001 is easier to read with a space after each group of four digits:

$$1001\ 0001\ 0100.0010\ 01$$ ▬

The bit at the extreme left of a binary number is called the *high-order* or *most significant bit (MSB)*. The bit at the extreme right of the number is the *low-order* or *least significant bit (LSB)*.

TABLE 23•1

POSITION	PLACE VALUE	
10	2^{10} =	1024
9	2^9 =	512
8	2^8 =	256
7	2^7 =	128
6	2^6 =	64
5	2^5 =	32
4	2^4 =	16
3	2^3 =	8
2	2^2 =	4
1	2^1 =	2
0	2^0 =	1
−1	2^{-1} =	0.5
−2	2^{-2} =	0.25
−3	2^{-3} =	0.125
−4	2^{-4} =	0.0625
−5	2^{-5} =	0.03125
−6	2^{-6} =	0.015625

Compare these place values to those in the decimal system shown in Figure 1•1.

Place Value

We saw in Chapter 1 that a positional number system is one in which the position of a digit determines its value, and that each position in a number has a *place value* equal to the base of the number system raised to the position number.

The place values in the binary number system are

$$\ldots\quad 2^4\quad 2^3\quad 2^2\quad 2^1\quad 2^0\quad .\quad 2^{-1}\quad 2^{-2}\quad \ldots$$

or

$$\ldots\quad 16\quad 8\quad 4\quad 2\quad 1\quad .\quad \tfrac{1}{2}\quad \tfrac{1}{4}\quad \ldots$$

binary point ⬆

A more complete list of place values for a binary number is given in Table 23•1.

Expanded Notation

Thus the value of any digit in a number is the product of that digit and the place value. The value of the entire number is then the sum of these products.

▬ **Example 4:**
(a) The decimal number 526 can be expressed as

$$5 \times 10^2 + 2 \times 10^1 + 6 \times 10^0$$

or

$$5 \times 100 + 2 \times 10 + 6 \times 1$$

or

$$500 + 20 + 6$$

(b) The binary number 1011 can be expressed as

$$1 \times 2^3 + 0 \times 2^2 + 1 \times 2^1 + 1 \times 2^0$$

or

$$1 \times 8 + 0 \times 4 + 1 \times 2 + 1 \times 1$$

or

$$8 + 0 + 2 + 1$$

Numbers written in this way are said to be in *expanded notation*.   ▬

Converting Binary Numbers to Decimal

Simply write the binary number in expanded notation (omitting those where the bit is 0), and add the resulting values.

▬ **Example 5:** Convert the binary number

$$1001.011$$

to decimal.

Solution: In expanded notation,

$$1001.011 = 1 \times 8 + 1 \times 1 + 1 \times \frac{1}{4} + 1 \times \frac{1}{8}$$

$$= 8 + 1 + \frac{1}{4} + \frac{1}{8}$$

$$= 9\frac{3}{8}$$

$$= 9.375$$ ▬

Largest Decimal Number Obtainable with n Bits

The largest possible 3-bit binary number is

$$1\ 1\ 1 = 7$$

or

$$2^3 - 1$$

The largest possible 4-bit binary number is

$$1\ 1\ 1\ 1 = 15$$

or

$$2^4 - 1$$

Similarly, the largest n-bit binary number is

Largest n-Bit Binary Number	$2^n - 1$	**17**

▬ **Example 6:** If a computer stores numbers with 15 bits, what is the largest decimal number that can be represented?

Solution: The largest decimal number is

$$2^{15} - 1 = 32\ 767$$ ▬

Significant Digits

In Example 6 we saw that a 15-bit binary number could represent a decimal number no greater than 32 767. Thus it took 15 binary digits to represent five decimal digits. As a rule of thumb, *it takes about three bits for each decimal digit.*

Stated another way, if we have a computer that stores numbers with 15 bits, we should assume that the decimal numbers it prints do not contain more than five significant digits.

■ **Example 7:** If we want a computer to print decimal numbers containing seven significant digits, how many bits must it use to store those numbers?

Solution: Using our rule of thumb, we need

$$3 \times 7 = 21 \text{ bits}$$

■

Converting Decimal Numbers to Binary

To convert a decimal *integer* to binary, we first divide it by 2, obtaining a quotient and a remainder. We write down the remainder, and divide the quotient by 2, getting a new quotient and remainder. We then repeat this process until the quotient is zero.

■ **Example 8:** Convert the decimal integer 59 to binary.

Solution: We divide 59 by 2, getting a quotient of 29 and a remainder of 1. Then dividing 29 by 2 gives a quotient of 14 and a remainder of 1. These calculations, and those that follow can be arranged in a table, as follows.

	Remainder	
2)59		
2)29	1 LSB	
2)14	1	
2)7	0	Read
2)3	1	up
2)1	1	
2)0	1 MSB	

The conversion can, of course, be checked by converting back to decimal.

Our binary number then consists of the digits in the remainders, with those at the *top* of the column appearing to the *right* in the binary number. Thus

$$59_{10} = 111011_2$$

■

To convert a decimal *fraction* to binary, we first multiply it by 2, remove the integral part of the product, and multiply by 2 again. The procedure is then repeated.

■ **Example 9:** Convert the decimal fraction 0.546875 to binary.

Solution: We multiply the given number by 2, getting 1.09375. We remove the integral part, 1, leaving 0.09375, which we again multiply by 2, getting 0.1875. We repeat the computation until we get a product that has a fractional part of zero, as in the following table.

$$
\begin{array}{rl}
0.546875 & \text{Integral part}\\
\times \quad\quad 2 & \\
\hline
\mathbf{1}.09375 & 1 \ \ \text{MSB}\\
\times \quad\quad 2 & \\
\hline
\mathbf{0}.1875 & 0\\
\times \quad\quad 2 & \\
\hline
\mathbf{0}.375 & 0\\
\times \quad\quad 2 & \\
\hline
\mathbf{0}.75 & 0\\
\times \quad\quad 2 & \\
\hline
\mathbf{1}.50 & 1\\
\times \quad\quad 2 & \\
\hline
\mathbf{1}.00 & 1 \ \ \text{LSB}\\
\end{array}
$$

Read down

Notice that we remove the integral part, shown in boldface, before multiplying by 2.

We stop now that the fractional part of the product (1.00) is zero. The column containing the integral parts is now our binary number, with the digits at the top appearing at the *left* of the binary number. So

$$0.546875_{10} = .1000\ 11_2$$

Note that this is the reverse of what we did when converting a decimal integer to binary.

In Example 9 we were able to find an exact binary equivalent of a decimal fraction. This is not always possible, as shown in the following example.

— Example 10: Convert the decimal fraction 0.743 to binary.

Solution: We follow the same procedure as before and get the following values.

$$
\begin{array}{rl}
0.743 & \\
\times \quad\quad 2 & \text{Integral Part}\\
\hline
\mathbf{1}.486 & 1\\
\times \quad\quad 2 & \\
\hline
\mathbf{0}.972 & 0\\
\times \quad\quad 2 & \\
\hline
\mathbf{1}.944 & 1\\
\times \quad\quad 2 & \\
\hline
\mathbf{1}.888 & 1\\
\times \quad\quad 2 & \\
\hline
\mathbf{1}.776 & 1\\
\times \quad\quad 2 & \\
\hline
\mathbf{1}.552 & 1\\
\times \quad\quad 2 & \\
\hline
\mathbf{1}.104 & 1\\
\times \quad\quad 2 & \\
\hline
\mathbf{0}.208 & 0\\
\times \quad\quad 2 & \\
\hline
\mathbf{0}.416 & 0\\
\end{array}
$$

It is becoming clear that this computation can continue indefinitely. This shows that *not all decimal fractions can be exactly converted to binary*. This inability to make an exact conversion is an unavoidable source of inaccuracy in some computations. To decide how far to carry out computation, we use the rule of thumb that each decimal digit requires about three binary bits to give the same accuracy. Thus our original three digit number requires about nine bits, which we already have. The result of our conversion is, then,

$$0.743_{10} \approx .101\ 111\ 100_2$$ ▬

To convert a decimal number having both an integer part and a fractional part to binary, convert each part separately as shown above, and combine.

▬ **Example 11:** Convert the number 59.546875 to binary.

Solution: From the preceding examples,

$$59 = 11\ 1011$$

and

$$0.546875 = .1000\ 11$$

So

$$59.546875 = 11\ 1011.1000\ 11$$ ▬

Converting Binary Fractions to Decimal

We use Table 23•1 (page 706) to find the decimal equivalent of each binary bit located to the right of the binary point, and add.

▬ **Example 12:** Convert the binary fraction 0.101 to decimal.

Solution: From Table 23•1,

$$
\begin{array}{llll}
0.1 & = 2^{-1} & = 0.5 \\
\underline{0.001} & = 2^{-3} & = \underline{0.125} \\
\end{array}
$$

Add: $\quad 0.101 \qquad = 0.625$ ▬

The procedure is no different when converting a binary number that has both a whole and a fractional part.

▬ **Example 13:** Convert the binary number 10.01 to decimal.

Solution: From Table 23•1,

$$
\begin{array}{lll}
10 & = 2 \\
\underline{0.01} & = \underline{0.25} \\
\end{array}
$$

Add: $\quad 10.01 = 2.25$ ▬

Exercise 1 The Binary Number System

Conversion between Binary and Decimal

Convert each binary number to decimal:

1. 10   **2.** 01   **3.** 11
4. 1001   **5.** 0110   **6.** 1111

7. 1101   **8.** 0111   **9.** 1100
10. 1011   **11.** 0101   **12.** 1101 0010
13. 0110 0111   **14.** 1001 0011   **15.** 0111 0111
16. 1001 1010 1000 0010

Convert each decimal number to binary:

17. 5   **18.** 9
19. 2   **20.** 7
21. 72   **22.** 28
23. 93   **24.** 17
25. 274   **26.** 937
27. 118   **28.** 267
29. 8375   **30.** 2885
31. 82740   **32.** 72649

Convert each decimal fraction below to binary. Retain eight bits to the right of the binary point.

33. 0.5   **34.** 0.25   **35.** 0.75
36. 0.375   **37.** 0.3   **38.** 0.8
39. 0.55   **40.** 0.35   **41.** 0.875
42. 0.4375   **43.** 0.3872   **44.** 0.8462

Convert each binary fraction to decimal:

45. 0.1   **46.** 0.11   **47.** 0.01
48. 0.011   **49.** 0.1001   **50.** 0.0111

Convert each decimal number below to binary. Keep eight bits to the right of the binary point.

51. 5.5   **52.** 2.75
53. 4.375   **54.** 29.381
55. 948.472   **56.** 2847.22853

Convert each binary number to decimal:

57. 1.1   **58.** 10.11
59. 10.01   **60.** 101.011
61. 1 1001.0110 1   **62.** 10 1001.1001 101

Calculator

63. Some calculators can convert directly between binary and decimal numbers. Some will do this only for integers. Check your calculator manual to see if you can perform these operations, and, if so, try it on any of the problems above.

23•2

The Hexadecimal Number System

Hexadecimal Numbers

Hexadecimal numbers (or *hex* for short) are obtained by grouping the bits in a binary number into sets of four, and representing each such set by a single number or letter. A hex number one-fourth the length of the binary number is thus obtained.

Base 16

Since a 4-bit group of binary digits can have a value between 0 and 15, we need 16 symbols to represent all these values. The base of hexadecimal numbers is thus 16. We use the digits from 0 to 9, and the capital letters A to F, as in Table 23•2.

TABLE 23•2 Hexadecimal and Octal Number Systems

Table 23•2 also shows octal numbers, which we will use later.

DECIMAL	BINARY	HEXADECIMAL	OCTAL
0	0000	0	0
1	0001	1	1
2	0010	2	2
3	0011	3	3
4	0100	4	4
5	0101	5	5
6	0110	6	6
7	0111	7	7
8	1000	8	10
9	1001	9	11
10	1010	A	12
11	1011	B	13
12	1100	C	14
13	1101	D	15
14	1110	E	16
15	1111	F	17

Converting Binary to Hexadecimal

Group the bits into sets of four starting at the binary point, adding zeros as needed to fill out the groups. Then assign to each group the appropriate letter or number from Table 23•2.

■ **Example 14:** Convert 10110100111001 to hexadecimal.

Solution: Grouping, we get

$$10 \quad 1101 \quad 0011 \quad 1001$$

or

$$0010 \quad 1101 \quad 0011 \quad 1001$$

From Table 23•2:   2   D   3   9

So the hexadecimal equivalent is 2D39. Hexadecimal numbers are sometimes written with the subscript 16, as in

$$2D39_{16}$$

The procedure is no different for binary fractions.

■ **Example 15:** Convert 101111.0011111 to hexadecimal.

Solution: Grouping from the binary point gives us

$$10 \quad 1111 \quad . \quad 0011 \quad 111$$

or

$$0010 \quad 1111 \quad . \quad 0011 \quad 1110$$

From Table 23•2:   2   F   .   3   E

or 2F.3E.

Binary–Octal Conversions

To convert from binary to octal, write the bits of the binary number in groups of three, starting at the binary point. Then write the octal equivalent for each group.

■ **Example 19:** Convert the binary number 1 1010 0011 0110 to octal.

Solution: Group the bits in sets of three from the binary point:

$$001 \quad 101 \quad 000 \quad 110 \quad 110$$

Give the octal equivalents: 1   5   0   6   6

The octal equivalent of 1 1010 0011 0110 is 15066.   ■

To convert from octal to binary, simply reverse the procedure shown in the preceding example.

■ **Example 20:** Convert the octal number 7364 to binary.

Solution: We write the group of 3 bits corresponding to each octal digit.

$$7 \quad\; 3 \quad\; 6 \quad\; 4$$
$$111 \quad 011 \quad 110 \quad 100$$

or 1110 1111 0100.   ■

Exercise 3 The Octal Number System

Convert each binary number to octal.

1. 110	**2.** 010	**3.** 111
4. 101	**5.** 11 0011	**6.** 01 1010
7. 0110 1101	**8.** 1 1011 0100	**9.** 100 1001
10. 1100 1001		

Convert each octal number to binary.

11. 26	**12.** 35	**13.** 623
14. 621	**15.** 5243	**16.** 1153
17. 63150	**18.** 2346	

Calculator

19. Some calculators can convert directly between octal, binary, and decimal numbers. Some will do this only for integers. Check your calculator manual to see if you can perform these operations, and, if so, try it on any of the problems above.

23•4

BCD Codes

In Section 23•1 we converted decimal numbers into binary. Recall that each bit had a place value equal to 2 raised to the position number. Thus the binary number 10001 is equal to

$$2^4 + 2^0 = 16 + 1 = 17$$

We shall now refer to numbers such as 10001 as *straight binary*.

With a BCD or *binary-coded-decimal* code, a decimal number is not converted *as a whole* to binary, but rather *digit by digit*. For example, the 1 in the decimal number 17 is 0001 in 4-bit binary, and the 7 is equal to 0111. Thus

$$17 = 10001 \text{ in straight binary}$$

and

$$17 = 0001\ 0111 \text{ in BCD}$$

When we converted the digits in the decimal number 17 in the preceding example, we used the same 4-bit binary equivalents as in Table 23•2. The bits have the place values 8, 4, 2, and 1, and BCD numbers written in this manner are said to be in *8421 code*.

Converting Decimal Numbers to BCD

Simply convert each decimal digit to its equivalent 4-bit code.

■ **Example 21:** Convert the decimal number 25.3 to 8421 BCD code.

Solution: We find the BCD equivalent of each decimal digit from Table 23•3.

$$
\begin{array}{ccccc}
2 & 5 & . & 3 \\
0010 & 0101 & . & 0011
\end{array}
$$

or 0010 0101.0011. ■

TABLE 23•3 Binary-Coded-Decimal Numbers

DECIMAL	8421	2421	5211
0	0000	0000	0000
1	0001	0001	0001
2	0010	0010	0011
3	0011	0011	0101
4	0100	0100	0111
5	0101	1011	1000
6	0110	1100	1010
7	0111	1101	1100
8	1000	1110	1110
9	1001	1111	1111

Converting from BCD to Decimal

Separate the BCD number into 4-bit groups, and write the decimal equivalent of each group.

■ **Example 22:** Convert the 8421 BCD number 1 0011.0101 to decimal.

Solution: We have

$$
\begin{array}{ccccc}
0001 & 0011 & . & 0101 \\
\end{array}
$$

From Table 23•3: $\quad$ 1 $\quad$ 3 $\quad$. $\quad$ 5

or 13.5. ■

Other BCD Codes

There are other BCD codes in use which represent each decimal digit by a 6-bit binary number or an 8-bit binary number, and other 4-bit codes in which the place values are other than 8421. Some of these are shown in Table 23•3. Each is used in the same way as shown for the 8421 code.

■ **Example 23:** Convert the decimal number 825 to 2421 BCD code.

Solution: We convert each decimal digit separately,

$$
\begin{array}{ccc}
8 & 2 & 5 \\
1110 & 0010 & 1011
\end{array}
$$
■

Other Computer Codes

In addition to the binary, hexadecimal, octal, and BCD codes we have discussed, there are many other codes used in the computer industry. Numbers can be represented by the *excess-3 code* or the *Gray code*. There are error-detecting and parity-checking codes. Other codes are used to represent letters of the alphabet and special symbols, as well as numbers. Some of these are the *Morse code*, the American Standard Code for Information Interchange or *ASCII* (pronounced *as-key*) *code*, the Extended Binary-Coded-Decimal Interchange Code or *EBCDIC* (pronounced *eb-si-dik*) *code*, and the *Hollerith code* used for punched cards.

Space does not permit discussion of each code. However, if you have understood the manipulation of the codes we have described, you should have no trouble when faced with a new one.

Exercise 4   BCD Codes

Convert each decimal number to 8421 BCD:

1. 62   **2.** 25   **3.** 274
4. 284   **5.** 42.91   **6.** 5.014

Convert each 8421 BCD number to a decimal number:

7. 1001   **8.** 101   **9.** 110 0001
10. 100 0111   **11.** 11 0110.1000   **12.** 11 1000.1000 1

CHAPTER 23   REVIEW PROBLEMS

1. Convert the binary number 110.001 to decimal.
2. Convert the binary number 1100.0111 to hex.
3. Convert the hex number 2D to BCD.
4. Convert the binary number 1100 1010 to decimal.
5. Convert the hex number 2B4 to octal.
6. Convert the binary number 110 0111.011 to octal.
7. Convert the decimal number 26.875 to binary.
8. Convert the hexadecimal number 5E.A3 to binary.
9. Convert the octal number 534 to decimal.
10. Convert the BCD number 1001 to hex.
11. Convert the octal number 276 to hex.
12. Convert the 8421 BCD number 1001 0100 0011 to decimal.
13. Convert the decimal number 8362 to hex.
14. Convert the octal number 2453 to BCD.
15. Convert the BCD number 1001 0010 to octal.
16. Convert the decimal number 482 to octal.
17. Convert the octal number 47135 to binary.

18. Convert the hexadecimal number 3D2.A4F to decimal.
19. Convert the BCD number 0111 0100 to straight binary.
20. Convert the decimal number 382.4 to 8421 BCD.

Writing

21. A financial expert, trying to trim the college budget, has suggested dropping the study of binary numbers. "Why do we need other numbers?" he asks. "Plain numbers were good enough when I went to school."

Write a letter to this financial expert, explaining why, in this computer age, "plain" numbers are not enough. Include specific examples of the use of binary numbers. Be polite but forceful, and limit your letter to one page.

24

Inequalities and Linear Programming

OBJECTIVES

When you have completed this chapter, you should be able to:

- Graph linear inequalities on the number line.
- Graph linear inequalities on the coordinate axes.
- Graph a system of linear inequalities.
- Solve conditional inequalities graphically and algebraically.
- Use inequalities to determine the range of a function or relation.
- Solve absolute value inequalities.
- Solve linear programming problems.

So far we have dealt only with equations, where one expression is equal to another, and our aim was to solve them—that is, to find any set of values of the variables that makes the equation true. In this chapter we work with *inequalities*, in which one expression is not necessarily equal to another, but may be greater than or less than the other expression. We will graph inequalities, and also solve them. Here we seek a whole range of values of the variable to satisfy the inequality.

We then introduce *linear programming* (a term that should not be confused with *computer programming*), which plays an important part in certain business decisions. It helps us decide how to allocate resources in order to reduce costs and maximize profit—a concern of technical people as well as management. We then write a computer program to do linear programming.

24•1 Definitions

Inequalities

An *inequality* is a statement that one quantity is greater than, or less than, another quantity.

■ **Example 1:** The statement $a > b$ means "a is greater than b." ■

Parts of an Inequality

$$a > b$$

left side or member —⌐⌐⌐— right side or member

inequality sign

Inequality Symbols

In Section 1•1 we introduced the inequality symbols $>$ and $<$. These can be combined with the equal sign to produce the compound symbols $\geq$ and $\leq$, which mean "greater than or equal to" and "less than or equal to." Further, a slash through any of these symbols indicates the negation of the inequality.

■ **Example 2:** The statement $a \not> b$ means "a is not greater than b." ■

Sense of an Inequality

The *sense* of an inequality refers to the *direction* in which the inequality sign points. We use this term mostly when operating on an inequality, where certain operations will *change the sense*, whereas others will not.

Conditional and Unconditional Inequalities

Just as we have conditional equations and identities, we also have conditional and unconditional inequalities. As with equations, a conditional inequality is one that is satisfied only by certain values of the unknown, whereas unconditional equalities are true for any values of the unknown.

■ **Example 3:** The statement $x - 2 > 5$ is a conditional inequality because it is true only for values of x greater than 7. ■

In this chapter we limit ourselves to the *real* numbers.

■ **Example 4:** The statement $x^2 + 5 > 0$ is an unconditional inequality (also called an *absolute* inequality) because for any value of x, positive, negative, or zero, x^2 cannot be negative. Thus $x^2 + 5$ is always greater than zero. ■

Linear and Nonlinear Inequalities

A *linear* inequality is defined in the same way as a linear equation, where all variables are of *first degree* or less. Other inequalities are called *nonlinear*.

■ **Example 5:** The inequalities

$$x + 2 > 3x - 5$$

and

$$2x - 3y \geq 4$$

are linear, while the inequalities

$$x^2 - 3 < 2x$$

and

$$y \leq x^3 + 2x - 3$$

are nonlinear. —

Inequalities with Three Members

The inequality $3 < x$ has two members, left and right. However, many inequalities have *three* members.

— **Example 6:** The statement $3 < x < 9$ means "x is greater than 3 and less than 9," or "x is a number between 3 and 9." The given inequality is really a combination of the two inequalities

$$x > 3$$

and

$$x < 9$$

It is sometimes called a *double inequality*. —

Common Error	It is incorrect to write the two inequalities $$x < 3 \quad \text{and} \quad x > 9$$ as $$3 > x > 9$$ because there is no number that is less than 3 and also greater than 9.

— **Example 7:** Combine the two inequalities

$$x > -6 \quad \text{and} \quad x \leq 22$$

into a double inequality.

Solution: We write

$$-6 < x \leq 22$$

—

Intervals

The *interval* of an inequality is the set of all numbers between the left member and the right member, called the *end points* of the interval, and may include one or both end points. An end point is *included* if it has the possibility of equality, i.e., its sign is $\geq$ or $\leq$ rather than just $>$ or $<$. An interval is called *open* or *closed* depending on whether or not the end points are included.

An interval is often denoted by enclosing it and its end points in parentheses or brackets. We use parentheses for an open interval and brackets for a closed interval, or a combination of the two if one end is open and the other is closed.

■ **Example 8:** Some inequalities and their notations are:

Inequality	Notation	Open or Closed
(a) $2 \leq x \leq 3$	[2, 3]	Closed
(b) $4 < x < 5$	(4, 5)	Open
(c) $6 < x \leq 7$	(6, 7]	Open on left, closed on right

■

Graphing Intervals

An inequality can be represented on the number line by graphing the interval. An open end point is usually shown as an open circle, while a closed end point is shown solid.

■ **Example 9:** The three inequalities of Example 8 are graphed in Figure 24•1.

FIGURE 24•1

The interval is called *unbounded* if it has only one end point, and extends indefinitely in one direction.

■ **Example 10:**

(a) The inequality $x < 1$ is shown graphically in Figure 24•2. It is said to be open on the right and unbounded on the left. The interval notation for the inequality $x < 1$ is $(-\infty, 1)$.

FIGURE 24•2

(b) The inequality $x \geq 2$ is also shown in Figure 24•2. It is said to be closed on the left and unbounded on the right. The interval notation for this inequality is $[2, \infty)$.

■

Graphing Inequalities Having Two Variables

An inequality having *two variables* can be represented by a *region*, in the *xy* plane. To graph an inequality, we first graph the corresponding equality with a dashed curve. Then, if points on the line satisfy the given inequality, we replace the dashed curve by a solid one. If the points above (or below) the curve satisfy the inequality, we shade the region above (or below) the curve.

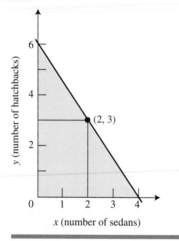

FIGURE 24•3 Points within the shaded region satisfy the inequality $y > x + 1$.

FIGURE 24•4

FIGURE 24•5

■ **Example 11:** Graph the inequality $y > x + 1$.

Solution: We graph the line $y = x + 1$ (Fig. 24•3) using a solid line if points on the line satisfy the given inequality, or a dashed line if they do not. Here, we need a dashed line. All points in the shaded region above the dashed line satisfy the given equality. For example, if we substitute the values for the point (1, 3) into our inequality, we get

$$3 > 1 + 1$$

which is true. So (1, 3) will be in the region that satisfies the inequality $y > x + 1$. This trial point helps us choose the region to shade (here, the region above the line) and serves as a check for our work. ■

■ **Example 12:** A certain automobile company can make a sedan in 3 h and a hatchback in 2 h. How many of each type of car can be made if the working time is not to exceed 12 h?

Solution: We let

$$x = \text{number of sedans made in 12 h}$$

and

$$y = \text{number of hatchbacks made in 12 h}$$

We look at the time it takes to make each vehicle. Since each sedan takes 3 h to make, it will take $3x$ hours to make the x sedans. Similarly, it takes $2y$ hours for the hatchbacks. So we get the inequality which states that the sum of the times is less than or equal to 12 h.

$$3x + 2y \le 12$$

We plot the equation $3x + 2y = 12$ in Figure 24•4. Any point on the line or in the shaded region satisfies the inequality. For example, the company could make two sedans and three hatchbacks in the 12 h period, or it could make no cars at all, or it could make four sedans and no hatchbacks, and so on. It could not, however, make three sedans and three hatchbacks in the allotted 12 h. ■

Sometimes we want to graph two inequalities on the same axes. This is a way to solve two inequalities simultaneously.

■ **Example 13:** Figure 24•5 shows a graph of the two inequalities

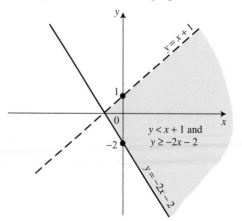

$$y < x + 1 \quad \text{and} \quad y \geq -2x - 2$$

Points within the shaded region simultaneously satisfy both inequalities. ▬

Exercise 1 Definitions

Kinds of Inequalities

Label each inequality as conditional, unconditional, linear, or nonlinear.

1. $x^2 > -4$
3. $3x^2 - 2x \leq 6$
5. $3x + 3 \geq x - 7$

2. $x + 2 < 3 - 4x$
4. $3x^4 + 5 > 0$
6. $x^2 - 3x + 2 > 7$

Inequalities with Three Members

Rewrite each double inequality as two separate inequalities.

7. $5 < x < 9$
9. $-11 < x \leq 1$

8. $-2 \leq x < 7$
10. $22 < x \leq 53$

Rewrite each pair of inequalities as a double inequality.

11. $x > 5, x < 8$
13. $x \geq -1, x < 24$

12. $x > -4, x < 1$
14. $x > 12, x \leq 13$

Intervals

Graph each inequality on the number line.

15. $x > 5$
17. $x < 3$
19. $x \geq -2$
21. $x \leq 1$

16. $2 < x < 5$
18. $-1 \leq x \leq 3$
20. $4 \leq x < 7$
22. $-4 < x \leq 0$

Write the inequality corresponding to each given interval, and graph.

23. $(-\infty, 8)$
26. $[10, \infty)$
29. $(4, 22]$

24. $(-\infty, 5]$
27. $(3, 12)$
30. $[-11, 5)$

25. $(-3, \infty)$
28. $[-2, 7]$

Graphing Inequalities Having Two Variables

Graph each inequality.

31. $y < 3x - 2$
33. $2x - y < 3$

32. $x + y \geq 1$
34. $y > -x^2 + 4$

Graph the region in which both inequalities are satisfied.

35. $y > -x + 3$
$\quad y < 2x - 2$
37. $y > x^2 - 4$
$\quad y < 4 - x^2$

36. $y < x^2 - 2$
$\quad y \geq x$

38. The supply voltage V to a certain device is required to be over 100 V, but not over 150 V. Express this as an inequality.

39. A manufacturer makes skis and snowshoes. A pair of skis takes 2.5 h to make and a pair of snowshoes takes 3.1 h. Write and graph an inequality to represent the number of pairs of skis and snowshoes that can be made in 8 h.

Calculator

40. Some graphics calculators can graph inequalities, and even shade the region in which the inequalities are satisfied. Check your manual, and if you have this capability use it to graph any of the inequalities in this exercise.

24·2 Solving Inequalities

Unlike the solution to a conditional equation, which is one or more discrete values of the variable, the solution to a conditional inequality will usually be an infinite set of values. We first show graphical methods for finding these values, and then give an algebraic method. For each method we will first solve linear inequalities and then nonlinear inequalities.

Graphical Solution of Inequalities

We will show two graphical methods. The first method is to graph both sides of the inequality, and then identify the intervals for which the inequality is true. We can make our graphs by a point-to-point plot, or with a graphics calculator or graphing utility on a computer.

Our first example will be the solution of a linear inequality.

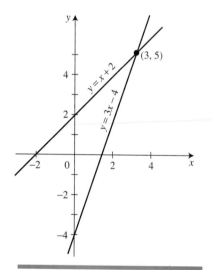

FIGURE 24·6

■ **Example 14:** Graphically solve the linear inequality

$$3x - 4 > x + 2$$

Solution: On the same axes, we graph

$$y = 3x - 4 \quad \text{and} \quad y = x + 2$$

as in Figure 24·6. The interval for which $3x - 4$ is greater than $x + 2$ is clearly

$$x > 3$$

or

$$(3, \infty)$$

■

Our second graphical method is to move all terms to one side of the inequality, and to graph the resulting expression. We then identify the intervals for which this inequality is true. We will illustrate this method by solving a nonlinear inequality.

■ **Example 15:** Solve the nonlinear inequality

$$x^2 - 3 > 2x$$

Solution: Rearranging gives

$$x^2 - 2x - 3 > 0$$

We now plot the function

$$y = x^2 - 2x - 3$$

as shown in Figure 24•7.

FIGURE 24•7 The points $x = -1$ and $x = 3$ where the curve crosses the x axis are called *critical values*. $x < -1$ and $x > 3$ are solutions because those x values satisfy the inequality.

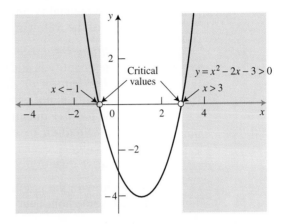

Note that our solutions to the inequality are all *values of x* that make the inequality true, that is, those values of x that here make y positive. The curve (a parabola) is above the x axis when $x < -1$ and $x > 3$. These values of x are the solutions to our inequality, because, for these values, $x^2 - 2x - 3 > 0$. The intervals containing the solutions are thus

$$(-\infty, -1) \quad \text{and} \quad (3, \infty) \qquad \blacksquare$$

Checking a Solution

We can gain confidence in our solution by substituting values of x into the inequality. Those values within the range of our solution should check, while all others should not.

■ **Example 16:** For the inequality of Example 15, the values of, say, $x = 4$ and $x = -2$ should check, while $x = 1$ should not. Substituting $x = 4$ into our original inequality gives

$$4^2 - 3 > 2(4)$$

or

$$16 - 3 > 8$$

which is true. Similarly, the value $x = -2$ gives

$$(-2)^2 - 3 > 2(-2)$$

or

$$4 - 3 > -4$$

which is also true. On the other hand, a value between -1 and 3, such as $x = 1$, gives

$$1^2 - 3 > 2(1)$$

or

$$-2 \not> 2$$

which is not true, as expected. ■

Algebraic Solution

The object of an *algebraic solution* to a conditional inequality is to locate the *critical values* (the points like those in Figure 24•7 where the curve crossed the x axis). To do this it is usually a good idea to transpose all terms to one side of the inequality and simplify the expression as much as possible. We make use of the following principles for operations with inequalities:

1. *Addition or subtraction:* The sense of an inequality is not changed if the same quantity is added to or subtracted from both sides.
2. *Multiplication or division by a positive quantity:* The sense of an inequality is not changed if both sides are multiplied or divided by the same *positive* quantity.
3. *Multiplication or division by a negative quantity:* The sense of an inequality *is reversed* if both sides are multiplied or divided by the same *negative* quantity.

As we did with the graphical solution, we will first solve a linear inequality and then some nonlinear inequalities.

━━ **Example 17:** Solve the linear inequality $21x - 23 < 2x + 15$.

Solution: Rearranging gives us

$$19x < 38$$

Dividing by 19, we get

$$x < 2$$

FIGURE 24•8

or $(-\infty, 2)$, as shown in Figure 24•8. ━━

When solving a nonlinear inequality, we usually get more than one critical value, which divide the x axis into more than two intervals. To decide which of these intervals contain the correct values, we test each for algebraic sign, as shown in the following example.

━━ **Example 18:** Solve the nonlinear inequality $2x - \dfrac{x^2}{2} > -\dfrac{21}{2}$.

Solution: Multiplying by 2, we have

$$4x - x^2 > -21$$

Rearranging yields

$$4x - x^2 + 21 > 0$$

or

$$-x^2 + 4x + 21 > 0$$

Multiplying by -1, which reverses the sense of the inequality, we obtain

$$x^2 - 4x - 21 < 0$$

Factoring gives us

$$(x - 7)(x + 3) < 0$$

The critical values are those that make the left side equal zero, $x = 7$ and $x = -3$. These divide the x axis into three intervals,

$$x < -3 \qquad -3 < x < 7 \qquad x > 7$$

Which of these is correct? We can decide by computing the sign of $(x - 7)(x + 3)$ in each interval. Since this product is supposed to be less than zero, we choose the interval(s) in which the product is negative. Thus

INTERVAL	$(x - 7)$	$(x + 3)$	$(x - 7)(x + 3)$
$x < -3$	–	–	+
$-3 < x < 7$	–	+	–
$x > 7$	+	+	+

The *sign pattern* for $(x - 7)(x + 3)$ is shown in Figure 24•9. The signs are correct in only one interval, so our solution is

$$x > -3 \qquad \text{and} \qquad x < 7$$

FIGURE 24•9

or $(-3, 7)$ in interval notation. Note that this is the interval for which the graph of $y = x^2 - 4x - 21$ is *below* the x axis (Fig. 24•10). ▬

Inequalities containing the $\geq$ or $\leq$ signs are solved the same way as in the preceding examples, except that now the endpoint of an interval may be included in the solution.

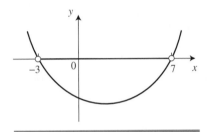

FIGURE 24•10

▬ **Example 19:** Solve the nonlinear inequality $x^3 - x^2 \geq 2x$.

Solution: Rearranging and factoring gives

$$x^3 - x^2 - 2x \geq 0$$
$$x(x^2 - x - 2) \geq 0$$
$$x(x + 1)(x - 2) \geq 0$$

The critical values are then

$$x = -1 \qquad x = 0 \qquad x = 2$$

We now analyze the signs, as in Example 18, looking for those intervals in which the product $x(x + 1)(x - 2)$ is positive.

INTERVAL	x	$(x + 1)$	$(x - 2)$	$x(x + 1)(x - 2)$
$x < -1$	–	–	–	–
$-1 < x < 0$	–	+	–	+
$0 < x < 2$	+	+	–	–
$x > 2$	+	+	+	+

Our solution is then

$$-1 \leq x \leq 0 \quad \text{and} \quad x \geq 2$$

Note that the endpoints $x = -1$, 0, and 2 are included in the solution. In interval notation, the solutions are $[-1, 0]$ and $[2, \infty)$.

   If we had graphed the inequality (Fig. 24•11), we would have selected the two intervals that correspond to values on the curve that are on or above the x axis. ▬

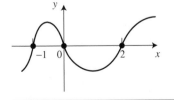

FIGURE 24•11

Our next example shows the algebraic and graphical solution of a double inequality.

■ **Example 20:** Solve the inequality

$$-5 < 3x + 4 \le 9$$

Algebraic Solution: We can manipulate both inequalities at the same time.

$$-9 < 3x \le 5$$

$$-3 < x \le 5/3$$

or $(-3, 5/3]$ in interval notation.

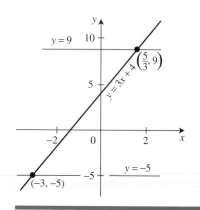

Graphical Solution: We graph the three functions

$$y = -5 \qquad y = 3x + 4 \qquad y = 9$$

on the same axes (Fig. 24•12). The interval for which $3x + 4$ lies between -5 and 9 is $(-3, 5/3]$. ■

FIGURE 24•12

Our final example shows a graphical solution to a difficult nonlinear inequality.

■ **Example 21:** Graphically solve the following inequality. Work to three significant digits.

$$3.72x^3 - 6.26x^2 > 3.27x - 4.57$$

Solution: On the same axes we graph

$$y = 3.72x^3 - 6.26x^2 \qquad \text{and} \qquad y = 3.27x - 4.57$$

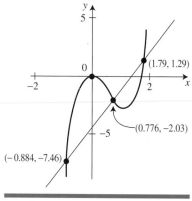

(Fig. 24•13). Using TRACE and ZOOM, we find the coordinates of the three critical points to be $(-0.884, -7.46)$, $(0.776, -2.03)$, and $(1.79, 1.29)$. The intervals for which the inequality is true are then

$$(-0.884, 0.776) \quad \text{and} \quad (1.79, \infty) \qquad \blacksquare$$

FIGURE 24•13

Inequalities Containing Absolute Values

Recall from Section 1•1 that the *absolute value* of a quantity is its *magnitude* and is always positive.

■ **Example 22:**

(a) $|5| = 5$ (b) $|-5| = 5$ ■

It would thus be correct to say that the quantity inside the absolute value sign could be 5 or -5, so if we see the expression $|x| > 2$, we know that either x or $-x$, will be greater than 2.

$|x| > 2$ is equivalent to $x > 2$ and $-x > 2$

expression with
absolute value signs

two inequalities, without
absolute value signs

The two inequalities can be written $x > 2$ and $x < -2$ because multiplying the right-hand inequality by -1 reverses the sense of the inequality.

Similarly, $|x| < 2$ is equivalent to $x < 2$ and $-x < 2$, or (after multiplying on the right by -1) $x < 2$ and $x > -2$. Stated as a rule,

$$|x| < a \quad \text{is equivalent to} \quad -a < x < a$$
$$|x| > a \quad \text{is equivalent to} \quad x < -a \quad \text{or} \quad x > a$$

To solve algebraically an inequality containing an absolute value sign, replace the inequality by a double inequality or by two inequalities having no absolute value signs. Solve each inequality as shown before.

To graphically solve an inequality containing an absolute value sign, simply graph both sides of the inequality and note the intervals in which the inequality is true. If you wish, you may move all terms to one side of the inequality before graphing, as in the second graphical method.

We will show both methods in the following examples.

■ **Example 23:** Solve the inequality $|3x - 2| \leq 5$.

Algebraic Solution: We replace the given inequality with the double inequality

$$-5 \leq 3x - 2 \leq 5$$

Solving, we get

$$-3 \leq 3x \leq 7$$
$$-1 \leq x \leq 7/3$$

In interval notation, our solution is $[-1, 7/3]$.

Graphical Solution: We graph

$$y = |3x - 2| \quad \text{and} \quad y = 5$$

on the same axes (Fig. 24•14). The interval for which $|3x - 2|$ is less than or equal to 5 is the same as found algebraically.   ■

■ **Example 24:** Solve the inequality $|7 - 3x| > 4$.

Algebraic Solution: We replace this inequality with

$$(7 - 3x) > 4 \quad \text{or} \quad (7 - 3x) < -4$$

Subtracting 7, we obtain

$$-3x > -3 \quad \text{or} \quad -3x < -11$$

Dividing by -3 and reversing the sense yields

$$x < 1 \quad \text{or} \quad x > \frac{11}{3}$$

So x may have values less than 1 or greater than $3\frac{2}{3}$. In interval notation, the solution is

$$(-\infty, 1) \quad \text{or} \quad (11/3, \infty)$$

Graphical Solution: We graph

$$y = |7 - 3x| \quad \text{and} \quad y = 4$$

These rules are, of course, equally true for the ≤ or ≥ relationships.

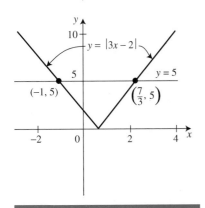

FIGURE 24•14

On a graphics calculator, use the ABS key to obtain an absolute value. Thus we would enter

$$Y1 = ABS (3X - 2)$$

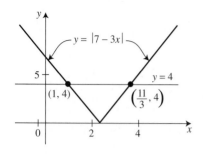

FIGURE 24·15

on the same axes (Fig. 24•15). The interval for which $|7 - 3x|$ is greater than 4 is the same as found algebraically. ▬

Finding the Domain of a Function

We can use inequalities to find the domain of a function or relation, those values of x for which the function or relation has real values. This is useful in graphing to locate, in advance, those regions in which the function exists.

▬ **Example 25:** Find the values of x for which the relation $x^2 - y^2 - 4x + 3 = 0$ is real.

Solution: We solve for y,

$$y^2 = x^2 - 4x + 3$$

$$y = \pm\sqrt{x^2 - 4x + 3}$$

For y to be real, the quantity under the radical sign must be nonnegative, so we seek the values of x that satisfy the inequality

$$x^2 - 4x + 3 \geq 0$$

Factoring gives

$$(x - 1)(x - 3) \geq 0$$

The critical values are then $x = 1$ and $x = 3$. Analyzing the signs, we obtain

INTERVAL	$(x - 1)$	$(x - 3)$	$(x - 1)(x - 3)$
$x < 1$	−	−	+
$1 < x < 3$	+	−	−
$x > 3$	+	+	+

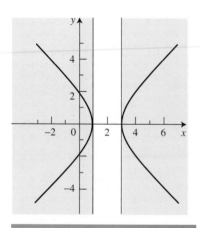

FIGURE 24·16

We conclude that the function exists for the ranges $x \leq 1$ and $x \geq 3$, but not for $1 < x < 3$. This information helps when graphing the curve, for we now know where the curve does and does not exist. (The curve is actually a hyperbola, Figure 24•16, which is studied in analytic geometry.) ▬

Exercise 2 Solving Inequalities

Solve each inequality:

1. $2x - 5 > x + 4$

2. $x + 2 < 3 - 2x$

3. $x^2 + 4 \geq 2x^2 - 5$

4. $2x^2 + 15x \leq -25$

5. $2x^2 - 5x + 3 > 0$

6. $6x^2 < 19x - 10$

7. $\dfrac{x}{5} + \dfrac{x}{2} \geq 4$

8. $\dfrac{x + 1}{2} - \dfrac{x - 2}{3} \leq 4$

9. $1 < x + 3 < 8$

10. $12 > 2x - 1 > -3$

11. $-2 \leq 2x + 4 \leq 6$

12. $10 > 8 + x \geq 2$

Inequalities Containing Absolute Values

Solve each inequality:

13. $|3x| > 9$
14. $2|x + 3| < 8$
15. $5|x| > 8$
16. $|3x + 2| \leq 11$
17. $|2 - 3x| \geq 8$
18. $3|x + 2| > 21$
19. $|x + 5| > 2x$
20. $|x + 7| > 3x$
21. $|3 - 5x| \leq 4 - 3x$
22. $|x + 1| \geq 2x - 1$

Finding the Domain of a Function

For what values of x is each expression below real?

23. $\sqrt{x^2 + 4x - 5}$
24. $\sqrt{x^3 - 4x^2 - 12x}$
25. $y^2 = x^2 - x - 6$
26. $x^2 + y^2 + x - 2 = 0$

Applications

27. A certain machine is rented for \$155 per day, and it costs \$25 per hour to operate. The total cost per day for this machine is not to exceed \$350. Write an inequality for this situation, and find the maximum permissible hours of operation.

28. A computer salesperson earns an annual salary of \$25 500 and also gets a 37.5% commission on sales. How much must be sold in order to make an annual income of at least \$50 000?

29. A company can make a camera lens for \$12.75 and sell it for \$39.99. It also has overhead costs of \$2884 per week. Find the minimum number of lenses that must be sold for the company to make a profit.

Graphics Calculator or Computer

30. Use a graphics calculator or a graphing utility on a computer to solve graphically any of the inequalities in this exercise. Also use it to solve the following inequalities, working to three significant digits:

31. $2.81x^2 - 4.73 < 1.75$
32. $11.2 - 4.72x^2 \geq 2.23x + 3.05$
33. $4.77x^2 - 7.14 < 4.72 - 2.33x$
34. $4.73 \leq 5.75x - 1.17x^2$

24•3

We will do problems with only two variables here. To see how to solve problems with more than two variables, look up the *simplex method* in a text on linear programming.

Linear Programming

Linear programming is a method for finding the maximum value of some function (usually representing *profit*) when the variables it contains are themselves restricted to within certain limits. The function that is maximized is called the *objective function*, and the limits on the variables are called *constraints*. The constraints will be in the form of inequalities.

We show the method by means of examples.

━ **Example 26:** Find the values of x and y that will make z a maximum, where the objective function is

$$z = 5x + 10y$$

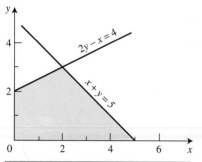

FIGURE 24•17 Feasible solutions

and *x* and *y* are positive and subject to the constraints

$$x + y \leq 5$$

and

$$2y - x \leq 4$$

Solution: We plot the two inequalities (Fig. 24•17). The only permissible values for *x* and *y* are the coordinates of points on the edges of or within the shaded region. These are called *feasible solutions*.

But which (x, y) pair selected from all those in the shaded region will give the greatest value of *z*? In other words, which of the infinite number of feasible solutions is the *optimum* solution?

To help us answer this, let us plot the equation $z = 5x + 10y$ for different values of *z*. For example, when $z = 0$,

$$5x + 10y = 0$$

$$y = -\frac{x}{2}$$

and, when $z = 10$,

$$5x + 10y = 10$$

$$y = -\frac{x}{2} + 1$$

and so on. We get a *family* of parallel straight lines, each with a slope of $-\frac{1}{2}$ (Fig. 24•18). The point *P* at which the line having the greatest *z* value intersects the region gives us the *x* and *y* values we seek. Such a point will always occur at a *corner* or *vertex* of the region. Thus, instead of plotting the family of lines, it is only necessary to compute *z* at the vertices of the region. The coordinates of the vertices are called the *basic feasible solutions*. Of these, the one that gives the greatest *z* is the *optimum solution*.

In our problem, the vertices are (0, 0), (0, 2), (5, 0), and *P*, whose coordinates we get by simultaneous solution of the equations of the boundary lines,

$$
\begin{aligned}
x + \ y &= \ 5 \\
x - 2y &= -4
\end{aligned}
$$

and

Subtracting,

$$
\begin{aligned}
3y &= \ 9 \\
y &= \ 3
\end{aligned}
$$

FIGURE 24•18 Optimum solution at *P*

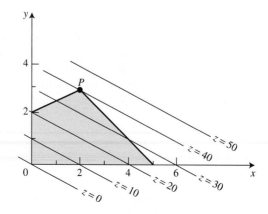

Substituting back,

$$x = 2$$

Therefore, P has the coordinates $(2, 3)$. Now compute z at each vertex:

$$\text{at } (0, 0) \quad z = 5(0) + 10(0) = \ \ 0$$
$$\text{at } (0, 2) \quad z = 5(0) + 10(2) = 20$$
$$\text{at } (5, 0) \quad z = 5(5) + 10(0) = 25$$
$$\text{at } (2, 3) \quad z = 5(2) + 10(3) = 40$$

Our optimum solution is $x = 2$, $y = 3$, which gives the largest z.   ▬

▬ **Example 27:** Find the nonnegative values of x and y that will maximize the function $z = 2x + y$ with the *four* constraints

$$y - \ \ x \leq \ \ 6$$
$$x + 4y \leq 40$$
$$x + \ \ y \leq 16$$
$$2x - \ \ y \leq 20$$

Solution: We graph the inequalities (Fig. 24•19) and compute the points of intersection. This gives the six basic feasible solutions:

$$(0,0) \quad (0, 6) \quad (3.2, 9.2) \quad (8, 8) \quad (12, 4) \quad (10, 0)$$

<table>
<tr><td>

We have not shown the work in finding the points of intersection. They are found, as before, by using TRACE and ZOOM on a graphics utility, or by simultaneously solving the equations of the intersecting lines.

FIGURE 24•19 The coordinates of the corners of the shaded region are the basic feasible solutions. One of these is the optimum solution.

</td></tr>
</table>

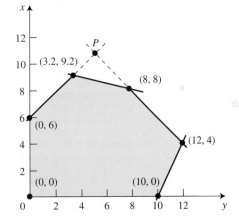

We now compute z at each point of intersection.

POINT	$z = 2x + y$	
$(0, 0)$	$z = 2(0) + 0$	$= 0$
$(0, 6)$	$z = 2(0) + 6$	$= 6$
$(3.2, 9.2)$	$z = 2(3.2) + 9.2$	$= 15.6$
$(8, 8)$	$z = 2(8) + 8$	$= 24$
$(12, 4)$	$z = 2(12) + 4$	$= 28$
$(10, 0)$	$z = 2(10) + 0$	$= 20$

The greatest z (28) occurs at $x = 12$, $y = 4$, which is thus our optimum solution. ▬

Applications

Our applications will usually be business problems, where our objective function z (the one we maximize) represents profit, and our variables x and y represent the quantities of two products to be made. A typical problem is to determine how much of each product should be manufactured so that the profit is a maximum.

▬ **Example 28:** Each month a company makes x stereos and y television sets. The manufacturing hours, material costs, testing time, and profit for each is as follows:

	MANUFACTURING TIME	MATERIAL COSTS	TEST TIME	PROFIT
Stereo	4.00 h	$95.00	1.00 h	$45.00
Television	5.00 h	$48.00	2.00 h	$38.00
Available	180 h	$3600	60.0 h	

Also shown in the table is the maximum amount of manufacturing and testing time, and the cost of material available per month. How many of each item should be made for maximum profit?

Solution: First, why should we make any television sets at all, if we get more profit on stereos? The answer is that we are limited by the money available. In 180 h we could make

$$180 \div 4.00 = 45.0 \text{ stereos}$$

However, 45 stereos, at $95 each, would require $4275, and there is only $3600 available. Then why not make

$$\$3600 \div 95.00 = 37.0 \text{ stereos}$$

using all our money on the most profitable item? This would leave us with manufacturing time unused but no money left to make any television sets.

Thus we wonder if we could do better by making fewer than 37 stereos, and using the extra time and money to make some television sets. We seek the *optimum* solution. We start by writing the equations and inequalities to describe our situation.

Our total profit z will be the profit per item times the number of items made:

$$z = 45.00x + 38.00y$$

The manufacturing time must not exceed 180 h, so

$$4.00x + 5.00y \le 180$$

The materials cost must not exceed $3600, so

$$95.00x + 48.00y \le 3600$$

And the test time must not exceed 60 h, so

$$x + 2.00y \le 60.0$$

This gives us our objective function and three constraints. We plot the constraints in Figure 24•20.

FIGURE 24•20

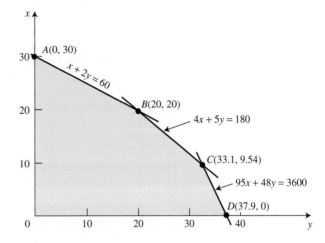

If we had used a graphics utility to make our graph, we would now use TRACE and ZOOM to find the points of intersection to three significant digits. Otherwise, we find the vertices of the region by simultaneously solving pairs of equations. To find point A, we set $x = 0$ in the equation

$$x + 2.00y = 60.0$$

and get

$$y = 30.0,$$

or

$$A(0, 30.0)$$

To find point B, we solve simultaneously

$$x + 2.00y = 60.0$$
$$4.00x + 5.00y = 180.0$$

and get

$$B(20.0, 20.0)$$

Again, the actual work is omitted here. To find point C, we solve the equations

$$4.00x + 5.00y = 180$$
$$95.00x + 48.00y = 3600$$

and get

$$x = 33.1, y = 9.54,$$

or

$$C(33.1, 9.54)$$

To find point D, we use the equation

$$95.00x + 48.00y = 3600$$

Letting $y = 0$ gives $x = 37.9$, or

$$D(37.9, 0)$$

We then evaluate the profit z at each vertex (omitting the point 0, 0 at which $z = 0$).

$$\text{At } A(0, 30.0) \qquad z = 45.00(0) \quad + 38.00(30.0) = \$1140$$
$$\text{At } B(20.0, 20.0) \quad z = 45.00(20.0) + 38.00(20.0) = \$1660$$
$$\text{At } C(33.1, 9.54) \quad z = 45.00(33.1) + 38.00(9.54) = \$1852$$
$$\text{At } D(37.9, 0) \qquad z = 45.00(37.9) + 38.00(0) \quad = \$1706$$

Thus our maximum profit, \$1852, is obtained when we make 33.1 stereos and 9.54 televisions sets. ▬

Linear Programming on the Computer

The computer can reduce the work of linear programming, especially when the number of constraints gets large. The following algorithm is for a problem with two variables and any number of constraints.

1. Using Eq. 63, find the point of intersection of any two of the given boundary lines.
2. If the point of intersection is within the region of permissible solutions, go to Step 3. If not, go to Step 5. (This will eliminate points such as P in Figure 24•19.)
3. Compute z at the point of intersection.
4. If z is the largest so far, save it and the coordinates of the point. If not, discard it.
5. If there are combinations of equations yet unused, go to Step 1.
6. Print the largest z and the coordinates of the point at which it occurs.

A flowchart for this computation is shown in Figure 24•21.

As in the examples, we seek only nonnegative values of x and y.

Exercise 3 Linear Programming

1. Maximize the function $z = x + 2y$ under the constraints
$$x + y \leq 5 \quad \text{and} \quad x - y \geq -2$$

2. Maximize the function $z = 4x + 3y$ under the constraints
$$x - 2y \geq -2 \quad \text{and} \quad x + 2y \leq 4$$

3. Maximize the function $z = 5x + 4y$ under the constraints
$$7x + 4y \leq 35, \quad 2x - 3y \leq 7, \quad \text{and} \quad x - 2y \geq -5$$

4. Maximize the function $z = x + 2y$ under the constraints
$$x - y \geq -5, \quad x + 5y \leq 45, \quad \text{and} \quad x + y \leq 15$$

For Problems 5, 6, and 7, round your answer to the nearest integer.

5. A company makes pulleys and sprockets. A pulley takes 3 min to make, requires \$1.25 in materials, and gives a profit of \$2.10. A sprocket takes 4 min to make, requires \$1.30 in materials, and gives a profit of \$2.35. The time to make x pulleys and y sprockets is not to exceed 8 h, and the cost for materials must not exceed \$175. How many of each item should be made for maximum profit?

FIGURE 24•21 Flowchart for linear programming by computer

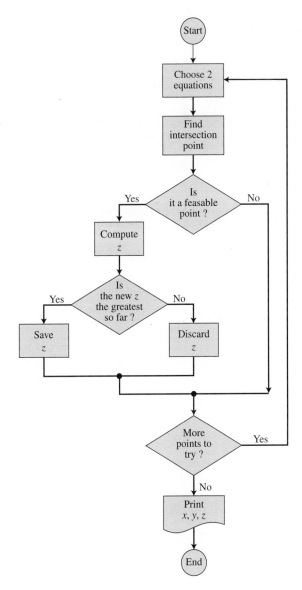

6. A company makes two computers. Model A requires 225 hours of labor and $223 in material, and yields a profit of $1975. Model B requires 67 hours of labor and $118 in material, and yields a profit of $824. There are 172 000 hours and $240 000 available per month to make the computers. How many of each computer must be made each month for maximum profit?

7. Each week a company makes x disk drives and y monitors. The manufacturing hours, material costs, inspection time, and profit for each are as follows:

	MANUFACTURING TIME (h)	MATERIAL COSTS	INSPECTION TIME (h)	PROFIT
Disk drive	5	$ 21	4.5	$34
Monitor	3	28	4	22
Available	50	320	50	

Also shown in the table are the maximum amount of manufacturing and inspection time available per week and the funds available for material. How many of each item should be made per week for maximum profit?

Computer

8. Using the flowchart (Fig. 24•21) as a guide, write a computer program to do linear programming. Try it on any of the problems in this exercise.
9. Some computer algebra systems, such as *Mathematica*, can solve linear programming problems. Consult your manual for the proper instructions and use it to solve any of the problems in this exercise.

CHAPTER 24 REVIEW PROBLEMS

1. Rewrite as two separate inequalities:
$$-11 < x \leq 1$$

2. Rewrite as an inequality:
$$x \geq -1, x < 24.$$

Graph on the number line and give the interval notation for each:

3. $x < 8$ 4. $2 \leq x < 6$

Write the inequality corresponding to each given interval, and graph:

5. $(8, \infty)$ 6. $[-4, 9)$

Solve each inequality algebraically or graphically:

7. $2x - 5 > x + 3$
8. $|2x| < 8$
9. $|x - 4| > 7$
10. $x^2 > x + 6$

11. Maximize the function $z = 7x + y$ under the constraints
$$2x + 3y \leq 5 \quad \text{and} \quad x - 4y \geq -4$$
12. A company makes four-cylinder engine blocks and six-cylinder engine blocks. A "four" requires 4 h of machine time and 5 h of labor, and gives a profit of $172. A "six" needs 5 h on the machine and 3 h of labor, and yields $195 in profit. If 130 h of labor and 155 h of machine time are available,

how many (to the nearest integer) of each engine block should be made for maximum profit?

Find the values of x for which each relation is real.

13. $\sqrt{x^2 + 8x + 15}$
14. $\sqrt{x^2 - 10x + 16}$
15. $y^2 = x^2 + 5x - 14$
16. $x^2 - y^2 - 10x + 9 = 0$

Solve each double inequality.

17. $-4.73 < x - 3 \leq 5.82$
18. $2.84 \leq x + 5 < 7.91$

19. Solve graphically to three significant digits.
$$1.27 - 2.24x + 1.84x^2 < 3.87x - 2.44x^2$$

20. A gear factory can make a bevel gear for $1.32 and sell it for $4.58. It also has overhead costs of $1845 per week for the bevel gear department. Find the minimum number that must be sold for the company to make a profit on bevel gears.

Writing

21. A job applicant says on her résumé that she knows linear programming, and the personnel director of your company insists that she fits your request for a "programmer." Write a memo to the personnel director explaining the difference between linear programming and computer programming.

25

Sequences, Series, and the Binomial Theorem

When you have completed this chapter, you should be able to:

- Identify various types of sequences and series.
- Write the general term or a recursion relation for many series.
- Compute any term or the sum of any number of terms of an arithmetic progression or a geometric progression.
- Compute any term of a harmonic progression.
- Insert any number of arithmetic means, harmonic means, or geometric means between two given numbers.
- Compute the sum of an infinite geometric progression.
- Solve applications problems using series.
- Raise a binomial to a power using the binomial theorem.
- Find any term in a binomial expansion.

We start this chapter with a general introduction to sequences and series. Sequences and series are of great interest, since a computer or calculator uses series internally to calculate many functions, such as the sine of an angle, the logarithm of a number, and so on. We then cover some specific sequences, such as the *arithmetic progression* and the *geometric progression*. Progressions are used to describe such things as the sequence of heights reached by a swinging pendulum on subsequent swings, or the monthly balance on a savings account that is growing with compound interest.

We finish this chapter with an introduction to the *binomial theorem*. The binomial theorem enables us to expand a binomial, such as $(3x^2 - 2y)^5$, without actually having to multiply the terms. It is also useful in deriving formulas in calculus, statistics, and probability.

25•1

Sequences and Series

Sequences

A *sequence*

$$u_1, u_2, u_3, \ldots, u_n$$

is a set of quantities, called *terms*, arranged in the same order as the positive integers.

■ **Example 1:**

(a) The sequence $1, \frac{1}{2}, \frac{1}{3}, \frac{1}{4}, \frac{1}{5}, \ldots, 1/n$ is called a *finite sequence*, because it has a finite number of terms, n.

(b) The sequence $1, \frac{1}{2}, \frac{1}{3}, \frac{1}{4}, \frac{1}{5}, \ldots, 1/n, \ldots$ is called an *infinite sequence*. The three dots at the end indicate that the sequence continues indefinitely.

(c) The sequence $3, 7, 11, 15, \ldots$ is called an *arithmetic sequence*, or *arithmetic progression* (AP), because each term after the first is equal to the sum of the preceding term and a constant. That constant (4 in this example) is called the *common difference*.

(d) The sequence $2, 6, 18, 54, \ldots$ is called a *geometric sequence*, or *geometric progression* (GP), because each term after the first is equal to the *product* of the preceding term and a constant. That constant (3 in this example) is called the *common ratio*.

(e) The sequence $1, 1, 2, 3, 5, 8, \ldots$ is called a *Fibonacci sequence*. Each term after the first is the sum of the two preceding terms. ■

Series

A *series* is the indicated sum of a sequence.

$$u_1 + u_2 + u_3 + \cdots + u_n + \cdots$$	**441**

■ **Example 2:**

(a) The series $1 + \frac{1}{2} + \frac{1}{3} + \frac{1}{4} + \frac{1}{5}$ is called a *finite series*. It is also called a *positive series* because all its terms are positive.

(b) The series $x - x^2 + x^3 - \cdots x^n \cdots$ is an *infinite series*. It is also called an *alternating series* because the signs of the terms alternate in sign.

(c) The series $6 + 9 + 12 + 15 + \cdots$ is an *infinite arithmetic series*. The terms of this series form an AP.

(d) $1 - 2 + 4 - 8 + 16 - \cdots$ is an *infinite, alternating, geometric series*. The terms of this series form a GP. ■

General Term

The *general term* u_n in a sequence or series is an expression involving n (where $n = 1, 2, 3, \ldots$) by which we can obtain any term. The general term is also called the nth term. If we have an expression for the general term, we can then find any specific term of the sequence or series.

■ **Example 3:** The general term of a certain series is

$$u_n = \frac{n}{2n + 1}$$

Write the first three terms of the series.

Solution: Substituting $n = 1$, $n = 2$, and $n = 3$, in turn, we get

$$u_1 = \frac{1}{2(1) + 1} = \frac{1}{3} \qquad u_2 = \frac{2}{2(2) + 1} = \frac{2}{5} \qquad u_3 = \frac{3}{2(3) + 1} = \frac{3}{7}$$

so our series is

$$\frac{1}{3} + \frac{2}{5} + \frac{3}{7} + \cdots + \frac{n}{2n + 1} + \cdots$$

■

Graphing a Sequence

We can graph a sequence if, as in Example 3, the general term is known.

■ **Example 4:** Graph the sequence given in Example 3.

Solution: *Graphing by hand:* We let $n = 1, 2, 3, \ldots$ and compute the value of as many terms as we wish. We then plot the points,

$$(1, \tfrac{1}{3}), (2, \tfrac{2}{5}), (3, \tfrac{3}{7}) \ldots$$

as in Figure 25•1.

Using a graphing utility: We graph the function

$$u = \frac{n}{2n + 1}$$

as in Figure 25•2, and place dots at $x = 1, 2, 3, \ldots$ to represent the terms of the series. ■

FIGURE 25•1

FIGURE 25•2

Recursion Relations

The words *recurrance* and *recursive* are sometimes used instead of *recursion*. We have used recursion relations before, for compound interest in Section 20•1, and for exponential growth in Section 20•2.

We have seen that we can find the terms of a series, given an expression for the nth term. Sometimes we can find each term from one or more immediately preceding terms. The relationship between a term and those preceding it is called a *recursion relation* or *recursion formula*.

■ **Example 5:** Each term (after the first) in the series $1 + 4 + 13 + 40 + \cdots$ is found by multiplying the preceding term by 3 and adding 1. The recursion relation is then

$$u_n = 3u_{n-1} + 1$$

■

Named for Leonardo Fibonacci (c. 1170–c. 1250), an Italian number theorist and algebraist who studied this sequence. He is also known as *Leonardo of Pisa*.

■ **Example 6:** In a *Fibonacci sequence*

$$1, 1, 2, 3, 5, 8, 13, 21, 34, \ldots$$

each term after the first is the sum of the two preceding terms. Its recursion relation is

$$u_n = u_{n-1} + u_{n-2}$$

■

Series by Computer

Computers now make series easier to study than before. If we have either an expression for the general term of a series or the recursion formula, we can use a computer to generate large numbers of terms. By inspecting them, we can get a good idea about how the series behaves.

■ **Example 7:** Table 25•1 shows a portion of a computer printout of 80 terms of the series

$$\frac{1}{e} + \frac{2}{e^2} + \frac{3}{e^3} + \cdots + \frac{n}{e^n} + \cdots$$

Shown for each term u_n are the sum of that term and all preceding terms, called the *partial sum*, and the ratio of that term to the one preceding. We notice several things about this series.

1. The terms get smaller and smaller, and approach a value of zero (Fig. 25•3).
2. The partial sums approach a limit (0.920674).
3. The ratio of two successive terms approaches a limit that is less than 1.

What do these facts tell us about this series? We'll see in the following section.

TABLE 25•1

n	TERM u_n	PARTIAL SUM S_n	RATIO
1	0.367879	0.367879	
2	0.270671	0.638550	0.735759
3	0.149361	0.787911	0.551819
4	0.073263	0.861174	0.490506
5	0.033690	0.894864	0.459849
6	0.014873	0.909736	0.441455
7	0.006383	0.916119	0.429193
8	0.002684	0.918803	0.420434
9	0.001111	0.919914	0.413864
10	0.000454	0.920368	0.408755
.	.	.	.
.	.	.	.
.	.	.	.
75	0.000000	0.920674	0.372851
76	0.000000	0.920674	0.372785
77	0.000000	0.920674	0.372720
78	0.000000	0.920674	0.372657
79	0.000000	0.920674	0.372596
80	0.000000	0.920674	0.372536

Convergence or Divergence of an Infinite Series

When we use a series to do computations, we cannot, of course, work with an infinite number of terms. In fact, for practical computation, we prefer as few terms as possible, as long as we get the accuracy that is needed. We want a series in which the terms decrease rapidly and approach zero, and for

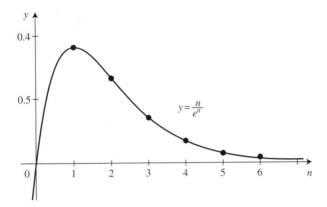

which the sum of the first several terms is not too different from the sum of all the terms of the series. Such a series is said to *converge* on some limit. A series that does not converge is said to *diverge*.

There are many tests for convergence. A particular test may tell us with certainty if the series converges or diverges. Sometimes, though, a test will fail and we must try another test. Here we consider only three tests.

1. *Magnitude of the terms:* If the terms of an infinite series do not approach zero, the series diverges. However, if the terms do approach zero, we cannot say with certainty whether the series converges. Thus, having the terms approach zero is a necessary, but not a sufficient, condition for convergence.
2. *Sum of the terms:* If the sum of the first *n* terms of a series reaches a limiting value as we take more and more terms, the series converges. Otherwise, the series diverges.
3. *Ratio test:* We compute the ratio of each term to the one preceding it, and see how that ratio changes as we go further out in the series. If that ratio approaches a number that is
   (a) less than 1, the series converges.
   (b) greater than 1, the series diverges.
   (c) equal to 1, the test is not conclusive.

■ **Example 8:** Does the series of Example 7 converge or diverge?

Solution: We apply the three tests by inspecting the computed values.

1. The terms approach zero, so this test is not conclusive.
2. The sum of the terms appears to approach a limiting value (0.920674), indicating convergence.
3. The ratio of the terms appears to approach a value of less than 1, indicating convergence.

Thus the series appears to converge.

Note that we say *appears to converge*. The computer run, while convincing, is still not a *proof* of convergence.

■ **Example 9:** Table 25•2 shows part of a computer run for the series

$$1 + \frac{1}{2} + \frac{1}{3} + \cdots + \frac{1}{n} + \cdots$$

TABLE 25·2

n	TERM u_n	PARTIAL SUM S_n	RATIO
1	1.000000	1.000000	
2	0.500000	1.500000	0.500000
3	0.333333	1.833333	0.666667
4	0.250000	2.083334	0.750000
5	0.200000	2.283334	0.800000
6	0.166667	2.450000	0.833333
7	0.142857	2.592857	0.857143
8	0.125000	2.717857	0.875000
9	0.111111	2.828969	0.888889
10	0.100000	2.928969	0.900000
.	.	.	.
.	.	.	.
.	.	.	.
75	0.013333	4.901356	0.986667
76	0.013158	4.914514	0.986842
77	0.012987	4.927501	0.987013
78	0.012821	4.940322	0.987180
79	0.012658	4.952980	0.987342
80	0.012500	4.965480	0.987500
.	.	.	.
.	.	.	.
.	.	.	.
495	0.002020	6.782784	0.997980
496	0.002016	6.784800	0.997984
497	0.002012	6.786813	0.997988
498	0.002008	6.788821	0.997992
499	0.002004	6.790825	0.997996
500	0.002000	6.792825	0.998000

Does the series converge or diverge?

Solution: Again we apply the three tests.

1. We see that the terms are getting smaller, so this test is not conclusive.
2. The ratio of the terms appears to approach 1, so this test also is not conclusive.
3. The partial sum S_n does not seem to approach a limit, but appears to keep growing even after 495 terms.

It thus appears that this series diverges.   ▬

Exercise 1 Sequences and Series

Write the first five terms of each series, given the general term.

1. $u_n = 3n$
2. $u_n = 2n + 3$
3. $u_n = \dfrac{n + 1}{n^2}$
4. $u_n = \dfrac{2^n}{n}$

Deduce the general term of each series. Use it to predict the next two terms.

5. $2 + 4 + 6 + \cdots$

6. $1 + 8 + 27 + \cdots$

7. $\dfrac{2}{4} + \dfrac{4}{5} + \dfrac{8}{6} + \dfrac{16}{7} + \cdots$

8. $2 + 5 + 10 + \cdots$

Deduce a recursion relation for each series. Use it to predict the next two terms.

9. $1 + 5 + 9 + \cdots$

10. $5 + 15 + 45 \cdots$

11. $3 + 9 + 81 + \cdots$

12. $5 + 8 + 14 + 26 + \cdots$

Computer

Write a program or use a spreadsheet to generate the terms of a series, given the general term or a recursion relation. Have the program compute and print each term, the partial sum, and the ratio of that term to the preceding one. Use the program to determine whether each of the following series converges or diverges.

13. $1 + \dfrac{1}{2} + \dfrac{1}{3} + \dfrac{1}{4} + \cdots + \dfrac{1}{n} + \cdots$

14. $\dfrac{3}{2} + \dfrac{9}{8} + \dfrac{27}{24} + \dfrac{81}{64} + \cdots + \dfrac{3^n}{n \cdot 2^n} + \cdots$

15. $1 + \dfrac{4}{7} + \dfrac{9}{49} + \dfrac{16}{343} + \cdots + \dfrac{n^2}{7^{n-1}} + \cdots$

Graphics Calculator

16. Some graphics calculators will generate the terms of a sequence if you enter the expression for the nth term, the first and last values of n, and the increment for n (usually 1). Check your manual for the proper instructions, and use your calculator to do Problems 1 to 4 of this exercise.

25·2

Arithmetic Progressions

Recursion Formula

We stated earlier that an *arithmetic progression* (or AP) is a sequence of terms in which each term after the first equals the sum of the preceding term and a constant, called the common difference d. If a_n is any term of an AP, the recursion formula for an AP is

AP: Recursion Formula	$a_n = a_{n-1} + d$	**236**

Each term of an AP after the first equals the sum of the preceding term and the common difference.

■ **Example 10:** The sequences

(a) 1, 5, 9, 13, . . . $(d = 4)$
(b) 20, 30, 40, 50, . . . $(d = 10)$
(c) 75, 70, 65, 60, . . . $(d = -5)$

are arithmetic progressions. The common difference for each is given in parentheses. We see that the series is increasing when d is positive and decreasing when d is negative.   ■

General Term

For an AP whose first term is a and whose common difference is d, the terms are

$$a, a + d, a + 2d, a + 3d, a + 4d, \ldots$$

We see that each term is the sum of the first term and a multiple of d, where the coefficient of d is one less than the number n of the term. So the nth term a_n is

AP: General Term	$a_n = a + (n - 1)d$	**237**

The general term is sometimes called the *last* term, but this is not an accurate name since the AP continues indefinitely.

The nth *term of an AP is found by adding the first term and* $(n - 1)$ *times the common difference.*

■ **Example 11:** Find the twentieth term of an AP that has a first term of 5 and a common difference of 4.

Solution: By Eq. 237, with $a = 5$, $n = 20$, and $d = 4$,

$$a_{20} = 5 + 19(4) = 81$$ ■

Of course, Eq. 237 can be used to find any of the four quantities (a, n, d, or a_n) given the other three.

■ **Example 12:** Write the AP whose eighth term is 19 and whose fifteenth term is 33.

Solution: Applying Eq. 237 twice gives

$$33 = a + 14d$$

$$19 = a + 7d$$

We now have two equations in two unknowns, which we solve simultaneously. Subtracting the second from the first gives $14 = 7d$, so $d = 2$. Also, $a = 33 - 14d = 5$, so the general term of our AP is

$$a_n = 5 + (n - 1)2$$

and the AP is then

$$5, 7, 9, \ldots$$ ■

AP: Sum of n Terms

Let us derive a formula for the sum s_n of the first n terms of an AP. Adding term by term gives

$$s_n = a + (a + d) + (a + 2d) + \cdots + (a_n - d) + a_n \qquad (1)$$

or, written in reverse order,

$$s_n = a_n + (a_n - d) + (a_n - 2d) + \cdots + (a + d) + a \qquad (2)$$

Adding (1) and (2) term by term gives

$$2s_n = (a + a_n) + (a + a_n) + (a + a_n) + \cdots$$
$$= n(a + a_n)$$

Dividing both sides by 2 gives the formula

AP: Sum of n Terms	$s_n = \dfrac{n}{2}(a + a_n)$	**238**

The sum of n terms of an AP is half the product of n and the sum of the first and nth terms.

■ **Example 13:** Find the sum of 10 terms of the AP

$$2, 5, 8, 11, \ldots$$

Solution: From Eq. 237, with $a = 2$, $d = 3$, and $n = 10$,

$$a_{10} = 2 + 9(3) = 29$$

Then, from Eq. 238,

$$s_{10} = \frac{10(2 + 29)}{2} = 155 \qquad ■$$

We get another form of Eq. 238 by substituting the expression for a_n from Eq. 237:

AP: Sum of n Terms	$s_n = \dfrac{n}{2}[2a + (n - 1)d]$	**239**

This form is useful for finding the sum without first computing the nth term.

■ **Example 14:** We repeat Example 13 without first having to find the tenth term. From Eq. 239,

$$s_{10} = \frac{10[2(2) + 9(3)]}{2} = 155 \qquad ■$$

Sometimes the sum is given and we must find one of the other quantities in the AP.

■ **Example 15:** How many terms of the AP 5, 9, 13, . . . give a sum of 275?

Solution: We seek n so that $s_n = 275$. From Eq. 239, with $a = 5$ and $d = 4$,

$$275 = \frac{n}{2}[2(5) + (n - 1)4]$$

$$= 5n + 2n(n - 1)$$

Removing parentheses and collecting terms gives the quadratic equation

$$2n^2 + 3n - 275 = 0$$

From the quadratic formula,

$$n = \frac{-3 \pm \sqrt{9 - 4(2)(-275)}}{2(2)} = 11 \quad \text{or} \quad -12.5$$

We discard the negative root and get 11 terms as our answer. ■

Arithmetic Means

The first term a and last (nth) term a_n of an AP are sometimes called the *extremes*, while the intermediate terms, $a_2, a_3, \ldots, a_{n-1}$, are called *arithmetic means*. We now show, by example, how to insert any number of arithmetic means between two extremes.

■ **Example 16:** Insert five arithmetic means between 3 and −9.

Solution: Our AP will have seven terms, with a first term of 3 and a seventh term of −9. From Eq. 237,

$$-9 = 3 + 6d$$

from which $d = -2$. The progression is then

$$3, 1, -1, -3, -5, -7, -9$$

and the five arithmetic means are 1, −1, −3, −5, and −7. ■

Average Value

Let us insert a single arithmetic mean between two numbers.

■ **Example 17:** Find a single arithmetic mean m between the extremes a and b.

Solution: The sequence is a, m, b. The common difference d is $m - a = b - m$. Solving for m gives

$$2m = b + a$$

Dividing by 2 gives

$$m = \frac{a + b}{2}$$

which agrees with the common idea of an *average* of two numbers as the sum of those numbers divided by 2. ■

Harmonic Progressions

A sequence is called a *harmonic progression* if the reciprocals of its terms form an arithmetic progression.

■ **Example 18:** The sequence

$$1, \frac{1}{3}, \frac{1}{5}, \frac{1}{7}, \frac{1}{9}, \frac{1}{11}, \ldots$$

is a harmonic progression because the reciprocals of the terms, 1, 3, 5, 7, 9, 11, . . . form an AP. ■

It is not possible to derive an equation for the *n*th term or for the sum of a harmonic progression. However, we can solve problems involving harmonic progressions by taking the reciprocals of the terms and using the formulas for the AP.

■ **Example 19:** Find the tenth term of the harmonic progression

$$2, \frac{2}{3}, \frac{2}{5}, \ldots$$

Solution: We write the reciprocals of the terms,

$$\frac{1}{2}, \frac{3}{2}, \frac{5}{2}, \ldots$$

and note that they form an AP with $a = \frac{1}{2}$ and $d = 1$. The tenth term of the AP is then

$$a_n = a + (n - 1)d$$

$$a_{10} = \frac{1}{2} + (10 - 1)(1)$$

$$= \frac{19}{2}$$

The tenth term of the harmonic progression is the reciprocal of $\frac{19}{2}$, or $\frac{2}{19}$. ■

Harmonic Means

To insert harmonic means between two terms of a harmonic progression, we simply take the reciprocals of the given terms, insert arithmetic means between those terms, and take reciprocals again.

■ **Example 20:** Insert three harmonic means between $\frac{2}{9}$ and 2.

Solution: Taking reciprocals, our AP is

$$\frac{9}{2}, \underline{\quad}, \underline{\quad}, \underline{\quad}, \frac{1}{2}$$

In this AP, $a = \frac{9}{2}$, $n = 5$, and $a_5 = \frac{1}{2}$. We can find the common difference d from the equation

$$a_n = a + (n - 1)d$$

$$\frac{1}{2} = \frac{9}{2} + 4d$$

$$-4 = 4d$$

$$d = -1$$

Having the common difference, we can fill in the missing terms of the AP,

$$\frac{9}{2}, \ \frac{7}{2}, \ \frac{5}{2}, \ \frac{3}{2}, \ \frac{1}{2}$$

Taking reciprocals again, our harmonic progression is

$$\frac{2}{9}, \frac{2}{7}, \frac{2}{5}, \frac{2}{3}, 2$$

■

Exercise 2 Arithmetic Progressions

General Term

1. Find the fifteenth term of an AP with first term 4 and common difference 3.
2. Find the tenth term of an AP with first term 8 and common difference 2.
3. Find the twelfth term of an AP with first term −1 and common difference 4.
4. Find the ninth term of an AP with first term −5 and common difference −2.
5. Find the eleventh term of the AP

$$9, 13, 17, \ldots$$

6. Find the eighth term of the AP

$$-5, -8, -11, \ldots$$

7. Find the ninth term of the AP

$$x, x + 3y, x + 6y, \ldots$$

8. Find the fourteenth term of the AP

$$1, \frac{6}{7}, \frac{5}{7}, \ldots$$

Write the five terms of each AP:

9. First term is 3 and thirteenth term is 55
10. First term is 5 and tenth term is 32
11. Seventh term is 41 and fifteenth term is 89
12. Fifth term is 7 and twelfth term is 42

13. Find the first term of an AP whose common difference is 3 and whose seventh term is 11.
14. Find the first term of an AP whose common difference is 6 and whose tenth term is 77.

Sum of an Arithmetic Progression

15. Find the sum of the first 12 terms of the AP: 3, 6, 9, 12, . . .
16. Find the sum of the first five terms of the AP: 1, 5, 9, 13, . . .
17. Find the sum of the first nine terms of the AP: 5, 10, 15, 20, . . .
18. Find the sum of the first 20 terms of the AP: 1, 3, 5, 7, . . .
19. How many terms of the AP 4, 7, 10, . . . will give a sum of 375?
20. How many terms of the AP 2, 9, 16, . . . will give a sum of 270?

Arithmetic Means

21. Insert two arithmetic means between 5 and 20.
22. Insert five arithmetic means between 7 and 25.
23. Insert four arithmetic means between -6 and -9.
24. Insert three arithmetic means between 20 and 56.

Harmonic Progressions

25. Find the fourth term of the harmonic progression
$$\frac{3}{5}, \frac{3}{8}, \frac{3}{11}, \ldots$$

26. Find the fifth term of the harmonic progression
$$\frac{4}{19}, \frac{4}{15}, \frac{4}{11}, \ldots$$

Harmonic Means

27. Insert two harmonic means between $\frac{7}{9}$ and $\frac{7}{15}$.
28. Insert three harmonic means between $\frac{6}{21}$ and $\frac{6}{5}$.

Applications

29. *Loan Repayment:* A person agrees to repay a loan of $10,000 with an annual payment of $1000 plus 8% of the unpaid balance. **(a)** Show that the interest payments alone form the AP: $800, $720, $640, . . . **(b)** Find the total amount of interest paid.

30. *Simple Interest:* A person deposits $50 in a bank on the first day of each month, at the same time withdrawing all interest earned on the money already in the account. **(a)** If the rate is 1% per month, computed monthly, write an AP whose terms are the amounts withdrawn each month. **(b)** How much interest will have been earned in the 36 months following the first deposit?

To find the amount of depreciation for each year, divide the total depreciation (initial value − scrap value) by the number of years of depreciation.

31. *Straight-Line Depreciation:* A certain milling machine has an initial value of $150 000 and a scrap value of $10 000 twenty years later. Assuming that the machine depreciates the same amount each year, find its value after 8 years.

32. *Salary or Price Increase:* A person is hired at a salary of $40 000 and receives a raise of $2500 at the end of each year. Find the total amount earned during 10 years.

33. *Freely Falling Body:* A freely falling body falls $a/2$ metres during the first second, $3a/2$ metres during the next second, $5a/2$ metres during the third second, and so on, where $a \approx 9.8$ m/s². Find the total distance the body falls during the first 10 s.

34. Using the information of Problem 33, show that the total distance s fallen in t seconds is $s = \frac{1}{2}at^2$.

Graphics Calculator

35. Some graphics calculators will compute the sum of a progression. You first indicate the progression by entering the expression for the nth term, the first and last values of n, and the increment for n (usually 1). Check your manual for the proper instructions, and use your calculator to solve Problems 15 to 20 of this exercise.

Computer

36. Some computer algebra systems, such as *Maple*, can compute the sum of a progression, once the progression is entered. If your CAS has this capability, use it to solve Problems 15 to 20 of this exercise.

25•3

Geometric Progressions

Recursion Formula

A geometric sequence or *geometric progression* (GP) is one in which each term after the first is formed by multiplying the preceding term by a factor r, called the *common ratio*. Thus, if a_n is any term of a GP, the recursion relation is

GP: Recursion Formula	$a_n = ra_{n-1}$	**240**

Each term of a GP after the first equals the product of the preceding term and the common ratio.

■ **Example 21:** Some geometric progressions, with their common ratios given, are

(a) 2, 4, 8, 16, . . . $(r = 2)$
(b) 27, 9, 3, 1, $\frac{1}{3}$, . . . $(r = \frac{1}{3})$
(c) −1, 3, −9, 27, . . . $(r = -3)$ ■

General Term

For a GP whose first term is a and whose common ratio is r, the terms are

$$a, \ ar, \ ar^2, \ ar^3, \ ar^4, \ \ldots$$

We see that each term after the first is the product of the first term and a power of r, where the power of r is one less than the number n of the term. So the nth term a_n is

GP: General Term	$a_n = ar^{n-1}$	**241**

The nth term of a GP is found by multiplying the first term by the n − 1 power of the common ratio.

■ **Example 22:** Find the sixth term of a GP with first term 5 and common ratio 4.

Solution: We substitute into Equation 241 for the general term of a GP, with $a = 5$, $n = 6$, and $r = 4$.

$$a_6 = 5(4^5) = 5(1024) = 5120 \qquad ■$$

GP: Sum of n Terms

We find a formula for the sum s_n of the first n terms of a GP (also called the sum of n terms of a geometric series) by adding the terms of the GP:

$$s_n = a + ar + ar^2 + ar^3 + \cdots + ar^{n-2} + ar^{n-1} \qquad (1)$$

Multiplying each term in (1) by r gives

$$rs_n = ar + ar^2 + ar^3 + \cdots + ar^{n-1} + ar^n \qquad (2)$$

Subtracting (1) from (2) term by term, we get

$$(1 - r)s_n = a - ar^n$$

Dividing both sides by $(1 - r)$ gives

GP: Sum of n Terms	$s_n = \dfrac{a(1 - r^n)}{1 - r}$	**242**

■ **Example 23:** Find the sum of the first six terms of the GP in Example 22.

Solution: We substitute into Eq. 242 using $a = 5$, $n = 6$, and $r = 4$.

$$s_n = \frac{a(1 - r^n)}{1 - r} = \frac{5(1 - 4^6)}{1 - 4} = \frac{5(-4095)}{-3} = 6825$$

■

We can get another equation for the sum of a GP in terms of the nth term a_n. We substitute into Eq. 242, using $ar^n = r(ar^{n-1}) = ra_n$:

GP: Sum of n Terms	$s_n = \dfrac{a - ra_n}{1 - r}$	**243**

■ **Example 24:** Repeat Example 23, given that the sixth term (found in Example 22) is $a_6 = 5120$.

Solution: Substitution, with $a = 5$, $r = 4$, and $a_6 = 5120$, yields

$$s_n = \frac{a - ra_n}{1 - r} = \frac{5 - 4(5120)}{1 - 4} = 6825$$

as before.

■

Geometric Means

As with the AP, the intermediate terms between any two terms are called *means*. A single number inserted between two numbers is called the *geometric mean* between those numbers.

■ **Example 25:** Insert a geometric mean b between two numbers a and c.

Solution: Our GP is a, b, c. The common ratio r is then

$$r = \frac{b}{a} = \frac{c}{b}$$

from which $b^2 = ac$ or

This is not new. We studied the mean proportional in Chapter 19.

Geometric Mean	$b = \pm\sqrt{ac}$	59

The geometric mean, or mean proportional, between two numbers is equal to the square root of their product. ▬

▬ **Example 26:** Find the geometric mean between 3 and 48.

Solution: Letting $a = 3$ and $c = 48$ gives us

$$b = \pm\sqrt{3(48)} = \pm12$$

Our GP is then

$$3, \mathbf{12}, 48$$

or

$$3, \mathbf{-12}, 48$$

Note that we get *two* solutions. ▬

To insert *several* geometric means between two numbers, we first find the common ratio.

▬ **Example 27:** Insert four geometric means between 2 and $15\frac{3}{16}$.

Solution: Here $a = 2$, $a_6 = 15\frac{3}{16}$, and $n = 6$. Then

$$a_6 = ar^5$$

$$15\frac{3}{16} = 2r^5$$

$$r^5 = \frac{243}{32}$$

$$r = \frac{3}{2}$$

Having r, we can write the terms of the GP. They are

$$2, \ 3, \ 4\frac{1}{2}, \ 6\frac{3}{4}, \ 10\frac{1}{8}, \ 15\frac{3}{16}$$ ▬

Exercise 3 Geometric Progressions

1. Find the fifth term of a GP with first term 5 and common ratio 2.
2. Find the fourth term of a GP with first term 7 and common ratio -4.
3. Find the sixth term of a GP with first term -3 and common ratio 5.
4. Find the fifth term of a GP with first term -4 and common ratio -2.
5. Find the sum of the first 10 terms of the GP in Problem 1.
6. Find the sum of the first nine terms of the GP in Problem 2.
7. Find the sum of the first eight terms of the GP in Problem 3.
8. Find the sum of the first five terms of the GP in Problem 4.

Geometric Means

9. Insert a geometric mean between 5 and 45.

10. Insert a geometric mean between 7 and 112.

11. Insert a geometric mean between -10 and -90.

12. Insert a geometric mean between -21 and -84.

13. Insert two geometric means between 8 and 216.

14. Insert two geometric means between 9 and -243.

15. Insert three geometric means between 5 and 1280.

16. Insert three geometric means between 144 and 9.

Applications

17. *Exponential Growth*: Using the equation for exponential growth,

$y = ae^{nt}$	**199**

with $a = 1$ and $n = 0.5$, compute values of y for $t = 0, 1, 2, \ldots, 10$. Show that, while the values of t form an AP, the values of y form a GP. Find the common ratio.

18. *Exponential Decay*: Repeat Problem 17 with the formula for exponential decay:

$y = ae^{-nt}$	**201**

19. *Cooling:* A certain iron casting is at 982°C and cools so that its temperature at each minute is 10% less than its temperature the preceding minute. Find its temperature after 1.00 h.

20. *Light through an Absorbing Medium:* Sunlight passes through a glass filter. Each millimetre of glass absorbs 20% of the light passing through it. What percentage of the original sunlight will remain after passing through 5.0 mm of the glass?

21. *Radioactive Decay:* A certain radioactive material decays so that after each year the radioactivity is 8% less than at the start of that year. How many years will it take for its radioactivity to be 50% of its original value?

22. *Pendulum:* Each swing of a certain pendulum is 85.0% as long as the swing before. If the first swing is 365 mm, find the entire distance traveled in eight swings.

23. *Bouncing Ball:* A ball dropped from a height of 3.00 m rebounds to half its height on each bounce. Find the total distance traveled when it hits the ground for the fifth time.

24. *Population Growth:* Each day the size of a certain colony of bacteria is 25% larger than on the preceding day. If the original size of the colony was 10 00$\overline{0}$ bacteria, find its size after five days.

25. A person has two parents, and each parent has two parents, and so on. We can write a GP for the number of ancestors as 2, 4, 8, ... Find the total number of ancestors in five generations, starting with the parents' generation.

One of the most famous and controversial references to arithmetic and geometric progressions was made by Thomas Malthus in 1798. He wrote: *"Population, when unchecked, increases in a geometrical ratio, and subsistence for man in an arithmetical ratio."*

This is called the *equally tempered scale* and is usually attributed to Johann Sebastian Bach (1685–1750).

26. *Musical Scale:* The frequency of the A note above middle C is, by international agreement, equal to 440 Hz. A note one *octave* higher is at twice that frequency, or 880 Hz. The octave is subdivided into 12 *half-tone* intervals, where each half-tone is higher than the one preceding by a factor equal to the twelfth root of 2. Write a GP showing the frequency of each half-tone, from 440 to 880 Hz. Work to two decimal places.

27. *Chemical Reactions:* Increased temperature usually causes chemicals to react faster. If a certain reaction proceeds 15% faster for each 10°C increase in temperature, by what factor is the reaction speed increased when the temperature rises by 50°C?

28. *Mixtures:* A radiator contains 30% antifreeze and 70% water. One-fourth of the mixture is removed and replaced by pure water. If this procedure is repeated three more times, find the percentage of the antifreeze in the final mixture.

29. *Energy Consumption:* If the Canadian energy consumption is 7.00% higher each year, by what factor will the energy consumption have increased after 10.0 years?

30. *Atmospheric Pressure:* The pressures measured at 2.0 km intervals above sea level form a GP, with each value smaller than the preceding by a factor of 0.819. If the pressure at sea level is 760 mm Hg, find the pressure at an altitude of 8.0 km.

31. *Compound Interest:* A person deposits $10 000 in a bank giving 6% interest, compounded annually. Find to the nearest dollar the value of the deposit after 50 years.

32. *Inflation:* The price of a certain house, now $126 000, is expected to increase by 5% each year. Write a GP whose terms are the value of the house at the end of each year, and find the value of the house after five years.

33. *Depreciation:* When calculating depreciation by the *declining-balance method*, a taxpayer claims as a deduction a fixed percentage of the book value of an asset each year. The new book value is then the last book value less the amount of the depreciation. Thus, for a machine having an initial book value of $100 000 and a depreciation rate of 40%, the first year's depreciation is 40% of $100 000, or $40 000, and the new book value is $100 000 − $40 000 = $60 000. Thus the book values for each year form a GP,

$$\$100\,000, \$60\,000, \$36\,000, \ldots$$

Find the book value after five years.

Graphics Calculator

34. Some graphics calculators will compute the sum of a progression. You first indicate the progression by entering the expression for the *n*th term, the first and last values of *n*, and the increment for *n* (usually 1). Check your manual for the proper instructions, and use your calculator to solve Problems 5 to 8 of this exercise.

Computer

35. Some computer algebra systems, such as *Maple*, can compute the sum of a progression, once the progression is entered. If your CAS has this capability, use it to solve Problems 5 to 8 of this exercise.

25•4

Infinite Geometric Progressions

Sum of an Infinite Geometric Progression

Before we derive a formula for the sum of an infinite geometric progression, let us explore the idea graphically and numerically.

We have already determined that the sum of n terms of any geometric progression with a first term a and a common ratio r is (Eq. 242)

$$sn = \frac{a(1 - r^n)}{1 - r}$$

so a graph of s_n versus n should tell us about the sum changes as n increases.

■ Example 28: Graph the sum s_n versus n for the GP

$$1, 1.2, 1.2^2, 1.2^3, \ldots$$

for $n = 0$ to 20.

Solution: Here, $a = 1$ and $r = 1.2$, so

$$s_n = \frac{1 - 1.2^n}{1 - 1.2} = \frac{1.2^n - 1}{0.8}$$

The sum s_n is graphed in Figure 25•4. Note that the sum continues to increase. We say that this progression *diverges.* ■

Decreasing GP

If the common ratio r in a GP is less than 1, each term in the progression will be less than those preceding it. Such a progression is called a *decreasing* GP.

■ Example 29: Graph the sum s_n versus n for the GP

$$1, 0.8, 0.8^2, 0.8^3, \ldots$$

for $n = 0$ *to* 20.

Solution: Here, $a = 1$ and $r = 0.8$, so

$$s_n = \frac{1 - 0.8^n}{1 - 0.8} = \frac{1 - 0.8^n}{0.2}$$

The sum is graphed in Figure 25•5. Note that the sum appears to reach a limiting value, so we say that this progression *converges.* The sum appears to be approaching a value of 5.

FIGURE 25•4

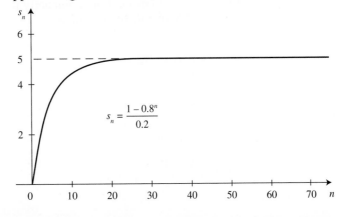

FIGURE 25•5

TABLE 25•3

TERM		SUM
1	9.0000	9.0000
2	3.0000	12.0000
3	1.0000	13.0000
4	0.3333	13.3333
5	0.1111	13.4444
6	0.0370	13.4815
7	0.0123	13.4938
8	0.0041	13.4979
9	9.0014	13.4993
10	0.0005	13.4998
11	0.0002	13.4999
12	0.0001	13.5000
13	0.0000	13.5000
14	0.0000	13.5000
15	0.0000	13.5000
16	0.0000	13.5000
17	0.0000	13.5000
18	0.0000	13.5000

We've used limit notation briefly in Section 20•2, and here we show a little more. Limits are usually covered more completely in a calculus course.

Our graphs have thus indicated that the sum of an infinite number of terms of a decreasing GP appears to approach a limit. Let us now verify that fact numerically.

■ **Example 30:** Find the sum of infinitely many terms of the GP

$$9, 3, 1, \tfrac{1}{3} \ldots$$

Solution: Knowing that $a = 9$ and $r = \tfrac{1}{3}$, we can use a computer to compute each term and keep a running sum (Table 25•3). Notice that the terms get smaller and smaller, and the sum appears to approach a value of around 13.5. ■

We will confirm the value found in the preceding example after we have derived a formula for the sum of an infinite geometric progression.

Limit Notation

In order to derive a formula for the sum of an infinite geometric progression, we need to introduce limit notation. Such notation will also be of great importance in the study of calculus.

First, we use an arrow ($\rightarrow$) to indicate that a quantity *approaches* a given value.

■ **Example 31:**
(a) $x \rightarrow 5$ means that x gets closer and closer to the value 5.
(b) $n \rightarrow \infty$ means that n grows larger and larger, without bound.
(c) $y \rightarrow 0$ means that y continuously gets closer and closer to zero. ■

If some function $f(x)$ approaches some value L as x approaches a, we could write this as

$$f(x) \rightarrow L \quad \text{as} \quad x \rightarrow a$$

or, in more compact notation,

Limit Notation	$\lim\limits_{x \to a} f(x) = L$	336

Limit notation lets us write compactly the value to which a function is tending, as in the following example.

■ **Example 32:**
(a) $\lim\limits_{b \to 0} b = 0$

(b) $\lim\limits_{b \to 0} (a + b) = a$

(c) $\lim\limits_{b \to 0} \dfrac{a + b}{c + d} = \dfrac{a}{c + d}$

(d) $\lim\limits_{x \to 0} \dfrac{x + 1}{x + 2} = \dfrac{1}{2}$ ■

A Formula for the Sum of an Infinite, Decreasing Geometric Progression

As the number of terms n of a geometric progression increases without bound, the term a_n will become smaller and approach zero. Using our new notation we may write

$$\lim_{n \to \infty} a_n = 0 \quad \text{when} \quad |r| < 1$$

Thus, in the equation for the sum of n terms (Eq. 243),

$$s_n = \frac{a - ra_n}{1 - r}$$

the expression ra_n will approach zero as n approaches infinity, so the sum s_∞ of infinitely many terms (called the sum to infinity) is

$$s_\infty = \lim_{n \to \infty} \frac{a - ra_n}{1 - r} = \frac{a}{1 - r}$$

Thus, letting $S = s_\infty$, the sum to infinity,

GP: Sum to Infinity	$S = \dfrac{a}{1 - r} \quad \text{when} \quad |r| < 1$	**244**

■ **Example 33:** Find the sum of infinitely many terms of the GP

$$9, 3, 1, \frac{1}{3}, \dots$$

Solution: Here $a = 9$ and $r = \frac{1}{3}$, so

$$S = \frac{a}{1 - r} = \frac{9}{1 - 1/3} = \frac{9}{2/3} = 13\frac{1}{2}$$

This agrees with the value we found numerically in Example 30.   ■

Repeating Decimals

A *finite decimal* (or terminating decimal) is one that has a finite number of digits to the right of the decimal point, followed by zeros. An *infinite decimal* (or nonterminating decimal) has an infinite string of digits to the right of the decimal point. A *repeating decimal* (or periodic decimal) is one that has a block of one or more digits that repeats indefinitely. It can be proved that, when one integer is divided by another, we get either a finite decimal or a repeating decimal. Irrational numbers, on the other hand, yield *nonrepeating decimals*.

■ **Example 34:**

(a) $\frac{3}{4} = 0.75000000000 \dots$ (finite decimal)

(b) $\frac{3}{7} = 0.428571\ 428571\ 428571 \dots$ (infinite repeating decimal)

(c) $\sqrt{2} = 1.414213562 \dots$ (infinite nonrepeating decimal)   ■

We can write a repeating decimal as a rational fraction by writing the repeating part as an infinite geometric series, as shown in the following example.

■ **Example 35:** Write the number 4.85151 . . . as a rational fraction.

Solution: We rewrite the given number as

$$4.8 + 0.051 + 0.00051 + \cdots$$

The terms of this series, except for the first, form an infinite GP where $a = 0.051$ and $r = 0.01$. The sum S to infinity is then

$$S = \frac{a}{1 - r} = \frac{0.051}{1 - 0.01} = \frac{0.051}{0.99} = \frac{51}{990} = \frac{17}{330}$$

Our given number is then equal to $4.8 + S$, so

$$4.85151 = 4 + \frac{8}{10} + \frac{17}{330} = 4\frac{281}{330} \qquad \blacksquare$$

Exercise 4 Infinite Geometric Progressions

Evaluate each limit.

1. $\lim\limits_{b \to 0} (b - c + 5)$

2. $\lim\limits_{b \to 0} (a + b^2)$

3. $\lim\limits_{b \to 0} \dfrac{3 + b}{c + 4}$

4. $\lim\limits_{b \to 0} \dfrac{a + b + c}{b + c - 5}$

Find the sum of the infinitely many terms of each GP.

5. 144, 72, 36, 18, . . .

6. $8, 4, 1, \frac{1}{4}, \ldots$

7. 10, 2, 0.4, 0.08, . . .

8. $1, \frac{1}{4}, \frac{1}{16}, \ldots$

Write each decimal number as a rational fraction.

9. $0.5\overline{75}\ldots$

10. $0.69\overline{69}\ldots$

11. $7.681\overline{81}\ldots$

12. $5.86111\ldots$

13. Each swing of a certain pendulum is 78% as long as the one before. If the first swing is 260 mm, find the entire distance traveled by the pendulum before it comes to rest.

14. A ball dropped from a height of 6.0 m rebounds to three-fourths of its height on each bounce. Find the total distance traveled by the ball before it comes to rest.

15. *Zeno's Paradox:* "A runner can never reach a finish line a kilometre away because first he would have to run half a kilometre, and then must run half of the remaining distance, or a quarter of a kilometre, and then half of that, and so on. Since there are an infinite number of distances that must be run, it will take an infinite length of time, and so the runner will never reach the finish line." Show that the distances to be run form an infinite series,

$$\frac{1}{2}, \frac{1}{4}, \frac{1}{8}, \cdots$$

Then disprove the paradox by actually finding the sum of that series and showing that the sum is *not* infinite.

Named for Zeno of Elea (c. 490–c. 435 B.C.), a Greek philosopher and mathematician. He wrote several famous paradoxes, including this one.

25·5

The Binomial Theorem

Powers of a Binomial

Recall that a binomial, such as $(a + b)$, is a polynomial with two terms. By actual multiplication we can show that

$$(a + b)^1 = a + b$$

$$(a + b)^2 = a^2 + 2ab + b^2$$

$$(a + b)^3 = a^3 + 3a^2b + 3ab^2 + b^3$$

$$(a + b)^4 = a^4 + 4a^3b + 6a^2b^2 + 4ab^3 + b^4$$

We now want a formula for $(a + b)^n$ with which to expand a binomial without actually carrying out the multiplication. In the expansion of $(a + b)^n$, where n is a positive integer, we note the following patterns:

1. There are $n + 1$ terms.
2. The power of a is n in the first term, decreases by 1 in each later term, and reaches 0 in the last term.
3. The power of b is 0 in the first term, increases by 1 in each later term, and reaches n in the last term.
4. Each term has a total degree of n (that is, the sum of the degrees of the variables is n).
5. The first coefficient is 1. Further, the product of the coefficient of any term and its power of a, divided by the number of the term, gives the coefficient of the next term. (This property gives a *recursion formula* for the coefficients of the binomial expansion.)

Expressed as a formula, we have

$$(a + b)^n = a^n + na^{n-1}b + \frac{n(n - 1)}{2} a^{n-2}b^2 + \frac{n(n - 1)(n - 2)}{2(3)} a^{n-3}b^3$$

$$+ \cdots + b^n$$

■ **Example 36:** Use the binomial theorem to expand $(a + b)^5$.

Solution: From the binomial theorem,

$$(a + b)^5 = a^5 + 5a^4b + \frac{5(4)}{2} a^3b^2 + \frac{5(4)(3)}{2(3)} a^2b^3 + \frac{5(4)(3)(2)}{2(3)(4)} ab^4 + b^5$$

$$= a^5 + 5a^4b + 10a^3b^2 + 10a^2b^3 + 5ab^4 + b^5$$

which can be verified by actual multiplication.　　　　　　　　　　　■

If the expression contains only one variable, we can verify the expansion graphically.

■ **Example 37:** Use the result from the preceding example to expand $(x + 1)^5$, and verify graphically.

Solution: Substituting $a = x$ and $b = 1$ into the preceding result gives

$$(x + 1)^5 = x^5 + 5x^4 + 10x^3 + 10x^2 + 5x + 1$$

We will use the binomial theorem to obtain the values in a *binomial probability distribution*, in the following chapter on statistics.

To verify graphically we plot on the same axes,

$$y_1 = (x + 1)^5$$

and

$$y_2 = x^5 + 5x^4 + 10x^3 + 10x^2 + 5x + 1$$

FIGURE 25•6 Graphs of $y = (x + 1)^5$ and $y = x^5 + 5x^4 + 10x^3 + 10x^2 + 5x + 1$

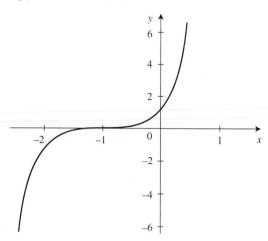

The two graphs, Figure 25•6, are identical. This is not a *proof* that our expansion is correct, but certainly gives us more confidence in our result. ▬

Binomial Expansion on the Computer

With a computer algebra system, simply type in the expression to be expanded, and give the EXPAND command.

Factorial Notation

Many calculators have a key for evaluating factorials.

We now introduce *factorial notation*. For a positive integer n, factorial n, written $n!$, is the product of all the positive integers less than or equal to n.

$$n! = 1 \cdot 2 \cdot 3 \cdots n$$

Of course, it does not matter in which order we multiply the numbers. We may also write

$$n! = n(n - 1) \cdots 3 \cdot 2 \cdot 1$$

▬ **Example 38:**
(a) $3! = 1 \cdot 2 \cdot 3 = 6$
(b) $5! = 1 \cdot 2 \cdot 3 \cdot 4 \cdot 5 = 120$
(c) $\dfrac{6! \, 3!}{7!} = \dfrac{6! \, (2)(3)}{7(6!)} = \dfrac{6}{7}$
(d) $0! = 1$ by definition ▬

Binomial Theorem Written with Factorial Notation

The use of factorial notation allows us to write the binomial theorem more compactly. Thus

Binomial Theorem	$(a + b)^n = a^n + na^{n-1}b + \dfrac{n(n - 1)}{2!} a^{n-2}b^2 + \dfrac{n(n - 1)(n - 2)}{3!} a^{n-3}b^3 + \cdots + b^n$	**245**

■ **Example 39:** Using the binomial formula, expand $(a + b)^6$.

Solution: There will be $(n + 1)$ or seven terms. Let us first find the seven coefficients. The first coefficient is always 1, and the second coefficient is always n, or 6. We calculate the remaining coefficients in the following table.

TERM	COEFFICIENT
1	1
2	$n = 6$
3	$\dfrac{n(n - 1)}{2!} = \dfrac{6(5)}{1(2)} = 15$
4	$\dfrac{n(n - 1)(n - 2)}{3!} = \dfrac{6(5)(4)}{1(2)(3)} = 20$
5	$\dfrac{n(n - 1)(n - 2)(n - 3)}{4!} = \dfrac{6(5)(4)(3)}{1(2)(3)(4)} = 15$
6	$\dfrac{n(n - 1)(n - 2)(n - 3)(n - 4)}{5!} = \dfrac{6(5)(4)(3)(2)}{1(2)(3)(4)(5)} = 6$
7	$\dfrac{n(n - 1)(n - 2)(n - 3)(n - 4)(n - 5)}{6!} = \dfrac{6(5)(4)(3)(2)(1)}{1(2)(3)(4)(5)(6)} = 1$

The seven terms thus have the coefficients

$$1 \quad 6 \quad 15 \quad 20 \quad 15 \quad 6 \quad 1$$

and our expansion is

$$(a + b)^6 = a^6 + 6a^5b + 15a^4b^2 + 20a^3b^3 + 15a^2b^4 + 6ab^5 + b^6 \quad ■$$

Pascal's Triangle

We now have expansions for $(a + b)^n$, and for values of n from 1 to 6, to which we add $(a + b)^0 = 1$. Let us now write the coefficients only of the terms of each expansion.

```
Exponent n
    0                        1
    1                      1   1
    2                    1   2   1
    3                  1   3   3   1
    4                1   4   6   4   1
    5              1   5  10  10   5   1
    6            1   6  15  20  15   6   1
```

Named for Blaise Pascal (1623–1662), the French geometer, probabilist, combinatorist, physicist, and philosopher.

This array is called *Pascal's triangle*. We may use it to predict the coefficients of expansions with powers higher than 6 by noting that each number in the triangle is equal to the sum of the two numbers above it (thus the 15 in the lowest row is the sum of the 5 and the 10 above it). When expanding a binomial, we may take the coefficients directly from Pascal's triangle, as shown in the following example.

━ **Example 40:** Expand $(1 - x)^6$, obtaining the binomial coefficients from Pascal's triangle.

Solution: From Pascal's triangle, for $n = 6$, we read the coefficients

$$1 \quad 6 \quad 15 \quad 20 \quad 15 \quad 6 \quad 1$$

We now substitute into the binomial formula with $n = 6$, $a = 1$, and $b = -x$. When one of the terms of the binomial is negative, as here, we must be careful to include the minus sign whenever that term appears in the expansion. Thus

$$(1 - x)^6 = [1 + (-x)]^6$$
$$= 1^6 + 6(1^5)(-x) + 15(1^4)(-x)^2 + 20(1^3)(-x)^3$$
$$+ 15(1^2)(-x)^4 + 6(1)(-x)^5 + (-x)^6$$
$$= 1 - 6x + 15x^2 - 20x^3 + 15x^4 - 6x^5 + x^6 \qquad ━$$

If either term in the binomial is itself a power, a product, or a fraction, it is a good idea to enclose that entire term in parentheses before substituting.

━ **Example 41:** Expand $(3/x^2 + 2y^3)^4$.

Solution: The binomial coefficients are 1   4   6   4   1. We substitute $3/x^2$ for a and $2y^3$ for b.

$$\left(\frac{3}{x^2} + 2y^3\right)^4 = \left[\left(\frac{3}{x^2}\right) + (2y^3)\right]^4$$
$$= \left(\frac{3}{x^2}\right)^4 + 4\left(\frac{3}{x^2}\right)^3 (2y^3) + 6\left(\frac{3}{x^2}\right)^2 (2y^3)^2 + 4\left(\frac{3}{x^2}\right)(2y^3)^3 + (2y^3)^4$$
$$= \frac{81}{x^8} + \frac{216y^3}{x^6} + \frac{216y^6}{x^4} + \frac{96y^9}{x^2} + 16y^{12} \qquad ━$$

Sometimes we may not need the entire expansion but only the first few terms.

━ **Example 42:** Find the first four terms of $(x^2 - 2y^3)^{11}$.

Solution: From the binomial formula, with $n = 11$, $a = x^2$, and $b = (-2y^3)$,

$$(x^2 - 2y^3)^{11} = [(x^2) + (-2y^3)]^{11}$$
$$= (x^2)^{11} + 11(x^2)^{10}(-2y^3) + \frac{11(10)}{2}(x^2)^9(-2y^3)^2$$
$$+ \frac{11(10)(9)}{2(3)}(x^2)^8(-2y^3)^3 + \cdots$$
$$= x^{22} - 22x^{20}y^3 + 220x^{18}y^6 - 1320x^{16}y^9 + \cdots \qquad ━$$

A *trinomial* may be expanded by the binomial formula by grouping the terms, as in the following example.

■ **Example 43:** Expand $(1 + 2x - x^2)^3$ by the binomial formula.

Solution: Let $z = 2x - x^2$. Then

$$(1 + 2x - x^2)^3 = (1 + z)^3 = 1 + 3z + 3z^2 + z^3$$

Substituting back,

$$(1 + 2x - x^2)^3 = 1 + 3(2x - x^2) + 3(2x - x^2)^2 + (2x - x^2)^3$$

$$= 1 + 6x + 9x^2 - 4x^3 - 9x^4 + 6x^5 - x^6$$ ■

General Term

We can write the general or rth term of a binomial expansion $(a + b)^n$ by noting the following pattern.

1. The power of b is one less than r. Thus a fifth term would contain b^4, and the rth term would contain b^{r-1}.
2. The power of a is n minus the power of b. Thus a fifth term would contain a^{n-5+1}, and the rth term would contain a^{n-r+1}.
3. The coefficient of the rth term is

$$\frac{n!}{(r - 1)! \, (n - r + 1)!}$$

Expressed as a formula,

General Term	In the expansion for $(a + b)^n$, rth term $= \dfrac{n!}{(r - 1)!(n - r + 1)!} \, a^{n-r+1}b^{r-1}$	**246**

■ **Example 44:** Find the eighth term of $(3a + b^5)^{11}$.

Solution: Here, $n = 11$ and $r = 8$. So $n - r + 1 = 4$. Substitution yields

$$\frac{n!}{(r - 1)! \, (n - r + 1)!} = \frac{11!}{7! \, 4!} = 330$$

Then

$$\text{the eighth term} = 330(3a)^{11-8+1}(b^5)^{8-1}$$

$$= 330(81a^4)(b^{35}) = 26\,730a^4b^{35}$$ ■

Proof of the Binomial Theorem

We have shown that the binomial theorem is true for $n = 1, 2, 3, 4,$ or 5. But what about some other exponent, say $n = 50$? To show that the theorem works for any positive integral exponent, we give the following proof.

We first show that if the binomial theorem is true for some exponent $n = k$, it is also true for $n = k + 1$. We assume that

$$(a + b)^k = a^k + ka^{k-1}b + \cdots + Pa^{k-r}b^r + Qa^{k-r-1}b^{r+1}$$

$$+ Ra^{k-r-2}b^{r+2} + \cdots + b^k \qquad (1)$$

where we show three intermediate terms with coefficients P, Q, and R. Multiplying both sides of (1) by $(a + b)$ gives

We have not written the b^r term or the b^{r+3} term because we do not have expressions for their coefficients, and they are not needed for the proof.

$$(a + b)^{k+1} = a^{k+1} + ka^kb + \cdots + Pa^{k-r+1}b^r + Qa^{k-r}b^{r+1}$$
$$+ Ra^{k-r-1}b^{r+2} + \cdots + ab^k + \cdots + a^kb + \cdots$$
$$+ Pa^{k-r}b^{r+1} + Qa^{k-r-1}b^{r+2} + Ra^{k-r-2}b^{r+3} + \cdots + b^{k+1}$$
$$(a + b)^{k+1} = a^{k+1} + (k + 1)a^kb + \ldots + (P + Q)a^{k-r}b^{r+1}$$
$$+ (Q + R)a^{k-r-1}b^{r+2} + \ldots + ab^k + b^{k+1} \qquad (2)$$

after combining like terms. Does (2) obey the binomial theorem? First, the power of b is 0 in the first term and increases by 1 in each later term, reaching $k + 1$ in the last term, so property 3 is met. Thus there are $k + 1$ terms containing b, plus the first term that does not, making a total of $k + 2$ terms, so property 1 is met. Next, the power of a is $k + 1$ in the first term and decreases by 1 in each succeeding term until it equals 0 in the last term, making the total degree of each term equal to $k + 1$, so properties 2 and 4 are met. Further, the coefficient of the first term is 1 and the coefficient of the second term is $k + 1$, which agrees with property 5. Finally, in order to satisfy property 5 for the intermediate terms, the identity

$$(P + Q)\frac{n - r}{r + 2} = Q + R$$

must be true. But since

$$Q = \frac{P(n - r)}{r + 1} \quad \text{and} \quad R = \frac{Q(n - r - 1)}{r + 2}$$

we must show that

$$\left[P + \frac{P(n - r)}{r + 1}\right]\frac{n - r}{r + 2} = \frac{P(n - r)}{r + 1} + \frac{P(n - r)(n - r - 1)}{(r + 1)(r + 2)}$$

Working each side separately, we combine each over a common denominator.

$$\frac{P(n - r)(r + 1)}{(r + 1)(r + 2)} + \frac{P(n - r)(n - r)}{(r + 1)(r + 2)}$$

$$= \frac{P(n - r)(r + 2)}{(r + 1)(r + 2)} + \frac{P(n - r)(n - r - 1)}{(r + 1)(r + 2)}$$

Since the denominators are the same on both sides, we simply have to show that the numerators are identical. Factoring gives us

$$P(n - r)(r + 1 + n - r) = P(n - r)(r + 2 + n - r - 1)$$
$$P(n - r)(n + 1) = P(n - r)(n + 1)$$

This type of proof is called mathematical induction.

This proves that (2) satisfies property 5 as well, and completes the proof that, if the binomial theorem is true for some exponent $n = k$, it is also true for the exponent $n = k + 1$. But since we have shown, by direct multiplication, that the binomial theorem *is true* for $n = 5$, it must be true for $n = 6$. And since it is true for $n = 6$, it must be true for $n = 7$, and so on, for all the positive integers.

Fractional and Negative Exponent

We have shown that the binomial formula is valid when the exponent n is a positive integer. We shall not prove it here, but the binomial formula also holds when the exponent is negative or fractional. However, we now obtain an infinite series, called a binomial series, with no last term. Further, the binomial series is equal to $(a + b)^n$ only if the series converges.

■ **Example 45:** Write the first four terms of the infinite binomial expansion for $\sqrt{5 + x}$.

Solution: We replace the radical with a fractional exponent and substitute into the binomial formula in the usual way:

$$(5 + x)^{1/2} = 5^{1/2} + \left(\frac{1}{2}\right)5^{-1/2}x + \frac{(1/2)(-1/2)}{2}5^{-3/2}x^2$$

$$+ \frac{(1/2)(-1/2)(-3/2)}{6}5^{-5/2}x^3 + \cdots$$

$$= \sqrt{5} + \frac{x}{2\sqrt{5}} - \frac{x^2}{8(5)^{3/2}} + \frac{x^3}{16(5)^{5/2}} - \cdots$$

Switching to decimal form and working to five decimal places, we get

$$(5 + x)^{1/2} \approx 2.23607 + 0.22361x - 0.01118x^2 + 0.00112x^3 - \cdots \quad ■$$

We now ask if this series is valid for any x. Let's try a few values. For $x = 0$,

$$(5 + 0)^{1/2} \approx 2.23607$$

which checks within the number of digits retained. For $x = 1$,

$$(5 + 1)^{1/2} = \sqrt{6} \approx 2.23607 + 0.22361 - 0.01118 + 0.00112 - \cdots$$

$$\approx 2.44962$$

which compares with a value of $\sqrt{6}$ of 2.44949. Not bad, considering that we are using only four terms of an infinite series.

To determine the effect of larger values of x, we have used a computer to generate eight terms of the binomial series. Into it we have substituted various x values, from 0 to 11, and compared the value obtained by series with those obtained from a calculator.

x	$\sqrt{5+x}$ BY SERIES	$\sqrt{5+x}$ BY CALCULATOR	ERROR
0	2.236068	2.236068	0
2	2.645766	2.645751	0.000015
4	3.002957	3	0.002957
6	3.379908	3.316625	0.063283
8	4.148339	3.605551	0.543788
11	9.723964	4	5.723964

These values are plotted in Figure 25•7.

Notice that the accuracy gets worse as x gets larger, with useless values being obtained when x is 6 or greater. This illustrates the fact that

A binomial series is equal to $(a + b)^n$ only if the series converges, and that occurs when $|a| > |b|$.

Our series in Example 45 thus converges when $x < 5$.

FIGURE 25·7

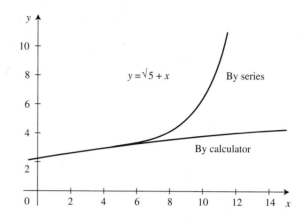

The binomial series, then, is given by the following formula.

Binomial Series	$$(a + b)^n = a^n + na^{n-1}b + \frac{n(n-1)}{2!}a^{n-2}b^2 + \frac{n(n-1)(n-2)}{3!}a^{n-3}b^3 + \cdots$$ where $|a| > |b|$	247

The binomial series is often written with $a = 1$ and $b = x$, so we give that form here also.

Binomial Series	$$(1 + x)^n = 1 + nx + \frac{n(n-1)}{2!}x^2 + \frac{n(n-1)(n-2)}{3!}x^3 + \cdots$$ where $|x| < 1$	248

■ **Example 46:** Expand to four terms,

$$\frac{1}{\sqrt[3]{1/a - 3b^{1/3}}}$$

Solution: We rewrite the given expression without radicals or fractions, and then expand.

$$\frac{1}{\sqrt[3]{1/a - 3b^{1/3}}} = [(a^{-1}) + (-3b^{1/3})]^{-1/3}$$

$$= (a^{-1})^{-1/3} - \frac{1}{3}(a^{-1})^{-4/3}(-3b^{1/3}) + \frac{2}{9}(a^{-1})^{-7/3}(-3b^{1/3})^2$$

$$- \frac{14}{81}(a^{-1})^{-10/3}(-3b^{1/3})^3 + \cdots$$

$$= a^{1/3} + a^{4/3}b^{1/3} + 2a^{7/3}b^{2/3} + \frac{14}{3}a^{10/3}b + \cdots$$

■

Exercise 5 The Binomial Theorem

Factorial Notation

Evaluate each factorial.

1. $6!$　　　　**2.** $8!$　　　　**3.** $\dfrac{7!}{5!}$

4. $\dfrac{11!}{9!\,2!}$　　　　**5.** $\dfrac{7!}{3!\,4!}$　　　　**6.** $\dfrac{8!}{3!\,5!}$

Binomials Raised to an Integral Power

Verify each expansion below. Obtain the binomial coefficients by formula or from Pascal's triangle, as directed by your instructor.

7. $(x + y)^7 = x^7 + 7x^6y + 21x^5y^2 + 35x^4y^3 + 35x^3y^4 + 21x^2y^5 + 7xy^6 + y^7$

8. $(4 + 3b)^4 = 256 + 768b + 864b^2 + 432b^3 + 81b^4$

9. $(3a - 2b)^4 = 81a^4 - 216a^3b + 216a^2b^2 - 96ab^3 + 16b^4$

10. $(x^3 + y)^7 = x^{21} + 7x^{18}y + 21x^{15}y^2 + 35x^{12}y^3 + 35x^9y^4 + 21x^6y^5 + 7x^3y^6 + y^7$

11. $(x^{1/2} + y^{2/3})^5 = x^{5/2} + 5x^2y^{2/3} + 10x^{3/2}y^{4/3} + 10xy^2 + 5x^{1/2}y^{8/3} + y^{10/3}$

12. $(1/x + 1/y^2)^3 = 1/x^3 + 3/x^2y^2 + 3/xy^4 + 1/y^6$

13. $(a/b - b/a)^6 = (a/b)^6 - 6(a/b)^4 + 15(a/b)^2 - 20 + 15(b/a)^2 - 6(b/a)^4 + (b/a)^6$

14. $(1/\sqrt{x} + y^2)^4 = x^{-2} + 4x^{-3/2}y^2 + 6x^{-1}y^4 + 4x^{-1/2}y^6 + y^8$

15. $(2a^2 + \sqrt{b})^5 = 32a^{10} + 80a^8b^{1/2} + 80a^6b + 40a^4b^{3/2} + 10a^2b^2 + b^{5/2}$

16. $(\sqrt{x} - c^{2/3})^4 = x^2 - 4x^{3/2}c^{2/3} + 6xc^{4/3} - 4x^{1/2}c^2 + c^{8/3}$

Verify the first four terms of each binomial expansion.

17. $(x^2 + y^3)^8 = x^{16} + 8x^{14}y^3 + 28x^{12}y^6 + 56x^{10}y^9 + \cdots$

18. $(x^2 - 2y^3)^{11} = x^{22} - 22x^{20}y^3 + 220x^{18}y^6 - 1320x^{16}y^9 + \cdots$

19. $(a - b^4)^9 = a^9 - 9a^8b^4 + 36a^7b^8 - 84a^6b^{12} + \cdots$

20. $(a^3 + 2b)^{12} = a^{36} + 24a^{33}b + 264a^{30}b^2 + 1760a^{27}b^3 + \cdots$

Trinomials

Verify each expansion.

21. $(2a^2 + a + 3)^3 = 8a^6 + 12a^5 + 42a^4 + 37a^3 + 63a^2 + 27a + 27$

22. $(4x^2 - 3xy - y^2)^3 = 64x^6 - 144x^5y + 60x^4y^2 + 45x^3y^3 - 15x^2y^4 - 9xy^5 - y^6$

23. $(2a^2 + a - 4)^4 = 16a^8 + 32a^7 - 104a^6 - 184a^5 + 289a^4 + 368a^3 - 416a^2 - 256a + 256$

General Term

Write the requested term of each binomial expansion, and simplify.

24. Seventh term of $(a^2 - 2b^3)^{12}$

25. Eleventh term of $(2 - x)^{16}$

26. Fourth term of $(2a - 3b)^7$
27. Eighth term of $(x + a)^{11}$
28. Fifth term of $\left(x - 2\sqrt{y}\right)^{25}$
29. Ninth term of $(x^2 + 1)^{15}$

Binomials Raised to a Fractional or Negative Power

Verify the first four terms of each infinite binomial series.

30. $(1 - a)^{2/3} = 1 - 2a/3 - a^2/9 - 4a^3/81 \ldots$
31. $\sqrt{1 + a} = 1 + a/2 - a^2/8 + a^3/16 \ldots$
32. $(1 + 5a)^{-5} = 1 - 25a + 375a^2 - 4375a^3 \ldots$
33. $(1 + a)^{-3} = 1 - 3a + 6a^2 - 10a^3 \ldots$
34. $1/\sqrt[6]{1 - a} = 1 + a/6 + 7a^2/72 + 91a^3/1296 \ldots$

Graphics Utility

35. Use a graphics utility to graph each binomial and four terms of the expansion for Problems 30 to 34, and compare the results you get with those obtained manually. Choose a value of a with an absolute value less than 1.

Computer

36. Use a computer algebra system to expand any of the binomials in this exercise.

CHAPTER 25   REVIEW PROBLEMS

1. Find the sum of seven terms of the AP $-4, -1, 2, \ldots$.
2. Find the tenth term of $(1 - y)^{14}$.
3. Insert four arithmetic means between 3 and 18.
4. How many terms of the AP $-5, -2, 1, \ldots$ will give a sum of 63?
5. Insert four harmonic means between 2 and 12.
6. Find the twelfth term of an AP with first term 7 and common difference 5.
7. Find the sum of the first 10 terms of the AP $1, 2\frac{2}{3}, 4\frac{1}{3}, \ldots$.

Expand each binomial:

8. $(2x^2 - \sqrt{x}/2)^5$
9. $(a - 2)^5$
10. $(x - y^3)^7$

11. Find the fifth term of a GP with first term 3 and common ratio 2.
12. Find the fourth term of a GP with first term 8 and common ratio -4.

Evaluate each limit:

13. $\lim_{b \to 0} (2b - x + 9)$
14. $\lim_{b \to 0} (a^2 + b^2)$

Find the sum of infinitely many terms of each GP:

15. $4, 2, 1, \ldots$
16. $\frac{1}{4}, -\frac{1}{16}, \frac{1}{64}, \ldots$
17. $1, -\frac{2}{5}, \frac{4}{25}, \ldots$

Write each decimal number as a rational fraction:

18. $0.86\overline{86} \ldots$
19. $0.54\overline{44} \ldots$

20. Find the seventh term of the harmonic progression $3, 3\frac{3}{7}, 4, \ldots$
21. Find the sixth term of a GP with first term 5 and common ratio 3.
22. Find the sum of the first seven terms of the GP in Problem 21.

23. Find the fifth term of a GP with first term -4 and common ratio 4.

24. Find the sum of the first seven terms of the GP in Problem 23.

25. Insert two geometric means between 8 and 125.

26. Insert three geometric means between 14 and 224.

Evaluate each factorial.

27. $\dfrac{4!\,5!}{2!}$ **28.** $\dfrac{8!}{4!\,4!}$ **29.** $\dfrac{7!\,3!}{5!}$ **30.** $\dfrac{7!}{2!\,5!}$

Find the first four terms of each binomial expansion.

31. $\left(\dfrac{2x}{y^2} - y\sqrt{x}\right)^7$

32. $(1 + a)^{-2}$

33. $\dfrac{1}{\sqrt{1 + a}}$

34. Expand, using the binomial theorem, $(1 - 3a + 2a^2)^4$.

35. Find the eighth term of $(3a - b)^{11}$.

36. Find the tenth term of an AP with first term 12 if the sum of the first 10 terms is 10.

Writing

37. State in your own words the difference between an arithmetic progression and a geometric progression. Give a real-world example of each.

26

Introduction to Statistics and Probability

O B J E C T I V E S

When you have completed this chapter, you should be able to:

- Identify data as continuous, discrete, or categorical.
- Represent data as an *x*–*y* graph, scatter plot, bar graph, pie chart, stem and leaf plot, or box plot.
- Organize data into frequency distributions, frequency histograms, frequency polygons, and cumulative frequency distributions.
- Calculate the mean, the weighted mean, the median, and the mode.
- Find the range, the quartiles, the deciles, the percentiles, the variance, and the standard deviation.
- Calculate the probabilities for frequency distributions, including the binomial and normal distributions.
- Estimate population means, standard deviations, and proportions, within a given confidence interval.
- Make control charts for statistical process control.
- Fit a straight line to a set of data using the method of least squares.

Why study statistics? There are several reasons. First, for your work you may have to interpret statistical data or you may even need to collect such data and make inferences from it. You may, perhaps, be asked to determine if replacing a certain machine on a production line actually reduced the number of defective parts made. Further, a knowledge of statistics may help you to evaluate the claims made in news reports, polls, and advertisements. A toothpaste manufacturer may claim that their product "significantly reduces" tooth decay. A pollster may claim that 52% of the electorate is going to vote for candidate Jones. A newspaper may show a chart that pictures oil consumption going down. It is easy to use statistics to distort the truth, either on purpose or unintentionally. Some knowledge of the subject may help you to separate fact from distortion.

In this chapter we introduce many new terms. We then show how to display statistical data in graphical and numerical form. How reliable are those statistical data? To answer that question we include a brief introduction to *probability*, which enables us to describe the "confidence" we can place on those statistics.

Definitions and Terminology

26•1

Populations and Samples

In statistics, an entire group of people or things is called a *population* or *universe*. A population can be *infinite* or *finite*. A small part of the entire group chosen for study is called a *sample*.

■ **Example 1:** In a study of the heights of students at Tech College, the entire student body is our *population*. This is a *finite* population. Instead of studying every student in the population, we may choose to work with a *sample* of only 100 students. ■

■ **Example 2:** Suppose that we want to determine what percentage of tosses of a coin will be heads. Then all possible tosses of the coin is an example of an *infinite* population. Theoretically, there is no limit to the number of tosses that can be made. ■

Parameters and Statistics

We often use just a few numbers to describe an entire population. Such numbers are called *parameters*. The branch of statistics in which we use parameters to describe a population is referred to as *descriptive statistics*.

■ **Example 3:** For the population of all students at Tech College, a computer read the height of each student and computed the average height of all students. It found this *parameter*, average height, to be 1.72 m. ■

Similarly, we use just a few numbers to describe a sample. Such numbers are called *statistics*. When we then use these sample statistics to *infer* things about the entire population, we are engaging in what is called *inductive statistics*.

■ **Example 4:** From the population of all students in Tech College, a sample of 100 students was selected. The average of their heights was found to be 1.72 m. This is a sample *statistic*. From it we infer that, for the entire population, the average height is 1.72 m plus or minus some *standard error*. We show how to compute standard error in Section 26.6. ■

Thus parameters describe populations, while statistics describe samples. The first letters of the words help us to keep track of which goes with which:

Population **P**arameter

versus

Sample **S**tatistic

Variables

In statistics we distinguish between data that are *continuous* (obtained by measurement), *discrete* (obtained by counting), or *categorical* (belonging to one of several categories).

■ **Example 5:** A survey at Tech College asked each student for (a) height, *continuous data*; (b) number of courses taken, *discrete data*; and (c) whether they were in favor (yes or no) of eliminating final exams, *categorical data*. ■

A *variable*, as in algebra, is a quantity that can take on different values within a problem; *constants* do not change value. We call variables *continuous*, *discrete*, or *categorical*, depending on the type of data they represent.

■ **Example 6:** If, in the survey of Example 5, we let

$$H = \text{student's height}$$

$$N = \text{number of courses taken}$$

$$F = \text{opinion on eliminating finals}$$

then H is a continuous variable, N is a discrete variable, and F is a categorical variable. ■

Ways to Display Data

Statistical data are usually presented as a table of values or displayed in a graph or chart. Common types of graphs are the *x–y* graph, scatter plot, bar graph, or pie chart. Here we give examples of the display of discrete and categorical data. We cover display of continuous data in Section 26•2.

■ **Example 7:** Table 26•1 shows the number of skis made per month by the Ace Ski Company. We show these discrete data as an *x–y* graph, a scatter plot, a bar chart, and a pie chart (Fig. 26•1). ■

■ **Example 8:** Table 26•2 shows the number of skis of various types made in a certain year by the Ace Ski Company. We show these discrete data as an *x–y* graph, a bar chart, and a pie chart (Fig. 26•2). ■

TABLE 26•1

MONTH	PAIRS SOLD
Jan.	13 946
Feb.	7 364
Mar.	5 342
Apr.	3 627
May	1 823
June	847
July	354
Aug.	425
Sept.	3 745
Oct.	5 827
Nov.	11 837
Dec.	18 475
Total	73 612

TABLE 26•2

TYPE	PAIRS SOLD
Downhill	35 725
Racing	7 735
Jumping	2 889
Cross-country	27 263
Total	73 612

Exercise 1 Definitions and Terminology

Types of Data

Label each type of data as continuous, discrete, or categorical:

1. The number of people in each county that voted for Jones
2. The life of certain 100 W light bulbs
3. The blood types of patients at a certain hospital
4. The number of Ford cars sold each day
5. The models of Ford cars sold each day
6. The mass in kilograms of steers in a given herd

(a) *x–y* graph

(b) Scatter plot

(c) Bar chart

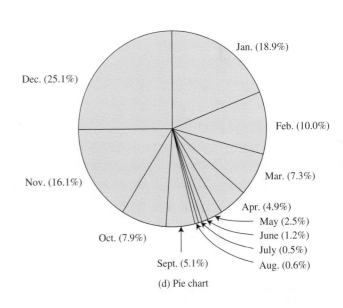

(d) Pie chart

FIGURE 26·1

Graphical Representation of Data

7. The following table shows the population of a certain town for the years 1920–1930.

YEAR	POPULATION	YEAR	POPULATION
1920	5364	1926	7245
1921	5739	1927	7734
1922	6254	1928	8148
1923	7958	1929	8545
1924	7193	1930	8623
1925	6837		

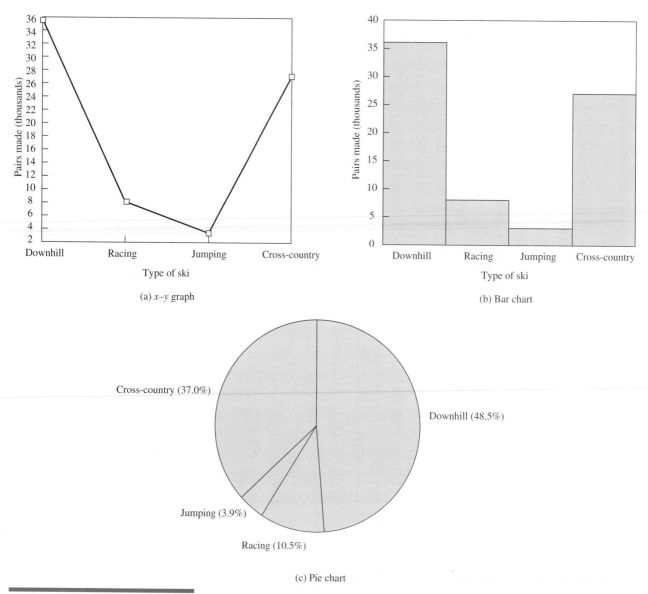

(a) x–y graph

(b) Bar chart

(c) Pie chart

FIGURE 26·2

Make a scatter plot and an x–y graph of the population versus the year.

8. Make a bar for the data of Problem 7.

9. In a certain election, the tally was:

CANDIDATE	NUMBER OF VOTES
Smith	746 000
Jones	623 927
Doe	536 023
Not Voting	163 745

Make a bar chart showing the election results.

10. Make a pie chart showing the election results of Problem 9. To make the pie chart, simply draw a circle and subdivide the area of the circle into four sectors. Make the central angle (and hence the area) of each sector proportional to the votes obtained by each candidate as a percentage of the total voting population. Label the percentage in each sector.

Graphics Calculator

11. Many graphics calculators can draw x–y graphs, scatter plots, and bar graphs. The data to be entered, however, must be in numerical form; thus the months January, February, . . . would be entered as 1, 2, ... Use your graphics calculator to draw any of the graphs in this exercise of which it is capable.

Computer

12. Many spreadsheet programs can draw x–y graphs, scatter plots, and bar graphs. Unlike with the graphics calculator, the data on the x axis can, for certain graphs, be words. Use a spreadsheet to draw any of the graphs in this exercise.

13. There are a number of computer software packages, such as *Minitab*, designed especially for statistics. These can draw all the common statistical graphs. Use one of them for any of the graphs in this exercise.

26•2

Frequency Distributions

Raw Data

Data that have not been organized in any way are called *raw data*. Data that have been sorted into ascending or descending order are called an *array*. The *range* of data is the difference between the largest and the smallest number in that array.

▬ Example 9: Five students were chosen at random and their heights were measured (in metres). The *raw data* obtained were:

$$1.42 \quad 1.85 \quad 1.48 \quad 1.45 \quad 1.72$$

If we sort the numbers into ascending order, we get the *array*:

$$1.42 \quad 1.45 \quad 1.48 \quad 1.72 \quad 1.85$$

The *range* of the data is

$$1.85 - 1.42 = 0.43 \text{ m} \qquad ▬$$

Grouped Data

For discrete and categorical data, we have seen that x–y plots and bar charts are effective. These graphs can also be used for *continuous* data, but first we must collect those data into groups. Such groups are usually called *classes*. We do this by dividing the range into a convenient number of *intervals*. Each interval has an upper and a lower *limit* or *class boundary*. The *class width* is equal to the upper class boundary minus the lower class limit. The intervals are chosen so that a given data point cannot fall directly on a class boundary. We call the center of each interval the *class midpoint*.

Frequency Distribution

Once the classes have been defined, we may tally the number of measurements falling within each class. Such a tally is called a *frequency distribution*. The number of entries in a given class is called the *absolute frequency*. That number, divided by the total number of entries, is called the *relative frequency*. The relative frequency is often expressed as a percentage. To make a frequency distribution:

1. Subtract the smallest number in the data from the largest to find the range of the data.
2. Divide the range into class intervals, usually of a length between 5 and 20. Avoid class limits that coincide with actual data by defining the limits to half a unit greater accuracy than the accuracy of the given data.
3. Get the class frequencies by tallying the number of observations that falls within each class.
4. Get the relative frequency of each class by dividing its class frequency by the total number of observations.

■ **Example 10:** Table 26•3 gives the grades of 30 students. Group these raw data into convenient classes. Choose the class width, the class midpoints, and the class limits. Find the absolute frequency and relative frequency of each class.

TABLE 26•3

85.0	62.5	94.6	76.3	77.4	78.9	58.4	86.4	88.4	69.8
91.3	75.0	69.6	86.4	79.5	74.7	65.7	88.6	90.6	69.7
86.7	70.5	78.4	86.4	94.6	60.7	79.8	97.2	85.7	78.5

Solution:

1. The highest value in the data is 97.2 and the lowest is 58.4, so

$$\text{range} = 97.2 - 58.4 = 38.8$$

2. If we divide the range into five classes, we get a class width of 38.8/5 or 7.76. If we divide the range into 20 classes, we get a class width of 1.94. A convenient width between those two values is 5, so

$$\text{let class width} = 5.0$$

Let us further choose class midpoints of 55, 60, . . . 95, so that our class limits are then

$$52.5, 57.5, 62.5, \ldots, 97.5$$

We must avoid ambiguity about in which class to place a grade like 62.5. Our data are given to the nearest tenth, so let us define our class limits to the nearest 0.05 unit. We then let our class limits be

$$52.45\text{–}57.44, \quad 57.45\text{–}62.44, \ldots, 92.45\text{–}97.44$$

3. Our next step is to tally the number of grades falling within each class and get a frequency distribution, shown in Table 26•4.

4. We then divide each frequency by 30 to get the relative frequency.

TABLE 26•4 Frequency Distribution of Student Grades

CLASS LIMITS	CLASS MIDPOINT	TALLY	ABSOLUTE FREQUENCY	RELATIVE FREQUENCY	
52.45–57.44	55		0	0/30	(0%)
57.45–62.44	60	//	2	2/30	(6.7%)
62.45–67.44	65	//	2	2/30	(6.7%)
67.45–72.44	70	////	4	4/30	(13.3%)
72.45–77.44	75	////	4	4/30	(13.3%)
77.45–82.44	80	////	5	5/30	(16.7%)
82.45–87.44	85	////+ /	6	6/30	(20%)
87.45–92.44	90	////+	4	4/30	(13.3%)
92.45–97.44	95	///	3	3/30	(10%)
Totals			30	30/30	(100%)

Frequency Histogram

A *frequency histogram* is a bar chart in which each bar is centered at its class midpoint. The width of each bar is equal to the class width, and the height of each bar is equal to the frequency. Either the absolute or the relative frequency can be used for the histogram, or the vertical axis can show both.

■ **Example 11:** We show a frequency histogram for the data of Example 10 in Figure 26•3. Note that the vertical scales show both absolute frequency and relative frequency. ■

FIGURE 26•3

Since all the bars have the same width, the *areas* of the bars are proportional to the heights of the bars. The areas are thus proportional to the class frequencies. If one bar in a relative frequency histogram has a height of 20%, that bar will contain 20% of the area of the whole graph. Thus there is a 20% chance that one grade chosen at random will fall within that class. We will make use of this connection between areas and probabilities in Section 26•4.

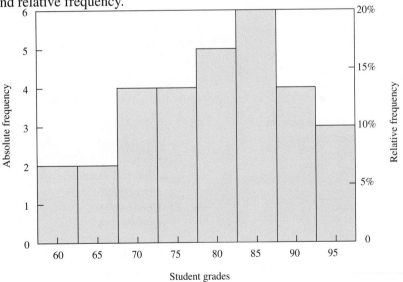

Frequency Polygon

A *frequency polygon* is simply an *x–y* graph in which frequency is plotted against class midpoint. As with the histogram, it can show either absolute or relative frequency, or both.

■ **Example 12:** We show a frequency polygon for the data of Example 10 in Figure 26•4.

FIGURE 26•4 A frequency polygon for the data of Example 10. Note that this polygon could have been obtained by connecting the midpoints of the tops of the bars in Figure 26•3.

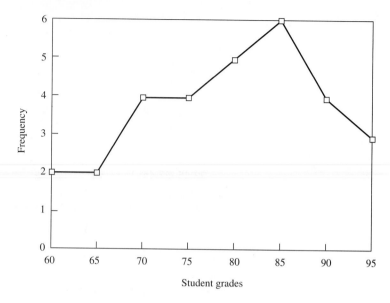

Cumulative Frequency Distributions

We obtain a *cumulative* frequency distribution by summing all values *less than* a given class limit. The graph of a cumulative frequency distribution is called a *cumulative frequency polygon*, or *ogive*.

■ **Example 13:** Make and graph a cumulative frequency distribution for the data of Example 10.

Solution: We compute the cumulative frequencies by adding up the values below the given limits (Table 26•5) and plot them in Figure 26.5.

TABLE 26•5 Cumulative Frequency Distribution for Student Grades

GRADE	CUMULATIVE ABSOLUTE FREQUENCY	CUMULATIVE RELATIVE FREQUENCY	
Under 62.45	2	2/30	(6.7%)
Under 67.45	4	4/30	(13.3%)
Under 72.45	8	8/30	(26.7%)
Under 77.45	12	12/30	(40%)
Under 82.45	17	17/30	(56.7%)
Under 87.45	23	23/30	(76.7%)
Under 92.45	27	27/30	(90%)
Under 97.45	30	30/30	(100%)

FIGURE 26•5

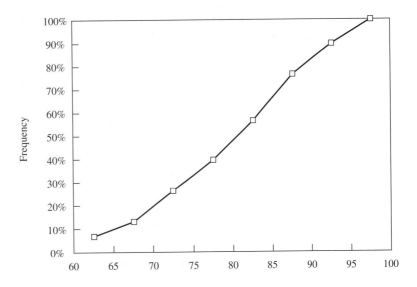

Stem and Leaf Plots

A fast and easy way to get an idea of the distribution of a new set of data is to make a stem and leaf plot. We will show how by means of an example.

■ **Example 14:** Make a stem and leaf plot for the data in Table 26•3.

Solution: Let us choose as the *stem* of our plot the first digit of each grade. These range from 5 to 9, representing grades from 50 to 90. Then opposite each number on the stem we write all the values in the table starting with that number:

STEM	LEAVES								
5	8.4								
6	2.5	9.8	9.6	5.7	9.7	0.7			
7	6.3	7.4	8.9	5.0	9.5	4.7	0.5	8.4	9.8 8.5
8	5.0	6.4	8.4	6.4	8.6	6.7	6.4	5.7	
9	4.6	1.3	0.6	4.6	7.2				

We sometimes go on to arrange the leaves in numerical order (not shown here). You may also choose to drop the decimal points.

To see the shape of the distribution, simply turn the page on its side. Notice the similarity in shape to that of Figure 26•3.

Also note that the stem and leaf plot *preserves the original data*. Thus we could exactly reconstruct Table 26•3 from this plot, while such a reconstruction is not possible from the grouped data of Table 26•4. ■

Exercise 2 Frequency Distributions

Frequency Distributions

1. The masses in kilograms of 40 students at Tech College are

58	62	52	67	72	68	70	74
70	63	65	52	74	67	70	75
78	76	66	70	50	68	53	69
75	78	72	67	53	58	74	70
54	64	58	69	75	57	53	73

(a) Determine the range of the data. **(b)** Make an absolute frequency distribution, using class widths of 2 kg. **(c)** Make a relative frequency distribution.

2. The times (in minutes) for 30 racers to complete a cross-country ski race are

61.4	72.5	88.2	71.2	48.5	48.9	54.8	71.4	99.2	74.5
84.6	73.6	69.3	49.6	59.3	71.4	89.4	92.4	48.4	66.3
85.7	59.3	74.9	59.3	72.7	49.4	83.8	50.3	72.8	69.3

(a) Determine the range of the data. **(b)** Make an absolute frequency distribution using class widths of 5 min. **(c)** Make a relative frequency distribution.

3. The prices (in dollars) of various computer printers in a distributor's catalogue are

850	625	946	763	774	789	584	864	884	698
913	750	696	864	795	747	657	886	906	697
867	705	784	864	946	607	798	972	857	785

(a) Determine the range of the data. **(b)** Make an absolute frequency distribution, using class widths of $50. **(c)** Make a relative frequency distribution.

Frequency Histograms and Frequency Polygons

Draw a histogram, showing both absolute and relative frequency, for the data of:

4. Problem 1   **5.** Problem 2   **6.** Problem 3

Draw a frequency polygon, showing both absolute and relative frequency, for the data of:

7. Problem 1   **8.** Problem 2   **9.** Problem 3

Cumulative Frequency Distributions

Make a cumulative frequency distribution, showing **(a)** absolute frequency and **(b)** relative frequency, for the data of:

10. Problem 1   **11.** Problem 2   **12.** Problem 3

Draw a cumulative frequency polygon, showing both absolute and relative frequency, for the data of:

13. Problem 10   **14.** Problem 11   **15.** Problem 12

Stem and Leaf Plot

Make a stem and leaf plot for the data of:

16. Problem 1   **17.** Problem 2   **18.** Problem 3

Graphics Calculator and Computer

19. Use your graphics calculator to produce any of the histograms or frequency polygons in this exercise.

20. Some spreadsheets such as *Lotus 123* have commands for automatically making a frequency distribution, and can also draw frequency histograms and polygons. If you have such a spreadsheet available, use it for any of the problems in this exercise.

21. Use any available statistical software for the computer, such as *Minitab*, to produce any of the distributions or plots in this exercise.

26·3

Numerical Description of Data

We saw in Section 26·2 how we can describe a set of data by a frequency distribution, a frequency histogram, a frequency polygon, or a cumulative frequency distribution. We can also describe a set of data with just a few numbers, and this more compact description is more convenient for some purposes. For example, if, in a report, you wanted to describe the heights of a group of students, and did not want to give the entire frequency distribution, you might simply say:

The mean height is 1.47 m with a standard deviation of 0.0889 m.

The *mean* is a number that shows the *center* of the data; the *standard deviation* is a measure of the *spread* of the data. As mentioned earlier, the mean and the standard deviation may be found either for an entire population (and are thus population parameters) or for a sample drawn from that population (and are thus sample statistics).

Thus to describe a population or a sample, we need numbers that give both the center of the data and the spread. Further, for sample statistics, we need to give the uncertainty of each figure. This will enable us to make inferences about the larger population.

■ **Example 15:** A student recorded the running times for a sample of participants in a race. From that sample she inferred (by methods we'll learn later) that, for the entire population of racers,

$$\text{mean time} = 23.65 \pm 0.84 \text{ minutes}$$

$$\text{standard deviation} = 5.83 \pm 0.34 \text{ minutes}$$ ■

The mean time is called a *measure of central tendency*. We show how to calculate the mean, and other measures of central tendency, later in this section. The standard deviation is called a *measure of dispersion*. We also show how to compute it, and other measures of dispersion, in this section. The "plus-or-minus" values show a degree of uncertainty, called the *standard error*. The uncertainty ± 0.84 min, is called the *standard error of the mean*, and the uncertainty, ± 0.34 min, is called the *standard error of the standard deviation*. We show how to calculate standard errors in Section 26·6.

Measures of Central Tendency: The Mean

There is a story, probably untrue, about a statistician who drowned in a lake that had an average depth of one-third of a metre.

Some common measures of the center of a distribution are the mean, the median, and the mode. The arithmetic mean, or simply the *mean*, of a set of measurements is equal to the sum of the measurements divided by the number of measurements. It is what we commonly call the *average*. It is the most commonly used measure of central tendency. If our n measurements are x_1, $x_2, \ldots, x_n$, then

$$\Sigma x = x_1 + x_2 + \cdots + x_n$$

The Greek symbol Σ (sigma) is used to represent "the sum of." The mean, which we call $\bar{x}$ (x bar), is then

Arithmetic Mean	$\bar{x} = \dfrac{\Sigma x}{n}$	**249**

The arithmetic mean of n measurements is the sum of those measurements divided by n.

We can calculate the mean for a sample or for the entire population. However, we use a *different symbol* in each case.

$\bar{x}$ is the sample mean

μ (mu) is the population mean

■ **Example 16:** Find the mean of the following sample.

$$746 \quad 574 \quad 645 \quad 894 \quad 736 \quad 695 \quad 635 \quad 794$$

Solution: Adding the values gives

$$\Sigma x = 746 + 574 + 645 + 894 + 736 + 695 + 635 + 794 = 5719$$

Then, with $n = 8$,

$$\bar{x} = \frac{5719}{8} = 715$$

rounded to three digits. ■

Weighted Mean

When all the data are not of equal importance, we may compute a *weighted mean*, where the values are weighted according to their importance.

■ **Example 17:** A student has grades of 83, 59, and 94 on three one-hour exams, a grade of 82 on the final exam which is equal in weight to two one-hour exams, and a grade of 78 on a laboratory report, which is worth 1.5 one-hour exams. Compute the weighted mean.

Solution: If a one-hour exam is assigned a weight of 1, then we have a total of the weights of

$$\Sigma w = 1 + 1 + 1 + 2 + 1.5 = 6.5$$

To get a weighted mean we add up the products of each grade and its weight, and divide by the total weight.

$$\text{weighted mean} = \frac{83(1) + 59(1) + 94(1) + 82(2) + 78(1.5)}{6.5} = 79.5 \quad \blacksquare$$

In general the weighted mean is

$$\text{Weighted mean} = \frac{\Sigma(wx)}{\Sigma w}$$

Midrange

We have already noted that the range of a set of data is the difference between the highest and lowest numbers in the set. The *midrange* is simply the value midway between the two extreme values.

$$\text{Midrange} = \frac{\text{highest value} + \text{lowest value}}{2}$$

■ **Example 18:** The midrange for the values

$$3, 5, 6, 6, 7, 11, 11, 15$$

is

$$\text{midrange} = \frac{3 + 15}{2} = 9 \quad \blacksquare$$

Mode

Our next measure of central tendency is the *mode*.

Mode	The mode of a set of numbers is the measurement that occurs most often in the set. (There may be more than one measurement which qualifies.)	**251**

A set of numbers may have no mode, one mode, or more than one mode.

■ **Example 19:**
(a) The set   1   3   3   5   6   7   7   7   9   has the mode 7.
(b) The set   1   1   3   3   5   5   7   7   has no mode.
(c) The set   1   3   3   3   5   6   7   7   7   9   has two modes, 3 and 7.
    It is called *bimodal*.   ■

Median

To find the *median*, we simply arrange the data in order of magnitude and pick the *middle value*. For an even number of measurements, we take the mean of the two middle values.

Median	The median of a set of numbers arranged in order of magnitude is the middle value of an odd number of measurements, or the mean of the two middle values of an even number of measurement.	**250**

■ **Example 20:** Find the median of the data in Example 16.

Solution: We rewrite the data in order of magnitude:

$$574 \quad 635 \quad 645 \quad 695 \quad 736 \quad 746 \quad 794 \quad 894$$

The two middle values are 695 and 736. Taking their mean gives

$$\text{median} = \frac{695 + 736}{2} = 715.5$$ ■

The Five-Number Summary

The median of that half of a set of data from the minimum value up to and including the median is called the *lower hinge*. Similarly, the median of the upper half of the data is called the *upper hinge*.

The group of values including the lowest value in a set of data, together with the highest value, the median, and the two hinges, is called a *5-number summary* of the data.

■ **Example 21:** For the data

$$12 \quad 17 \quad 18 \quad 20 \quad 22 \quad 28 \quad 32 \quad 34 \quad 49 \quad 52 \quad 59 \quad 66$$

the median is $(28 + 32)/2 = 30$, so

This 5-number summary for this set of data may be written

$$[12, 20, 30, 49, 66]$$ ■

Box Plots

A graph of the values in the 5-number-summary is called a *box plot*.

■ **Example 22:** A box plot for the data of Example 21 is given in Figure 26•6.   ■

FIGURE 26•6 A Box plot. It is also called a *Box and Whisker* diagram.

Measures of Dispersion

We will usually use the mean to describe a set of numbers, but it alone can be misleading.

■ **Example 23:** Each of the following sets of numbers,

$$1 \quad 1 \quad 1 \quad 1 \quad 1 \quad 1 \quad 1 \quad 1 \quad 1 \quad 91$$

and

$$10 \quad 10 \quad 10 \quad 10 \quad 10 \quad 10 \quad 10 \quad 10 \quad 10 \quad 10$$

has a mean value of 10 but the sets are otherwise quite different. Each set has a sum of 100; in the first set most of this sum is concentrated in a single value, but in the second set the sum is *dispersed* among all the values. ▬

Thus we need some *measure of dispersion* of a set of numbers. Four common ones are the range, the percentile range, the variance, and the standard deviation. We will cover each of these.

Range

We have already introduced range in Section 26•2, and we define it here.

Range	The range of a set of numbers is the difference between the largest and the smallest number in the set.	**252**

▬ **Example 24:** For the set of numbers

$$6 \quad 3 \quad 9 \quad 12 \quad 44 \quad 2 \quad 53 \quad 1 \quad 8$$

the largest value is 53 and the smallest is 1, so the range is

$$53 - 1 = 52$$ ▬

We sometimes give the range by stating the end values themselves. Thus in Example 24 we might say that the range is from 1 to 53.

Quartiles, Deciles, and Percentiles

For a set of data arranged in order of magnitude, we have seen that the median divides the data into two equal parts. There are as many numbers below the median as there are above it.

Similarly, we can determine two more values that divide each half of the data in half again. We call these values *quartiles*. One-fourth of the values will fall into each quartile. The quartiles are labeled Q_1, Q_2, and Q_3. Thus, Q_2 is the median.

Those values that divide the data into 10 equal parts we call deciles and label them D_1, D_2, ... Those values that divide the data into 100 equal parts are percentiles, labeled P_1, P_2, ... Thus the 25th percentile is the same as the first quartile ($P_{25} = Q_1$). The median is the 50th percentile, the fifth decile, and the second quartile ($P_{50} = D_5 = Q_2$). The 70th percentile is the seventh decile ($P_{70} = D_7$).

One measure of dispersion sometimes used is to give the range of values occupied by some given percentiles. Thus we have a *quartile range*, *decile range*, and *percentile range*. For example, the quartile range is the range from the first to the third quartile.

▬ **Example 25:** Find the quartile range for the set of data

$$2 \quad 4 \quad 5 \qquad 7 \quad 8 \quad 11 \qquad 15 \quad 18 \quad 19 \qquad 21 \quad 24 \quad 25$$

Solution: The quartiles are

$$Q_1 = \frac{5 + 7}{2} = 6$$

Note that the quartiles are not in the same locations as the upper and lower hinges. The hinges here would be at 7 and 19.

$$Q_2 = \text{the median} = \frac{11 + 15}{2} = 13$$

$$Q_3 = \frac{19 + 21}{2} = 20$$

Then

$$\text{quartile range} = Q_3 - Q_1 = 20 - 6 = 14 \qquad \blacksquare$$

We see that half the values fall within the quartile range. We may similarly compute the range of any percentiles or deciles. The range from the 10th to the 90th percentile is the one commonly used.

Variance

We now give another measure of dispersion called the *variance*, but we must first mention deviation. We define the *deviation* of any number x in a set of data as the difference between that number and the mean $\bar{x}$ of that set of data.

■ **Example 26:** A certain set of measurements has a mean of 48.3. What are the deviations of the values 24.2 and 69.3 in that set?

Solution: The deviation of 24.2 is

$$24.2 - 48.3 = -24.1$$

and the deviation of 69.3 is

$$69.3 - 48.3 = 21.0 \qquad \blacksquare$$

To get the *variance* of a population of n numbers, we add up the squares of the deviations of each number in the set and divide by n.

Population Variance	$\sigma^2 = \dfrac{\Sigma(x - \bar{x})^2}{n}$	**253**

For large samples (over 30 or so), the variance found by either formula is practically the same.

For finding the variance of a *sample*, it is more accurate to divide by $n - 1$ rather than n. As with the mean, we use one symbol for the sample variance and a different symbol for the population variance:

$$s^2 \text{ is the sample variance}$$

$$\sigma^2 \text{ is the population variance}$$

Sample Variance	$s^2 = \dfrac{\Sigma(x - \bar{x})^2}{n - 1}$	**254**

■ **Example 27:** Compute the variance for the population

$$1.74 \quad 2.47 \quad 3.66 \quad 4.73 \quad 5.14 \quad 6.23 \quad 7.29 \quad 8.93 \quad 9.56$$

Solution: We first compute the mean, $\bar{x}$.

$$\bar{x} = \frac{1.74 + 2.47 + 3.66 + 4.73 + 5.14 + 6.23 + 7.29 + 8.93 + 9.56}{9}$$

$$= 5.53$$

We then subtract the mean from each of the nine values to obtain deviations. The deviations are then squared and added, as in the following table:

MEASUREMENT x	DEVIATION $x - \overline{x}$	DEVIATION SQUARED $(x - \overline{x})^2$
1.74	−3.79	14.35
2.47	−3.06	9.35
3.66	−1.87	3.49
4.73	−0.80	0.64
5.14	−0.39	0.15
6.23	0.70	0.49
7.29	1.76	3.11
8.93	3.40	11.58
9.56	4.03	16.26
$\Sigma x = 49.75$	$\Sigma(x - \overline{x}) = 0$	$\Sigma(x - \overline{x})^2 = 59.41$

The variance σ^2 is then

$$\sigma^2 = \frac{59.41}{9} = 6.60$$

Standard deviation

Once we have the variance, it is a simple matter to get the *standard deviation*. It is the most common measure of dispersion.

Standard Deviation	The standard deviation of a set of numbers is the positive square root of the variance.	**255**

As before, we use s for the sample standard deviation and σ for the population standard deviation.

■ **Example 28:** Find the standard deviation for the data of Example 27.

Solution: We have already found the variance in Example 27.

$$\sigma^2 = 6.60$$

Taking the square root gives the standard deviation

$$\sqrt{6.60} = 2.57$$

To get an intuitive feel for the standard deviation, we now compute it for several data sets consisting of 12 numbers which can range from 1 to 12 (Fig. 26•7). In the first set, all the numbers have the same value, 6, and in the last set every number is different. The data sets in between have differing amounts of repetition. To the right of each data set is a relative frequency histogram and the population standard deviation (computation not shown).

Note that the most compact distribution has the lowest standard deviation, and as the distribution spreads the standard deviation increases.

For a final demonstration, let us again take twelve numbers in two groups of six equal values (Fig. 26•8). Now let us separate the two groups, first by one interval and then by two intervals. Again notice that the standard deviation increases as the data moves further from the mean.

From these two demonstrations we may conclude that *the standard deviation increases whenever data moves away from the mean.*

FIGURE 26·7

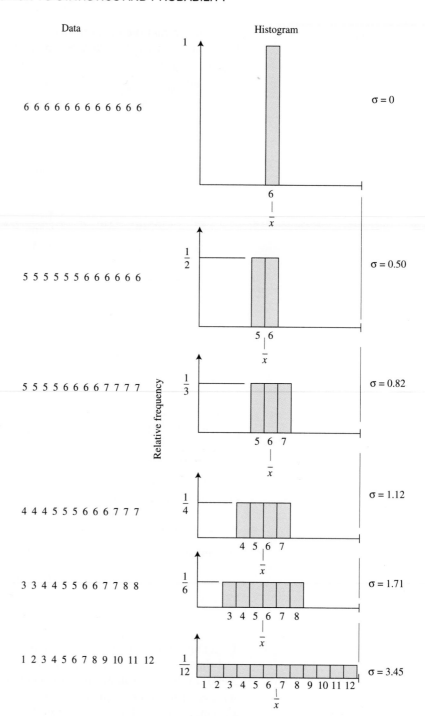

Exercise 3 Numerical Description of Data

The Mean

1. Find the mean of the following set of grades:

85 74 69 59 60 96 84 48 89 76 96 68 98 79 76

2. Find the mean of the following set of masses:

173 127 142 164 163 153 116 199

FIGURE 26·8

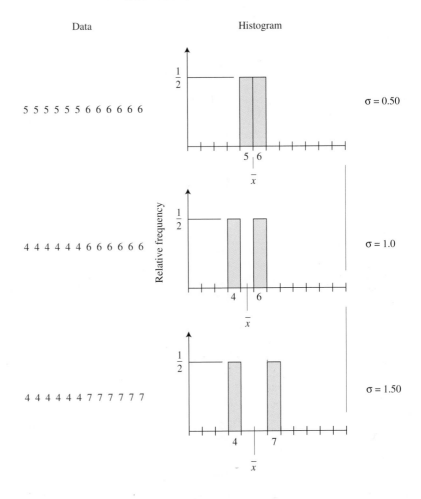

Data

Histogram

5 5 5 5 5 6 6 6 6 6 6

$\sigma = 0.50$

4 4 4 4 4 4 6 6 6 6 6 6

$\sigma = 1.0$

4 4 4 4 4 4 7 7 7 7 7 7

$\sigma = 1.50$

3. Find the mean of the masses in Exercise 2, Problem 1 (page 782).

4. Find the mean of the times in Exercise 2, Problem 2.

5. Find the mean of the prices in Exercise 2, Problem 3.

Weighted Mean

6. A student's grades and the weight of each grade are given in the following table. Find their weighted mean.

	GRADE	WEIGHT
Hour exam	83	5
Hour exam	74	5
Quiz	93	1
Final exam	79	10
Report	88	7

7. A student receives hour-test grades of 86, 92, 68, and 75, a final exam grade of 82, and a project grade of 88. Find the weighted mean, if each hour-test counts for 15% of his grade, the final exam counts for 30% and the project counts for 10%.

Midrange

8. Find the midrange of the grades in Problem 1.
9. Find the midrange of the masses in Problem 2.

The Mode

10. Find the mode of the grades in Problem 1.
11. Find the mode of the masses in Problem 2.
12. Find the mode of the masses in Exercise 2, Problem 1 (page 782).
13. Find the mode of the times in Exercise 2, Problem 2.
14. Find the mode of the prices in Exercise 2, Problem 3.

The Median

15. Find the median of the grades in Problem 1.
16. Find the median of the masses in Problem 2.
17. Find the median of the masses in Exercise 2, Problem 1 (page 782).
18. Find the median of the times in Exercise 2, Problem 2.
19. Find the median of the prices in Exercise 2, Problem 3.

Five-Number Summary

20. Give the 5-number summary for the grades in Problem 1.
21. Give the 5-number summary for the masses in Problem 2.

Boxplot

22. Make a box plot using the results of Problem 20.
23. Make a box plot using the results of Problem 21.

Range

24. Find the range of the grades in Problem 1.
25. Find the range of the masses in Problem 2.

Percentiles

26. Find the quartiles and give the quartile range of the data:

28 39 46 53 69 71 83 94 102 117 126

27. Find the quartiles and give the quartile range of the data:

1.33 2.28 3.59 4.96 5.23 6.89 7.91 8.13 9.44 10.6 11.2 12.3

Variance and Standard Deviation

28. Find the variance and standard deviation of the grades in Problem 1. Assume that these grades are a sample drawn from a larger population.
29. Find the variance and standard deviation of the masses in Problem 2. Assume that these masses are a sample drawn from a larger population.
30. Find the population variance and standard deviation of the masses in Exercise 2, Problem 1 (page 782).
31. Find the population variance and standard deviation of the times in Exercise 2, Problem 2.
32. Find the population variance and standard deviation of the prices in Exercise 2, Problem 3.

Calculator

33. Many calculators, both graphics and nongraphics, have built-in functions for finding the mean, the sample or population variance, and the standard deviation. If you have such a calculator, use it for any of the problems in this exercise.

Computer

34. Most spreadsheet programs can find the mean, the sample or population variance, the standard deviation, counts, and the range. If you have such a program, use it for any of the problems in this exercise.

35. A statistics program for a computer can, of course, do any of the above calculations, and create box plots as well. Use it for any of the problems in this exercise.

36. Many computer algebra systems can compute the mean, standard deviation, variance, and other statistical measures. Check your manual for the proper instructions and use your CAS for any of the problems in this exercise.

26•4

Introduction to Probability

Why do we need probability to learn statistics? In Section 26•3 we learned how to compute certain sample statistics, such as the mean and the standard deviation. Knowing, for example, that the mean height $\bar{x}$ of a sample of students is 1.76 m, we might *infer* that the mean height μ of the entire population is 1.76 m. But how reliable is that number? Is μ equal to 1.76 m *exactly*? We'll see later that we give population parameters such as μ as a *range* of values, say, 1.76 ± 0.015 m, and we state the *probability* that the true mean lies within that range. We might say, for example, that there is a 68% chance that the true value lies within the stated range.

Further, we may report that the sample standard deviation is, say, 0.066 m. What does that mean? Of 1000 students, for example, how many can be expected to have a height falling within one standard deviation of the mean height at that college? We use probability to help us answer questions such as that.

Further, statistics are often used to "prove" many things, and it takes a knowledge of probability to help decide whether the claims are valid or are merely a result of chance.

■ **Example 29:** Suppose that a nurse measures the heights of 14-year-old students in a town located near a chemical plant. Of 100 students measured, she finds 75 students to be shorter than 1.50 m. Parents then claim that this is caused by chemicals in the air, but the company claims that such heights can occur by chance. We cannot resolve this question without a knowledge of probability. ■

We must distinguish between *statistical* probability and *mathematical* probability.

■ **Example 30:** We may toss a die 6000 times and count the number of times that "one" comes up, say 1006 times. We conclude that the chance of tossing a "one" is 1006 out of 6000, or about 1 in 6. This is an example of what is called *statistical* probability.

On the other hand, we may reason, without even tossing the die, that each face has an equal chance of coming up. Since there are six faces, the chance of tossing a "one" is 1 in 6. This is an example of *mathematical probability*. ▬

We first give a brief introduction to mathematical probability and then apply it to statistics.

Probability That a Single Event Will Occur

Suppose that an event A can happen in m ways out of a total of n equally likely ways. The probability $P(A)$ that A will occur is defined as

Probability That a Single Event Will Occur	$$P(A) = \frac{m}{n}$$	**256**

Note that the probability $P(A)$ is a number between 0 and 1. $P(A) = 0$ means that there is no chance that A will occur. $P(A) = 1$ means that it is certain that A will occur. Also note that, if the probability that A will occur is $P(A)$, the probability that A *will not* occur is $1 - P(A)$.

▬ **Example 31:** A bag contains 15 balls, 6 of which are red. Assuming that any ball is as likely to be drawn as any other, the probability of drawing a red ball from the bag is $\frac{6}{15}$ or $\frac{2}{5}$. The probability of drawing a ball that is not red is $\frac{9}{15}$ or $\frac{3}{5}$. ▬

▬ **Example 32:** A nickel and a dime are tossed once each. What is (a) the probability $P(A)$ that both coins will show heads; (b) the probability $P(B)$ that not both coins will show heads?
The possible outcomes of a single toss of each coin are

NICKEL	DIME
Heads	Heads
Heads	Tails
Tails	Heads
Tails	Tails

Thus, there are four equally likely outcomes. For event A (both heads), there is only one favorable outcome (heads, heads). Thus

$$P(A) = \frac{1}{4} = 0.25$$

Event B (that not both coins will show heads) can happen in three ways (HT, TH, and TT). Thus $P(B) = \frac{3}{4} = 0.75$. Or, alternatively,

$$P(B) = 1 - P(A) = 0.75$$ ▬

Probability of Two Events Both Occurring

If $P(A)$ is the probability that A will occur, and $P(B)$ is the probability that B will occur, the probability $P(A, B)$ that *both* A and B will occur is

Probability That Two Events Will Both Occur	$P(A, B) = P(A)P(B)$	**257**

Independent events are those in which the outcome of the first in no way affects the outcome of the second.

The probability that two independent events will both occur is the product of their individual probabilities.

The rule above can be extended as follows:

Probability That Several Events Will All Occur	$P(A, B, C, \ldots) = P(A)P(B)P(C) \cdots$	**258**

The probability that several independent events, A, B, C, . . . , will all occur is the product of the probabilities for each.

■ **Example 33:** What is the probability that in tossing a coin three times all results will be heads?

Solution: Each toss is independent of the others, and the probability of getting a head on a single toss is $\frac{1}{2}$. Thus the probability of three heads being tossed is

$$\left(\frac{1}{2}\right)\left(\frac{1}{2}\right)\left(\frac{1}{2}\right) = \frac{1}{8}$$

or 1 in 8. If we were to make, say, 800 sets of tosses, we would expect to toss three heads about 100 times.   ■

Probability That Either of Two Events Will Occur

If $P(A)$ and $P(B)$ are the probabilities that events A and B will occur, the probability $P(A + B)$ that *either A or B* or both will occur is

Probability That Either of Two Events Will Occur	$P(A + B) = P(A) + P(B) - P(A, B)$	**259**

The probability that either A or B or both will occur is the sum of the individual probabilities for A and B, less the probability that both will occur.

■ **Example 34:** In a certain cup production line, 6% are chipped, 8% are cracked, and 2% are both chipped and cracked. What is the probability that a cup picked at random will be either chipped or cracked, or both?

Solution: If $P(C)$ = probability of being chipped = 0.06

and $\qquad P(S)$ = probability of being cracked = 0.08

and $\qquad P(C, S) = 0.02$, then

$$P(C + S) = 0.06 + 0.08 - 0.02 = 0.12$$

We would thus predict that 12 out of 100 chosen would be chipped or cracked, or both chipped and cracked. ▬

Probability That Two Mutually Exclusive Events Will Occur

Mutually exclusive events A and B are those that cannot both occur at the same time. Thus the probability $P(A, B)$ of both A and B occurring is zero.

▬ **Example 35:** A tossed coin lands either heads or tails. Thus the probability $P(H, T)$ of a single toss being both heads and tails is

$$P(H, T) = 0$$ ▬

Setting $P(A, B) = 0$ in Eq. 259 gives

Probability That Two Mutually Exclusive Events Will Occur	$P(A + B) = P(A) + P(B)$	**260**

The probability that either of two mutually exclusive events will occur in a certain trial is the sum of the two individual probabilities.

We can generalize this to n mutually exclusive events. The probability that one of n mutually exclusive events will occur in a certain trial is the sum of the n individual probabilities.

▬ **Example 36:** In a certain school, 10% of the students have red hair and 20% have black hair. If we select one student at random, what is the probability that this student will have either red or black hair?

Solution: The probability $P(A)$ of having red hair is 0.1 and the probability $P(B)$ of having black hair is 0.2, and the two events (having red hair or having black hair) are mutually exclusive. Thus, the probability $P(A + B)$ that a student will have either red or black hair is

$$P(A + B) = 0.1 + 0.2 = 0.3$$ ▬

Random Variables

In Section 26•1 we defined continuous, discrete, and categorical variables. Now we define a *random* variable.

Suppose there is a process or experiment whose outcome is a real number X. If the process is repeated, then X can assume specific values, each determined by chance, each with a certain probability of occurrence. X is then called a *random variable*.

▬ **Example 37:** The process of rolling a pair of dice once results in a single numerical value X, whose value is determined by chance, but whose value has a definite probability of occurrence. Repeated rollings of the dice may result in other values of X, which can take on the values

$$2, 3, 4, 5, 6, 7, 8, 9, 10, 11, 12$$

Here X is a random variable. ▬

Discrete and Continuous Random Variables

A *discrete* random variable can take on a finite number of variables. Thus the value X obtained by rolling a pair of dice is a discrete random variable.

A *continuous* random variable may have infinitely many values on a continuous scale, with no gaps.

■ **Example 38:** An experiment measuring the temperatures T of major cities at any given hour gives values that are determined by chance, depending on the whims of nature, but each value has a definite probability of occurrence. The random variable T is continuous, because temperatures are read on a continuous scale. ■

Probability Distributions

A probability distribution is sometimes called a *probability density function*, a *relative frequency function*, or a *frequency function*.

If a process or experiment has X different outcomes, where X is a discrete random variable, we say that the probability of a particular outcome is $P(X)$. If we calculate $P(X)$ for each X, we have what is called a *probability distribution*. Such a distribution may be presented as a table, a graph, or a formula.

■ **Example 39:** Make a probability distribution for a single roll of a single die.

Solution: Let X equal the number of the face that turns up and $P(X)$ be the probability that that face will turn up. That is, $P(5)$ is the probability of rolling a five. Since each number has an equal chance of being rolled, we have

X	P(X)
1	$\frac{1}{6}$
2	$\frac{1}{6}$
3	$\frac{1}{6}$
4	$\frac{1}{6}$
5	$\frac{1}{6}$
6	$\frac{1}{6}$

FIGURE 26•9 Probability distribution for the toss of a single die

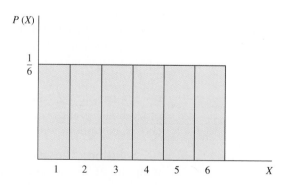

We graph this probability distribution in Figure 26•9. ■

■ **Example 40:** Make a probability distribution for the two-coin toss experiment of Example 32.

Solution: Let X be the number of heads tossed and $P(X)$ be the probability of x heads being tossed. The experiment has four possible outcomes (HH, HT, TH, TT). The outcome $X = 0$ (no heads) can occur in only one way (TT), so the probability $P(0)$ of not tossing a head is one in four, or $\frac{1}{4}$. The probabilities of the other outcomes are found in a similar way. They are:

X	P(X)
0	$\frac{1}{4}$
1	$\frac{1}{2}$
2	$\frac{1}{4}$

which is shown graphically in Figure 26•10.

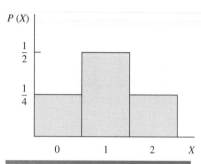

FIGURE 26•10 Probability distribution

Probabilities as Areas on a Probability Distribution

The probability of an event occurring can be associated with a geometric *area* of the probability distribution or relative frequency distribution.

■ **Example 41:** For the distribution in Figure 26•10, each bar has a width of one unit, so the total shaded area is

$$1(\tfrac{1}{4}) + 1(\tfrac{1}{2}) + 1(\tfrac{1}{4}) = 1 \text{ square unit}$$

The bar representing the probability of tossing a "0" has an area of $\frac{1}{4}$, which is equal to the probability that that event will occur. The areas of the other two bars also give the values of their probabilities. ■

Probabilities from a Relative Frequency Histogram

Suppose we were to repeat the two-coin toss experiment or the preceding example a very large number of times, and draw a relative frequency histogram of our results. That relative frequency histogram *would be identical to the probability distribution of Figure 26•10.* The relative frequency of tossing a "0" would be $\frac{1}{4}$, of a "1" would be $\frac{1}{2}$, and of a "2" would be $\frac{1}{4}$.

We thus may think of a probability distribution as being the limiting value of a relative frequency distribution as the number of observations increases, in fact, the distribution for a *population.*

Thus we can obtain probabilities from a relative frequency histogram for a population, or from one obtained using a large number of observations.

■ **Example 42:** For the relative frequency histogram for the population of students' grades (Fig. 26•3, page 779), find the probability that a student chosen at random will have received a grade between 92.45 and 97.45.

Solution: The given grades are represented by the bar having a class midpoint of 95 and a relative frequency of 10%. Since the relative frequency distribution for a population probability is no different from the probability distribution, the grade of a student chosen at random has a 10% chance of falling within that class. ■

Probability of a Variable Falling Between Two Limits

Further, the probability of a variable falling *between two limits* is given by the area of the probability distribution or relative frequency histogram for that variable, between those limits.

■ **Example 43:** Using the relative frequency histogram shown in Figure 26.3 (page 779), find the chance that a student chosen at random will have a grade that falls between 62.5 and 77.5.

Solution: This range spans three classes in Table 26.4, having relative frequencies of 6.7%, 13.3%, and 13.3%. The chance of falling within one of the three is

$$6.7 + 13.3 + 13.3 = 33.3\%$$

so the probability is $\frac{1}{3}$. ■

Think of a sheet of paper on which the distribution is drawn lying face up on the ground during a snowfall. The probability that a snowflake will fall within any region is proportional to the area of that region.

Thus we have shown that the *area between two limits on a probability distribution or a relative frequency histogram for a population is a measure of the probability of a measurement falling within those limits*. This idea will be used again when we compute probabilities from a *continuous* probability distribution such as the normal curve.

Binomial Experiments

A *binomial experiment* is one that can have only two possible outcomes.

■ **Example 44:** Some binomial experiments are:
(a) A tossed coin shows either heads or tails.
(b) A manufactured part is either accepted or rejected.
(c) A voter either chooses Smith for Parliament or does not choose Smith for Parliament. ■

Binomial Probability Formula

We call the occurrence of an event a *success* and the nonoccurrence of that event a *failure*. Let us denote the probability of success of a single trial of a binomial experiment by p. Then the probability of failure, q, must be $(1 - p)$.

■ **Example 45:** If the probability is 80% ($p = 0.8$) that a single part drawn at random from a production line is accepted, then the probability is 20% ($q = 1 - 0.8$) that a part is rejected. ■

There are tables given in statistics books that can be used instead of the formula.

If we repeat a binomial experiment n times, we will have x successes, where

$$x = 0, 1, 2, 3, \ldots, n$$

The probability $P(x)$ of having x successes in n trials is given by

Does this formula look a little familiar? We will soon connect the binomial distribution with what we have already learned about the binomial theorem.

Binomial Probability Formula	$P(x) = \dfrac{n!}{(n - x)! \, x!} \, p^x q^{n-x}$	**262**

■ **Example 46:** For the production line of Example 45, find the probability that of 10 parts taken at random from the line 6 will be acceptable.

Solution: Here, $n = 10$, $x = 6$, and $p = 0.8$, $q = 0.2$, from before. Substituting into the formula gives

$$P(6) = \frac{10!}{(10 - 6)! \, 6!} (0.8)^6 \, (0.2)^{10-6}$$

$$= \frac{10!}{4! \, 6!} (0.8)^6 \, (0.2)^4 = 0.0881$$

or about 9%.

Binomial Distribution

In the preceding example we computed a single probability, that 6 out of 10 parts drawn at random will be acceptable. We can also compute the probabilities of having 0, 1, 2, ..., 10 acceptable parts in a group of ten. If we compute all ten possible probabilities, we will then have a *probability distribution*.

■ **Example 47:** For the production line of Example 45, find the probability that of ten parts taken at random from the line, 0, 1, 2, ..., 10 will be acceptable.

Solution: Computing the probabilities in the same way as in the preceding example (work not shown), we get the following binomial distribution.

x	P(x)
0	0
1	0
2	0.0001
3	0.0008
4	0.0055
5	0.0264
6	0.0881
7	0.2013
8	0.3020
9	0.2684
10	0.1074
Sum	1.0000

This binomial distribution is shown graphically in Figure 26•11.

FIGURE 26•11

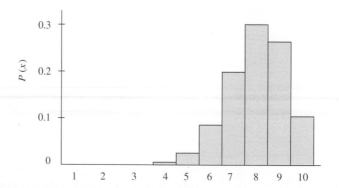

Binomial Distribution Obtained by Binomial Theorem

Refer back to Section 25•6 for a refresher on the binomial theorem.

The *n* values in a binomial distribution for *n* trials may be obtained by using the binomial theorem to expand the binomial

$$(q + p)^n$$

where *p* is the probability of success of a single trial and $q = (1 - p)$ is the probability of failure of a single trial, as before.

━ **Example 48:** Use the binomial theorem, Eq. 245, to obtain the binomial distribution of Example 47.

Solution: We expand $(q + p)^n$ using $q = 0.2, p = 0.8$, and $n = 10$.

$(0.2 + 0.8)^{10}$

$= (0.2)^{10}(0.8)^0 + 10(0.2)^9(0.8)^1 + \dfrac{10(9)}{2!}(0.2)^8(0.8)^2$

$\quad + \dfrac{10(9)(8)}{3!}(0.2)^7(0.8)^3 + \dfrac{10(9)(8)(7)}{4!}(0.2)^6(0.8)^4$

$\quad + \dfrac{10(9)(8)(7)(6)}{5!}(0.2)^5(0.8)^5 + \dfrac{10(9)(8)(7)(6)(5)}{6!}(0.2)^4(0.8)^6$

$\quad + \dfrac{10(9)(8)(7)(6)(5)(4)}{7!}(0.2)^3(0.8)^7 + \dfrac{10(9)(8)(7)(6)(5)(4)(3)}{8!}(0.2)^2(0.8)^8$

$\quad + \dfrac{10(9)(8)(7)(6)(5)(4)(3)(2)}{9!}(0.2)^1(0.8)^9 + \dfrac{10!}{10!}(0.2)^0(0.8)^{10}$

$= 0 + 0 + 0.0001 + 0.0008 + 0.0055 + 0.0264 + 0.0881$

$\quad + 0.2013 + 0.3020 + 0.2684 + 0.1074$

As expected, we get the same values as given by binomial probability formula. ━

Exercise 4 Introduction to Probability

Probability of a Single Event

1. We draw a ball from a bag that contains 8 green balls and 7 blue balls. What is the probability that a ball drawn at random will be green?

2. A card is drawn from a deck containing 13 hearts, 13 diamonds, 13 clubs, and 13 spades. What chance is there that a card drawn at random will be a heart?

3. If we toss four coins, what is the probability of getting two heads and two tails? [*Hint:* This experiment has 16 possible outcomes (HHHH, HHHT,. . . , TTTT).]

4. If we toss four coins, what is the probability of getting one head and three tails?

5. If we throw two dice, what is the probability that their sum will be 9? [*Hint:* List all possible outcomes, (1, 1), (1, 2), and so on, and count those that have a sum of 9.]

6. If two dice are thrown, what is the probability that their sum is 7?

Probability That Several Events Will All Occur

7. A die is rolled twice. What is the probability that both rolls will give a 6?

8. We draw four cards from a deck, replacing each before the next is drawn. What chance is there that all four draws will be a red card?

Probability That Either of Two Events Will Occur

9. At a certain school, 55% of the students have brown hair, 15% have blue eyes, and 7% have both brown hair and blue eyes. What is the probability that a student chosen at random will have either brown hair or blue eyes or both?

10. Find the probability that a card drawn from a deck will be either a "picture" card (jack, queen, or king) or a spade or a spade picture card.

Probability of Mutually Exclusive Events

11. What chance is there of tossing a sum of 7 or 9 when two dice are tossed? You may use your results from Problems 5 and 6 here.

12. On a certain production line, 5% of the parts are underweight and 8% are overweight. What is the probability that one part selected at random is either underweight or overweight?

Probability Distributions

13. For the relative frequency histogram for the population of student's grades (Fig. 26•3, page 779), find the probability that a student chosen at random will have achieved a grade between 67.5 and 72.5.

14. Using the relative frequency histogram of Figure 26•3, find the chance that a student chosen at random will have a grade between 72.5 and 82.5.

Binomial Distribution

A binomial experiment is repeated n times, with a probability p of success on one trial. Find the probability $P(x)$ of x successes, if:

15. $n = 5, p = 0.4, x = 3$
16. $n = 7, p = 0.8, x = 4$
17. $n = 7, p = 0.8, x = 6$
18. $n = 9, p = 0.3, x = 6$

Find all the terms in each probability distribution, and graph.

19. $n = 5, p = 0.8$
20. $n = 6, p = 0.3$

21. What is the probability of tossing 7 heads in 10 tosses of a fair coin?

22. If male and female births are equally likely, what is the probability of five births being all girls?

23. If the probability of producing a defective floppy disk is 0.15, what is the probability of getting 10 bad disks in a sample of 15?

24. A certain multiple-choice test has 20 questions, each of which has four choices, only one of which is correct. If a student were to guess every answer, what is the probability of getting 10 correct?

Computer

25. Any mathematical software that can evaluate factorials and exponents can be used to give values from the binomial probability formula. Some software, however, has the formula built in, and one just has to enter the required information. *Derive*, for example, takes the command

BINOMIAL_DENSITY(k, n, p)

and returns the *k*th value in the binomial distribution having *n* terms and a probability of success of *p*. Some statistical software will give the *entire* distribution. In *Minitab*, for example, the commands

MTB>PDF;
SUBC>BINOMIAL n = 10 p = 0.8

would return the probability distribution for our production line in Example 45. If such software is available, use your computer to find the distributions in Problems 19 and 20.

26·5

The Normal Curve

In the preceding section we showed some discrete probability distributions and studied the binomial distribution, one of the most useful of the discrete distributions. Now we introduce *continuous* probabilities and go on to study the most useful of these, the *normal curve*.

Continuous Probability Distributions

Suppose now that we collect data from a "large" population. Suppose, for example, that we record the age of every mother giving birth to a child in a given year. Since the population is large, we can use very narrow class widths and still have many observations that fall within each class. If we do so, our relative frequency histogram [Fig. 26•12(a)] will have very narrow bars, and our relative frequency polygon [Fig. 26•12(b)] will be practically *a smooth curve*.

We get probabilities from the smooth curve just as we did from the relative frequency histogram. *The probability that an observation will fall between two limits a and b is proportional to the area bounded by the curve and the x axis, between those limits.* Let us designate the total area under the curve as 100% (or $P = 1$). Then the probability of an observation falling between two limits is equal to the area between those two limits.

━━ **Example 49:** Suppose that 40% of the entire area under the curve in Figure 26•12(b) lies between the limits 25 and 30. That means that there is a 40% chance ($P = 0.4$) that one mother chosen at random will be between 25 and 30 years of age.   ━━

Normal Distribution

The frequency distribution for many real-life observations, such as a person's height, is found to have a typical "bell" shape. We have seen that the chance that one observation will fall between two limits is equal to the area under the relative frequency histogram [such as Fig. 26•12(a)] between those limits. But how are we to get those areas for a curve such as Figure 26•12(b)?

(a)

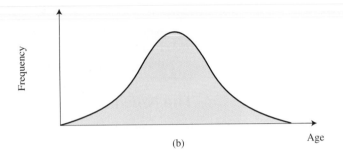

(b)

It is named for Carl Friedrich, the Gauss (1777–1855) whose *Gauss–Seidel method* we studied in Chapter 10. Some consider him to be one of the greatest mathematicians of all time. Many theorems and proofs are named after him.

One way is to make a *mathematical model* of the probability distribution, and from it get the area of any section of the distribution. One such mathematical model is called the *normal distribution*, *normal curve*, or *Gaussian distribution*.

The normal distribution is obtained by plotting the equation

Don't be frightened by this equation. We will not be calculating with it but give it only to show where the normal curve and Table 26•6 come from.

Normal Distribution	$y = \dfrac{1}{\sigma\sqrt{2\pi}}e^{-(x-\mu)^2/(2\sigma^2)}$	**261**

The normal curve (Fig. 26•13) is bell-shaped and is symmetrical about its mean μ. It closely matches many frequency distributions in the real world.

To use the normal curve to determine probabilities, we must know the areas between any given limits. Since the equation of the curve is known, it is possible, by methods too advanced to show here, to compute these areas.

FIGURE 26•13 The normal curve

FIGURE 26•14

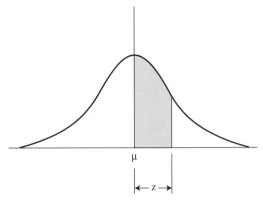

They are given in Table 26•6. The areas are given "within z standard deviations of the mean." This means that each area given is that which lies between the mean and z standard deviations *on one side* of the mean, as shown in Figure 26•14.

The number z is called the *standardized variable*, or *normalized variable*. When used for educational testing it is often called the *standard score*, or *z score*. Since the normal curve is symmetrical about the mean, the given values apply to either the left or the right side.

TABLE 26•6 Areas under the Normal Curve within z Standard Deviations of the Mean

z	AREA	z	AREA
0.1	0.0398	2.1	0.4821
0.2	0.0793	2.2	0.4861
0.3	0.1179	2.3	0.4893
0.4	0.1554	2.4	0.4918
0.5	0.1915	2.5	0.4938
0.6	0.2258	2.6	0.4952
0.7	0.2580	2.7	0.4965
0.8	0.2881	2.8	0.4974
0.9	0.3159	2.9	0.4981
1.0	0.3413	3.0	0.4987
1.1	0.3643	3.1	0.4990
1.2	0.3849	3.2	0.4993
1.3	0.4032	3.3	0.4995
1.4	0.4192	3.4	0.4997
1.5	0.4332	3.5	0.4998
1.6	0.4452	3.6	0.4998
1.7	0.4554	3.7	0.4999
1.8	0.4641	3.8	0.4999
1.9	0.4713	3.9	0.5000
2.0	0.4772	4.0	0.5000

More extensive tables can be found in most statistics books.

■ **Example 50:** Find the area under the normal curve between the following limits: from one standard deviation to the left of the mean, to one standard deviation to the right of the mean.

Solution: From Table 26•6, the area between the mean and one standard deviation is 0.3413. By symmetry, the same area lies to the other side of the mean. The total is thus 2(0.3413), or 0.6826. Thus *about 68% of the area*

under the normal curve lies within one standard deviation of the mean (Fig. 26•13). Thus $100\% - 68\%$, or 32% of the area, lies in the "tails," or 16% in each tail. ▬

▬ **Example 51:** Find the area under the normal curve between 0.8 standard deviation to the left of the mean, to 1.1 standard deviations to the right of the mean (Fig. 26•15).

FIGURE 26•15

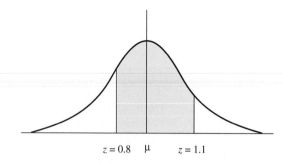

$z = 0.8$ μ $z = 1.1$

Solution: From Table 26•6, the area between the mean and 0.8 standard deviation ($z = 0.8$) is 0.2881. Also, the area between the mean and 1.1 standard deviations ($z = 1.1$) is 0.3643. The combined area is thus

$$0.2881 + 0.3643 = 0.6524$$

or 65.24% of the total area. ▬

▬ **Example 52:** Find the area under the tail of the normal curve to the right of $z = 1.4$ (Fig. 26•16).

FIGURE 26•16

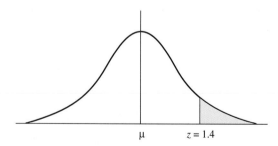

μ $z = 1.4$

Solution: From Table 26•6, the area between the mean and $z = 1.4$ is 0.4192. Since the total area to the right of the mean is $\frac{1}{2}$, the area in the tail is

$$0.5000 - 0.4192 = 0.0808$$

or 8.08% of the total area. ▬

Since, for a normal distribution, the probability that a measurement will fall within a given interval is equal to the area under the normal curve within that interval, we can use the areas to assign probabilities. We must first convert the measurement x to the standard variable z, which tells the number of standard deviations between x and the mean $\bar{x}$. To get the value of z, we simply find the difference between x and $\bar{x}$, and divide that difference by the standard deviation,

$$z = \frac{x - \bar{x}}{s}$$

■ **Example 53:** Suppose that the heights of 2000 students have a mean of 1.76 m with a standard deviation of 0.085 m. Assuming the heights to have a normal distribution, predict the number of students (a) shorter than 1.65 m; (b) taller than 1.78 m; (c) between 1.65 m and 1.78 m.

Solution:

(a) Let us compute z for $x = 1.65$ m. The mean $\bar{x}$ is 1.76 m and the standard deviation s is 3.2, so

$$z = \frac{1.65 - 1.76}{0.085} = -1.294 (-1.3)$$

From Table 26·6, with $z = 1.3$ we read an area of 0.4032. The area in the tail to the left of $z = -1.3$ is thus

$$0.5000 - 0.4032 = 0.0968$$

Thus there is a 9.68% chance that a student will be shorter than 1.65 m. Since there are 2000 students, we predict that

$$9.68\% \text{ of } 2000 \text{ students} = 194 \text{ students}$$

will be within this range.

(b) For a height of 1.78 m, the value of z is

$$z = \frac{1.78 - 1.76}{0.085} = 0.235$$

The area between the mean and $z = 0.235$ interpolates a value of 0.093, so to the right of $z = 0.235$ is

$$0.5000 - 0.0935 = 0.407$$

Since there is a 40.7% chance that a student will be taller than 1.78 m, we predict that 0.407(2000) or 814 students will be within that range.

(c) Since 194 + 814 or 1008 students are either shorter than 1.65 m or taller than 1.78 m, we predict that students will be between these two heights.

■

Since the normal curve is symmetrical about the mean, either a positive or a negative value of z will give the same area. Thus, for compactness, Table 26·6 shows only positive values of z.

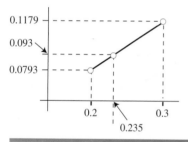

FIGURE 26·17 Interpolation. Table 26·6 gives an area value for $z = 0.2$ and for $z = 0.3$. To find the area value for $z = 0.235$, we can construct a simple graph. This technique is called *interpolation.*

Exercise 5 The Normal Curve

Use Table 26·6 for the following problems.

1. Find the area under the normal curve between the mean and 1.5 standard deviations in Figure 26·18.

2. Find the area under the normal curve between 1.6 standard deviations on both sides of the mean in Figure 26·19.

3. Find the area in the tail of the normal curve to the left of $z = -0.8$ in Figure 26·20.

4. Find the area in the tail of the normal curve to the right of $z = 1.3$ in Figure 26·21.

FIGURE 26•18

FIGURE 26•19

FIGURE 26•20

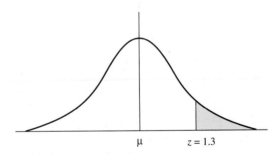

FIGURE 26•21

5. The distribution of the masses of 1000 students at Tech College has a mean of 74.0 kg with a standard deviation of 8.18 kg. Assuming that the masses are normally distributed, predict the number of students who have masses between 60.0 kg and 78.0 kg.

6. For the data of Problem 5, predict the number of students who will have less than 60.0 kg mass.

7. For the data of Problem 5, predict the number of students who will have more than 88.0 kg mass.

8. On a test given to 500 students, the mean grade was 82.6 with a standard deviation of 7.4. Assuming a normal distribution, predict the number of A grades (90 or over).

9. For the test of Problem 8, predict the number of failing grades (59 or less).

10. Computation of the gas consumption of a new car model during a series of trials gives a set of data that is normally distributed with a mean of 8.55 L/100 km and a standard deviation of 0.822 L/100 km. Find the probability that the same car will get at least 7.81 L/100 km on the next trial.

Graphics Calculator and Computer

11. Some graphics calculators will draw the normal curve. Check your manual to see how to do this, if possible. If you can draw the curve, you can then use TRACE to find values on the curve.

12. Some mathematics software has the normal curve built in. In *Derive*, for example, the command

$$\text{NORMAL}(z, -, 1)$$

will return the value of z from $-\infty$ to $+z$, for a normal curve with a mean of 0 and a standard deviation of 1. To get the value of z as measured *from the mean*, as in Table 26•6, we must subtract $\frac{1}{2}$ from the value returned by this command.

26•6 Standard Errors

When we draw a random sample from a population, it is usually to *infer* something about that population. Typically, from our sample we compute a *statistic* (such as the sample mean $\bar{x}$) and use it to infer a population *parameter* (such as the population mean μ).

━━ **Example 54:** A researcher measured the heights of a randomly drawn sample of students at Tech College and calculated the mean height of that sample. It was

$$\text{mean height } \bar{x} = 1.710 \text{ m}$$

From this he inferred that the mean height of the entire population of students at Tech College was

$$(\text{mean height } \mu =) \ 1.710 \text{ m} \qquad \qquad ━━$$

In general,

$$\text{population parameter} \approx \text{sample statistic}$$

How accurate is the population parameter that we find in this way? We know that all measurements are approximate, and we usually give some indication of the accuracy of a measurement. In fact, a population parameter such as the mean height is often given in the form

$$\text{mean height } \mu = 1.710 \pm 0.0061 \text{ m}$$

where ± 0.0061 is called the *standard error* of the mean. In this section we show how to compute the standard error of the mean and the standard error of the standard deviation.

Further, when we give a range of values for a statistic, we know it is possible that another sample can have a mean that lies outside that range. In fact, the true mean itself can lie outside the given range. That is why a statistician will *give the probability* that the true mean falls within the given range.

■ **Example 55:** Using the same example of heights at Tech College, we might say that

$$\text{mean height } \mu = 1.71 \pm 0.0061 \text{ m}$$

with a 68% chance that the mean student height μ falls within the range

$$1.71 - 0.0061 \quad \text{to} \quad 1.71 + 0.0061$$

or from 1.70 m to 1.72 m.   ■

We call the interval 1.71 ± 0.0061 m a *68% confidence interval*. This means that there is a 68% chance that the true population mean falls within the given range. So the complete way to report a population parameter is

$$\text{population parameter} = \text{sample statistic} \pm \text{standard error}$$

within a given confidence interval. We will soon show how to compute this confidence interval, and others as well, but first we must lay some groundwork.

Frequency Distribution of a Statistic

Suppose that you draw a sample of, say, 40 heights from the population of students in your school, and find the mean $\bar{x}$ of those heights, say 1.66 m. Now measure another 40 heights from the same population and find another $\bar{x}$, say 1.76 m. Then repeat, drawing one sample of 40 after another, and for each compute the statistic $\bar{x}$. This collection of $\bar{x}$s now has a frequency distribution of its own (called the $\bar{x}$ distribution) with its own mean and standard deviation.

We now ask: *How is the $\bar{x}$ distribution related to the original distribution?* To answer this we need a statistical theorem called the *central limit theorem*, which we give here without proof.

Standard Error of the Mean

If we were to draw *all possible* samples of size n from a given population, and for each sample compute the mean $\bar{x}$, and then make a frequency distribution of the $\bar{x}$'s, the central limit theorem states that:

1. The mean of the $\bar{x}$ distribution is the same as the mean μ of the population from which the samples were drawn.
2. The standard deviation of the $\bar{x}$ distribution is equal to the standard deviation σ of the population divided by the square root of the sample size n. The standard error of a sampling distribution of a statistic such as $\bar{x}$ is often called its *standard error*. We'll denote the standard error of $\bar{x}$ by $\text{SE}_{\bar{x}}$, so,

$$\text{SE}_{\bar{x}} = \frac{\sigma}{\sqrt{n}}$$

3. For a "large" sample (over 30 or so) the $\bar{x}$ distribution is approximately a normal distribution, even if the population from which the samples were drawn is not a normal distribution.

We will illustrate parts of the central limit theorem with an example.

Example 56: Consider the population of 256 integers from 100 to 355 (Table 26•7). The frequency distribution of these integers [Fig. 26•22(a)] shows that each class has a frequency of 32. We computed the population mean μ by adding all the integers and dividing by 256 and got 227. We also got a population standard deviation σ of 74.

TABLE 26•7

174	230	237	173	214	242	113	177	238	175	303	172	114	179	307	176
190	246	253	189	194	258	129	193	254	191	319	188	130	111	108	103
206	262	269	205	210	274	145	209	270	207	335	204	146	127	124	119
222	278	285	221	226	290	161	225	286	223	351	220	162	143	140	135
300	229	302	228	296	233	298	232	301	239	236	231	304	241	306	240
316	245	318	244	312	249	314	248	317	255	252	247	320	257	322	256
332	261	334	260	328	265	330	264	333	271	268	263	336	273	338	272
348	277	350	276	344	281	346	280	349	287	284	279	352	289	354	288
166	102	109	165	170	234	105	169	110	167	295	164	106	171	299	168
182	118	125	181	186	250	121	185	126	183	311	180	122	187	315	184
198	134	141	197	202	266	137	201	142	199	327	196	138	203	331	200
178	150	157	213	218	282	153	217	158	215	343	212	154	219	347	216
292	101	294	100	297	107	104	235	293	195	323	192	305	115	112	243
308	117	310	116	313	123	120	251	309	211	339	208	321	131	128	259
324	133	326	132	329	139	136	267	325	227	355	224	337	147	144	275
340	149	342	148	345	155	152	283	341	159	156	151	353	163	160	291

FIGURE 26•22

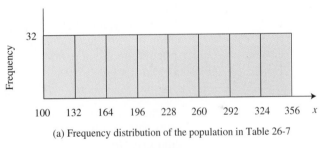

(a) Frequency distribution of the population in Table 26-7

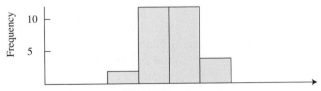

(b) Sampling distribution of the means (frequency distribution of the means of 32 samples drawn from the population in Table 26-7)

The calculations in this example were done by computer, but you will not need a computer to make use of the results of this demonstration.

Then 32 samples of 16 integers each were drawn from the population. For each sample we got the sample mean $\bar{x}$. The 32 values we got for $\bar{x}$ are

234 229 236 235 227 232 229 224 266 230 218 212 234 226 237 216
170 222 220 218 232 247 262 277 265 252 238 225 191 204 216 223

We now make a frequency distribution for the sample means, which is called a *sampling distribution* of the mean [Fig. 26•21(b)]. We further compute the mean of the sample means and get 229, nearly the same value as for the population mean μ. The standard deviation of the sample means is computed to be 20. We see that:

1. The mean of the $\bar{x}$ distribution (229) is approximately equal to the mean μ of the population (227).
2. By the central limit theorem, the standard deviation $SE_{\bar{x}}$ of the $\bar{x}$ distribution is found by dividing σ by the square root of the sample size.

$$SE_{\bar{x}} = \frac{\sigma}{\sqrt{n}} = \frac{74}{\sqrt{16}} = 18.5$$

This compares well with the actual standard deviation of the $\bar{x}$ distribution, which was 20.

We now take the final step and show how to predict the population mean μ from the mean $\bar{x}$ and standard deviation s *of a single sample*. We also give the probability that our prediction is correct.

Predicting μ from a Single Sample

If the standard deviation of the $\bar{x}$ distribution, $SE_{\bar{x}}$, is small, most of the $\bar{x}$s will be near the center μ of the population. Thus a particular $\bar{x}$ has a good chance of being close to μ, and will hence be a good estimator of μ. Conversely, a large $SE_{\bar{x}}$ means that a given $\bar{x}$ will be a poor estimator of μ.

However, since the frequency distribution of the $\bar{x}$s is normal, the chance that a single $\bar{x}$ will lie within one standard deviation of the mean is 68%. Conversely, the mean μ has a 68% chance of lying within one standard deviation of a *single randomly chosen $\bar{x}$*. Thus there is a 68% chance that the true population mean μ falls within the interval

$$\bar{x} \pm SE_{\bar{x}}$$

In this way we can estimate the population mean μ from a *single sample*. Not only that, but we are able to give a range of values within which μ must lie, and give *the probability* that μ will fall within that interval.

There is just one difficulty: To compute the standard error $SE_{\bar{x}}$ by the central limit theorem, we must divide the population standard deviation σ by the square root of the sample size, but σ *is not usually known*. Thus it is common practice to use the sample standard deviation s instead. Thus the standard error of the mean is approximated by the following formula (valid if the population is large).

Standard Error of the Mean $\bar{x}$	$SE_{\bar{x}} = \dfrac{\sigma}{\sqrt{n}} \approx \dfrac{s}{\sqrt{n}}$	**263**

Example 57: For the population of 256 integers (Table 26·7), the central limit theorem says that 68% of the sample means should fall within one standard error of μ, or within the interval 227 ± 18.5. Is this statement correct?

Solution: We count the number of sample means that actually do fall within this interval and get 23, which is 72% of the total number of samples.

■ **Example 58:** One of the 32 samples in Example 56 has a mean of 234 and a standard deviation s of 67. Use these figures to estimate the mean μ of the population.

Solution: Computing the standard error from Eq. 263, with $s = 67$ and $n = 16$, gives

$$\text{SE}_{\bar{x}} \approx \frac{67}{\sqrt{16}} = 17$$

We may then predict that there is a 68% chance that μ will fall within the range

$$\mu = 234 \pm 17$$

We see that the true population mean does fall within that range.   ■

■ **Example 59:** The heights of 64 randomly chosen students at Tech College were measured. The mean $\bar{x}$ was found to be 1.73 m and the standard deviation s was 0.0561 mm. Estimate the mean μ of the entire population of students at Tech College.

Solution: From Eq. 263, with $s = 0.0561$ m and $n = 64$,

$$\text{SE}_{\bar{x}} \approx \frac{s}{\sqrt{n}} = \frac{0.0561 \text{ m}}{\sqrt{64}} = 0.0070$$

We may then state that there is a 68% chance that the mean height μ of all students at Tech College is

$$\mu = 1.73 \pm 0.0070 \text{ m}$$

In other words, the true mean has a 68% chance of falling within the interval

$$1.724 \text{ to } 1.738 \text{ m}$$ ■

Confidence Intervals

The interval 1.724 to 1.738 m found in Example 59 is called the *68% confidence interval*. Similarly, there is a 95% chance that the population mean falls within *two* standard errors of the mean,

$$\mu = \bar{x} \pm 2\text{SE}_{\bar{x}}$$

so we call it the *95% confidence interval*.

■ **Example 60:** For the data of Example 59, find the 95% confidence interval.

Solution: We had found that $\text{SE}_{\bar{x}}$ was 0.0070 m. Thus we may state that μ will lie within the interval

$$1.731 \pm 2(0.0070) \text{ m}$$

or

$$1.731 \pm 0.0140 \text{ m}$$

This is the 95% confidence interval.   ■

We find other confidence intervals in a similar way.

Standard Error of the Standard Deviation

We may compute standard errors for sample statistics other than the mean. The most common is for the standard deviation. The standard error of the standard deviation is called SE_s, and is given by

Standard Error of the Standard Deviation	$SE_s = \dfrac{\sigma}{\sqrt{2n}}$	264

where, again, we use the sample standard deviation s if we don't know σ.

■ **Example 61:** A single sample of size 32 drawn from a population is found to have a standard deviation s of 21.55. Give the population standard deviation σ with a confidence level of 68%.

Solution: From Eq. 264, with $\sigma \approx s = 21.55$ and $n = 32$,

$$SE_s = \frac{21.55}{\sqrt{2(32)}} = 2.69$$

Thus there is a 68% chance that σ falls within the interval

$$21.55 \pm 2.69$$

■

Standard Error of a Proportion

Consider a binomial experiment in which the probability of occurrence (called a *success*) of an event is p and the probability of nonoccurrence (a *failure*) of that event is q (or $1 - p$). For example, for the toss of a die, the probability of success in rolling a 3 is $p = \frac{1}{6}$ and the probability of failure in rolling a 3 is $q = \frac{5}{6}$.

If we threw the die n times, and recorded the proportion of successes, it would be close to, but probably not equal to, p. Suppose we then threw the die another n times and got another proportion, and then another n times, and so on. If we do this enough times, the proportion of successes of our samples would form a normal distribution with a mean equal to p and a standard deviation given by

Standard Error of a Proportion	$SE_p = \sqrt{\dfrac{p(1 - p)}{n}}$	265

■ **Example 62:** Find the 68% confidence interval for rolling a 3 for a die tossed 150 times.

Solution: Using Eq. 265, with $p = \frac{1}{6}$ and $n = 150$

$$SE_p = \sqrt{\frac{\left(\frac{1}{6}\right)\left(\frac{5}{6}\right)}{150}} = 0.030$$

Thus there is a 68% probability that in 150 rolls of a die, the proportion of 3s will lie between $\frac{1}{6} + 0.03$ and $\frac{1}{6} - 0.03$.

■

We can use the proportion of success in a single sample to estimate the proportion of success of an entire population. Since we will not usually know p for the population, we use the proportion of successes found from the sample when computing SE_p.

▬ **Example 63:** In a poll of 152 students at Tech College, 87 said that they would vote for Jones for president of the student union. Estimate the support for Jones among the entire student body.

  Solution: In the sample, $\frac{87}{152} = 0.572$ support Jones. So we estimate that her support among the entire student body is 57.2%. To compute the confidence interval, we need the standard error. With $n = 152$, and using 0.572 as an approximation to p, we get

$$SE_p \approx \sqrt{\frac{0.572(1 - 0.572)}{152}} = 0.040$$

We thus expect that there is a 68% chance that the support for Jones is

$$0.572 \pm 0.040$$

or that she will capture between 53.2% and 61.2% of the vote of the entire student body. ▬

Exercise 6 Standard Errors

1. The heights of 49 randomly chosen students at Tech College were measured. Their mean $\bar{x}$ was found to be 1.765 m and their standard deviation s was 0.0597 m. Estimate the mean μ of the entire population of students at Tech College with a confidence level of 68%.
2. For the data of Problem 1, estimate the population mean with a 95% confidence level.
3. For the data of Problem 1, estimate the population standard deviation with 68% confidence interval.
4. For the data of Problem 1, estimate the population standard deviation with a 95% confidence interval.
5. A single sample of size 32 drawn from a population is found to have a mean of 164 and a standard deviation s of 16.31. Give the population mean with a confidence level of 68%.
6. For the data of Problem 5, estimate the population mean with a 95% confidence interval.
7. For the data of Problem 5, estimate the population standard deviation with a 68% confidence interval.
8. For the data of Problem 5, estimate the population standard deviation with a 95% confidence interval.
9. Find the 68% confidence interval for drawing a heart from a deck of cards, for 200 draws from the deck, replacing the card each time before the next draw.
10. In a survey of 950 viewers, 274 said that they watched a certain program. Estimate the proportion of viewers in the entire population that watched that program, given the 68% confidence interval.

26•7

The subject of statistics usually requires an entire textbook to cover, and SPC is often an entire chapter in such a book, or may take an entire textbook by itself. Obviously we can only scratch the surface here.

Process Control

Statistical Process Control

Statistical process control, or SPC, is perhaps the most important application of statistics for technology students. Process control involves continuous testing of samples from a production line. Any manufactured item will have chance variations in weight, dimensions, color, and so forth. As long as the variations are due only to chance, we say that the process is *in control*.

■ **Example 64:** The diameters of steel balls on a certain production line have harmless chance variations between 1.995 mm and 2.005 mm. The production process is said to be in control. ▬

However, as soon as there is variation because of some cause other than chance, we say that the process is no longer in control.

■ **Example 65:** During a certain week some of the steel balls from the production line of the preceding example were found to have diameters over 2.005. The process was now *out of control*. ▬

One problem of process control is to detect when a process is out of control so that those other causes may be eliminated.

■ **Example 66:** The period during which the process was out of control in the preceding example was found to occur when the factory air conditioning was out of operation during a heat wave. Now the operators are instructed to stop the production line during similar occurrences. ▬

Control Charts

The main tool of SPC is the *control chart*. The idea behind a control chart is simple. We pull samples off a production line at regular time intervals, measure them in some way, and graph those measurements over time. We then establish upper and lower limits between which the sample is acceptable, but outside of which it is not acceptable.

■ **Example 67:** Figure 26•23 shows a control chart for the diameters of samples of steel balls of the preceding examples. One horizontal line shows

FIGURE 26•23 A control chart

FIGURE 26•24

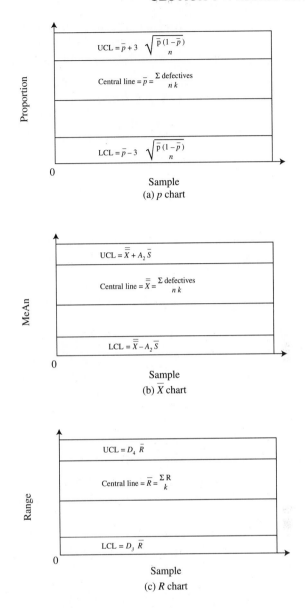

(a) *p* chart

(b) $\overline{X}$ chart

(c) *R* chart

the mean value of the diameter, while the other two give the upper and lower *control limits*. Note that the diameters fluctuate randomly between the control limits until the start of the heat wave, and then go out of control.

To draw a control chart, we must decide what variables we want to measure, and what statistical quantities we want to compute. Then we must calculate the control limits. A sample can be tested for a categorical variable (such as pass/fail) or for a continuous variable (such as the ball diameter). When testing a categorical variable we usually compute the *proportion* of those items that pass. When testing a continuous variable, we usually compute the *mean*, *standard deviation*, or *range*.

We will draw three control charts: one for the proportion of a categorical variable, called a *p chart*, a second for the mean of a continuous variable, called an $\overline{X}$ *chart*, and a third for the range of a continuous variable, called an

R chart. The formulas for computing the central line and the control limits are summarized in Figure 26•24. We will illustrate the construction of each chart with an example.

The p Chart

■ **Example 68:** Make a control chart for the proportion of defective light bulbs coming off a certain production line.

Solution:

1. *Choose a sample size n and the testing frequency.*

Let us choose to test a sample of 1000 bulbs every day for 21 days.

2. *Collect the data. Count the number d of defectives in each sample of 1000. Obtain the proportion defective p for each sample by dividing the number of defectives d by the sample size n.*

The collected data and the proportion defective are given in Table 26•8

TABLE 26•8 Daily Samples of 1000 Light Bulbs per Day for 21 Days

DAY	NUMBER DEFECTIVE	PROPORTION DEFECTIVE
1	63	0.063
2	47	0.047
3	59	0.059
4	82	0.082
5	120	0.120
6	73	0.073
7	58	0.058
8	55	0.055
9	39	0.039
10	99	0.099
11	85	0.085
12	47	0.047
13	46	0.046
14	87	0.087
15	90	0.090
16	67	0.067
17	85	0.085
18	24	0.024
19	77	0.077
20	58	0.058
21	103	0.103
	1464	

3. *Start the control chart by plotting p versus time.*

The proportion defective *p* is plotted daily in Figure 26•25(a).

4. *Compute the average proportion defective p̄ by dividing the total number of defectives for all samples by the total number of items measured.*

FIGURE 26•25

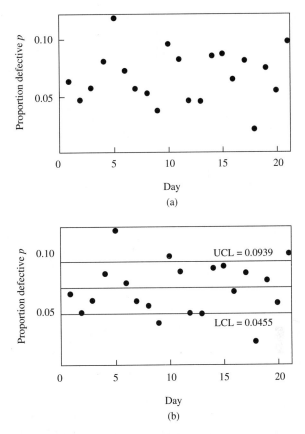

(a)

(b)

The total number of defectives is 1464 and the total number of bulbs tested is $1000(21) = 21\ 000$, so

$$\bar{p} = \frac{1464}{21\ 000} = 0.0697$$

We are assuming here that our sampling distribution is approximately normal.

5. *Compute the standard error SE_p. From Section 26•6, the standard error for a proportion, in which the probability is p of success of a single event is given by Equation 265,*

$$SE_p = \sqrt{\frac{p(1-p)}{n}}$$

Since we do not know p, we use $\bar{p}$ as an estimator for p.

$$SE_p = \sqrt{\frac{\bar{p}(1-\bar{p})}{n}} = \sqrt{\frac{0.0697(1-0.0697)}{1000}} = 0.00805$$

6. *Choose a confidence interval. Recall from Section 26•6 that one standard error will give a 68% confidence interval, two standard errors will give a 95% confidence interval, three standard errors, a 99.7% level, and so forth (Fig. 26•26). Set the control limits at these values.*

If the calculation of the lower limit gives a negative number, then we have no lower control limit.

We will use 3 standard errors, which is the most commonly used interval. Thus,

upper control limit $= \bar{p} + 3SE_p = 0.0697 + 3(0.00805) = 0.0939$

lower control limit $= \bar{p} - 3SE_p = 0.0697 - 3(0.00805) = 0.0455$

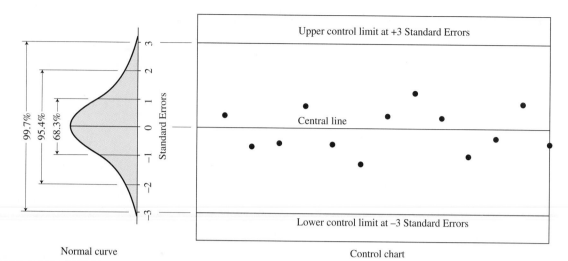

Normal curve   Control chart

FIGURE 26•26 Relationship between the normal curve and the control chart. Note that the upper and lower limits are placed at 3 standard errors from the mean, so that there is a 99.7% chance that a sample will fall between those limits.

The next step would be to *analyze* the finished control chart. We would look for points that are out of control and try to determine their cause. We do not have space here for this discussion, which can be found in any SPC book.

We would also *adjust the control limits*, if in our calculation of the limits we used values that we now see are outside those limits. Since those values are not the result of chance, but are caused by some production problem, they should not be used in calculating the permissible variations due to chance. Thus we would normally recompute the control limits without using those values. We omit that step here.

7. *Draw a horizontal at $\overline{p}$, and upper and lower control limits at $\overline{p} \pm 3SE_p$.* These are shown in the control chart in Figure 26•25(b).

Control Chart for a Continuous Variable

We construct a control chart for a continuous variable in much the same way as for a categorical variable. The variables commonly charted are the mean, and either the range or the standard deviation. The range is usually preferred over the standard deviation because it is simple to calculate, and easier to understand by factory personnel who may not be familiar with statistics. We will now make control charts for the mean and range, commonly called the $\overline{X}$ and R charts.

The $\overline{X}$ and R Charts

We again illustrate the method with an example. As is usually done, we will construct both charts at the same time.

Example 69: Make $\overline{X}$ and R control charts for a sampling of the wattages of the lamps on a production line.

Solution:

1. *Choose a sample size n and the testing frequency.*

Since the measurement of wattage is more time consuming than just simple counting of defectives, let us choose a smaller sample size than before, say 5 bulbs every day for 21 days.

2. *Collect the data.*

We measure the wattage in each sample of 5 bulbs. For each sample we compute the sample mean $\overline{X}$ and the sample range R. These are given in Table 26•9.

TABLE 26•9 Daily Samples of Wattages of 5 Lamps per Day for a Period of 21 Days

DAY	WATTAGE OF FIVE SAMPLES					MEAN X	RANGE R
1	105.6	92.8	92.6	101.5	102.5	99.0	13.02
2	106.2	100.4	106.6	108.3	109.2	106.1	8.79
3	108.6	103.3	101.8	96.0	98.8	101.7	12.58
4	95.5	106.3	106.1	97.8	101.0	101.3	10.78
5	98.4	91.5	106.3	91.6	93.2	96.2	14.81
6	101.9	102.5	94.5	107.7	108.6	103.0	14.06
7	96.7	94.8	106.9	103.4	96.2	99.6	12.15
8	99.3	107.5	94.8	102.1	108.2	102.4	13.32
9	98.0	108.3	94.8	98.6	102.8	100.5	13.47
10	109.3	98.6	92.2	106.7	96.9	100.8	17.09
11	98.8	95.0	99.4	104.8	96.2	98.9	9.71
12	91.2	103.3	95.3	103.2	108.9	100.4	17.67
13	98.5	102.8	106.4	108.6	94.2	102.1	14.41
14	100.8	108.1	104.7	108.6	97.0	103.8	11.58
15	109.0	102.6	90.5	91.3	90.5	96.8	18.58
16	100.0	104.0	99.5	92.9	93.4	98.0	11.06
17	106.3	106.2	107.6	90.4	102.9	102.7	17.17
18	103.4	91.8	105.7	106.9	106.3	102.8	15.15
19	99.7	106.8	99.6	106.6	90.1	100.6	16.67
20	98.4	104.5	94.5	101.7	96.2	99.0	10.03
21	102.2	103.0	90.3	94.0	103.5	98.6	13.19
					Sums	2114	285.3
					Averages	100.7	13.58

3. *Start the control chart by plotting* $\overline{X}$ *and R versus time.*

The mean and range are plotted daily as in Figure 26•27.

4. *Compute the average mean* $\overline{\overline{X}}$ *and the average range* $\overline{R}$*.*

We take the average of the 21 means,

$$\overline{\overline{X}} = \frac{\Sigma \overline{X}}{21} = \frac{2114}{21} = 100.7$$

and the average of the ranges is

$$\overline{R} = \frac{\Sigma R}{21} = \frac{285.3}{21} = 13.58$$

5. *Compute the control limits.*

When making $\overline{X}$ and R charts, we normally do not have the standard deviation to use in computing the control limits. The average range $\overline{R}$, multiplied by a suitable constant, is usually used to give the control limits for both the mean and the range charts. For the mean, the 3-standard-errors control limits are

$$\overline{\overline{X}} \pm A_2 \overline{R}$$

FIGURE 26·27

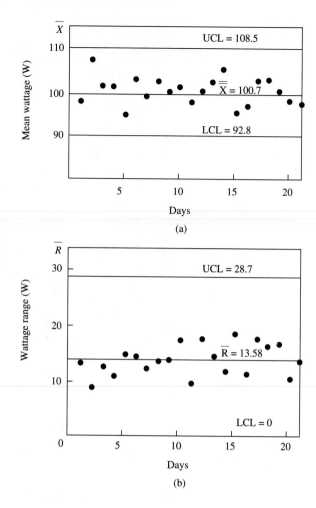

(a)

(b)

where A_2 is a constant depending on sample size, given in Table 26·10. The control limits for the range are

$$D_3\overline{R} \quad \text{and} \quad D_4\overline{R}$$

where D_3 and D_4 are also from the table.

TABLE 26·10 Factors for Computing Control Chart Lines

n	2	3	4	5	6	7	8	9	10
A_2	1.880	1.023	0.729	0.577	0.483	0.419	0.373	0.337	0.308
D_3	0	0	0	0	0	0.076	0.136	0.184	0.223
D_4	3.268	2.574	2.282	2.114	2.004	1.924	1.864	1.816	1.777

Excerpted from the *ASTM Manual on Presentation of Data and Control Chart Analysis.* (1976). For larger sample sizes consult a book on SPC.

For a sample size of 5, $A_2 = 0.577$, so the control limits for the mean are

$$\text{UCL} = 100.7 + 0.577(13.58) = 108.5$$

and

$$LCL = 100.7 - 0.577(13.58) = 92.8$$

Also from the table, $D_3 = 0$ and $D_4 = 2.114$, so the control limits for the range are

$$UCL = 2.114(13.58) = 28.7$$

and

$$LCL = 0(13.58) = 0$$

6. *Draw the central line and the upper and lower control limits.*

These are shown in the control chart [Fig. 26•27(b)].

Exercise 7 Process Control

1. The proportion of defectives for samples of 1000 tennis balls per day for 20 days is as follows:

DAY	NUMBER DEFECTIVE	PROPORTION DEFECTIVE
1	31	0.031
2	28	0.028
3	26	0.026
4	27	0.027
5	30	0.030
6	26	0.026
7	26	0.026
8	27	0.027
9	29	0.029
10	27	0.027
11	27	0.027
12	26	0.026
13	31	0.031
14	30	0.030
15	27	0.027
16	27	0.027
17	25	0.025
18	26	0.026
19	30	0.030
20	28	0.028
	554	

Find the values for the central line, and the upper and lower control limits.

2. Draw a p chart for the data of Problem 1.

3. The proportion of defectives for samples of 500 calculators per day for 20 days is as follows:

DAY	NUMBER DEFECTIVE	PROPORTION DEFECTIVE
1	153	0.306
2	174	0.348
3	139	0.278
4	143	0.286
5	156	0.312
6	135	0.270
7	141	0.282
8	157	0.314
9	125	0.250
10	126	0.252
11	155	0.310
12	174	0.348
13	138	0.276
14	165	0.330
15	144	0.288
16	166	0.332
17	145	0.290
18	153	0.306
19	132	0.264
20	169	0.338
	2990	

Find the values for the central line, and the upper and lower control limits.

4. Draw a p chart for the data of Problem 3.

5. Five pieces of pipe are taken from a production line each day for 20 days, and their lengths are measured. Find the values for the central line, and the upper and lower control limits for the mean.

6. Draw a p chart for the data of Problem 5.

7. Draw an $\overline{X}$ chart for the data of Problem 5.

8. Draw an R chart for the data of Problem 5.

9. Five circuit boards are taken from a production line each day for 20 days, and weighed (grams). Find the values for the central line, and the upper and lower control limits for the mean.

10. Draw a p chart for the data of Problem 9.

11. Draw an $\overline{X}$ chart for the data of Problem 9.

12. Draw an R chart for the data of Problem 9.

Computer

13. Some statistics software for the computer, such as *Minitab*, can be used to draw control charts. One simply enters the raw data and specifies which kind of chart is required, and the program automatically sets the central line and the control limits and draws the chart. Some software will even detect out-of-control or nonrandom behavior in the data. If you have such software, use it to draw any of the control charts in this exercise.

TABLE FOR PROBLEM 5

DAY	MEASUREMENTS OF FIVE SAMPLES (mm)				
1	201.7	184.0	201.3	183.9	192.6
2	184.4	184.2	207.2	194.4	193.1
3	217.2	212.9	198.7	185.1	196.9
4	201.4	201.8	182.5	195.0	215.4
5	214.3	197.2	219.8	219.9	194.5
6	190.9	180.6	181.9	203.6	185.1
7	189.5	209.5	207.6	215.2	200.0
8	182.2	216.4	190.7	189.0	204.2
9	184.9	217.3	185.7	183.0	189.7
10	211.2	194.8	208.6	209.4	183.3
11	197.1	189.5	200.1	197.7	187.9
12	207.1	203.1	218.4	199.3	219.1
13	199.1	207.1	205.8	197.4	189.4
14	198.9	196.1	210.3	210.6	217.0
15	215.2	200.8	205.0	186.6	181.6
16	180.2	216.8	182.5	206.3	191.7
17	219.3	195.1	182.2	207.4	191.9
18	204.0	209.9	196.4	202.3	206.9
19	202.2	216.3	217.8	200.7	215.1
20	185.0	194.1	191.2	186.3	201.6
21	181.6	187.8	188.2	191.7	200.1

TABLE FOR PROBLEM 9

DAY	MEASUREMENTS OF FIVE SAMPLES (grams)				
1	16.7	19.5	11.1	18.8	11.8
2	15.0	14.5	14.5	18.4	11.5
3	14.3	16.5	13.3	14.0	14.4
4	19.3	14.0	14.6	15.0	18.0
5	16.2	13.6	16.8	12.4	16.6
6	14.3	16.7	18.4	18.3	16.5
7	13.5	15.5	13.7	19.8	11.6
8	15.6	12.3	16.8	18.3	11.8
9	13.3	15.4	16.1	17.0	12.2
10	17.6	18.6	12.4	19.9	19.3
11	19.0	12.8	14.7	19.6	15.8
12	12.3	12.2	14.9	15.5	12.9
13	16.3	12.3	18.6	14.0	11.3
14	11.4	15.8	13.9	19.1	10.5
15	12.5	11.4	14.1	12.4	14.9
16	18.1	15.1	19.2	15.2	17.6
17	18.7	13.7	11.0	17.0	12.7
18	11.3	11.5	13.4	13.1	13.9
19	16.6	18.7	12.1	14.7	11.2
20	11.2	10.5	16.2	11.0	16.2
21	12.8	18.7	10.4	16.8	17.1

26·8

The word *regression* was first used in the nineteenth century when these methods were used to determine the extent by which the heights of children of tall or short parents *regressed* or got closer to the mean height of the population.

Glance back at Section 20·7 where we did some curve fitting using logarithmic and semilogarithmic graph paper.

Regression

Curve Fitting

In statistics, *curve fitting*, the fitting of a curve to a set of data points, is called *regression*. The fitting of a straight line to data points is called linear regression, while the fitting of some other curve is called *nonlinear regression*. Fitting a curve to *two* sets of data is called *multiple regression*. We will cover linear regression in this section.

Scatter Plot

We mentioned scatter plots in Section 26·1. A scatter plot is simply a plot of all the data points. It can be made by hand, by graphics calculator, or by computer.

■ **Example 70:** Scatter plots for three sets of data are shown in Figure 26·28. In Figure 26·28(b), the point (6, 7) is called an *outlier*. Such points are usually suspected of being the result of an error, and are sometimes discarded. ▬

Correlation Coefficient

In Figure 26·28 we see that some data are more scattered than others. The *correlation coefficient r* gives a numerical measure of this scattering. For a set of n xy pairs, the correlation coefficient is given by

FIGURE 26·28

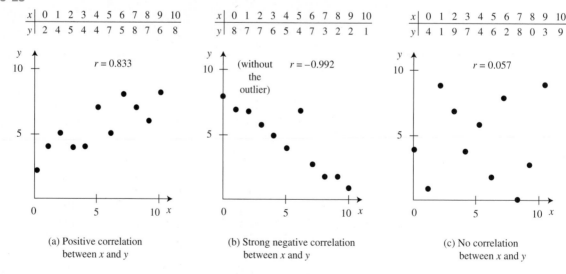

(a) Positive correlation between x and y

(b) Strong negative correlation between x and y

(c) No correlation between x and y

Correlation Coefficient	$r = \dfrac{n\Sigma xy - \Sigma x\,\Sigma y}{\sqrt{n\Sigma x^2 - (\Sigma x)^2}\sqrt{n\Sigma y^2 - (\Sigma y)^2}}$	266

The formula looks complicated, but is really easy to use when doing the computation in table form.

■ **Example 71:** Find the correlation coefficient for the data in Figure 26•28(a).

Solution: We make a table giving x and y, the product of x and y, and the squares of x and of y. We then sum each column.

x	y	xy	x^2	y^2
0	2	0	0	4
1	4	4	1	16
2	5	10	4	25
3	4	12	9	16
4	4	16	16	16
5	7	35	25	49
6	5	30	36	25
7	8	56	49	64
8	7	56	64	49
9	6	54	81	36
10	8	80	100	64
Sums 55	60	353	385	364
Σx	Σy	Σxy	Σx^2	Σy^2

Then, from Eq. 266, with $n = 11$,

$$r = \frac{n\Sigma xy - \Sigma x\,\Sigma y}{\sqrt{n\Sigma x^2 - (\Sigma x)^2}\sqrt{n\Sigma y^2 - (\Sigma y)^2}}$$

$$= \frac{11(353) - 55(60)}{\sqrt{11(385) - (55)^2}\sqrt{11(364) - (60)^2}} = 0.833$$

■

The correlation coefficient can vary from $+1$ (perfect positive correlation) through zero (no correlation) to -1 (perfect negative correlation). For comparison with the data in Figure 26•28(a), the correlation coefficient for the data in (b) and (c) is found to be $r = -0.992$ (after discarding the outlier) and $r = 0.057$, respectively (work not shown).

Linear Regression

In linear regression, the object is to find the constants m and b for the equation of a straight line (Eq. 289)

$$y = mx + b$$

that best fit a given set of data points. The simplest way to do this is to fit a straight line by eye on a scatter plot, and measure the slope and y intercept of that line.

■ **Example 72:** Find, by eye, the equation of the straight line that best fits the following data.

x	1	2	3	4	5	6	7	8
y	3.249	3.522	4.026	4.332	4.900	5.121	5.601	5.898

Solution: We draw a scatter diagram (Fig. 26•29). Then, using a ruler, we draw a line through the data, trying to balance those points above the line

FIGURE 26•29

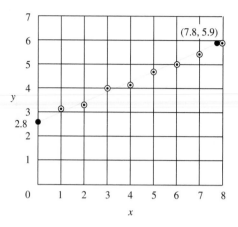

with those below. We then read the y intercept, and the rise of the line in a chosen run.

$$y \text{ intercept } b = 2.8$$

The rise is 3.1 in a run of 7.8, so the slope is

$$(\text{slope } m =) \text{ rise/run} = 3.1/7.8 = 0.40$$

The equation of the fitting line is then

$$y = 0.40x + 2.8$$

Method of Least Squares

Sometimes the points may be too scattered to enable drawing a good-fitting line, or perhaps we desire more accuracy than can be obtained when fitting by eye. Then we may want a method that does not require any manual steps, so that it can be computerized. One such method is the *method of least squares.*

Let us define a *residual* as the vertical distance between a data point and the approximating curve (Fig. 26•30). The method of least squares is a method to fit a straight line to a data set so that *the sum of the squares of the residuals is a minimum,* hence the name "least squares."

With this method, the slope and y intercept of the least-squares-line are given by

We give these equations without proof here. They are derived using calculus.

$\text{Slope } m = \dfrac{n\Sigma xy - \Sigma x\, \Sigma y}{n\Sigma x^2 - (\Sigma x)^2}$	**267**
$y \text{ intercept } b = \dfrac{\Sigma x^2 \Sigma y - \Sigma x\, \Sigma xy}{n\Sigma x^2 - (\Sigma x)^2}$	

FIGURE 26•30 Definition of a residual

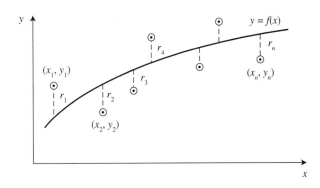

These equations are easy to use, as you will see in the following example.

■ **Example 73:** Repeat Example 72 using the method of least squares.

Solution: We tabulate the given values in Table 26•11.

In the third column of Table 26•11, we tabulate the squares of the abscissas given in column 1, and in the fourth column we list the products of x and y. The sums are given below each column.

TABLE 26•11

x	y	x²	xy
1	3.249	1	3.249
2	3.522	4	7.044
3	4.026	9	12.08
4	4.332	16	17.33
5	4.900	25	24.50
6	5.121	36	30.73
7	5.601	49	39.21
8	5.898	64	47.18
$\Sigma x = 36$	$\Sigma y = 36.649$	$\Sigma x^2 = 204$	$\Sigma xy = 181.3$

This is not the only way to fit a line to a data set, but it is widely regarded as the one that gives the "best fit."

Substituting these sums into Eq. 267, and letting $n = 8$,

$$\text{slope} = \frac{8(181.3) - 36(36.65)}{8(204) - (36)^2} = 0.3904$$

and

$$y \text{ intercept} = \frac{204(36.65) - 36(181.3)}{8(204) - (36)^2} = 2.824$$

which agree well with our graphically obtained values. The equation of our best-fitting line is then

$$y = 0.3904x + 2.824$$

Note the close agreement with the values we obtained by eye, slope $= 0.40$ and y intercept $= 2.8$. ■

Exercise 8 Regression

Correlation Coefficient

Find the correlation coefficient for each set of data:

1.		2.		3.	
−8	−6.238	−20	82.29	−11.0	−65.30
−6.66	−3.709	−18.5	73.15	−9.33	−56.78
−5.33	−0.712	−17.0	68.11	−7.66	−47.26
−4	1.887	−15.6	59.31	−6.00	−37.21
−2.66	4.628	−14.1	53.65	−4.33	−27.90
−1.33	7.416	−12.6	45.90	−2.66	−18.39
0	10.2	−11.2	38.69	−1.00	−9.277
1.33	12.93	−9.73	32.62	0.66	0.081
2.66	15.70	−8.26	24.69	2.33	9.404
4	18.47	−6.8	18.03	4.00	18.93
5.33	21.32	−5.33	11.31	5.66	27.86
6.66	23.94	−3.86	3.981	7.33	37.78
8	26.70	−2.4	−2.968	9.00	46.64
9.33	29.61	−0.93	−9.986	10.6	56.69
10.6	32.35	0.53	−16.92	12.3	64.74
12	35.22	2	−23.86	14.0	75.84

Method of Least Squares

Find the least-squares-line for each set of data:

4. From Problem 1
5. From Problem 2
6. From Problem 3

Graphics Calculator

7. Many graphics calculators can automatically compute the correlation coefficient for a set of data. Check your manual for the proper instructions and use it to solve Problems 1 to 3 in this exercise.
8. Some graphics calculators can graph a least-squares-line for a given set of data, and some can do nonlinear regression. If you have this capability, use it to solve Problems 4 to 6 of this exercise.

Computer

6. Many computer programs, including *Lotus 123*, *Derive*, *Maple*, *Math-Cad*, and *Minitab*, can do all or some of the following: find a correlation coefficient, make scatter plots, find least-squares-lines, do nonlinear regression. If you are able to, use your computer to do any of Problems 1 to 6 in this exercise.

CHAPTER 26 REVIEW PROBLEMS

Label each type of data as continuous, discrete, or categorical.

1. The life of certain radios

2. The number of houses sold each day

3. The colors of the cars at a certain dealership

4. The sales figures for a certain product for the years 1986–1996 are:

YEAR	NUMBER SOLD
1986	1344
1987	1739
1988	2354
1989	2958
1990	3153
1991	3857
1992	3245
1993	4736
1994	4158
1995	5545
1996	6493

Make an *x–y* graph of the sales versus the year.

5. Make a bar graph for the data of problem 4.

6. If we toss three coins, what is the probability of getting one head and two tails?

7. If we throw two dice, what chance is there that their sum is 8?

8. A die is rolled twice. What is the probability that both rolls will give a 2?

9. At a certain factory, 72% of the workers have brown hair, 6% are left-handed, and 3% have both brown hair and are left-handed. What is the probability that a worker chosen at random will have either brown hair or be left-handed or both?

10. What is the probability of tossing a 5 or a 9 when two dice are tossed?

11. Find the area under the normal curve between the mean and 0.5 standard deviation to one side of the mean.

12. Find the area under the normal curve between 1.1 standard deviations on both sides of the mean.

13. Find the area in the tail of the normal curve to the left of $z = 0.4$.

14. Find the area in the tail of the normal curve to the right of $z = 0.3$.

Use the following table of data for Problems 16 to 29.

146	153	183	148	116	127	162	153
168	161	117	153	116	125	173	131
117	183	193	137	188	159	154	112
174	182	144	144	133	167	192	145
162	138	137	154	141	129	137	152

15. Determine the range of the data.

16. Make a frequency distribution using class widths of 5. Show both absolute and relative frequencies.

17. Draw a frequency histogram showing both absolute and relative frequencies.

18. Draw a frequency polygon showing both absolute and relative frequencies.

19. Make a cumulative frequency distribution.

20. Draw a cumulative frequency polygon.

21. Find the mean.

22. Find the median.

23. Find the mode.

24. Find the variance.

25. Find the standard deviation.

26. Predict the population mean with a 68% confidence interval.

27. Predict the population mean with a 95% confidence interval.

28. Predict the population standard deviation with a 68% confidence interval.

29. Predict the population standard deviation with a 95% confidence interval.

30. On a test given to 300 students, the mean grade was 79.3 with a standard deviation of 11.6. Assuming a normal distribution, estimate the number of A grades (90 or over).

31. For the data of Problem 30, estimate the number of failing grades (59 or less).

32. Determine the quartiles and give the quartile range of the data:

118 133 135 143 164 173 179 199 212 216 256

33. Determine the quartiles and give the quartile range of the data:

167 245 327 486 524 639 797 853 974 1136 1162 1183

34. The proportion defective for samples of 700 keyboards per day for 20 days is as follows:

DAY	NUMBER DEFECTIVE	PROPORTION DEFECTIVE
1	123	0.176
2	122	0.175
3	125	0.178
4	93	0.132
5	142	0.203
6	110	0.157
7	98	0.140
8	120	0.172
9	139	0.198
10	142	0.203
11	128	0.183
12	132	0.188
13	92	0.132
14	114	0.163
15	92	0.131
16	105	0.149
17	146	0.208
18	113	0.162
19	122	0.175
20	92	0.131
	2351	

Find the values of the central line and the upper and lower control limits, and make a control chart for the proportion defective.

35. Five castings per day are taken from a production line each day for 21 days, and weighed. Their masses, in grams, are as follows:

DAY	MEASUREMENTS OF FIVE SAMPLES				
1	1134	1168	995	992	1203
2	718	1160	809	432	650
3	971	638	1195	796	690
4	598	619	942	1009	833
5	374	395	382	318	329
6	737	537	692	562	960
7	763	540	738	969	786
8	777	1021	626	786	472
9	1015	1036	1037	1063	1161
10	797	1028	1102	796	536
11	589	987	765	793	481
12	414	751	1020	524	1100
13	900	613	1187	458	661
14	835	957	680	845	1023
15	832	557	915	934	734

DAY	MEASUREMENTS OF FIVE SAMPLES				
16	353	829	808	626	868
17	472	798	381	723	679
18	916	763	599	338	1026
19	331	372	318	304	354
20	482	649	1133	1022	320
21	752	671	419	715	413

Find the values of the central line and the upper and lower control limits, and make a control chart for the mean of the masses.

36. Find the values of the central line and upper and lower control limits, and make a control chart for the range of the masses in Problem 35.

37. Find the correlation coefficient and the least-squares-fit for the following data:

X	Y
5	6.882
11.2	−7.623
17.4	−22.45
23.6	−36.09
29.8	−51.13
36.0	−64.24
42.2	−79.44
48.4	−94.04
54.6	−107.8
60.8	−122.8
67.0	−138.6
73.2	−151.0
79.4	−165.3
85.6	−177.6
91.8	−193.9
98	−208.9

38. For the relative frequency histogram for the population of students' grades (Fig. 26•3), find the probability that a student chosen at random will have received a grade between 72.5 and 87.5.

39. Find the 68% confidence interval for drawing a king from a deck of cards, for 200 draws from the deck, replacing the card each time before the next draw.

40. In a survey of 120 shoppers, 71 said that they preferred Brand A potato chips over Brand B. Estimate the proportion of shoppers in the entire population that would prefer Brand A, given the 68% confidence interval.

41. Give an example of one statistical claim (such as an advertisement, commercial, political message) that you have heard or read lately that has made you skeptical. State your reasons for being suspicious, and point out how the claim could otherwise have been presented to make it more plausible.

Team Project

42. A certain diode has the following characteristics:

VOLTAGE ACROSS DIODE (V)	CURRENT THROUGH DIODE (mA)
0	0
5	2.063
10	5.612
15	10.17
20	15.39
25	21.30
30	27.71
35	34.51
40	42.10
45	49.95
50	58.11

Graph the data using the methods of Section 20•7. Then apply the method of least squares to find the slope and y intercept of the straight line obtained. Using those values, write and graph an equation for the current as a function of the voltage. How does your graphed equation compare with the plot of the original points?

Some of the formulas included in this summary do not appear elsewhere in the text. They are included because we hope that this summary will provide a handy reference, not only for your current course but also for other courses, and for your technical work after graduation. The page number in the right-hand column indicates where the formula or equation is first discussed.

Summary of Facts and Formulas

	No.				Page
ALGEBRAIC LAWS	1	Commutative Law	Addition	$a + b = b + a$	10
	2		Multiplication	$ab = ba$	13
	3	Associative Law	Addition	$a + (b + c) = (a + b) + c = (a + c) + b$	10
	4		Multiplication	$a(bc) = (ab)c = (ac)b = abc$	13
	5	Distributive Law		$a(b + c) = ab + ac$	13
RULES OF SIGNS	6	Addition and Subtraction		$a + (-b) = a - (+b) = a - b$	8
	7			$a + (+b) = a - (-b) = a + b$	9
	8	Multiplication		$(+a)(+b) = (-a)(-b) = +ab$	14
	9			$(+a)(-b) = (-a)(+b) = -(+a)(+b) = -ab$	15
	10	Division		$\dfrac{+a}{+b} = \dfrac{-a}{-b} = -\dfrac{-a}{+b} = -\dfrac{+a}{-b} = \dfrac{a}{b}$	19
	11			$\dfrac{+a}{-b} = \dfrac{-a}{+b} = -\dfrac{-a}{-b} = -\dfrac{a}{b}$	19
PERCENTAGE	12			Amount = base × rate, $A = BP$	41
	13			Percent change $= \dfrac{\text{new value} - \text{original value}}{\text{original value}} \times 100$	43
	14			Percent error $= \dfrac{\text{measured value} - \text{known value}}{\text{known value}} \times 100$	44
	15			Percent concentration of ingredient $A = \dfrac{\text{amount of } A}{\text{amount of mixture}} \times 100$	45
	16			Percent efficiency $= \dfrac{\text{output}}{\text{input}} \times 100$	44

	No.				Page
BINARY NUMBERS	17	Largest n-Bit Binary Number		$2^n - 1$	707
	18	Addition		$0 + 0 = 0$ $0 + 1 = 1$ $1 + 0 = 1$ $1 + 1 = 0$ with carry to next column	
	19	Subtraction		$0 - 0 = 0$ $0 - 1 = 1$ with borrow from next column $1 - 0 = 1$ $1 - 1 = 0$ $10 - 1 = 1$	
	20			Subtracting B from A is equivalent to adding the twos complement of B to A.	
	21	Multiplication		$0 \times 0 = 0$ $0 \times 1 = 0$ $1 \times 0 = 0$ $1 \times 1 = 1$	
	22	Division		$0 \div 0$ is not defined $1 \div 0$ is not defined $0 \div 1 = 0$ $1 \div 1 = 1$	
	23	Complements	n-Bit Ones Complement of x	$(2^n - 1) - x$	
	24			The ones complement of a number can be written by changing the 1s to 0s and the 0s to 1s.	
	25		n-Bit Twos Complement of x	$2^n - x$	
	26			To find the twos complement of a number, first write the ones complement, and add 1.	
	27	Negative Binary Numbers		If M is a positive binary number, then $-M$ is the twos complement of M.	

No.				Page
28		Definition	$a^n = \underbrace{a \cdot a \cdot a \cdot \ldots \cdot a}_{n \text{ factors}}$	65
29		Products	$x^a \cdot x^b = x^{a+b}$	66
30		Quotients	$\dfrac{x^a}{x^b} = x^{a-b} \quad (x \neq 0)$	66
31		Powers	$(x^a)^b = x^{ab} = (x^b)^a$	67
32	Laws of Exponents	Product Raised to a Power	$(xy)^n = x^n \cdot y^n$	67
33		Quotient Raised to a Power	$\left(\dfrac{x}{y}\right)^n = \dfrac{x^n}{y^n} \quad (y \neq 0)$	68
34		Zero Exponent	$x^0 = 1 \quad (x \neq 0)$	69
35		Negative Exponent	$x^{-a} = \dfrac{1}{x^a} \quad (x \neq 0)$	69
36	Fractional Exponents		$a^{1/n} = \sqrt[n]{a}$	364
37			$a^{m/n} = \sqrt[n]{a^m} = \left(\sqrt[n]{a}\right)^m$	364
38		Root of a Product	$\sqrt[n]{ab} = \sqrt[n]{a}\sqrt[n]{b}$	365
39	Rules of Radicals	Root of a Quotient	$\sqrt[n]{\dfrac{a}{b}} = \dfrac{\sqrt[n]{a}}{\sqrt[n]{b}}$	366
40		Root of a Power	$\sqrt[n]{a^m} = \left(\sqrt[n]{a}\right)^m$	
41	Binomials	Difference of Two Squares	$a^2 - b^2 = (a - b)(a + b)$	76
42		Sum of Two Cubes	$a^3 + b^3 = (a + b)(a^2 - ab + b^2)$	232
43		Difference of Two Cubes	$a^3 - b^3 = (a - b)(a^2 + ab + b^2)$	232
44	Trinomials	Test for Factorability	$ax^2 + bx + c$ is factorable if $b^2 - 4ac$ is a perfect square	22
45		Leading Coefficient $= 1$	$x^2 + (a + b)x + ab = (x + a)(x + b)$	76
46		General Quadratic Trinomial	$acx^2 + (ad + bc)x + bd = (ax + b)(cx + d)$	76
47		Perfect Square Trinomials	$a^2 + 2ab + b^2 = (a + b)^2$	77
48			$a^2 - 2ab + b^2 = (a - b)^2$	77
49	Factoring by Grouping		$ac + ad + bc + bd = (a + b)(c + d)$	

Row labels (left vertical headers): EXPONENTS (28–37), RADICALS (38–40), SPECIAL PRODUCTS AND FACTORING (41–49)

	No.				Page
FRACTIONS	50	Simplifying		$\dfrac{ad}{bd} = \dfrac{a}{b}$	240
	51	Multiplication		$\dfrac{a}{b} \cdot \dfrac{c}{d} = \dfrac{ac}{bd}$	243
	52	Division		$\dfrac{a}{b} \div \dfrac{c}{d} = \dfrac{a}{b} \cdot \dfrac{d}{c} = \dfrac{ad}{bc}$	244
	53	Addition and Subtraction	Same Denominators	$\dfrac{a}{b} \pm \dfrac{c}{b} = \dfrac{a \pm c}{b}$	248
	54		Different Denominators	$\dfrac{a}{b} \pm \dfrac{c}{d} = \dfrac{ad}{bd} \pm \dfrac{bc}{bd} = \dfrac{ad \pm bc}{bd}$	250
PROPORTION	55	In the Proportion $a{:}b = c{:}d$	The product of the means equals the product of the extremes.	$ad = bc$	
	56		The extremes may be interchanged.	$d{:}b = c{:}a$	
	57		The means may be interchanged.	$a{:}c = b{:}d$	
	58		The means may be interchanged with the extremes.	$b{:}a = d{:}c$	
	59	Mean Proportional	In the Proportion	$a{:}b = b{:}c$	
			Geometric Mean	$b = \pm\sqrt{ac}$	539
VARIATION	60	$k =$ Constant of Proportionality	Direct	$y \propto x$ or $y = kx$	541
	61		Inverse	$y \propto \dfrac{1}{x}$ or $y = \dfrac{k}{x}$	554
	62		Joint	$y \propto xw$ or $y = kxw$	559

	No.					Page

	No.					Page
SYSTEMS OF LINEAR EQUATIONS	63	Algebraic Solution		$a_1x + b_1y = c_1$ $a_2x + b_2y = c_2$	$x = \dfrac{b_2c_1 - b_1c_2}{a_1b_2 - a_2b_1}$ and $y = \dfrac{a_1c_2 - a_2c_1}{a_1b_2 - a_2b_1}$ where $a_1b_2 - a_2b_1 \neq 0$	289
	64			$a_1x + b_1y + c_1z = k_1$ $a_2x + b_2y + c_2z = k_2$ $a_3x + b_3y + c_3z = k_3$	$x = \dfrac{b_2c_3k_1 + b_1c_2k_3 + b_3c_1k_2 - b_2c_1k_3 - b_3c_2k_1 - b_1c_3k_2}{a_1b_2c_3 + a_3b_1c_2 + a_2b_3c_1 - a_3b_2c_1 - a_1b_3c_2 - a_2b_1c_3}$ $y = \dfrac{a_1c_3k_2 + a_3c_2k_1 + a_2c_1k_3 - a_3c_1k_2 - a_1c_2k_3 - a_2c_3k_1}{a_1b_2c_3 + a_3b_1c_2 + a_2b_3c_1 - a_3b_2c_1 - a_1b_3c_2 - a_2b_1c_3}$ $z = \dfrac{a_1b_2k_3 + a_3b_1k_2 + a_2b_3k_1 - a_3b_2k_1 - a_1b_3k_2 - a_2b_1k_3}{a_1b_2c_3 + a_3b_1c_2 + a_2b_3c_1 - a_3b_2c_1 - a_1b_3c_2 - a_2b_1c_3}$	319
	65	Determinants	Value of a Determinant	Second Order	$\begin{vmatrix} a_1 & b_1 \\ a_2 & b_2 \end{vmatrix} = a_1b_2 - a_2b_1$	309
	66			Third Order	$\begin{vmatrix} a_1 & b_1 & c_1 \\ a_2 & b_2 & c_2 \\ a_3 & b_3 & c_3 \end{vmatrix} = a_1b_2c_3 + a_3b_1c_2 + a_2b_3c_1 -$ $(a_3b_2c_1 + a_1b_3c_2 + a_2b_1c_3)$	315
	67			Minors	The signed minor of element b in the determinant $\begin{vmatrix} a & b & c \\ d & e & f \\ g & h & i \end{vmatrix}$ is $-\begin{vmatrix} d & f \\ g & i \end{vmatrix}$	316
	68				To find the value of a determinant: 1. Choose any row or any column to develop by minors. 2. Write the product of every element in that row or column and its signed minor. 3. Add these products to get the value of the determinant.	317
	69		Cramer's Rule		The solution for any variable is a fraction whose denominator is the determinant of the coefficients, and whose numerator is also the determinant of the coefficients, except that the column of coefficients of the variable being solved for is replaced by the column of constants.	319
	70			Two Equations	$x = \dfrac{\begin{vmatrix} c_1 & b_1 \\ c_2 & b_2 \end{vmatrix}}{\begin{vmatrix} a_1 & b_1 \\ a_2 & b_2 \end{vmatrix}}$ and $y = \dfrac{\begin{vmatrix} a_1 & c_1 \\ a_2 & c_2 \end{vmatrix}}{\begin{vmatrix} a_1 & b_1 \\ a_2 & b_2 \end{vmatrix}}$	311
	71			Three Equations	$x = \dfrac{\begin{vmatrix} k_1 & b_1 & c_1 \\ k_2 & b_2 & c_2 \\ k_3 & b_3 & c_3 \end{vmatrix}}{\Delta}$, $y = \dfrac{\begin{vmatrix} a_1 & k_1 & c_1 \\ a_2 & k_2 & c_2 \\ a_3 & k_3 & c_3 \end{vmatrix}}{\Delta}$, $z = \dfrac{\begin{vmatrix} a_1 & b_1 & k_1 \\ a_2 & b_2 & k_2 \\ a_3 & b_3 & k_3 \end{vmatrix}}{\Delta}$ Where $\Delta = \begin{vmatrix} a_1 & b_1 & c_1 \\ a_2 & b_2 & c_2 \\ a_3 & b_3 & c_3 \end{vmatrix} \neq 0$	318

	No.				Page
SYSTEMS OF LINEAR EQUATIONS (Continued)	72	**Properties of Determinants**	Zero Row or Column	If all elements in a row (or column) are zero, the value of the determinant is zero.	323
	73		Identical Rows or Columns	The value of a determinant is zero if two rows (or columns) are identical.	323
	74		Zeros below the Principal Diagonal	If all elements below the principal diagonal are zeros, then the value of the determinant is the product of the elements along the principal diagonal.	323
	75		Interchanging Rows with Columns	The value of a determinant is unchanged if we change the rows to columns and the columns to rows.	324
	76		Interchange of Rows or Columns	A determinant will change sign when we interchange two rows (or columns).	324
	77		Multiplying by a Constant	If each element in a row (or column) is multiplied by some constant, the value of the determinant is multiplied by that constant.	324
	78		Multiples of One Row or Column Added to Another	The value of a determinant is unchanged when the elements of a row (or column) are multiplied by some factor, and then added to the corresponding elements of another row or column.	325
MATRICES	79	**Addition**	Commutative Law	$A + B = B + A$	338
	80		Associative Law	$A + (B + C) = (A + B) + C$ $= (A + C) + B$	338
	81		Addition and Subtraction	$\begin{pmatrix} a & b \\ c & d \end{pmatrix} + \begin{pmatrix} w & x \\ y & z \end{pmatrix} = \begin{pmatrix} a+w & b+x \\ c+y & d+z \end{pmatrix}$	338
	82	**Multiplication**	Conformable Matrices	The product AB of two matrices A and B is defined only when the number of columns in A equals the number of rows in B.	338
	83		Commutative Law	$AB \neq BA$ Matrix multiplication is *not* commutative.	343
	84		Associative Law	$A(BC) = (AB)C = ABC$	339
	85		Distributive Law	$A(B + C) = AB + AC$	339
	86		Dimensions of the Product	$(m \times p)(p \times n) = (m \times n)$	339
	87		Product of a Scalar and a Matrix	$k\begin{pmatrix} a & b \\ c & d \end{pmatrix} = \begin{pmatrix} ka & kb \\ kc & kd \end{pmatrix}$	338
	88		Scalar Product of a Row Vector and a Column Vector	$(a \quad b \quad \cdots) \begin{pmatrix} x \\ y \\ \cdot \\ \cdot \end{pmatrix} = (ax + by + \cdots)$	340
	89		Tensor Product of a Column Vector and a Row Vector	$(2 \times 1)(1 \times 2) \quad (2 \times 2)$ $\begin{pmatrix} a \\ b \end{pmatrix} \; (x \quad y) = \begin{pmatrix} ax & ay \\ bx & by \end{pmatrix}$	344
	90		Product of a Row Vector and a Matrix	$(1 \times 2) \; (2 \times 3) \qquad (1 \times 3)$ $(a \quad b)\begin{pmatrix} u & v & w \\ x & y & z \end{pmatrix} = (au + bx \quad av + by \quad aw + bz)$	340

		No.			Page
MATRICES (Continued)	Matrix Multiplication (Continued)	91	Product of a Matrix and a Column Vector	$(2 \times 2)(2 \times 1) \quad (2 \times 1)$ $\begin{pmatrix} a & b \\ c & d \end{pmatrix} \begin{pmatrix} x \\ y \end{pmatrix} = \begin{pmatrix} ax + by \\ cx + dy \end{pmatrix}$	343
		92	Product of Two Matrices	$(2 \times 3) \quad (3 \times 2) \qquad (2 \times 2)$ $\begin{pmatrix} a & b & c \\ d & e & f \end{pmatrix} \begin{pmatrix} u & x \\ v & y \\ w & z \end{pmatrix} = \begin{pmatrix} au + bv + cw & ax + by + cz \\ du + ev + fw & dx + ey + fz \end{pmatrix}$	343
		93	Product of a Matrix and Its Inverse	$\mathbf{A}\mathbf{A}^{-1} = \mathbf{A}^{-1}\mathbf{A} = 1$	349
		94	Multiplying by the Unit Matrix	$\mathbf{AI} - \mathbf{IA} = \mathbf{A}$	348
	Solving Systems of Equations	95	Matrix Form for a System of Equations	$\mathbf{AX} = \mathbf{B}$	353
		96	Elementary Transformations of a Matrix	1. Interchange any rows. 2. Multiply a row by a nonzero constant. 3. Add a constant multiple of one row to another row.	350
		97	Unit Matrix Method	When we transform the coefficient matrix **A** into the unit matrix **I**, the column vector **B** gets transformed into the solution set.	334
		98	Solving a Set of Equations Using the Inverse	$\mathbf{X} = \mathbf{A}^{-1}\mathbf{B}$	354
QUADRATICS		99	General Form	$ax^2 + bx + c = 0$	381
		100	Quadratic Formula	$x = \dfrac{-b \pm \sqrt{b^2 - 4ac}}{2a}$	390
		101	The Discriminant	If a, b, and c are real, and: if $b^2 - 4ac > 0$ the roots are real and unequal. if $b^2 - 4ac = 0$ the roots are real and equal. if $b^2 - 4ac < 0$ the roots are not real.	392
		102	Polynomial of Degree n	$a_0 x^n + a_1 x^{n-1} + \cdots + a_{n-1}x + a_n$	404
		103	Factor Theorem	If a polynomial equation $f(x) = 0$ has a root r, then $(x - r)$ is a factor of the polynomial $f(x)$; conversely, if $(x - r)$ is a factor of a polynomial $f(x)$, then r is a root of $f(x) = 0$.	404

	No.				Page
INTERSECTING LINES	104	Opposite angles of two intersecting straight lines are equal.			156
	105	If two parallel straight lines are cut by a transversal, corresponding angles are equal and alternate interior angles are equal.			157
	106	If two lines are cut by a number of parallels, the corresponding segments are proportional.			158
QUADRILATERALS	107		Square	Area $= a^2$	171
	108		Rectangle	Area $= ab$	171
	109		Parallelogram: Diagonals bisect each other	Area $= bh$	171
	110		Rhombus: Diagonals intersect at right angles	Area $= ah$	171
	111		Trapezoid	Area $= \dfrac{(a + b)h}{2}$	171
POLYGON	112	n sides	Sum of Angles $= (n - 2)\,180°$		161
CIRCLES	113		Circumference $= 2\pi r = \pi d$		172
	114		Area $= \pi r^2 = \dfrac{\pi d^2}{4}$		172
	115		Central angle θ (radians) $= \dfrac{s}{r}$		451
	116		Area of sector $= \dfrac{rs}{2} = \dfrac{r^2\theta}{2}$		449
	117		1 revolution $= 2\pi$ radians $= 360°$ $1° = 60$ min 1 min $= 60$ sec		183
	118		The angle between two lines drawn from the two ends of the diameter of a semicircle to any single point on the circumference will be a right angle.		174
	119		Tangents to a Circle	Tangent AP is perpendicular to radius OA.	173
	120			Tangent $AP = $ tangent BP OP bisects angle APB	174
	121		Intersecting Chords	$ab = cd$	173

	No.				Page
SOLIDS	122		Cube	Volume $= a^3$	177
	123			Surface area $= 6a^2$	177
	124		Rectangular Parallel-epiped	Volume $= lwh$	177
	125			Surface area $= 2(lw + hw + lh)$	177
	126		Any Cylinder or Prism	Volume $=$ (area of base)(altitude)	177
	127		Right Cylinder or Prism	Lateral area (not including bases) $=$ (perimeter of base)(altitude)	177
	128		Sphere	Volume $= \dfrac{4}{3}\pi r^3$	177
	129			Surface area $= 4\pi r^2$	177
	130		Any Cone or Pyramid	Volume $= \dfrac{1}{3}$(area of base)(altitude)	177
	131		Right Circular Cone or Regular Pyramid	Lateral area $= \dfrac{1}{2}$(perimeter of base) $\times$ (slant height)	177
	132		Any Cone or Pyramid	Volume $= \dfrac{h}{3}(A_1 + A_2 + \sqrt{A_1A_2})$	177
	133		Right Circular Cone or Regular Pyramid	Lateral area $= \dfrac{s}{2}$(sum of base perimeters) $= \dfrac{s}{2}(P_1 + P_2)$	177
SIMILAR FIGURES	134		Corresponding dimensions of plane or solid similar figures are in proportion.		549
	135		Areas of similar plane or solid figures are proportional to the squares of any two corresponding dimensions.		550
	136		Volumes of similar solid figures are proportional to the cubes of any two corresponding dimensions.		550

	No.				Page
ANY TRIANGLE	137	Areas		$\text{Area} = \dfrac{1}{2}bh$	163
	138			Hero's Formula: $\text{Area} = \sqrt{s(s-a)(s-b)(s-c)}$ where $s = \dfrac{1}{2}(a+b+c)$	163
	139		Sum of the Angles	$A + B + C = 180°$	163
	140		Law of Sines	$\dfrac{a}{\sin A} = \dfrac{b}{\sin B} = \dfrac{c}{\sin C}$	425
	141		Law of Cosines	$a^2 = b^2 + c^2 - 2bc \cos A$ $b^2 = a^2 + c^2 - 2ac \cos B$ $c^2 = a^2 + b^2 - 2ab \cos C$	429
	142		Exterior Angle	$\theta = A + B$	164
SIMILAR TRIANGLES	143	If two angles of a triangle equal two angles of another triangle, the triangles are similar.			164
	144	Corresponding sides of similar triangles are in proportion.			164
RIGHT TRIANGLES	145		Pythagorean Theorem	$a^2 + b^2 = c^2$	165
	146	Trigonometric Ratios	Sine	$\sin \theta = \dfrac{y}{r} = \dfrac{\text{opposite side}}{\text{hypotenuse}}$	187
	147		Cosine	$\cos \theta = \dfrac{x}{r} = \dfrac{\text{adjacent side}}{\text{hypotenuse}}$	187
	148		Tangent	$\tan \theta = \dfrac{y}{x} = \dfrac{\text{opposite side}}{\text{adjacent side}}$	187
	149		Cotangent	$\cot \theta = \dfrac{x}{y} = \dfrac{\text{adjacent side}}{\text{opposite side}}$	187
	150		Secant	$\sec \theta = \dfrac{r}{x} = \dfrac{\text{hypotenuse}}{\text{adjacent side}}$	187
	151		Cosecant	$\csc \theta = \dfrac{r}{y} = \dfrac{\text{hypotenuse}}{\text{opposite side}}$	187
	152	Reciprocal Relations	(a) $\sin \theta = \dfrac{1}{\csc \theta}$ (b) $\cos \theta = \dfrac{1}{\sec \theta}$ (c) $\tan \theta = \dfrac{1}{\cot \theta}$		188
	153		In a right triangle, the altitude to the hypotenuse forms two right triangles which are similar to each other and to the original triangle.		162
	154	A and B Are Complementary Angles	Cofunctions	(a) $\sin A = \cos B$ (b) $\cos A = \sin B$ (c) $\tan A = \cot B$ (d) $\cot A = \tan B$ (e) $\sec A = \csc B$ (f) $\csc A = \sec B$	198
CONGRUENT TRIANGLES	155	Two Triangles Are Congruent If	Two angles and a side of one are equal to two angles and the corresponding side of the other (ASA), (AAS).		162
	156		Two sides and the included angle of one are equal, respectively, to two sides and the included angle of the other (SAS).		164
	157		Three sides of one are equal to the three sides of the other (SSS).		164
COORDINATE SYSTEMS	158		Rectangular	$x = r \cos \theta$	494
	159			$y = r \sin \theta$	494
	160		Polar	$r = \sqrt{x^2 + y^2}$	494
	161			$\theta = \arctan \dfrac{y}{x}$	494

No.			Page

			Page
162	Quotient Relations	$\tan \theta = \dfrac{\sin \theta}{\cos \theta}$	502
163		$\cot \theta = \dfrac{\cos \theta}{\sin \theta}$	502
164	Pythagorean Relations	$\sin^2 \theta + \cos^2 \theta = 1$	503
165		$1 + \tan^2 \theta = \sec^2 \theta$	503
166		$1 + \cot^2 \theta = \csc^2 \theta$	503
167	Sum or Difference of Two Angles	$\sin(\alpha \pm \beta) = \sin \alpha \cos \beta \pm \cos \alpha \sin \beta$	511
168		$\cos(\alpha \pm \beta) = \cos \alpha \cos \beta \mp \sin \alpha \sin \beta$	511
169		$\tan(\alpha \pm \beta) = \dfrac{\tan \alpha \pm \tan \beta}{1 \mp \tan \alpha \tan \beta}$	513
170	Double-Angle Relations	$\sin 2\alpha = 2 \sin \alpha \cos \alpha$	516
171		(a) $\cos 2\alpha = \cos^2 \alpha - \sin^2 \alpha$ (b) $\cos 2\alpha = 1 - 2\sin^2 \alpha$ (c) $\cos 2\alpha = 2\cos^2 \alpha - 1$	516
172		$\tan 2\alpha = \dfrac{2 \tan \alpha}{1 - \tan^2 \alpha}$	517
173	Half-Angle Relations	$\sin \dfrac{\alpha}{2} = \pm \sqrt{\dfrac{1 - \cos \alpha}{2}}$	519
174		$\cos \dfrac{\alpha}{2} = \mp \sqrt{\dfrac{1 + \cos \alpha}{2}}$	520
175		(a) $\tan \dfrac{\alpha}{2} = \dfrac{1 - \cos \alpha}{\sin \alpha}$ (b) $\tan \dfrac{\alpha}{2} = \dfrac{\sin \alpha}{1 + \cos \alpha}$ (c) $\tan \dfrac{\alpha}{2} = \pm \sqrt{\dfrac{1 - \cos \alpha}{1 + \cos \alpha}}$	521
176	Sum or Difference of Two Functions	$\sin \alpha + \sin \beta = 2 \sin \tfrac{1}{2}(\alpha + \beta) \cos \tfrac{1}{2}(\alpha - \beta)$	
177		$\sin \alpha - \sin \beta = 2 \cos \tfrac{1}{2}(\alpha + \beta) \sin \tfrac{1}{2}(\alpha - \beta)$	
178		$\cos \alpha + \cos \beta = 2 \cos \tfrac{1}{2}(\alpha + \beta) \cos \tfrac{1}{2}(\alpha - \beta)$	
179		$\cos \alpha - \cos \beta = 2 \sin \tfrac{1}{2}(\alpha + \beta) \sin \tfrac{1}{2}(\alpha - \beta)$	
180	Product of Two Functions	$\sin \alpha \sin \beta = \tfrac{1}{2}\cos(\alpha - \beta) - \tfrac{1}{2}\cos(\alpha + \beta)$	
181		$\cos \alpha \cos \beta = \tfrac{1}{2}\cos(\alpha - \beta) + \tfrac{1}{2}\cos(\alpha + \beta)$	
182		$\sin \alpha \cos \beta = \tfrac{1}{2}\sin(\alpha + \beta) + \tfrac{1}{2}\sin(\alpha - \beta)$	
183	Inverse Trigonometric Functions	$\theta = \arcsin C = \arctan \dfrac{C}{\sqrt{1 - C^2}}$	192
184		$\theta = \arccos D = \arctan \dfrac{\sqrt{1 - D^2}}{D}$	192

TRIGONOMETRIC IDENTITIES

	No.				Page
LOGARITHMS	185	Definition of e		$\lim\limits_{k \to \infty}\left(1 + \dfrac{1}{k}\right)^{k} = e$	573
	186	Exponential to Logarithmic Form		If $b^{x} = y$, then $x = \log_{b} y$ $(y > 0, b > 0, b \neq 1)$	582
	187	Laws of Logarithms	Products	$\log_{b} MN = \log_{b} M + \log_{b} N$	587
	188		Quotients	$\log_{b} \dfrac{M}{N} = \log_{b} M - \log_{b} N$	588
	189		Powers	$\log_{b} M^{p} = p \log_{b} M$	589
	190		Roots	$\log_{b} \sqrt[q]{M} = \dfrac{1}{q} \log_{b} M$	591
	191		Log of 1	$\log_{b} 1 = 0$	591
	192		Log of the Base	$\log_{b} b = 1$	592
	193	Log of the Base Raised to a Power		$\log_{b} b^{n} = n$	592
	194	Base Raised to a Logarithm of the Same Base		$b^{\log_{b} x} = x$	592
	195	Change of Base		$\log N = \dfrac{\ln N}{\ln 10} \cong \dfrac{\ln N}{2.3026}$	593

No.				Page
196	Power Function		$y = ax^n$	545
197	Exponential Function		$y = a(b)^{nx}$	610
198	Series Approximation		$b^x = 1 + x \ln b + \dfrac{(x \ln b)^2}{2!} + \dfrac{(x \ln b)^3}{3!} + \cdots \qquad (b > 0)$	586
199	Exponential Growth		$y = ae^{nt}$	573
200			Doubling Time or Half-Life $\quad t = \dfrac{\ln 2}{n}$	598
201	Exponential Decay		$y = ae^{-nt}$	574
202	Exponential Growth to an Upper Limit		$y = a(1 - e^{-nt})$	574
203	Time Constant		$T = \dfrac{1}{\text{growth rate } n}$	575
204	Recursion Relation for Exponential Growth		$y_t - By_{t-1}$	577
205	Nonlinear Growth Equation		$y_t = By_{t-1}(1 - y_{t-1})$	577
206	Series Approximations		$e = 2 + \dfrac{1}{2!} + \dfrac{1}{3!} + \dfrac{1}{4!} + \cdots$	580
207			$e^x = 1 + x + \dfrac{x^2}{2!} + \dfrac{x^3}{3!} + \dfrac{x^4}{4!} + \cdots$	581

SOME USEFUL FUNCTIONS

	No.				Page
SOME USEFUL FUNCTIONS (Continued)	208	Logarithmic Function		$y = \log_b x$ $(x > 0, b > 0, b \neq 1)$	584
	209	Series Approximation		$\ln x = 2a + \dfrac{2a^3}{3} + \dfrac{2a^5}{5} + \dfrac{2a^7}{7} + \cdots$ where $a = \dfrac{x-1}{x+1}$	586
	210	Sine Wave of Amplitude a		$y = a \sin(bx + c)$	467
	211			$\text{Period} = \dfrac{360}{b} \text{ deg/cycle} = \dfrac{2\pi}{b} \text{ rad/cycle}$	465
	212			$\text{Frequency} = \dfrac{b}{360} \text{ cycle/deg} = \dfrac{b}{2\pi} \text{ cycle/rad}$	465
	213			$\text{Phase shift} = -\dfrac{c}{b}$	468
	214	Addition of a Sine Wave and a Cosine Wave		$A \sin \omega t + B \cos \omega t = R \sin(\omega t + \phi)$ where $R = \sqrt{A^2 + B^2}$ and $= \phi \arctan \dfrac{B}{A}$	488
	215	Series Approximations		$\sin x = x - \dfrac{x^3}{3!} + \dfrac{x^5}{5!} - \dfrac{x^7}{7!} + \cdots$	1190
	216			$\cos x = 1 - \dfrac{x^2}{2!} + \dfrac{x^4}{4!} - \dfrac{x^6}{6!} + \cdots$	1213

	No.					Page
COMPLEX NUMBERS	217	Powers of j			$j = \sqrt{-1}, j^2 = -1, j^3 = -1, j^4 = 1, j^5 = j$, etc.	619
	218		Rectangular Form		$a + jb$	618
	219			Sums	$(a + jb) + (c + jd) = (a + c) + j(b + d)$	618
	220			Differences	$(a + jb) - (c + jd) = (a - c) + j(b - d)$	618
	221			Products	$(a + jb)(c + jd) = (ac - bd) + j(ad + bc)$	619
	222			Quotients	$\dfrac{a + jb}{c + jd} = \dfrac{ac + bd}{c^2 + d^2} + j\dfrac{bc - ad}{c^2 + d^2}$	621
	223		Trigonometric Form		$a + jb = r(\cos\theta + j\sin\theta)$	625
	224			where	$a = r\cos\theta$	625
	225				$b = r\sin\theta$	625
	226				$r = \sqrt{a^2 + b^2}$	625
	227				$\theta = \arctan\dfrac{b}{a}$	625
	228		Polar Form		$r\underline{/\theta} = a + jb$	625
	229			Products	$r\underline{/\theta} \cdot r'\underline{/\theta'} = rr'\underline{/\theta + \theta'}$	627
	230			Quotients	$r\underline{/\theta} \div r'\underline{/\theta'} = \dfrac{r}{r'}\underline{/\theta - \theta'}$	627
	231			Roots and Powers	DeMoivre's Theorem: $(r\underline{/\theta})^n = r^n\underline{/n\theta}$	628
	232		Exponential Form	Euler's Formula	$re^{j\theta} = r(\cos\theta + j\sin\theta)$	631
	233			Products	$r_1 e^{j\theta_1} \cdot r_2 e^{j\theta_2} = r_1 r_2 e^{j(\theta_1 + \theta_2)}$	632
	234			Quotients	$\dfrac{r_1 e^{j\theta_1}}{r_2 e^{j\theta_2}} = \dfrac{r_1}{r_2} e^{j(\theta_1 - \theta_2)}$	632
	235			Powers and Roots	$(re^{j\theta})^n = r^n e^{jn\theta}$	634

For number 226, the diagram shows:

Imaginary axis (vertical) and Real axis (horizontal), with a vector r at angle θ to point $(a + jb)$, where a is the horizontal component and b is the vertical component.

	No.				Page
PROGRESSIONS	236	**Arithmetic Progression** **Common Difference** $= d$	Recursion Formula	$a_n = a_{n-1} + d$	745
	237		General Term	$a_n = a + (n-1)d$	746
	238		Sum of n Terms	$s_n = \dfrac{n(a + a_n)}{2}$	747
	239			$s_n = \dfrac{n[2a + (n-1)d]}{2}$	747
	240	**Geometric Progression** **Common Ratio** $= r$	Recursion Formula	$a_n = ra_{n-1}$	752
	241		General Term	$a_n = ar^{n-1}$	752
	242		Sum of n Terms	$s_n = \dfrac{a(1 - r^n)}{1 - r}$	753
	243			$s_n = \dfrac{a - ra_n}{1 - r}$	753
	244		Sum to Infinity	$S = \dfrac{a}{1 - r}$ where $|r| < 1$	759
BINOMIAL THEOREM	245	Binomial Expansion		$(a + b)^n = a^n + na^{n-1}b + \dfrac{n(n-1)}{2!}a^{n-2}b^2 + \dfrac{n(n-1)(n-2)}{3!}a^{n-3}b^3 + \cdots + b^n$	763
	246	General Term		$r\text{th term} = \dfrac{n!}{(r-1)!(n-r+1)!}a^{n-r+1}b^{r-1}$	765
	247	**Binomial Series**		$(a + b)^n = a^n + na^{n-1}b + \dfrac{n(n-1)}{2!}a^{n-2}b^2 + \dfrac{n(n-1)(n-2)}{3!}a^{n-3}b^3 + \cdots$ where $|a| > |b|$	768
	248			$(1 + x)^n = 1 + nx + \dfrac{n(n-1)}{2!}x^2 + \dfrac{n(n-1)(n-2)}{3!}x^3 + \cdots$ where $|x| < 1$	768
STATISTICS AND PROBABILITY	249	Measures of Central Tendency	Arithmetic Mean	$\bar{x} = \dfrac{\sum x}{n}$	785
	250		Median	The median of a set of numbers arranged in order of magnitude is the middle value, or the mean of the two middle values.	786
	251		Mode	The mode of a set of numbers is the measurement(s) that occur most often in the set.	786
	252	Measures of Dispersion	Range	The range of a set of numbers is the difference between the largest number and the smallest number in the set.	787
	253		Population Variance σ^2	$\sigma^2 = \dfrac{\sum(x - \bar{x})^2}{n}$	789
	254		Sample Variance s^2	$s^2 = \dfrac{\sum(x - \bar{x})^2}{n - 1}$	789
	255		Standard Deviation s	The standard deviation of a set of numbers is the positive square root of the variance.	791
	256	Probability	Of a Single Event	$P(A) = \dfrac{\text{number of ways in which } A \text{ can happen}}{\text{number of equally likely ways}}$	795
	257		Of Two Events Both Occurring	$P(A, B) = P(A)P(B)$	795
	258		Of Several Events All Occurring	$P(A, B, C, \ldots) = P(A)P(B)P(C)\ldots$	796
	259		Of Either of Two Events Occurring	$P(A + B) = P(A) + P(B) - P(A, B)$	796
	260		Of Two Mutually Exclusive Events Occurring	$P(A + B) = P(A) + P(B)$	797
	261	Gaussian Distribution		$y = \dfrac{1}{\sigma\sqrt{2\pi}}e^{-(x - \mu)^2/2\sigma^2}$	805

No.				Page

STATISTICS AND PROBABILITY (Continued)

No.			Formula	Page
262	Binomial Probability Formula		$P(x) = \dfrac{n!}{(n-x)!\,x!}\, p^x q^{n-x}$	800
263	Standard Error	Of the Mean	$SE_{\bar{x}} = \dfrac{\sigma}{\sqrt{n}} = \dfrac{s}{\sqrt{n}}$	813
264		Of the Standard Deviation	$SE_s = \dfrac{\sigma}{\sqrt{2n}}$	815
265		Of a Proportion	$SE_p = \sqrt{\dfrac{p(1-p)}{n}}$	815
266	Correlation Coefficient		$r = \dfrac{n\sum xy - \sum x \sum y}{\sqrt{n\sum x^2 - (\sum x)^2}\,\sqrt{n\sum y^2 - (\sum y)^2}}$	
267	Least Squares Line		Slope $m = \dfrac{n\sum xy - \sum x \sum y}{n\sum x^2 - (\sum x)^2}$	830
			y intercept $b = \dfrac{\sum x^2 \sum y - \sum x \sum xy}{n\sum x^2 - (\sum x)^2}$	830

BOOLEAN ALGEBRA AND SETS — Boolean Operators

No.		Truth Table	Venn Diagram	Switch Diagram	Logic Gate	
268	AND	$\begin{array}{ccc} A & B & A\cdot B \\ 0 & 0 & 0 \\ 0 & 1 & 0 \\ 1 & 0 & 0 \\ 1 & 1 & 1 \end{array}$	Intersection $A \cap B = \{x : x \in A, x \in B\}$	In Series	AND Gate AB	
269	OR	$\begin{array}{ccc} A & B & A+B \\ 0 & 0 & 0 \\ 0 & 1 & 1 \\ 1 & 0 & 1 \\ 1 & 1 & 1 \end{array}$	Union $A \cup B = \{x : x \in A \text{ or } x \in B\}$	In Parallel	OR Gate $A+B$	
270	NOT	$\begin{array}{cc} A & \overline{A} \\ 0 & 1 \\ 1 & 0 \end{array}$	Complement $A^c = \{x : x \in U, x \in A\}$		Inverter $\overline{A}$	
271	Exclusive OR	$\begin{array}{ccc} A & B & A \oplus B \\ 0 & 0 & 0 \\ 0 & 1 & 1 \\ 1 & 0 & 1 \\ 1 & 1 & 0 \end{array}$	$A \oplus B = \{x : x \in A \text{ or } x \in B, x \in A \cap B\}$		Exclusive OR Gate $A \oplus B$	

No.			AND	OR	Page
272		Commutative Laws	(a) $AB \equiv BA$	(b) $A + B \equiv B + A$	
273		Boundedness Laws	(a) $A \cdot 0 \equiv 0$	(b) $A + 1 \equiv 1$	
274		Identity Laws	(a) $A \cdot 1 \equiv A$	(b) $A + 0 \equiv A$	
275		Idempotent Laws	(a) $AA \equiv A$	(b) $A + A \equiv A$	
276		Complement Laws	(a) $A \cdot \overline{A} \equiv 0$	(b) $A + \overline{A} \equiv 1$	
277		Associative Laws	(a) $A(BC) \equiv (AB)C$	(b) $A + (B + C) \equiv (A + B) + C$	
278		Distributive Laws	(a) $A(B + C) \equiv AB + AC$	(b) $A + BC \equiv (A + B)(A + C)$	
279			(a) $A(\overline{A} + B) \equiv AB$	(b) $A + \overline{A} \cdot B \equiv A + B$	
280		Absorption Laws	(a) $A(A + B) \equiv A$	(b) $A + (AB) \equiv A$	
281		DeMorgan's Laws	(a) $\overline{A \cdot B} \equiv \overline{A} + \overline{B}$	(b) $\overline{A + B} \equiv \overline{A} \cdot \overline{B}$	
282		Involution Law	$\overline{\overline{A}} \equiv A$		

BOOLEAN ALGEBRA AND SETS (Continued)

Laws of Boolean Algebra

	No.					Page
	283		Distance Formula		$d = \sqrt{(\Delta x)^2 + (\Delta y)^2} = \sqrt{(x_2 - x_1)^2 + (y_2 - y_1)^2}$	648
	284		Slope m		$m = \dfrac{\text{rise}}{\text{run}} = \dfrac{\Delta y}{\Delta x} = \dfrac{y_2 - y_1}{x_2 - x_1}$	140
	285				$m = \tan(\text{angle of inclination}) = \tan\theta$ $0 \le \theta < 180°$	649
THE STRAIGHT LINE	286		Equation of Straight Line	General Form	$Ax + By + C = 0$	654
	287			Parallel to x Axis	$y = b$	656
	288			Parallel to y Axis	$x = a$	656
	289			Slope-Intercept Form	$y = mx + b$	142
	290			Two-Point Form	$\dfrac{y - y_1}{x - x_1} = \dfrac{y_2 - y_1}{x_2 - x_1}$	656
	291			Point-Slope Form	$m = \dfrac{y - y_1}{x - x_1}$	645
	292			Intercept Form	$\dfrac{x}{a} + \dfrac{y}{b} = 1$	
	293			Polar Form	$r\cos(\theta - \beta) = p$	
	294		If L_1 and L_2 are parallel, then		$m_1 = m_2$	650
	295		If L_1 and L_2 are perpendicular, then		$m_1 = \dfrac{1}{m_2}$	650
	296		Angle of Intersection		$\tan\phi = \dfrac{m_2 - m_1}{1 + m_1 m_2}$	651
CONIC SECTIONS	297	Any Conic	General Second-Degree Equation		$Ax^2 + Bxy + Cy^2 + Dx + Ey + F = 0$	665
	298		Translation of Axes		To translate or shift the axes of a curve to the left by a distance h and downward by a distance k, replace x by $(x - h)$ and y by $(y - k)$ in the equation of the curve.	665
	299		Eccentricity		$e = \dfrac{\cos\beta}{\cos\alpha}$	
	300				$e = 0$ for the Circle $0 < e < 1$ for the Ellipse $e = 1$ for the Parabola $e > 1$ for the Hyperbola	
	301		Definition of a Conic		$PF = e \cdot PD$	
	302		Polar Equation for the Conics		$r = \dfrac{ke}{1 - e\cos\theta}$	

	No.				Page
CONIC SECTIONS (Continued)	303	Circle of Radius r	A circle is a plane curve all points of which are at a fixed distance (the radius) from a fixed point (the center).		663
	304			Standard Form	$x^2 + y^2 = r^2$	664
	305				$(x - h)^2 + (y - k)^2 = r^2$	664
	306		General Form		$x^2 + y^2 + Dx + Ey + F = 0$	665
	307	Parabola	A parabola is the set of points (P) in a plane, each of which is equidistant from a fixed point, the focus (F), and a fixed line, the directrix (D). $$PF = PD$$		671
	308			Standard Form	$y^2 = 4px$	672
	309				$x^2 = 4py$	673
	310				$(y - k)^2 = 4p(x - h)$	674
	311				$(x - h)^2 = 4p(y - k)$	674
	312		General Form		$Cy^2 + Dx + Ey + F = 0$ or $Ax^2 + Dx + Ey + F = 0$	675
	313		Focal Width		$L = |4p|$	674
	314		Area			Area $= \dfrac{2}{3} ab$	

	No.			Page
CONIC SECTIONS (Continued)	315	Ellipse	An ellipse is the set of all points in a plane such that the sum of the distances from each point (P) on the ellipse to two fixed points (F and F') called the foci is constant. $$PF + PF' = 2a$$	681
	316		Standard Form	$$\frac{x^2}{a^2} + \frac{y^2}{b^2} = 1$$ $$a > b$$	684
	317			$$\frac{y^2}{a^2} + \frac{x^2}{b^2} = 1$$ $$a > b$$	685
	318			$$\frac{(x - h)^2}{a^2} + \frac{(y - k)^2}{b^2} = 1$$ $$a > b$$	686
	319			$$\frac{(y - k)^2}{a^2} + \frac{(x - h)^2}{b^2} = 1$$ $$a > b$$	686
	320		General Form	$Ax^2 + Cy^2 + Dx + Ey + F = 0$ $A \neq C$, but has the same sign	687
	321		Distance from Center to Focus	$c = \sqrt{a^2 - b^2}$	675
	322		Focal Width	$L = \dfrac{2b^2}{a}$	689
	323			Eccentricity $e = \dfrac{a}{b} = \dfrac{c}{a}$	
	324		Area $= \pi ab$		

No.				Page
325			A hyperbola is the set of all points in a plane such that the distances from each point (P) to two fixed points (F' and F) called the foci have a constant difference. $$PF' - PF = 2a$$	691
326			$$\dfrac{x^2}{a^2} - \dfrac{y^2}{b^2} = 1$$	693
327		Standard Form	$$\dfrac{y^2}{a^2} - \dfrac{x^2}{b^2} = 1$$	693
328			$$\dfrac{(x - h)^2}{a^2} - \dfrac{(y - k)^2}{b^2} = 1$$	697
329			$$\dfrac{(y - k)^2}{a^2} - \dfrac{(x - h)^2}{b^2} = 1$$	697
330		General Form	$$Ax^2 + Cy^2 + Dx + Ey + F = 0$$ $A \neq C$, but has the opposite sign	698
331		Distance from Center to Focus	$$c = \sqrt{a^2 - b^2}$$	694
332		Slope of Asymptotes	Transverse Axis Horizontal — Slope $= \pm\dfrac{b}{a}$	694
333			Transverse Axis Vertical — Slope $= \pm\dfrac{a}{b}$	694
334		Length of Latus Rectum	$$L = \dfrac{2b^2}{a}$$	
335			Axes Rotated 45°: $$xy = k$$	699

CONIC SECTIONS (Continued) — Hyperbola

		No.			Page
DIFFERENTIAL CALCULUS		336	Limit Notation	$\lim\limits_{x \to a} f(x) = L$	759
		337	Increments	$\Delta x = x_2 - x_1, \Delta y = y_2 - y_1$	647
		338	Definition of the Derivative	$\dfrac{dy}{dx} = \lim\limits_{\Delta x \to 0} \dfrac{\Delta y}{\Delta x} = \lim\limits_{\Delta x \to 0} \dfrac{f(x + \Delta x) - f(x)}{\Delta x}$ $= \lim\limits_{\Delta x \to 0} \dfrac{(y + \Delta y) - y}{\Delta x}$	847
		339	The Chain Rule	$\dfrac{dy}{dx} = \dfrac{dy}{du} \cdot \dfrac{du}{dx}$	864
	Rules for Derivatives	340	Of a Constant	$\dfrac{d(c)}{dx} = 0$	857
		341	Of a Power Function	$\dfrac{d}{dx} x^n = n x^{n-1}$	876
		342	Of a Constant Times a Function	$\dfrac{d(cu)}{dx} = c \dfrac{du}{dx}$	870
		343	Of a Constant Times a Power of x	$\dfrac{d}{dx} cx^n = cn x^{n-1}$	857
		344	Of a Sum	$\dfrac{d}{dx}(u + v + w) = \dfrac{du}{dx} + \dfrac{dv}{dx} + \dfrac{dw}{dx}$	860
		345	Of a Function Raised to a Power	$\dfrac{d(cu^n)}{dx} = cn u^{n-1} \dfrac{du}{dx}$	864
		346	Of a Product	$\dfrac{d(uv)}{dx} = u \dfrac{dv}{dx} + v \dfrac{du}{dx}$	868
		347	Of a Product of Three Factors	$\dfrac{d(uvw)}{dx} = uv \dfrac{dw}{dx} + uw \dfrac{dv}{dx} + vw \dfrac{du}{dx}$	869
		348	Of a Product of n Factors	The derivative is an expression of n terms, each term being the product of $n - 1$ of the factors and the derivative of the other factor.	869
		349	Of a Quotient	$\dfrac{d}{dx}\left(\dfrac{u}{v}\right) = \dfrac{v \dfrac{du}{dx} - u \dfrac{dv}{dx}}{v^2}$	870

No.				Page
350		Of the Trigonometric Functions	$$\dfrac{d(\sin u)}{dx} = \cos u\,\dfrac{du}{dx}$$	1045
351			$$\dfrac{d(\cos u)}{dx} = -\sin u\,\dfrac{du}{dx}$$	1041
352			$$\dfrac{d(\tan u)}{dx} = \sec^2 u\,\dfrac{du}{dx}$$	1044
353			$$\dfrac{d(\cot u)}{dx} = -\csc^2 u\,\dfrac{du}{dx}$$	1045
354			$$\dfrac{d(\sec u)}{dx} = \sec u \tan u\,\dfrac{du}{dx}$$	1045
355			$$\dfrac{d(\csc u)}{dx} = -\csc u \cot u\,\dfrac{du}{dx}$$	1045
356	Rules for Derivatives (Continued)	Of the Inverse Trigonometric Functions	$$\dfrac{d(\sin^{-1} u)}{dx} = \dfrac{1}{\sqrt{1-u^2}}\dfrac{du}{dx} \qquad -1 < u < 1$$	1048
357			$$\dfrac{d(\cos^{-1} u)}{dx} = \dfrac{-1}{\sqrt{1-u^2}}\dfrac{du}{dx} \qquad -1 < u < 1$$	1048
358			$$\dfrac{d(\tan^{-1} u)}{dx} = \dfrac{1}{1+u^2}\left(\dfrac{du}{dx}\right)$$	1048
359			$$\dfrac{d(\cot^{-1} u)}{dx} = \dfrac{-1}{1+u^2}\left(\dfrac{du}{dx}\right)$$	1048
360			$$\dfrac{d(\sec^{-1} u)}{dx} = \dfrac{1}{u\sqrt{u^2-1}}\left(\dfrac{du}{dx}\right) \qquad |u| > 1$$	1048
361			$$\dfrac{d(\csc^{-1} u)}{dx} = \dfrac{-1}{u\sqrt{u^2-1}}\left(\dfrac{du}{dx}\right) \qquad |u| > 1$$	1048
362		Of Logarithmic and Exponential Functions	(a) $\dfrac{d}{dx}(\log_b u) = \dfrac{1}{u}\log_b e\,\dfrac{du}{dx}$ (b) $\dfrac{d}{dx}(\log_b u) = \dfrac{1}{u \ln b}\left(\dfrac{du}{dx}\right)$	1051
363			$$\dfrac{d}{dx}(\ln u) = \dfrac{1}{u}\left(\dfrac{du}{dx}\right)$$	951
364			$$\dfrac{d}{dx}\,b^u = b^u\,\dfrac{du}{dx}\ln b$$	1056
365			$$\dfrac{d}{dx}\,e^u = e^u\,\dfrac{du}{dx}$$	1057
366	Graphical Applications	Maximum and Minimum Points	To find maximum and minimum points (and other stationary points) set the first derivative equal to zero and solve for x.	891
367		First-Derivative Test	The first derivative is negative to the left of, and positive to the right of, a minimum point. The reverse is true for a maximum point.	892
368		Second-Derivative Test	If the first derivative at some point is zero, then, if the second derivative is 1. positive, the point is a minimum. 2. negative, the point is a maximum. 3. zero, the test fails.	892
369		Ordinate Test	Find y a small distance to either side of the point to be tested. If y is greater there, we have a minimum; if less, we have a maximum.	892
370		Inflection Points	To find points of inflection, set the second derivative to zero and solve for x. Test by seeing whether the second derivative changes sign a small distance to either side of the point.	855
371		Newton's Method	$$x_{n+1} = x_n - \dfrac{f(x_n)}{f'(x_n)}$$	905
372	Differentials	Differential of y	$$dy = f'(x)\,dx$$	877
373		Approximations Using Differentials	$$\Delta y \cong \dfrac{dy}{dx}\,\Delta x$$	850

DIFFERENTIAL CALCULUS (Continued)

	No.				Page
DIFFERENTIAL CALCULUS (Continued)	374	**The Definite Integral**	The Indefinite Integral	$$\int F'(x)\,dx = F(x) + C$$	940
	375			$$\int f(x)\,dx = F(x) + C \quad \text{where } f(x) = F'(x)$$	941
	376		The Fundamental Theorem	$$\int_a^b f(x)\,dx = F(b) - F(a)$$	961
	377		Properties of the Definite Integral	$$\int_a^b c\,f(x)\,dx = c\int_a^b f(x)\,dx$$	
	378			$$\int_a^b [f(x) + g(x)]\,dx = \int_a^b f(x)\,dx + \int_a^b g(x)\,dx$$	
	379			$$\int_a^b f(x)\,dx = -\int_b^a f(x)\,dx$$	
	380			$$\int_a^b f(x)\,dx = \int_a^c f(x)\,dx + \int_c^b f(x)\,dx$$	
	381	**Approximate Area under a Curve**	Midpoint Method	$$A \cong \sum_{i=1}^n f(x_i^*)\,\Delta x$$ where $f(x_i^*)$ is the height of the ith panel at its midpoint	966
	382		Average Ordinate Method	$$A \cong y_{\text{avg}}\,(b - a)$$	1092
	383		Trapezoid Rule	With unequal spacing $$A \cong \frac{1}{2}[(x_1 - x_0)(y_1 + y_0) + (x_2 - x_1)(y_2 - y_1) + \cdots + (x_n - x_{n-1})(y_n + y_{n-1})]$$	1092
	384			With equal spacing, $h = x_1 - x_0$: $$A \cong h\left[\frac{1}{2}(y_0 - y_n) + y_1 + y_2 + \cdots + y_{n-1}\right]$$	1092
	385		Prismoidal Formula	$$A = \frac{h}{3}(y_0 + 4y_1 + y_2)$$	1094
	386		Simpson's Rule	$$A \cong \frac{h}{3}(y_0 + 4y_1 + 2y_2 + 4y_3 + \cdots + 4y_{n-1} + y_n)$$	1095
	387	**Exact Area under a Curve**	Defined by Riemann Sums	$$A = \lim_{\Delta x \to 0} \sum_{i=1}^n f(x_i^*)\,\Delta x = \int_a^b f(x)\,dx$$	969
	388		By Integration	$$A = \int_a^b f(x)\,dx = F(b) - F(a)$$	971
	389		Area between Two Curves	$$A = \int_a^b [f(x) - g(x)]\,dx$$	

No.					Page
390		Disk Method		Volume $= dV = \pi r^2\, dh$	
391		Disk Method		$V = \pi \int_a^b r^2\, dh$	995
392		Ring Method		$dV = \pi\, (r_o^2 - r_i^2)\, dh$	
393		Ring Method		$V = \pi \int_a^b (r_o^2 - r_i^2)\, dh$	998
394		Shell Method		$dV = 2\pi\, rh\, dr$	1031
395		Shell Method		$V = 2\pi \int_a^b rh\, dr$	997

APPLICATIONS OF THE DEFINITE INTEGRAL

Volumes of Solids of Revolution

No.					Page
396(a)	Length of Arc		Rectilinear Form	$s = \int_a^b \sqrt{1 + \left(\dfrac{dy}{dx}\right)^2}\, dx$	1005
396(b)			Polar Form $r = f(\theta)$	$L = \int_a^b \sqrt{r^2 + \left(\dfrac{dr}{d\theta}\right)^2}$	1005
396(c)			Parametric Form	$L = \int_{t_1}^{t_2} \sqrt{\left(\dfrac{dx}{dt}\right)^2 + \left(\dfrac{dy}{dt}\right)^2}$	1005
397			Rectilinear Form	$s = \int_c^d \sqrt{1 + \left(\dfrac{dx}{dy}\right)^2}\, dy$	1006
398	Surface Area		About x Axis: $S = 2\pi \int_a^b y\sqrt{1 + \left(\dfrac{dy}{dx}\right)^2}\, dx$		1009
399			About y Axis: $S = 2\pi \int_a^b x\sqrt{1 + \left(\dfrac{dy}{dx}\right)^2}\, dx$		1010
400	Centroids	Of Plane Area:	$\bar{x} = \dfrac{1}{A}\int_a^b x(y_2 - y_1)\, dx$		1014
401			$\bar{y} = \dfrac{1}{2A}\int_a^b (y_1 + y_2)(y_2 - y_1)\, dx$		1014
402		Of Solid of Revolution of Volume V:	About x Axis: $\bar{x} = \dfrac{\pi}{V}\int_a^b xy^2\, dx$		1018
403			About y Axis: $\bar{y} = \dfrac{\pi}{V}\int_c^d yx^2\, dy$		1018

APPLICATIONS OF THE DEFINITE INTEGRAL (Continued)

No.						Page

<table>
<tr><td rowspan="15">APPLICATIONS OF THE DEFINITE INTEGRAL (Continued)</td></tr>
</table>

No.			Diagram	Formula	Page
404			Thin Strip: $p \bullet$ A (r)	$I_p = Ar^2$	1028
405	Moment of Inertia	Of Areas	Extended Area: $dA = y\,dx$	$I_x = \dfrac{1}{3}\int y^3\,dx$	1030
406				$I_y = \int x^2 y\,dx$	1030
407				Polar $I_0 = I_x + I_y$	
408				Radius of Gyration: $r = \sqrt{\dfrac{I}{A}}$	1029
409			(s) $\bullet A$ B A	Parallel Axis Theorem: $I_B = I_A + As^2$	
410		Of Masses	$p \bullet$ (r) M	$I_p = Mr^2$	
411			Disk: r dh	$dI = \dfrac{m\pi}{2} r^4\,dh$	
412			Ring: r_0 r_i dh	$dI = \dfrac{m\pi}{2}(r_0^4 - r_1^4)\,dh$	
413			Shell: dr r h	$dI = 2\pi m r^3 h\,dr$	1031
414			Solid of Revolution:	Disk Method: $I = \dfrac{m\pi}{2}\displaystyle\int_a^b r^4\,dh$	1033
415			0 a b h	Shell Method: $I = 2\pi m \displaystyle\int r^3 h\,dr$	1032
416			(s) $\bullet$ B A	Parallel Axis Theorem: $I_B = I_A + Ms^2$	
417	Average and rms Values		$y = f(x)$ 0 a b x	Average Ordinate: $y_{\text{avg}} = \dfrac{1}{b-a}\displaystyle\int_a^b f(x)\,dx$	1069
418				Root-Mean-Square Value: $\text{rms} = \sqrt{\dfrac{1}{b-a}\displaystyle\int_a^b [f(x)]^2\,dx}$	1070

About Axis of Revolution (Polar Moment of Inertia) applies to rows 411–415.

No.					Page
419		Variables Separable		$f(y)\,dy = g(x)\,dx$	1107
420		Integrable Combinations		$x\,dy + y\,dx = d(xy)$	1111
421				$\dfrac{x\,dy - y\,dx}{x^2} = d\!\left(\dfrac{y}{x}\right)$	1111
422				$\dfrac{y\,dx - x\,dy}{y^2} = d\!\left(\dfrac{x}{y}\right)$	1111
423	First-Order			$\dfrac{x\,dy - y\,dx}{x^2 + y^2} = d\!\left(\tan^{-1}\dfrac{y}{x}\right)$	1111
424		Homogeneous		$M\,dx + N\,dy = 0$ (Substitute $y = vx$)	1114
425		First-Order Linear	Form	$y' + Py = Q$	1116
426			Integrating Factor	$R = e^{\int P\,dx}$	1117
427			Solution	$ye^{\int P\,dx} = \int Qe^{\int P\,dx}\,dx$	1118
428		Right Side Zero — Form		$ay'' + by' + cy = 0$	1134
429		Auxiliary Equation		$am^2 + bm + c = 0$	1135
	Second-Order	Form of Solution	Roots of Auxiliary Equation	Solution	
430			Real and Unequal	$y = c_1 e^{m_1 x} + c_2 e^{m_2 x}$	1135
431			Real and Equal	$y = c_1 e^{mx} + c_2 x e^{mx}$	1137
432			Nonreal	(a) $y = e^{ax}(C_1 \cos bx + C_2 \sin bx)$ or (b) $y = Ce^{ax} \sin(bx + \phi)$	1138
433		Right Side Not Zero — Form		$ay'' + by' + cy = f(x)$	1133
434		Complete Solution		$y = \underset{\substack{\uparrow \\ \text{complementary} \\ \text{function}}}{y_c} + \underset{\substack{\uparrow \\ \text{particular} \\ \text{integral}}}{y_p}$	1142
435		Bernoulli's Equation		$\dfrac{dy}{dx} + Py = Qy^n$ (Substitute $z = y^{1-n}$)	1119

DIFFERENTIAL EQUATIONS

	No.					Page
DIFFERENTIAL EQUATIONS (Continued)	436		Laplace Transform	Definition	$\mathscr{L}[f(t)] = \int_0^\infty f(t)e^{-st}\,dt$	1157
	437			Inverse Transform	$\mathscr{L}^{-1}[F(s)] = f(t)$	1163
	438	**Numerical Solution**	Euler's Method		$x_q = x_p + \Delta x$ $y_q = y_p + m_p\,\Delta x$	1105
	439		Modified Euler's Method		$x_q = x_p + \Delta x$ $y_q = y_p + \left(\dfrac{m_p + m_q}{2}\right)\Delta x$	1175
	440		Runge-Kutta Method		$x_q = x_p + \Delta x$ $y_q = y_p + m_{\mathrm{avg}}\,\Delta x$ where $\quad m_{\mathrm{avg}} = \left(\dfrac{1}{6}\right)(m_p + 2m_r + 2m_s + m_q)$ and $\quad m_p = f'(x_p, y_p)$ $m_r = f'\left(x_p + \dfrac{\Delta x}{2}, y_p + m_p\dfrac{\Delta x}{2}\right)$ $m_s = f'\left(x_p + \dfrac{\Delta x}{2}, y_p + m_r\dfrac{\Delta x}{2}\right)$ $m_q = f'(x_p + \Delta x, y_p + m_s\,\Delta x)$	1177

		No.				Page
INFINITE SERIES	Power Series	441	Notation		$u_1 + u_2 + u_3 + \cdots + u_n + \cdots$	740
		442	Tests for Convergence	Limit Test	$\lim\limits_{n\,=\,\infty} u_n = 0$	1187
		443		Partial Sum Test	$\lim\limits_{n \to \infty} S_n = S$	1186
		444		Ratio Test	If $\lim\limits_{n \to \infty}\left\lvert\dfrac{u_n + 1}{u_n}\right\rvert$ (a) is less than 1, the series converges. (b) is greater than 1, the series diverges. (c) is equal to 1, the test fails.	1188
		445	Maclaurin's Series		$f(x) = f(0) + f'(0)x + \dfrac{f''(0)}{2!}x^2 + \cdots + \dfrac{f^{(n)}(0)}{n!}x^n + \cdots$	1190
		446	Taylor's Series		$f(x) = f(a) + f'(a)(x - a) + \dfrac{f''(a)}{2!}(x - a)^2 + \cdots + \dfrac{f^{(n)}(a)}{n!}(x - a)^n + \cdots$	1198
		447		Remainder after n Terms	$R_n = \dfrac{(x - a)^n}{n!}f^{(n)}(c)$ where c lies between a and x.	
	Fourier Series	448	Period of 2π		$f(x) = \dfrac{a_0}{2} + a_1 \cos x + a_2 \cos 2x + a_3 \cos 3x + \cdots + a_n \cos nx + \cdots$ $+ b_1 \sin x + b_2 \sin 2x + b_3 \sin 3x + \cdots + b_n \sin nx + \cdots$	1206
		449		where	$a_0 = \dfrac{1}{\pi}\int_{-\pi}^{\pi} f(x)\,dx$	1207
		450			$a_n = \dfrac{1}{\pi}\int_{-\pi}^{\pi} f(x) \cos nx\,dx$	1208
		451			$b_n = \dfrac{1}{\pi}\int_{-\pi}^{\pi} f(x) \sin nx\,dx$	1208
		452	Period of $2L$		$f(x) = \dfrac{a_0}{2} + a_1 \cos\dfrac{\pi x}{L} + a_2 \cos\dfrac{2\pi x}{L} + a_3 \cos\dfrac{3\pi x}{L} + \cdots$ $+ b_1 \sin\dfrac{\pi x}{L} + b_2 \sin\dfrac{2\pi x}{L} + b_3 \sin\dfrac{3\pi x}{L} + \cdots$	1219
		453		where	$a_0 = \dfrac{1}{L}\int_{-L}^{L} f(x)\,dx$	1219
		454			$a_n = \dfrac{1}{L}\int_{-L}^{L} f(x) \cos\dfrac{n\pi x}{L}\,dx$	1219
		455			$b_n = \dfrac{1}{L}\int_{-L}^{L} f(x) \sin\dfrac{n\pi x}{L}\,dx$	1219
		456	Waveform Symmetries	Odd and Even Functions	(a) Odd functions have Fourier Series with only sine terms (and no constant term). (b) Even functions have Fourier Series with only cosine terms (and an even function may have a constant term).	1214
		457		Half-Wave Symmetry	A waveform that has half-wave symmetry has only odd harmonics in its Fourier Series.	1215
		458	Bessel Equation of Order p		$x^2 \cdot y'' + x \cdot y' + (x^2 - p^2) \cdot y = 0$	1204
		459	Bessel Function $J_0(x)$		$J_0(x) = 1 - \dfrac{x^2}{4} + \dfrac{x^4}{64} - \dfrac{x^6}{2304} + \cdots$	1206
		460	Bessel Function $J_1(x)$		$J_1(x) = \left(\dfrac{x}{2}\right)\left[1 - \dfrac{1}{1! \cdot 2!}\left(\dfrac{x}{2}\right)^2 + \dfrac{1}{2! \cdot 3!}\left(\dfrac{x}{2}\right)^4 + \dfrac{1}{3! \cdot 4!}\left(\dfrac{x}{2}\right)^6 + \cdots\right]$	1206
		461	Bessel Function of the First Order with $p = 0$		$J_0(x) = \dfrac{1}{\pi}\int_0^{\pi} \cos(x \cdot \cos\theta)\,d\theta$	1206
		462	Lommel Integral		$J_0(x) = \dfrac{\left(\dfrac{x}{2}\right)^n}{\pi \cdot (2n)!\,\dfrac{1}{n!2^{2n}}}\int_0^{\pi} \sin^{2n}\theta \cdot \cos(x \cdot \cos\theta)\,d\theta$	1206

	No.		APPLICATIONS		Page
MIXTURES	A1	Mixture Containing Ingredients $A, B, C, \ldots$	Total amount of mixture = amount of A + amount of B + $\cdots$		106
	A2		Final amount of each ingredient = initial amount + amount added − amount removed		106
	A3	Combination of Two Mixtures	Final amount of A = amount of A from mixture 1 + amount of A from mixture 2		107
	A4	Fluid Flow	Amount of flow = flow rate × elapsed time $A = QT$		
WORK	A5		Amount done = rate of work × time worked		263
	A6		Constant Force	Work = force × distance = Fd	1024
	A7		Variable Force	Work = $\int_a^b F(x)\, dx$	1024
FINANCIAL	A8	Unit Cost	Unit cost = $\dfrac{\text{total cost}}{\text{number of units}}$		
	A9	Interest: Principal a Invested at Rate n for t years Accumulates to Amount y	Simple	$y = a(1 + nt)$	
	A10		Compounded Annually	(a) $y = a(1 + n)^t$	570
				(b) Recursion Relation $y_t = y_{t-1}(1 + n)$	569
	A11		Compounded m times/year	$y = a\left(1 + \dfrac{n}{m}\right)^{mt}$	570
STATICS	A12		Moment about Point a	$M_a = Fd$	110
	A13	Equations of Equilibrium (Newton's First Law)	The sum of all horizontal forces = 0		110
	A14		The sum of all vertical forces = 0		110
	A15		The sum of all moments about any point = 0		110
	A16		Coefficient of Friction	$\mu = \dfrac{F}{N}$	150

	No.					Page
MOTION	A17	Linear Motion		Uniform Motion (Constant Speed)	Distance = rate × time	263
	A18		Uniformly Accelerated (Constant Acceleration a, Initial Velocity v_0) For free fall, $a = g = 9.807$ m/s^2	Displacement at Time t	$s = v_0 t + \dfrac{at^2}{2}$	976
	A19			Velocity at Time t	$v = v_0 + at$	976
	A20			Newton's Second Law	$F = ma$	267
	A21		Nonuniform Motion	Average Speed	Average speed $= \dfrac{\text{total distance travelled}}{\text{total time elapsed}}$	
	A22			Displacement	$s = \displaystyle\int v\, dt$	974
	A23			Instantaneous Velocity	$v = \dfrac{ds}{dt}$	912
	A24				$v = \displaystyle\int a\, dt$	974
	A25			Instantaneous Acceleration	$a = \dfrac{dv}{dt} = \dfrac{d^2 s}{dt^2}$	913
	A26	Rotation	Uniform Motion	Angular Displacement	$\theta = \omega t$	455
	A27			Linear Speed of Point at Radius r	$v = \omega r$	450
	A28		Nonuniform Motion	Angular Displacement	$\theta = \displaystyle\int \omega\, dt$	977
	A29			Angular Velocity	$\omega = \dfrac{d\theta}{dt}$	917
	A30				$\omega = \displaystyle\int \alpha\, dt$	977
	A31			Angular Acceleration	$\alpha = \dfrac{d\omega}{dt} = \dfrac{d^2 \theta}{dt^2}$	917
	A32	Curvilinear Motion	x and y Components	Displacement	(a) $x = \displaystyle\int v_x\, dt$ (b) $y = \displaystyle\int v_y\, dt$	914
	A33			Velocity	(a) $v_x = \dfrac{dx}{dt}$ (b) $v_y = \dfrac{dy}{dt}$	914
	A34				(a) $v_x = \displaystyle\int a_x\, dt$ (b) $v_y = \displaystyle\int a_y\, dt$	976
	A35			Acceleration	(a) $a_x = \dfrac{dv_x}{dt} = \dfrac{d^2 x}{dt^2}$ (b) $ay = \dfrac{dv_y}{dt} = \dfrac{d^2 y}{dt^2}$	914

	No.						Page
MECHANICAL VIBRATIONS	A36		Free Vibrations $(P = 0)$	Simple Harmonic Motion (No Damping)		$x = x_0 \cos \omega_n t$	
	A37				Undamped Angular Velocity	$\omega_n = \sqrt{\dfrac{k \cdot a}{m}}$	
	A38				Natural Frequency	$f_n = \dfrac{\omega_n}{2\pi}$	
	A39			Under-damped		$x = x_0 e^{-at} \cos \omega_d t$	
	A40	$P \sin \omega t$			Damped Angular Velocity	$\omega_n = \sqrt{\dfrac{ka}{m}}$	
	A41	Coefficient of friction $= c$		Overdamped		$x = C_1 e^{m_1 t} + C_2 e^{m_2 t}$	
	A42		Forced Vibrations	Maximum Deflection		$x_0 = \dfrac{P \cdot a}{m\sqrt{4a^2\omega^2 + (\omega_n^2 - \omega^2)^2}}$	

	No.				Page
MATERIAL PROPERTIES	A43	Density		$\text{Density} = \dfrac{\text{mass}}{\text{volume}}$	
	A44	Mass		$\text{Mass} = \dfrac{\text{force}}{\text{acceleration}}$	
	A45	Specific Gravity		$\text{SG} = \dfrac{\text{density of substance}}{\text{density of water}}$	565
	A46	Pressure	Total Force on a Surface	$\text{Force} = \text{pressure} \times \text{area}$	1021
	A47		Force on a Submerged Surface	$F = \delta \int y\, dA$	1021
	A48			$F = \delta \bar{y} A$	1022
	A49	pH		$\text{pH} = -10 \log \text{concentration}$	606
TEMPERATURE	A50	Conversions between Degrees Celsius (C) and Degrees Fahrenheit (F)		$C = \dfrac{5}{9}(F - 32)$	
	A51			$F = \dfrac{9}{5}C + 32$	
STRENGTH OF MATERIALS	A52	Tension or Compression	Normal Stress	$\sigma = \dfrac{P}{a}$	
	A53		Strain	$\epsilon = \dfrac{e}{L}$	
	A54		Modulus of Elasticity and Hooke's Law	$E = \dfrac{PL}{ae}$	
	A55			$E = \dfrac{\sigma}{\epsilon}$	
	A56	Thermal Expansion Temperature change $= \Delta t$ Coefficient of thermal expansion $= \alpha$	Elongation	$e = \alpha L\, \Delta t$	
	A57		New Length	$L = L_0(1 + \alpha \Delta t)$	
	A58		Strain	$\epsilon = \dfrac{e}{L} = \alpha \Delta t$	
	A59		Stress, If Restrained	$\sigma = E\epsilon = E\alpha\, \Delta t$	
	A60		Force, If Restrained	$P = a\sigma = aE\alpha\, \Delta t$	
	A61		Force Needed to Deform a Spring	$F = \text{spring constant} \times \text{distance} = kx$	543

No.				Page
A62	Ohm's Law		$\text{Current} = \dfrac{\text{voltage}}{\text{resistance}} \quad I = \dfrac{V}{R}$	564
A63	Combinations of Resistors	In Series	$R = R_1 + R_2 + R_3 + \ldots$	12
A64		In Parallel	$\dfrac{1}{R} = \dfrac{1}{R_1} + \dfrac{1}{R_2} + \dfrac{1}{R_3} + \ldots$	273
A65	Power Dissipated in a Resistor		$\text{Power} = P = VI$	128
A66			$P = \dfrac{V^2}{R}$	236
A67			$P = I^2 R$	128
A68	Kirchhoff's Laws	Loops	The sum of the voltage rises and drops around any closed loop is zero.	273
A69		Notes	The sum of the currents entering and leaving any node is zero.	
A70	Resistance Change with Temperature		$R = R_1[1 + \alpha(t - t_1)]$	273
A71	Resistance of a Wire		$R = \dfrac{\rho L}{A}$	256
A72	Combinations of Capacitors	In Series	$\dfrac{1}{C} = \dfrac{1}{C_1} + \dfrac{1}{C_2} + \dfrac{1}{C_3} + \ldots$	
A73		In Parallel	$C = C_1 + C_2 + C_3 + \cdots$	34
A74	Charge on a Capacitor at Voltage V		$Q = CV$	

ELECTRICAL TECHNOLOGY

No.			Sinusoidal Form	Complex Form	Page
A75		Alternating Voltage	$v = V_m \sin(\omega t + \phi_1)$	$V = V_m \underline{/\phi_1}$	639
A76		Alternating Current	$i = I_m \sin(\omega t + \phi_2)$	$I = I_m \underline{/\phi_2}$	639
A77		Period	$P = \dfrac{2\pi}{\omega}$ seconds		484
A78		Frequency	$f = \dfrac{1}{P} = \dfrac{\omega}{2\pi}$ hertz		485
A79		Current	$i = \dfrac{dq}{dt}$		909
A80		Charge	$q = \int i\, dt$ coulombs		979
A81	Capacitor	Instantaneous Current	$i = C\dfrac{dv}{dt}$		909
A82	Capacitor	Instantaneous Voltage	$v = \dfrac{1}{C}\int i\, dt$ volts		979
A83	Capacitor	Current When Charging or Discharging	Series *RC* Circuit	$i = \dfrac{E}{R} e^{-t/RC}$	580
A84	Capacitor	Voltage When Discharging		$v = E(1 - e^{-t/RC})$	
A85	Capacitor	Voltage When Discharging		$v = Ee^{-t/RC}$	1129
A86	Inductor	Instantaneous Current	$i = \dfrac{1}{L}\int v\, dt$ amperes		980
A87	Inductor	Instantaneous Voltage	$v = L\dfrac{di}{dt}$		910
A88	Inductor	Current When Charging	Series *RL* Circuit	$i = \dfrac{E}{R}(1 - e^{-Rt/L})$	579
A89	Inductor	Current When Discharging		$i = \dfrac{E}{R} e^{-Rt/L}$	
A90	Inductor	Voltage When Charging or Discharging		$v = Ee^{-Rt/L}$	1129

(Row group label on left: ELECTRICAL TECHNOLOGY (Continued))

No.					Page
ELECTRICAL TECHNOLOGY (Continued)	A91	*Series RLC* Circuit (Source with R, L, C)	DC Source	Resonant Frequency	$\omega_n = \sqrt{\dfrac{1}{LC}}$	1147
	A92			No Resistance: The Series *LC* Circuit	$i = \dfrac{E}{\omega_n L} \sin \omega_n t$	1149
	A93			Underdamped	$i = \dfrac{E}{\omega_d L} e^{-at} \sin \omega_d t$	1148
	A94				where $\omega_d = \sqrt{\omega_n^2 - \dfrac{R^2}{4L^2}}$	1148
	A95			Overdamped	$i = \dfrac{E}{2j\omega_d L}\left[e^{(-a+j\omega_d)t} - e^{(-a-j\omega_d)t}\right]$	1150
	A96		AC Source	Inductive Reactance	$X_L = \omega L$	210
	A97			Capacitive Reactance	$X_C = \dfrac{1}{\omega C}$	210
	A98			Total Reactance	$X = X_L - X_C$	210
	A99			Magnitude of Impedance	$\lvert Z \rvert = \sqrt{R^2 + X^2} = \sqrt{R^2 + \left(\omega L - \dfrac{1}{\omega C}\right)^2}$	210
	A100			Phase Angle	$\phi = \arctan \dfrac{X}{R}$	210
	A101			Complex Impedance	$Z = R + jX = Z\,\underline{/\phi} = Ze^{j\phi}$	639
	A102			Steady-State Current	$i_{ss} = \dfrac{E}{Z} \sin(\omega t - \phi)$	1152
	A103	Ohm's Law for AC			$\mathbf{V} = \mathbf{Z}\mathbf{I}$	640
	A104	Decibels Gained or Lost			$G = 10 \log_{10} \dfrac{P_2}{P_1}$ dB	606

The measurement system in use in Canada is *Le Système International d'Unités*, commonly called SI. It is frequently necessary to convert quantities expressed in one system of measurement to units in another system, or to convert from one unit to another in the same system. This appendix provides a basic SI table and several conversion tables, organized by type of measurement (length, area, etc.), giving equivalents for a single unit of a number of measures. The equivalents may be in different units within the same measurement system or they may be in units of another system.

SI Units and Conversion Factors

INTERNATIONAL SYSTEM OF UNITS (SI)			
NAME	**UNIT**	**SYMBOL**	**RELATED**
Length	metre	m	
Time	second	s	
Mass	kilogram	kg	
Electric Current	ampere	A	
Substance Quantity	mole	mol	
Temperature (absolute)	kelvin	K	
Luminous Intensity	candela	cd	
Force	newton	N	$kg \cdot m/s^2$
Capacity	litre	L	
Volume	cubic metre	m^3	
Area	square metre	m^2	
Pressure	pascal	Pa	N/m^2
Work or Energy	joule	J	$N \cdot m$
Power	watt	W	J/s
Density	mass/unit of volume	kg/m^3	
Charge (electrical)	coulomb	C	
Electrical Potential	volt	V	
Capacitance	farad	F	
Inductance	henry	H	
Resistance	Ohm	Ω	
Temperature	°Celsius	°C	
Frequency	hertz	Hz	
Heat Quantity	joule	J	

The first seven units (in the highlighted box) are the *Base Units of SI*.

ANGLES	
1 degree	60 minutes
	0.01745 radian
	3600 seconds
	2.778×10^{-3} revolution
1 minute of arc	0.01667 degree
	2.909×10^{-4} radian
	60 seconds
1 radian	0.1592 revolution
	57.296 degrees
	3438 minutes
1 second of arc	2.778×10^{-4} degrees
	0.01667 minute

UNIT	EQUALS
LENGTH	
1 angstrom	1×10^{-10} metre
	1×10^{-4} micrometre (micron)
1 centimetre	10^{-2} metre
	0.3937 inch
1 foot	12 inches
	0.3048 metre
1 inch	25.4 millimetres
	2.54 centimetres
1 kilometre	3281 feet
	0.5400 nautical mile
	0.6214 statute mile
	1094 yards
1 light-year	9.461×10^{12} kilometres
	5.879×10^{12} statute miles
1 metre	10^{10} angstroms
	3.281 feet
	39.37 inches
	1.094 yards
1 micron	10^{4} angstroms
	10^{-4} centimetre
	10^{-6} metre
1 nautical mile (International)	8.439 cables
	6076 feet
	1852 metres
	1.151 statute miles
1 statute mile	5280 feet
	8 furlongs
	1.609 kilometres
	0.8690 nautical mile
1 yard	3 feet
	0.9144 metre

UNIT	EQUALS
AREA	
1 acre	4047 square metres
	43 560 square feet
1 are	0.02471 acre
	1 square decametre
	100 square metres
1 hectare	2.471 acres
	100 ares
	10 000 square metres
1 square foot	144 square inches
	0.09290 square metre
1 square inch	6.452 square centimetres
1 square kilometre	247.1 acres
1 square metre	10.76 square feet
1 square mile	640 acres
	2.788×10^7 square feet
	2.590 square kilometres

VOLUME	
1 board-foot	144 cubic inches
1 bushel (U.S.)	1.244 cubic feet
	35.24 litres
1 cord	128 cubic feet
	3.625 cubic metres
1 cubic foot	7.481 gallons (U.S. liquid)
	28.32 litres
1 cubic inch	0.01639 litre
	16.39 millilitres
1 cubic metre	35.31 cubic feet
	10^6 cubic centimetre
1 cubic millimetre	6.102×10^{-5} cubic inch
1 cubic yard	27 cubic feet
	0.7646 cubic metre
1 gallon (imperial)	277.4 cubic inches
	4.546 litres
1 gallon (U.S. liquid)	231 cubic inches
	3.785 litres
1 kilolitre	35.31 cubic feet
	1.308 cubic yards
	220 imperial gallons
1 litre	10^3 cubic centimetres
	10^6 cubic millimetres
	10^{-3} cubic metre
	61.02 cubic inches

UNIT	EQUALS
MASS	
1 gram	10^{-3} kilogram
	6.854×10^{-5} slug
1 kilogram	1000 grams
	0.06854 slug
1 slug	14.59 kilograms
	14 590 grams
1 tonne (metric ton)	1000 kilograms

UNIT	EQUALS
FORCE	
1 dyne	10^{-5} newton
1 newton	10^{5} dynes
	0.2248 pound
	3.597 ounces
1 pound	4.448 newtons
	16 ounces
1 ton	2000 pounds

UNIT	EQUALS
VELOCITY	
1 foot/minute	0.3048 metre/minute
	0.011 364 mile/hour
1 foot/second	1097 kilometres/hour
	18.29 metres/minute
	0.6818 mile/hour
1 kilometre/hour	3281 feet/hour
	54.68 feet/minute
	0.6214 mile/hour
1 kilometre/minute	3281 feet/minute
	37.28 miles/hour
1 knot	6076 feet/hour
	101.3 feet/minute
	1.852 kilometres/hour
	30.87 metres/minute
	1.151 miles/hour
1 metre/hour	3.281 feet/hour
1 mile/hour	1.467 feet/second
	1.609 kilometres/hour

UNIT	EQUALS
POWER	
1 British thermal unit/hour	0.2929 watt
1 Btu/pound	2.324 joules/gram
1 Btu/second	1.414 horsepower
	1.054 kilowatts
	1054 watts
1 horsepower	42.44 Btu/minute
	550 footpounds/second
	746 watts
1 kilowatt	3414 Btu/hour
	737.6 footpounds/second
	1.341 horsepower
	10^3 joules/second
	999.8 international watts
1 watt	44.25 footpounds/minute
	1 joule/second
	1 newton·metre/second

	PRESSURE
1 atmosphere	1.013 bars
	14.70 pounds/square inch
	760 torrs
	101 kilopascals
1 bar	10^6 baryes
	14.50 pounds-force/square inch
1 barye	10^{-6} bar
1 inch of mercury	0.033 86 bar
	70.73 pounds/square foot
1 pascal	1 newton/square metre
1 pound/square inch	0.068 03 atmosphere

ENERGY	
1 British thermal unit	1054 joules
	1054 watt·seconds
1 foot-pound	1.356 joules
	1.356 newton·metres
1 joule	0.7376 foot-pound
	1 watt·second
	0.2391 calories
1 kilowatthour	3410 British thermal units
	1.341 horsepower·hours
1 newton·metre	0.7376 foot-pounds
1 watthour	3.414 British thermal units
	2655 foot-pounds
	3600 joules

Source: Adapted from P. Calter, *Schaum's Outline of Technical Mathematics*, McGraw-Hill Book Company, New York, 1979.

Table of Integrals

Note: Many integrals have alternate forms that are not shown here. Don't be surprised if another table of integrals gives an expression that looks very different from one listed here.

Basic forms

1. $\int du = u + C$

2. $\int af(x)\,dx = a\int f(x)\,dx = aF(x) + C$

3. $\int [f(x) + g(x) + h(x) + \cdots]\,dx = \int f(x)\,dx + \int g(x)\,dx + \int h(x)\,dx + \cdots + C$

4. $\int x^n\,dx = \dfrac{x^{n+1}}{n+1} + C \qquad (n \neq -1)$

5. $\int u^n\,du = \dfrac{u^{n+1}}{n+1} + C \qquad (n \neq -1)$

6. $\int u\,dv = uv - \int v\,du$

7. $\int \dfrac{du}{u} = \ln |u| + C$

8. $\int e^u\,du = e^n + C$

9. $\int b^n\,du = \dfrac{b^u}{\ln b} + C \qquad (b > 0, b \neq 1)$

Trigonometric functions

10. $\int \sin u\,du = -\cos u + C$

11. $\int \cos u\,du = \sin u + C$

12. $\int \tan u\,du = -\ln |\cos u| + C$

13. $\int \cot u\,du = \ln |\sin u| + C$

14. $\int \sec u\,du = \ln |\sec u + \tan u| + C$

15. $\int \csc u\,du = \ln |\csc u - \cot u| + C$

Squares of the *trigonometric functions*	16. $\int \sin^2 u \, du = \dfrac{u}{2} - \dfrac{\sin 2u}{4} + C$
	17. $\int \cos^2 u \, du = \dfrac{u}{2} + \dfrac{\sin 2u}{4} + C$
	18. $\int \tan^2 u \, du = \tan u - u + C$
	19. $\int \cot^2 u \, du = -\cot u - u + C$
	20. $\int \sec^2 u \, du = \tan u + C$
	21. $\int \csc^2 u \, du = -\cot u + C$

Cubes of the *trigonometric functions*	22. $\int \sin^3 u \, du = \dfrac{\cos^3 u}{3} - \cos u + C$
	23. $\int \cos^3 u \, du = \sin u - \dfrac{\sin^3 u}{3} + C$
	24. $\int \tan^3 u \, dx = \dfrac{1}{2} \tan^2 u + \ln|\cos u| + C$
	25. $\int \cot^3 u \, dx = -\dfrac{1}{2} \cot^2 u - \ln|\sin u| + C$
	26. $\int \sec^3 u \, du = \dfrac{1}{2} \sec u \tan u + \dfrac{1}{2} \ln|\sec u + \tan u| + C$
	27. $\int \csc^3 u \, du = -\dfrac{1}{2} \csc u \cot u + \cot u \dfrac{1}{2} \ln|\csc u - \cot| u + C$

Miscellaneous *trigonometric forms*	28. $\int \sec u \tan u \, du = \sec u + C$
	29. $\int \csc u \cot u \, du = -\csc u + C$
	30. $\int \sin^2 u \cos^2 u \, du = \dfrac{u}{8} - \dfrac{1}{32} \sin 4u + C$
	31. $\int u \sin u \, du = \sin u - u \cos u + C$
	32. $\int u \cos u \, du = \cos u + u \sin u + C$
	33. $\int u^2 \sin u \, du = 2u \sin u - (u^2 - 2) \cos u + C$
	34. $\int u^2 \cos u \, du = 2u \cos u + (u^2 - 2) \sin u + C$
	35. $\int \sin^{-1} u \, du = u \sin^{-1} u + \sqrt{1 - u^2} + C$
	36. $\int \tan^{-1} u \, du = u \tan^{-1} u - \ln \sqrt{1 + u^2} + C$

Exponential and *logarithmic forms*	37. $\int u e^{au} \, du = \dfrac{e^{au}}{a^2} (au - 1) + C$
	38. $\int u^2 e^{au} \, du = \dfrac{e^{au}}{a^3} (a^2 u^2 - 2au + 2) + C$
	39. $\int u^n e^n \, du = u^n e^n - n \int u^{n-1} e^n \, du$
	40. $\int \dfrac{e^u \, du}{u^n} = \dfrac{-e^n}{(n-1)u^{n-1}} + \dfrac{1}{n-1} \int \dfrac{e^u \, du}{u^{n-1}} \qquad (n \neq 1)$

Exponential and logarithmic forms	41. $\displaystyle\int e^{au}\sin bu\,du = \frac{e^{au}}{a^2 + b^2}(a\sin bu - b\cos bu) + C$

41. $\displaystyle\int e^{au}\sin bu\,du = \frac{e^{au}}{a^2 + b^2}(a\sin bu - b\cos bu) + C$

42. $\displaystyle\int e^{au}\cos bu\,du = \frac{e^{au}}{a^2 + b^2}(a\cos bu + b\sin bu) + C$

43. $\displaystyle\int \ln u\,du = u(\ln u - 1) + C$

44. $\displaystyle\int u^n \ln|u|\,du = u^{n+1}\left[\frac{\ln|u|}{n+1} - \frac{1}{(n+1)^2}\right] + C \qquad (n \neq -1)$

Forms involving $a + bu$

45. $\displaystyle\int \frac{u\,du}{a + bu} = \frac{1}{b^2}[a + bu - a\ln|a + bu|] + C$

46. $\displaystyle\int \frac{u^2\,du}{a + bu} = \frac{1}{b^3}\left[\frac{1}{2}(a + bu)^2 - 2a(a + bu) + a^2\ln|a + bu|\right] + C$

47. $\displaystyle\int \frac{u\,du}{(a + bu)^2} = \frac{1}{b^2}\left[\frac{a}{a + bu} + \ln|a + bu|\right] + C$

48. $\displaystyle\int \frac{u^2\,du}{(a + bu)^2} = \frac{1}{b^3}\left[a + bu - \frac{a^2}{a + bu} - 2a\ln|a + bu|\right] + C$

49. $\displaystyle\int \frac{du}{u(a + bu)} = \frac{-1}{a}\ln\left|\frac{a + bu}{u}\right| + C$

50. $\displaystyle\int \frac{du}{u^2(a + bu)} = \frac{-1}{au} + \frac{b}{a^2}\ln\left|\frac{a + bu}{u}\right| + C$

51. $\displaystyle\int \frac{du}{u(a + bu)^2} = \frac{1}{a(a + bu)} - \frac{1}{a^2}\ln\left|\frac{a + bu}{u}\right| + C$

52. $\displaystyle\int u\sqrt{a + bu}\,du = \frac{2(3bu - 2a)}{15b^2}(a + bu)^{3/2} + C$

53. $\displaystyle\int u^2\sqrt{a + bu}\,du = \frac{2(15b^2u^2 - 12abu + 8a^2)}{105b^3}(a + bu)^{3/2} + C$

54. $\displaystyle\int \frac{u\,du}{\sqrt{a + bu}} = \frac{2(bu - 2a)}{3b^2}\sqrt{a + bu} + C$

55. $\displaystyle\int \frac{u^2\,du}{\sqrt{a + bu}} = \frac{2(3b^2u^2 - 4abu + 8a^2)}{15b^3}\sqrt{a + bu} + C$

Forms involving $u^2 \pm a^2$ $(a > 0)$

56. $\displaystyle\int \frac{du}{a^2 + b^2u^2} = \frac{1}{ab}\tan^{-1}\frac{bu}{a} + C$

57. $\displaystyle\int \frac{du}{u^2 - a^2} = \frac{1}{2a}\ln\left|\frac{u - a}{u + a}\right| + C$

58. $\displaystyle\int \frac{u^2\,du}{u^2 - a^2} = u + \frac{a}{2}\ln\left|\frac{u - a}{u + a}\right| + C$

59. $\displaystyle\int \frac{u^2\,du}{u^2 + a^2} = u - a\tan^{-1}\frac{u}{a} + C$

60. $\displaystyle\int \frac{du}{u(u^2 \pm a^2)} = \frac{\pm 1}{2a^2}\ln\left|\frac{u^2}{u^2 \pm a^2}\right| + C$

Forms involving $\sqrt{a^2 \pm u^2}$ and $\sqrt{u^2 \pm a^2}$ $(a > 0)$

61. $\displaystyle\int \frac{du}{\sqrt{a^2 - u^2}} = \operatorname{Sin}^{-1}\frac{u}{a} + C$

62. $\displaystyle\int \frac{du}{\sqrt{u^2 \pm a^2}} = \ln\left|u + \sqrt{u^2 \pm a^2}\right| + C$

63. $\displaystyle\int \frac{u^2\,du}{\sqrt{u^2 \pm a^2}} = \frac{u}{2}\sqrt{u^2 \pm a^2} \mp \frac{a^2}{2}\ln\left|u + \sqrt{u^2 \pm a^2}\right| + C$

64. $\displaystyle\int \frac{du}{u\sqrt{u^2 + a^2}} = \frac{1}{a}\ln\left|\frac{u}{a + \sqrt{u^2 + a^2}}\right| + C$

Forms involving
$\sqrt{a^2 \pm u^2}$
and
$\sqrt{u^2 \pm a^2}$
$(a > 0)$

65. $\displaystyle\int \frac{du}{u\sqrt{u^2 - a^2}} = \frac{1}{a} \sec^{-1} \frac{u}{a} + C$

66. $\displaystyle\int \sqrt{u^2 \pm a^2} \, du = \frac{u}{2} \sqrt{u^2 \pm a^2} \pm \frac{a^2}{2} \ln \left| u + \sqrt{u^2 \pm a^2} \right| + C$

67. $\displaystyle\int \frac{\sqrt{u^2 + a^2} \, du}{u} = \sqrt{u^2 + a^2} - a \ln \left| \frac{a + \sqrt{u^2 + a^2}}{u} \right| + C$

68. $\displaystyle\int \frac{\sqrt{u^2 - a^2} \, du}{u} = \sqrt{u^2 - a^2} - a \sec^{-1} \frac{u}{a} + C$

69. $\displaystyle\int \sqrt{a^2 - u^2} \, du = \frac{u}{2} \sqrt{a^2 - u^2} + \frac{a^2}{2} \sin^{-1} \frac{u}{a} + C$

70. $\displaystyle\int u^2 \sqrt{a^2 - u^2} \, du = \frac{-u}{4} (a^2 - u^2)^{3/2} + \frac{a^2 u}{8} \sqrt{a^2 - u^2} + \frac{a^4}{8} \sin^{-1} \frac{u}{a} + C$

71. $\displaystyle\int \frac{\sqrt{a^2 - u^2} \, du}{u} = \sqrt{a^2 - u^2} - a \ln \left| \frac{a + \sqrt{a^2 - u^2}}{u} \right| + C$

72. $\displaystyle\int \frac{\sqrt{a^2 - u^2} \, du}{u^2} = \frac{-\sqrt{a^2 - u^2}}{u} - \sin^{-1} \frac{u}{a} + C$

73. $\displaystyle\int \frac{u^2 \, du}{\sqrt{a^2 - u^2}} = \frac{-u}{2} \sqrt{a^2 - u^2} + \frac{a^2}{2} \sin^{-1} \frac{u}{a} + C$

Answers to Selected Problems

CHAPTER ONE

Exercise 1

1. $7 < 10$ **3.** $-3 < 4$ **5.** $\frac{3}{4} = 0.75$ **7.** -18 **9.** 13   **11.** 4   **13.** 2   **15.** 5   **17.** 5
19. 2.00   **21.** 55.86   **23.** 2.96   **25.** 278.38   **27.** 745.6   **29.** 0.5   **31.** 34.9   **33.** 0.8
35. 7600   **37.** 274 800   **39.** 2860   **41.** 484 000   **43.** 29.6   **45.** 8370

Exercise 2

1. -1090 **3.** -1116 **5.** 105 233   **7.** 1789   **9.** -1129 **11.** -850 **13.** 1827
15. 4931   **17.** 593.44   **19.** -0.00031 **21.** 472 100 km^2 **23.** 350 mm   **25.** 41.1 Ω

Exercise 3

1. $73\overline{0}0$ **3.** 0.525   **5.** $-17\ 800$ **7.** 22.9   **9.** \$3320   **11.** \$1441   **13.** \$1 570 000
15. 17 180 rev   **17.** 1751 degrees

Exercise 4

1. 163   **3.** -0.347 **5.** 0.7062   **7.** 70 840   **9.** 17   **11.** 371.708 m   **13.** 10
15. 0.00144   **17.** -0.00000253 **19.** -175 **21.** 0.2003   **23.** 0.0901   **25.** 0.9930   **27.** 313Ω
29. 0.279

Exercise 5

1. 8   **3.** -8 **5.** 1   **7.** 1   **9.** 1   **11.** -1 **13.** 100   **15.** 1   **17.** 1000   **19.** 0.01
21. 10 000   **23.** 0.00001   **25.** 1.035   **27.** -112 **29.** 0.0146   **31.** 0.0279   **33.** 59.8
35. -0.0000193 **37.** 125 W   **39.** 878×10^6 mm^3 **41.** 5   **43.** 7   **45.** -2 **47.** 7.01
49. 4.45   **51.** 62.25   **53.** -7.28 **55.** -1.405 **57.** 4480 Ω

Exercise 6

1. 3340   **3.** -5940 **5.** 5   **7.** 3   **9.** 121   **11.** 27   **13.** 27   **15.** 24   **17.** 12
19. 2   **21.** 30   **23.** 46.2   **25.** 978   **27.** 2.28   **29.** 0.160   **31.** 59.8   **33.** 55.8
35. 3.51   **37.** 7.17   **39.** 3.23   **41.** 0.871   **43.** 7.93

Exercise 7

1. 10^2 **3.** 10^{-4} **5.** 10^8 **7.** 0.01   **9.** 0.1   **11.** 1.86×10^5 **13.** 2.5742×10^4
15. 9.83×10^4 **17.** 2850   **19.** 90 000   **21.** 0.003667   **23.** 10   **25.** 10^3 **27.** 10^3

29. 10^7 **31.** 10^2 **33.** 400 **35.** 2.1×10^9 **37.** 2×10^6 **39.** 2×10^{-9} **41.** 7.0×10^5
43. 10.70×10^3 **45.** 3.1×10^{-2} **47.** 1.55×10^6 **49.** 2.11×10^4 **51.** 1.7×10^2
53. $9.79 \times 10^6 \, \Omega$ **55.** $2.72 \times 10^{-6} \, W$ **57.** $6.77 \times 10^{-5} \, F$ **59.** 118 h

Exercise 8

1. 15 km **3.** 38 μF **5.** 6.82 kN/m² **7.** 8210 kJ/s

Exercise 9

1. 17 **3.** −37 **5.** 14 **7.** 14.1 **9.** 233 **11.** 8.00 **13.** $3975 **15.** 53.3°C
17. $13 266

Exercise 10

1. 372% **3.** 0.55% **5.** 40.0% **7.** 70.0% **9.** 0.23 **11.** 2.875 **13.** $\frac{3}{8}$ **15.** $1\frac{1}{2}$
17. 102 tonnes **19.** 220 kg **21.** 120 L **23.** 1090 Ω **25.** $1400 **27.** 519 **29.** $28\frac{1}{8}$
31. $10\overline{0}$ **33.** 107 km **35.** $50\overline{0} **37.** 50% **39.** 20% **41.** $33\frac{1}{3}$% **43.** 11.6%
45. 1.5% **47.** 96.6% **49.** 31.3% **51.** 11% **53.** 5.99% **55.** 66.64% **57.** 73%
59. 2.3% **61.** 112.5 and 312.5 V **63.** 37.5% **65.** 25 L

Exercise 11

1. 540 mm ± 22.2 mm (±4.1%) **3.** 500 Ω ± 5% **5.** 29 ± 7.5% **7.** $11.4 \times 10^6 \, mm^3 \pm 12\%$

Review Problems

1. 83.35 **3.** 88.1 **5.** 0.346 **7.** 94.7 **9.** 5.46 **11.** 6.8 **13.** 30.6 **15.** 17.4
17. (a) 179 (b) 1.08 (c) 4.86 (d) 45 700 **19.** 70.2% **21.** 3.63×10^6 **23.** 30 830 kW
25. 3.2% **27.** 7×10^{11} bbl **29.** 10 200 **31.** 4.16×10^{-10} **33.** 2.42 **35.** $-\frac{2}{3} < -0.660$
37. 2370 **39.** −1.72 **41.** 64.5% **43.** 484 N **45.** 160 m **47.** 22.0% **49.** 7216
51. 4.939 **53.** 109 **55.** 0.207 **57.** 14.7 **59.** 6.20 **61.** 2 **63.** 83.4 **65.** 3.08 hectares
67. 9.07 **69.** 75.2% **71.** 0.0737 **73.** 7.239 **75.** 121 **77.** 1.21 **79.** 0.30
81. 1440 ± 3% **83.** V = 1.27 m³ ± 18%

CHAPTER TWO

Exercise 1

1. 2 **3.** 1 **5.** 5 **7.** $b/4$ **9.** $3/2a$

Exercise 2

1. $12x$ **3.** $-10ab$ **5.** $2m - c$ **7.** $4a - 2b - 3c - d - 17$ **9.** $11x + 10ax$
11. $-26x^3 + 2x^2 + x - 31$ **13.** 0 **15.** $20 - 2ay^3$ **17.** $18b^2 - 3ac - 2d$
19. $7m^2 - 5m^3 + 15ab - 4q - z$ **21.** $5.83(a + b)$ **23.** $3a^2 - 3a + x - b$ **25.** $-1.1 - 4.4x$
27. $4a^2 - 5a + y + 1$ **29.** $2a + 2b - 2m$ **31.** $6m - 3z$ **33.** $5w + 2z + 6x$ **35.** $a + 12$

Exercise 3

1. 16 **3.** −27 **5.** 0.0001 **7.** a^8 **9.** y^{2a-2} **11.** 10^{a+b} **13.** y^3 **15.** x **17.** 100
19. x **21.** x^{12} **23.** a^{xy} **25.** x^{2a+2} **27.** $8x^3$ **29.** $27a^3b^3c^3$ **31.** $-1/27$ **33.** $8a^3/27b^6$
35. $1/a^2$ **37.** $y^3/27$ **39.** $9b^6/4a^2$ **41.** $2/x^2 + 3/y^3$ **43.** x^{-1} **45.** x^2y^{-2} **47.** $a^{-3}b^{-2}$
49. 1 **51.** $\frac{1}{9}$ **53.** 1

Exercise 4

1. x^5 **3.** $10a^3b^4$ **5.** $36a^6b^5$ **7.** $-8p^4q^4$ **9.** $2a^2 - 10a$ **11.** $x^2y - xy^2 + x^2y^2$
13. $-12p^3q - 8p^2q^2 + 12pq^3$ **15.** $6a^3b^3 - 12a^3b^2 + 9a^2b^3 + 3a^2b^2$ **17.** $a^2 + ac + ab + bc$
19. $x^3 - xy + 3x^2y - 3y^2$ **21.** $9m^2 - 9n^2$ **23.** $49c^2d^4 - 16y^6z^2$ **25.** $x^4 - y^4$ **27.** $a^2 - ac - c - 1$

29. $m^3 - 5m^2 - m + 14$ **31.** $x^8 - x^2$ **33.** $-z^3 + 2z^2 - 3z + 2$ **35.** $a^3 + y^3$ **37.** $a^3 - y^3$
39. $x^3 - px^2 - mx^2 + mpx + nx^2 - npx - mnx + mnp$ **41.** $m^5 - 1$ **43.** $9a^2x - 6abx + b^2x$
45. $x^3 - 3x - 2$ **47.** $x^3 - cx^2 + bx^2 - bcx + ax^2 - acx + abx - abc$ **49.** $-c^5 - c^4 + c + 1$
51. $4a^6 - 10a^4c^2 + 14a^4 - 25a^2c^2 + 10a^2$ **53.** $a^3 + a^2c - ab^2 + b^2c - b^3 + 2abc - ac^2 + bc^2 - c^3 + a^2b$
55. $n^5 - 34n^3 + 57n^2 - 20$ **57.** $a^2 + 2ac + c^2$ **59.** $m^2 - 2mn + n^2$ **61.** $A^2 + 2AB + B^2$
63. $14.4a^2 - 16.7ax + 4.84x^2$ **65.** $4c^2 - 12cd + 9d^2$ **67.** $a^2 - 2a + 1$ **69.** $y^4 - 40y^2 + 400$
71. $a^2 + 2ab + b^2 + 2ac + 2bc + c^2$ **73.** $x^2 + 2x - 2xy - 2y + y^2 + 1$
75. $x^4 + 2x^3y + 3x^2y^2 + 2xy^3 + y^4$ **77.** $a^3 + 3a^2b + 3ab^2 + b^3$ **79.** $p^3 - 9p^2q + 27pq^2 - 27q^3$
81. $a^3 - 3a^2b + 3ab^2 - b^3$ **83.** $3a + 3b + 3c$ **85.** $p - q$ **87.** $31y - 5z$ **89.** $2x - 4$
91. $7 - 5x$

Exercise 5

1. z^2 **3.** $-5xyz$ **5.** $2f$ **7.** $-2xz$ **9.** $-5xy^2$ **11.** $3c$ **13.** $-5y$ **15.** $-3w$
17. $7n$ **19.** $4b$ **21.** b^2 **23.** x^{m-n} **25.** $4s$ **27.** -24 **29.** $-5z/xy$ **31.** $-5n^2/m^2x$
33. $3ab$ **35.** $3x^5$ **37.** $42/y$ **39.** $-4x$ **41.** $2a^2 - a$ **43.** $7x^2 - 1$ **45.** $3x^4 - 5x^2$
47. $2x^2 - 3x$ **49.** $a + 2c$ **51.** $ax - 2y$ **53.** $2x + y$ **55.** $ab - c$ **57.** $xy - x^2 - y^2$
59. $1 - a - b$ **61.** $a - 3b + c^2$ **63.** $x - 2y + y^2/x$ **65.** $m + 2 - 3m/n$ **67.** $a - b - c$
69. $ab - 2 - 3b^2$ **71.** $5a - 10x - 2$ **73.** $x + 8$ **75.** $x - 6 + 15/(x + 2)$ **77.** $a + 5$
79. $9a^2 + 6ab + 4b^2$ **81.** $5x + 13 - 35/(3 - x)$ **83.** $-3a - 2$ **85.** $x^4 + x + 1 + R(x^2 + x + 1)$
87. $x^2 + 3x + 1$ **89.** $a + b - c$ **91.** $c^2 + c + 2$ **93.** $x^3 + 2x^2 - 6x + 5$ **95.** $4x^3 - 3x^2 - x + 6$
97. $2x^3 - x^2 + 5$

Review Problems

1. $b^6 - b^4x^2 + b^4x^3 - b^2x^5 + b^2x^4 - x^6$ **3.** 3.86×10^{14} **5.** $9x^4 - 6mx^3 - 6m^3x + 10m^2x^2 + m^4$
7. $8x^3 + 12x^2 + 6x + 1$ **9.** $6a^2x^5$ **11.** $16a^2 - 24ab + 9b^2$ **13.** $x^2y^2 - 6xy + 8$
15. $4a^2 - 12ab + 9b^2$ **17.** $ab - b^4 - a^2b$ **19.** $16m^4 - c^4$ **21.** $2a^2$ **23.** $24 - 8y$
25. $6x^3 + 9x^2y - 3xy^2 - 6y^3$ **27.** $13w - 6$ **29.** $a^5 + 32c^5$ **31.** $(a - c)^{m-2}$ **33.** $x + y$
35. $b^3 - 9b^2 + 27b - 27$ **37.** $x^2/2y^3$ **39.** $x^2 + 2x - 8$ **41.** 8.01×10^6 **43.** $10x^3y^4$
45. $x^3 + 3x^2 - 4x$ **47.** 1.77×10^8 **49.** $6a^3b^3$

CHAPTER 3

Exercise 1

1. 33   **3.** 4/5   **5.** 1/2   **7.** 1/2   **9.** 4   **11.** 3   **13.** -1.38 **15.** 1   **17.** $-1/2$
19. 2   **21.** 5   **23.** 28   **25.** 3   **27.** 3   **29.** 35   **31.** $-5/23$ **33.** 5/6   **35.** 19/5
37. 1   **39.** 3/25   **41.** 0   **43.** -0.0549 **45.** $3/a$ **47.** $5/c + 1$ **49.** $\dfrac{3b + c - a}{b}$

Exercise 2

1. $5x + 8$ **3.** x and $83 - x$ **5.** x and $25 - x$ **7.** A, $2A$, and $180 - 3A$ **9.** $82x$ km   **11.** 5
13. 57, 58, 59   **15.** 14   **17.** 6   **19.** 4   **21.** 20   **23.** 14   **25.** 81

Exercise 3

1. 8 technicians   **3.** $130 137   **5.** 57 000 L   **7.** $64.29 to brother, $128.57 to uncle, $257.14 to bank
9. $94 000   **11.** $12 000

Exercise 4

1. 1333 L   **3.** 485 kg of 18% mixture, 215 kg of 31% mixture   **5.** 1380 kg   **7.** 1.29 L   **9.** 26 kg
11. 27.7 kg   **13.** 85.3 mW

Exercise 5

1. 1.53 m   **3.** $R_1 = 3.4$ kN downwards; $R_2 = 13.9$ kN upwards   **5.** 3390 mm
7. 34.7 kN right end, 42.9 kN left end

Review Problems

1. 12   **3.** 5   **5.** 0   **7.** $10\frac{1}{2}$ **9.** 2   **11.** 4   **13.** 4   **15.** 6   **17.** $-5/7$ **19.** -6
21. 9.27   **23.** 7   **25.** 6   **27.** 470 mm, 530 mm   **29.** 12 kg   **31.** $13 500   **33.** 4.2 km

35. $-13/5$ **37.** 13   **39.** $-5/7$ **41.** $-5/2$ **43.** $-7/3$ **45.** $-6/b$ **47.** $\dfrac{a + 10}{2}$
49. $\dfrac{5a - c + 8}{a}$

CHAPTER 4

Exercise 1

1. Is a function   **3.** Not a function   **5.** Not a function   **7.** Yes   **9.** $y = x^3$ 11. $y = x + 2x^2$
13. $y = (2/3)(x - 4)$ **15.** The amount by which 5 exceeds x **17.** Twice the cube root of x
19. $A = bh/2$ **21.** $V = 4\pi r^3/3$ **23.** $d = 80t$ km   **25.** $H = 125t - gt^2/2$
27. Domain $= -10, -7, 0, 5, 10$; Range $= 3, 7, 10, 20$ **29.** $x \ge 7, y \ge 0$ **31.** $x \ne 0$, all y
33. $x \ne 9, y \ne 1$ **35.** $x < 1, y > 0$ **37.** $x \ge 1, y \ge 0$ **39.** $-5 \le y \le 70$

Exercise 2

1. Explicit   **3.** Implicit   **5.** x is independent, y is dependent
7. x and y are independent, w is dependent   **9.** x and y are independent, z is dependent   **11.** $y = 2/x + 3$
13. $y = (2x^2 + x)/3$ **15.** $e = PL/aE$ **17.** 6   **19.** -21 **21.** 12.5   **23.** -5 **25.** -15
27. 5/4   **29.** $2a^2 + 4$ **31.** $5a + 5b + 1$ **33.** $9\frac{1}{2}$ **35.** 142   **37.** 20   **39.** -52 **41.** 18
43. $1.06 \times 10^4 \, \Omega, 1.08 \times 10^4 \, \Omega, 1.11 \times 10^4 \, \Omega$

Exercise 3

1. $2x^2 + 3$ **3.** $4 - 3x^3$ **5.** -77 **7.** $y = (8 - x)/3$ **9.** $y = (x - 10)/2$

Review Problems

1. (a) Is a function (b) Not a function (c) Not a function   **3.** $S = 4\pi r^2$
5. (a) Explicit, y independent, w dependent (b) Implicit   **7.** $w = (3 - x^2 - y^2)/2$ **9.** $7x^2$ **11.** 6

13. 28   **15.** 13/90   **17.** y is less than five times the cube of x **19.** $x = \pm\sqrt{\dfrac{6 - y}{3}}$

CHAPTER 5

Exercise 1

1. Fourth   **3.** Second   **5.** Fourth   **7.** First and fourth   **9.** $x = 7$
11. $E(-1.8, -0.7), F(-1.4, -1.4), G(1.4, -0.6), H(2.5, -1.8)$
13.   **15.**   **17.** $(4, -5)$

Exercise 2

1.   **3.**   **5.**

7.

9.

11.

13.

15.

Exercise 3

1. 2   **3.** −1   **5.** 1   **7.** −11/7   **9.**

11.

13.

15.

17.

Exercise 4

9.

11.

Exercise 5

1.

3.

5.

7.

9.

11.

Exercise 6

1.

3.

5.

7.

9.

Review Problems

1.

3.

5.

7.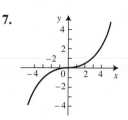

9. $y = 5x^2 + 24x - 12$

11.

13.

15.

CHAPTER 6

Exercise 1

1. (a) $62.8°$ **(b)** $64.6°$ **(c)** $37.7°$ **3.** 5.05 **5.** $A = C = 46.3°$; $B = D = 134°$

Exercise 2

1. $19\ 200   **3.** 6050 mm   **5.** 25 m, 33.5 m, 61.8 m   **7.** 35.4 m   **9.** 35.4 m   **11.** 4.93 m
13. 10.8 m   **15.** 14.7 mm   **17.** 990 mm   **19.** 17.6 hectares   **21.** 2.62 m   **23.** 5.2 mm

Exercise 3

1. 423 square units   **3.** 248 square units   **5.** $3042   **7.** $348   **9.** $2635   **11.** $1763

Exercise 4

1. 7.16 m   **3.** 401 mm   **5.** 104 m   **7.** 127 hectares   **9.** 0.74 unit   **11.** 44.7 units
13. 2200 mm   **15.** 69.1 m²   **17.** 2470 mm

Exercise 5

1. 1042.5 m³   **3. (a)** 4.2 m   **(b)** 150 m³   **5.** 2.9×10^6 mm³   **7.** 14.5 mm   **9.** 25 mm
11. 492×10^3 mm²   **13.** 1180 kg   **15.** 1.16×10^6 mm³   **17.** 1.72×10^9, 6.96×10^6 **19.** 15.8, 1.12
21. 100 kg

Review Problems

1. 2400 km/h   **3.** 2.88 m   **5.** 13 m   **7.** 175 000 square units   **9.** 1200 mm   **11.** 17.5 m
13. 161°   **15.** 213×10^3 mm³   **17.** 617×10^3 mm²   **19.** 1150m²   **21.** 87.8×10^6 mm³
23. 311.5×10^6 mm³   **25.** 116×10^3 mm³

CHAPTER 7

Exercise 1

1. 0.485 rad   **3.** 0.615 rad   **5.** 3.5 rad   **7.** 0.7595 rev   **9.** 0.191 rev   **11.** 0.2147 rev
13. 162°   **15.** 171°   **17.** 29.45°   **19.** 244° 57′45″   **21.** 161° 54′36″   **23.** 185° 58′19″

Exercise 2

1. 0.50, 0.87, 0.58, 1.73, 1.15, 2.00   **3.** 0.24, 0.97, 0.25, 4.01, 1.03, 4.13   **5.** 53°   **7.** 63°
9. 0.528, 0.849, 0.622, 1.61, 1.18, 1.89   **11.** 0.447, 0.894, 0.500   **13.** 0.832, 0.555, 1.50
15. 0.491, 0.871, 0.564   **17.** 0.9793   **19.** 3.0415   **21.** 0.9319   **23.** 1.0235
25. 0.955, 0.296, 3.230   **27.** 0.546, 0.838, 0.652   **29.** 0.677, 0.736, 0.920   **31.** 2.05   **33.** 2.89
35. −10.9

Exercise 3

1. 30.0°   **3.** 31.9°   **5.** 28.9°   **7.** 3/5, 4/5, 3/4   **9.** 5/13, 12/13, 5/12   **11.** 75.0°   **13.** 40.5°
15. 13.6°

Exercise 4

1. $B = 47.1°$, $b = 167$, $c = 228$ **3.** $b = 1.08$, $A = 58.1°$, $c = 2.05$ **5.** $B = 0.441$ rad, $b = 134$, $c = 314$
7. $a = 6.44$, $c = 11.3$, $A = 34.8°$ **9.** $a = 50.3$, $c = 96.5$, $B = 58.6°$ **11.** $c = 470$, $A = 54.3°$, $B = 35.7°$
13. $a = 2.80$, $A = 35.2°$, $B = 54.8°$ **15.** $b = 25.6$, $A = 46.9°$, $B = 43.1°$ **17.** $b = 48.5$, $A = 40.4°$, $B = 49.6°$
19. $a = 414$, $A = 61.2°$, $B = 28.8°$ **21.** cos 52°   **23.** cot 71°   **25.** tan 26.8°   **27.** cot 54° 46′
29. cos 1.10 rad

Exercise 5

1. 402 m   **3.** 88 m   **5.** 64.9 m   **7.** 36.46 m   **9.** 128 m   **11.** 21.4 km, 14.7 km
13. 692 km, S58°32′W   **15.** 249 km North, 260 km East   **17.** 30.2°, 6240 mm   **19.** 37.6°   **21.** 141, 114
23. 63°, 117°   **25.** 1250 mm   **27.** 67.83 mm   **29.** 94 mm   **31.** 140.46 mm   **33.** 8.66 mm, 4.33 mm

Exercise 6

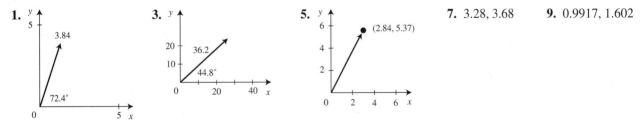

7. 3.28, 3.68   **9.** 0.9917, 1.602

11. 616, 51.7°   **13.** 8811, 56.70°   **15.** 2.42, 31.1°   **17.** 616, 38.3°   **19.** 69.2, 32.5°
21. 9.14, 54.8°   **23.** 1090, 34.0°   **25.** 6.97, 57.1°

Exercise 7

1. 118 N   **3.** 155 kg   **5.** 25.7°   **7.** 48.5 kN   **9.** 119 km.h   **11.** 5.70 m/min, 1.76 min
13. 18 km/h   **15.** $X = 354\ \Omega$, $Z = 372\ \Omega$ **17.** 7.13 Ω, 53.7°

Review Problems

1. 38° 12′, 0.667 rad, 0.106 rev   **3.** 157.3 deg, , 157° 18′, 0.4369 rev
5. 0.919, 0.394, 2.33, 0.429, 2.54, 1.09, 66.8°   **7.** 0.600, 0.800, 0.750, 1.33, 1.25, 1.67, 36.9°
9. 0.9558, 0.2940, 3.2506, 0.3076, 3.4009, 1.0463   **11.** 0.8674, 0.4976, 1.7433, 0.5736, 2.0098, 1.1528   **13.** 34.5°
15. 70.7°   **17.** 65.88°   **19.** $B = 61.5°$, $a = 2.02$, $c = 4.23$ **21.** 356, 810   **23.** 473, 35.5°
25. 2.21 m   **27.** 0.5120   **29.** 1.3175   **31.** 2.1742   **33.** 60.1°   **35.** 46.5°   **37.** 46.5°

39. 16.6 **41.** 3.79 **43.**
49. $\phi = 35.74°$

45. 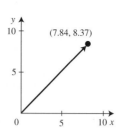 **47.** 32.2, 57.4°

CHAPTER 8

Exercise 1

1. $y^2(3 + y)$ **3.** $x^3(x^2 − 2x +3)$ **5.** $a(3 + a − 3a^2)$ **7.** $5(x + y)[1 +3(x +y)]$
9. $(1/x)(3 +2/x − 5/x^2)$ **11.** $a^2(5b +6c)$ **13.** $xy(4x +cy +3y^2)$ **15.** $3ay(a^2 − 2ay + 3y^2)$
17. $cd(5a − 2cd +b)$ **19.** $4x^2(2y^2 +3z^2)$ **21.** $ab(3a + c − d)$ **23.** $L_0(1 + \alpha t)$
25. $R_1[1 + \alpha (t − t_1)]$ **27.** $t (v_0 + at/2)$ **29.** $4 \pi D/3)(r_2^3 − r_1^3)$

Exercise 2

1. $(2 − x)(2 + x)$ **3.** $(3a − x)(3a + x)$ **5.** $4(x − y)(x + y)$ **7.** $(x − 3y)(x + 3y)$
9. $(3c − 4d)(3c + 4d)$ **11.** $(3y − 1)(3y + 1)$ **13.** $(m − n)(m + n)(m^2 + n^2)$ **15.** $(m^n − n^m)(m^n +n^m)$
17. $(a^2 − b)(a^2 + b)(a^4 + b^2)(a^8 + b^4)$ **19.** $(5x^2 − 4y^3)(5x^2 + 4y^3)$ **21.** $(4a^2 − 11)(4a^2 + 11)$
23. $(5a^2b^2 − 3)(5a^2b^2 + 3)$ **25.** $\pi(r_2 − r_1)(r_2 + r_1)$ **27.** $4\pi(r_1 − r_2)(r_1 + r_2)$ **29.** $m(v_1 − v_2)(v_1 + v_2)/2$
31. $\pi h(R − r)(R + r)$

Exercise 3

1. Not factorable **3.** Factorable **5.** Factorable **7.** $(x − 7)(x − 3)$ **9.** $(x − 9)(x − 1)$
11. $(x + 10)(x − 3)$ **13.** $(x + 4)(x + 3)$ **15.** $(x − 7)(x + 3)$ **17.** $(x + 4)(x + 2)$ **19.** $(b − 5)(b − 3)$
21. $(b − 4)(b + 3)$ **23.** $2(y − 10)(y − 3)$ **25.** $3(w + 4)(w + 8)$ **27.** $(x + 7y)(x + 12y)$
29. $(a + 3b)(a − 2b)$ **31.** $(a + 9x)(a − 7x)$ **33.** $(a − 24bc)(a + 4bc)$
35. $(a + 48bc)(a + bc)$ **37.** $(a + b + 1)(a + b − 8)$ **39.** $(x^2 − 5y^2)(x − 2y)(x + 2y)$
41. $(t − 20)(t − 120)$ **43.** $(x − 10)(x − 100)$

Exercise 4

1. $(a^2 + 4)(a + 3)$ **3.** $(x − 1)(x^2 + 1)$ **5.** $(x − b)(x + 3)$ **7.** $(x − 2)(3 + y)$
9. $(x + y − 2)(x + y + 2)$ **11.** $(m − n + 2)(m + n − 2)$ **13.** $(x + 3)(a + b)$ **15.** $(a + b)(a − c)$
17. $(2 + x^2)(a + b)$ **19.** $(2a − c)(3a + b)$ **21.** $(a + b)(b − c)$ **23.** $(x − a − b)(x + a + b)$

Exercise 5

1. $(4x − 1)(x − 3)$ **3.** $(5x + 1)(x + 2)$ **5.** $(3b + 2)(4b − 3)$ **7.** $(2a − 3)(a + 2)$
9. $(x − 7)(5x − 3)$ **11.** $3(x + 1)(x + 1)$ **13.** $(3x + 2)(x − 1)$ **15.** $2(2x − 3)(x − 1)$
17. $(2a − 1)(2a + 3)$ **19.** $(3a − 7)(3a + 2)$ **21.** $(7x^3 − 3y)(7x^3 +5y)$ **23.** $(4x^3 + 1)(x^3 + 3)$
25. $(5x^{2n} + 1)(x^{2n} + 2)$ **27.** $3[(a + x)^n + 1][(a + x)^n − 2]$ **29.** $5(t − 1)(t − 3)$

Exercise 6

1. $(x + 2)^2$ **3.** $(y − 1)^2$ **5.** $2(y − 3)^2$ **7.** $(3 + x)^2$ **9.** $(3x + 1)^2$ **11.** $9(y − 1)^2$
13. $4(2 + a)^2$ **15.** $(7a − 2)^2$ **17.** $(x + y)^2$ **19.** $(aw + b)^2$ **21.** $(x + 5a)^2$ **23.** $(x +4y)^2$
25. $(z^3 + 8)^2$ **27.** $(7 − x^3)^2$ **29.** $(a − b)^2(a + b)^2$ **31.** $(2a^n + 3b^n)^2$

Exercise 7

1. $(4 + x)(16 − 4x + x^2)$ **3.** $2(a − 2)(a^2 + 2a + 4)$ **5.** $(x − 1)(x^2 + x + 1)$ **7.** $(x +1)(x^2 − x +1)$
9. $(a +4)(a^2 − 4a +16)$ **11.** $(x + 5)(x^2 − 5x + 25)$ **13.** $8(3 − a)(9 + 3a +a^2)$ **15.** $(7 +4x)(49 − 28x + 16x^2)$ **17.** $(y^3 + 4x)(y^6 − 4xy^3 + 16x^2)$ **19.** $(3x^5 + 2a^2)(9x^{10} − 6x^5a^2 + 4a^4)$
21. $(2a^{2x} − 5b^x)(4a^{4x} + 10a^{2x}b^x + 25b^{2x})$ **23.** $(4x^n − y^{3n})(16x^{2n} + 4x^ny^{3n} +y^{6n})$ **25.** $(4\pi/3)(r_2 − r_1)(r_2^2 + r_2r_1 + r_1^2)$

Review Problems

1. $(x - 5)(x + 3)$ **3.** $(x^3 - y^2)(x^3 + y^2)$ **5.** $(2x - 1)(x + 2)$
7. $(a - b + c + d)[(a - b)^2 - (a - b)(c + d) + (c + d)^2]$ **9.** $(x/y)(x - 1)$ **11.** $(y + 5)(x - 2)$
13. $(x - y)(1 - b)$ **15.** $(y + 2 - z)(y + 2 + z)$ **17.** $(x - 3)(x - 4)$
19. $(4x^{2n} + 9y^{4n})(2x^n + 3y^{2n})(2x^n - 3y^{2n})$ **21.** $(3a + 2z^2)^2$ **23.** $(x^m + 1)^2$ **25.** $(x - y - z)(x - y + z)$
27. $(1 + 4x)(1 - 4x)$ **29.** $x^2(3x + 1)(3x - 1)$ **31.** $(p - q - 3)[(p - q)^2 + 3(p - q) + 9]$
33. $(3a - 2w)(9a^2 + 6aw + 4w^2)$ **35.** $4(2x - y)^2$ **37.** $(3b + y)(2a + x)$ **39.** $2(y^2 - 3)(y^2 + 3)$
41. $(1/R)(V_2 - V_1)(V_2 + V_1)$

CHAPTER 9

Exercise 1

1. $x \neq 0$ **3.** $x \neq 5$ **5.** $x \neq 2, x \neq 1$ **7.** 0.5833 **9.** 0.9375 **11.** 3.6667 **13.** $7/16$
15. $11/16$ **17.** $7/9$ **19.** -1 **21.** $d - c$ **23.** $\frac{2}{3}$ **25.** $\frac{15}{7}$ **27.** $a/3$
29. $3m/4p^2$ **31.** $(2a - 3b)/2a$ **33.** $x/(x - 1)$ **35.** $\dfrac{x + 2}{x^2 + 2x + 4}$ **37.** $\dfrac{n(m - 4)}{3(m - 2)}$ **39.** $\dfrac{2(a + 1)}{a - 1}$
41. $\dfrac{x + z}{x^2 + xz + z^2}$ **43.** $\dfrac{a - 2}{a - 3}$ **45.** $\dfrac{(x - 1)}{2y}$ **47.** $\dfrac{2}{3(x^4 y^4 - 1)}$ **49.** $\dfrac{x + y}{x - y}$ **51.** $\dfrac{(b - 3 + a)}{5}$

Exercise 2

1. $2/15$ **3.** $6/7$ **5.** $2\frac{2}{15}$ **7.** $75/8$ **9.** $1\frac{1}{2}$ **11.** $a^4 b^4/2y^{2n}$ **13.** $7p^2/4xz$ **15.** $x - a$
17. $ab/(x^2 - y^2)$ **19.** $cd/(x^2 - y^2)^2$ **21.** $\dfrac{(x - 1)(x + 4)}{(x + 3)(x - 5)}$ **23.** $\dfrac{(x + 1)(x + 2)}{(x - 4)(x - 3)}$ **25.** $\dfrac{(2x - 3)(x + 1)}{(x - 1)(x - 6)}$
27. $1\frac{15}{16}$ **29.** $9/128$ **31.** $5/18$ **33.** $5\frac{1}{4}$ **35.** b^2 **37.** $8a^3/3\,dxy$ **39.** $(3an + cm)(x^4 - y^4)$
41. $1/(c - d)$ **43.** $1/(x + 2)$ **45.** $\dfrac{6(x - 1)}{x + 2}$ **47.** $\dfrac{(p + 2)^2}{(p - 1)^2}$ **49.** $\dfrac{(z - 1)(z + 4)}{(z + 3)(z - 5)}$ **51.** $1\frac{2}{3}$
53. $2\frac{5}{12}$ **55.** $9\frac{2}{5}$ **57.** $x + 1/x$ **59.** $\dfrac{2}{x} - \dfrac{1}{2}$ **61.** $3m/4\pi r^3$ **63.** $2P/(a + b)h$ **65.** $4\pi d^3/3$

Exercise 3

1. 1 **3.** $1/7$ **5.** $5/3$ **7.** $7/6$ **9.** $19/16$ **11.** $7/18$ **13.** $13/5$ **15.** $-92/15$
17. $67/35$ **19.** $8/3$ **21.** $13/4$ **23.** $91/16$ **25.** $6/a$ **27.** $(a + 3)/y$ **29.** x **31.** $x/(a - b)$
33. $19/(a + 1)$ **35.** $19a/10x$ **37.** $\dfrac{2ax - 3x + 12}{6x}$ **39.** $(5b - a)/6$ **41.** $\dfrac{9 - x}{x^2 - 1}$ **43.** $\dfrac{2b(2a - b)}{a^2 - b^2}$
45. $\dfrac{2x^2 - 1}{x^4 - x^2}$ **47.** $\dfrac{2(3x^2 + 2x - 3)}{x^3 - 7x - 6}$ **49.** $\dfrac{x^2 - 2x}{(x - 3)(x + 3)}$ **51.** $\dfrac{5x^2 + 7x + 16}{x^3 - 8}$ **53.** $\dfrac{-d}{(x + 1)(x + d + 1)}$
55. $\dfrac{d(x^2 + dx - 1)}{x(x + d)}$ **57.** $(x^2 + 1)/x$ **59.** $2/(x^2 - 1)$ **61.** $(3a - a^2 - 2)/a$ **63.** $(abx + a + b)/ax$
65. 9 km/day   **67.** $2/25$ min   **69.** $11/8$ machines   **71.** $\dfrac{2h(a + b) - \pi d^2}{4}$ **73.** $\dfrac{V_1 V_2 d + V V_2 d_1 + V V_1 d_2}{V V_1 V_2}$

Exercise 4

1. $85/12$ **3.** $65/132$ **5.** $69/95$ **7.** $\dfrac{3(4x + y)}{4(3x - y)}$ **9.** $y/(y - x)$ **11.** $\dfrac{5(3a^2 + x)}{3(20 + x)}$
13. $\dfrac{2(3acx + 2d)}{3(2acx + 3d)}$ **15.** $\dfrac{2x^2 - y^2}{x - 3y}$ **17.** $\dfrac{(x + 2)(x - 1)}{(x + 1)(x - 2)}$ **19.** 1 **21.** $\dfrac{4}{3(a + 1)}$ **23.** 1
25. $\dfrac{x + y + z}{x - y + z}$ **27.** $\dfrac{pL_1 L_2}{A_2 L_1 + A_1 L_2}$

Exercise 5

1. 12 **3.** 20 **5.** 14 **7.** 72 **9.** 24 **11.** 7 **13.** 24 **15.** 24 **17.** $\frac{5}{2}$ **19.** 12
21. 17 **23.** $\frac{3}{13}$ **25.** $-\frac{2}{3}$ **27.** $-\frac{11}{4}$ **29.** $\frac{1}{2}$ **31.** No solution **33.** -2 **35.** 4
37. 8 **39.** 2

Exercise 6

1. 150 **3.** 5 and 6 **5.** 15 and 35 **7.** 20 h **9.** 457 km **11.** 2 days **13.** $5\frac{5}{6}$ days
15. 2.4 h **17.** 4.2 h **19.** 12.4 h **21.** 7.8 weeks **23.** 5.6 winters **25.** 6.125 h **27.** \$11 360
29. \$1500, \$2000

Exercise 7

1. $bc/2a$ **3.** $\dfrac{bz - ay}{a - b}$ **5.** $\dfrac{a^2d + 3d^2}{4ac + d^2}$ **7.** $\dfrac{b + cd}{a^2 + a - d}$ **9.** $2z/a + 3w$ **11.** $(b - m)/3$

13. $(c - m)(a - b - d)$ **15.** b **17.** $\dfrac{2c + bc + 3b}{3 - 2b + c}$ **19.** $\dfrac{w}{w(w + y) - 1}$ **21.** $(p - q)/3p$

23. $(5b - 2a)/3$ **25.** $\dfrac{a^2(c + 1)(c - a)}{c^2}$ **27.** $\dfrac{ab}{a + b}$ **29.** $\dfrac{ab}{b - a}$ **31.** $md/(m + n)$ and $nd/(m + n)$

33. $\dfrac{anm}{nm - m - n}$ **35.** $\dfrac{L - L_0}{L_0\alpha}$ **37.** PL/Ee **39.** $(kAt_1 - qL)/kA$ **41.** $\dfrac{RR_1}{R_1 - R}$

43. $\dfrac{R_1(1 + \alpha t) - R}{R_1\alpha}$ **45.** $\dfrac{M - Fx}{R_1 - F}$ **47.** $\dfrac{m_2(25 - x)}{x - 10}$ **49.** $E/(ay + \frac{1}{2}v^2)$

Review Problems

1. $2ab/(a - b)$ **3.** $1/(3m - 1)$ **5.** $a^2 + 1 + 1/a^2$ **7.** a/c **9.** $4/(4 - x^2)$ **11.** 0
13. $\dfrac{a^2 + ab + b^2}{a + b}$ **15.** $(2a - 3c)/2a$ **17.** $3a/(a + 2)$ **19.** $\dfrac{x - y - z}{x + y - z}$ **21.** $\dfrac{a + b - c - d}{a - b + c - d}$
23. $(b + 5)/(c - a)$ **25.** 1 **27.** 11 **29.** $(r - pq)/(p - q)$ **31.** $q(p + 1)/(p^2 + r)$
33. 7 **35.** 24 **37.** 3 **39.** 6.35 days **41.** $19\frac{29}{45}$ **43.** $2ax^2y/7w$ **45.** $C = \dfrac{C_1C_2}{C_2 + C_1}$

CHAPTER 10

Exercise 1

1. $(2, -1)$ **3.** $(1, 2)$ **5.** $(-0.24, 0.90)$ **7.** $(3, 5)$ **9.** $(-3, 3)$ **11.** $(1, 2)$ **13.** $(3, 2)$
15. $(15, 6)$ **17.** $(3, 4)$ **19.** $(2, 3)$ **21.** $(1.63, 0.0971)$ **23.** $m = 2, n = 3$ **25.** $w = 6, z = 1$
27. $(9.36, 4.69)$ **29.** $v = 1.05, w = 2.58$

Exercise 2

1. $(60, 36)$ **3.** $(87/7, 108/7)$ **5.** $(15, 12)$ **7.** $m = 4, n = 3$ **9.** $r = 3.77, s = 1.23$
11. $(1/2, 1/3)$ **13.** $(1/3, 1/2)$ **15.** $(1/10, 1/12)$ **17.** $w = 1/36, z = 1/60$
21. **23.** **25.** $\dfrac{bs - cr}{a(b - c)}, \dfrac{r - s}{b - c}$ **27.** $(-3q, -2p)$

Exercise 3

1. 8 and 16   **3.** 4/21   **5.** 82   **7.** 7 and 41   **9.** 9×16 **11.** $x = 3.4$ km, $y = 0.772$ km
13. 2.14 m/s and 1.6 m/s   **15.** 2.13 km/h and 8.52 km/h   **17.** $v_0 = 3.8$ mm/s, $a = 36.2$ mm/s^2
19. \$2500 at 4%   **21.** \$2684 and \$1716   **23.** \$6000 for 2 years   **25.** 2740 kg mixture, 271 kg sand
27. 5.57 kg peat, 11.6 kg vermiculite   **29.** $T_1 = 490$ N, $T_2 = 185$ N   **31.** Carpenter, 25 days; helper, 37.5 days
33. 12 000 L/h and 18 000 L/h   **35.** 92 700 people and 162 000 people
37. $I_1 = 13.1$ mA, $I_2 = 22.4$ mA   **39.** $R_1 = 27.6 \, \Omega$, $\alpha = 0.00511$

Exercise 4

1. (15, 20, 25)   **3.** (1, 2, 3)   **5.** (5, 6, 7)   **7.** (1, 2, 3)   **9.** (3, 4, 5)   **11.** (6.18, 13.7, 18.1)
13. (2, 3, 1)   **15.** (1/2, 1/3, 1/4)   **17.** $(1, -1, 1/2)$ **19.** $(a/11, 5a/11, 7a/11)$
21. $[(a + b - c), (a - b + c), (-a + b + c)]$ **23.** 876   **25.** 361
27. 6.38 mA, 0.275 mA, -2.53 mA   **29.** $F_1 = 426$ N, $F_2 = 1080$ N, $F_3 = 362$ N

Review Problems

1. (3, 5)   **3.** (5, -2)   **5.** (2, -1, 1)   **7.** $\left(\dfrac{-9}{5}, \dfrac{54}{5}, \dfrac{-21}{5} \right)$ **9.** (8, 10)   **11.** (2, 3)

13. $[(a + b - c)/2, (a - b + c)/2, (b - a + c)/2]$ **15.** (7, 5)   **17.** (6, 8, 10)   **19.** (2, 3, 1)
21. (13, 17)   **23.** (2, 9)   **25.** 8 days

CHAPTER 11

Exercise 1

1. -14 **3.** 15   **5.** -27 **7.** 17.3   **9.** $-2/5$ **11.** $ad - bc$ **13.** $\sin^2 \theta - 3 \tan \theta$
15. $3i_1 \cos \theta - i_2 \sin \theta$ **17.** (3, 5)   **19.** $(-3, 3)$ **21.** (1, 2)   **23.** (3, 2)   **25.** (15, 6)
27. (3, 4)   **29.** (2, 3)   **31.** (1.63, 0.0967)   **33.** $m = 2, n = 3$ **35.** $w = 6, z = 1$

37. $(-6/13, 30/13)$ **39.** $\left(\dfrac{dp - bq}{ad - bc}, \dfrac{aq - cp}{ad - bc} \right)$ **41.** (3, 4)

Exercise 2

1. 11   **3.** 45   **5.** 48   **7.** -28 **9.** (5, 6, 7)   **11.** (15, 20, 25)   **13.** (1, 2, 3)
15. (3, 4, 5)   **17.** (6, 8, 10)   **19.** $(-2.30, 4.80, 3.09)$ **21.** (3, 6, 9)   **23.** $(2, -1, 5)$

Exercise 3

1. 2   **3.** 18   **5.** -66 **7.** $x = 2, y = 3, z = 4, w = 5$ **9.** $x = -4, y = -3, z = 2, w = 5$
11. $x = a - c, y = b + c, z = 0, w = a - b$ **13.** $x = 4, y = 5, z = 6, w = 7, u = 8$
15. $v = 3, w = 2, x = 4, y = 5, z = 6$ **17.** \$40 000, \$30 000, \$24 000, \$26 000
19. 102 kg, 98 kg, 218 kg, 182 kg

Review Problems

1. 20   **3.** 0   **5.** -3 **7.** 0   **9.** 18   **11.** 15   **13.** 0   **15.** -29 **17.** 133
19. $x = -4, y = -3, z = 2, w = 1$ **21.** (3, 5)   **23.** (4, 3)   **25.** (5, 1)   **27.** (2, 5)   **29.** (2, 1)
31. (3, 2)   **33.** (9/7, 37/7)   **35.** $x = -0.972, y = 2.28, z = 1.38, u = -0.385, v = 2.48$

CHAPTER 12

Exercise 1

1. A, B, D, E, F, I   **3.** C, H   **5.** I   **7.** B, I   **9.** F   **11.** 6   **13.** 4×3 **15.** 2×4

17. $\begin{pmatrix} 0 & 0 \\ 0 & 0 \\ 0 & 0 \\ 0 & 0 \end{pmatrix}$ **19.** If $y = 6, x = 2, w = 7$, and $z = 8$

Exercise 2

1. $(12 \quad 13 \quad 5 \quad 8)$ 　　**3.** $\begin{pmatrix} 14 \\ -10 \\ 6 \\ 14 \end{pmatrix}$ 　　**5.** $\begin{pmatrix} 7 & 1 & -4 & -7 \\ -9 & -4 & 9 & 2 \\ 3 & 7 & -3 & -9 \\ -1 & -4 & -5 & 6 \end{pmatrix}$ 　　**7.** $(-15 \quad -27 \quad 6 \quad -21 \quad -9)$

9. $\begin{pmatrix} -12 & -6 & 9 & 0 \\ 3 & -18 & -9 & 12 \end{pmatrix}$ 　　**11.** $7\begin{pmatrix} 3 & 1 & -2 \\ 7 & 9 & 4 \\ 2 & -3 & 8 \\ -6 & 10 & 12 \end{pmatrix}$ 　　**13.** $\begin{pmatrix} 6 & 16 & 3 \\ -16 & 8 & 19 \\ 31 & -14 & 15 \end{pmatrix}$ 　　**17.** 35 　　**19.** -61

21. $(10 \quad 27 \quad -14 \quad 15 \quad -7)$ 　　**23.** $(-60 \quad 18 \quad 10)$ 　　**25.** $(15 \quad 2 \quad 40 \quad 2 \quad 34)$ 　　**27.** $\begin{pmatrix} 19 & -13 \\ 17 & -43 \end{pmatrix}$

29. $\begin{pmatrix} -20 & 10 \\ 8 & -2 \\ -4 & 16 \end{pmatrix}$ 　　**31.** $\begin{pmatrix} 6 & -10 \\ 3 & -5 \end{pmatrix}$ 　　**33.** $\begin{pmatrix} 0 & 2 \\ 2 & 0 \\ -10 & -6 \\ -5 & 0 \end{pmatrix}$ 　　**35.** $\begin{pmatrix} 2 & 0 & -2 & 1 \\ 8 & 8 & -1 & 2 \\ 2 & 2 & 2 & 6 \end{pmatrix}$

37. $\mathbf{AB} = \begin{pmatrix} 1 & 2 & -1 \\ -2 & 9 & 2 \\ -1 & -2 & 1 \end{pmatrix} \quad \mathbf{BA} = \begin{pmatrix} 5 & -2 & 2 \\ 4 & -2 & 0 \\ -2 & 3 & 8 \end{pmatrix}$ 　　**39.** $\begin{pmatrix} 778 & 1050 \\ 1225 & 1653 \end{pmatrix}$ 　　**41.** $\begin{pmatrix} 5 \\ 1 \end{pmatrix}$ 　　**43.** $\begin{pmatrix} 13 \\ -1 \\ 10 \end{pmatrix}$

Exercise 3

1. $\begin{pmatrix} 0 & -0.2 \\ 0.125 & 0.1 \end{pmatrix}$ 　　**3.** $\begin{pmatrix} 0.118 & 0.059 \\ -0.02 & 0.157 \end{pmatrix}$ 　　**5.** $\begin{pmatrix} 0.074 & 0.168 & 0.057 \\ 0.148 & -0.164 & 0.115 \\ 0.090 & 0.094 & -0.041 \end{pmatrix}$

7. $\begin{pmatrix} 0.500 & 0 & -0.500 & 0 \\ 10.273 & -0.545 & -13.091 & 1.364 \\ -4.727 & 0.455 & 5.909 & -0.636 \\ -4.591 & 0.182 & 5.864 & -0.455 \end{pmatrix}$

Review Problems

1. $(2 \quad 12 \quad 10 \quad -2)$ 　　**3.** 86 　　**5.** $\begin{pmatrix} 0.063 & 0.250 \\ -0.188 & 0.250 \end{pmatrix}$ 　　**7.** $\begin{pmatrix} 7 & 2 & 6 \\ 9 & 0 & 3 \end{pmatrix}$ 　　**9.** $x = -4, y = -3, z = 2, w = 1$

11. $(2, \quad -1, \quad 1)$ 　　**13.** $(3, \quad 5)$ 　　**15.** -0.557 mA, 0.188 mA, -0.973 mA, -0.271 mA

CHAPTER 13

Exercise 1

1. $3/x$ 　　**3.** 2 　　**5.** $a/4b^2$ 　　**7.** a^3/b^2 　　**9.** p^3/q 　　**11.** 1 　　**13.** $1/(16a^6b^4c^{12})$ 　　**15.** $1/(x+y)$
17. $m^4/(1 - 6m^2n)^2$ 　　**19.** $2/x + 1/y^2$ 　　**21.** $1/(3m)^3 - 2/n^2$ 　　**23.** $x^{2n} + 2x^ny^m + y^{2m}$ 　　**25.** $x/2y^7$
27. p 　　**29.** x^{m^2} 　　**31.** $b/3$ 　　**33.** $9y^2/4x^2$ 　　**35.** $27q^3y^3/8p^3x^3$ 　　**37.** $9a^8b^6/25x^4y^2$

39. $4^na^{6n}x^{6n}/9^nb^{4n}y^{2n}$ 　　**41.** $3p^2/2q^2x^4z^3$ 　　**43.** $5^pw^{2p}/2^pz^p$ 　　**45.** $25n^4x^8/9m^6y^6$ 　　**47.** $\dfrac{(1+a)^2(b-1)}{(1-a+a^2)(b+1)^2}$

49. $x^7(x-y)^2$ 　　**51.** $9a^{2n} + 6a^nb^n + 4b^{2n}$ 　　**53.** $\dfrac{(x+1)^2(y-1)}{(y+1)^2(x^2-x+1)}$ 　　**55.** $(7/15)a^{n-m+2}x^{2-n}y^{n-3}$

57. $a^3(5a^2 - 16b^2)$ 　　**59.** $(a^{4-m}b^{n-3})/5$ 　　**61.** $x^3(x^2 + y^2)$ 　　**63.** $(a+b)^4/(a^2+b^2)^2$

Exercise 2

1. $\sqrt[4]{a}$ 　　**3.** $\sqrt[4]{z^3}$ 　　**5.** $\sqrt{m-n}$ 　　**7.** $\sqrt[3]{y/x}$ 　　**9.** $b^{1/2}$ 　　**11.** y 　　**13.** $(a+b)^{1/n}$ 　　**15.** xy
17. $3\sqrt{2}$ 　　**19.** $3\sqrt{7}$ 　　**21.** $-2\sqrt[3]{7}$ 　　**23.** $a\sqrt{a}$ 　　**25.** $6x\sqrt{y}$ 　　**27.** $2x^2\sqrt[3]{2y}$ 　　**29.** $6y^2\sqrt[5]{xy}$

31. $a\sqrt{a-b}$ **33.** $3\sqrt{m^3+2n}$ **35.** $x\sqrt[3]{x-a^2}$ **37.** $(a-b)(a+b)\sqrt{a}$ **39.** $\sqrt{21}/7$
41. $\sqrt[3]{2}/2$ **43.** $\sqrt[3]{6}/3$ **45.** $\sqrt{2x}/2x$ **47.** $a\sqrt{15ab}/5b$ **49.** $\sqrt[3]{x}/x$ **51.** $x\sqrt[3]{18}/3$
53. $(x-y)\sqrt{x^2+xy}$ **55.** $\dfrac{(m+n)\sqrt{m^2-mn}}{m-n}$ **57.** $\dfrac{(2a-6)\sqrt{6a}}{3a}$

Exercise 3

1. $\sqrt{6}$ **3.** $\sqrt{6}$ **5.** $25\sqrt{2}$ **7.** $-7\sqrt[3]{2}$ **9.** $-5\sqrt[3]{5}$ **11.** $-\sqrt[4]{3}$ **13.** $10x\sqrt{2y}$ **15.** $11\sqrt{6}/10$
17. $(a+b)\sqrt{x}$ **19.** $(x-2a)\sqrt{y}$ **21.** $-4a\sqrt{3x}$ **23.** $(5a+3c)\sqrt[3]{10b}$ **25.** $(a^2b^2c^2-2a+bc)\sqrt[5]{a^3bc^2}$
27. $6\sqrt{2x}$ **29.** $\dfrac{25}{18y}\sqrt{3x}$ **31.** 45 **33.** $16\sqrt{5}$ **35.** $24\sqrt[3]{5}$ **37.** $6\sqrt[6]{72}$ **39.** $10\sqrt[6]{72}$
41. $6x\sqrt{3ay}$ **43.** $2\sqrt[3]{x^3y^3}$ **45.** $\sqrt[4]{a^2b}$ **47.** $2xy\sqrt[6]{x^4yz^3}$ **49.** $2\sqrt{15}-6$ **51.** $x^2\sqrt{1-xy}$ **53.** a^2-b **55.** $16x-12\sqrt{xy}-10y$ **57.** $9y$ **59.** $9x^3\sqrt[3]{4x}$ **61.** $9-30\sqrt{a}+25a$ **63.** $250x\sqrt{2x}$
65. $250ax$ **67.** $3/4$ **69.** $\sqrt[6]{18}/4$ **71.** $3\sqrt[3]{2a}/a$ **73.** $4\sqrt[3]{18}/3+\sqrt[3]{4}+3$ **75.** $3/2$
77. $\dfrac{2\sqrt[6]{a^5b^2c^3}}{ac}$ **79.** $\dfrac{1}{2c}\sqrt[12]{a^2bc^{10}}$ **81.** $\dfrac{8+5\sqrt{2}}{2}$ **83.** $4\sqrt{ax}/a$ **85.** $6\sqrt[3]{2x}/x$
87. $\dfrac{30+17\sqrt{30}}{28}$ **89.** $\dfrac{a^2-a\sqrt{b}}{a^2-b}$ **91.** $\dfrac{x-2\sqrt{xy}+y}{x-y}$
93. $\dfrac{5\sqrt{3x}-5\sqrt{xy}+\sqrt{6xy}-\sqrt{2y}}{6x-2y}$ **95.** $\dfrac{3\sqrt{6a}-4\sqrt{3ab}+6\sqrt{10ab}-8\sqrt{5b}}{9a-8b}$

Exercise 4

1. 36 **3.** 4 **5.** 13.8 **7.** 8 **9.** 8 **11.** 7 **13.** 4.79 **15.** 3 **17.** 8 **19.** 0.347
21. No solution **23.** 7 **25.** 1412 mm, 290 mm **27.** 3.91 m, 4.77 m **29.** $C=1/(\omega^2L\pm\omega\sqrt{Z^2-R^2})$

Review Problems

1. $2\sqrt{13}$ **3.** $3\sqrt[3]{6}$ **5.** $\sqrt[3]{2}$ **7.** $9x\sqrt[4]{x}$ **9.** $(a-b)x\sqrt[3]{(a-b)^2x}$ **11.** $\dfrac{\sqrt{a^2-4}}{a+2}$ **13.** $x^2\sqrt{1-xy}$
15. $-\dfrac{1}{46}(6+15\sqrt{2}-4\sqrt{3}-10\sqrt{6})$ **17.** $\dfrac{2x^2+2x\sqrt{x^2-y^2}-y^2}{y^2}$ **19.** $26\sqrt[3]{x^2}$ **21.** $\sqrt[6]{a^3b^2}$
23. $9+12\sqrt{x}+4x$ **25.** $7\sqrt{2}$ **27.** $25\sqrt{2}/12$ **29.** $\sqrt{2b}/2b$ **31.** $72\sqrt{2}$ **33.** 10 **35.** 14
37. 15.2 **39.** $x^{2n-1}+(xy)^{n-1}+x^ny^{n-2}+y^{2n-3}$ **41.** $27x^3y^6/8$ **43.** $8x^9y^6$ **45.** $3/w^2$ **47.** $1/3x$
49. $1/x-2/y^2$ **51.** $1/9x^2+y^8/4x^4$ **53.** $p^{2a-1}+(pq)^{a-1}+p^aq^{a-2}+q^{2a-3}$ **55.** p^2/q **57.** r^2/s^3 **59.** 1

CHAPTER 14

Exercise 1

1. $0, 2/5$ **3.** $0, 9/2$ **5.** ±3 **7.** ±1 **9.** $0, 0.355$ **11.** $3, -5$ **13.** $5, -4$ **15.** $2, -1$
17. $-1, -2$ **19.** $9, -2$ **21.** $-4, -8$ **23.** $16, -4$ **25.** $5/2, -1$ **27.** $3/2, -4$ **29.** $1/5, -3$
31. $2, -1$ **33.** $1/6, -5/4$ **35.** $6, -3$ **37.** $1/2, -2/3$ **39.** $9, -4$ **41.** $1, -1/6$
43. $4, -2/3$ **45.** $5, -17/3$ **47.** ±6 **49.** $1, -13/6$ **51.** $-a, -3a$ **53.** $-2b, -4b/3$
55. $-3y^2/7, -2y^2/3$ **57.** $x^2-11x+28=0$ **59.** $15x^2-19x+6=0$ **61.** $6x^2+31x+35=0$
63. $x^2-2x-4=0$ **65.** $6, 15/4$ **67.** 4 (-21 doesn't check) **69.** 2 (-2 doesn't check)

Exercise 2

1. $4\pm\sqrt{14}$ **3.** $(-7\pm\sqrt{61})/2$ **5.** $(3\pm\sqrt{89})/8$ **7.** $(-3\pm\sqrt{21})/3$ **9.** $(-7\pm\sqrt{129})/8$
11. $0.485, -6.74$

Exercise 3

1. $3.17, 8.83$ **3.** $3.89, -4.87$ **5.** $1.96, -5.96$ **7.** $0.401, -0.485$ **9.** $0.170, -0.599$
11. $2.87, 0.465$ **13.** $0.907, -2.57$ **15.** $5.87, -1.87$ **17.** $12.0, -14.0$ **19.** $5.08, 10.9$
21. $0.132, -15.1$ **23.** $2.31, 0.623$ **25.** Real, unequal **27.** Not real **29.** Not real

Exercise 4

1. 2/3 or 3/2   **3.** 4 and 11   **5.** 5 and 15   **7.** 4 × 6 m   **9.** 150 × 300 mm   **11.** 162 × 200 m
13. 52.8 mm   **15.** 164.5 mm   **17.** 240 km/h   **19.** 80 km/h   **21.** 9 h and 12 h   **23.** 7 m/day
25. At each end   **27.** 0.64 s and 8.3 s   **29.** 125 Ω and 655 Ω   **31.** 0.38 A and 0.77 A
33. −0.5 A and 0.1 A   **35.** −1.1 V

Exercise 5

1.   **3.**   **7.**   **9.** 20 mm   **11.** 1.9 m

Exercise 6

1. $\sqrt[3]{2}$, $\sqrt[3]{4}$ **3.** 2, 1   **5.** 1 (0 doesn't check)   **7.** −1, −1/27   **9.** 1, −64
11. $\sqrt[3]{2}/8$ (8.69 doesn't check)   **13.** 625 (256 doesn't check)   **15.** 496 (243 doesn't check)

Exercise 7

1. 3, −5   **3.** −1   **5.** 3/2, −4   **7.** 4/3, −8/3   **13.** −0.930, 0.157, 0.773
15. −0.961, 0.293, 0.668   **17.** 0.629, 3.32

Exercise 8

1. (6, 2)   **3.** (3, 2), (−5, 6)   **5.** (2, 3), (−46, 15)   **7.** (2.61, −1.2), (−2.61, −1.2)
9. (4.86, 0.845), (4.86, −0.845)   **11.** (4, −7), (7, −4)   **13.** (2.04, 2.01), (−0.838, −2.57)
15. (1.26, 1.07), (0.491, −0.381)

Review Problems

1. 6, −1   **3.** ±2, ±3   **5.** 0, 5   **7.** 0, −2   **9.** 5, −2/3   **11.** 1, 1/2   **13.** ±3
15. 1.79, −2.79   **17.** 4, 9   **19.** 0.692, −0.803   **21.** ±$\sqrt{10}$ **23.** 1/2, −2   **25.** 0, 9   **27.** 1, 512
29. ±5   **31.** 3.54, −2.64   **33.** 0.777, −2.49   **35.** 0.716, −2.32   **37.** 1.49, −1.26
39. (7.41, −0.41), (−0.41, 7.41)   **41.** 2, 4, −3   **43.** (1.68, 1.16), (−2.68, 3.34)   **45.** 202 bags
47. 15 × 30 m   **49.** 4.63 km/h   **51.** 1.5 s   **53.** 128 × 404 or 256 × 202 mm   **55.** 3.56 km/h
57. 3.6 m × 3.6 m   **59.** Original voltage = 144 v

CHAPTER 15

Exercise 1

1. II   **3.** IV   **5.** I   **7.** II   **9.** II or III   **11.** IV   **13.** III   **15.** pos   **17.** pos

19. pos   **21.** neg

	sin	cos	tan		r	sin	cos	tan	cot	sec	csc
23.	+	−	−	**29.**	12.65	0.949	−0.316	−3.00	−0.333	−3.16	1.05
25.	−	+	−	**31.**	17.0	−0.471	−0.882	0.533	1.88	−1.13	−2.13
27.	+	−	−	**33.**	5.00	0	1.00	0	—	1.00	—

	sin	cos	tan		sin	cos	tan		sin	cos	tan
35.	−3/5	−4/5	3/4	**41.**	0.9816	−0.1908	−5.145	**47.**	0.8090	−0.5878	−1.376
37.	−2/$\sqrt{5}$	−1/$\sqrt{5}$	2	**43.**	−0.4848	0.8746	−0.5543	**49.**	0.9108	−0.4128	−2.206
39.	2/3	−$\sqrt{5}$/3	−2/$\sqrt{5}$	**45.**	−0.8898	0.4563	−1.950	**51.**	−0.2264	−0.9740	0.2324

	sin	cos	tan
53.	−0.1959	0.9806	−0.1998
55.	−0.8480	−0.5299	1.600

57. 0.8192   **59.** 1.906   **61.** 1.711   **63.** 1.111   **65.** 135°, 315°

67. 33.2°, 326.8°   **69.** 81.1°, 261.1°   **71.** 90°, 270°   **73.** 219.5°, 320.5°   **75.** 60.1°, 240.1°
77. 227.4°, 312.6°   **79.** 34.2°, 325.8°   **81.** 102.6°, 282.6°   **83.** 1/2   **85.** 0   **87.** 1   **89.** 0
91. 0   **93.** −1   **95.** 0   **97.** 1/2   **99.** 1   **101.** 0

Exercise 2

| | ANGLES | | | SIDES | | |
	A	B	C	a	b	c
1.	32.8°		101°			413
3.	108°	29.2°		29.3		
5.		71.1°			8.20	6.34
7.	104°			21.7		15.7
9.	23.0°			42.8	89.7	
11.	106.4°			90.74		29.55
13.			150°		34.1	82.0

Exercise 3

| | ANGLES | | | SIDES | | |
	A	B	C	a	b	c
1.	44.2°	29.8°				21.7
3.		48.7°	63.0°	22.6		
5.	56.9°	95.8°				70.1
7.		25.5°	19.5°	452		
9.	45.6°	80.4°	54.0°			
11.		30.8°	34.2°	82.8		
13.	69.0°	44.0°				8.95
15.		10.3°	11.7°	3.69		
17.	66.21°	72.02°				1052
19.	69.7°	51.7°	58.6°			

Exercise 4

1. 30.8 m and 85.6 m   **3.** 32.3°, 60.3°, 87.4°   **5.** N 48.8° W   **7.** S 59.5° E   **9.** 598 km
11. 28.3 m   **13.** 77.3 m, 131 m   **15.** 32.4 m   **17.** 337 mm   **19.** 337 mm   **21.** 1860 mm
23. 53.8 mm and 78.2 mm   **25.** 419   **27.** $A = 45°, B = 60°, C = 75°, AC = 1220, AB = 1360$ **29.** 6.67 m

Exercise 5

1. 521 at 10.0°   **3.** 87.1 at 31.9°   **5.** 6708 at 41.16°   **7.** 37.3 N at 20.5°   **9.** 121 N at N 59.8° W
11. 1720 N at 29.8° from larger force   **13.** 44.2° and 20.7°   **15.** Wind, S 37.4° E; plane, S 84.8° W
17. 413 km/h at N 41.2° E   **19.** 632 km/h, 3.09°   **21.** 26.9 A, 32.3°   **23.** 39.8 at 26.2°

Review Problems

1. $A = 24.1°, B = 20.9°, c = 77.6$ **3.** $A = 61.6°, C = 80.0°, b = 1.30$ **5.** $B = 20.2°, C = 27.8°, a = 82.4$
7. IV   **9.** II   **11.** negative   **13.** negative   **15.** negative   **17.** −0.800   −0.600   1.33
19. 1200 at 36.3°   **21.** 22.1 at 121°   **23.** 1.11 km

	sin	cos	tan
25.	0.0872	−0.9962	−0.0875
27.	0.7948	−0.6069	−1.3095

29. 0.4698   **31.** 1.469   **33.** S 3.5° E   **35.** 130.8°, 310.8°   **37.** 47.5°, 132.5°
39. 80.0°, 280.0°   **41.** 6954 N at 17.0°   **43.** −2240 mm/s, 4720 mm/s

CHAPTER 16

Exercise 1

1. 0.834 rad　　**3.** 0.615 rad　　**5.** 9.74 rad　　**7.** 0.279 rev　　**9.** 0.497 rev　　**11.** 0.178 rev
13. 162°　　**15.** 21.3°　　**17.** 65.3°　　**19.** π/3　　**21.** 11π/30　　**23.** 7π/10　　**25.** 13π/30
27. 20π/9　　**29.** 9π/20　　**31.** $22\frac{1}{2}°$　　**33.** 147°　　**35.** 20°　　**37.** 158°　　**39.** 24°　　**41.** 15°
43. 0.8660　　**45.** 0.4863　　**47.** −0.3090　　**49.** 1.067　　**51.** −2.747　　**53.** −0.8090　　**55.** −0.2582
57. 0.5854　　**59.** 0.8129　　**61.** 1.337　　**63.** 0.2681　　**65.** 1.309　　**67.** 1.116　　**69.** 0.5000
71. 0.1585　　**73.** 1.23×10^4 mm²　　**75.** 4860 mm²　　**77.** 57.9 mm

Exercise 2

	r	θ	s
1.			6.07 m
3.			230 m
5.			43.5 m
7.		2.21 rad	
9.		1.24 rad	
11.	8.9 mm		
13.	125 m		

15. 6064 km　　**17.** 596 m　　**19.** 245 mm　　**21.** 3.226×10^8 km

23. 0.251 m　　**25.** $r = 355$ mm, $R = 710$ mm, $\theta = 60.8°$　　**27.** 9920 km　　**29.** 141 mm　　**31.** 26.7 m

Exercise 3

1. 184 rad/s, 11 100 deg/s　　**3.** 12.9 rev/min, 1.35 rad/s　　**5.** 8.02 rev/min, 0.840 rad/s
7. 4350°　　**9.** 0.00749 s　　**11.** 356 rev/min　　**13.** 1.62 m/s　　**15.** 1659 km/h　　**17.** 57.6 rad/s

Review Problems

1. 77.1°　　**3.** 20°　　**5.** 165°　　**7.** 2.42 rad/s　　**9.** 5π/3　　**11.** 23π/18　　**13.** 0.3420
15. 1.000　　**17.** −0.01827　　**19.** 153 rev/min　　**21.** 537 km/h　　**23.** 1.1089　　**25.** −0.8812
27. −1.0291　　**29.** 0.9777　　**31.** 0.9097　　**33.** 222 mm

CHAPTER 17

Exercise 1

1. $P = 2$ s, $f = \frac{1}{2}$ cycle/s, amplitude = 7

15.

$y = 2 \sin 3x$
Period $= \dfrac{2\pi}{3}$
Amplitude $= 2$

17.

$y = \sin 3\pi x$
Period $= 2/3$
Amplitude $= 1$

19.

$y = \sin(x - 1)$
Period $= 2\pi$
Amplitude $= 1$
Phase shift $= 1$

21.

$y = \sin\left(x + \dfrac{\pi}{2}\right)$
Period $= 2\pi$
Amplitude $= 1$
Phase shift $= -\dfrac{\pi}{2}$

23. (a) $y = \sin 2x$ **(b)** $y = \sin(x - \pi/2)$ **(c)** $y = 2 \sin(x - \pi)$ **25.** $y = -2 \sin(x/3 + \pi/12)$

27.

29.

31.

Exercise 2

1.

$y = 3 \cos x$
Amplitude $= 3$
Period $= 2\pi$
Phase shift $= 0$

3.

$y = 2 \cos 3x$
Amplitude $= 2$
Period $= \dfrac{2\pi}{3}$
Phase shift $= 0$

5.

$y = 3 \cos\left(x - \dfrac{\pi}{4}\right)$
Amplitude $= 3$
Period $= 2\pi$
Phase shift $= \dfrac{\pi}{4}$

7.

$y = 2 \tan x$

9.

$y = 3 \tan 2x$

11.

$y = 2 \tan(3x - 2)$

13.

15.

17.

19.

$y = x + \sin x$ $y = x$
$y = \sin x$

21.

$y = \dfrac{2}{x}$ $y = \dfrac{2}{x} - \sin x$
$y = \sin x$

23.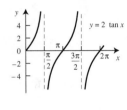

$y = \sin x$
$y = \cos 2x$
$y = \sin x + \cos 2x$

25.

$y = 2 \sin 2x$
$y = \cos 3x$ $y = 2 \sin 2x - \cos 3x$

27. (graph)

29. (graph)

Exercise 3

1. $P = 0.0147$ s, $\omega = 427$ rad/s   **3.** $P = 0.0002$ s, $\omega = 31\ 400$ rad/s   **5.** $f = 8$ Hz, $\omega = 50.3$ rad/s
7. 3.33 s   **9.** $P = 0.0138$ s, $f = 72.4$ Hz   **11.** $P = 0.0126$ s, $f = 79.6$ Hz
13. $P = 400$ ms, $a = 10$, $\phi = 1.1$ rad   **15.** $y = 5 \sin(750t + 15°)$

17. 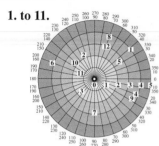 $y = 3 \sin 377t$

19. $y = 375 \sin\left(55t + \frac{\pi}{4}\right)$

21. $y = 35.7 \sin(\omega t + 45.4°)$ **23.** $y = 843 \sin(\omega t - 28.2°)$ **25.** $y = 9.40 \sin(\omega t + 51.7°)$
27. $y = 660 \sin(wt + 56.5°)$
29. $v_{max} = 4.27$ V, $P = 13.6$ ms, $f = 73.7$ Hz, $\phi = 27° = 0.471$ rad, $v(0.12) = -2.11$ V
31. $i = 49.2 \sin(220t + 63.2°)$mA

Exercise 4

1. to 11.   **27.**   **29.**   **31.**

33.

35. $(6.71, 63.4°)$ **37.** $(5.00, 36.9°)$ **39.** $(7.61, 231°)$ **41.** $(597, 238°)$
43. $(3.41, 3.66)$ **45.** $(298, -331)$ **47.** $(2.83, -2.83)$ **49.** $(12.3, -8.60)$
51. $(-7.93, 5.76)$ **53.** $x^2 + y^2 = 2y$ **55.** $x^2 + y^2 = 1 - y/x$
57. $x^2 + y^2 = 4 - x$ **59.** $r \sin \theta + 3 = 0$ **61.** $r = 1$ **63.** $\sin \theta = r \cos^2 \theta$

65.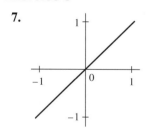

67. $r = 2.35 \sin^2 \theta + 2.94 \cos^2$

Exercise 5

7.   **9.**   **11.**   **13.**

15.   **17.**   **19.**   **21.**

Review Problems

1.
$y = 3 \sin 2x$
Period $= \pi$
Amplitude $= 3$

3.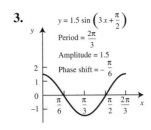
$y = 1.5 \sin\left(3x + \dfrac{\pi}{2}\right)$
Period $= \dfrac{2\pi}{3}$
Amplitude $= 1.5$
Phase shift $= -\dfrac{\pi}{6}$

5.
$y = 2.5 \sin\left(4x + \dfrac{2\pi}{9}\right)$
Period $= \dfrac{\pi}{2}$
Amplitude $= 2.5$
Phase shift $= -\dfrac{\pi}{18}$

7. $y = 5 \sin(2x/3 + \pi/9)$

9.

11. and 13.

15.

17. $(6.52, 144°)$ **19.** $(2.54, 2.82)$ **21.** $(2.73 - 2.64)$ **23.** $x^2 + y^2 = 2x$
25. $r = 1/(5 \cos \theta + 2 \sin \theta)$ **27.** $P = 0.00833\ s$, $\omega = 754$ rad/s   **29.** $3.33\ s$

31.

33. (a) $y = 101 \sin(\omega t - 15.2°)$ **(b)** $y = 3.16 \sin(\omega t + 56.8°)$ **35.**

CHAPTER 18

Exercise 1

1. $(\sin x - 1)/\cos x$ **3.** $1/\cos \theta$ **5.** $1/\cos \theta$ **7.** $-\tan^2 x$ **9.** $\sin \theta$ **11.** $\sec \theta$ **13.** $\tan x$
15. $\cos \theta$ **17.** $\sin \theta$ **19.** 1 **21.** 1 **23.** $\sin x$ **25.** $\sec x$ **27.** $\tan^2 x$ **29.** $-\tan^2 \theta$

Exercise 2

1. $\frac{1}{2}(\sqrt{3} \sin \theta + \cos \theta)$ **3.** $\frac{1}{2}(\sin x + \sqrt{3} \cos x)$ **5.** $-\sin x$ **7.** $\sin \theta \cos 2\phi + \cos \theta \sin 2\phi$
9. $(\tan 2\theta - \tan 3\alpha)/(1 + \tan 2\theta \tan 3\alpha)$ **11.** $-\cos \theta - \sin \theta$ **13.** $-\sin x$
33. $y = 11\,200 \sin(\omega t + 41.0°)$ **35.** $y = 112 \sin(\omega t + 41.4°)$

Exercise 3

1. 1 **3.** $\sin 2x$ **5.** 2

Exercise 5

1. 30°, 150°   **3.** 45°, 225°   **5.** 60°, 120°, 240°, 300°   **7.** 90°   **9.** 30°, 150°, 210°, 330°
11. 45°, 135°, 225°, 315°   **13.** 0°, 45°, 180°, 225°   **15.** 60°, 120°, 240°, 300°   **17.** 60°, 180°, 300°
19. 120°, 240°   **21.** 0°, 60°, 120°, 180°, 240°, 300°   **23.** 135°, 315°   **25.** 0°, 60°, 180°, 300°

Exercise 6

1. 22.0°   **3.** 281.5°   **5.** 81.8°   **7.** 75.4°   **9.** 33.2°

Review Problems

13. 1   **15.** $2 \csc^2\theta$ **17.** 1   **19.** 1   **21.** 1   **23.** $-\tan\theta$ **25.** 120°, 240°   **27.** 45°, 225°
29. 15°, 45°, 75°, 135°, 195°, 225°, 255°, 315°   **31.** 90°, 306.9°   **33.** 189.3°, 350.7°   **35.** 60°, 300°
37. 55.6°   **39.** 74.3°   **41.** $78.2 \sin(\omega t + 52.5°)$

CHAPTER 19

Exercise 1

1. 9/2   **3.** 8/3   **5.** 8   **7.** 8   **9.** $3x$ **11.** $-5a$ **13.** $(x + 2)/x$ **15.** ± 12 **17.** ± 15
19. 30, 42   **21.** 24, 32   **23.** elder = \$40 000, younger = \$35 000   **25.** 9, 11   **27.** 300 turns

Exercise 2

1. 197   **3.** 71.5   **5.** $x = 15, y = 55$ **7.** $x = 138, y = 140, 152$ **9.** 438 km   **11.** 137
13. 5067 kw   **15.** 911 m   **17.** 1.8 m³

Exercise 3

1. 2050   **3.** 79.3   **5.** 2799   **7.** 66.7   **9.** $x = 27.5, y = 8\,842$ **11.** $x = 122, y = 203$
13.

15. 396 m   **17.** 5.8 s   **19.** 765 W   **21.** 1.73   **23.** f4   **25.** f11

27. 137×10^3 mm³   **29.** 236 tonnes   **31.** 94 m²   **33.** 93 mm   **35.** 28 900 m²

Exercise 4

1. 1420   **3.** y is halved   **5.** $x = 91.5, y = 61.5$ **7.** $x = 9236, y = 1443$ **9.** 41.4% increase
11.

13. 760 Pa   **15.** 4.5×10^{-6} dyne   **17.** 530 N   **19.** 200 lux   **21.** 5.3 m

23. 0.91   **25.** $33\frac{1}{3}$% increase

Exercise 5

1. 352   **3.** 4.2% increase   **5.** $w = 116$ $x = 43.5$ $y = 121$ **7.** 13.9   **9.** $y = 4.08x^{3/2}/w$
11. $13\frac{3}{4}$% decrease   **13.** 1/3   **15.** 9/4   **17.** 169 W   **19.** 3.58 m³   **21.** 3.0 weeks
23. 57.64 kN   **25.** 394 times/s   **27.** 2.21

Review Problems

1. 1040   **3.** 10.4% increase   **5.** 121 L/min   **7.** 1.73   **9.** 29 yr   **11.** shortened by 8 mm
13. 8.5   **15.** 22 h 52 min   **17.** 337×10^6 km or 437×10^3 km   **19.** 420 N   **21.** 2.8
23. 45% increase   **25.** 2074 L   **27.** 102 m²   **29.** 28.3 mm   **31.** 17.6 m²   **33.** 12.7 tonnes
35. 23.4 kg   **37.** $608   **39.** 1.5   **41.** 762 000 mm²

CHAPTER 20

Exercise 1

1.   **3.**   **5.**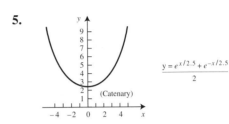

7. $4852   **9. (a)** $6.73   **(b)** $7.33   **(c)** $7.39   **11.** $1823

Exercise 2

1. 284 units   **3.** 12.4 million   **5.** 18.2 million barrels   **7.** 506°C   **9.** 0.101 A   **11.** 569.5°C
13. 192 mm Hg   **15.** 72 mA   **17.** 30%

Exercise 3

1. $\log_3 81 = 4$ **3.** $\log_4 4096 = 6$ **5.** $\log_x 995 = 5$ **7.** $10^2 = 100$ **9.** $5^3 = 125$ **11.** $3^{57} = x$
13. $5^y = x$ **15.**

$$y = \log_e x$$

17. 1.4409   **19.** 0.7731   **21.** 1.6839   **23.** 2.9222   **25.** 1.4378

27. −2.1325   **29.** 4.5437   **31.** 38.4   **33.** 187 000   **35.** 1.39×10^{-3} **37.** 5.93×10^{-3}
39. 9530   **41.** 1.07×10^{-4} **43.** 3.8774   **45.** 7.7685   **47.** −0.1684   **49.** −4.7843
51. −9.9825   **53.** 10.5558   **55.** 17.22   **57.** 2.408   **59.** 0.6942   **61.** 2.550   **63.** 7.572×10^6
65. 1.063×10^{-8}

Exercise 4

1. $\log 2 - \log 3$ **3.** $\log a + \log b$ **5.** $\log x + \log y + \log z$ **7.** $\log 3 + \log x - \log 4$
9. $-\log 2 - \log x$ **11.** $\log a + \log b + \log c - \log d$ **13.** $\log 12$ **15.** $\log 3/2$ **17.** $\log 27$
19. $\log a^3 c^4/b^2$ **21.** $\log xy^2z^3/ab^2c^3$ **23.** $\log[\sqrt{x + 2}(x - 2)]$ **25.** $2^x = xy^2$ **27.** $a^2 + 2b^2 = 0$
29. $p - q = 100$ **31.** 1   **33.** 2   **35.** x **37.** $3y$ **39.** 549.0   **41.** 322   **43.** 2.735
45. 12.58   **47.** 3.634   **49.** 3.63   **51.** 1.639   **53.** 2.28   **55.** 195   **57.** −8.796   **59.** 5.46

Exercise 5

1. 2.81   **3.** 16.1   **5.** 2.46   **7.** 1.17   **9.** 5.10   **11.** 1.49   **13.** 0.239   **15.** −3.44
17. 1.39   **19.** 0   **21.** $3e^{4.159x}$ **23.** 0.0147 s   **25.** 1.5 s   **27.** 8528 m   **29.** 2.0 rad
31. 2.4 yr   **33.** 7.95 yr   **35.** 9.9 yr   **37.** 3.4%

Exercise 6

1. 2 **3.** 1/3 **5.** 2/3 **7.** 2/3 **9.** 2 **11.** 3 **13.** 25 **15.** 6 **17.** 3/2
19. 47.5 **21.** −11.0, 9.05 **23.** 10/3 **25.** 22 **27.** 0.928 **29.** 0.916 **31.** 12 **33.** 101
35. 50 000 **37.** 7.0 years **39.** 3.5 **41.** 713.4 mm Hg **43.** 1300 kW **45.** −3.01 dB
47. 17.5 years **49.** 10^{-7} **51.** $4\overline{0}$

Exercise 7

1. $y = 2x^3$

3. $y = x^{.5}$

5. $y = 5\sqrt{x}$ 15.8

7. $y = 1/x$

9. $y = 2x^{2/3}$ 9.28

11. $y = 2000x^{-2.97}$

13. $y = x^{.5}$

15. $y = e^{-x}$ 0.0067

17. $y = 3^{x/4}$ 3.95

19. $y = 5e^{-x}$ 0.034

21. $y = 2.5^x$

23. $i = 16.5\,v^{0.598}$

25.

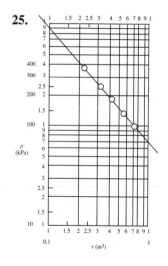

Review Problems

1. $\log_x 352 = 5.2$ **3.** $\log_{24} x = 1.4$ **5.** $x^{124} = 5.2$ **7.** 3/4 **9.** 1/128 **11.** $\log 3 + \log x - \log z$
13. $\log 10$ **15.** $\log(\sqrt{p}/\sqrt[4]{q})$ **17.** 2.5611 **19.** 701.5 **21.** 0.3365 **23.** 2.943 **25.** 4.4394
27. −4.7410 **29.** 4.362 **31.** 2.101 **33.** 13.44 **35.** 3.17 **37.** 1.00×10^{-3} **39.** $2071
41. 828 rev/min **43.** 23 years **45.** $y = e^{v/3}$

CHAPTER 21

Exercise 1

1. $j3$ **3.** $j/2$ **5.** $4 + j2$ **7.** $-5 + j3/2$ **9.** $j5$ **11.** $-1 + j$ **13.** $2a + j2$
15. $3/4 + j/6$ **17.** $4.03 + j1.20$ **19.** j **21.** j **23.** $j14$ **25.** -15 **27.** $-j96$ **29.** -25
31. $6 - j8$ **33.** $8 + j20$ **35.** $36 + j8$ **37.** $42 - j39$ **39.** $21 - j20$ **41.** $2 + j3$
43. $p - jq$ **45.** $n + jm$ **47.** $j2$ **49.** 2 **51.** $2 + j$ **53.** $-5/2 + j/2$ **55.** $11/34 - j41/34$
57. $0.833 \pm j1.28$ **59.** $1.00 \pm j2.24$ **61.** $(x + j3)(x - j3)$ **63.** $(2y + jz)(2y - jz)$

Exercise 2

1., 3., 5., 7., 9.

Exercise 3

1. $6.40\underline{/38.7°}$, $6.40(\cos 38.7° + j \sin 38.7°)$ **3.** $5\underline{/323°}$, $5(\cos 323° + j \sin 323°)$
5. $5.39\underline{/202°}$, $5.39(\cos 202° + j \sin 202°)$ **7.** $10.3\underline{/209°}$, $10.3(\cos 209° + j \sin 209°)$
9. $8.06\underline{/240°}$, $8.06(\cos 240° + j \sin 240°)$ **11.** $1.63 + j2.52$, $3\underline{/57°}$
13. $-7.79 + j4.50$, $9\underline{/150°}$ **15.** $3.70 + j4.01$, $5.46\underline{/47.3°}$ **17.** $4.64 + j7.71$, $9(\cos 59° + j \sin 59°)$
19. $4.21 - j5.59$, $7(\cos 307° + j \sin 307°)$ **21.** $15(\cos 40° + j \sin 40°)$ **23.** $16.1(\cos 54.9° + j \sin 54.9°)$
25. $56\underline{/60°}$ **27.** $2(\cos 25° + j \sin 25°)$ **29.** $4.70(\cos 50.2° + j \sin 50.2°)$ **31.** $10\underline{/60°}$
33. $8(\cos 45° + j \sin 45°)$ **35.** $49\underline{/40°}$ **37.** $7.55\underline{/26°}$, $7.55\underline{/206°}$
39. $3.36\underline{/24.3°}$, $3.36\underline{/144.3°}$, $3.36\underline{/264.3°}$ **41.** $13.8 + j7.41$, $-13.8 - j7.41$

Exercise 4

1. $3.61e^{j0.983}$ **3.** $3e^{j0.873}$ **5.** $2.5e^{j\pi/6}$ **7.** $5.4e^{j\pi/12}$
9. $-4.95 + j0.706$, $5\underline{/172°}$, $5(\cos 172° + j \sin 172°)$ **11.** $0.156 + j2.19$, $2.2\underline{/85.9°}$, $2.2(\cos 85.9° + j \sin 85.9°)$
13. $18e^{j6}$ **15.** $21e^{j4}$ **17.** $3.6e^{j7}$ **19.** $3e^{j3}$ **21.** $11e^{j3}$ **23.** $3e^{j}$ **25.** $9e^{j10}$ **27.** $8e^{j3}$

Exercise 5

1. $4.59 + j5.28$, $7\underline{/49°}$ **3.** $54.8 + j185$, $193\underline{/73.5°}$ **5.** $-31.2 + j23.3$, $39\underline{/143°}$ **7.** $8 - j2$
9. $38.3 + j60.2$ **11.** $8.67 + j6.30$ **13.** $29 - j29$ **15.** $12(\cos 32° - j \sin 32°)$
17. $3.08\underline{/32°}$

Exercise 6

1. $177\underline{/25°}$ **3.** $40\underline{/-90°}$ **5.** $102\underline{/0°}$ **7.** $212 \sin \omega t$ **9.** $424 \sin (\omega t - 90°)$ **11.** $11 \sin \omega t$
13. $155 + j0$, $155\underline{/0°}$ **15.** $0 - j18$, $18\underline{/270°}$ **17.** $72 - j42$, $83.4\underline{/-30.3°}$ **19.** $552 - j572$, $795\underline{/-46.0°}$
21. (a) $v = 603 \sin(\omega t + 85.3°)$ **(b)** $v = 293 \sin(\omega t - 75.5°)$

Review Problems

1. $3 + j2$, $3.61\underline{/33.7°}$, $3.61(\cos 33.7° + j \sin 33.7°)$, $3.61e^{j0.588}$
3. $-2 + j7$, $7.28\underline{/106°}$, $7.28(\cos 106° + j \sin 106°)$, $7.28e^{j1.85}$ **5.** j **7.** $9 + j2$ **9.** $60.8 + j45.6$
11. $11 + j7$ **13.** $12(\cos 38° + j \sin 38°)$ **15.** $33/17 - j21/17$ **17.** $2(\cos 45° + j \sin 45°)$
19. and 21.   **23.** $7 - j24$ **25.** $125(\cos 30° + j \sin 30°)$ **27.** $32\underline{/32°}$
29. $0.884\underline{/-45°}$

CHAPTER 22

Exercise 1

1. 3   **3.** 9   **5.** 6.60   **7.** 3.34   **9.** 6.22   **11.** −7.90   **13.** 26   **15.** 9.06   **17.** 4.66
19. 1.615   **21.** −1.080   **23.** 61.5°   **25.** 110°   **27.** 93.8°   **29.** −1/2   **31.** 0.541
33. 0.1862   **35.** 0.276   **37.** 166°   **39.** 164°   **41.** 35.5°   **43.** 125°   **45.**

47.

49. $2.25x − y − 1.48 = 0$ **51.** $5.52x + 0.39y − 22.9 = 0$ **53.** $2x + y + 7 = 0$

55. $3x − y + 6 = 0$ **57.** $2x − 3y − 6.9 = 0$ **59.** $3x + 4y − 8 = 0$ **61.** $4x − y − 17 = 0$
63. $3x + y − 19 = 0$ **65.** $0.472x + y + 3.52 = 0$ **67.** $x − 0.40y + 4.31 = 0$ **69.** $x = −3$
71. $2x − y − 2 = 0$ **73.** $x + 2y − 2 = 0$ **75.** 78.6 mm   **77.** 612 m   **79.** 1260 m   **81.** 0.911°
83. 33.7°   **85.** $F = kL − kL_0$ **87.** 10.5 m/s, 64.3 m/s   **89.** 150.1 Ω   **93.** $P = 103 + 12.4x, x = 8.46\ m$
95. $t = −0.789x + 25.0, x = 31.7$ cm, $m = 0.789$ **97.** $y = P + t(S − P)/L$, \$5555

Exercise 2

1. $x^2 + y^2 = 49$ **3.** $(x − 2)^2 + (y − 3)^2 = 25$ **5.** $(x − 5)^2 + (y + 3)^2 = 16$ **7.** $C(0, 0), r = 7$
9. $C(2, −4), r = 4$ **11.** $C(3, −5), r = 6$ **13.** $C(4, 0), r = 4$ **15.** $C(5, −6), r = 6$
17. $C(−3, 1), r = 5$ **19.** $x^2 + y^2 − 2x − 2y − 23 = 0$ **21.** $4x + 3y = 25$ **23.** $4x − 3y + 10 = 0$
25. (3, 0), (2, 0), (0, 1), (0, 6)   **27.** (2, 3) and (−3/2, −1/2)   **31.** 2.62 m
33. $(x − 1828)^2 + y^2 − 3048^2 = 0, 2x = w = 2102$ mm

Exercise 3

1. $F(2, 0), L = 8$ **3.** $F(0, −3/7), L = 12/7$ **5.** $x^2 + 8y = 0$ **7.** $3y^2 = 4x$
9. $V(3, 5), F(6, 5), L = 12, y = 5$ **11.** $V(3, −1), F(3, 5), L = 24, x = 3$
13. $V(2, −1), F(13/8, −1), L = 3/2, y = −1$ **15.** $V(3/2, 5/4), F(3/2, 1), L = 1, x = 3/2$
17. $y^2 − 8x − 4y + 12 = 0$ **19.** $y^2 + 4x − 2y + 9 = 0$ **21.** $2y^2 + 4y − x − 4 = 0$ **23.** $y^2 = 3(10^8x)$
25. 3.20 m   **27.** $x^2 = 109y$, 22.9 m   **29.** 0.563 m   **31.** $x^2 = −366(y − 22.9)$ **33.** 21.8 mm

Exercise 4

1. $V(\pm 5, 0), F(\pm 3, 0)$ **3.** $V(\pm 2, 0), F(\pm 1, 0)$ **5.** $V(0, \pm 4), F(0, \pm 2)$ **7.** $\dfrac{x^2}{25} + \dfrac{y^2}{9} = 1$
9. $\dfrac{x^2}{36} + \dfrac{y^2}{4} = 1$ **11.** $\dfrac{x^2}{169} + \dfrac{y^2}{25} = 1$ **13.** $\dfrac{3x^2}{115} + \dfrac{7y^2}{115} = 1$
15. $C(2, −2); V(6, −2), (−2, −2); F(4.65, −2), (−0.65, −2)$ **17.** $C(−2, 3); V(1, 3), (−5, 3); F(0,3), (−4, 3)$
19. $C(1, −1); V(5, −1), (−3, −1); F(4, −1), (−2, −1)$ **21.** $C(−3, 2); V(−3, 7), (−3, −3); F(−3, 6), (−3, −2)$
23. $\dfrac{x^2}{9} + \dfrac{(y − 3)^2}{36} = 1$ **25.** $\dfrac{(x + 2)^2}{12} + \dfrac{(y + 3)^2}{16} = 1$ **27.** (1,2), (1, −2)   **29.** 608 mm   **31.** 200 mm
33. 2146 mm

Exercise 5

1. $V(\pm 4, 0)$, $F(\pm\sqrt{41}, 0)$, $a = 4$, $b = 5$, slope $= \pm 5/4$ **3.** $V(\pm 3, 0)$, $F(\pm 5, 0)$, $a = 3$, $b = 4$, slope $= \pm 4/3$

5. $V(\pm 4, 0)$, $F(\pm 2\sqrt{5}, 0)$, $a = 4$, $b = 2$, slope $= \pm 1/2$ **7.** $\dfrac{x^2}{25} - \dfrac{y^2}{144} = 1$ **9.** $\dfrac{x^2}{9} - \dfrac{y^2}{7} = 1$

11. $\dfrac{y^2}{16} - \dfrac{x^2}{16} = 1$ **13.** $\dfrac{y^2}{25} - \dfrac{3x^2}{64} = 1$

15. $C(2, -1)$; $a = 5$, $b = 4$; $F(8.4, -1)$, $F'(-4.4, -1)$; $V(7, -1)$, $V'(-3, -1)$; slope $= \pm 4/5$

17. $C(2, -3)$; $a = 3$, $b = 4$; $F(7, -3)$, $F'(-3, -3)$; $V(5, -3)$, $V'(-1, -3)$; slope $= \pm 4/3$

19. $C(-1, -1)$; $a = 2$, $b = \sqrt{5}$; $F(-1, 2)$, $F'(-1, -4)$; $V(-1, 1)$, $V'(-1, -3)$; slope $= \pm 2/\sqrt{5}$

21. $\dfrac{(y - 2)^2}{16} - \dfrac{(x - 3)^2}{4} = 1$ **23.** $\dfrac{(x - 1)^2}{4} - \dfrac{(y + 2)^2}{12} = 1$ **25.** $xy = 36$ **27.** $\dfrac{x^2}{324} - \dfrac{y^2}{352} = 1$

29. $pv = 2.85$

Review Problems

1. 4 **3.** -1.44 **5.** $147°$ **7.** $-2b/a$ **9.** $m = 3/2$, $b = -7/2$ **11.** $7x - 3y + 32 = 0$

13. $5x - y + 27 = 0$ **15.** $7x - 3y + 21 = 0$ **17.** $y = 5$ **19.** -3 **21.** $x + 3 = 0$ **23.** 23.0

35. Parabola, $V(-3, 3)$, $F(-3, 2)$ **37.** Ellipse, $C(4,5)$; $a = 10$, $b = 6$; $F(4, 13)$, $(4, -3)$; $V(4, 15)$, $(4, -5)$

39. Circle, $C(0, 0)$, $r = 3$ **41.** $x^2 + y^2 - 8x + 6y = 0$ **43.** $(x - 1)^2 - 9(y - 1)^2 = 16$

45. $625x^2 - 84y^2 = 10\,000$ **47.** $(y + 7)^2 = 4(x - 3)$ **49.** $(-1, -3)$ and $(-3, -1)$ **51.** $\dfrac{x^2}{6.25} - \dfrac{y^2}{36} = 1$

53. 25.44 m and 3.76 m

CHAPTER 23

Exercise 1

1. 2 **3.** 3 **5.** 6 **7.** 13 **9.** 12 **11.** 5 **13.** 103 **15.** 119 **17.** 101 **19.** 10

21. 0100 1000 **23.** 0101 1101 **25.** 1 0001 0010 **27.** 0111 0110

29. 10 0000 1011 0111 **31.** 1 0100 0011 0011 0100 **33.** 0.1 **35.** 0.11 **37.** 0.0100 1100

39. 0.1000 1100 **41.** 0.111 **43.** 0.0110 0011 **45.** 0.5 **47.** 0.25 **49.** 0.5625

51. 101.1 **53.** 100.011 **55.** 11 1011 0100.0111 1000 **57.** 1.5 **59.** 2.25 **61.** 25.40625

Exercise 2

1. D **3.** 9 **5.** 93 **7.** D8 **9.** 92A6 **11.** 9.3 **13.** 1.38 **15.** 0110 1111

17. 0100 1010 **19.** 0010 1111 0011 0101 **21.** 0100 0111 1010 0010 **23.** 0101.1111

25. 1001.1010 1010 **27.** 242 **29.** 51 **31.** 14 244 **33.** 62 068 **35.** 3.9375

37. 2748.8671875 **39.** 27 **41.** 399 **43.** AB5 **45.** 6C8

Exercise 3

1. 6 **3.** 7 **5.** 63 **7.** 155 **9.** 111 **11.** 01 0110 **13.** 1 1001 0011

15. 1010 1010 0011 **17.** 0110 0110 0110 1000

Exercise 4

1. 0110 0010 **3.** 0010 0111 0100 **5.** 0100 0010.1001 0001 **7.** 9 **9.** 61 **11.** 36.8

Review Problems

1. 6.125 **3.** 0100 0101 **5.** 1264 **7.** 1 1010.111 **9.** 348 **11.** BE **13.** 20AA

15. 134 **17.** 0100 1110 0101 1101 **19.** 0100 1010

CHAPTER 24

Exercise 1

1. unconditional, nonlinear **3.** conditional, nonlinear **5.** conditional, linear **7.** $x > 5$ and $x < 9$
9. $x > -11$ and $x \le 1$ **11.** $5 < x < 8$ **13.** $-1 \le x < 24$ **15.**

17.

19. $x \ge -2$ **21.** $x \le 1$ **23.** $x < 8$

25. $x > -3$ **27.** $3 < x < 12$ **29.** $4 < x \le 22$ **31.**

33. **35.**

37.

Exercise 2

1. $x > 9$ **3.** $-3 \le x \le 3$ **5.** $x < 1$ or $x > 3/2$ **7.** $x \ge 40/7$ **9.** $-2 < x < 5$
11. $-3 \le x \le 1$ **13.** $x > 3$ or $x < -3$ **15.** $x > 8/5$ or $x < -8/5$ **17.** $x \ge 10/3$ or $x \le -2$
19. $x < 5$ **21.** $x \ge -1/2$ or $x \le 7/8$ **23.** $x \le -5$ or $x \ge 1$ **25.** $x \le -2$ or $x \ge 3$
27. $25x + 155 \le 350$, 7.8 h **29.** 106 lenses per week **31.** $-1.52 < x < 1.52$ **33.** $-1.84 < x < 1.35$

Exercise 3

1. $x = 1.5, y = 3.5$ **3.** $x = 2.78, y = 3.89$ **5.** 69 pulleys, 68 sprockets **7.** 8 disk drives, 4 monitors

Review Problems

1. $x > -11$ and $x \le 1$ **3.** $(-\infty, 8)$ **5.** **7.** $x > 8$

9. $x < -3$ or $x > 11$ **11.** $x = 2.5, y = 0$

13. $x \le -5$ or $x \ge -3$ **15.** $x \le -7$ or $x \ge 2$ **17.** $-1.73 < x \le 8.82$ **19.** $0.253 < x < 1.18$

CHAPTER 25

Exercise 1

1. $3 + 6 + 9 + 12 + 15 + \cdots + 3n + \cdots$ **3.** $2 + 3/4 + 4/9 + 5/16 + 6/25 + \cdots + (n + 1)/n^2 + \cdots$
5. $u_n = 2n$; 8, 10 **7.** $\cdots u_n = 2^n/(n + 3)$; 32/8, 64/9 **9.** $u_n = u_{n-1} + 4$; 13, 17
11. $u_n = (u_{n-1})^2$; 6561, 43 046 721 **13.** Diverges **15.** Converges

Exercise 2

1. 46 **3.** 43 **5.** 49 **7.** $x + 24y$ **9.** $3, 7\frac{1}{3}, 11\frac{2}{3}$ 16, $20\frac{1}{3}, \cdots$ **11.** 5, 11, 17, 23, 29, $\cdots$
13. -7 **15.** 234 **17.** 225 **19.** 15 **21.** 10, 15 **23.** $-6\frac{3}{5}, -7\frac{1}{5}, -7\frac{4}{5}, -8\frac{2}{5}$ **25.** 3/14
27. 7/11, 7/13 **29.** \$ 4400 **31.** \$94 000 **33.** 490 m

Exercise 3

1. 80 **3.** −9375 **5.** 5115 **7.** −292 968 **9.** ±15 **11.** ±30 **13.** 24, 72
15. ±20, 80, ±320 **17.** $e^{1/2}$ or 1.649 **19.** 1.76°C **21.** 8.3 years **23.** 8.625 m **25.** 62
27. 2.0 **29.** 1.97 **31.** \$184 202 **33.** \$7776

Exercise 4

1. $5 - c$ **3.** $3/(c + 4)$ **5.** 288 **7.** 12.5 **9.** 19/33 **11.** $7\frac{15}{22}$ **13.** 1182 mm **15.** Sum = 1

Exercise 5

1. 720 **3.** 42 **5.** 35 **25.** $512\,512x^{10}$ **27.** $330x^4a^7$ **29.** $6435x^{14}$

Review Problems

1. 35 **3.** 6, 9, 12, 15 **5.** $2\frac{2}{5}$, 3, 4, 6 **7.** 85 **9.** $a^5 - 10a^4 + 40a^3 - 80a^2 + 80a - 32$ **11.** 48
13. $9 - x$ **15.** 8 **17.** 5/7 **19.** 49/90 **21.** 1215 **23.** −1024 **25.** 20, 50 **27.** 1440
29. 252 **31.** $128x^7/y^{14} - 448x^{13/2}/y^{11} + 672x^6/y^8 - 560x^{11/2}/y^5 + \cdots$
33. $1 - a/2 + 3a^2/8 - 5a^3/16 + \cdots$ **35.** $-26\,730a^4b^7$

CHAPTER 26

Exercise 1

1. Discrete **3.** Categorical **5.** Categorical **7.** **9.**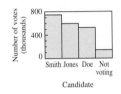

Exercise 2

1. (a) Range = 78 − 50 = 28   **3. (a)** Range = 972 − 584 = 388

			(b)	**(c)**	**10. (a)**	**10. (b)**
Class Mid-point	Class Limits		Abs. Freq.	Rel. Freq.	Cumulative Frequency Abs.	Rel.
50.5	49.5	51.5	1	2.5%	1	2.5%
52.5	51.5	53.5	5	12.5%	6	15.0%
54.5	53.5	55.5	1	2.5%	7	17.5%
56.5	55.5	57.5	1	2.5%	8	20.0%
58.5	57.5	59.5	3	7.5%	11	27.5%
60.5	59.5	61.5	0	0.0%	11	27.5%
62.5	61.5	63.5	2	5.0%	13	32.5%
64.5	63.5	65.5	2	5.0%	15	37.5%
66.5	65.5	67.5	4	10.0%	19	47.5%
68.5	67.5	69.5	4	10.0%	23	57.5%
70.5	69.5	71.5	5	12.5%	28	70.0%
72.5	71.5	73.5	3	7.5%	31	77.5%
74.5	73.5	75.5	6	15.0%	37	92.5%
76.5	75.5	77.5	1	2.5%	38	95.0%
78.5	77.5	79.5	2	5.0%	40	100%

			(b)	**(c)**	**12. (a)**	**12. (b)**
Class Mid-point	Class Limits		Rel. Abs. Freq.	Freq. (%)	Cumulative Frequency Abs.	Rel. (%)
525	500.1	550	0	0.0	0	0.0
575	550.1	600	1	3.3	1	3.3
625	600.1	650	2	6.7	3	10.0
675	650.1	700	4	13.3	7	23.3
725	700.1	750	3	10.0	10	33.3
775	750.1	800	7	23.3	17	56.7
825	800.1	850	1	3.3	18	60.0
875	850.1	900	7	23.3	25	83.3
925	900.1	950	4	13.3	29	96.7
975	950.1	1000	1	3.3	30	100.0

7. **9.**

13. **15.**

17.

3									
4	8.5	8.9	9.6	8.4	9.4				
5	4.8	9.3	9.3	9.3	0.3				
6	1.4	9.3	6.3	9.3					
7	2.5	1.2	1.4	4.5	3.6	1.4	4.9	2.7	2.8
8	8.2	4.6	9.4	5.7	3.8				
9	9.2	2.4							
10									

Exercise 3

1. 77   **3.** 66 kg   **5.** $796   **7.** 81.6   **9.** 157.5   **11.** none   **13.** 59.3 min   **15.** 76
17. 67.5 kg   **19.** $792   **21.** 116, 142, 158, 164, 199   **23.**   **25.** 83
27. 4.28 and 10.02, 5.74   **29.** 697.4, 26.4   **31.** 201, 14.2   116 142 158 164 199

Exercise 4

1. 8/15   **3.** 0.375   **5.** 1/9   **7.** 1.36   **9.** 0.63   **11.** 5/18   **13.** 0.133   **15.** 0.230
17. 0.367   **19.**   **21.** 0.117   **23.** 7.68×10^{-6}

Exercise 5

1. 0.4332   **3.** 0.2119   **5.** 656 students   **7.** 44 students   **9.** 1

Exercise 6

1. 1764.54 ± 8.53 mm   **3.** 8.53 ± 0.86 mm   **5.** 164 ± 2.88 **7.** 16.31 ± 2.04 **9.** 0.25 ± 0.031

Exercise 7

1. and 2.   **3. and 4.**   **5. and 7.**

6. and 8.   **9. and 11.**   **12.**

Exercise 8

1. 1.00   **3.** 1.00   **5.** $y = -4.79x - 14.5$

Review Problems

1. Continuous   **3.** Categorical   **5.**   **7.** 5/36   **9.** 0.75   **11.** 0.1915   **13.** 0.3446
15. 81

17.   **21.** $\bar{x} = 150$ **23.** 137 and 153   **25.** $s = 22.1$ **27.** 150 ± 7.0

29. 22.1 ± 4.94 **31.** 13   **33.** $Q_1 = 407, Q_2 = 718, Q_3 = 1055$; quartile range = 648   **35.**
37. $-1.00, y = -2.31x + 18.1$ **39.** 0.0769 ± 0.0188

Index to Applications

Index to Graphics Calculator Instructions and Exercises

Index to CAS Instructions and Exercises

Index to Writing Questions

Index to Team Projects

General Index